discovering advanced mathematics

D0452718

AS mathematics

John Berry
Roger Fentem
Bob Francis
Ted Graham

series editor
John Berry

project contributors
Steve Dobbs, Howard Hampson, Penny Howe, Rob Lincoln, Sue de Pomerai, Claire Rowland, Stuart Rowlands, Stewart Townend, John White

Published by HarperCollins*Publishers* Limited
77–85 Fulham Palace Road
Hammersmith
London W6 8JB

www.**Collins**Education.com
On-line Support for Schools and Colleges

© HarperCollins*Publishers*
First published 2000

10 9 8 7 6 5 4

ISBN 000 322502 X

John Berry, Roger Fentem, Bob Francis and Ted Graham assert the moral right to be identified as the authors of this work.

All rights reserved. No part of this publication may be reproduced, stored in a retrieval system, or transmitted in any form or by any means, electronic, mechanical, photocopying, recording or otherwise, without either the prior permission of the Publisher or a licence permitting restricted copying in the United Kingdom issued by the Copyright Licensing Agency Ltd., 90 Tottenham Court Road, London W1P 0LP.
British Library Cataloguing in Publication Data.

Cover Design: Terry Bambrook
Internal Design and Illustration: Ken Vail Graphic Design
Project Editor: Joan Miller
Pure and Statistics questions updating: Roger Luther
Key Skills Consultants: Val Beamish and Andy Conway, Harrow College
Index: Bill Houston
Printed and Bound: Bath Press

Acknowledgements
We are grateful to the following Awarding Bodies for permission to reproduce questions from their past examination papers and specimen papers. The Awarding Bodies accept no responsibility whatsoever for the accuracy or method of working in the answers given, which are solely the responsibilty of the authors and publishers.
Edexcel
OCR
AQA (AEB)
AQA (NEAB)

We are grateful to the following for their permission to reproduce copyright photographs: cover: Tony Stone Images/Jeremy Walker; p15 Science Photo Library; p420 John Birdsall; p459 Andrew Lambert.

Every effort has been made to contact all copyright holders. If any hav been inadvertantly overlooked, the publisher would be pleased to make full acknowledgement at the first opportunity.

You might also like to visit:
www.**fire**and**water**.com
The book lover's website

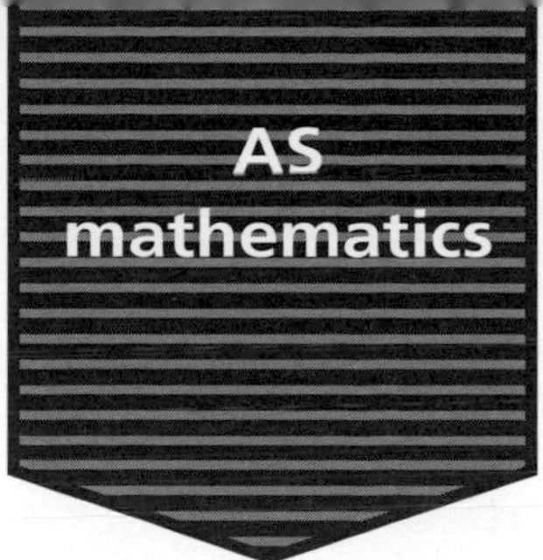

Contents

Preface

discovering advanced mathematics: AS mathematics

Mathematics is not just an important subject in its own right, but also a tool for solving problems. Mathematics at Advanced level is changing to reflect this: during the A-level course you must study at least one area of the application of mathematics. This is what we mean by 'mathematical modelling'. Of course, mathematicians have been applying mathematics to problems in mechanics and statistics for many years. But now, the process has been formally included throughout A-level mathematics.

Curriculum 2000 offers many more students the opportunity to study for an AS-level qualification in mathematics by selecting either a mechanics module or a statistics module with the two compulsory pure modules. In this book we offer students a complete AS text.

A third innovation is the recognition that graphical and numerical methods play an important part in the teaching and learning of mathematics. This book shows how much easier it is to study this topic now that we have programmable calculators and computers. Curriculum 2000 expects you to know how to use appropriate technology in mathematics and be aware that this technology has limitations.

We have revised *discovering advanced mathematics* to meet the needs of the new A- and AS- specifications and the Common Core for mathematics. This book provides opportunities to study advanced mathematics while learning about modelling and problem solving. We show how to make best use of new technology, including graphic calculators.

In every chapter in this book, you will find:

- an introduction that explains a new idea or technique in a helpful context;
- plenty of worked examples to show you how the techniques are used;
- exercises in two sets, classwork problems for work in class and homework problems that 'mirror' the classwork problems so that you can practice the same work in a self-study sessions;
- consolidation exercises that test you in the same way as real examination questions;
- real questions from all the awarding bodies;
- icons to show opportunities where you could develop Key Skills, with further notes in the section at the back of the book.

And then, once you have finished the chapter, modelling and problem solving exercises to help you pull together all of the ideas in the chapter.

I hope that you will enjoy studying advanced mathematics by working through this book. The authors thank the many people involved in developing the *discovering advanced mathematics* series.

John Berry, Series Editor, *April 2000*

Problem-solving in mathematics

WHAT IS MATHEMATICS?

Let us begin our Advanced Level studies in mathematics by asking the question, *What is mathematics?* Some people call it the analysis of pattern. Some say that it is a language of communication. Others say that mathematics is the art of problem-solving.

In fact, all three definitions are appropriate and, in many cases, all three are applicable at the same time. There are many occasions in this book when we analyse a pattern to generalise a mathematical idea, and we use the language of mathematics to communicate that idea. To begin with, though, we emphasise the art of problem-solving, using mostly the mathematics techniques that are familiar from GCSE studies.

This opening chapter looks at problem-solving in mathematics under five broad headings, each of which features several related problems. These five areas are:

A linear models,
B quadratic models,
C other non-linear models,
D exponential models,
E wave models.

The first problem in each section is laid out on a right-hand page so that you can try solving it on your own. It is then followed by a fully worked solution on the two following pages, which you can use to check your work and clarify any ideas you found tricky. Following this, in each section there are two or three problems for you to tackle without any help. There are answers to these problems at the back of the book.

For each problem you may be asked to:

- complete a table of values,
- draw a graph to illustrate the relationship between two variables,
- solve the problem using your graph,
- formulate, where appropriate, an algebraic relationship between the variables,
- check and extend your work using a graphics calculator or computer package.

Much of the mathematics in this book springs from the type of problems set in this chapter. You could work through the whole of this chapter at the beginning of this A Level course, to get a flavour of the types of models to be found in mathematics. Alternatively you could use each section separately as an introduction to one of the main chapters which follow. Wherever appropriate, you will see mathematics in context as well as in theory. Applications of mathematics will appear throughout each topic as it is developed, so you can both use and apply mathematics as well as learn new mathematics for its own sake.

Throughout the book you will be encouraged to use both graphics calculators and computers effectively. In this chapter there are numerous opportunities to confirm and extend your results using a graphics calculator, once you have obtained initial solutions by drawing graphs by hand. Once you have modelled a problem on your calculator, you can very easily change the ground rules and investigate 'What happens if ... ?' Equally, you could solve these problems with the help of a spreadsheet or graph plotter. Use whatever technology you have at hand to bring your mathematics to life.

Example 1.1

Linear models

Problem

> *Yellacabs* taxis charge their customers a fixed cost of £1 plus 40 pence per mile.

1 *Copy and complete the following table of values.*

Distance, d (miles)	0	5	10	15	20
Cost, c (£)	1	3			

2 *Using suitable scales, draw a graph to show the cost of a journey against the number of miles travelled.*

3 *From your graph find:*
a) *the cost of a journey of 8 miles,*
b) *how far you can travel for £6.20.*

> Another taxi-firm, *Maxitaxis*, have no fixed charge, but customers pay 60 pence per mile.

4 *On the same axes, draw a graph of cost against distance for* ***Maxitaxis.***

5 *Use your graphs to:*
a) *find which firm is cheaper, and by how much, for a journey of:*
i) *3 miles,* ***ii)*** *12 miles,*
b) *find which firm offers the greater travelling distance for a cost of £7.50.*

6 *Devise a simple strategy for choosing between* ***Yellacabs*** *and* ***Maxitaxis*** *if you are a potential customer.*

7 *Find formulae, one for* ***Yellacabs*** *and one for* ***Maxitaxis****, connecting the cost of a journey (in £) and the distance travelled (in miles).*

Exploration 1.1

CALCULATOR ACTIVITY

Check your work using a graphics calculator

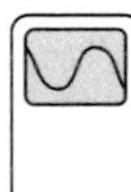

- Firstly scale your axes using the range settings:

  $x_{min} = 0$; $x_{max} = 20$; $x_{scl} = 5$
  $y_{min} = -2$; $y_{max} = 10$; $y_{scl} = 1$.

- Using variables x and y (instead of d and c), enter equations:

  $y = 0.4x + 1, y = 0.6x$.

- Use the TRACE facility to confirm all your results.
- Use the ZOOM facility to obtain the desired degree of accuracy.

Problem solution

1 *A taxi fare with **Yellacabs** consists of a fixed cost of £1 plus a variable cost of 40 pence for each mile travelled. So:*
a 5-mile journey would cost £1 + 5 × 40 pence = £3
a 10-mile journey would cost £1 + 10 × 40 pence = £5.

The complete table is shown here.

Distance, d (miles)	0	5	10	15	20
Cost, c (£)	1	3	5	7	9

2 *The graph below shows the cost of a journey in a **Yellacab** against the number of miles travelled.*

3 *From the graph we can read off:*
***a)** an 8-mile journey costs £4.20,*
***b)** for £6.20 you can travel a distance of 13 miles.*

***Note:** If you use 2 mm graph paper, you will be able to obtain a reasonably accurate result in this case. Sometimes, though, only an estimate is possible, due to the scales chosen.*

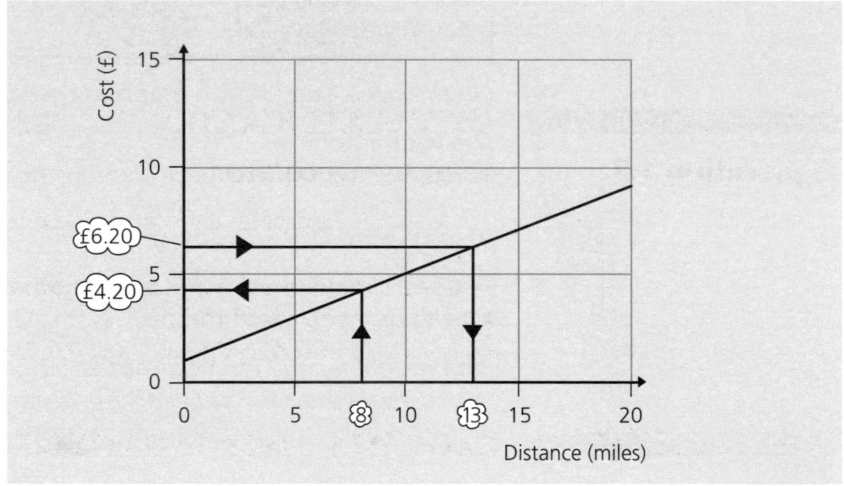

4 ***Maxitaxis** charge 60 pence per mile (i.e. no fixed cost, just a variable cost), which is equivalent to £3 for every five miles.*

*This graph shows the cost against distance for **Maxitaxis** on the same grid.*

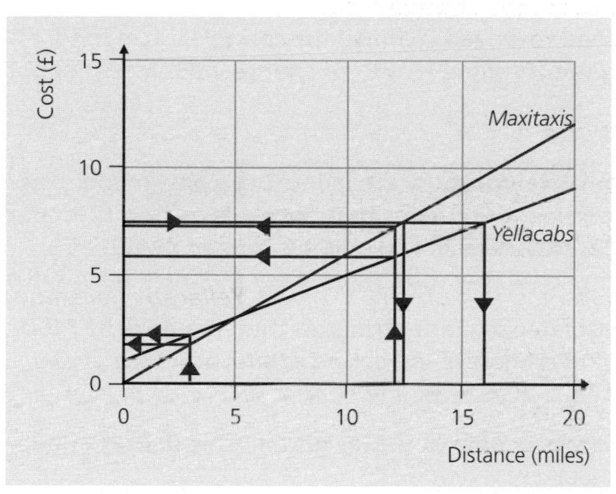

5 *From the graph we can read off :*

*a) i) For a 3-mile journey, **Maxitaxis** are cheaper by 40 pence,*

*ii) For a 12-mile journey, **Yellacabs** are cheaper by £1.40.*

*b) **Yellacabs** offer 16.25 miles compared with **Maxitaxis** who offer 12.5 miles. So:*

6 *For journeys less than five miles **Maxitaxis** are cheaper, for journeys greater than five miles **Yellacabs** are cheaper.*

7 *Let c represent cost and d represent distance, then the formulae relating cost and distance for the two firms are:*

Yellacabs: $c = 0.4d + 1$ ***Maxitaxis:*** $c = 0.6d$

variable cost (0.4d) *fixed cost* (1) *variable cost* (0.6d)

CALCULATOR ACTIVITY

Exploration 1.2

Graphics calculator

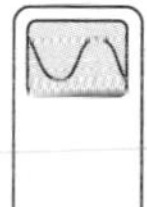

You can use a graphics calculator to investigate changes in ways of charging customers.

Find out how your answers to questions **3** to **6** would change if, say:

- *Yellacabs* increased their mileage rate to 50 pence,
- *Maxitaxis* introduced a fixed charge, but reduced their mileage rate.

EXERCISES

1 **Stretching a spring**

A spring stretches by 1 cm for every 100 g of load.

When the spring carries a load of 300 g the length of the spring is 10 cm.

a) Copy and complete the table of values for length of spring in centimetres against mass of a load in grams.

Mass of load (g)	0	100	200	300	400	500
Length of spring (cm)				10		

b) Using suitable scales, draw a graph to show the length of the spring against load.

c) From your graph find:
i) the length of the spring when the load is 180 g,
ii) the unstretched length of the spring,
iii) how large a load you need to make the spring 12.3 cm long.
d) Find a formula connecting the length of spring and mass of load.

2 Marketing a new bicycle

The *Everest Mountain Bike Company* are launching a new model. The market research department estimates that, averaged over a 12-month period, the demand for the new bike would be 200 per month at a price of £150, reducing by 20 per month for every £10 increase in price.

The production control department estimates that at a price of £150 they could supply 100 per month, increasing production capacity by 15 per month for every £10 increase in price.

a) Copy and complete this table of values for monthly demand and supply against price.

Price (£)	150	160	170	180	190	200	210
Demand	200						
Supply	100						

b) On the same axes draw graphs of demand against price and supply against price.
c) What price should be charged for supply to equal demand? How many bikes per month could the company sell at this price?
d) For what range of prices would you think this model to be valid?
e) Find formulae connecting **i)** demand and price, **ii)** supply and price.

3 World record for the mile

The table shows some of the world records (in minutes : seconds) set for the mile from 1913 to 1985.

Athlete	Year	Time taken	Athlete	Year	Time taken
John Paul Jones	1913	4:14.4	Roger Bannister	1954	3:59.4
Paavo Nurmi	1923	4:10.4	Peter Snell	1964	3:54.1
Glen Cunningham	1933	4:06.8	John Walker	1975	3:49.4
Arne Andersson	1943	4:02.6	Steve Cram	1985	3:46.3

a) Using suitable scales plot times taken against year of race.
b) Draw in a line of best fit and find an equation for it.
c) Predict the likely year when the mile will be run in:
i) 3:40, **ii)** 3:30.
d) Is it reasonable to use the same method to estimate when we are likely to see the first three-minute mile?

Example 1.2

Quadratic models

Problem

Chris is a keen cricketer.

He is practising throwing the ball from the boundary to the wicket-keeper, a distance of 50 m.

An equation to describe the flight-path (trajectory) of the ball is

$y = x - 0.02x^2$

where y represents the height (in metres) of the ball when it has travelled x metres horizontally.

1 *Copy and complete the following table of values.*

x (metres)	0	10	20	30	40	50
y (metres)						

2 *Using suitable scales, draw a graph to show the height of the ball (y metres) against x, the horizontal distance travelled, also in metres.*

3 *From your graph find:*
a) *the height of the ball when $x = 8$,*
b) *how far the ball is, horizontally, from Chris when it is at a height of 10 m,*
c) *the maximum height of the ball during its flight.*

Trevor and Winston also throw the ball from the boundary and aim for the wicket-keeper.

Equations describing the trajectories for their throws are as follows:

Trevor: $y = x - 0.025x^2$ Winston: $y = x - 0.018x^2$

4 *On the same axes, draw graphs to represent these two trajectories.*

5 *Re-work question **3**, for both Trevor and Winston.*

6 *How far from the wicket-keeper will the ball land when:*
a) *Trevor throws the ball,*
b) *Winston throws the ball?*

CALCULATOR ACTIVITY

Exploration 1.3

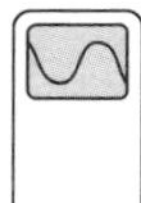

- Check your work using a graphics calculator.

Problem solution

1 *The complete table is shown below.*

x (metres)	0	10	20	30	40	50
y (metres)	0	8	12	12	8	0

2 *The graph below shows the height of the ball (y metres) against x, the horizontal distance travelled.*

3 *From the graph we can read off:*

a) when $x = 8$, height of ball (y) = 6.7 m,

b) when the ball is at a height of 10 metres, it is either about 14 m or about 36 m from Chris,

c) the maximum height of the ball is 12.5 m, when it is 25 m from Chris, half-way to the wicket-keeper.

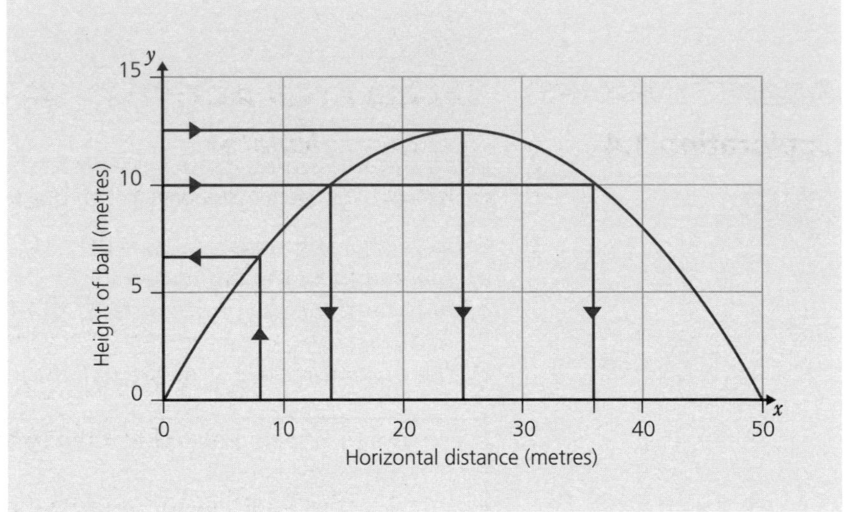

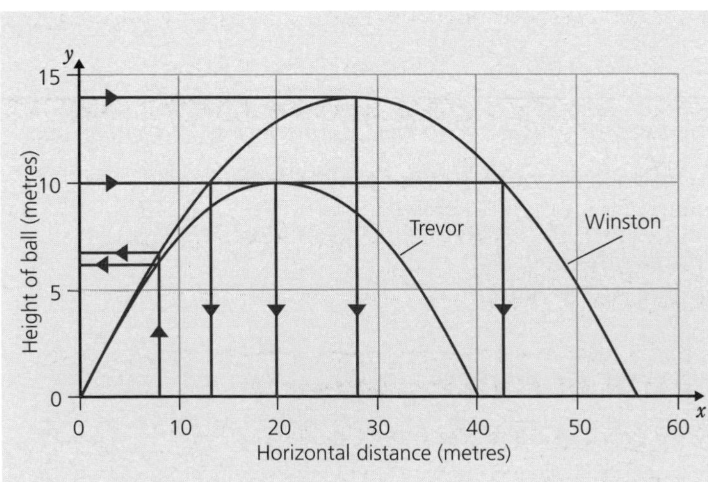

4 *When Trevor and Winston throw the cricket ball from the boundary, both throw the ball at the same angle to the ground, but with different speeds, as shown in the graph (left). Trevor's throw fails to reach the wicket-keeper, whereas Winston's throw sails over the wicket-keeper's head!*

5 *From the graph we can read off the following results.*
Trevor:
- ***a)*** *When $x = 8$, height of ball (y) = 6.4 m.*
- ***b)*** *When the ball is at a height of 10 metres, it is 20 m from Trevor.*
- ***c)*** *The maximum height of the ball is 10 m, when it is 20 m from Trevor, less than half-way to the wicket-keeper.*

Winston:
- ***a)*** *When $x = 8$ m, height of ball (y) = 6.85 m.*
- ***b)*** *When the ball is at a height of 10 metres, it is either about 13.5 m or about 42.5 m from Winston.*
- ***c)*** *The maximum height of the ball is about 13.9 m, when it is 28 m from Winston, more than half-way to the wicket-keeper.*

6
- ***a)*** *When Trevor throws the ball, it lands 10 metres short of the wicket-keeper.*
- ***b)*** *When Winston throws the ball, it lands about 5.5 metres beyond the wicket-keeper.*

CALCULATOR ACTIVITY

Exploration 1.4

Graphics calculator

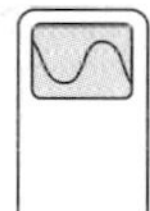

- Firstly scale your axes using the range settings:

$x_{min} = 0$; $x_{max} = 70$; $x_{scl} = 10$
$y_{min} = -5$; $y_{max} = 15$; $y_{scl} = 2$.

Enter equations: $y = x - 0.02x^2$ (Chris),
$y = x - 0.025x^2$ (Trevor),
$y = x - 0.018x^2$ (Winston).

- Use the TRACE facility to confirm all your results.
- Use the ZOOM facility to obtain the desired degree of accuracy.

EXERCISES

1.2

1 **Picture framing**

Ubeen Framed offer a picture-framing service.
The cost of framing square pictures is made up of two parts:
cost of glass: 50 pence per square foot,
cost of frame: £1.50 per foot.

a) Copy and complete the following table of values for total cost (in £) against length of side of frame (in feet).

Length of side of frame (feet)	1	2	3	4	5
Cost (£)					

b) Using suitable scales, draw a graph to show the cost against the length of side.

c) From your graph find:

i) the cost of framing a picture of side 2 feet 6 inches,

ii) how large a picture you could have framed for £25.

d) Find a formula connecting the cost and the length of side of the frame.

e) *Ubeen Framed* also offer a home delivery service, within the local area, for which they charge a fixed fee of £5.

i) On the same axes, draw a graph of total cost (including home delivery) against length of frame.

ii) Re-work part **c)**, assuming the picture is delivered to the customer's home.

iii) How is the formula in **d)** altered?

2 Stopping distance

The highway code contains information about shortest stopping distances for cars on a dry surface, summarised by the following table.

Speed (mph)	Thinking distance (ft)	Braking distance (ft)	Stopping distance (ft)
20	20	20	
30	30		75
40	40	80	
50	50		175
70	70	245	

a) Given that
stopping distance = thinking distance + braking distance,
copy and complete the table.

b) Plot a graph of stopping distance (in feet) against speed (in mph).

c) Use your graph to estimate:

i) the shortest stopping distance for a car travelling at 60 mph,

ii) the speed of a car which stopped in 70 feet.

d) Find a relationship between the overall stopping distance, d, and speed, v, of the form:

$$d = v + kv^2.$$

e) Using your equation from **d)**, check your results to **b)** and **c)** on a graphics calculator.

f) In wet conditions, the minimum recommended *braking* distance is doubled. On the same axes plot a graph of stopping distance (in feet) against speed (in mph) for wet conditions. How are your answers to **c)** modified for wet conditions?

Example 1.3

Other non-linear models

Problem

An open box is to be formed by cutting four squares of side x cm from the corners of a sheet of card 20 cm square.

You are asked to investigate how the volume of the box varies as x varies.

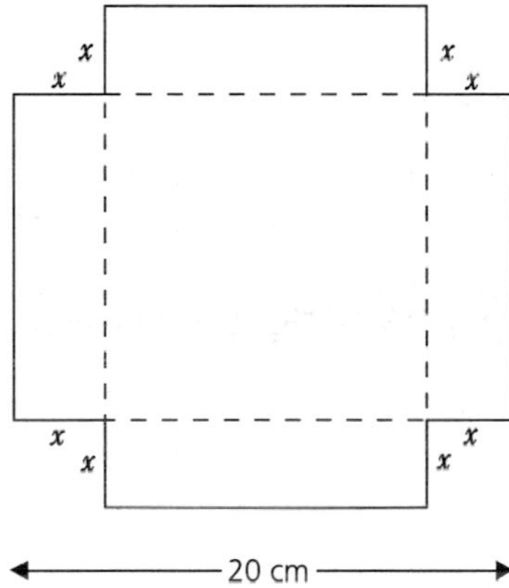

1 *Find a formula connecting the volume of the box, V cm^3, and the length x cm.*

2 *Copy and complete the following table of values.*

x (cm)	0	2	4	6	8	10
V (cm^3)						

3 *Using suitable scales, draw a graph to show the volume, V cm^3, of the box against the length x cm.*

4 *From your graph find:*
a) *the volume for which **i)** $x = 2.5$ cm, **ii)** $x = 6.6$ cm,*
b) *which x-values correspond to a volume of 0.5 litre,*
c) *the value of x for which the box has maximum volume. What is the maximum volume?*

CALCULATOR ACTIVITY

Exploration 1.5

- Check your work using a graphics calculator.

Problem solution

1 *The dimensions of the open box are:*

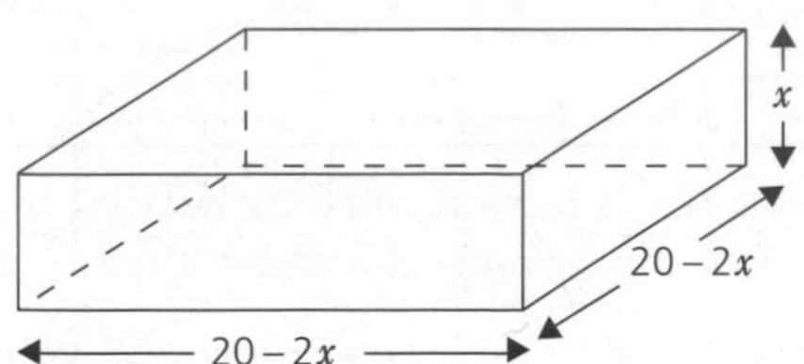

length and width = $20 - 2x$
height = x.
Therefore the volume is given by:
$V = x(20 - 2x)^2$.

2 *Using the formula we can obtain the complete table of values, as shown below.*

x (cm)	0	2	4	6	8	10
V (cm^3)	0	512	576	384	128	0

3 *The graph below shows the volume (V) against the value of x.*

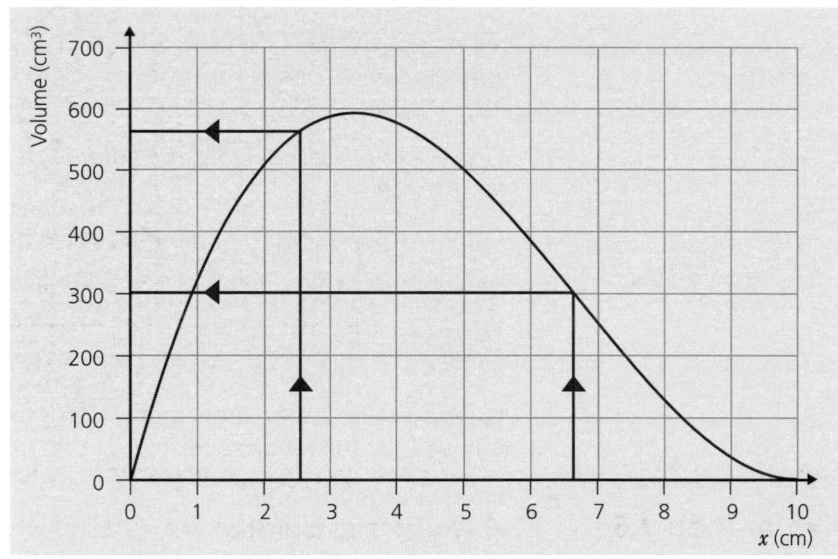

4 *From the graphs (above and opposite) we can read off:*

a) ***i)*** *when* $x = 2.5$, $V = 562.5$,
ii) *when* $x = 6.6$, $V = 305$
(see the diagram above),

b) *when* $V = 0.5$ litre $= 500\,\text{cm}^3$, $x = 1.9$ *or* 5
(see the diagram opposite, top)

c) *maximum volume is* $V = 593$, *when* $x = 3.33$ *(see the diagram opposite, beneath).*

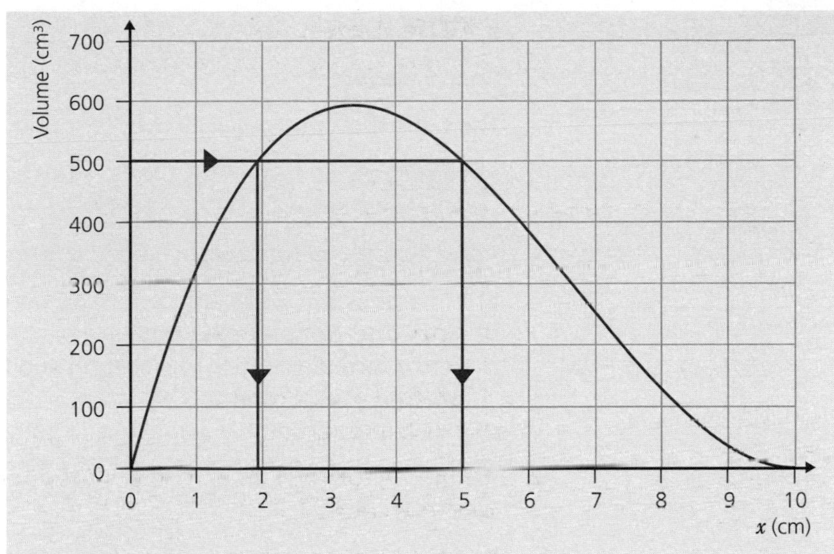

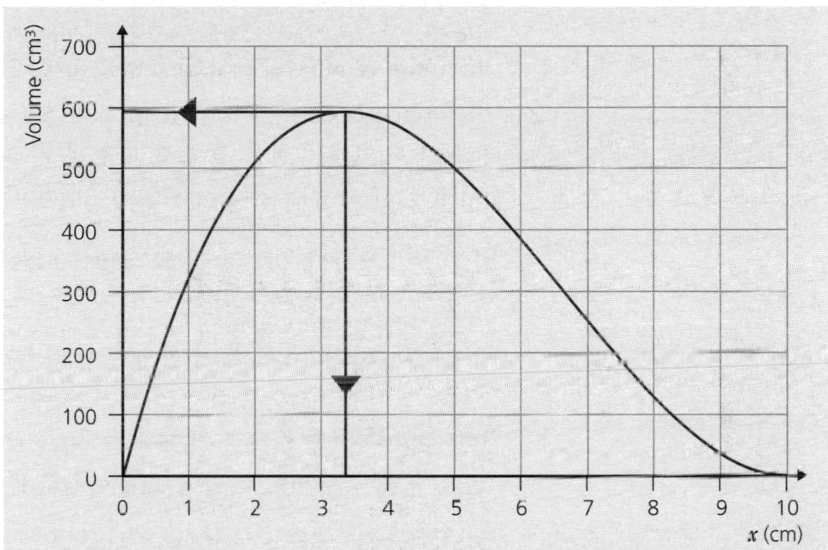

CALCULATOR ACTIVITY

Exploration 1.6

Graphics calculator

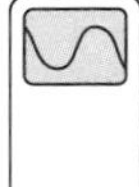

- Firstly scale your axes using the range settings:

  $x_{min} = 0$; $x_{max} = 10$; $x_{scl} = 1$
  $y_{min} = -100$; $y_{max} = 700$; $y_{scl} = 100$.

- Using variables x and y (instead of x and V), enter the equation:

  $y = x(20 - 2x)^2$.

- Use the TRACE facility to confirm all your results.
- Use the ZOOM facility to obtain the desired degree of accuracy.

EXERCISES

1.3

1 **Sound waves**

The table shows the wavelengths of sound waves of various frequencies.

Frequency, f (cycles per second)	50	100	150	200		300
Wavelength, w (metres)	6.60	3.30	2.20		1.32	

a) How does the wavelength depend on the frequency?
b) Copy and complete the table.
c) Find a formula relating wavelength and frequency in the form: $w = \frac{k}{f}$, where k is a constant.
d) Draw a graph of wavelength, w, against frequency, f.
e) What wavelength corresponds to a frequency of 400 cycles per second?
f) What frequency corresponds to a wavelength of 1.5 metres?

2 **Gravity**

The force of gravity, F newtons, on a mass of 1 kg, at a distance d kilometres from the centre of the Earth, is inversely proportional to d^2.

The radius of the Earth is about 6400 km and the force of gravity on a mass of 1 kg, at the surface of the Earth is about 10 newtons.

a) Find a formula relating F and d in the form: $F = \frac{k}{d^2}$, where k is a constant.
b) Draw a graph of F against d for suitable values of d.
c) What would you expect F to be on an object 10 000 km from the surface of the Earth?
d) At what height above the Earth's surface would F fall to 8 newtons?

3 **Nets and boxes**

A box is to be made, from a sheet of card, to have a volume of 500 cm^3.

If it is to have a square base, what dimensions would you choose to minimise the surface area for:

a) an open box (i.e. a box without a lid)
i) Let the length of side of base be x cm and its height be h cm. Explain why $h = \frac{500}{x^2}$.
ii) Show that the formula for the surface area, A, in terms of x, for the open box is $A = x^2 + \frac{2000}{x}$.
iii) Copy and complete the table for the open box.

x	2	4	6	8	10	12	14	16
A	1004	516						

iv) Plot a graph of surface area, A, against length of base, x.
v) What dimensions would you choose to minimise the total surface area?
b) a closed box.

Example 1.4

Exponential models

Problem

A colony of bacteria has a population of 1 million at midday on Sunday.

During the next week, the colony's population **doubles** every 24 hours.

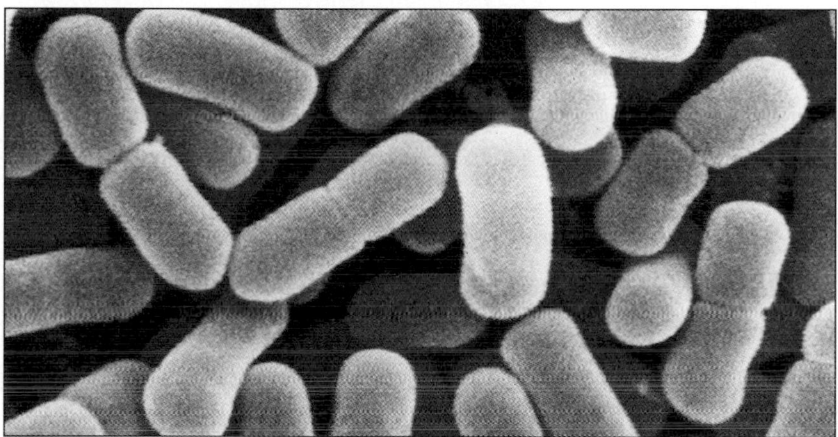

1 *Copy and complete the following table of population values, taken at midday each day (day 0 is Sunday, day 1 is Monday, etc.).*

Day	0	1	2	3	4	5	6	7
Population (millions)	1	2	4					

2 *Using suitable scales, draw a graph to show how the population grows during the week.*

3 *From your graph find:*

a) the population at midnight on Thursday,
b) the day and time by which the population has reached 70 million,
c) the rate at which the population is growing on:
i) Wednesday (midday), ii) Friday (midnight).

4 *Find a formula that gives population in millions (P) after t days.*

Exploration 1.7

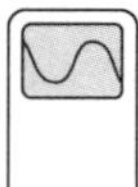

CALCULATOR ACTIVITY

■ Check your work using a graphics calculator.

Problem solution

1 *Since the population is 1 million on day 0 and doubles every 24 hours, the populations on subsequent days are all powers of 2.*

The complete table is shown below.

Day	0	1	2	3	4	5	6	7
Population (millions)	1	2	4	8	16	32	64	128

2 *The graph below shows the population (in millions) against the number of days.*

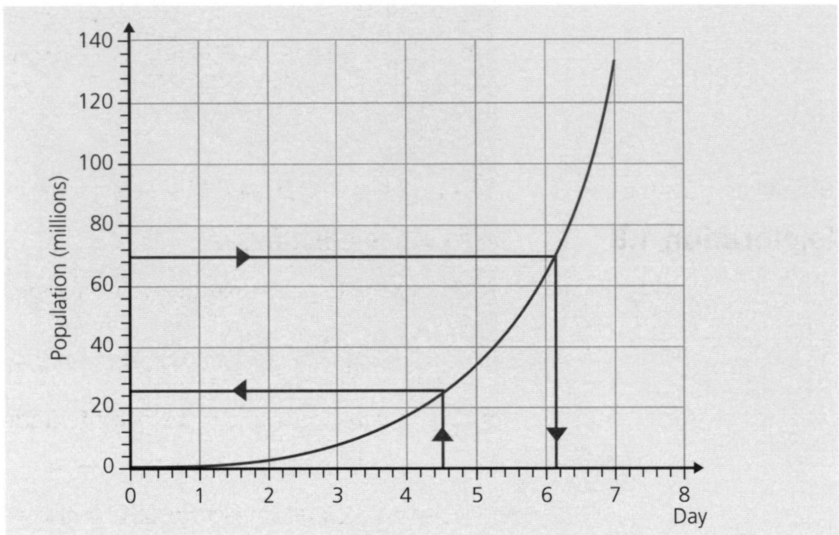

3 *From the graph we can read off the following results.*

a) *The population at midnight on Thursday is about 23 million.*

b) *The population reaches 70 million by about 3 am on Saturday.*

c) *The rate at which the population is growing at any one time is estimated by finding the gradient of the tangent to the graph. To do this, we draw in the tangent and choose two suitable points on the tangent from which a right-angled triangle may be constructed. The gradient of the line is the difference in population values divided by the difference in times. The graph on the next page shows the method to estimate the rate at which the population is growing on Wednesday (midday), day 3 and Friday (midnight), day 5.5.*

d) *The rates at which the population is growing are given by:*

i) *on Wednesday (midday):* $\frac{11}{2} = 5.5$ *million per day,*

ii) *on Friday (midnight):* $\frac{90}{3} = 30$ *million per day.*

4 *Let P represent population and t represent time, then the formula relating population (in millions) and time (in days) is:*

$P = 2^t$.

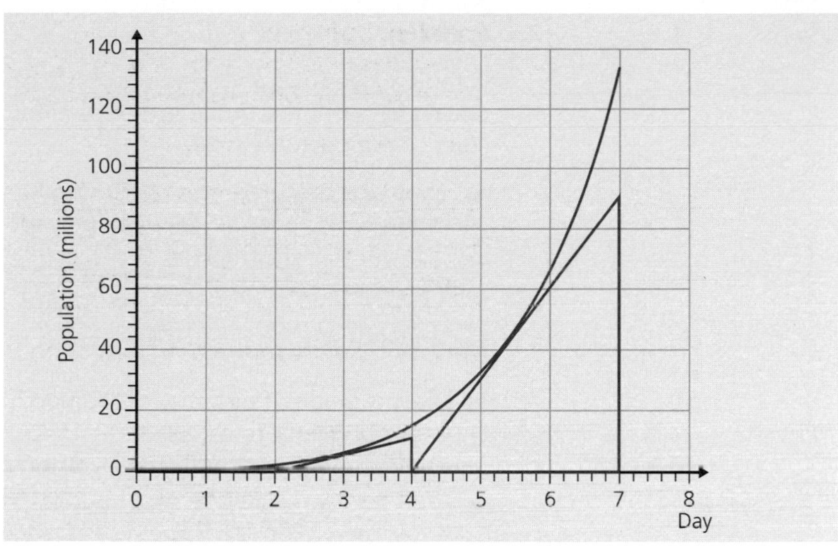

CALCULATOR ACTIVITY

Exploration 1.8

Graphics calculator

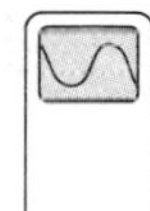

- Firstly scale your axes using the range settings:

  $x_{min} = 0$; $x_{max} = 7$; $x_{scl} = 1$
  $y_{min} = -20$; $y_{max} = 140$; $y_{scl} = 10$.

- Using variables x and y (instead of t and P), enter the equation: $y = 2^x$.
- Use the TRACE facility to confirm all your results.
- Use the ZOOM facility to obtain the desired degree of accuracy.

EXERCISES

1.4

1 Growing trees

The quantity of timber in a fast growing forest is estimated to increase by 15% per annum. After planting, the quantity of timber is 10 units.

a) Copy and complete the table of values, showing quantities of timber over a five-year period.

Time, t (years)	0	1	2	3	4	5
Quantity of timber, q	10	11.5				

b) Draw a graph of quantity of timber, q, against time in years, t.
c) Use your graph to estimate:
  i) the quantity of timber after $2\frac{1}{2}$ years,
  ii) the time it takes for the quantity of timber to double its initial size.
d) Find a formula that gives q in terms of t.
e) Check your results to **a)**, **b)** and **c)** using a graphics calculator.

2 **Half-life**

A radioactive substance has a half-life of one week, i.e. every week it decays by half of its value at the beginning of the week. Its initial level of radioactivity is 20.

a) Copy and complete the table of values, showing levels of radioactivity over a five-week period.

Time, t (weeks)	0	1	2	3	4	5
Radioactivity, r	20	10				

b) Draw a graph of quantity of radioactivity, r, against time in weeks, t.
c) Use your graph to estimate:
  i) the amount of radioactivity after 10 days,
  ii) the time it takes for the radioactivity to reach 10% of its initial value.
d) Find a formula that gives r in terms of t.
e) Check your results to **a)**, **b)** and **c)** using a graphics calculator.

3 **Cooling**

A flask of water is at a temperature of 100°C. After five minutes it has cooled to 80°C.

a) Assuming that the fall in temperature in any five-minute period is proportional to the temperature at the beginning of the period, copy and complete the following table of values.

Time, t (minutes)	0	5	10	15	20	25
Temperature, T (°C)	100	80	64			

b) Draw a graph of temperature, T, against time in minutes, t.
c) Use your graph to estimate:
  i) the temperature after 8 minutes,
  ii) the time it takes for the water to cool to 50°C.
d) Find a formula that gives T in terms of t.
e) Check your results to **a)**, **b)** and **c)** using a graphics calculator.

Example 1.5

KEY SKILLS
N 3.1
N 3.2
N 3.3
IT 3.1

Wave models

Problem

The height of the tide in Portbury harbour during a period of 12 hours (midnight to midday) is given in the table below.

Time (hours)	0	1	2	3	4	5	6	7	8	9	10	11	12
Height (metres)	6.6	5.5	4.0	2.5	1.4	1.0	1.4	2.5	4.0	5.5	6.6	7.0	6.6

1 *Using suitable scales, draw a graph to show the height of the tide against time.*

2 *From your graph find:*
a) the height of the tide at:
i) 02.30, ii) 09.45,
b) the times at which the height was:
i) 4.0 metres, ii) 6.0 metres,
c) the time of:
i) low tide, ii) high tide.

3 *Fishing vessels can safely leave or enter the harbour provided the depth of water is at least two metres. For how long is it not safe for a boat to enter or leave the harbour?*

A formula that gives the height in terms of time is $h = 3\cos\big(30(t+1)\big)+4$.

Check that the values in the table above may be found by substituting values of t in this equation.

Exploration 1.9

CALCULATOR ACTIVITY

Check your work using a graphics calculator

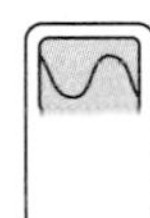

- Firstly make sure that you are in degree MODE.
- Secondly scale your axes using the range settings:

$x_{min} = 0$; $x_{max} = 12$; $x_{scl} = 1$
$y_{min} = 0$; $y_{max} = 8$; $y_{scl} = 1$.

- Using variables x and y (instead of t and h), enter the equation:

$$y = 3\cos\big(30(x+1)\big)+4.$$

- Use the TRACE facility to confirm all your results.
- Use the ZOOM facility to obtain the desired degree of accuracy.

Problem solution

1 *The graph below shows the height of tide against time for the period of time midnight to midday.*

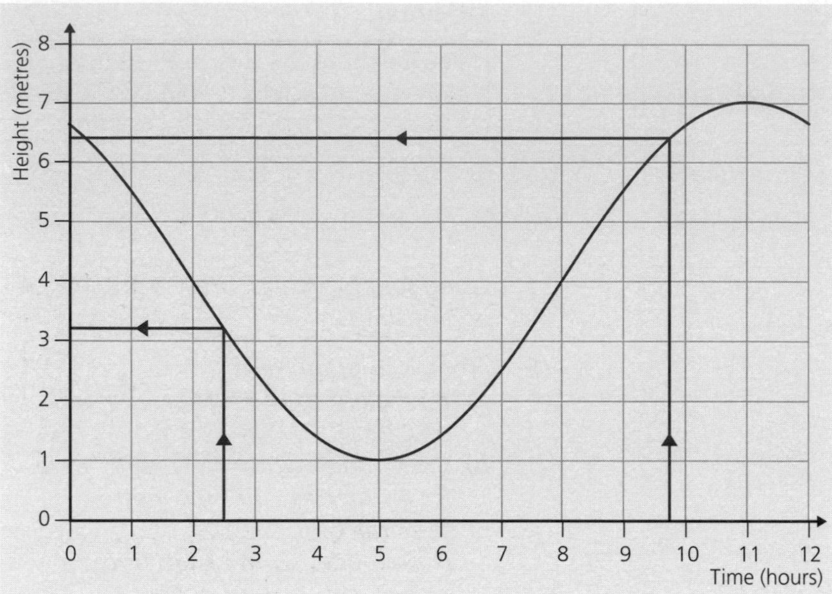

2 ***a)*** *From the graph above we can read off the height of tide:*

i) *at 02.30 = 3.2 metres,*

ii) *at 09.45 = 6.4 metres.*

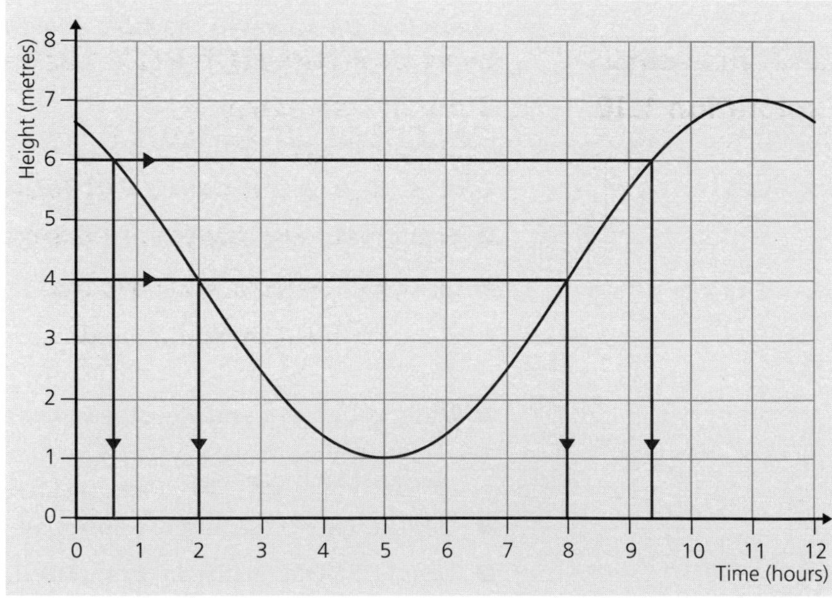

b) *From the graph above we can read off that the height of tide was:*

i) *4.0 metres at 02.00 and 08.00,*

ii) *6.0 metres at 00.36 and 09.24.*

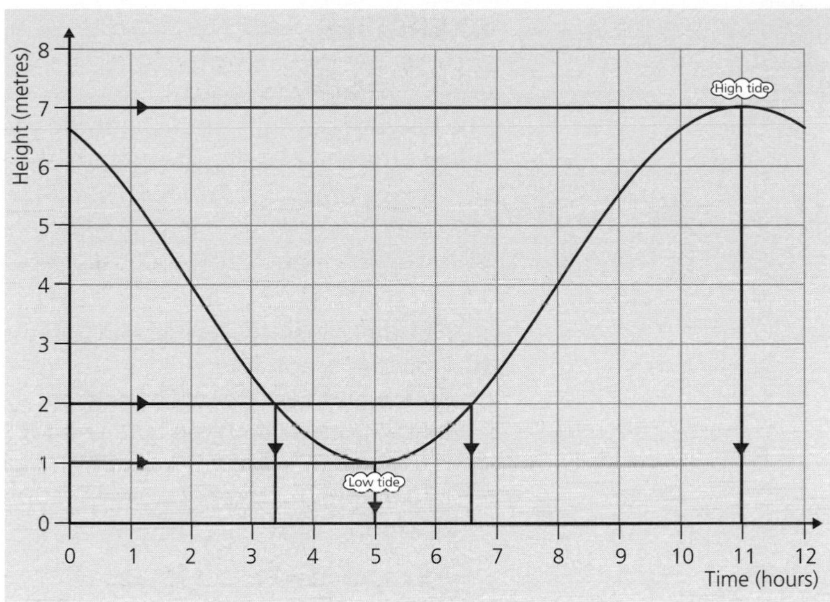

c) *From the graph above, we can read off:*
i) *low tide was at 05.00,*
ii) *high tide was at 11.00.*

3 *Also from the graph above, we can deduce that the tide is two metres in depth at about 03.25 and 06.35, so it is not safe for a boat to enter or leave harbour for a period of just over three hours.*

CALCULATOR ACTIVITY

Exploration 1.10

Graphics calculator

Modify the equation you were given, i.e. $h = 3\cos\big(30(t+1)\big) + 4$, to model the movement of the tide to take account of, say:

- change in height of high and low tide,
- change in times of high and low tide,
- change in the time between successive high tides.

EXERCISES

1.5

1 Hours of daylight

The hours of daylight throughout the year for Casterton are as follows (on the 21st day of each month).

March	April	May	June	July	Aug.	Sept.	Oct.	Nov.	Dec.	Jan.	Feb.
12	15	17.2	18	17.2	15	12	9	6.8	6	6.8	9

a) Plot the values on a graph and join the points with a smooth curve.
b) From the graph find:
 i) the number of hours of daylight on 1 October,
 ii) the period when the hours of day light are less than 7.5 hours.
c) If h represents the number of hours of daylight on the twenty-first of a month, m, formulate an equation, to give h in terms of m, of the form:

$$h = c + a\sin(bm)$$

where $m = 0$ for March, $m = 1$ for April, ..., $m = 11$ for February, and a, b and c are constants to be found.
d) Use your equation from **c)** to plot the graph on a graphical calculator and check your results from **a)** and **b)**.

2 The big wheel

A Ferris wheel at a fair ground has radius 8 m.

When in motion it completes one revolution in 36 seconds.

a) Copy and complete the table of values, showing height above the ground of a particular car against time.

Time (seconds)	0	3	6	9	12	15	18	21	24	27	30	33	36
Height (metres)	1	2.1	5	9	13	15.9	17						1

b) Using suitable scales, draw a graph of height against time.
c) From the graph find:
 i) the height of a Ferris wheel car after 25 seconds,
 ii) the period of time during which the car is more than 15 m above the ground.
d) If h represents the height of a Ferris wheel car t seconds after the wheel starts to move, find an equation, to give h in terms of t, of the form $h = c - a\cos(bt)$.
e) Use your equation from **d)** to plot the graph on a graphical calculator and check yours results from **a)**, **b)** and **c)**.

Summary

In each of these sections you have been solving real problems using mathematics.

*This is called **mathematical modelling**. Most of this book is about the **mathematical methods** that are needed to solve problems and to develop further techniques. For example, you will need **algebra** to be able to understand rates of change. However, it is important to be able to use your mathematics to solve real problems. So the theme of mathematical modelling will run through the book.*

*An important part of solving a real problem is called the **mathematical model**. For the problems in this chapter the mathematical models are described by **graphs** or **equations**. The following table illustrates this using two of the problems in this chapter.*

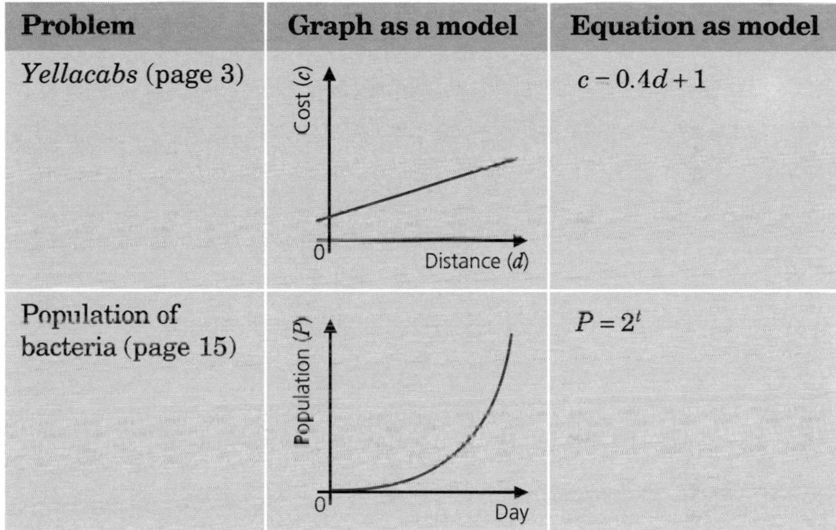

Problem	Graph as a model	Equation as model
Yellacabs (page 3)		$c = 0.4d + 1$
Population of bacteria (page 15)		$P = 2^t$

Here is a list of skills that may be required to solve a real problem:

- *understand the problem,*
- *choose suitable variables (and units),*
- *label the variables,*
- *find the relationship between the variables.*

*For example, in the **Yellacabs** problem it was appropriate to choose the cost (£) and distance (miles) as variables. We labelled these variables c and d. The relationship between c and d is then* $c = 0.4d + 1$.

Having found a mathematical model for a situation, the model is then used in two ways:

- *to describe the situation,*
- *to make predictions about the future.*

*For example, in the taxis problem we had graphical models for **Yellacabs** and **Maxitaxis**.*

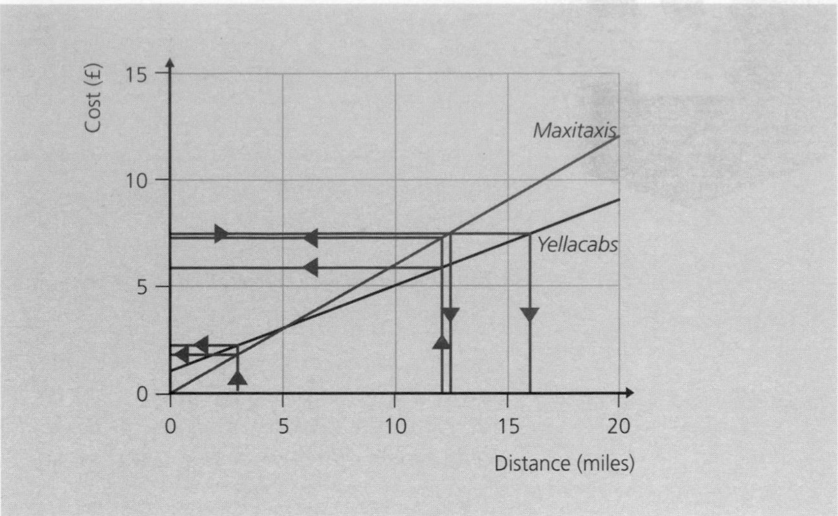

These graphs are a ***description*** *of the situation. The graphs were used to* ***predict*** *when Yellacabs are cheaper.*

Sometimes we need more data to check the model and in the light of the checking process we may refine our model to give a better description and (hopefully) predictions.

This whole process of problem solving can be represented in the following diagram.

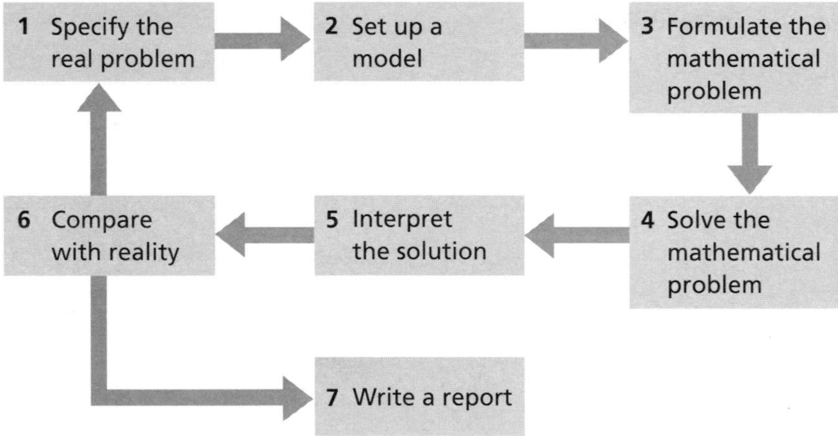

This diagram will appear regularly in the margin as we use mathematics in problem-solving. You do not need to remember the diagram. It is there to help you identify the problem-solving skills that you will be developing as part of your advanced mathematics course.

As you work through this book, you will learn new mathematical methods, which will give you better tools to describe and predict.

Basic algebra

In this chapter we:

- *review the basic techniques of solving linear equations and inequalities*
- *manipulate expressions involving brackets*
- *practise making a variable the subject of an equation.*
- *explore the law of indices for manipulating powers of numbers and variables*
- *explore the manipulation of surds.*

SIMPLE LINEAR EQUATIONS

Solving for x

An **equation** is a mathematical statement that two quantities are equal. It can thought of as a balance. To maintain the balance we have to do the same to both sides (e.g. subtract 5, divide by 9, multiply by 4, etc.).

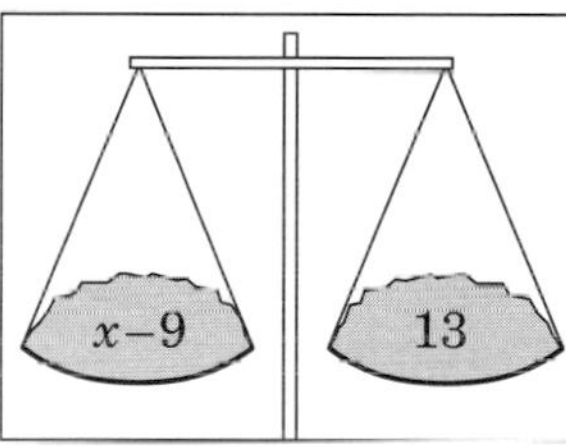

Exploration 2.1

Balancing equations

- For each equation, find a value for x that makes it balance.

1 $x + 7 = 12$

2 $5x = 45$

3 $\dfrac{x}{4} = 7$

4 $3x - 4 = 23$

5 $25 - 4x = 9$

6 $2x - 7 = 8 - 3x$

- In each case describe what you did to solve the equation.

Solving equations

For any equation we may be able to find the solution without writing anything down. In solving equations we use the fact that addition is the inverse of subtraction (and vice-versa) and multiplication is the inverse of division (and vice-versa). However, a more formal approach is essential when there is more manipulation to do. We need a strategy for solving equations.

The following examples illustrate how to solve equations by 'doing the same to both sides', in each case to find the value of x (or the unknown given).

Example 2.1

Solve $x - 9 = 13$.

Solution

Add 9 to both sides $\Rightarrow$ $x - 9 + 9 = 13 + 9$ $\Rightarrow$ $x = 22$

Example 2.2

Solve $30 = 8x$.

Solution

Divide both sides by 8 $\Rightarrow$ $\dfrac{30}{8} = x$ $\Rightarrow$ $x = 3.75$

Example 2.3

Solve $5t + 18 = 3$.

Solution

Subtract 18 from both sides $\Rightarrow$ $5t + 18 - 18 = 3 - 18$

$\Rightarrow$ $5t = -15$

Divide both sides by 5 $\Rightarrow$ $\dfrac{5}{5}t = \dfrac{-15}{5}$

$\Rightarrow$ $t = -3$

Example 2.4

Solve $10 - 2x = x - 12$.

Solution

Add 2x to both sides $\Rightarrow$ $10 - 2x + 2x = x - 12 + 2x$

Collect like terms $\Rightarrow$ $10 = 3x - 12$

Add 12 to both sides $\Rightarrow$ $10 + 12 = 3x - 12 + 12$

$\Rightarrow$ $22 = 3x$

Divide both sides by 3 $\Rightarrow$ $\dfrac{22}{3} = \dfrac{3}{3}x$

$\Rightarrow$ $x = 7\frac{1}{3}$

Example 2.5

Solve $\dfrac{3y+2}{4} = 2y$.

Solution

Multiply both sides by 4 $\Rightarrow$ $4 \times \dfrac{3y+2}{4} = 4 \times 2y$

$\Rightarrow$ $3y + 2 = 8y$

Subtract 3y from both sides $\Rightarrow$ $3y + 2 - 3y = 8y - 3y$

$\Rightarrow$ $2 = 5y$

Divide both sides by 5 $\Rightarrow$ $\dfrac{2}{5} = \dfrac{5}{5}y$

$\Rightarrow$ $y = 0.4$

For each example, check that the value obtained does solve the equation by ensuring that, with this value for the unknown, the equation balances.

e.g. for example 2.3: $t = -3$

LHS $= 5 \times (-3) + 18 = -15 + 18 = 3 =$ RHS

EXERCISES

2.1 CLASSWORK

Solve the following equations, in each case checking that the value obtained does balance the equation.

1	$x + 11 = 30$	**2**	$7 = x - 2.5$
3	$5x = 75$	**4**	$\frac{1}{3}x = 13$
5	$2x - 5 = 11$	**6**	$7 = 5x + 22$
7	$30 - x = 11$	**8**	$7 = 57 - 5m$
9	$20 = 8 - 3x$	**10**	$5x - 3 = 3 - x$
11	$25 - m = 6m + 11$	**12**	$7 - 2x = 2x - 7$
13	$\dfrac{7x-5}{5} = 3x$	**14**	$\dfrac{20-3r}{5} = r$

EXERCISES

2.1 HOMEWORK

Solve the following equations, in each case checking that the value obtained does balance the equation.

1	$x - 15 = 68$	**2**	$8 = 7.7 + m$
3	$14 = 5x$	**4**	$\frac{1}{8}x = 3.5$
5	$12 = 4x - 12$	**6**	$11 + 8x = 81$
7	$0 = 8t + 28$	**8**	$4 = 5 - 3x$
9	$z = 2 + 11z$	**10**	$3 - 6x = x - 18$
11	$3x - 1 = 6 - x$	**12**	$12 + 8x - 15x$
13	$\dfrac{9x+7}{5} = 8$	**14**	$\dfrac{119-x}{11} = 3x$

Exploration 2.2

Brackets

We often need to find the area of something.

■ Find the areas of the following shapes in two different ways.

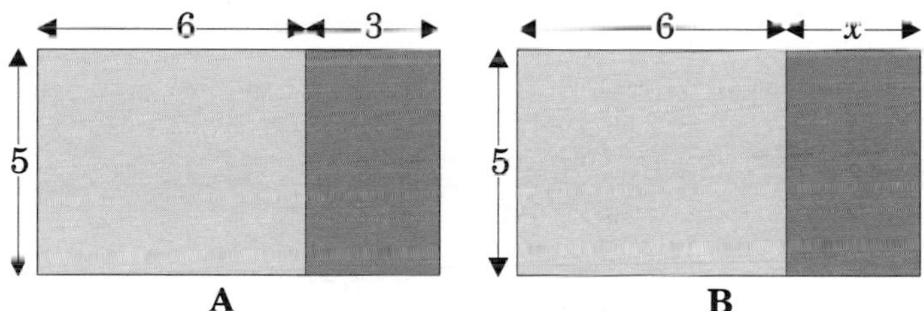

The area of rectangle A may be found as

$5 \times (6 + 3)$ or $5 \times 6 + 5 \times 3$

Either way the area is 45 square units.

The area of rectangle B may be thought of as
$5 \times (6 + x)$ or $5 \times 6 + 5 \times x$

This leads to the algebraic idea of multiplying out or **expanding** brackets.

■ Multiply the 5 by the 6 *and* by the x.

$5(6 + x) = 30 + 5x$.

Exploration 2.3

Diagrams to represent equations

■ Draw a diagram to illustrate $3(10 - x) = 30 - 3x$.

We can take the approach used in the last exploration, but in reverse.

area PUTS = area PQRS – area UQRT
$\rightarrow 3(10 - x) = 30 - 3x$

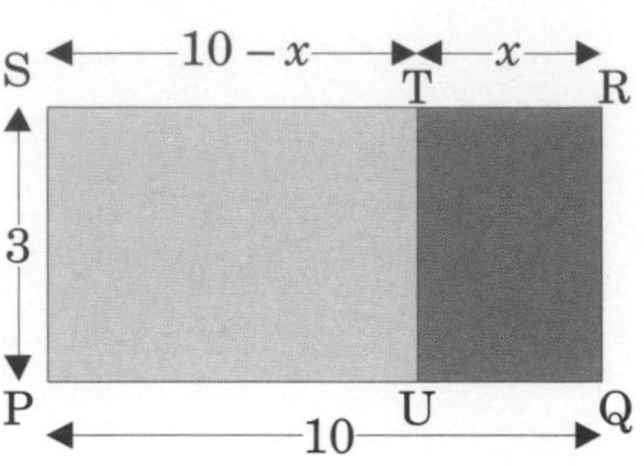

The following examples use similar techniques.

Example 2.6

Multiply out these brackets.

a) $7(x - 10)$ ***b)*** $a(12 - 5x)$
c) $2x(x + 3)$ ***d)*** $-3a(2s - 7t)$

Solution

a) $7(x - 10) = 7(x + (-10))$
$= 7x + (-70)$
$= 7x - 70$

Treating 'subtracting a positive' as 'adding a negative' helps to get the signs right.

b) $a(12 - 5x) = a \times 12 - a \times 5x$
$= 12a - 5ax$

Rearrange the products, writing them with the number first, followed by variables in alphabetical order.

c) $2x(x + 3) = 2x \times x + 2x \times 3$
$= 2x^2 + 6x$

Simplifying products as before, $x \times x$ becomes x^2.

d) $-3a(2s - 7t) = -3a(2s + (-7t))$
$= -3a \times 2s + (-3a) \times (-7t)$
$= -6as + 21at$

Treat 'subtracting a positive' as 'adding a negative' and remember that rules for multiplying directed numbers apply.

Example 2.7

Simplify the following expressions.

a) $3(x - 2y) - 5(x + 3y)$ ***b)*** $(10a - 3)b - 2a(5b - 1)$
c) $3x(2x + 3) - (7 + 4x)$

Solution

a) $3(x - 2y) - 5(x + 3y)$ $= 3(x + (-2y)) + (-5)(x + 3y)$
$= 3x + (-6y) + (-5x) + (-15y)$
$= 3x - 5x - 6y - 15y$
$= -2x - 21y$

b) $(10a - 3)b - 2a(5b - 1) = (10a + (-3))b + (-2a)(5b + (-1))$
$= 10ab + (-3b) + (-10ab) + 2a$
$= 10ab - 3b - 10ab + 2a$
$= 2a - 3b$

c) $3x(2x + 3) - (7 + 4x) = 3x(2x + 3) + (-1)(7 + 4x)$
$= 6x^2 + 9x + (-7) + (-4x)$
$= 6x^2 + 9x - 7 - 4x$
$= 6x^2 + 5x - 7$

Shortcuts

We can put together the ideas from this section to form a set of rules that may be applied to expanding brackets, to give some shortcuts to the calculations.

Rule	**Example**	
$a(b + c) = ab + ac$	$3(x + 5) = 3x + 15$	(1)
$a(b - c) = ab - ac$	$5(p - q) = 5p - 5q$	(2)
$-a(b + c) = -ab - ac$	$-r(s + t) = -rs - rt$	(3)
$-a(b - c) = -ab + ac$	$-x(x - 4) = -x^2 + 4x$ or $4x - x^2$	(4)

Notice the pattern of the operation signs in each case.

The reverse of expanding brackets is called **factorising**.

Rules (1) and (2) in reverse give $ab + ac = a(b + c)$ and $ab - ac = a(b - c)$

In both cases a is the **common factor**. In practice we try to make a the highest common factor (HCF), which is often obtained by inspection.

Example 2.8

Factorise the following.

a) $3r + 12s$ **b)** $25x - 15$
c) $6x^2 - 21x$ **d)** $12e + 4f - 20$

Solution

a) *HCF is 3:* $3r + 12s = 3 \times r + 3 \times 4s = 3(r + 4s)$
b) *HCF is 5:* $25x - 15 = 5 \times 5x - 5 \times 3 = 5(5x - 3)$
c) *HCF is 3x:* $6x^2 - 21x = 3x \times 2x - 3x \times 7 = 3x(2x - 7)$
d) *HCF is 4:* $12e + 4f - 20 = 4 \times 3e + 4 \times f - 4 \times 5 = 4(3e + f - 5)$

Example 2.9

Simplify and factorise the following.

a) $(8x + 2y) - (3x - 8y)$
b) $7x(1 - 3x) + x(5 + x)$

Solution

a) $(8x + 2y) - (3x - 8y) = 8x + 2y - 3x + 8y$
$= 5x + 10y = 5 \times x + 5 \times 2y$
$= 5(x + 2y)$

b) $7x(1 - 3x) + x(5 + x) = 7x - 21x^2 + 5x + x^2$
$= 12x - 20x^2 = 4x \times 3 - 4x \times 5x$
$= 4x(3 - 5x)$

EXERCISES

Multiply out the brackets.

a) $3(x + 4)$ b) $-3(x - 4)$
c) $-4(x + 5)$ d) $7(2p - 3q)$
e) $2x(x - 3)$ f) $2x(x + 3)$
g) $-3p(q - 2r)$ h) $-3p(q + 2r)$
i) $5a(a - b + c)$ j) $5a(a + b - c)$
k) $-2r(-3r + 5s - t)$ l) $-2r(3r - 5s + t)$

2 Simplify the following.

a) $3(x + 1) + 2(x + 4)$ b) $3(x + 1) - 2(x + 4)$
c) $4(1 - 2x) + 3(3x - 4)$ d) $4(1 - 2x) - 3(3x - 4)$
e) $x(2x - 1) + 2x(x + 4)$ f) $x(2x - 1) - 2x(x + 4)$
g) $4(x + 5) - 3(x + 2) + 5(x - 1)$ h) $a(b + c) + a(b - c) - a(b + c)$
i) $2p - 3q - (5p + 2q)$ j) $8(x - y) - (3x - 4y)$

3 Factorise each of these fully.

a) $10a - 5b$ b) $7x + 21$
c) $12y + 3$ d) $12xy - 3x$
e) $7x^2 - 5x$ f) $7t^2 - 35t$
g) $a^2b - ab^2$ h) $15cd + 20de$
i) $5r - 20s + 15t$ j) $30xy + 6x^2 - 15x$

EXERCISES

2.2 HOMEWORK

1 Multiply out the brackets.

a) $6(3x + 2)$ b) $-8(9x + 8)$
c) $2(5 - 7x)$ d) $-(4x - 3)$
e) $8(8a - 2b)$ f) $-4(9b - 6a)$
g) $4m(7m + 6)$ h) $-x(9 + x)$
i) $-4x(5x - 1)$ j) $5t(-5 - 2t)$
k) $x(x + y - z)$ l) $-y(x - y - z)$
m) $-3a(8a - 8b + c)$ n) $4a(2a - 3b - 1)$

2 Simplify the following.

a) $9(x + 7) + 6(x + 7)$ b) $5 - (x - 3)$
c) $9(x - 7) - 6(x + 1)$ d) $7(6x - 1) + 3(5 - 4x)$
e) $5(4 + 2t) - (14 - 2t)$ f) $-(7x + 1) - 3(9 + 8x)$
g) $9x(7x - 6) + 2x(8 + 2x)$ h) $5x(5x + 2) - 4(3x - 7)$
i) $(6x - 7) - 2(x + 1) + 3(3 - x)$ j) $x(y + z) - x(y - z) + 2x(y + z)$
k) $7(6x - 5) - x + 7 - 7(5 + 3x)$ l) $8(a - 5b) - (4a + b) + (a - 6b)$

3 Factorise each of these fully.

a) $28x + 24$ b) $42 - 35a$ c) $3 - 3x$ d) $4m^2 + 10m$
e) $8y^2 - 3y$ f) $2a^2 + 18a$ g) $8x^2y - 7xy^2$ h) $3ab + 6a^2d$
i) $x + 7xy - x^2$ j) $24t^2 - 30t - 42tu^2$

LINEAR EQUATIONS WITH BRACKETS

We can now use the ideas built up in the section above to solve equations with brackets.

Example 2.10

Solve $4(x-5)=19$.

Solution

Multiply out $\Rightarrow 4x-20=19$

Add 20 to both sides $\Rightarrow 4x-20+20=19+20$

$\Rightarrow 4x=39$

Divide both sides by 4 $\Rightarrow \frac{4x}{4}=\frac{39}{4}$

$\Rightarrow x=9.75$

Example 2.11

Solve $3(x+4)-5(x-1)=23$.

Multiply out $\Rightarrow 3x+12-5x+5=23$

Collect like terms $\Rightarrow -2x+17=23$

Subtract 17 from both sides $\Rightarrow -2x+17-17=23-17$

$\Rightarrow -2x=6$

Divide both sides by –2 $\Rightarrow \frac{-2x}{-2}=\frac{6}{-2}$

$\Rightarrow x=-3$

Example 2.12

Solve $5(2x-3)=22-(7x+3)$.

Solution

Multiply out $\Rightarrow 10x-15=22-7x-3$

Collect like terms $\Rightarrow 10x-15=19-7x$

Add 7x to both sides $\Rightarrow 10x-15+7x=19-7x+7x$

Collect like terms $\Rightarrow 17x-15=19$

Add 15 to both sides $\Rightarrow 17x-15+15=19+15$

$\Rightarrow 17x=34$

Divide both sides by 17 $\Rightarrow \frac{17}{17}x=\frac{34}{17}$

$\Rightarrow x=2$

EXERCISES

2.3 CLASSWORK

Solve the following equations

1 $2(x+1)=9$
2 $5(m-2)=17$
3 $2x=4(x+1)$
4 $5(8-x)=3x$
5 $3(x-1)-4(2x+3)=14$
6 $5(y+2)-3(y-5)=29$
7 $4(x-5)=7-5(3-2x)$
8 $7x-(2-x)=0$
9 $3(n+1)=10-(2n+3)$
10 $3y+7+3(y-1)=4(y+3)$
11 $4(r-1)+3(r+2)=5(r-4)$
12 $7-2(x-1)=3(2x-1)+2$

EXERCISES

2.3 HOMEWORK

Solve the following equations.

1 $8(3x-8)=26$
2 $2(5-3x)=70$
3 $7(x+2)=21x$
4 $2x-8=4(x+6)$
5 $8(x-2)-(7x-9)=-4$
6 $5(4-5t)+8(t-7)=32$
7 $7(4x+3)=8-(4x+3)$
8 $2x-5(x-7)=0$
9 $8(x+3)=8-(x+3)$
10 $4n-7+6(n+1)=8(n-4)$
11 $9(4x+1)-6(8-7x)=5(5x-1)$
12 $4x-6-(2x+3)=2-3(8x-2)$

LINEAR EQUATIONS WITH FRACTIONS

Exploration 2.4

Solving equations involving fractions

- What operations do we need to carry out, and in what order, to solve this equation?

$$\frac{7x+5}{4} = 2x - 3 \qquad (1)$$

- Refine the method to solve

$$\frac{5x-3}{7} = \frac{2x+1}{3} \quad (2) \quad \text{and} \quad \frac{2x}{3} - \frac{x}{5} = \frac{x+3}{6} \quad (3)$$

Solving the equations

In each case the first operation is to multiply both sides by the same number to eliminate the fractions.
For equation (1) we multiply both sides by 4.
For equation (2) we multiply both sides by 21.
For equation (3) we multiply both sides by 30.

Whenever we need to solve equations with fractions, first of all we multiply both sides by the **lowest common denominator**.

The following examples illustrate how this method can be applied in a variety of cases, including when a variable (such as x) appears in the denominator.

Example 2.13

Solve $\dfrac{5x-3}{7} = \dfrac{2x+1}{3}$.

Solution

Multiply both sides by 21	$\Rightarrow$	$\dfrac{21(5x-3)}{7} = \dfrac{21(2x+1)}{3}$
Simplify numerical fractions	$\Rightarrow$	$3(5x-3) = 7(2x+1)$
Multiply out	$\Rightarrow$	$15x - 9 = 14x + 7$
Subtract 14x from both sides	$\Rightarrow$	$15x - 9 - 14x = 14x + 7 - 14x$
	$\Rightarrow$	$x - 9 = 7$
Add 9 to both sides	$\Rightarrow$	$x - 9 + 9 = 7 + 9$
	$\Rightarrow$	$x = 16$

Example 2.14

Solve $\dfrac{2x}{3} - \dfrac{x}{5} = \dfrac{x+3}{6}$.

Solution

Multiply both sides by 30	$\Rightarrow$	$30\left(\dfrac{2x}{3} - \dfrac{x}{5}\right) = 30\left(\dfrac{x+3}{6}\right)$
	$\Rightarrow$	$\dfrac{30 \times 2x}{3} - \dfrac{30 \times x}{5} = \dfrac{30(x+3)}{6}$
Simplify numerical fractions	$\Rightarrow$	$20x - 6x = 5(x + 3)$
Simplify and multiply out	$\Rightarrow$	$14x = 5x + 15$
Subtract 5x from both sides	$\Rightarrow$	$14x - 5x = 5x + 15 - 5x$
	$\Rightarrow$	$9x = 15$
Divide both sides by 9	$\Rightarrow$	$\dfrac{9x}{9} = \dfrac{15}{9}$
	$\Rightarrow$	$x = 1\frac{2}{3}$

Example 2.15

Solve $\dfrac{t-4}{5}+\dfrac{2t-3}{10}=2.5$.

Solution

Multiply both sides by 10 $\Rightarrow \quad 10\left(\dfrac{t-4}{5}+\dfrac{2t-3}{10}\right)=10\times 2.5$

$\Rightarrow \quad \dfrac{10(t-4)}{5}+\dfrac{10(2t-3)}{10}=25$

$\Rightarrow \quad 2(t-4)+(2t-3)=25$

$\Rightarrow \quad 2t-8+2t-3=25$

$\Rightarrow \quad 4t-11=25$

Add 11 to both sides $\Rightarrow \quad 4t-11+11=25+11$

$\Rightarrow \quad 4t=36$

Divide both sides by 4 $\Rightarrow \quad \dfrac{4t}{4}=\dfrac{36}{4}$

$\Rightarrow \quad t=9$

Example 2.16

Solve $\dfrac{2y-3}{y}=\dfrac{5}{4}$.

Solution

Multiply both sides by 4y $\Rightarrow \quad \dfrac{4y(2y-3)}{y}=\dfrac{5\times 4y}{4}$

$\Rightarrow \quad 4(2y-3)=5y$

$\Rightarrow \quad 8y-12=5y$

Add 12 to both sides $\Rightarrow \quad 8y-12+12=5y+12$

Subtract 5y from both sides $\Rightarrow \quad 8y-5y=5y+12-5y$

$\Rightarrow \quad 3y=12$

Divide both sides by 3 $\Rightarrow \quad \dfrac{3}{3}y=\dfrac{12}{3}$

$\Rightarrow \quad y=4$

EXERCISES

2.4 CLASSWORK

Solve the following equations.

1 $\dfrac{x}{2}+7=12$

2 $\dfrac{x}{3}+10=2x$

3 $\dfrac{5x}{6}=\dfrac{1}{4}$

4 $\dfrac{4x}{3}=\dfrac{x}{2}+5$

5 $\dfrac{m}{5}-\dfrac{m}{6}=0.5$

6 $\dfrac{y+3}{4}-\dfrac{y-3}{5}=2$

7 $\dfrac{3u+5}{4}=2-\dfrac{10+u}{6}$

8 $\dfrac{2x}{15}-\dfrac{x-6}{12}-\dfrac{3x}{20}=\dfrac{3}{2}$

9 $\dfrac{12}{x}=-4$

10 $\dfrac{8-x}{x}=\dfrac{3}{5}$

11 $\dfrac{3x}{x-2}=4$

12 $\dfrac{3x-1}{2x-1}=2$

13 $\dfrac{15}{2y}+\dfrac{10}{3y}=\dfrac{5}{6}$

14 $\dfrac{30}{2x+1}=\dfrac{14}{x}$

15 $\dfrac{9}{x+1}-\dfrac{15}{3x-1}=0$

EXERCISES

2.4 HOMEWORK

Solve the following equations.

1 $\frac{x}{4} - 1 = 5$

2 $\frac{2t}{3} + 5 = 9t$

3 $\frac{6x}{5} = \frac{4}{3}$

4 $\frac{x}{9} = \frac{5x}{6} + 13$

5 $\frac{x}{8} + \frac{x}{12} = 1$

6 $\frac{n}{4} - 7 = \frac{6n}{7}$

7 $\frac{9x+3}{7} = \frac{1-8x}{2}$

8 $\frac{2x}{21} = \frac{x-15}{33}$

9 $\frac{6n+7}{9} + \frac{8n}{3} = 3$

10 $\frac{5-9x}{8} - 2 = \frac{x}{4}$

11 $\frac{x+4}{14} + \frac{4x-5}{35} - \frac{9}{10} = \frac{x}{5}$

12 $\frac{9x+2}{6} - \frac{1-3x}{7} = \frac{x+6}{3}$

13 $\frac{31}{x} = 10$

14 $\frac{8x+1}{x} = 2$

15 $\frac{5x-1}{x} = \frac{8}{9}$

16 $\frac{x}{x+3} = 6$

17 $\frac{x-4}{9-3x} = \frac{5}{6}$

18 $\frac{3}{4u} - \frac{u+1}{5u} = 2$

19 $\frac{6}{2x-1} = \frac{5}{4x+3}$

20 $\frac{45}{7x+4} + \frac{53}{2-5x} = 0$

SIMPLIFYING EXPRESSIONS

Exploration 2.5

Simplifying expressions with fractions

- What operations do we need to carry out, to simplify this expression?

$$\frac{x}{3} - \frac{x}{4} + \frac{5x}{6} \qquad (1)$$

- Refine the method to simplify this expression.

$$\frac{1}{x} + \frac{2}{1-x} \qquad (2)$$

Simplifying the equation

In each case, the first operation is to find the lowest common denominator, which is the same as the lowest common multiple of all the denominators.

For expression (1) the lowest common denominator is 12, so we write each fraction over 12 and then simplify the numerator, to find the answer.

$$\frac{4x - 3x + 10x}{12} = \frac{11x}{12}$$

For expression (2) we follow the same steps but now the lowest common denominator is $x(1-x)$.

$$\frac{(1-x) + 2x}{x(1-x)} = \frac{1+x}{x(1-x)}$$

Whenever we simplify expressions involving fractions first of all we put all the fractions over the lowest common denominator. The following examples illustrate how to simplify algebraic expressions.

Example 2.17

Find the highest common factor of $x^2 + x$ and $x^2 - x$, and hence simplify $\frac{x^2 + x}{x^2 - x}$.

Solution

Factorise both expressions $\Rightarrow$ $x^2 + x = x(x + 1)$
$x^2 - x = x(x - 1)$

$\Rightarrow$ $\frac{x^2 + x}{x^2 - x} = \frac{x(x + 1)}{x(x - 1)}$

Divide numerator and denominator by x $\Rightarrow$ $\frac{x(x + 1)}{x(x - 1)} = \frac{x + 1}{x - 1}$

Example 2.18

Simplify $\frac{1}{x} + \frac{x}{x - 1}$.

Solution

Find the lowest common denominator $x(x - 1)$

Write each fraction in terms of the lowest common denominator $\Rightarrow$ $\frac{1}{x} = \frac{x - 1}{x(x - 1)}$

$\frac{x}{x - 1} = \frac{x^2}{x(x - 1)}$

Simplify $\Rightarrow$ $\frac{1}{x} + \frac{x}{x - 1} = \frac{x - 1}{x(x - 1)} + \frac{x^2}{x(x - 1)} = \frac{x^2 + x - 1}{x(x - 1)}$

Example 2.19

Simplify $\frac{a}{a^2 + 2a} - \frac{(a - 1)}{a} + \frac{(a + 1)}{(a + 2)}$.

Solution

Factorise $a^2 + 2a$ $\Rightarrow$ $a^2 + 2a = a(a + 2)$

Find the lowest common denominator.

This is the lowest common multiple of $a(a + 2)$, a and $(a + 2)$, which is $a(a + 2)$.

Write each fraction in terms of the lowest common denominator $\Rightarrow$ $\frac{a}{a^2 + 2a} = \frac{a}{a(a + 2)}$

$\frac{a - 1}{a} = \frac{(a - 1)(a + 2)}{a(a + 2)}$

$\frac{a + 1}{a + 2} = \frac{a(a + 1)}{a(a + 2)}$

Combine the fractions and simplify the numerator

$$\Rightarrow \frac{a - (a - 1)(a + 2) + a(a + 1)}{a(a + 2)} = \frac{a - (a^2 + a - 2) + a^2 + a}{a(a + 2)} = \frac{a + 2}{a(a + 2)} = \frac{1}{a}$$

EXERCISES

2.5 CLASSWORK

Find the lowest common multiple for each of these groups of expressions.

1 $x - 1, 3(x + 1), (x + 1)^2$

2 $a - 1, (a - 1)(a + 1), 2(a + 1)$

3 $(x - a)^2, (x - a)(x + a)$

4 $y^2 - 2y, (y - 2)(y - 1)$

Simplify these expressions.

5 $\dfrac{x^2 - 3x}{x - 3}$ **6** $\dfrac{(a^3 + 2a)(a - 1)}{a(a^2 - a)}$

7 $\dfrac{2}{3x} + \dfrac{3}{4x}$ **8** $\dfrac{1}{x + 1} + \dfrac{1}{1 - x}$

9 $\dfrac{a}{2 - a} + \dfrac{4}{4 - a}$ **10** $1 + \dfrac{1}{x(x + 1)}$

11 $\dfrac{y + 3}{(y - 1)(y + 1)} - \dfrac{3}{2(y - 1)}$ **12** $\dfrac{1}{(x - a)(x - b)} + \dfrac{1}{(a - b)(a - x)}$

EXERCISES

2.5 HOMEWORK

Find the lowest common multiple for each of these groups of expressions.

1 $x + 1, (x - 1), x(x + 1)^2$ **2** $x - 1, (x - 1)(x + 2), 2(x + 2)$

3 $3(x + 1), 6(x + 1)^3$ **4** $y^2 - ay, y^2 + ay, (y - 1)(y + 2)$

Simplify these expressions.

5 $\dfrac{x^2 + 4x}{x + 4}$ **6** $\dfrac{(a^2 + 2a)(a + 1)}{a(a^2 + a)}$

7 $\dfrac{3}{2x} + \dfrac{4}{3x}$ **8** $\dfrac{1}{x + 2} + \dfrac{1}{2 - x}$

9 $\dfrac{y}{3 + y} - \dfrac{1}{1 - y}$ **10** $2 + \dfrac{a + 1}{a(a - 1)}$

11 $\dfrac{3}{x^2 - x} - \dfrac{4}{x^2 - 1}$ **12** $\dfrac{1}{a - 1} + \dfrac{a}{a + 1} - \dfrac{a + 1}{2a}$

CHANGING THE SUBJECT OF A FORMULA

28° in the shade!

What does 28° mean? Weather reports seem to switch randomly from the Celsius scale to the Fahrenheit. The formula $f = 32 + 1.8c$ is used to convert temperatures in Celsius (°C) into temperatures in Fahrenheit (°F).

When $c = 20$, $f = 32 + 1.8 \times 20 = 68$

We can rearrange the formula to convert temperatures in °F to temperatures in °C.

Rearranging a formula is called **changing the subject**.

In the example above, we began with f as the subject of a formula and wanted to rearrange it to make c the subject.

Treat $f = 32 + 1.8c$ as an equation which can be solved for c. The steps we might take are:

Subtract 32 from both sides $\Rightarrow f - 32 = 32 + 1.8c - 32$

$\Rightarrow f - 32 = 1.8c$

Divide both sides by 1.8 $\Rightarrow \dfrac{f - 32}{1.8} = \dfrac{1.8c}{1.8}$

$\Rightarrow c = \dfrac{f - 32}{1.8}$

Given any temperature in Fahrenheit, this rearranged formula may be used to give the temperature in Celsius.

When $f = 98.6$, $c = \dfrac{98.6 - 32}{1.8} = 37$

We often find that a formula may be rearranged to change the subject, in this way. We simply treat it as an equation and solve for the variable we want to make the subject.

The following examples illustrate a variety of cases.

Example 2.20

In mechanics or physics, a common equation of motion is $v = u + at$. This describes how the velocity of an object in uniform motion changes in relation to the starting velocity, the (constant) acceleration and the time of travel. Suppose we need to find the value of t. We need to make t the subject of $v = u + at$.

Solution

Treat the formula as an equation in t.

$$v = u + at$$

Subtract u from both sides $\Rightarrow v - u = u + at - u$

$\Rightarrow v - u = at$

Divide both sides by a $\Rightarrow \dfrac{v-u}{a} = \dfrac{at}{a}$

$\Rightarrow t = \dfrac{v-u}{a}$

Example 2.21

Make a the subject of $P = 2(a + b)$.

Solution

$$P = 2(a + b)$$

Multiply out the brackets $\Rightarrow P = 2a + 2b$

Subtract $2b$ from both sides $\Rightarrow P - 2b = 2a + 2b - 2b$

$\Rightarrow P - 2b = 2a$

Divide both sides by 2 $\Rightarrow \dfrac{P-2b}{2} = \dfrac{2a}{2}$

$\Rightarrow a = \dfrac{P-2b}{2}$ (1)

Alternatively, we could try a different approach, to give an equivalent formula.

$$P = 2(a + b)$$

Divide both sides by 2 $\Rightarrow \dfrac{P}{2} = \dfrac{2(a+b)}{2} = a + b$

Subtract b from both sides $\Rightarrow \dfrac{P}{2} - b = a + b - b$

$\Rightarrow a = \dfrac{P}{2} - b$ (2)

(1) and (2) are equivalent to each other – try substituting numerical values for b and P and check that you get the same value for a whichever rearrangement you use.

Example 2.22

Make p the subject of $\frac{q-ap}{m}=l$.

Solution

Treat the formula as an equation in p. $\frac{q-ap}{m}=l$

Multiply both sides by m $\Rightarrow$ $\frac{m(q-ap)}{m}=ml$

$\Rightarrow$ $q-ap=ml$

Add ap to both sides $\Rightarrow$ $q-ap+ap=ml+ap$

$\Rightarrow$ $q=ml+ap$

Subtract ml from both sides $\Rightarrow$ $q-ml=ml+ap-ml$

$\Rightarrow$ $q-ml=ap$

Divide both sides by a $\Rightarrow$ $\frac{q-ml}{a}=\frac{ap}{a}$

$\Rightarrow$ $p=\frac{q-ml}{a}$

Example 2.23

Rewrite $\frac{a}{b}+c=d$ in the form $b=\ldots$.

Solution

Treat the formula as an equation in b. $\frac{a}{b}+c=d$

Subtract c from both sides $\Rightarrow$ $\frac{a}{b}+c-c=d-c$

$\Rightarrow$ $\frac{a}{b}=d-c$

Multiply both sides by b $\Rightarrow$ $\frac{a}{b}\times b=b(d-c)$

$\Rightarrow$ $a=b(d-c)$

Divide both sides by $(d-c)$ $\Rightarrow$ $\frac{a}{d-c}=\frac{b(d-c)}{d-c}$

$\Rightarrow$ $b=\frac{a}{d-c}$

Example 2.24

Make s the subject of the formula $3s+t=7r-as$.

Treat the formula as an equation in s. $3s+t=7r-as$

Add as to both sides $\Rightarrow$ $3s+t+as=7r-as+as$

Collect like terms $\Rightarrow$ $3s+as+t=7r$

Subtract t from both sides $\Rightarrow$ $3s+as+t-t=7r-t$

$\Rightarrow$ $3s+as=7r-t$

Take out s as a common factor $\Rightarrow$ $s(3+a)=7r-t$

Divide both sides by $(3+a)$ $\Rightarrow$ $\frac{s(3+a)}{3+a}=\frac{7r-t}{3+a}$

$\Rightarrow$ $s=\frac{7r-t}{3+a}$

Example 2.25

Make x the subject of the formula $y = \frac{x+5}{3-x}$ *and find x when $y = 3$.*

$$y = \frac{x+5}{3-x}$$

Multiply both sides by $(3-x)$ $\Rightarrow$ $(3-x)y = \frac{x+5}{3-x}(3-x) = x+5$

Multiply out the brackets $\Rightarrow$ $3y - xy = x + 5$

Add xy to both sides $\Rightarrow$ $3y - xy + xy = x + 5 + xy$

Collect like terms $\Rightarrow$ $3y = x + xy + 5$

Subtract 5 from both sides $\Rightarrow$ $3y - 5 = x + xy + 5 - 5$

$\Rightarrow$ $3y - 5 = x + xy$

Take x out as a common factor $\Rightarrow$ $3y - 5 = x(1+y)$

Divide both sides by $(1+y)$ $\Rightarrow$ $\frac{3y-5}{1+y} = \frac{x(1+y)}{1+y}$

$\Rightarrow$ $x = \frac{3y-5}{1+y}$

When $y = 3$, $x = \frac{3 \times 3 - 5}{1+3} = \frac{9-5}{4} = 1$

EXERCISES

2.6 CLASSWORK

Make the variable shown in brackets the subject.

1	$v = u + at$	(u)	**2**	$A = \frac{1}{2}h(a+b)$	(a)
3	$u = a + (n-1)d$	(d)	**4**	$u = a + (n-1)d$	(n)
5	$5x - y = 12$	(y)	**6**	$5x - y = 12$	(x)
7	$4x + 5y = 20$	(y)	**8**	$4x + 5y = 20$	(x)
9	$\frac{3r+5}{s} = 8$	(s)	**10**	$\frac{5p-2q}{r} = w$	(p)
11	$\frac{a(b-c)}{d} = e$	(d)	**12**	$\frac{a(b-c)}{d} = e$	(b)
13	$\frac{3e}{g} = f - 7$	(e)	**14**	$\frac{3e}{g} = f - 7$	(g)
15	$3a + b = 5a - b$	(a)	**16**	$px + q = rx + s$	(x)
17	$5m - n = 4(3m+n)$	(m)	**18**	$5m + n = n(3m-4)$	(m)
19	$2(x-1) = a(b-x)$	(x)	**20**	$x(a+b) = d(x+b)$	(x)
21	$y = \frac{x+1}{x-1}$	(x)	**22**	$y = \frac{5-x}{2x-2}$	(x)

EXERCISES

2.6 HOMEWORK

Make the variable shown in brackets the subject.

1	$a = bx + c$	(x)	**2**	$v^2 = u^2 + 2as$	(s)
3	$s = \frac{1}{2}(u+v)t$	(t)	**4**	$s = \frac{1}{2}(u+v)t$	(v)
5	$y - y_1 = m(x - x_1)$	(m)	**6**	$c = 2\pi r$	(r)
7	$p = \frac{w}{g}f$	(w)	**8**	$A = 2\pi r^2 + 2\pi rh$	(h)
9	$7x - 9y = 3$	(y)	**10**	$g = \frac{x+3y}{a}$	(x)
11	$2m = \frac{3x-7y}{n}$	(n)	**12**	$\frac{3a-2b}{5} = m$	(b)

13	$\dfrac{3a}{2} = 9x - 1$	(a)	**14**	$m = \dfrac{y-b}{x-a}$	(y)
15	$2x + a = 8x + b$	(x)	**16**	$6a(x+y) = 4(x-7y)$	(x)
17	$m(x + y) = n(x - y)$	(y)	**18**	$x = \dfrac{y+3}{2-y}$	(y)
19	$f = \dfrac{8x-5f}{m}$	(f)	**20**	$y = \dfrac{m}{x} + c$	(x)

LINEAR INEQUALITIES

Exploration 2.6

What is an inequality?

- What do you understand by these expressions?
  $x < 7$ $\quad x \geq 10$ $\quad 0 \geq x$ $\quad -2 \leq x \leq 2$ $\quad 2 < x < 7$
- Illustrate these inequalities, using the real number line.
- Simplify **1** $3x + 1 < 13$ **2** $12 - 5x \leq 20$
  3 $3x - 5 < 6x + 10$ **4** $\dfrac{10-x}{3} > x + 5$
  5 $3 < 2x - 5 \leq 11$
- If $x > 5$ does it follow that $-x > -5$?
- What do you understand by $|x| > 3$?

Interpreting inequalities

An inequality such as $x < 7$ means that x can take any value less than 7. If x is a real number then the set of values satisfying the inequality may be illustrated by an **open** interval on the real number line.

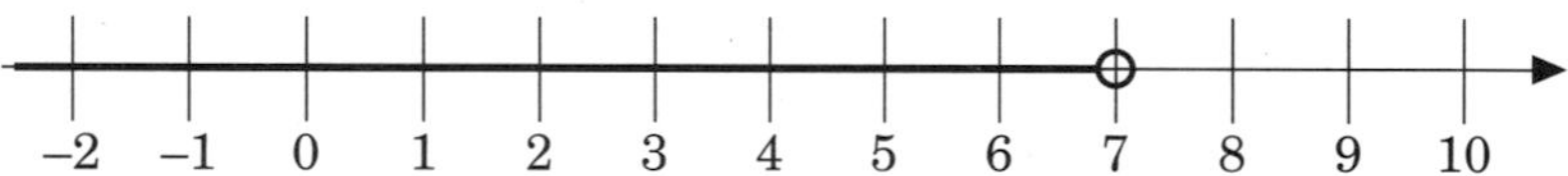

An inequality such as $-2 \leq x \leq 2$ means that x can take any value between –2 and 2 inclusive, illustrated by a **closed** interval on the real number line.

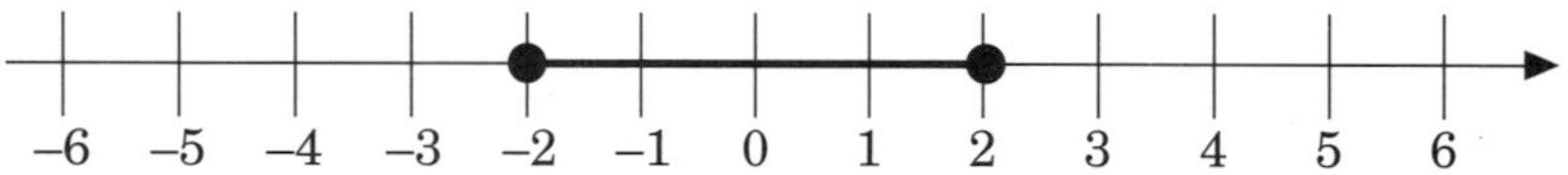

Inequalities such as $12 - 5x \leq 20$ may be simplified by manipulating the inequality, in a similar way to an equation.

$$12 - 5x \leq 20$$

Add $5x$ to both sides $\quad \Rightarrow \quad 12 - 5x + 5x \leq 20 + 5x$

$\Rightarrow \quad 12 \leq 20 + 5x$

Subtract 20 from both sides $\quad \Rightarrow \quad 12 - 20 \leq 20 + 5x - 20$

$\Rightarrow \quad -8 \leq 5x$

Divide both sides by 5 $\quad \Rightarrow \quad -\dfrac{8}{5} \leq \dfrac{5x}{5}$

$\Rightarrow \quad -1.6 \leq x$

This is equivalent to $x \geq -1.6$, reading the inequality from right to left. The **solution** to the inequality represents the set of values of x which are *greater than or equal* to –1.6.

We could take an alternative approach to simplifying $12 - 5x \le 20$.

$$12 - 5x \le 20$$

Subtract 12 from both sides $\Rightarrow 12 - 5x - 12 \le 20 - 12$

$\Rightarrow -5x \le 8$

Divide both sides by –5 and *reverse* the inequality sign $\Rightarrow \dfrac{-5x}{-5} \ge \dfrac{8}{-5}$

$\Rightarrow x \ge -1.6$

Note
When solving an inequality, if you multiply or divide by a negative number you *must* reverse the inequality.

For example:
$12 > 5 \Rightarrow -12 < -5$ or $x > 5 \Rightarrow -x < -5$

The modulus sign

The **modulus** of a number is its **absolute** value, i.e. its **magnitude**, ignoring its sign, and is denoted by enclosing it by a pair of vertical lines.

e.g. $|8.3| = 8.3$
$|-2| = 2$

Algebraic equations and inequalities may also involve the modulus sign.
e.g. $|x| = 5 \Rightarrow x = -5$ or $x = 5$
$|x| \le 5 \Rightarrow -5 \le x \le 5$
$|x| > 3 \Rightarrow x < -3$ or $x > 3$

Note how the last two inequalities may be illustrated.
$|x| \le 5 \Rightarrow -5 \le x \le 5$ which is a closed interval.

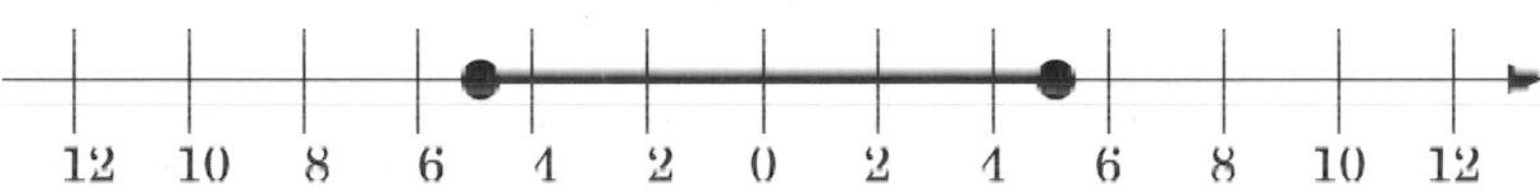

$|x| > 3 \Rightarrow x < -3$ or $x > 3$ which is two open intervals.

The following examples illustrate the simplification or solution of inequalities and how the solution set may be represented on the real number line.

Example 2.26

Simplify the inequality $3x - 5 < 6x + 10$.

Solution

$$3x - 5 < 6x + 10$$

Subtract 10 from both sides $\Rightarrow 3x - 5 - 10 < 6x + 10 - 10$

$\Rightarrow 3x - 15 < 6x$

Subtract 3x from both sides $\Rightarrow 3x - 15 - 3x < 6x - 3x$

$\Rightarrow -15 < 3x$

Divide both sides by 3 $\Rightarrow \dfrac{-15}{3} < \dfrac{3x}{3}$

$\Rightarrow -5 < x$ *or* $\Rightarrow x > -5$

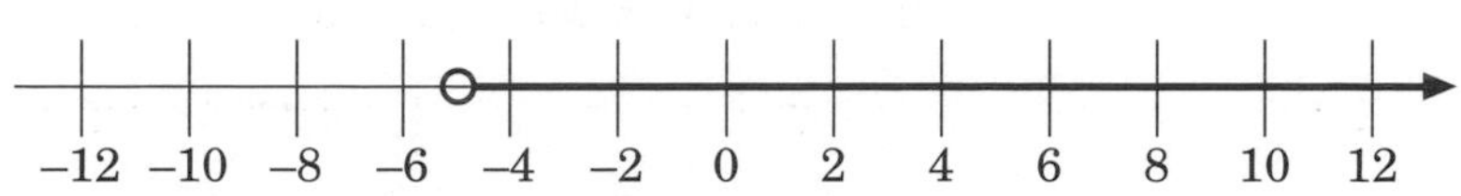

Example 2.27

Solve the inequality $\frac{8-x}{3} \geq x+5$.

Solution

$$\frac{8-x}{3} \geq x+5$$

Multiply both sides by 3 $\Rightarrow \frac{3(8-x)}{3} \geq 3(x+5)$

Multiply out the brackets $\Rightarrow 8-x \geq 3x+15$

Add x to both sides $\Rightarrow 8-x+x \geq 3x+15+x$

$\Rightarrow 8 \geq 4x+15$

Subtract 15 from both sides $\Rightarrow 8-15 \geq 4x+15-15$

$\Rightarrow -7 \geq 4x$

Divide both sides by 4 $\Rightarrow \frac{-7}{4} \geq \frac{4x}{4}$

$\Rightarrow -1.75 \geq x$

or $\Rightarrow x \leq -1.75$

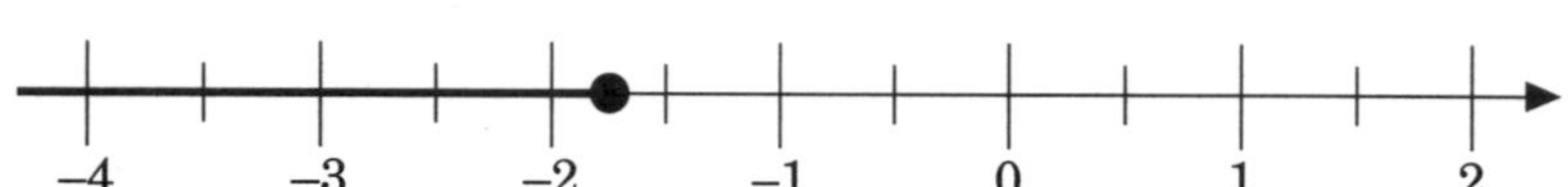

Example 2.28

Find the values of x which satisfy $3 < 2x - 5 \leq 11$.

Solution

Treat the double inequality as two separate inequalities.

i.e. ***a)*** $3 < 2x - 5$ ***b)*** $2x - 5 \leq 11$

a) $3 < 2x - 5$

Add 5 to both sides $\Rightarrow 3+5 < 2x-5+5$

$\Rightarrow 8 < 2x$

Divide both sides by 2 $\Rightarrow \frac{8}{2} < \frac{2}{2}x$

$\Rightarrow 4 < x \quad (1)$

or $\Rightarrow x > 4$

b) $2x - 5 \leq 11$

Add 5 to both sides $\Rightarrow 2x-5+5 \leq 11+5$

$\Rightarrow 2x \leq 16$

Divide both sides by 2 $\Rightarrow \frac{2}{2}x \leq \frac{16}{2}$

$\Rightarrow x \leq 8 \quad (2)$

Combining inequalities (1) and (2) gives the solution set. $4 < x \leq 8$

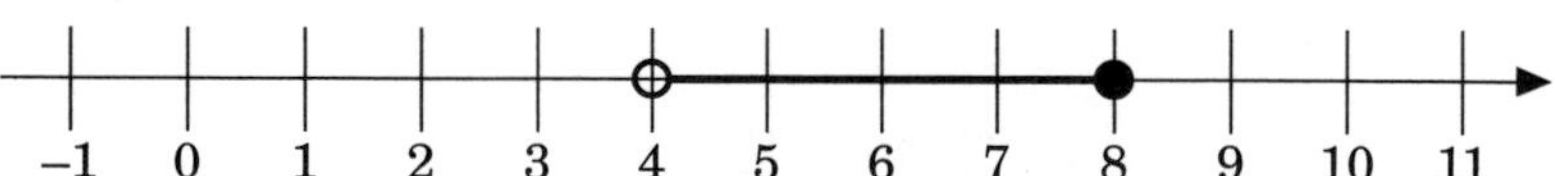

Example 2.29

Solve the inequality $|5x - 8| \geq 12$.

Solution

$|5x - 8| \geq 12$ *means* ***a)*** $5x - 8 \leq -12$ ***b)*** $5x - 8 \geq 12$

a)

$$5x - 8 \le -12$$

Add 8 to both sides $\Rightarrow \quad 5x - 8 + 8 \le -12 + 8$

$\Rightarrow \quad 5x \le -4$

Divide both sides by 5 $\Rightarrow \quad \dfrac{5x}{5} \le \dfrac{-4}{5}$

$\Rightarrow \quad x \le -0.8 \qquad (1)$

b)

$$5x - 8 \ge 12$$

Add 8 to both sides $\Rightarrow \quad 5x - 8 + 8 \ge 12 + 8$

$\Rightarrow \quad 5x \ge 20$

Divide both sides by 5 $\Rightarrow \quad \dfrac{5x}{5} \ge \dfrac{20}{5}$

$\Rightarrow \quad x \ge 4 \qquad (2)$

Combining inequalities (1) and (2) gives the solution set.

$x \le -0.8$ *or* $x \ge 4$

Note

Inequalities (1) and (2) cannot be combined into a single inequality because they represent two **disjoint** solution sets on the number line, as shown below.

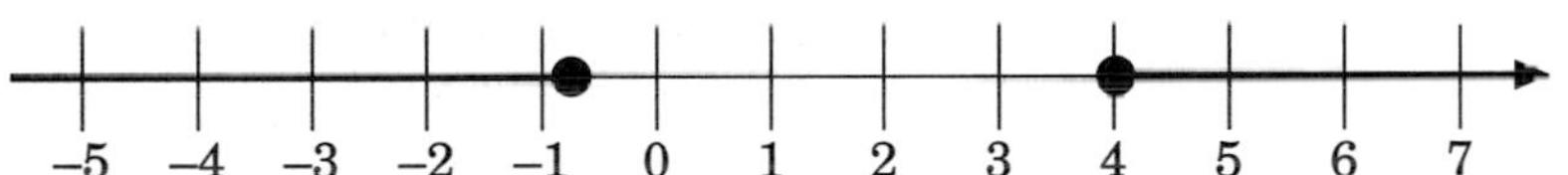

EXERCISES

2.7 CLASSWORK

Solve the following inequalities and illustrate the result on the real number line.

1. $3x + 2 > 8$
2. $5x - 3 \ge 17$
3. $4(x - 3) < 16$
4. $3x - 8 \ge 4x + 3$
5. $14 - 3x < 5x + 6$
6. $3(x + 1) \ge 5(4 - x)$
7. $\dfrac{3x+5}{2} < 4x - 3$
8. $\dfrac{5-2x}{4} \ge \dfrac{7-x}{5}$
9. $7 \le 3x + 1 \le 16$
10. $15 < 9 - 2x < 31$
11. $2x - 3 < 5$ or $2x - 3 > 17$
12. $12 - 5x < 2 \le 12 + 5x$
13. $|2x + 3| \le 7$
14. $|10x - 4| \ge 16$

EXERCISES

2.7 HOMEWORK

Solve the following inequalities and illustrate the result on the real number line.

1. $5x - 1 < 3$
2. $6 \ge x + 1$
3. $\dfrac{8x+7}{7} < 2$
4. $8x + 3 > 5x - 21$
5. $4x \ge 7 - 5x$
6. $4(9 - 8x) \ge 5(3x + 1)$
7. $\dfrac{3x+2}{4} < 4x + 7$
8. $\dfrac{6x+7}{2} > \dfrac{8-7x}{3}$
9. $-10 < 6x + 2 < 68$
10. $14 \ge 19 - 3x \ge 7$
11. $9x - 2 < 7$ or $9x - 2 > 43$
12. $3 + 4x > 2x - 5 > 1 - x$
13. $|x - 8| \le 3$
14. $25 \le |5x - 8|$

LAWS OF INDICES

In this section we shall explore the ideas of indices and powers and show the dramatic effect they have on numbers. To do this, we shall carry out an annotated exploration of a situation that frequently occurs in a biochemistry laboratory.

Exploration 2.7 *Examining indices*

Suppose that the size of a colony of bacteria doubles each day. At midnight (00:00) on a particular day (day 0) it is estimated that there are 1 million bacteria. Some of the figures are given in this table.

Day	–3	–2	–1	0	1	2	3	4	5
Size (in millions)			0.5	1	2				
Size (as a power of 2)									

- Study the patterns made by the figures, then copy and complete the table to show the size of the colony at 00:00 on various days before and after day 0.
- Give the population size (in millions) as a power of 2.

By studying the figures for days 1, 2, 3, ..., we can see that on day n the population size, P, is given by $P = 2^n$. Extending the definition to $n = 0, -1, -2, -3$ gives:

$$2^0 = 1 \qquad 2^{-1} = 0.5 = \frac{1}{2} \qquad 2^{-2} = 0.25 = \frac{1}{2^2} \qquad 2^{-3} = 0.125 = \frac{1}{2^3}$$

Therefore we can generalise to obtain the results:

$$2^0 = 1 \quad \text{and} \quad 2^{-n} = \frac{1}{2^n} \qquad n = 1, 2, 3, \ldots$$

$$a^0 = 1 \quad \text{and} \quad a^{-n} = \frac{1}{a^n} \qquad n = 1, 2, 3, \ldots$$

where a is any positive number.

- Check that your calculator gives equivalent results for various values of a and n:
  e.g. $3^{-2} = \frac{1}{3^2}$ $\qquad 5^0 = 1 \qquad 1.1^{-5} = \frac{1}{1.1^5}$

The summary table of values may be extended like this.

Day	... –7	–6	–5	–4	–3	–2	–1	0	1	2	3	4	5	6	7 ...
Size	... 2^{-7}	2^{-6}	2^{-5}	2^{-4}	2^{-3}	2^{-2}	2^{-1}	2^0	2^1	2^2	2^3	2^4	2^5	2^6	2^7 ...

- By considering the population on day m and the population both n days later and n days earlier, find expressions for $2^m \times 2^n$ and $2^m \div 2^n$.
- At the end of one week, beginning with day 0, the population is 2^7. What will it be at the end of the next week? What will it be five weeks after day 0?

By inspecting the number pattern we see, for example, that:

$$2^2 \times 2^5 = 2^7 \qquad 2^3 \div 2^5 = 2^{-2} \qquad (2^7)^5 = 2^{35}$$

Generalising these results for powers of 2:

$$2^m \times 2^n = 2^{m+n} \qquad 2^m \div 2^n = 2^{m-n} \qquad (2^m)^n = 2^{mn}$$

For any positive number a:

$$a^m \times a^n = a^{m+n} \qquad a^m \div a^n = a^{m-n} \qquad (a^m)^n = a^{mn}$$

e.g. $5^4 \times 5^3 = 5^7 \qquad 1.6^2 \div 1.6^7 = 1.6^{-5} \qquad (3^5)^4 = 3^{20}$

These **rules of indices** also apply when m and/or n are negative:

e.g. $2.1^{-3} \times 2.1^5 = 2.1^2 \qquad 4^2 \div 4^{-5} = 4^7 \qquad (0.8^{-2})^3 = 0.8^{-6}$

■ Check these numerical examples on your calculator.

Now let's return to the bacterial colony, and assume growth is continuous.

■ What would you expect the population size to be at *midday* (12:00) on day 0, and at midday on day 1?

■ What would you expect the population size to be at 08:00 on day 0 and at 16:00 on day 1?

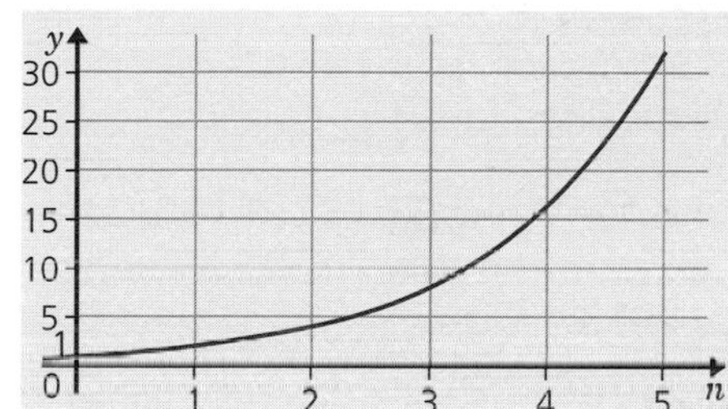

Assuming continuous growth, we can draw a graph of $P = 2^n$, treating n as a continuous variable.

At midday on day 0, $n = \frac{1}{2}$ and, from the graph, $P = 1.4$, correct to two significant figures (2 s.f.) which corresponds to $2^{\frac{1}{2}}$. From a calculator $2^{\frac{1}{2}} = 1.4142$ (5 s.f.).

Assuming the laws of indices still hold true, $(2^{\frac{1}{2}})^2 = 2^1 = 2$, i.e. $2^{\frac{1}{2}} \equiv \sqrt{2}$.

■ Use your calculator to check that $2^{\frac{1}{2}}$ and $\sqrt{2}$ give the same decimal expansion.

By similar reasoning, the population at 08:00 on day 0 ($\frac{1}{3}$ of the way through the day) should correspond to $2^{\frac{1}{3}} = 1.26$.
Since $(2^{\frac{1}{3}})^3 = 2$, $2^{\frac{1}{3}} \equiv \sqrt[3]{2}$, the cube root of 2.

The population at 16:00 on day 0 ($\frac{2}{3}$ of the way through the day) will be $2^{\frac{2}{3}} = 1.59$.

Since $2^{\frac{2}{3}} = \left(2^2\right)^{\frac{1}{3}} = \left(2^{\frac{1}{3}}\right)^2$, $\quad 2^{\frac{2}{3}} = \sqrt[3]{4} = \sqrt[3]{2^2} = \left(\sqrt[3]{2}\right)^2$

■ Check these equivalent values give the same decimal expansions.

Generalising this idea for powers of 2:

$$2^{\frac{m}{n}} = \left(2^m\right)^{\frac{1}{n}} \equiv \sqrt[n]{2^m} \quad \text{or} \quad 2^{\frac{m}{n}} = \left(2^{\frac{1}{n}}\right)^m \equiv \left(\sqrt[n]{2}\right)^m$$

For any positive number a:

$$a^{\frac{m}{n}} = \left(a^m\right)^{\frac{1}{n}} \equiv \sqrt[n]{a^m} \quad \text{or} \quad a^{\frac{m}{n}} = \left(a^{\frac{1}{n}}\right)^m \equiv \left(\sqrt[n]{a}\right)^m$$

e.g. $9^{\frac{3}{2}} = \left(9^3\right)^{\frac{1}{2}} = \sqrt{729} = 27$ or $9^{\frac{3}{2}} = \left(9^{\frac{1}{2}}\right)^3 = (3)^3 = 27$

Example 2.30

Simplify the following expressions.

a) $\dfrac{5^7 \times 5^3}{5^8}$ **b)** $5x^2 \times 3x^5$ **c)** $(7a^3b)^2$ **d)** $\dfrac{6p^3q^2r}{2pq^3r^2}$

Solution

a) $\dfrac{5^7 \times 5^3}{5^8} = \dfrac{5^{7+3}}{5^8} = 5^{10-8} = 5^2 = 25$

b) $5x^2 \times 3x^5 = 5 \times 3 \times x^2 \times x^5 = 15x^7$

c) $(7a^3b)^2 = 7a^3b \times 7a^3b = 49a^6b^2$

d) $\dfrac{6p^3q^2r}{2pq^3r^2} = 3p^{3-1}q^{2-3}r^{1-2} = 3p^2q^{-1}r^{-1} = \dfrac{3p^2}{qr}$

Example 2.31

Evaluate the following, without using a calculator.

a) 3^{-2} **b)** $16^{-\frac{1}{2}}$ **c)** $8^{\frac{4}{3}}$

Solution

a) $3^{-2} = \dfrac{1}{3^2} = \dfrac{1}{9}$ **b)** $16^{-\frac{1}{2}} = \dfrac{1}{16^{\frac{1}{2}}} = \dfrac{1}{\sqrt{16}} = \dfrac{1}{4} = 0.25$

c) $8^{\frac{4}{3}} = \sqrt[3]{8^4} = \sqrt[3]{4096} = 16$ *or* $8^{\frac{4}{3}} = \left(\sqrt[3]{8}\right)^4 = 2^4 = 16$

Example 2.32

Without using a calculator, find the missing numbers.

a) $n^3 = -64$ **b)** $n^{\frac{2}{3}} = 25$ **c)** $3^n = \dfrac{1}{243}$

d) $-216^n = -6$ **e)** $25^n = 0.2$

Solution

a) $n^3 = -64 \Rightarrow n = \sqrt[3]{-64} = -4$ *Check:* $(-4)^3 = -64$

b) $n^{\frac{2}{3}} = 25 \Rightarrow \left(\sqrt[3]{n}\right)^2 = 25 \Rightarrow \sqrt[3]{n} = 5 \Rightarrow n = 5^3 \Rightarrow n = 125$

c) *Since* $3^5 = 243, \dfrac{1}{3^5} = 243^{-1} \Rightarrow 3^5 = 243^{-1} \Rightarrow n = -5$

d) *Since* $-6^3 = -216, \sqrt[3]{-216} = -6 \Rightarrow -216^{\frac{1}{3}} = -6 \Rightarrow n = \frac{1}{3}$

e) *Since* $0.2 = \dfrac{1}{5}$ *and* $\sqrt{25} = 5, \dfrac{1}{\sqrt{25}} = \dfrac{1}{5} = 0.2 \Rightarrow n = -\dfrac{1}{2}$

General results

From Example 2.30 we see that the **square of a product** is the **product of the squares**.

e.g. $(7a^3b)^2 = 49a^6b^2$

Similarly, the **square of a quotient** is the **quotient of the squares**.

e.g. $\left(\dfrac{5x}{2y^2}\right)^2 = \dfrac{25x^2}{4y^4}$

Reversing the argument in both cases gives:

- the square root of a product is the product of the square roots,
- the square root of a quotient is the quotient of the square roots.

e.g. $\sqrt{49a^6b^2} = 7a^3b$ and $\sqrt{\dfrac{25x^2}{4y^4}} = \dfrac{5x}{2y^2}$

We can extend this to give the general results:

$$(ab)^{\frac{m}{n}} = a^{\frac{m}{n}}b^{\frac{m}{n}} \quad \text{and} \quad \left(\frac{a}{b}\right)^{\frac{m}{n}} = \frac{a^{\frac{m}{n}}}{b^{\frac{m}{n}}}$$

Which can be summarised as:

- the power of a product is the product of the powers,
- the power of a quotient is the quotient of the powers.

Example 2.33

Simplify the following expressions.

a) $\left(\dfrac{3r}{4st^2}\right)^3$ **b)** $\sqrt[3]{125x^3y^6}$

Solution

a) $\left(\dfrac{3r}{4st^2}\right)^3 = \dfrac{(3r)^3}{(4st^2)^3} = \dfrac{27r^3}{64s^3t^6}$

b) $\sqrt[3]{125x^3y^6} = (125x^3y^6)^{\frac{1}{3}} = 125^{\frac{1}{3}}(x^3)^{\frac{1}{3}}(y^6)^{\frac{1}{3}} = \sqrt[3]{125}\sqrt[3]{x^3}\sqrt[3]{y^6} = 5xy^2$

Example 2.34

Evaluate the following, without using a calculator.

a) $\sqrt{1\frac{7}{9}}$ **b)** $(2\frac{10}{27})^{\frac{4}{3}}$

Solution

a) $\sqrt{1\frac{7}{9}} = \sqrt{\dfrac{16}{9}} = \dfrac{\sqrt{16}}{\sqrt{9}} = \dfrac{4}{3} = 1\frac{1}{3}$

b) $(2\frac{10}{27})^{\frac{4}{3}} = \left(\dfrac{64}{27}\right)^{\frac{4}{3}} = \dfrac{64^{\frac{4}{3}}}{27^{\frac{4}{3}}} = \dfrac{(\sqrt[3]{64})^4}{(\sqrt[3]{27})^4} = \dfrac{4^4}{3^4} = \dfrac{256}{81} = 3\frac{13}{81}$

EXERCISES

2.8 CLASSWORK

1 Simplify the following expressions.

a) $\dfrac{3^4 \times 3^5}{3^7}$ **b)** $\dfrac{4^6}{4^3 \times 4^4}$ **c)** $\dfrac{(7^3)^4}{(7^4)^3}$ **d)** $7x^6 \times 5x^2$

e) $2a^2b^3 \times 4a^3b^2$ **f)** $(2ab)^5$ **g)** $(-4x^3y^2)^3$

h) $\dfrac{4r^2st \times 6rs^2t}{8rst^2}$ **i)** $\left(\dfrac{3a^2b^3c}{4abc^3}\right)^3$ **j)** $\sqrt{\dfrac{9p^6}{49q^2}}$

2 Evaluate the following without using a calculator.

a) 2^{-3} **b)** $49^{\frac{1}{2}}$ **c)** $49^{\frac{3}{2}}$ **d)** $\left(\frac{2}{3}\right)^4$ **e)** $\left(\frac{2}{3}\right)^{-4}$

f) $25^{-\frac{1}{2}}$ **g)** $\sqrt{6\frac{1}{4}}$ **h)** $\sqrt{12.25}$ **i)** $\sqrt[3]{3\frac{3}{8}}$ **j)** $\left(\frac{9}{16}\right)^{-\frac{1}{2}}$

3 Without using a calculator find the value of n.

a) $n^3 = -27$ **b)** $n^5 = 32$ **c)** $n^{-2} = \frac{1}{16}$ **d)** $n^{\frac{1}{3}} = \frac{2}{3}$

e) $n^{\frac{2}{3}} = 49$ **f)** $(-5)^n = 625$ **g)** $(-3)^n = \frac{1}{81}$ **h)** $225^n = -15$

i) $729^n = 9$ **j)** $64^n = \frac{1}{16}$ **k)** $1.44^n = \frac{5}{6}$

4 Explain why $\sqrt{a^2b^2} = ab$ but $\sqrt{a^2+b^2} \neq a+b$.

EXERCISES

2.8 HOMEWORK

1 Simplify the following expressions.

a) $\dfrac{2^7 \times 2^2}{2^4}$ **b)** $\dfrac{5^{11}}{5^2 \times 5^7}$ **c)** $\dfrac{(11^2)^5}{(11^5)^2}$

d) $3y^4 \times 5y^7$ **e)** $2abc \times 5a^3b^2c^3 \times 4a^4b^5c^2$ **f)** $(11a^2b)^9$

g) $(-3m^2n^3p^4)^5$ h) $\sqrt{\dfrac{5a^5b^3}{20ab^7}}$ i) $\dfrac{6x^2y \times 14x^3y^4}{21x^4y^7}$ j) $\left(\dfrac{5r^4s^2t^3}{7r^3s^4t^2}\right)^2$

2 Evaluate the following without using a calculator.

a) 2^{-5} b) $64^{\frac{1}{2}}$ c) $64^{\frac{3}{2}}$ d) $64^{-\frac{1}{2}}$

e) $\left(\frac{3}{4}\right)^3$ f) $\left(\frac{3}{4}\right)^{-3}$ g) $\left(\frac{125}{8}\right)^{-\frac{1}{3}}$ h) $\sqrt{3\frac{1}{16}}$

i) $\sqrt{20.25}$ j) $\sqrt[3]{2\frac{10}{27}}$

3 Without using a calculator, find the value of n.

a) $n^5 = 243$ b) $n^{-3} = \frac{1}{8}$ c) $n^2 = \frac{1}{100}$

d) $n^{\frac{1}{3}} = \frac{4}{5}$ e) $n^{-\frac{2}{3}} = \frac{1}{36}$ f) $625^n = 1$

g) $(-5)^n = -\frac{1}{125}$ h) $289^n = -17$ i) $1.2^n = \frac{25}{36}$

4 Choose various numbers to show the following results.

$\sqrt{a^2b^2} = ab$ $\sqrt{\dfrac{b^2}{a^2}} = \dfrac{b}{a}$ $\sqrt{a^2+b^2} \neq a+b$ $\sqrt{a^2-b^2} \neq a-b$

SURDS

When taking a square root, the answer may be positive or negative. A surd is the square root of a positive number, expressed in a form such as $\sqrt{x}$ or $\sqrt{a^2+b^2}$, without being evaluated numerically. This means that the value of $\sqrt{2}$, for example, is the exact value of the square root of 2, whereas the value given in a table or by a calculator will be an approximation. It is possible to manipulate surds, following the usual rules of operations in arithmetic.

Exploration 2.8

Finding diagonals

Rectangle A measures 2 units by 4 units.

- Express the length of the diagonal, d units, exactly.

Now suppose the rectangle is enlarged in two ways, one with scale factor 2, the other with scale factor $\frac{1}{2}$.

- Find the length of the diagonals of rectangles B and C exactly *in two different ways.*
- Account for any differences in the form of your answers.

Using surds

Using Pythagoras' theorem for rectangle A:

$$d^2 = 2^2 + 4^2 = 20$$

$$\Rightarrow \quad d = \sqrt{20}$$

Since rectangle B is an enlargement, scale factor 2, of rectangle A, the length of its diagonal is $2\sqrt{20}$, since $e = 2d$; similarly $f = \frac{1}{2}d = \frac{1}{2}\sqrt{20}$.

However, applying Pythagoras' theorem for rectangles B and C gives:

$$e^2 = 4^2 + 8^2 = 80 \Rightarrow e = \sqrt{80}$$

and $f^2 = 1^2 + 2^2 = 5 \Rightarrow f = \sqrt{5}$

Comparing the two different ways of finding e and f:

$$2\sqrt{20} \equiv \sqrt{80} \quad \text{and} \quad \tfrac{1}{2}\sqrt{20} \equiv \sqrt{5}$$

The equivalence of the results is justified by rules we discovered in the last section.

$$e = \sqrt{80} = \sqrt{4 \times 20} = \sqrt{4} \times \sqrt{20} = 2\sqrt{20}$$

$$f = \sqrt{5} = \sqrt{\frac{20}{4}} = \frac{\sqrt{20}}{\sqrt{4}} = \tfrac{1}{2}\sqrt{20}$$

The square roots used in these exact expressions are surds. The expression for e may be simplified by reducing the number inside the square root further.

$$e = 2\sqrt{20} = 2\sqrt{4 \times 5} = 2\sqrt{4} \times \sqrt{5} = 4\sqrt{5}$$

Comparing e with d and f gives these results:

$$d = 2\sqrt{5} \quad e = 4\sqrt{5} \quad f = \sqrt{5}$$

Exploration 2.9

Using surds

Function f is defined by $f(x) = x^2 - 4x - 3$.

- Find values for the x-coordinates of the points where the graph of $y = f(x)$ intersects the x-axis using surds:
  a) by completing the square,
  b) using the quadratic formula.
- Investigate the sum and product of the roots of the equation $f(x) = 0$.

Finding the roots

To find the x-coordinates of the points of intersection of the curve and the x-axis, we need to solve the equation $f(x) = 0$.

a) $x^2 - 4x - 3 = 0 \Rightarrow (x-2)^2 - 7 = 0$
$\Rightarrow (x-2)^2 = 7$
$\Rightarrow x - 2 = \pm\sqrt{7}$
$\Rightarrow x = 2 \pm \sqrt{7}$

b) $x^2 - 4x - 3 = 0$

$$\Rightarrow x = \frac{4 \pm \sqrt{(-4)^2 - 4 \times 1 \times (-3)}}{2} = \frac{4 + \sqrt{28}}{2}$$

$$= \frac{4 \pm \sqrt{4 \times 7}}{2} = \frac{4 \pm 2\sqrt{7}}{2} = 2 \pm \sqrt{7}$$

The equivalence of the two formats is demonstrated using the identity:

$$\sqrt{28} \equiv \sqrt{4 \times 7} = \sqrt{4} \times \sqrt{7} = 2\sqrt{7} \Rightarrow \tfrac{1}{2}\sqrt{28} = \sqrt{7}$$

Since the roots of the equation are $2 + \sqrt{7}$ and $2 - \sqrt{7}$ their *sum* is:

$$2 + \sqrt{7} + (2 - \sqrt{7}) = 4$$

and their *product* is:

$$(2 + \sqrt{7})(2 - \sqrt{7}) = 4 - 2\sqrt{7} + 2\sqrt{7} - 7 = 4 - 7 = -3$$

Notice that neither the sum nor the product involves surds. In fact, both are simply linked to the original equation. Can you see how?

Simplest form

It is usual to express surds in their simplest form. This means, for example, that $\sqrt{28}$ would be expressed as $2\sqrt{7}$, so that the number inside the square root sign has no square factors. This is called **minimising** the square root. A surd such as $\sqrt{21+8}$ would be expressed as $\sqrt{29}$, by **gathering like terms**.

Any expression involving surds is in its simplest form if:

- numbers inside the square roots are minimised,
- like terms are gathered together,
- fractions do not contain surds in the denominator.

The following examples illustrate how such expressions may be simplified.

Example 2.35

Simplify $7\sqrt{3}-\sqrt{48}+\sqrt{75}$.

Solution

$$7\sqrt{3}-\sqrt{48}+\sqrt{75}=7\sqrt{3}-\sqrt{16\times 3}+\sqrt{25\times 3}=7\sqrt{3}-4\sqrt{3}+5\sqrt{3}=8\sqrt{3}$$

Example 2.36

Simplify $\frac{5}{\sqrt{2}}-\frac{4}{\sqrt{3}}$.

Solution

$$\frac{5}{\sqrt{2}}-\frac{4}{\sqrt{3}}=\frac{5\sqrt{3}-4\sqrt{2}}{\sqrt{6}}=\frac{5\sqrt{3}\sqrt{6}-4\sqrt{2}\sqrt{6}}{6}=\frac{5\sqrt{18}-4\sqrt{12}}{6}$$

$$=\frac{5\sqrt{9\times 2}-4\sqrt{4\times 3}}{6}=\frac{5\times 3\sqrt{2}-4\times 2\sqrt{3}}{6}=\frac{15\sqrt{2}-8\sqrt{3}}{6}$$

Example 2.37

Simplify $\frac{5-\sqrt{2}}{4+\sqrt{3}}$.

Solution

$$\frac{5-\sqrt{2}}{4+\sqrt{3}}=\frac{(5-\sqrt{2})(4-\sqrt{3})}{(4+\sqrt{3})(4-\sqrt{3})}=\frac{20-4\sqrt{2}-5\sqrt{3}+\sqrt{6}}{16+4\sqrt{3}-4\sqrt{3}-3}=\frac{20-4\sqrt{2}-5\sqrt{3}+\sqrt{6}}{13}$$

Rationalising the denominator

In the last example we used a method called **rationalising the denominator**. Wherever a fraction has a denominator of the form $a+b\sqrt{c}$, where a, b and c are integers, multiplying both denominator and numerator by $a-b\sqrt{c}$ will remove the surds from the denominator, since:

$$(a+b\sqrt{c})(a-b\sqrt{c})=a^2+ab\sqrt{c}-ab\sqrt{c}-b^2c=a^2-b^2c$$

EXERCISES

2.9 CLASSWORK

Simplify the following surds.

1 $\sqrt{18}$ **2** $\sqrt{32}$ **3** $\sqrt{28}$ **4** $\sqrt{75}$ **5** $\sqrt{90}$

6 $\sqrt{345}$ **7** $\sqrt{507}$ **8** $\sqrt{60\,000}$ **9** $\sqrt{\frac{3}{4}}$ **10** $\sqrt{\frac{50}{9}}$

Express each of the following as a single surd in its simplest form.

11 $2\sqrt{3}+7\sqrt{3}-\sqrt{3}$ **12** $\sqrt{2}-\sqrt{18}+\sqrt{32}$

13 $\sqrt{45}+4\sqrt{5}-3\sqrt{20}$ **14** $2\sqrt{50}-\sqrt{72}+7\sqrt{8}$

15 $\sqrt{2}(5-\sqrt{2})$ **16** $\sqrt{2}^3-5\sqrt{2}+\sqrt{2}^5$

17 $(3-\sqrt{2})(2+3\sqrt{2})$ **18** $(\sqrt{3}+1)(3-2\sqrt{3})$

19 $(5+\sqrt{5})(5-\sqrt{5})$ **20** $(1-\sqrt{3})(1+\sqrt{3})$

Rationalise the denominators of the following fractions.

21 $\frac{5}{\sqrt{2}}$ **22** $\frac{1}{\sqrt{3}}$ **23** $\frac{7}{\sqrt{7}}$ **24** $\frac{3\sqrt{5}}{\sqrt{6}}$ **25** $\frac{1}{\sqrt{2}}-\frac{1}{\sqrt{3}}$

26 $\frac{5}{\sqrt{7}}+\frac{2}{3}$ **27** $\frac{1}{1+\sqrt{3}}$ **28** $\frac{7}{2+\sqrt{5}}$ **29** $\frac{\sqrt{3}-1}{\sqrt{2}-3}$ **30** $\frac{\sqrt{5}-\sqrt{3}}{\sqrt{5}+\sqrt{3}}$

EXERCISES

2.9 HOMEWORK

Simplify the following surds.

1 $\sqrt{44}$ **2** $\sqrt{125}$ **3** $\sqrt{7\,000\,000}$ **4** $\sqrt{320}$ **5** $\sqrt{261}$

6 $\sqrt{304}$ **7** $\sqrt{496}$ **8** $\sqrt{4205}$ **9** $\sqrt{\frac{32}{25}}$ **10** $\sqrt{\frac{27}{16}}$

Express each of the following as a single surd in its simplest form.

11 $4\sqrt{7}-3\sqrt{7}+6\sqrt{7}$ **12** $4\sqrt{2}-\sqrt{50}+\sqrt{98}$

13 $\sqrt{27}+2\sqrt{243}-\sqrt{75}$ **14** $\sqrt{3}^3-5\sqrt{3}+\sqrt{3}^5$

15 $\sqrt{3}(7+2\sqrt{3})$ **16** $(\sqrt{11}-\sqrt{11})(\sqrt{11}+\sqrt{11})$

17 $(3\sqrt{5}-1)(1+\sqrt{5})$ **18** $(\sqrt{7}-\sqrt{3})(\sqrt{7}+\sqrt{3})$

19 $(\sqrt{13}+1)(\sqrt{13}-13)$ **20** $(\sqrt{x}+\sqrt{y})(\sqrt{x}-\sqrt{y})$

Rationalise the denominators of the following fractions.

21 $\frac{7}{\sqrt{2}}$ **22** $\frac{-4}{\sqrt{5}}$ **23** $\frac{14}{\sqrt{7}}$ **24** $\frac{13}{\sqrt{13}}$ **25** $\frac{2\sqrt{7}}{\sqrt{12}}$

26 $\frac{1}{\sqrt{5}}+\frac{1}{\sqrt{3}}$ **27** $\frac{1}{2-\sqrt{3}}$ **28** $\frac{11}{5+\sqrt{3}}$ **29** $\frac{\sqrt{7}-1}{\sqrt{7}+1}$ **30** $\frac{\sqrt{5}-2}{1+\sqrt{2}}$

CONSOLIDATION EXERCISES FOR CHAPTER 2

1 Solve these equations.
a) $3-2x=5$ **b)** $12x+8=12+3x$ **c)** $\frac{9-x}{5}=7x$

2 Multiply out the brackets.
a) $5(6x-7)$ **b)** $-3p(5+8p)$

3 Simplify these expressions.
a) $4x(7x+3)-x(5-x)$ **b)** $2-(5x+2)$

4 Factorise these expressions.
a) $9a^2b+6ab^2$ **b)** $20xy+5x-20x^2$

5 Solve these equations.
a) $7(3x-9)=42$ **b)** $2(8x+7)-(x-1)=6$ **c)** $2x-8+6(1-2x)=9(x+4)$

6 Solve these equations.
a) $\frac{x}{7}+2=3x$ **b)** $\frac{x+7}{6}=\frac{6x-1}{9}$

c) $\dfrac{7x}{3} - 6 = \dfrac{4-3x}{8}$ d) $\dfrac{5x+1}{x} = 9$

7 Simplify these expressions.

a) $\dfrac{x^2 - 3x}{x - 3}$

b) $\dfrac{4}{x} - \dfrac{2}{(x-1)}$

c) $\dfrac{a+1}{a-1} + \dfrac{1}{a+1} + a$

d) $\dfrac{1}{x+1} - \dfrac{2}{x-1} + \dfrac{1}{x(x+1)^2}$

8 a) Make k the subject of $m + n = 2k + fm$.

b) Make c the subject of $\dfrac{ax-c}{a+b} = m$.

c) Make g the subject of $g = 4ag - 7b$.

d) Make y the subject of $x = \dfrac{2y-1}{3-y}$.

e) Make x the subject of $8(3x-4) = 8 - \dfrac{(9+x)}{m}$.

9 Solve these inequalities.

a) $8x + 1 < 9$ b) $7 < 4 - 3x \le 12$ c) $x + 2 < 9 < 2 - 7x$

10 Simplify the following expressions.

a) $\dfrac{7^2 \times 7^4 \times 7^0}{7^5 \times 7^3}$ b) $2a \times 5a^4$ c) $3a^2b^2 \times 2a^4b^5$

d) $\dfrac{6p^2q^3 \times 10pq^5}{15pq}$ e) $\sqrt{\dfrac{63r^{11}s^7t^3}{7r^3st^{-1}}}$ f) $\left(\dfrac{3x^2yz^3}{2xz}\right)^4$

11 Express each of the following in the form ka^x.

a) $(5a)^2$ b) $\dfrac{1}{a^3}$ c) $a^2 \times \sqrt{a}$ d) $\left(\dfrac{2}{a}\right)^4$

e) $\dfrac{4a}{\sqrt{a}}$ f) $\dfrac{\sqrt{a}}{a^2}$ g) $\sqrt{9a}$ h) $(3a^4)^3$

12 Solve the following equations for x.

a) $x^2 = 0.64$ b) $2^x = 128$ c) $0.5^x = 8$

d) $2.5^x = 6.25$ e) $x^{\frac{1}{4}} = \frac{1}{4}$ f) $5^x = 1$

g) $(-2)^x = \frac{1}{64}$ h) $(100\,000)^x = 10^{15}$ i) $441^x = -21$

13 Simplify the following expressions writing each in the form $x + y\sqrt{b}$ where x and y are integers or fractions.

a) $11\sqrt{3} - 2\sqrt{3} + 5\sqrt{3}$ b) $\sqrt{50} - 2\sqrt{2} + \sqrt{18}$ c) $\sqrt{5}^3 + 2\sqrt{5} - 4\sqrt{5}^5$

d) $\sqrt{2}(3 - 4\sqrt{2})$ e) $\dfrac{\sqrt{3}-2}{\sqrt{3}+5}$ f) $\dfrac{\sqrt{7}+1}{\sqrt{7}-1}$

g) $\dfrac{\sqrt{27}-\sqrt{3}}{\sqrt{75}+1}$ h) $\dfrac{(\sqrt{5}-1)(\sqrt{5}+2)}{\sqrt{5}+1}$

14 Rationalise the denominators of the following fractions.

a) $\frac{25}{\sqrt{5}}$ **b)** $\frac{8}{5\sqrt{2}}$ **c)** $\frac{10}{3-\sqrt{7}}$ **d)** $\frac{4-\sqrt{13}}{5+\sqrt{13}}$

15 **i)** Write down the exact value of 7^{-2}.

ii) Simplify $\frac{(x\sqrt{x})^3}{2x^4}$

(OCR, Question 1, Specimen Paper 1 2000)

16 Solve the inequality $|x-100|<10$.

Hence find the set of integers n that satisfy the inequality $|1.01^n - 100| < 10$.

(OCR, Question 2, Specimen Paper 2 2000)

Summary

This chapter was a review of basic algebraic techniques.

- Solving linear equations
- Solving linear inequalities
- Manipulating expressions involving brackets
- Making a variable the subject of an equation
- The modulus of a number is its absolute value, i.e. its magnitude, ignoring the sign. The magnitude (modulus) of x is denoted by $|x|$.
- The laws of indices are

$$a^m \times a^n = a^{m+n}$$

$$\frac{a^m}{a^n} = a^m \div a^n = a^{m-n}$$

$$\left(a^m\right)^n = a^{mn}$$

- A **surd** is an irrational number such as $\sqrt{2}$ or $\sqrt{3}$. Surds can be manipulated following the usual rules of arithmetic.
- $\left(a+\sqrt{b}\right)\left(a-\sqrt{b}\right) = a^2 - b$

Linear functions

In this chapter we:

- *explore the equation of a straight line*
- *discover algebraic relations between pairs of parallel and perpendicular lines.*

CARTESIAN COORDINATES

Exploration 3.1

Map references

The map shows part of south-west England, together with the national grid references of five places, given as coordinates.

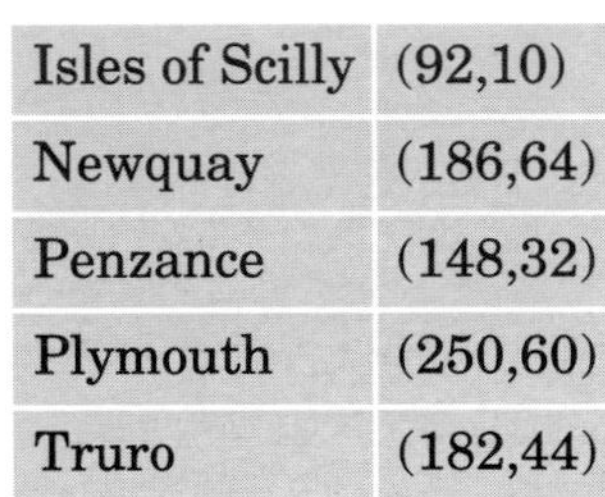

Isles of Scilly	(92,10)
Newquay	(186,64)
Penzance	(148,32)
Plymouth	(250,60)
Truro	(182,44)

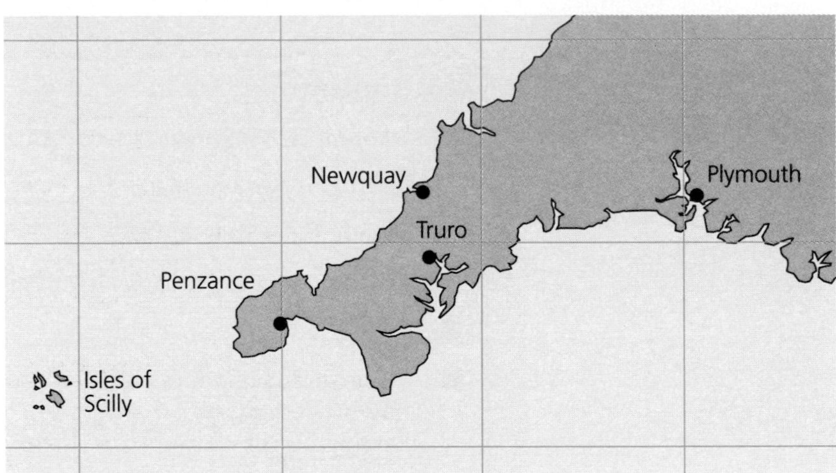

A helicopter flies directly from Penzance to the Isles of Scilly. On the way, it flies directly over a marker buoy which is equidistant between the two places.

- How far is it, as the helicopter flies, from Penzance to the Isles of Scilly?
- What is the national grid reference of the buoy?

Maps and coordinates

If we superimpose a right-angled triangle over the map, with Penzance and the Isles of Scilly at the ends of the hypotenuse and the other two sides running north–south and east–west, we can use Pythagoras' theorem to calculate the distance between the two places.

The lengths of the two perpendicular sides can be calculated by finding the difference in the east–west references and the difference in the north–south references.

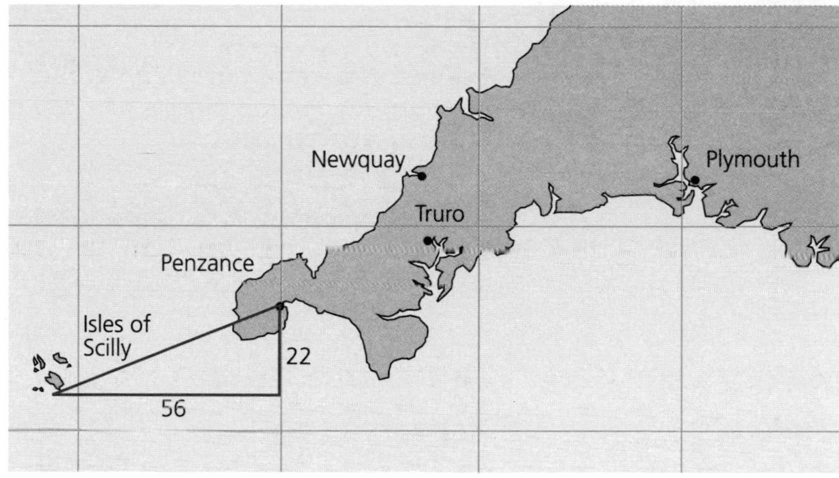

Therefore the distance from Penzance to the Isles of Scilly is given by:

$$\sqrt{(148-92)^2+(32-10)^2} = \sqrt{56^2+22^2}$$

$$= \sqrt{3620}$$

$$= 60 \text{ km (2 s.f.)}$$

The marker buoy is halfway between Penzance and the Isles of Scilly. Its grid reference is found by taking the average of the east–west references and the average of the north–south references for the two places.

east–west reference $\Rightarrow \dfrac{092+148}{2} = 120$

north–south reference $\Rightarrow \dfrac{010+032}{2} = 021$

The national grid coordinates of the marker buoy are (120, 021).

The general result

The results of the exploration can be generalised for any grid, given the coordinates of two points.

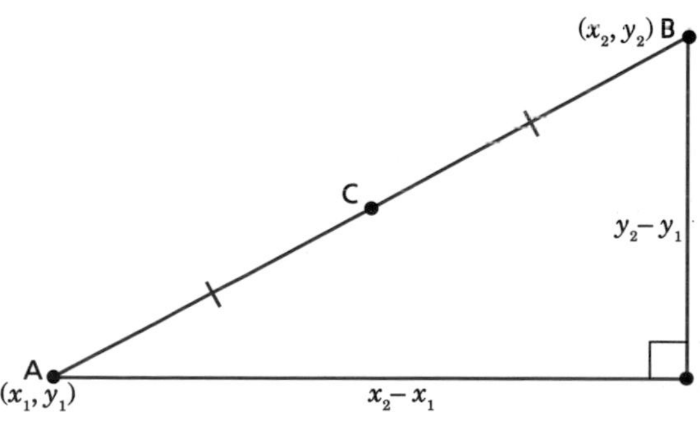

Let point A have coordinates (x_1, y_1) and point B have coordinates (x_2, y_2). Point C is the **midpoint** of the line AB.

$$AB = \sqrt{(x_2-x_1)^2+(y_2-y_1)^2}$$

Coordinates of C are $\left(\frac{1}{2}(x_1+x_2), \ \frac{1}{2}(y_1+y_2)\right)$

Example 3.1

Find the distance, as the helicopter flies, between Newquay and Plymouth and the coordinates of a point exactly halfway between Newquay and Plymouth.

Solution

First, draw a suitable right-angled triangle.

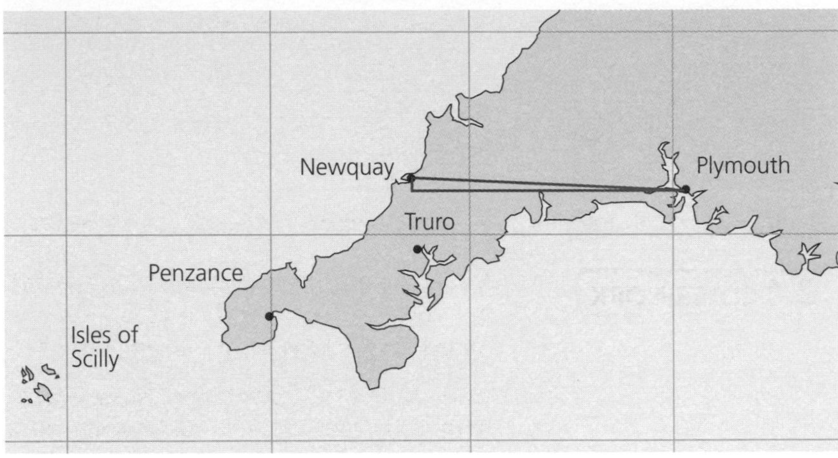

The distance from Newquay to Plymouth is:

$$\sqrt{(250-186)^2+(60-64)^2} = \sqrt{(64^2+(-4)^2)} = \sqrt{4112} = 64 \text{ km (2 s.f.)}$$

The coordinates of the halfway point are

$\left(\frac{1}{2}(186+250), \frac{1}{2}(64+60)\right)$ or $(218, 62)$.

Note: It would not make sense to quote the distance between Newquay and Plymouth to more than 2 significant figures (i.e. to the nearest kilometre), since the grid references are given to 2 s.f. Note also that the distance is roughly the difference in the east–west references, since the difference in the north–south references is relatively small.

Example 3.2

In ΔPQR, points P, Q and R have coordinates (–7, 6), (10, 2) and (–2, –4) respectively.

a) *Find the distance PQ.*
b) *Find the coordinates of M, the midpoint of PQ.*
c) *Show that $PQ^2 = PR^2 + QR^2$. What does this tell you about ΔPQR?*

Solution

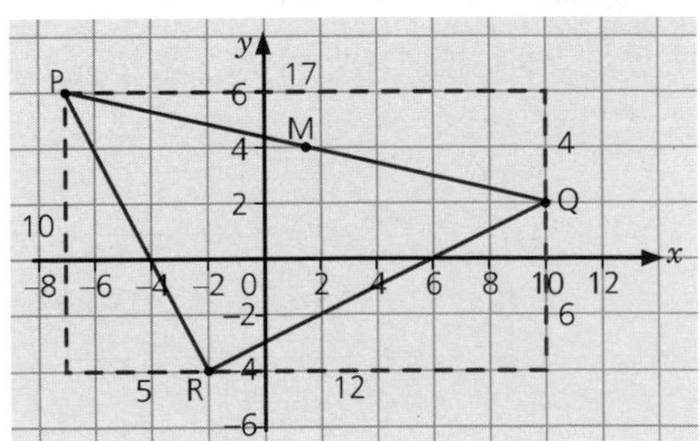

a) $PQ^2 = 17^2 + 4^2 = 305 \Rightarrow PQ = \sqrt{305} = 17.5$ (3 s. f.)

b) *Coordinates of M are* $\left(\frac{1}{2}(-7+10), \frac{1}{2}(6+2)\right)$ *or* $(1.5, 4)$.

c) $PR^2 = 10^2 + 5^2 = 125 \quad QR^2 = 6^2 + 12^2 = 180$

$\Rightarrow$ $PR^2 + QR^2 = 125 + 180 = 305 = PQ^2$, *as required.*

Since Pythagoras' theorem is only true for right-angled triangles, ΔPQR is a right-angled triangle with $\angle R = 90°$.

Example 3.3

A parallelogram has vertices A(–5, 4), B(1, 6), C(9, –2) and D(3,–4). Show that its diagonals bisect each other.

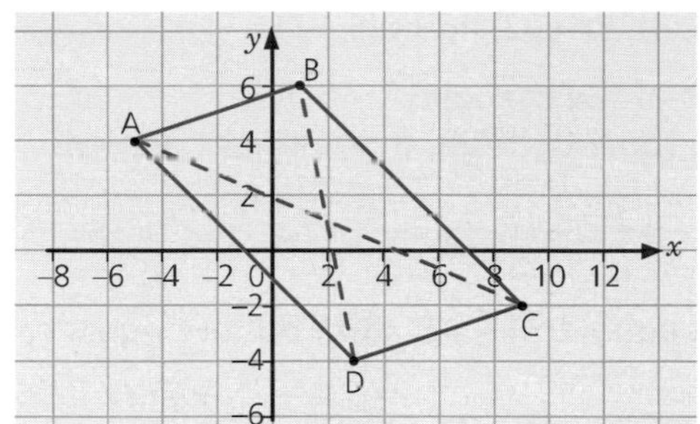

Solution

The midpoint of AC is $\left(\frac{1}{2}(-5+9),\ \frac{1}{2}(4+(-2))\right) = (2, 1)$

The midpoint of BD is $\left(\frac{1}{2}(1+3),\ \frac{1}{2}(6+(-4))\right) = (2, 1)$

Since the midpoints of AC and BD have the same coordinates, the diagonals must bisect each other.

EXERCISES

3.1 CLASSWORK

1 Using the map from Exploration 3.1, find the shortest distance between Penzance and Truro. Troon is exactly halfway between Penzance and Truro; find its grid reference.

2 Find the lengths of the following lines and the coordinates of their midpoints, illustrating your answers on a grid.

a) AB where A is (2, 1), B is (8, 4)
b) PQ where P is (3, 0), Q is (–5, 5)
c) RS where R is (–1, 5), S is (–4, –3)

3 A triangle XYZ has vertices X(6, 2), Y(2, 5) and Z(–1, 1).

a) Find the lengths of the sides of the triangle.
b) What type of triangle is ΔXYZ?
c) Find the coordinates of point M, the midpoint of XZ.
d) Calculate the area of ΔXYZ.

4 A triangle PQR has vertices at P(4, –2), Q(10, 2) and R(–2, 6). M is the midpoint of PQ and N is the midpoint of QR.

a) Find the coordinates of M and N.
b) Show that the length of PR is twice the length of MN.

5 A quadrilateral ABCD has vertices A(0, 5), B(–2, 1), C(1, 2) and D(6, 3). Points E, F, G and H are the midpoints of AB, BC, CD and DA respectively.

a) Find the coordinates of E, F, G and H.
b) Show that EFGH is a parallelogram.

EXERCISES

3.1 HOMEWORK

1 Using the map from Exploration 3.1, find the grid reference of the point midway between Plymouth and Penzance, and the shortest distance I would have to fly to get to Plymouth if I set off from there.

2 Using the points A(5, 2), B(–1, 2), C(–6, –7) and D (1, –9) find the lengths:

a) AB **b)** BC **c)** CD **d)** DA **e)** AC **f)** BD.

3 Using the points P(7, 4), Q(5, –6), R(–3, 5) and S(0, –8), find the midpoints of:

a) PQ b) PR c) PS d) QR e) QS f) RS.

4 A triangle ABC has vertices A(1, 9), B(–6, 2) and C(6, –3).

a) Find the lengths of the sides of the triangle.
b) Use Pythagoras' theorem to show that ABC is not a right-angled triangle.
c) Find the coordinates of point M, the midpoint of AC, and N, the midpoint of AB.
d) Explain why the area ABC is equal to $\frac{1}{2} \times AB \times CN$, but not equal to $\frac{1}{2} \times AC \times BM$.

5 A quadrilateral PQRS has vertices at P(–4, 8), Q(9, 6), R(11, –7) and S(–2, –5).

a) Find the lengths of the four sides of PQRS.
b) Find the midpoints of the diagonals PR and QS.
c) Without drawing a diagram, prove that PQRS is not square.

GRADIENTS

Exploration 3.2

Is there a rule?

The firm 'Have van will travel' produces a table of charges.

Time (hours)	2	4	6	8
Charge (£)	30	40	50	60

- What is the fixed charge and what is the variable charge for the service?

Finding a relationship

By plotting the data on a graph we can see more clearly the linear relationship between the cost and time.

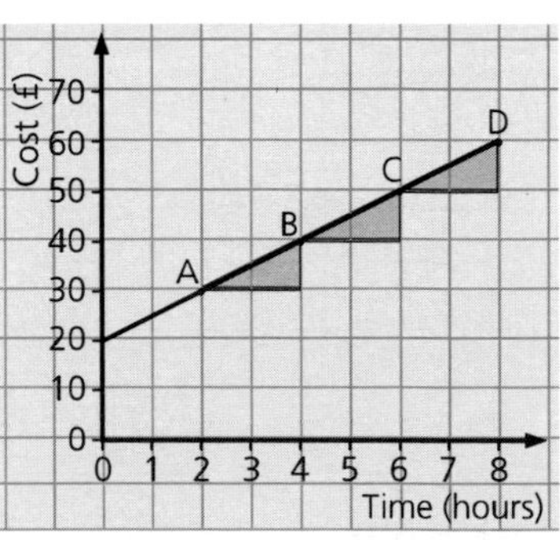

From the graph, we can read:

- the fixed charge is £20 (charge for 0 hours' hire)
- the variable charge is £5 per hour.

The variable charge is found from the **slope** or **gradient** of the line through the points, which is found by taking any two points on the line.

The gradient of the line is given by $\frac{\text{increase in cost}}{\text{increase in time}}$ between *any* two points on the line.

$$\text{Gradient of AB} = \frac{10}{2} = 5$$

$$\text{Gradient of BD} = \frac{20}{4} = 5$$

$$\text{Gradient of AD} = \frac{30}{6} = 5$$

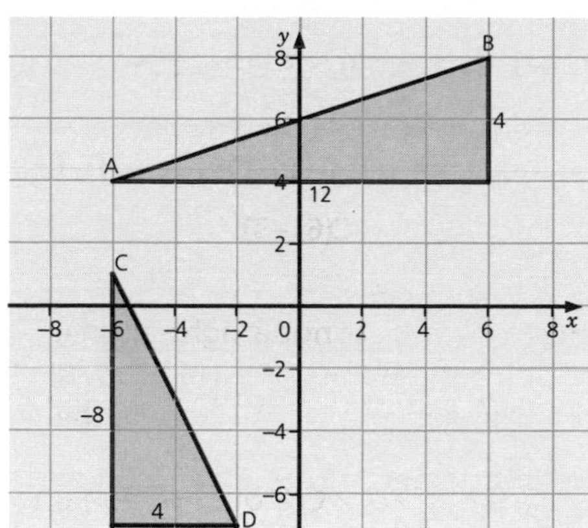

The gradient of the straight line is constant and represents the **rate of change** of cost with respect to time, i.e. the hourly rate.

For any straight line on any grid with variables x and y, the gradient is defined in a similar way.

$$\text{gradient} = \frac{\text{change in } y}{\text{change in } x}$$

For line AB: gradient = $\frac{4}{12} = \frac{1}{3}$ *y increases* by 1 for every increase of 3 in x

Line AB has a **positive** gradient.

For line CD: gradient = $\frac{-8}{4} = -2$ *y decreases* by 2 for every increase of 1 in x

Line CD has a **negative** gradient.

The general result

These examples lead to a general definition for the gradient between two points $P(x_1, y_1)$ and point $Q(x_2, y_2)$.

$$\text{gradient of PQ} = \frac{\text{change in } y}{\text{change in } x} = \frac{y_2 - y_1}{x_2 - x_1}$$

A line with a **positive** gradient slopes **upwards** from left to right.
A line with a **negative** gradient slopes **downward** from left to right.

Example 3.4

Three points A, B and C have coordinates (–3, –1), (2, 1) and (12, 5) respectively.

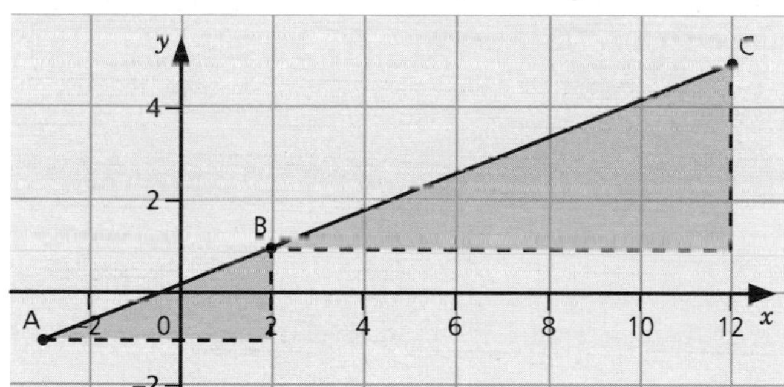

Show that these three points are collinear (lie on a straight line).

Solution

Gradient of AB $= \frac{1-(-1)}{2-(-3)} = \frac{2}{5} = 0.4$

Gradient of BC $= \frac{5-1}{12-2} = \frac{4}{10} = 0.4$

Point B is common to both lines AB and BC. This is sufficient to show that A, B and C are collinear.

Example 3.5

A quadrilateral has vertices P(0, 4), Q(–2, 1), R(0, –2) and S(4, –2). Find one pair of parallel sides and hence show that PQRS is a trapezium.

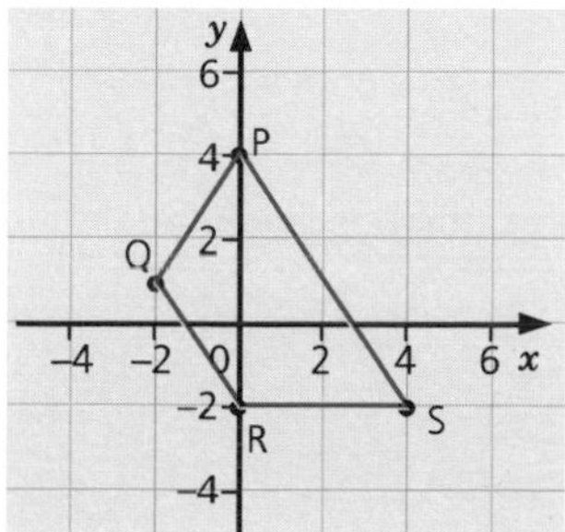

Solution

Start by plotting quadrilateral PQRS on a grid. From the graph, it seems that PS is parallel to QR. We can confirm this by showing that PS and QR have the same gradient.

Gradient of PS $= \frac{-6}{4} = -1.5$ *Gradient of QR* $= \frac{-3}{2} = -1.5$

Since lines PS and QR have the same gradient they must be parallel.

Parallel and perpendicular lines

We have seen that when two lines are **parallel** they have *equal* gradients. What happens when two lines are **perpendicular** to each other (intersect at right angles)?

Exploration 3.3

Perpendicular lines

Using the same scales on both axes, plot the points A(2, 10), B(10, 8) and C(6, 2) and join them to form a triangle.

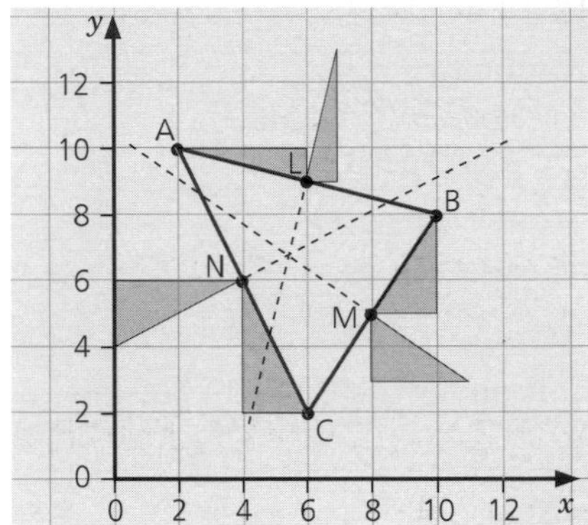

- Construct the perpendicular bisectors of AB, BC and CA and comment on what you find.

  The diagram shows triangle ABC. To construct a perpendicular bisector you need to find the midpoint and gradients.

  For line AB, the midpoint is L(6, 9). The gradient of AB is $-\frac{1}{4}$, i.e. for every 4 units *to the right* you move 1 unit *down*.

  For the perpendicular bisector, for every 1 unit to the *right* you move 4 units *up*. So the gradient of the perpendicular bisector is 4.

- Working similarly with BC and CA, verify the following summary.

Line	Gradient of line	Gradient of perpendicular bisector
AB	$-\frac{1}{4}$	4
BC	$\frac{3}{2}$	$-\frac{2}{3}$
CA	–2	$\frac{1}{2}$

- For each line, find the product of its gradient and the gradient of its perpendicular bisector. What can you say?

The general result

For each line in the exploration, the product of the two gradients is –1.

$$-\frac{1}{4}\times 4=-1 \qquad \frac{3}{2}\times -\frac{2}{3}=-1 \qquad -2\times\frac{1}{2}=-1$$

If two straight lines are perpendicular, the product of their gradients is –1.

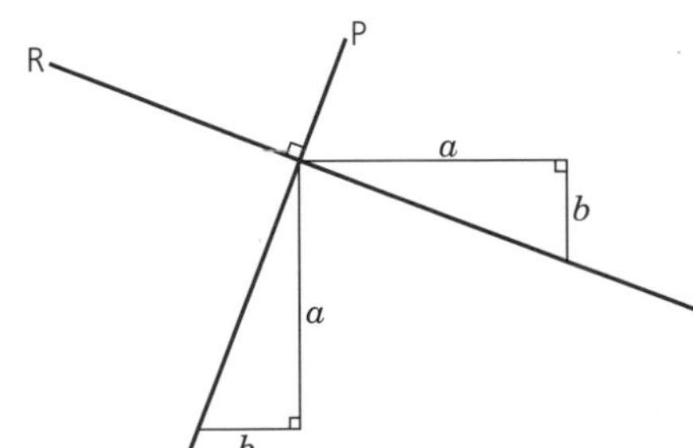

Gradient of PQ is $\frac{a}{b}$ Gradient of RS is $-\frac{b}{a}$

$$\frac{a}{b}\times -\frac{b}{a}=-1$$

Let $m=\frac{a}{b}$, then $-\frac{b}{a}=\frac{-1}{a/b}=-\frac{1}{m}$

Therefore, if a line has gradient m, a perpendicular line has gradient $-\frac{1}{m}$.

Example 3.6

*A quadrilateral has vertices P(–6, 6), Q(0, 10), R(8, –2) and S(2, –6).
By working out gradients, show that PQRS is a rectangle.*

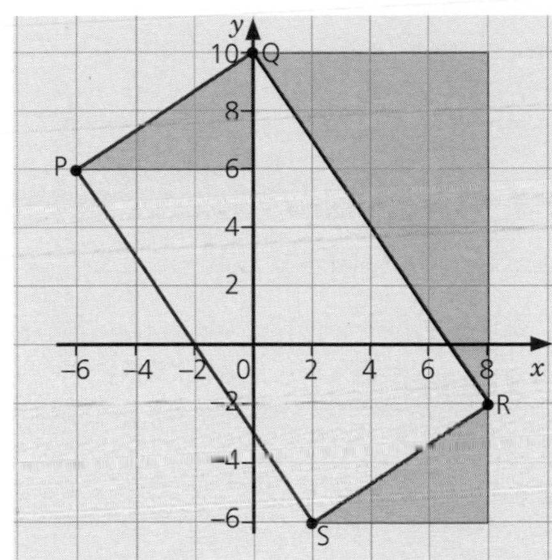

Solution

Gradient of PQ $= \frac{4}{6} = \frac{2}{3}$ *Gradient of RS* $= \frac{4}{6} = \frac{2}{3}$

Since their gradients are the same, PQ and RS are parallel.
Similarly, QR and PS are parallel.

Gradient of PQ $= \frac{2}{3}$ *Gradient of QR* $= \frac{-12}{8} = -\frac{3}{2}$

Since $\frac{2}{3} \times -\frac{3}{2} = -1$, *PQ is perpendicular to QR.*
Similarly, PQ is perpendicular to PS.

So the opposite sides are parallel and adjacent sides are perpendicular, which means that PQRS is a rectangle.

EXERCISES

3.2 CLASSWORK

Eight points have coordinates as follows.
A(3, 5) B(6, 10) C(8, 3) D(6, –2) E(0, –5) F(–4, –7) G(–1, –4) H(–4, 2)

1 Plot all eight points on a grid, using the same scale for both axes.

2 Find the gradients of the lines AF, HD, AD and CH.

3 Show that the points D, E and F are collinear.

4 Show that AC is parallel to DH.

5 Find another pair of parallel lines, giving a reason why you think they are parallel.

6 Show that BC is perpendicular to DG.

7 Find another pair of perpendicular lines, giving a reason why you think they are perpendicular.

8 A point I is such that ACDI is a square. Find the coordinates of I.

9 Using gradients show that ΔEFG is right angled.

EXERCISES

3.2 HOMEWORK

Six points have coordinates as follows.
L(8, 1) M(5, 2) N(0, 8) P(–5, 3) Q(–12, –2) R(2, –4)

1 Plot all six points on a grid, using the same scale for both axes.

2 Find the gradient of the lines MR, PM and QL.

3 Show that NM is perpendicular to LR.

4 Show that PN is not parallel to LR.

5 Find a point which is collinear to Q and R, and prove that it is collinear.

6 What is the gradient of a line that is perpendicular to PR? Which line is perpendicular to PR?

7 If T and U are points such that RLTU is a square, find possible coordinates of T and U.

8 V is a point such that MRV is a right-angled triangle with hypotenuse MV, which has a zero gradient. FInd the coordinates of V.

9 A circle is drawn with MV (as defined in question 9) as its diameter. Find the coordinates (x, y) of as many points as possible that lie on the circumference of this circle (x and y should only be whole numbers).

EQUATION OF A STRAIGHT LINE

Exploration 3.4

Straight-line relationships

Take another look at the 'Have van will travel' problem on page 58 at the beginning of the last section. From the graph we found that:

- the fixed charge is £20 (charge for 0 hours' hire)
- the variable charge is £5 per hour.

Find an equation that connects cost (c) with time (t).

Finding the equation

The cost of hiring a van (c) consists of a fixed charge of £20 plus a variable charge of £5t (£5 × number of hours of hire). Symbolically this is expressed as:

$$c = 20 + 5t$$

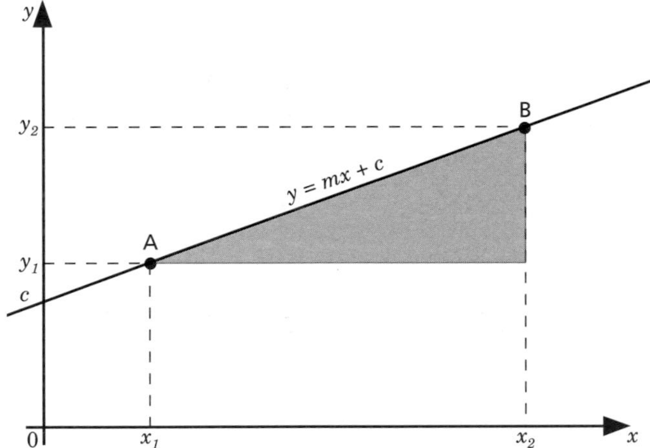

From the graph on page 58 we can see that 20 is the charge for 0 hours hire (the **intercept** on the cost axis) and the **gradient** of the straight line is 5. This principle can be applied generally to any straight-line graph on xy-axes with y-intercept $(0, c)$ and gradient m. The equation of the straight line is $y = mx + c$.

Note
When $x = 0$, $y = m \times 0 + c$, which equals c. So, the graph of $y = mx + c$ passes through $(0, c)$.

If A and B are two points on the line with coordinates (x_1, y_1) and (x_2, y_2) then in particular:

$$y_1 = mx_1 + c \quad (1) \qquad y_2 = mx_2 + c \quad (2)$$

Subtracting equation (1) from equation (2):

$$\begin{aligned}(2) - (1) \quad \Rightarrow \quad y_2 - y_1 &= (mx_2 + c) - (mx_1 + c)\\ &= mx_2 + c - mx_1 - c\\ &= mx_2 - mx_1\\ &= m(x_2 - x_1)\end{aligned}$$

$$\Rightarrow \quad m = \frac{y_2 - y_1}{x_2 - x_1}$$

This is the gradient of the line joining two points.

This confirms that m represents the gradient of the line passing through A and B.

Exploration 3.5

CALCULATOR ACTIVITY

Plotting straight lines

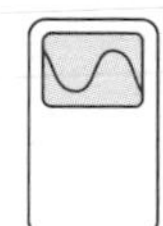

You will need a graphics calculator or graph plotter. Set x and y limits so that the origin is at the centre of the screen and both axes have the same scale.

Test your settings: the graph of $y = x$ should make a 45° angle with both x and y axes.

- Plot graphs of $y = x + c$ by choosing different values for c (e.g. –5, –2, 0, 1, 3, etc.).
- Plot graphs of $y = mx$ by choosing different values for m (e.g. –2, –1, 0.5, 0, 0.5, 1, 2, etc.).
- For the straight line $y = mx + c$, describe the effect of:

a) varying c whilst keeping m fixed
b) varying m whilst keeping c fixed
c) varying both m and c.

Special cases

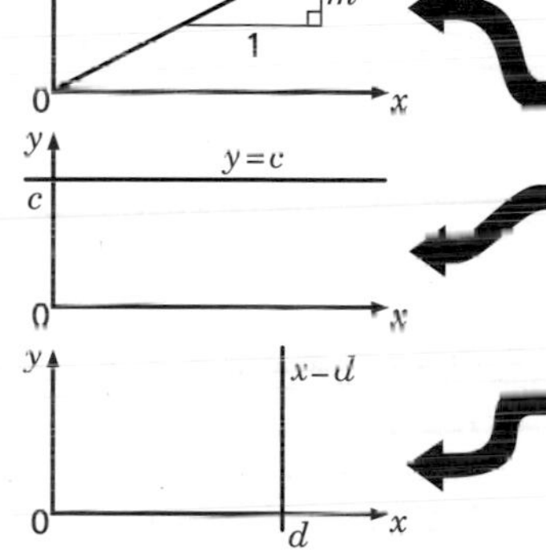

Nearly all straight lines have equations in the form $y = mx + c$. There are some special cases worth noting.

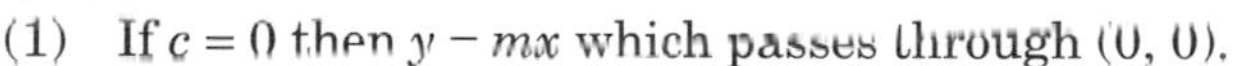

(1) If $c = 0$ then $y = mx$ which passes through (0, 0).

(2) If $m = 0$ then $y = c$, a line parallel to the x-axis ($y = 0$) passing through (0, c).

The problem line is one which is parallel to the y-axis. If it passes through (d, 0) then it has equation $x = d$. Note that in this case you cannot use $y = mx + c$ since m, the gradient, is not defined.

The following examples show how problems involving straight-line graphs and their equations may be tackled.

Example 3.7

Find the equation of the line with gradient 3 which passes through (0, 12). Where does it intersect the x-axis?

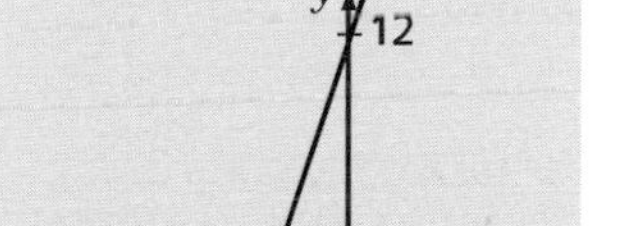

Solution

Gradient $= 3 \Rightarrow m = 3$ *and y-intercept is (0, 12)* $\Rightarrow c = 12$
Therefore the equation of the line is $y = 3x + 12$.
Let the point of intersection with the x-axis be (d, 0), i.e. when $y = 0, x = d$. *Then:*

$$\begin{aligned} 0 &= 3d + 12 \\ \Rightarrow -12 &= 3d \\ \Rightarrow d &= -4 \end{aligned}$$

The line intersects with the x-axis at (–4, 0).

These results are confirmed on the sketch graph.

Example 3.8

Find the gradient and y-intercept for each of these equations.

a) $y = 10 - 4x$ ***b)*** $3y = 2x - 9$ ***c)*** $5x + 2y = 10$

In each case, draw a sketch graph, clearly showing where the line intersects with the x and y axes.

Solution

a) $y = 10 - 4x$ *may be written* $y = -4x + 10$.

Gradient $= -4$ *and y-intercept is (0, 10)*
Let the x-intercept be (d, 0), i.e. when $y = 0$, $x = d$. Then:

$$0 = -4d + 10$$
$$\Rightarrow \quad 4d = 10$$
$$\Rightarrow \quad d = 2.5$$

The line intersects with the x-axis at (2.5, 0).

b) $3y = 2x - 9$ *may be written as* $y = \frac{2}{3}x - 3$

Gradient $= \frac{2}{3}$ *and y-intercept is (0, –3)*

Let the x-intercept be (d, 0). Then from the original equation:

$$3 \times 0 = 2d - 9$$
$$\Rightarrow \quad 9 = 2d$$
$$\Rightarrow \quad d = 4.5$$

The line intersects with the x-axis at (4.5, 0).

c) $5x + 2y = 10$ *may be written as* $y = -2.5x + 5$.

Gradient $= -2.5$ *and y-intercept is (0, 5)*
Let the x-intercept be (d, 0). Then from the original equation:

$$5d + 2 \times 0 = 10$$
$$\Rightarrow \quad 5d = 10$$
$$\Rightarrow \quad d = 2$$

The line intersects with the x-axis at (2, 0).

Example 3.9

Find the equation of the straight line parallel to $y = 12 - 5x$ passing through (2, –4).

Solution

$y = 12 - 5x$ *may be written* $y = -5x + 12$.
Gradient $= -5$

Since parallel lines have the same gradient, the required gradient is $m = -5$.
Let the equation be $y = -5x + c$.
Since the line passes through (2, –4), when $x = 2$, $y = -4$.

$$-4 = -5 \times 2 + c$$
$$\Rightarrow \quad c = 10 - 4 = 6$$

The equation of the line is $y = -5x + 6$
or $y = 6 - 5x$
or $5x + y = 6$.

Example 3.10

Find the equation of the straight line passing through P(–3, –1) and Q(5, 3) and show that the equation of the perpendicular bisector of PQ is $2x + y = 3$. Illustrate your answer with a sketch.

Solution

The gradient of the line through P and Q is $\dfrac{3-(-1)}{5-(-3)} = \dfrac{4}{8} = 0.5$

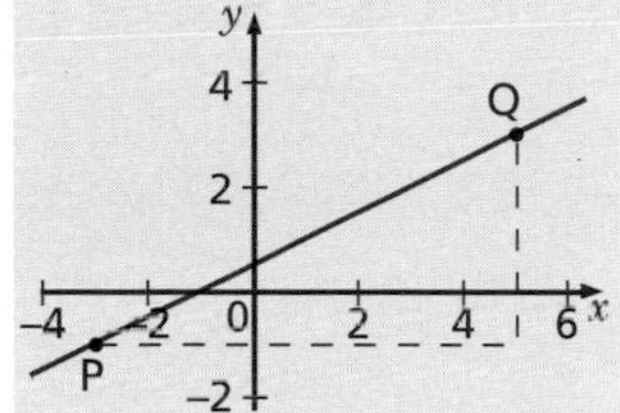

Let the equation be $y = 0.5x + c$.

Since the line passes through (5, 3):

$3 = 0.5 \times 5 + c \Rightarrow \quad c = 3 - 2.5 = 0.5$

The equation of the line is $y = 0.5x + 0.5$

or $2y = x + 1$

Now we need to find the equation of the perpendicular bisector of PQ.

Let M be the midpoint of PQ. Then the coordinates of M are:

$\left(\dfrac{-3+5}{2}, \dfrac{-1+3}{2}\right)$ or (1, 1).

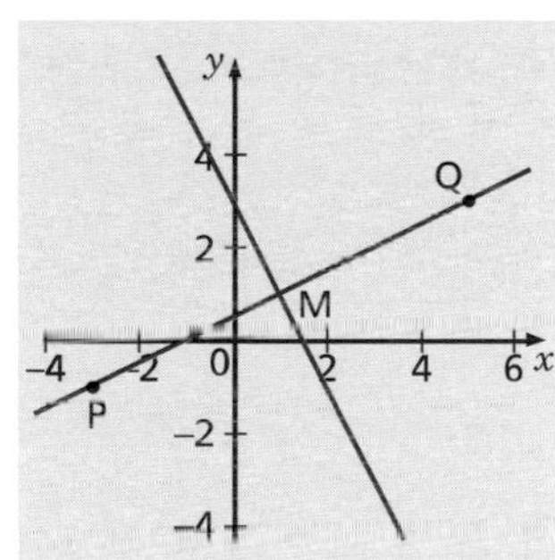

Since the gradient of PQ is 0.5, the gradient of its perpendicular bisector is $\dfrac{-1}{0.5} = -2$.

Therefore the equation of the perpendicular bisector is $y = -2x + c$, *and* $y = 1$ *when* $x = 1$.

$\Rightarrow \quad 1 = -2 \times 1 + c$

$c = 1 + 2 = 3$

The equation of the perpendicular bisector is: $y = -2x + 3$

or $2x + y = 3$.

The last two worked examples demonstrate two general methods for finding equations of straight lines, given certain initial information:

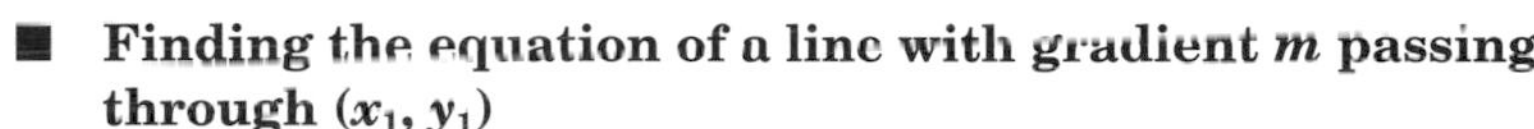

- **Finding the equation of a line with gradient m passing through (x_1, y_1)**

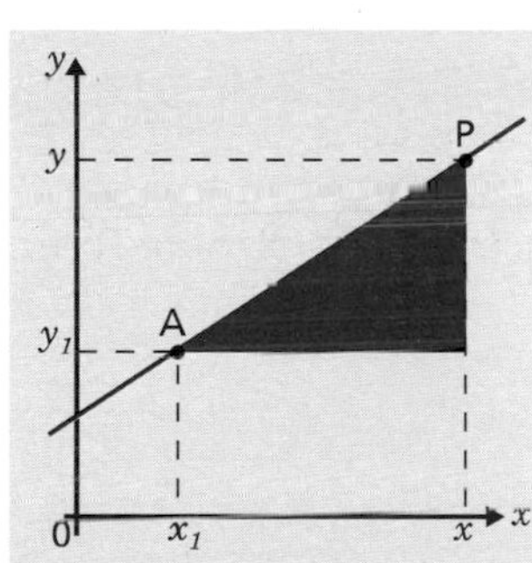

Let A(x_1, y_1) be the fixed point and P(x, y) be a variable point on the line with gradient m. Then:

$$\frac{y - y_1}{x - x_1} = m \qquad \Rightarrow \quad y - y_1 = m(x - x_1)$$

So the equation of the line with gradient –1.5 passing through (3, –0.5) is

$y - (-0.5) = -1.5(x - 3) \Rightarrow y + 0.5 = -1.5x + 4.5 \Rightarrow y = 4 - 1.5x$

or $\quad 2y + 3x = 8$.

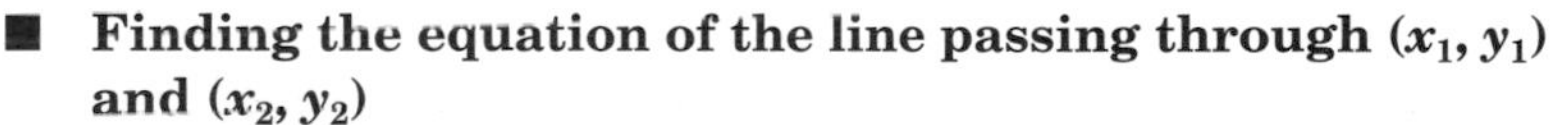

- **Finding the equation of the line passing through (x_1, y_1) and (x_2, y_2)**

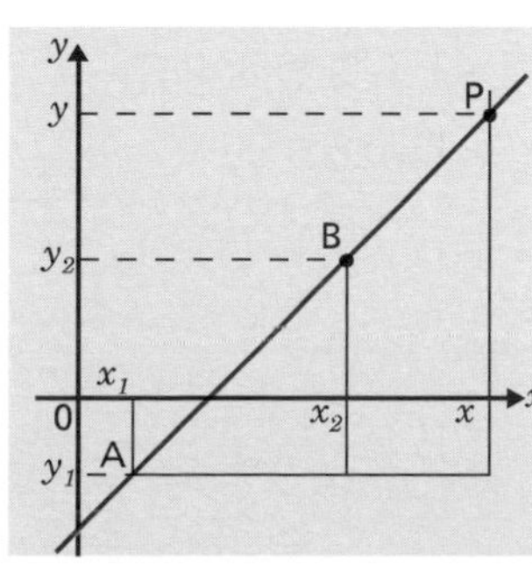

Let A(x_1, y_1) and B(x_2, y_2) be the fixed points and P(x, y) be the variable point on the line.

Since points A, B and P are collinear:

gradient AP = gradient AB

$$\Rightarrow \frac{y - y_1}{x - x_1} = \frac{y_2 - y_1}{x_2 - x_1} \Rightarrow \frac{y - y_1}{y_2 - y_1} = \frac{x - x_1}{x_2 - x_1}$$

So the equation of the line passing through (2, 7) and (5, 1) is given by:

$$\frac{y-7}{1-7} = \frac{x-2}{5-2} \Rightarrow \frac{y-7}{-6} = \frac{x-2}{3} \Rightarrow \frac{-6(y-7)}{-6} = \frac{-6(x-2)}{3}$$

$\Rightarrow y - 7 = -2(x - 2) \Rightarrow y - 7 = -2x + 4 \Rightarrow y = -2x + 11$
or $\quad 2x + y = 11$.

You may find both methods useful but in both cases you can always work from first principles, i.e. by finding values for m and c in the equation $y = mx + c$.

EXERCISES

3.3 CLASSWORK

1 Find the gradients and y-intercepts for lines with the following equations.

a) $y = 2x - 5$ **b)** $y = 10 - 3x$ **c)** $x + y = 7$
d) $4x + 5y = 30$ **e)** $2x - 6y + 9 = 0$ **f)** $\frac{1}{3}x + \frac{1}{4}y = 1$

2 For each of the following equations:

a) find the coordinates of the points where the line meets the x and y axes, i.e. $(d, 0)$ and $(0, c)$ respectively
b) sketch a graph, showing clearly $(0, c)$ and $(d, 0)$
c) confirm that the gradient $m = -\frac{c}{d}$.

i) $y = 2x + 8$ **ii)** $y = 12 - 4x$ **iii)** $y = 4 - \frac{2}{3}x$
iv) $2x + y = 10$ **v)** $3x - 4y = 18$ **vi)** $\frac{3}{5}y + \frac{1}{2}x = \frac{3}{2}$

3 Find the equations of the lines with the following gradients and y-intercepts, giving your answers in an appropriate form. Illustrate each answer with a sketch.

a) gradient = 3 y-intercept –5
b) gradient = –2 y-intercept 7
c) gradient = 0 y-intercept 8
d) gradient = –0.4 y-intercept –2.4
e) gradient = 2 y-intercept 3

4 Find the equations of the lines with the following gradients, passing through the points given. Give each equation in an appropriate form.

a) gradient = 4, passing through (5, –1)
b) gradient = –3, passing through (–1, 6)
c) gradient = $-\frac{2}{3}$, passing through (6, –3)

5 Find the equations of the lines which pass through the following pairs of points.

a) (2, 0) and (7, 1) **b)** (–4, –1) and (5, 2) **c)** (–2, 8) and (3, –5)

6 Points R and S have coordinates (6, 1) and (2, 5) respectively.

a) Find the coordinates of the midpoint of RS.
b) Find the gradient of RS.
c) Find the equation of the perpendicular bisector of RS.

7 A triangle has vertices A(5, 1), B(8, 4) and C(2, 5).

a) Find the equation of the line AB.
b) Find the equation of the line passing through C that is perpendicular to AB and meets AB at point D.
c) Show that point D has coordinates (5.5, 1.5).
d) Find the lengths of AB and CD and hence deduce the area of the triangle.

8 The line l has equation $3x + 4y = 21$. Find the equation of a line that is perpendicular to l and intersects l at a point on the line $y = x$.

EXERCISES

3.3 HOMEWORK

1 Find the gradients and y-intercepts for the lines with the following equations.

a) $y = x + 2$ **b)** $y = 2 - 3x$ **c)** $2x + y = 0$
d) $x + 2y + 7 = 0$ **e)** $\frac{1}{8}x + \frac{5}{4}y = 6$ **f)** $y = 7$

2 For each of the following equations, sketch a graph marking where the line crosses each of the axes, and state its gradient.

a) $y = 7x + 6$ **b)** $y = 6 - 4x$ **c)** $y = \frac{2}{9} - \frac{1}{3}x$ **d)** $7x + 5y = 9$

e) a line which passes through the x-axis at $\frac{-2}{3}$ and through the y-axis at $\frac{4}{9}$
f) a horizontal line which passes through the point (6.2, –7.1)

3 Find the equations of the lines with the following gradients and y-intercepts, giving your answers in an appropriate form. Illustrate each answer with a sketch.

a) gradient = 7 y-intercept 4 **b)** gradient = –9 y-intercept $\frac{2}{3}$
c) gradient – $\frac{4}{3}$ y-intercept $\frac{1}{4}$

4 Find the equations of the lines with the following gradients, passing through the given points. Give each equation in an appropriate form.

a) gradient = 3, passing through (8, 1)
b) gradient = –5, passing through (–1, 8)
c) gradient = $\frac{2}{3}$, passing through (4, –5)

5 Find the equations of the lines which pass through these pairs of points.

a) (2, 2) and (8, 7) **b)** (–7, 5) and (–2, –8) **c)** ($\frac{1}{2}$, –1) and (4, –2$\frac{1}{2}$)

6 Find the equations of the following lines and give your answers in the form $ax + by + c = 0$.

a) a line of gradient 3 and y-intercept 6
b) a line of gradient –$\frac{2}{3}$ which crosses the x-axis at (–3, 0)
c) a line of gradient –4 which passes through the point (–8, 5)
d) a line which passes through the points (4, –9) and (–2, 6)

7 Points A and B have coordinates (–3, 1) and (7, 4) repectively.

a) Find the coordinates of the midpoint of AB.
b) Find the gradient of AB.
c) Find the equation of the perpendicular bisector of AB.

8 The line $2x - 3y + 7 = 0$ passes through the x-axis at point P. Find the equation of the line which is perpendicular to $6x + 3y + 4 = 0$ and which passes through point P.

FITTING LINES TO DATA

Exploration 3.6

Line of best fit

In an experiment to measure the elasticity of a rubber band, a student hung various masses on one end of the rubber band and measured its stretched length. The results were as follows.

Mass in g x	100	200	300	400	500	600
Length in mm y	227	237	253	272	288	298

- Plot this data on graph paper.
- Draw in a straight line which best fits the data.
- Find the equation of the line of best fit.
- Use your equation to predict the length of the rubber band when a mass of 540 g is attached.
- Would it be sensible to use this model to predict the length when a mass of 1 kg is attached?

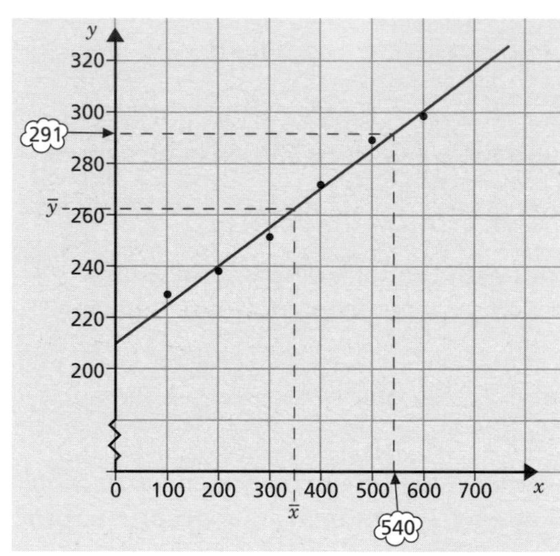

The graph shows the six data points joined with a line of best fit. A line of best fit should pass through $(\bar{x}, \bar{y})$ where $\bar{x}$ is the mean of the x-values and $\bar{y}$ is the mean of the y-values.

$$\bar{x} = \frac{100 + 200 + 300 + 400 + 500 + 600}{6} = 350$$

$$\bar{y} = \frac{227 + 237 + 253 + 272 + 288 + 298}{6} = 262.5$$

The point $(\bar{x}, \bar{y}) = (350, 262.5)$ is the **centroid**.

Now draw in the straight line passing through $(\bar{x}, \bar{y})$ which fits the data best.

Interpreting the results

From the graph, the gradient is about 0.15 (for every 100 g added, the rubber band stretches about 15 mm) and the y-intercept is at (0, 210) mm (the unstretched length is 210 mm). So $m = 0.15$ and $c = 210$.

Therefore the equation of the line of best fit is $y = 0.15x + 210$
For a mass of 540 grams, substitute $x = 540$:
$y = 0.15 \times 540 + 210 \quad \Rightarrow \quad y = 291$
The model predicts that a mass of 540 grams will stretch the band to a length of 291 mm.

Predicting a y-value using an x-value within the range of x-values given is called **interpolation**. Using an x-value from outside the range of x-values is called **extrapolation**. There are dangers in extrapolating. Attaching a mass of 1 kg may break the rubber band!

An alternative way of forming the equation of the line of best fit is to use its gradient (m) and the fact that it must pass through $(\bar{x}, \bar{y})$. This is especially useful if it is inconvenient to include $x = 0$ on your graph. The following example illustrates the method.

Example 3.11

In athletics, the times set by various world record holders for the mile, together with the date they broke the record are:

Roger Bannister	*6–5–54*	*3 minutes 59.4 seconds*
Derek Ibbotson	*19–7–57*	*3 minutes 57.2 seconds*
Peter Snell	*27–1–62*	*3 minutes 54.4 seconds*
Michel Jazy	*9–6–65*	*3 minutes 53.6 seconds*
Filbert Bayi	*17–5–75*	*3 minutes 51.0 seconds*
Seb Coe	*17–7–79*	*3 minutes 49.0 seconds*
Steve Cram	*27–7–85*	*3 minutes 46.3 seconds*

a) *Using suitable variables x and y, model the data using a straight-line equation.*

b) *Use your model to suggest a world record time for the mile in 1995.*

c) *When is it likely that the mile could be run in 3 minutes 30 seconds?*

d) *Is it reasonable to use this model to estimate when we are likely to see the first 3-minute mile?*

Solution

a) *Let x represent the year since 1900, and y represent the time in seconds above 3 minutes. Then we have:*

x	54.3	57.5	62.1	65.4	75.4	79.5	85.5
y	59.4	57.2	54.4	53.6	51.0	49.0	46.3

$\bar{x} = 68.5$ and $\bar{y} = 53.0$, so the line of best fit passes through (68.5, 53.0).

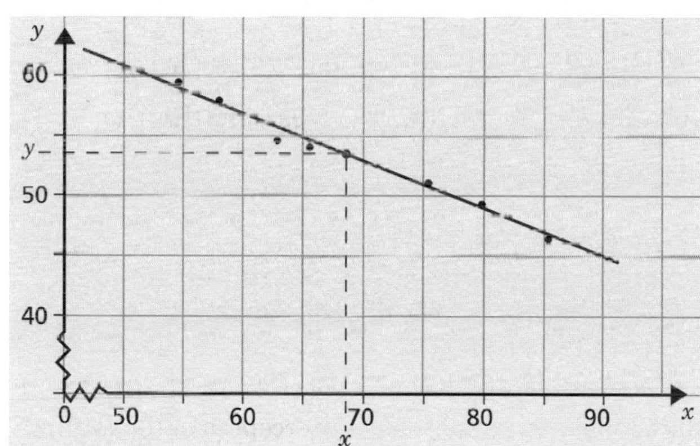

From the graph the gradient $m = -0.38$, therefore the equation of the line of best fit is

$y - \bar{y} = m(x - \bar{x})$

$\Rightarrow y - 53.0 = -0.38(x - 68.5)$

$\Rightarrow y - 53.0 = -0.38x + 26.03$

$\Rightarrow y = -0.38x + 79.03$

b) *To suggest the world record time for 1995, let $x = 95.5$ (representing a date mid-way through 1995).*

$\Rightarrow y = -0.38 \times 95.5 + 79.03$

$y = 42.74$

So we might expect a time of 3 minutes 42.7 seconds to have been set during 1995.

c) *To predict when the mile might be run in 3 minutes 30 seconds, let $y = 30$.*

$\Rightarrow 30 = -0.38x + 79.03$

$\Rightarrow 0.38x = 79.03 - 30 = 49.03$

$\Rightarrow x = 49.03/0.38 = 129.0$

So the model predicts that we shall have to wait until the year 2029!

d) *In **c)** we used the model to extrapolate. The reliability of the model for a prediction so far ahead is questionable. The model would give an even more unreliable prediction of the year in which we are likely to see a 3-minute mile.*

The model cannot be valid indefinitely since this would mean that eventually the mile would be run in no time at all!

EXERCISES

3.4 CLASSWORK

KEY SKILLS
IT 3.3
C 3.1b

1 The table shows some equivalent temperatures in °C and °F.

Temperature (in °C)	20	37	55	70	100
Temperature (in °F)	68	98.6	131	158	212

a) Plot points to represent these pairs of temperatures.
b) Find the equation of the line that fits the data exactly.
c) What temperature in °F corresponds to 0°C? What is the significance of this?
d) What temperature is the same in both scales?

2 A particular type of fish (North Seas haddock) has a lifetime of about 10 years. The table shows average masses of haddock at different times in their life.

Age (in years)	2	4	6	8	10
Mass (in grams)	250	500	820	1110	1300

a) Plot points to represent the mass of a fish at different ages.
b) Calculate the mean age and mean mass for the data given.
c) Find the equation of the line that fits the data best.
d) Use your equation to predict the mass at age 3 years.
e) At what age would you expect a haddock to have a mass of 1 kg?

3 A student conducted an experiment to discover the relationship between the resistance of a piece of wire and its temperature.

At five different temperatures her results were as shown in the table.

Temperature, T (in °C)	20	40	60	80	100
Resistance, R (in ohms)	18.1	21.0	23.8	26.9	30.0

a) Plot the data on a suitable graph.
b) Find the equation of the line of best fit in the form $R = aT + b$.
c) Interpret what a and b represent for the relationship.
d) Use your equation in **b)** to predict:
   i) the resistance in the wire at 130°C,
   ii) the temperature range for which the resistance is less than 10 ohms,
   iii) the temperature for which the resistance is zero – does this make sense?

EXERCISES

3.4 HOMEWORK

KEY SKILLS
IT 3.3
C 3.1b

1 In an attempt to find the thickness of the paper in a telephone book, the thickness of multiple pages was measured and the following data were noted.

Number of pages	506	220	423	104	0
Thickness (in mm)	33	14	27	7	0

a) Plot points to represent this data.
b) Find the equation of the line that you think best fits the data.
c) Estimate the thickness of a single sheet of telephone book paper.

2 The population of Scotland for certain years is given below.

Year	Total population
1821	2 091 521
1831	2 364 386
1841	2 620 184
1851	2 888 742
1881	3 735 573
1891	4 025 647
1921	4 882 497

a) Let x be the number of years after 1800 and y be the population of Scotland in millions. Plot points to represent this data in terms of x and y.
For the first piece of information $x = 21$ and $y = 2.09$ (3 s.f.).

b) Does this data seem to lie on a straight line? If so, find the equation of the line which best fits the data.

c) What do you think the population of Scotland was in 1931?

d) According to this model, what was the population of Scotland in 1700 ($x = -100$)?

e) Some more data on Scotland's population is given below.

Year	Total population
1891	4 025 647
1901	4 472 103
1911	4 760 904
1921	4 882 497
1931	4 842 554

Plot this data, and comment on what you have done through this question.

3 The times taken by the winners of the Women's Olympic 400 m freestyle swimming between 1956 and 1980 are given in the table below.

year	Winner	Time (minutes : seconds)
1956	*Lorraine Gapp*	*4:54.6*
1960	*Chris von Saltza*	*4:50.6*
1964	*Virginnia Duenkel*	*4:43.3*
1968	*Debbie Meyer*	*4:31.8*
1972	*Shane Gould*	*4:19.0*
1976	*Petra Thumer*	*4:09.9*
1980	*Ines Diers*	*4:08.8*

a) Let x be the number of years after 1950 and let y be the time taken (in seconds). Plot points to represent this data as (x, y) coordinates.

b) Draw in a line of best fit and find its equation.

c) Use the equation to predict:
   i) the time taken by the 1984 winner,
   ii) the time taken by the winner in the year 2000.

d) Comment on the validity of your predictions in **c)**.

CONSOLIDATION EXERCISES FOR CHAPTER 3

1 A, B and C are the points (0, 2), (4, 6) and (10, 0) respectively.

a) Find the lengths AB, BC and CA of the sides of the triangle ABC, and show that:
$AB^2 + BC^2 = CA^2$
Deduce the size of angle ABC.

b) Find the gradients of the lines AB and BC and show these can be used to confirm your answer in part a) for the size of angle ABC.
c) M is the midpoint of line CA. Show that MA = MB.

(MEI Specimen Paper, 1994)

2 The points P, Q and R have coordinates (2, 4), (7, –2) and (6, 2) respectively.

Find the equation of the straight line l which is perpendicular to the line PQ and which passes through the midpoint of PR.

(AEB Specimen Paper, 1994)

3 The speed of a car (in mph) accelerating away from traffic lights is noted from the speedometer at one-second time intervals. The results were as follows.

Time from start (t)	1	2	3	4	5	6	7	8
Speed of car (v)	5	11	16	21	27	30	39	45

a) Plot points to represent this data.
b) Find the equation of the line that you think best fits the data.
c) Estimate the acceleration of the car stating your units carefully.

4 The following set of data is taken from a study of primates.

Adult body weight (in grams)	6583	733	582	288	2490	7362	4173	3384
New born baby weight (in grams)	480	97	50	27	234	425	314	107

Source: Unit 5, Edate pack, originally from Ross C (1988) in Journal of Zoology 214: pp. 199–219

a) Rewrite this table in more usual form with the data in each row increasing.
b) Plot points to represent this data.
c) Find the equation of the line that you think best fits the data.
d) How would your line of best fit change if the primate with weight 3384 grams had not been included?
e) What would be your prediction of the birth weight of a gorilla with adult body weight 117 500 grams? The actual baby weight is 2122 grams. Comment on your answer.

5 The points A and B have coordinates (2, 16) and (12, –4) respectively. A straight line l_1, passes through A and B.

a) Find an equation for l_1, in the form $ax + by = c$.
The line l_2 passes through the point C with coordinates (–1, 1) and has gradient $\frac{1}{3}$

b) Find an equation for l_2.

(EDEXCEL, Question 6, Paper 1, January 2000)

6 A landscape gardener is given the following instructions about laying a rectangular lawn. The length x m is to be 2 m longer than the width. The width must be greater than 6.4 m and the area is to be less than 63 m^2.
By forming an inequality in x, find the set of possible values of x.

(EDEXCEL, Question 1, Specimen Paper 1 2000)

7 The point A has coordinates (7, 4). The straight lines with equations $x + 3y + 1 = 0$ and $2x + 5y = 0$ intersect at the point B. Show that one of these two lines is perpendicular to AB.

(OCR, Question 3, Specimen Paper 1 2000)

Summary

Straight lines

- The straight line through the points $P(x_1, y_1)$ and $Q(x_2, y_2)$ has the following properties:

  gradient $\dfrac{y_2 - y_1}{x_2 - x_1}$

  equation $\dfrac{y - y_1}{y_2 - y_1} = \dfrac{x - x_1}{x_2 - x_1}$.

- The midpoint of PQ has coordinates $\left(\frac{1}{2}(x_1 + x_2), \frac{1}{2}(y_1 + y_2)\right)$.

- The length of the line PQ is $\sqrt{(x_2 - x_1)^2 + (y_2 - y_1)^2}$.

Equation of a straight line

- The general equation of a straight line is $y = mx + c$
  where m is the gradient or slope of the line and
  c is called the intercept because the point $(0, c)$ is the intercept of the line with the y-axis.

Parallel and perpendicular lines

- If two straight lines are perpendicular then the product of their gradients is –1.

- The two lines $y = m_1x + c_1$ and $y = m_2x + c_2$ are
  parallel if $m_1 = m_2$
  perpendicular if $m_1 m_2 = -1$.

Quadratic functions

In this chapter we:

- *explore the properties of quadratic functions and their graphs*
- *investigate factorisation of quadratic functions*
- are *introduced to the method of 'completing the square'.*
- *solve quadratic equations by factorising, completing the square and using 'the quadratic formula'.*

PARABOLAE

Exploration 4.1 ***Fixed perimeter***

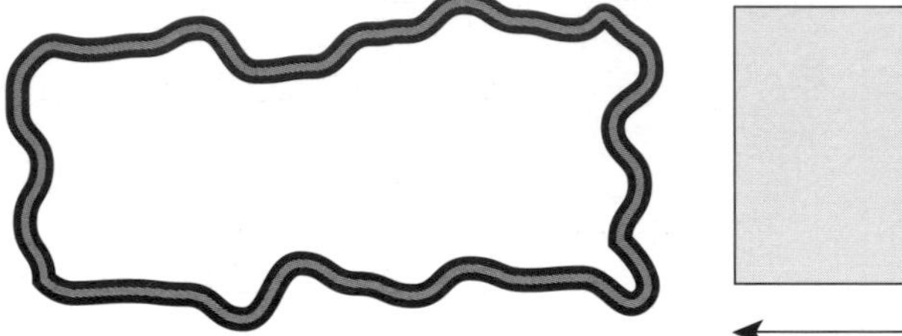

Make a loop of string 40 cm long and lay it out in the form of a rectangle.

- Investigate the area enclosed by the string.

1. How does the area (A) vary as the length of rectangle (x) varies?
2. What will the value of A be when $x = 7$?
3. What value of x will give $A = 75$?
4. What value of x will maximise the value of A?
   What shape is the rectangle then?
5. Find a formula connecting A with x. Use it to illustrate your answers to 2, 3 and 4.

   Describe any geometrical properties of the curve.

Interpreting the results

1. Since the rectangle is formed from a piece of string 40 cm long, the perimeter of the rectangle must be constant at 40 cm. The perimeter of a rectangle is twice the sum of adjacent sides, so the sum of the length and width of a rectangle is always half the perimeter, i.e.

$$\begin{aligned} \text{length} + \text{width} &= 20 \\ \Rightarrow \qquad \text{width} &= 20 - \text{length} \\ &= 20 - x \end{aligned}$$

Area = length × width

$\Rightarrow \; A = x(20 - x)$

2 In particular, when $x = 7$:
$A = 7 \times 13 = 91\ \text{cm}^2$

3 If $A = 75$, then $75 = x(20 - x)$
Looking carefully at this, we can see that $x = 5$ or 15 will satisfy the equation.

4 The area will be greatest if we form a square from the string.
When $x = 10$:
$A = 10 \times 10 = 100\ \text{cm}^2$

5 The solutions to 2, 3 and 4 can be read from the graph of $A = x(20 - x)$.

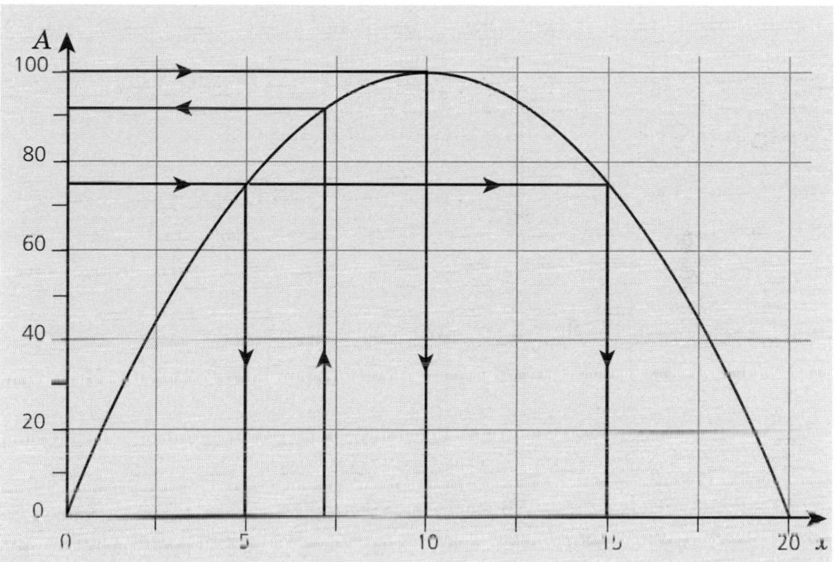

Parabolae as functions

The curve above is an example of a **parabola**. Every parabola is symmetrical and has a line of symmetry passing through the **vertex**. In our example the equation of the line of symmetry is $x = 10$ and the vertex has coordinates (10, 100).

All parabolae can be described by **quadratic functions**. The expression for the area of the rectangle may be expanded by multiplying out the brackets.

$$A = x(20 - x)$$
$$\Rightarrow A = 20x - x^2$$

Any expression with a term in x^2, with or without a term in x and with or without a constant, is a quadratic function. The following are all quadratic functions.

$y = x^2$
$y = 2x^2 - 5$
$y = x^2 + 5x - 6$
$s = 12t - 5t^2$

Example 4.1

Plot a graph of $y = x^2 - 2x - 15$ for $-4 \leq x \leq 6$.

From your graph find:

a) the values of x when $y = 0$,
b) the values of x when $y = -10$,
c) the equation of the line of symmetry and the coordinates of the vertex.

Solution

A table of values for $y = x^2 - 2x - 15$ gives:

x	–4	–3	–2	–1	0	1	2	3	4	5	6
y	9	0	–7	–12	–15	–16	–15	–12	–7	0	9

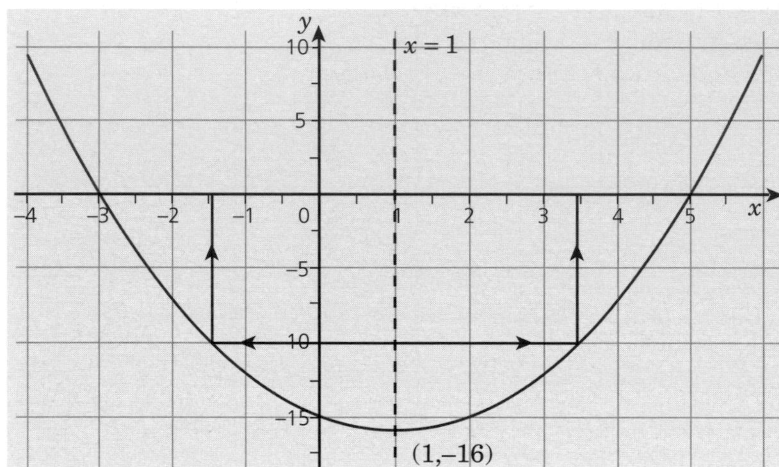

From the graph:

a) when $y = 0$, $x = -3$ or 5
b) when $y = -10$, $x = -1.45$ or 3.45
c) the line of symmetry has equation $x = 1$ and the vertex has coordinates (1, –16).

Example 4.2

An athlete is a shot-putter. On one occasion the flight path (or trajectory) of the shot is modelled by the equation:

$$y = -0.1x^2 + x + 1.5$$

where x represents the horizontal distance of the shot and y represents its height.
Plot a graph of y against x for $0 \leq x \leq 12$ and use it to find:

a) how far the shot travelled horizontally before hitting the ground,
b) the maximum height of the shot and the horizontal distance from the shot-putter when this occurred.

Solution

A suitable table of values might be as shown here.

x	0	2	4	6	8	10	12
y	1.5	3.1	3.9	3.9	3.1	1.5	–0.9

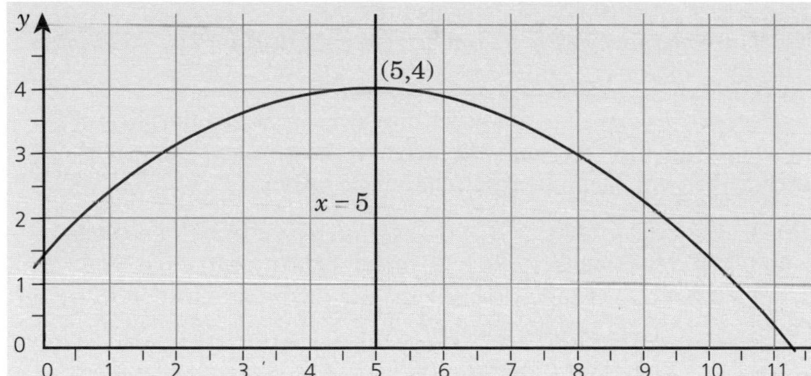

Looking at the table, notice the symmetry in the y-values. The highest y-value will occur between $x = 4$ and $x = 6$, when $x = 5$ and this point should be plotted as well.

a) *From the graph, when $y = 0$, $x = 11.3$ m.*
$\Rightarrow$ horizontal distance travelled by shot = 11.3 m

b) *The curve has its line of symmetry through $x = 5$, where the corresponding y-value on the curve is $y = 4$, which gives the maximum height of the shot, i.e. 4 metres.*

In the worked examples so far, the quadratic function has had terms in x^2, x and a constant. The general form of a quadratic function is:

$f(x) = ax^2 + bx + c$

where $f(x)$ is a function of x and a, b and c are constants, the only restriction being that $a \neq 0$.

e.g. $f(x) = 2x^2 - x + 5 \Rightarrow a = 2, b = -1, c = 5 \Rightarrow f(3) = 2 \times 3^2 - 3 + 5 = 20$
e.g. $f(x) = x^2 - 16 \Rightarrow a = 1, b = 0, c = -16 \Rightarrow f(-4) = (-4)^2 - 16 = 0$
e.g. $f(x) = 8 + 5x - x^2 \Rightarrow a = -1, b = 5, c = 8 \Rightarrow f(-2) = 8 + 5(-2) - (-2)^2 = -6$
The following exploration examines the effect that varying a, b or c has on the graph of the function.

CALCULATOR ACTIVITY

Exploration 4.2

Plotting parabolae

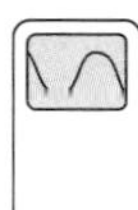

You will need a graphics calculator or graph plotter. Set x and y limits so that the origin is at the centre of the screen and both axes have the same scale. To test your settings, the graph of $y = x$ should make an angle of 45° with both axes.

- Plot graphs of $y = x^2 + c$ by choosing different values for c (e.g. –5, –2, 0, 1, 3 etc.).
- Plot graphs of $y = ax^2$ by choosing different values for a (e.g. –5, –2, –0.2, 0.3, 1, 3, 4 etc.).
- Plot graphs of $y = x^2 + bx$ by choosing different values for b (e.g. –5, –2, 0, 1, 3 etc.).
- For the parabola $y = ax^2 + bx + c$, describe the effect of:

1 varying c whilst keeping a and b fixed
2 varying b whilst keeping a and c fixed
3 varying a whilst keeping b and c fixed.

Interpreting the results

The effect of varying c for the function $y = x^2 + c$ is to translate the parabola parallel to the y-axis. Note that the parabola intersects with the y-axis at $(0, c)$.

Note: The constant c plays a similar role as it does for the straight-line graph $y = mx + c$.

The effect of varying a for the function $y = ax^2$ is to stretch the parabola parallel to the y-axis. Relative to the graph $y = x^2$, a is the **stretch factor** which can be fractional or negative.

Note: A negative value for a may be regarded as a positive stretch followed by a reflection in $y = 0$, e.g. consider the graph of $y = -3x^2$ as a stretch factor 3 of the graph $y = x^2$ followed by a reflection in the x-axis.

The effect of varying b for the function $y = x^2 + bx$ is less easy to interpret. As with varying c for the function $y = x^2 + c$, the effect is a translation, but this time in two directions: a translation through $-\frac{1}{2}b$ units parallel to the x-axis and a translation through $-(\frac{1}{2}b)^2$ units parallel to the y-axis. To examine the amounts by which the curve $y = x^2$ is translated, consider what happens to the vertex.

e.g. for $y = x^2 + 5x$, the vertex is at $(-2.5, -6.25)$.

EXERCISES

4.1 CLASSWORK

1 For each of the following quadratic functions:

a) plot a graph of the function,
b) find the coordinates of the y-intercept,
c) find the coordinates of the points where the graph intersects the x-axis,
d) draw in and give the equation of the line of symmetry,
e) write down the coordinates of the vertex.

i) $y = x^2 - 6x + 5$ **ii)** $y = -x^2 - 2x + 3$
iii) $y = 4x^2 + 8x - 5$ **iv)** $y = 25 + 5x - 2x^2$
v) $y = x^2 - 16$ **vi)** $y = 25 - 4x^2$
vii) $y = 3x^2 - 12x$ **viii)** $y = -(x^2 + 6x + 9)$

2 Find the coordinates of the vertex of the parabola $y = 9 - 7x - 2x^2$, given that it intersects the x-axis at $(-4.5, 0)$ and $(1, 0)$.

3 The St Louis arch in the USA is in the shape of a parabola. The height, y metres, of a point on the arch, in terms of its distance, x metres, from one side, can be modelled by the function $y = \frac{1}{48}x(192 - x)$. Draw a graph to represent the arch, and from your graph find:

a) the width of the arch at ground level,
b) the height of the arch,
c) the equation of its line of symmetry.

4 The spinal compression, H, of an athlete taking prolonged exercise, after t minutes, can be modelled by the function $H = 8.6 + 0.21t - 0.01t^2$.
Draw a graph of H against t for $0 \le t \le 50$ and from your graph find:

a) the time at which $H = 8$,
b) the time at which $H = 0$,
c) the time at which H reaches its greatest value and the value it takes at this time.

EXERCISES

4.1 HOMEWORK

1 Without plotting any points, state the coordinates where the following parabolae cut the y-axis.

a) $y = x^2 + 3x + 4$
b) $y = 3x^2 - 3x + 7$
c) $y = 5x^2$
d) $y = 2x - 6x^2$
e) $y = 4x - 7 - 5x^2$
f) $2y = 8x^2 + 4x - 7$

2 Find the equation of the line of symmetry of a parabola which passes through the x-axis at (–2, 0) and (3, 0).

3 Find the coordinates of the vertex of the parabola $y = 2x^2 - 25x + 63$, given that it crosses the x-axis at (3.5, 0) and (9, 0).

4 A ball is thrown up in the air. After t seconds the ball is h metres above the ground where $h = 1.4 + 2.3t - 4.9t^2$. Find:

a) how long it is before the ball hits the ground,
b) the time at which the ball is at its greatest height above the ground, and how high it is at that point.

BRACKETS

Sometimes, in some mathematical expressions, we can separate or group terms which have something in common, or which have to be considered as one item. We have already done this in earlier chapters, when we took out common factors.

Expanding

Exploration 4.3

Area of a rectangle

■ Find four different expressions for the area of this rectangle.

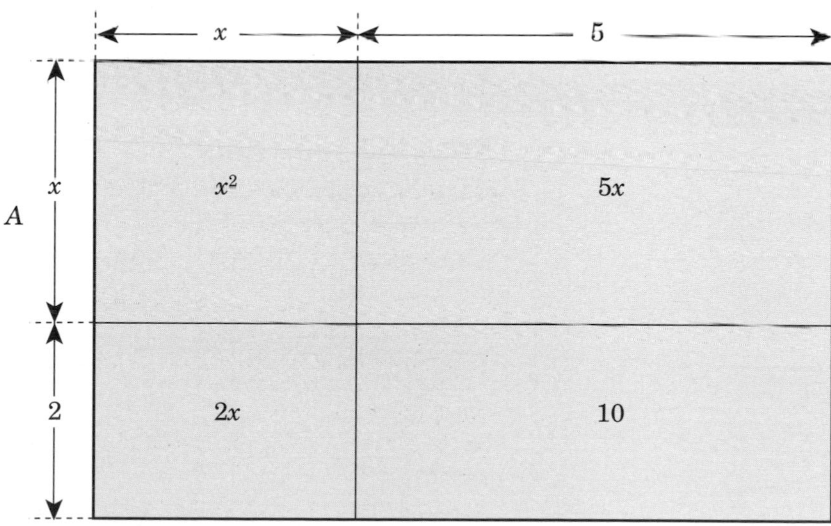

Summarising the results

Dividing the area into four smaller rectangles gives:

$$\begin{aligned}\text{area} &= x^2 + 5x + 2x + 10\\ &= x^2 + 7x + 10\end{aligned}$$

We can divide the rectangle into smaller parts, in different ways, to give these expressions.

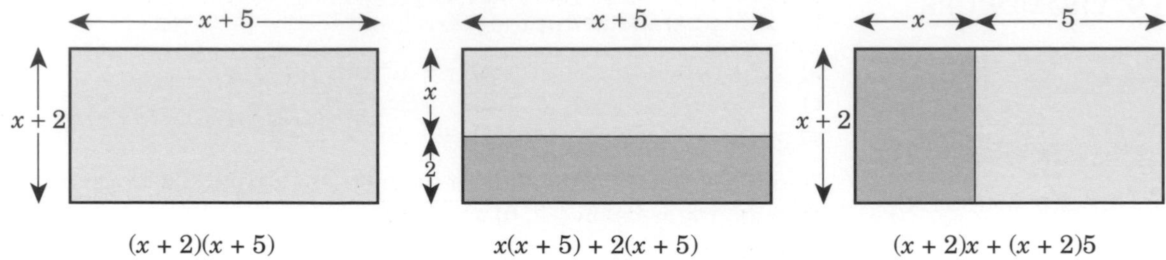

The four expressions are equivalent and illustrate ways in which pairs of brackets may be expanded.

$$(x + 2)(x + 5) \rightarrow \begin{cases} x(x + 5) + 2(x + 5) \\ (x + 2)x + (x + 2)5 \end{cases} \rightarrow x^2 + 5x + 2x + 10 \rightarrow x^2 + 7x + 10$$

The diagram shows how the expansion takes place in two stages. First we expand to give two sets of single brackets. Then we expand these and collect like terms. With practice, we can cut out the middle stage:

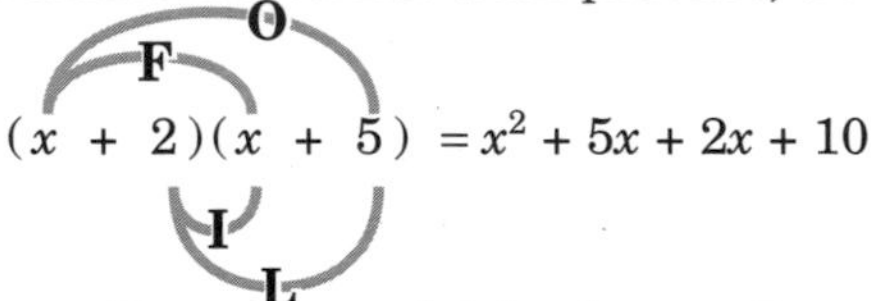

$$(x + 2)(x + 5) = x^2 + 5x + 2x + 10$$

where **F** means multiply the two first terms
O means multiply the two outside terms
I means multiply the two inside terms
L means multiply the two last terms.

Exploration 4.4

Expanding brackets

■ Use diagrams to illustrate that
$(x + 3)(x - 2) = x^2 + x - 6$ and $(x - 3)(x - 2) = x^2 - 5x + 6$

Possible solutions

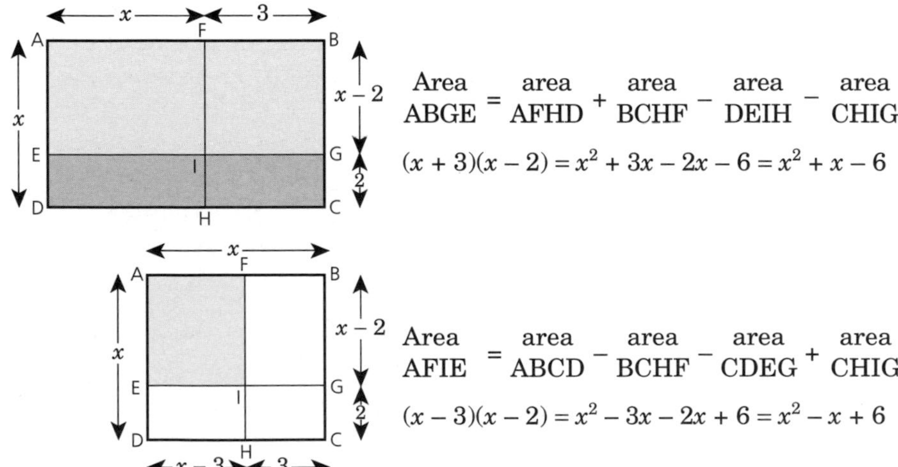

Example 4.3

Multiply out the brackets in the expression $(2x + 3)(x - 5)$.

Solution

$$\begin{aligned}(2x + 3)(x - 5) &= 2x(x - 5) + 3(x - 5) = 2x^2 - 10x + 3x - 15\\ &= 2x^2 - 7x - 15\end{aligned}$$

Example 4.4

Expand the brackets in the expression $(5x - 2)(8 - 3x)$.

Solution

$$\begin{aligned}(5x - 2)(8 - 3x) &= 5x(8 - 3x) - 2(8 - 3x) = 40x - 15x^2 - 16 + 6x\\ &= -15x^2 + 46x - 16\end{aligned}$$

Example 4.5

Multiply out the brackets and simplify this expression.
$(x - 7)(3x + 4) + (2x + 3)(2x - 3)$

Solution

$$\begin{aligned}(x - 7)(3x + 4) + (2x + 3)(2x - 3) &= x(3x + 4) - 7(3x + 4) + 2x(2x - 3) + 3(2x - 3)\\ &= 3x^2 + 4x - 21x - 28 + 4x^2 - 6x + 6x - 9\\ &= 3x^2 - 17x - 28 + 4x^2 - 9\\ &= 7x^2 - 17x - 37\end{aligned}$$

With practice, it is possible to find the final x-term by adding the two products which combine to give it. This is illustrated in the next example.

Example 4.6

Expand the brackets and simplify this expression.
$(3x - 1)(5 + 2x) - (4x - 3)^2$

Solution

$$\begin{aligned}(3x - 1)(5 + 2x) - (4x - 3)^2 &= (3x - 1)(5 + 2x) - (4x - 3)(4x - 3)\\ &= 6x^2 + 13x - 5 - (16x^2 - 24x + 9)\\ &= -10x^2 + 37x - 14\end{aligned}$$

Factorising expressions

When faced with a complicated mathematical expression, it is often useful to be able to simplify it in some way, such as taking out common factors. This is the reverse of expanding brackets and is called **factorising**, as we saw in Chapter 2, *Basic algebra*. We shall now look at ways of factorising quadratic functions (where possible).

If p and q are any two constants, then:

$$(x + p)(x + q) = x^2 + (p + q)x + pq$$

e.g. $(x + 5)(x + 2) = x^2 + (5 + 2)x + 5 \times 2$
$= x^2 + 7x + 10$

The constant term in the expansion is the **product** of the constants p and q and the coefficient of x is the **sum** of p and q. This result is very useful when factorising, since:

$$x^2 + (p + q)x + pq = (x + p)(x + q)$$

Example 4.7

Factorise the expression $x^2 + 5x + 6$.

Solution

Let $x^2 + 5x + 6 = x^2 + (p + q)x + pq$

We need to find two constants p *and* q *such that* $pq = 6$ *and* $p + q = 5$.

Possible values of p *and* q *to satisfy* $pq = 6$ *are* $p = 1, q = 6; p = 6, q = 1; p = 2, q = 3; p = 3, q = 2$.

By inspection, either $p = 2, q = 3$ or $p = 3, q = 2$ *will satisfy both conditions.*

$\Rightarrow \quad x^2 + 5x + 6 = (x + 2)(x + 3)$ *or* $x^2 + 5x + 6 = (x + 3)(x + 2)$

This method is used again in the following examples.

Example 4.8

Factorise the expression $x^2 - x - 12$.

Solution

Let $x^2 - x - 12 = x^2 + (p + q)x + pq$

Then $pq = -12$ *and* $p + q = -1$.

Possible combinations of p *and* q *to give a product of –12 are:*

p	1	–1	2	–2	3	–3	4	–4	6	–6	12	–12
q	–12	12	–6	6	–4	4	–3	3	–2	2	–1	1

but only $p = 3, q = -4$ *or* $p = -4, q = 3$ *give a sum of –1.*

$\Rightarrow \quad x^2 - x - 12 = (x + 3)(x - 4)$ *or* $x^2 - x - 12 = (x - 4)(x + 3)$

Note: As before, it does not matter which of the two factorised forms we take, since the same factors appear in both expressions, although in a different order.

Example 4.9

Factorise the expression $x^2 - 10x + 21$.

Solution

$x^2 - 10x + 21 = x^2 + (p + q)x + pq$

$\Rightarrow \quad p + q = -10$ *and* $pq = 21$

For a positive product and negative sum, both p *and* q *have to be negative numbers; by inspection:*

$p = -3$ *and* $q = -7$ *or* $p = -7$ *and* $q = -3$

since $-3 + (-7) = -10$ *and* $-7 + (-3) = -10$

$\Rightarrow \quad x^2 - 10x + 21 = (x - 3)(x - 7)$ *or* $x^2 - 10x + 21 = (x - 7)(x - 3)$

The examples so far suggest some useful clues.

$x^2 + 5x + 6 = (x + 2)(x + 3)$

positive product, positive sum $\Rightarrow$ both signs positive

$x^2 - x - 12 = (x + 3)\ x - 4)$

$x^2 + x - 12 = (x - 3)(x + 4)$

negative product $\Rightarrow$ different signs

$x^2 - 10x + 21 = (x - 3)(x - 7)$

positive product, negative sum $\Rightarrow$ both signs negative

Factorisation of $ax^2 + bx + c$

So far, the expressions we have been factorising have been of the form $x^2 + bx + c$. More complex factorisations occur when the coefficient of x^2 is not 1. We now have to consider the product of the two x terms as well as the product of the two constants. The most effective approach is to try the possibilities systematically until we find the correct factorisation.

Example 4.10

Factorise $2x^2 + 7x + 3$.

Solution

Both signs must be positive; possible combinations which give the correct products are:

$(x + 1)(2x + 3) = 2x^2 + 5x + 3$ ✗
$(x + 3)(2x + 1) = 2x^2 + 7x + 3$ ✓
$(2x + 1)(x + 3) = 2x^2 + 7x + 3$ ✓
$(2x + 3)(x + 1) = 2x^2 + 5x + 3$ ✗

Either of the ✓ lines gives the correct factorisation. We really need only try the first two, since the second two are equivalent to the first two.

Example 4.11

Factorise $6x^2 + 13x - 5$.

Solution

The signs must be different; possible combinations which give the correct products are:

$(x + 1)(6x - 5) = 6x^2 + x - 5$ ✗
$(x + 5)(6x - 1) = 6x^2 + 29x - 5$ ✗
$(2x + 1)(3x - 5) = 6x^2 - 7x - 5$ ✗
$(2x + 5)(3x - 1) = 6x^2 + 13x - 5$ ✓

Having found a correct factorisation there is no need to go further.

We could have tried the combination.

$(3x + 1)(2x - 5) = 6x^2 - 13x - 5$

which is almost correct, but the sign for the x term is wrong. This means that changing both signs in the factors will give the correct answer.

To factorise $15x^2 + x - 6$:
$(3x - 2)(5x + 3) = 15x^2 - x - 6$

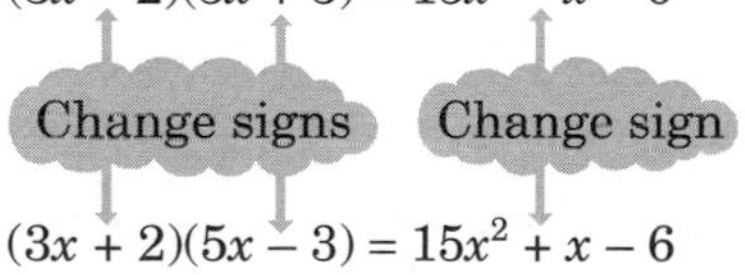

Change signs Change sign

$(3x + 2)(5x - 3) = 15x^2 + x - 6$

Difference of two squares

A special case of factorising involves the expansion of $(x - p)(x + p)$.

$$(x - p)(x + p) = x^2 - px + px - p^2$$
$$= x^2 - p^2$$
$$\Rightarrow \quad x^2 - p^2 = (x - p)(x + p)$$

Example 4.12

Factorise these expressions.

a) $x^2 - 9$ *b)* $16t^2 - 1$ *c)* $a^2 - b^2$
d) $10x^2 - 250$ *e)* $3y^3 - 3y$

Solution

Each expression is or can be factorised to give a difference of two squares.

a) $x^2 - 9 = x^2 - 3^2 = (x - 3)(x + 3)$

b) $16t^2 - 1 = (4t)^2 - 1^2$
$= (4t - 1)(4t + 1)$

c) $a^2 - b^2 = (a - b)(a + b)$

d) $10x^2 - 250 = 10(x^2 - 25)$
$= 10(x^2 - 5^2)$
$= 10(x - 5)(x + 5)$

e) $3y^3 - 3y = 3y(y^2 - 1^2) = 3y(y - 1)(y + 1)$

EXERCISES

4.2 CLASSWORK

1 Multiply out the brackets.

a) $(x + 5)(x + 8)$ **b)** $(x - 5)(x + 8)$
c) $(x - 5)(x - 8)$ **d)** $(2x - 1)(x + 9)$
e) $(4y - 3)(y - 2)$ **f)** $(3x + 4)(5x + 1)$
g) $(2t - 3)(2t + 5)$ **h)** $(3a + b)(a - 3b)$
i) $(4x + 1)^2$ **j)** $(2x - 3)^2$
k) $(4z + 1)(4z - 1)$ **l)** $(c - 7)(c + 7)$
m) $5(3x - 1)(x + 3)$ **n)** $3(2x - 5y)^2$

2 Expand the brackets and simplify each expression.

a) $(x - 7)(x + 3) + (x + 2)(x - 4)$
b) $(x + 3)(x + 10) - (x - 3)(x - 10)$
c) $(2x - 1)(x + 5) - (x - 4)^2$
d) $(3x - 2)(3x + 2) + (4x + 5)(x - 7)$
e) $(3a + b)(a - 5b) - (2a + b)^2$
f) $(2x - y)(3x - y) + (4x + 3y)(4x - 3y)$
g) $7(2x - 5)^2 - 3(4x + 3)(4x - 3)$

3 Factorise each of these expressions fully.

a) $x^2 + 9x + 20$ **b)** $x^2 - x - 20$
c) $x^2 + x - 20$ **d)** $x^2 - 12x + 35$
e) $y^2 - 2y - 63$ **f)** $x^2 + 6x + 9$
g) $x^2 - 14x + 49$ **h)** $2x^2 + 3x + 1$
i) $3x^2 + 17x + 20$ **j)** $2x^2 + 5xy - 3y^2$
k) $16a^2 - 40ab + 25b^2$ **l)** $60 + 95x + 20x^2$
m) $12x^2 + 60x + 75$ **n)** $2x^3 - x^2 - 21x$

4 Factorise each of these expressions fully.

a) $x^2 - 49$ **b)** $100 - t^2$
c) $p^2 - q^2$ **d)** $64s^2 - 25$
e) $121t^2 - 1$ **f)** $36a^2 - b^2$
g) $9e^2 - 49f^2$ **h)** $10x^2 - 40$
i) $45 - 20x^2$ **j)** $9x - 49x^3$
k) $320x^2 - 125$ **l)** $a^3b - ab^3$

EXERCISES

4.2 HOMEWORK

1 Multiply out the brackets.

a) $(x + 1)(x + 4)$ b) $(x - 1)(x + 4)$
c) $(x - 1)(x - 4)$ d) $(x - 1)(6x + 7)$
e) $(t - 8)(2t - 7)$ f) $(9x + 7)(3x + 4)$
g) $(4x - 7)(8x - 9)$ h) $(2x + y)(x - 2y)$
i) $(5x + 3)^2$ j) $(6x - 5)^2$
k) $(x - 8)(x + 8)$ l) $(7u + 2)(7u - 2)$
m) $8(9x + 4)(3x - 2)$ n) $9xy(3x + 2y)^2$

2 Expand the brackets and simplify each expression.

a) $(x - 4)(x + 5) + (x + 8)(x - 3)$
b) $(x - 3)(x - 9) + (x + 3)(x + 9)$
c) $(3x - 4)(x + 8) + (x - 6)^2$
d) $(2x + 7)(5x + 3) - (4x - 3)(2 - x)$
e) $(8a - b)(5a + 3b) - (a - 9b)^2$
f) $(x - 2y)(x + 2y) - (x + 2y)^2$
g) $5(2x + 9)(9x + 2) - 3(2x + 11)^2$

3 Factorise each of these expressions fully.

a) $x^2 + 7x + 10$ b) $x^2 - 3x - 10$
c) $x^2 - 7x + 10$ d) $-x^2 + 12x - 32$
e) $t^2 - 6t - 16$ f) $x^2 - 10x + 25$
g) $x^2 + 22x + 121$ h) $3x^2 - 16x + 5$
i) $6x^2 - 17x - 3$ j) $7a^2 + 13ab - 2b^2$
k) $81x^2 + 36xy + 4y^2$ l) $12x^2 + 14x - 40$
m) $200x^2 - 560x + 392$ n) $25x^3 - 195x^2 - 84x$

4 Factorise each of these expressions fully.

a) $x^2 - 16$ b) $49 - u^2$
c) $a^2 - 4b^2$ d) $36 - 16x^2$
e) $9x^2 - 1$ f) $4a^2 - 36b^2$
g) $64x^2 - 81y^2$ h) $45x^2 - 20$
i) $243p^2 - 48q^2$ j) $20a^3 - 5ab^2$
k) $81t - 16t^3$ l) $36x^3y - 100xy^3$

QUADRATIC EQUATIONS BY FACTORS

The general form of a quadratic function is $y = ax^2 + bx + c$, where a, b and c are constants and $a \neq 0$. A **family** of quadratics is a group which have something in common. The equations all take the same form and the curves are all the same general shape, but they may have slightly different properties.

Exploration 4.5

The family $y = k(x^2 - 9)$

Look carefully at these graphs. They all belong to the family $y = k(x^2 - 9)$, for different values of k.

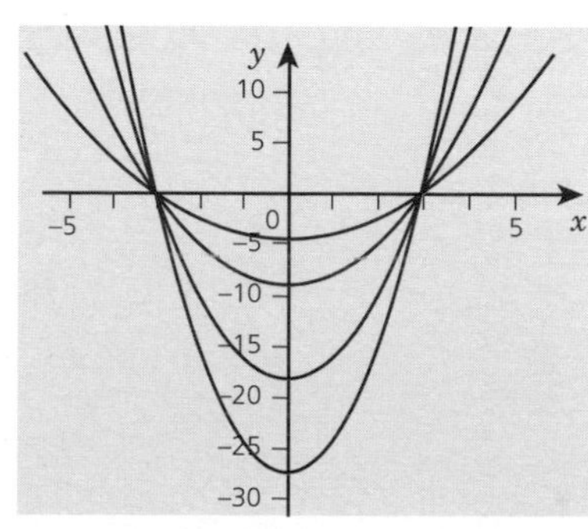

- Identify the values of k.
- Factorise $k(x^2 - 9)$.
- What do the four graphs all have in common?

Exploration 4.6

The family $y = k(5x - x^2)$

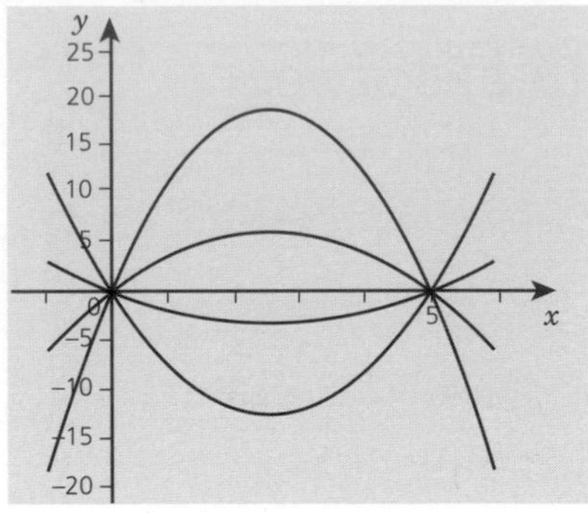

Now examine carefully another set of graphs. They all belong to the family $y = k(5x - x^2)$, for different values of k.

- Identify the values of k.
- Factorise $k(5x - x^2)$.
- What do the four graphs all have in common?

Exploration 4.7

The family $y = k(x^2 + 5x - 14)$

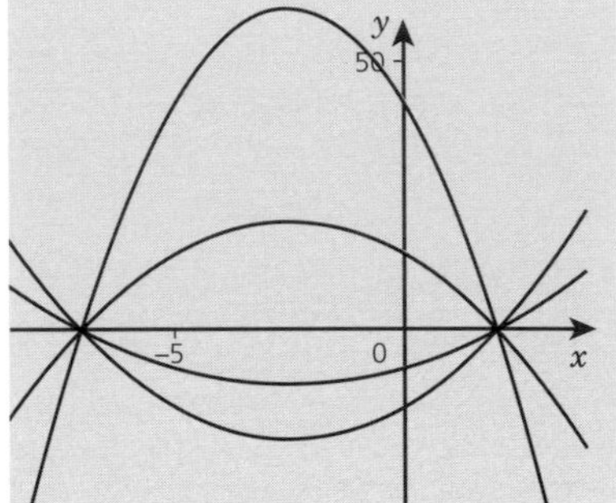

Finally study a third set of graphs. They all belong to the family $y = k(x^2 + 5x - 14)$, for different values of k.

- Identify the values of k.
- Factorise $k(x^2 + 5x - 14)$.
- What do the four graphs all have in common?

Interpreting the results

Each graph represents a quadratic function $f(x)$, which intersects with the x-axis in two places, i.e. the x-values for which $f(x) = 0$.

For varying values of k your findings might be summarised as:

Exploration	Quadratic function	Factorised form	x-values when $y = 0$
4.5	$k(x^2 - 9)$	$k(x + 3)(x - 3)$	−3, 3
4.6	$k(5x - x^2)$	$kx(5 - x)$	0, 5
4.7	$k(x^2 + 5x - 14)$	$k(x + 7)(x - 2)$	−7, 2

So by factorising the **quadratic function**, the x-values which solve the quadratic equation $f(x) = 0$, may be fairly easily identified. These x-values are called the **roots** of the quadratic equation. Factorising gives a product of factors which is zero. This means that one or other of the two factors (other than k) must be zero, which in turn gives the roots.

$k(x + 3)(x - 3) = 0 \quad \Rightarrow \quad x + 3 = 0 \text{ or } x - 3 = 0 \quad \Rightarrow \quad x = -3 \text{ or } x = 3$

$kx(5 - x) = 0 \quad \Rightarrow \quad x = 0 \text{ or } 5 - x = 0 \quad \Rightarrow \quad x = 0 \text{ or } x = 5$

$k(x + 7)(x - 2) = 0 \quad \Rightarrow \quad x + 7 = 0 \text{ or } x - 2 = 0 \quad \Rightarrow \quad x = -7 \text{ or } x = 2$

The value of the constant k does not affect the solution of the quadratic equation. Provided the quadratic function can be factorised, solutions may be found, as in the following examples.

Example 4.13

Solve the equation $7x^2 - 28 = 0$.

Solution

$$7x^2 - 28 = 0$$

Take out a constant factor $\Rightarrow 7(x^2 - 4) = 0$

This will factorise further $\Rightarrow 7(x - 2)(x + 2) = 0$

$\Rightarrow x = 2$ *or* $x = -2$

Example 4.14

Solve the equation $16x^2 = 100$.

Solution

$$16x^2 = 100$$

Rearrange in the form $f(x) = 0 \Rightarrow 16x^2 - 100 = 0$

Take out a constant factor $\Rightarrow 4(4x^2 - 25) = 0$

This will factorise further $\Rightarrow 4(2x - 5)(2x + 5) = 0$

$\Rightarrow 2x - 5 = 0$ *or* $2x + 5 = 0$

$\Rightarrow x = 2.5$ *or* $x = -2.5$

Note: For the last two examples we may use an alternative strategy:

$7x^2 - 28 = 0 \Rightarrow 7x^2 = 28 \Rightarrow x^2 = 4 \Rightarrow x = \pm\sqrt{4} = \pm 2$

$16x^2 = 100 \Rightarrow x^2 = 6.25 \Rightarrow x = \pm\sqrt{6.25} = \pm 2.5$

This works well provided the quadratic equation does not contain a term in x. This idea occurs again later.

Example 4.15

Solve the equation $15x^2 - 25x = 0$.

Solution

$$15x^2 - 25x = 0$$

Take out a constant factor $\Rightarrow 5(3x^2 - 5x) = 0$

This will factorise further $\Rightarrow 5x(3x - 5) = 0$

$\Rightarrow x = 0$ *or* $3x - 5 = 0$

$\Rightarrow x = 0$ *or* $x = 1\frac{2}{3}$

Example 4.16

Solve the equation $3x^2 - 24x + 45 = 0$.

Solution

$$3x^2 - 24x + 45 = 0$$

Take out a constant factor $\Rightarrow 3(x^2 - 8x + 15) = 0$

This will factorise further $\Rightarrow 3(x - 3)(x - 5) = 0$

$\Rightarrow x - 3 = 0$ *or* $x - 5 = 0$

$\Rightarrow x = 3$ *or* $x = 5$

Example 4.17

Solve the equation $3x^2 + 11x - 4 = 0$.

Solution

$$3x^2 + 11x - 4 = 0$$

Which will factorise $\Rightarrow (3x - 1)(x + 4) = 0$

$\Rightarrow 3x - 1 = 0$ *or* $x + 4 = 0$

$\Rightarrow x = \frac{1}{3}$ *or* $x = -4$

Some equations may not appear to be quadratic at first glance, but using some algebraic manipulation we can change them into a suitable form. The next two examples illustrate this.

Example 4.18

Solve the equation $x - \frac{8}{x} = 2$.

Solution

$$x - \frac{8}{x} = 2$$

Multiply both sides by x $\Rightarrow x^2 - 8 = 2x$

Rearrange $\Rightarrow x^2 - 2x - 8 = 0$

This will factorise $\Rightarrow (x-4)(x+2) = 0$

$\Rightarrow x = 4$ *or* $x = -2$

Example 4.19

Solve the equation $x^4 - 13x^2 + 36 = 0$.

Solution

$$x^4 - 13x^2 + 36 = 0$$

Change to a quadratic equation in x^2 $\Rightarrow (x^2)^2 - 13(x^2) + 36 = 0$

This will factorise $\Rightarrow (x^2 - 9)(x^2 - 4) = 0$

$\Rightarrow x^2 = 9 \Rightarrow x = \pm 3$

or $x^2 = 4 \Rightarrow x = \pm 2$

Solving problems

As we discovered earlier in this chapter, quadratic equations can sometimes be useful in solving problems. The next worked example extends a problem we met there and uses a quadratic equation to solve it.

Example 4.20

The height, y *metres, of a point on the St Louis arch,* x *metres from one side, can be modelled by the function* $y = \frac{x(192 - x)}{48}$.

How far apart are points on the arch which are 165 m above the ground?

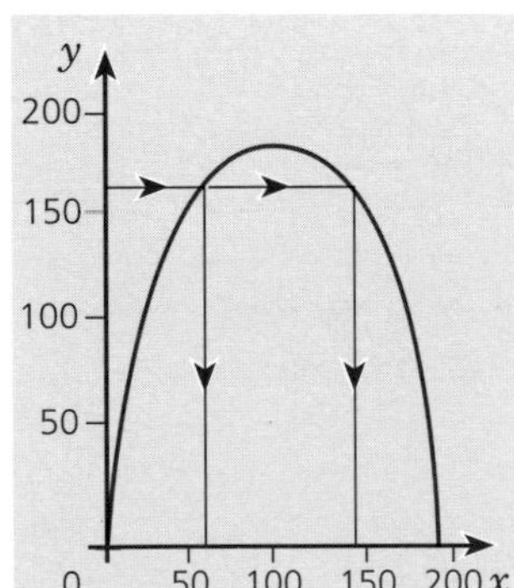

Solution

For a height of 165 m, let $y = 165$ *in the quadratic function.*

$$165 = \frac{x(192 - x)}{48}$$

Multiply both sides by 48 $\Rightarrow 7920 = x(192 - x)$

Rearrange $\Rightarrow x^2 - 192x + 7920 = 0$

This will factorise $\Rightarrow (x - 60)(x - 132) = 0$

$\Rightarrow x - 60 = 0$ *or* $x - 132 = 0$

$\Rightarrow x = 60$ *or* $x = 132$

This means that two points which are 165 m above the ground have corresponding x*-values 60 and 132, i.e. they are 72 metres apart.*

Notes

- If you found the factorising in the last example very difficult, there are alternative strategies which appear in the next section.

- Sometimes problems lead to quadratic equations where one of the roots is meaningless (e.g. a negative value for a physical quantity). In such cases the unwanted root is discarded.

A word of warning

From the explorations it is clear that the solution of a quadratic equation in the form $f(x) = 0$ occurs where the graph of $y = f(x)$ intersects with the x-axis. The roots occur at the points where the parabola intersects the x-axis. However, not all parabolae actually intersect with the x-axis. To put it another way, not all quadratic equations have roots!

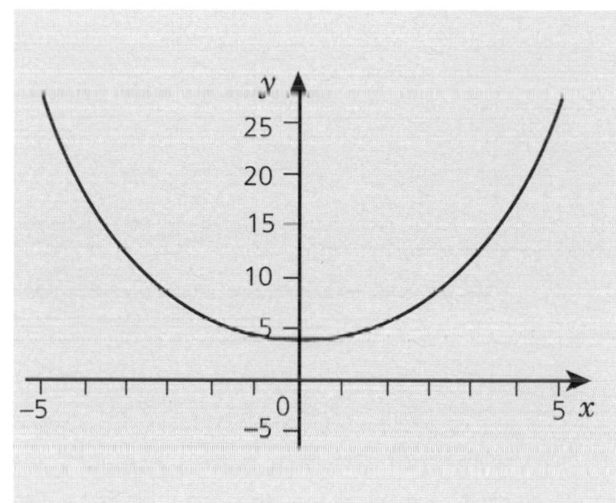

Consider the graph of $y = x^2 + 4$, i.e. $f(x) = x^2 + 4$.

Since the graph lies entirely above the x-axis, $f(x) = 0$ has no solutions.

Trying to solve the equation leads to:

$$x^2 + 4 = 0 \quad \Rightarrow \quad x^2 = -4 \quad \Rightarrow \quad x = \pm\sqrt{-4}$$

which is not possible, at least within the system of real numbers (try finding the square root of −4 on your calculator). There is no real number which has a square of −4. Whenever attempting to solve a quadratic equation leads to taking the square root of a negative number, the roots are said to be **imaginary**.

EXERCISES

4.3 CLASSWORK

For each of the quadratic functions, solve the equation $f(x) = 0$. In each case, sketch the curve $y = f(x)$ and mark on your solutions.

1 $f(x) = x^2 - 7x$
2 $f(x) = x^2 - 12x + 32$
3 $f(x) = x^2 - 6x + 9$
4 $f(x) = 8 + 2x - x^2$
5 $f(x) = 8x - x^2 - 16$
6 $f(x) = x^2 - 25$

Solve the following equations wherever possible. If the roots are imaginary, say so.

7 $x^2 - 17x = 0$
8 $3x^2 - 6x = 0$
9 $x^2 = -4x$
10 $x^2 = 49$
11 $x^2 - 25 = 0$
12 $3x^2 - 147 = 0$
13 $4x^2 - 9 = 0$
14 $p^2 + 51 = 0$
15 $81 + r^2 = 0$

Solve the following quadratic equations by factorising.

16 $x^2 + 5x + 6 = 0$
17 $x^2 + 15x + 54 = 0$
18 $x^2 - 4x + 3 = 0$
19 $t^2 - 3t - 40 = 0$
20 $x^2 + 3x - 4 = 0$
21 $x^2 - x - 12 = 0$
22 $t^2 - 2t + 1 = 0$
23 $2x^2 - 11x + 5 = 0$
24 $3x^2 - x - 14 = 0$
25 $6x^2 + 19x + 10 = 0$
26 $5y^2 + 33y - 14 = 0$
27 $7u - 6u^2 + 20 = 0$
28 $9x^2 + 12x + 4 = 0$
29 $5x^2 + 40x + 80 = 0$

Rearrange the following as quadratic equations and solve by factorising.

30 $x + 1 = \dfrac{6}{x}$
31 $2x - \dfrac{12}{x} = 5$
32 $x^4 - 13x^2 + 36 = 0$
33 $(x + 1)^2 + 3(x + 1) + 2 = 0$

34 A ball is thrown vertically upwards. Its height, h metres, after t seconds, is given by $h = 16t - 5t^2$.

At what times will the ball be at a height of 12 m?

35 A rectangular sports pitch is 25 metres longer than it is wide and has an area of 3150 m^2.

a) If x represents the width of the pitch, express both the length and the area in terms of x.
b) Solve a quadratic equation to find the dimensions of the pitch.

36 The diagram shows a right-angled triangle in which the shortest side is x cm.

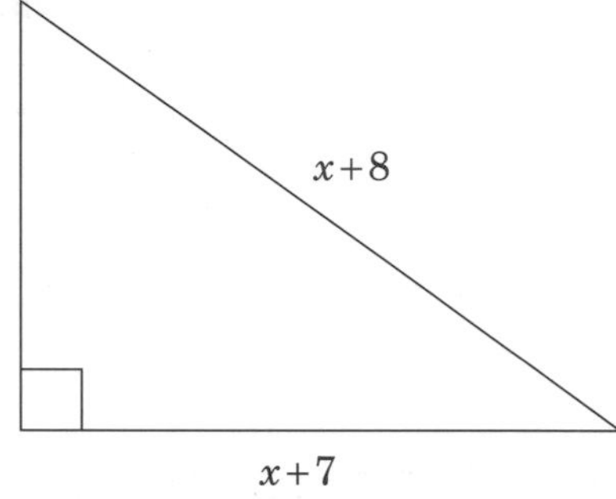

a) Use Pythagoras' theorem to formulate a quadratic equation in x.
b) Solve the quadratic equation to find the sides of the triangle.

EXERCISES

4.3 HOMEWORK

For each of the quadratic functions, solve the equation $f(x) = 0$, wherever possible. In each case, sketch the curve $y = f(x)$ and mark on any solutions.

1 $f(x) = x^2 + 2x$ **2** $f(x) = x^2 - 9$
3 $f(x) = 2x^2 + 5x - 3$ **4** $f(x) = 24 + 6x - 3x^2$
5 $f(x) = 6x^2 - 13x + 6$ **6** $f(x) = x^2 + 10$

Solve the following equations wherever possible.

7 $x^2 + 4x = 0$ **8** $x^2 = 3x$ **9** $3x^2 - 5x = 0$
10 $x^2 = 17$ **11** $x^2 - 26 = 0$ **12** $x^2 - 10 = 0$
13 $4x^2 - 64 = 0$ **14** $7s^2 + 19 = 0$ **15** $7t^2 + 35t = 0$

Solve the following quadratic equations by factorising.

16 $x^2 + 4x + 3 = 0$ **17** $x^2 + 20x + 51 = 0$
18 $x^2 - 12x + 32 = 0$ **19** $x^2 - 7x + 10 = 0$
20 $2y^2 - 12y + 18 = 0$ **21** $5x^2 - 5x - 30 = 0$
22 $x^2 - 2x + 1 = 0$ **23** $1 + 6y - 7y^2 = 0$
24 $y^2 + 5y - 14 = 0$ **25** $6x^2 + 7x - 3 = 0$
26 $15 - 4x - 4x^2 = 0$ **27** $9x^2 + 6x + 1 = 0$

Rearrange the following as quadratic equations and solve by factorising.

28 $6x + \frac{12}{x} = 17$ **29** $\frac{x}{4} + \frac{3}{x} = 2$

30 $(x - 1)(x - 2) = 20$ **31** $x^4 + 7x^2 = 8$

$x-2$ $x+2$ x

32 The diagram shows a right-angled triangle.

a) Use Pythagoras' theorem to formulate a quadratic equation in x.
b) Solve the quadratic equation to find the sides of the triangle.
c) Try to predict the dimensions of a right-angled triangle with sides of lengths $x - d$, x and $x + d$, in terms of a constant d.

33 **a)** The product of two consecutive odd numbers is 783. What are the numbers?
b) The product of two integers, which differ by 9, is 1540. Find the two integers.

34 **a)** Explain why a polygon, with n sides, has d diagonals where $d = \dfrac{n(n-3)}{2}$, $n \geq 0$.
b) A polygon has 44 diagonals. How many sides does it have?

QUADRATIC EQUATIONS

Completing the square

In the last section we saw how to solve quadratic equations such as $x^2 = 49$ and $4x^2 - 9 = 0$ using an alternative method.

$x^2 = 49 \Rightarrow x = \pm\sqrt{49} = \pm 7$
$4x^2 - 9 = 0 \Rightarrow 4x^2 = 9 \Rightarrow x^2 = 2.25 \Rightarrow x = \pm\sqrt{2.25} = \pm 1.5$

These are **rational roots**, since they can be expressed precisely as a whole number or a fraction.

This may be extended to equations which have roots that are not exact, e.g.

$5x^2 = 100 \Rightarrow x^2 = 20 \Rightarrow x = \pm\sqrt{20} = \pm 4.47$ (3 s.f.)
$x^2 - 93 = 0 \Rightarrow x^2 = 93 \Rightarrow x = \pm\sqrt{93} = \pm 9.64$ (3 s.f.)

These are **irrational** roots, since they cannot be expressed precisely as a whole number or a fraction. Accuracy is given correct to three significant figures (3 s.f.).

Going one stage further, we can solve quadratic equations such as those in the following examples.

Example 4.21

Solve the equation $(x - 3)^2 = 15$.

Solution

$(x - 3)^2 = 15$

Take the square root of both sides $\Rightarrow$ $x - 3 = \pm\sqrt{15}$
Rearrange $\Rightarrow$ $x = 3 \pm\sqrt{15}$
$\Rightarrow$ $x = -0.873$ *or* $x = 6.87$ (3 s.f.)

Example 4.22

Solve the equation $4(x+5)^2 - 59 = 0$.

Solution

		$4(x+5)^2 - 59 = 0$
Add 59 to both sides	$\Rightarrow$	$4(x+5)^2 = 59$
Divide both sides by 4	$\Rightarrow$	$(x+5)^2 = 14.75$
Take the square root of both sides	$\Rightarrow$	$x+5 = \pm\sqrt{14.75}$
Rearrange	$\Rightarrow$	$x = -5 \pm\sqrt{14.75}$
	$\Rightarrow$	$x = -8.84$ *or* $x = -1.16$ (3 s.f.)

The last two examples pave the way for a method which may be used on any quadratic equation which has a solution, but may not factorise. Firstly, complete the square for the function $f(x)$, then solve the equation $f(x) = 0$ as above. Study the following examples carefully.

Example 4.23

Solve the equation $x^2 - 8x - 11 = 0$.

Solution

		$x^2 - 8x - 11 = 0$
Complete the square	$\Rightarrow$	$(x-4)^2 - 27 = 0$
Add 27 to both sides	$\Rightarrow$	$(x-4)^2 = 27$
Take the square root of both sides	$\Rightarrow$	$x - 4 = \pm\sqrt{27}$
Rearrange	$\Rightarrow$	$x = 4 \pm\sqrt{27}$
	$\Rightarrow$	$x = -1.20$ *or* $x = -9.20$ (3 s.f.)

Example 4.24

Solve the equation $2x^2 + 8x + 3 = 0$.

Solution

		$2x^2 + 8x + 3 = 0$
Complete the square	$\Rightarrow$	$2(x+2)^2 - 5 = 0$
Add 5 to both sides	$\Rightarrow$	$2(x+2)^2 = 5$
Divide both sides by 2	$\Rightarrow$	$(x+2)^2 = 2.5$
Take the square root of both sides	$\Rightarrow$	$x + 2 = \pm\sqrt{2.5}$
Rearrange	$\Rightarrow$	$x = -2 \pm\sqrt{2.5}$
	$\Rightarrow$	$x = -3.58$ *or* $x = -0.419$ (3 s.f.)

Using the formula

The process of solving a quadratic equation by completing the square may be quite time-consuming. The structure of the solution is roughly the same each time, only the details are different. This leads to the idea of finding a general purpose formula for solving quadratic equations of the type:

$ax^2 + bx + c = 0$

where a, b and c are constants and $a \neq 0$. It is essential that $a \neq 0$, since in developing the formula we shall need to divide by a.

To solve the equation $ax^2 + bx + c = 0$

$$ax^2 + bx + c = 0$$

Complete the square $\Rightarrow a\left(x+\frac{b}{2a}\right)^2 - \frac{b^2}{4a} + c = 0$

Rearrange $\Rightarrow a\left(x+\frac{b}{2a}\right)^2 = \frac{b^2-4ac}{4a}$

Divide both sides by a $\Rightarrow \left(x+\frac{b}{2a}\right)^2 = \frac{b^2-4ac}{4a^2}$

Take the square root of both sides $\Rightarrow x+\frac{b}{2a} = \pm\sqrt{\frac{b^2-4ac}{4a^2}} = \pm\frac{\sqrt{b^2-4ac}}{2a}$

Rearrange $\Rightarrow x = \frac{-b\pm\sqrt{b^2-4ac}}{2a}$

This gives a general formula which can be used to solve any quadratic equation with real roots. Looking again at the formula, we can see that this will be the case provided $a \neq 0$ and $b^2 - 4ac$ is **not** negative. The expression $b^2 - 4ac$ is called the **discriminant** of the expression $ax^2 + bx + c$.

Exploration 4.8

Applying the formula

- Apply the formula to the following quadratic equations and see what happens.

a) $x^2 - 2x - 3 = 0$ **b)** $x^2 - 2x + 1 = 0$
c) $x^2 - 2x - 7 = 0$ **d)** $x^2 - 2x + 5 = 0$

Interpreting the results

a) $x^2 - 2x - 3 = 0 \Rightarrow a = 1, b = -2, c = -3$

$$\Rightarrow x = \frac{-(-2)\pm\sqrt{(-2)^2-4\times1\times(-3)}}{2\times1} = \frac{2\pm\sqrt{16}}{2}$$

$\Rightarrow x = -1$ or $x = 3$

b) $x^2 - 2x + 1 = 0 \Rightarrow a = 1, b = -2, c = 1$

$$\Rightarrow x = \frac{-(-2)\pm\sqrt{(-2)^2-4\times1\times1}}{2\times1} = \frac{2\pm\sqrt{0}}{2}$$

$\Rightarrow x = 1$

c) $x^2 - 2x - 7 = 0 \Rightarrow a = 1, b = -2, c = -7$

$$\Rightarrow x = \frac{-(-2)\pm\sqrt{(-2)^2-4\times1\times(-7)}}{2\times1} = \frac{2\pm\sqrt{32}}{2}$$

$\Rightarrow x = -1.83$ or $x = 3.83$ (3 s.f.)

d) $x^2 - 2x + 5 = 0 \Rightarrow a = 1, b = -2, c = 5$

$$\Rightarrow x = \frac{-(-2)\pm\sqrt{(-2)^2-4\times1\times5}}{2\times1} = \frac{2\pm\sqrt{-16}}{2}$$

$\Rightarrow$ There are no real roots.

In **a)** the discriminant is a perfect square, which means that the equation will factorise to give **rational** roots.

In **b)** the discriminant is zero, which means that the equation will factorise to give **repeated rational** roots.

In **c)** the discriminant is not a perfect square, which means that when completing the square (using the formula) the roots are **irrational**.

KEY SKILLS
C 3.1b

In **d)** the discriminant is negative, which means that there are no real roots to the equation, since you cannot take the square root of a negative number.

Exploration 4.9 *Solutions and the x-axis*

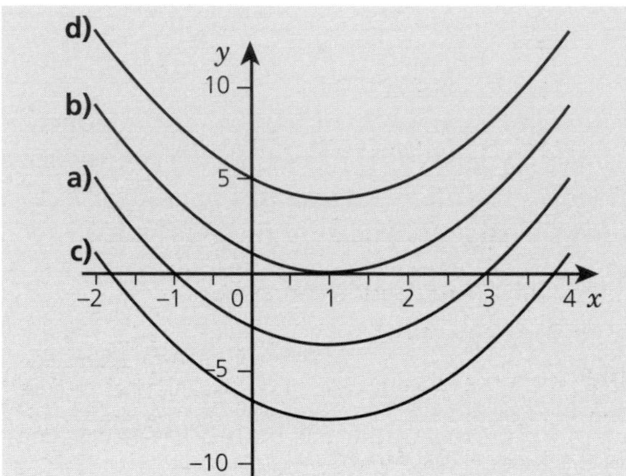

- Sketch the graphs of $y = \mathrm{f}(x)$ for each function in Exploration 4.8 and relate the solutions of the quadratic equations to where the curves intersect with the x-axis.

Interpreting the results

Taking the three graphs in turn:

a) $y = \mathrm{f}(x)$ intersects with the x-axis at $x = -1$ and $x = 3$.
b) $y = \mathrm{f}(x)$ touches the x-axis at $x = 1$.
c) $y = \mathrm{f}(x)$ intersects with the x-axis at $x = -1.83$ and $x = 3.83$. (3 s.f.)
d) $y = \mathrm{f}(x)$ does not intersect with the x-axis.

Manipulating equations

As we found earlier, there are equations which may not look at first like quadratic equations, but a little algebraic manipulation can turn them into quadratic equations. The next example illustrates such a situation, where the quadratic function does not factorise and the formula is applied.

Example 4.25

Solve the equation $x = \dfrac{(x+2)}{(x+5)}$.

Solution

$$x = \frac{(x+2)}{(x+5)}$$

Multiply both sides by $(x+5)$ $\Rightarrow \quad x(x+5) = x+2$
Multiply out the brackets $\Rightarrow \quad x^2 + 5x = x + 2$
Rearrange $\Rightarrow x^2 + 4x - 2 = 0$

Use the quadratic formula $\Rightarrow \quad x = \dfrac{-4 \pm \sqrt{16 - 4(1)(-2)}}{2} = \dfrac{-4 \pm \sqrt{24}}{2}$

$$\Rightarrow \quad x = \frac{-4 \pm 2\sqrt{6}}{2} = -2 \pm \sqrt{6}$$

$$\Rightarrow \quad x = 0.449 \textit{ or } x = -4.45 \text{ (3 s.f.)}$$

EXERCISES

4.4 CLASSWORK

Solve the following equations, wherever possible, by completing the square, giving your answers correct to 3 s.f. where necessary. If there are no real roots, say so.

1 $x^2 - 8x + 12 = 0$
2 $x^2 + 17x - 18 = 0$
3 $x^2 + 8x = 84$
4 $3x^2 + 10x + 3 = 0$
5 $9x^2 + 13x = 10$
6 $11x^2 - x = 12$
7 $3x^2 + 4x = 5$
8 $7x^2 + 8x + 2 = 0$

Solve the following equations, wherever possible, using the quadratic formula, giving your answers correct to 3 s.f. where necessary. If there are no real roots, say so.

9 $x^2 + 3x - 4 = 0$
10 $3x^2 - 11x + 6 = 0$
11 $x^2 - 3x + 1 = 0$
12 $3x^2 - 13x = 10$
13 $3x^2 - 5x = 7$
14 $10x^2 + 7x = 12$
15 $5x^2 + 4 = 7x$
16 $x^2 + 111x = 3400$

Rearrange the following as quadratic equations and solve.

17 $\dfrac{2x+3}{x+4} = \dfrac{x-5}{x+1}$
18 $\dfrac{x-2}{2x+1} = \dfrac{x-3}{x-1}$

19 The diagram shows a regular pentagon, with sides that are each 1 unit long. Each diagonal is of length d units.

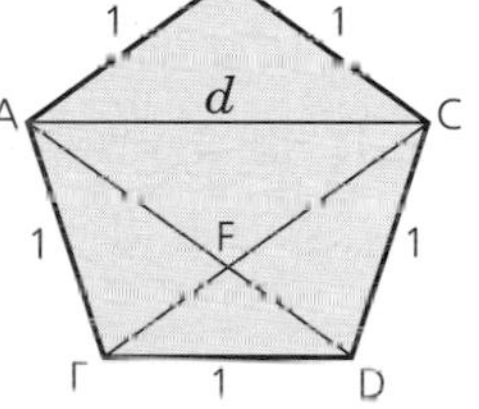

a) Explain why quadrilateral ABCF is a parallelogram.
b) Show that the length of DF = $d - 1$.
c) Using similar triangles, formulate an equation involving d and show that it can be rearranged to give $d^2 - d - 1 = 0$.
d) Solve the equation in **c)** to find the value of d.

EXERCISES

4.4 HOMEWORK

Solve the following equations, wherever possible, by completing the square, giving your answers correct to 3 s.f. where necessary. If there are no real roots, say so.

1 $x^2 + 12x + 20 = 0$
2 $x^2 - x - 20 = 0$
3 $x^2 - 11x = 180$
4 $7x^2 - 8x = 18$
5 $8x^2 + 38x = -3$
6 $x^2 - 6x + 3 = 0$
7 $x^2 + 9x + 4 = 0$
8 $3x^2 - 7x = 1$

Solve the following equations, wherever possible, using the quadratic formula, giving your answers correct to 3 s.f. where necessary. If there are no real roots, say so.

9 $x^2 + 8x + 7 = 0$
10 $2x^2 + x - 4 = 0$
11 $3x^2 - 2x - 2 = 0$
12 $5x^2 - 12x + 4 = 0$
13 $4x^2 + 5x + 2 = 0$
14 $7x^2 - 9x = 0$
15 $12x^2 - 25x + 12 = 0$
16 $7x^2 - 26x = 1008$

Rearrange the following as quadratic equations and solve.

17 $3x = \dfrac{1}{x+1} + 2$
18 $x + \dfrac{2x}{x+1} = 3$
19 $\dfrac{4}{x-1} - \dfrac{3}{x+7} = \dfrac{1}{18}$
20 $\dfrac{x-3}{x+2} = \dfrac{2x+1}{x-3}$

MATHEMATICAL MODELLING ACTIVITY

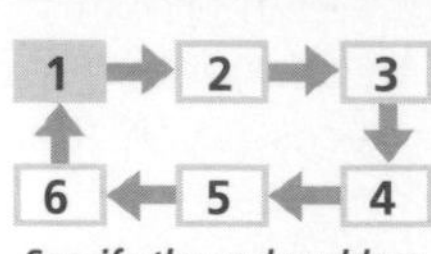

Specify the real problem

Problem statement

A fleet hire company leases cars to firms on a yearly basis, with a percentage discount in the leasing charge proportional to the number of cars leased.

1 How many cars must the fleet hire company lease to a single firm to maximise income?

2 How would your decision be affected if the fleet hire company wish to maximise profit?

Set up a model

Set up a model

The first stage in setting up a model is to identify the important variables:

- the size of a firm's fleet,
- the income for a contract with a given fleet size,
- the profit for a contract with a given fleet size.

Before formulating the problem mathematically, you will also need to make certain assumptions:

- the income I and profit P depend only on the fleet size S,
- the nominal lease charge is £2000 per car per year,
- the fleet hire company has a special offer: the lease charge per car is discounted by 1 per cent for each car in the fleet, e.g. a fleet size of 20 cars earns a 20 per cent discount,
- each car depreciates by £1000 each year.

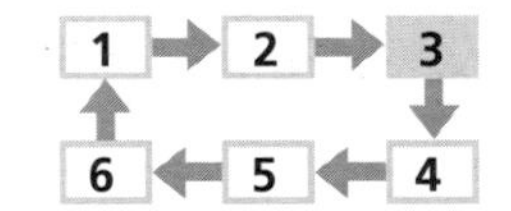

Formulate the mathematical problem

Mathematical problem

The total income is given by:

$$\begin{aligned} I &= 2000S - S \times 0.01 \times 2000S \\ &= 2000S - 20S^2 \end{aligned}$$

income before special offer

special offer discount

Assuming that each car depreciates by £1000 each year, the profit is given by:

$$\begin{aligned} P &= 2000S - 20S^2 - 1000S \\ &= 1000S - 20S^2 \end{aligned}$$

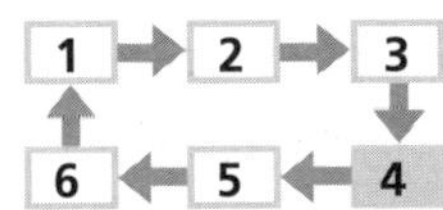

Solve the mathematical problem

Mathematical solution

$I = 2000S - 20S^2$ is a quadratic function in S.

Graphically you can read off the maximum income from the vertex of the parabola.

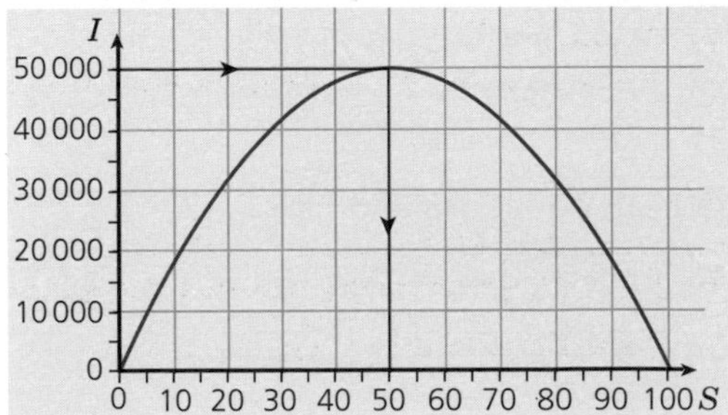

The maximum income of £50 000 is obtained from a contract for a fleet size of 50. Confirm these findings by plotting the graph using a graphics calculator.

The solution may also be found algebraically by completing the square:

$$\begin{aligned} I &= 2000S - 20S^2 \\ &= -20\{S^2 - 100S\} \\ &= -20\{(S-50)^2 - 2500\} \\ &= 50\,000 - 20(S-50)^2 \end{aligned}$$

You can now deduce that I has a maximum value of 50 000 when $S = 50$.

By repeating the analysis for the profit function, show that P has a maximum of 12 500 when $S = 25$.

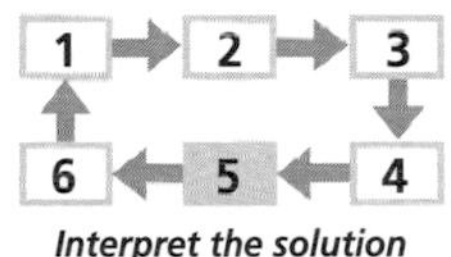

Interpret the solution

Interpretation

To maximise income, a fleet size of 50 cars produces an income of £50 000 but to maximise profit, the fleet size should be 25 cars, realising a profit of £12 500.

Note that the fleet size for maximum income, $S = 50$, means that the company just breaks even (zero profit) and for $S > 50$ the company makes a loss.

Refinement of the model

Investigate the effect of changes in

1 the annual lease charge
2 the percentage discount per car
3 the annual depreciation.

Introduce a threshold for the discounting process to start.

CONSOLIDATION EXERCISES FOR CHAPTER 4

1 Multiply out the brackets and simplify each expression.

a) $(x+9)(x-4)$ **b)** $(2x-3)(3x+2)$
c) $(5-2x)^2$ **d)** $(3x+4)(2x-5)+(x-7)(x+7)$
e) $(2x+9)^2-(4x+5)(x-3)$

2 Factorise each expression fully.

a) $x^2-20x+91$ **b)** $2x^2+21x-11$
c) $12x^2+38x+20$ **d)** $20x^2-120x+36$
e) $245x^2-5$

3 Complete the square for the following quadratic functions.

a) $f(x)=x^2-20x+91$ **b)** $f(x)=2x^2+20x+35$
c) $f(x)=8+x-x^2$ **d)** $f(x)=(2x-1)(2x-7)$

4 **a)** Express the quadratic function $y=4x^2+6x+7$ in the form $a(x+p)^2+q$.
b) Hence write down the coordinates of the vertex and the equation of the line of symmetry for the parabola.
c) Sketch the graph of $y=4x^2+6x+7$, labelling the vertex and the line of symmetry.

5 Sketch the curve with equation $y=x^2$.
On separate axes, sketch the following curves. Label each one, giving the coordinates of the vertex and the equation of the axis of symmetry.

a) $y=(x-2)^2+1$ **b)** $y=(x+1)^2-3$ **c)** $y=3(x-1)^2+5$

6 Complete the square for the function $f(x) = ax^2 + bx + c$.
Assuming that a is positive, and by considering the coordinates of the vertex, deduce conditions for which the graph of $f(x)$:

a) crosses the x-axis in two distinct places,
b) touches the x-axis at one point only,
c) lies entirely above the x-axis.

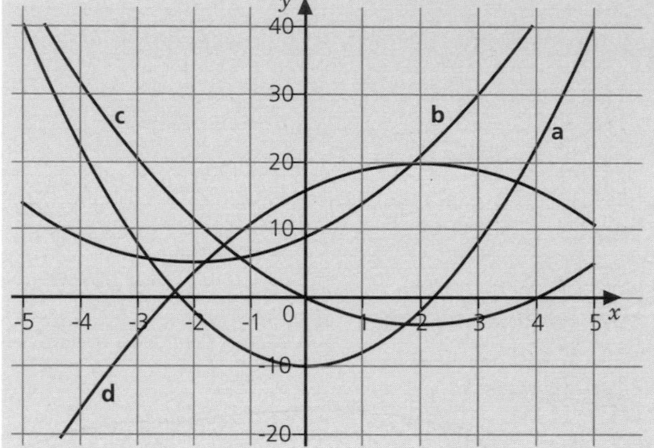

7 The diagram shows four parabolae.

By inspecting the points where they intersect with the axes, and the coordinates of the vertex, write down the equation for each one in the form $y = ax^2 + bx + c$.

8 Solve for x the equation $4x(x - 1) = 3$.
Hence, or otherwise, solve for y the equation $4(y + 3)(y + 2) = 3$.

9 Solve the equation $\dfrac{1}{x} + \dfrac{1}{3x - 2} = 2$.

10 By letting $y = 5^x$, solve the equation $5^{2x+1} - 6 \times 5^x + 1 = 0$.
Use a graphics calculator to confirm your answer.

11 Solve the following quadratic equations, giving the answers as surds in their simplest form.

a) $x^2 + 4x + 1 = 0$
b) $2x^2 - 5x + 1 = 0$
c) $3x^2 + x - 5 = 0$
d) $4x^2 - x - 7 = 0$

12 Use algebra to solve $(x - 1)(x + 2) = 18$.

(EDEXCEL, Question 2, Paper 1, June 1998)

13 Find, as surds, the roots of the equation $2(x + 1)(x - 4) - (x - 2)^2 = 0$.

(EDEXCEL, Question 4, Paper 1 Jan 1998)

14 A quadratic function is defined by $f(x) = x^2 + kx + 9$, where k is a constant. It is given that the equation $f(x) = 0$ has two distinct real roots. Find the set of values that k can take.

For the case where $k = -4\sqrt{3}$,

i) express $f(x)$ in the form $(x + a)^2 + b$, stating the values of a and b, and hence write down the least value taken by $f(x)$.

ii) solve the equation $f(x) = 0$, expressing your answer in terms of surds, simplified as far as possible.

(OCR, Question 7, Specimen Paper 1 2000)

Summary

Quadratic functions

- A quadratic function is of the general form $f(x) = ax^2 + bx + c$.
- The graph of a quadratic function is called a **parabola**.

Factorising

- The quadratic expression $ax^2 + bx + c$ may sometimes be factorised into the product of linear factors by inspection. For example:
  $x^2 - 2x - 15 = (x - 5)(x + 3)$
  $2x^2 + 9x + 4 = (2x + 1)(x + 4)$.
- Special cases of factorising are:
  a perfect square $(x + p)^2 = x^2 + 2px + p^2$
  the difference of two squares $(x - p)(x + p) = x^2 - p^2$.

Completing the square

- Any quadratic function $f(x) = ax^2 + bx + c$ can be written in the form $f(x) = a(x + p)^2 + q$
  This is called completing the square.
- For the parabola $y = ax^2 + bx + c$:
  the **line of symmetry** has equation $x = -p$
  the coordinates of the **vertex** are $(-p, q)$.

Quadratic equations

- In general a quadratic equation $ax^2 + bx + c = 0$ may have
  i) two real roots
  ii) one (repeated) real root
  iii) no real roots.

  Two real roots occur if the parabola $y = ax^2 + bx + c$ intersects the x-axis twice.

  One real root occurs if the parabola $y = ax^2 + bx + c$ touches the x-axis,
  i.e. the x-axis is a tangent to the parabola.

  The parabola may not intersect or touch the x-axis, in which case there are no real roots.
- The **formula** for solving a quadratic equation $ax^2 + bx + c = 0$ is

  $$x = \frac{-b \pm \sqrt{b^2 - 4ac}}{2a}$$

  Real roots occur if the **discriminant** $b^2 - 4ac$ is positive or zero.

Simultaneous equations and quadratic inequalities

In this chapter we:

- *see how to form pairs of simultaneous equations to model situations*
- *see how to solve linear simultaneous equations*
- *see how to solve a pair of simultaneous equations consisting of a quadratic equation and a linear equation*
- *see how to solve quadratic inequalities.*

SIMULTANEOUS EQUATIONS

Exploration 5.1

Best combinations

Imagine you are a landscape gardener and have been given the job of creating a floral display in the local park. You are given the following brief.

- Use daffodil and/or tulip bulbs only.
- The display should contain no more than 400 bulbs in total.
- Tulip bulbs cost 10 pence and daffodil bulbs cost 6 pence each.
- Total budget for bulbs = £30.

Find a combination of tulip and daffodil bulbs which total 400 and use up all the money.

Finding the combination

The two variables in this problem are the number of tulips and the number of daffodils. Let d represent the number daffodil bulbs and t the number of tulip bulbs purchased for the display.

The two constraints lead to two **inequalities**:

Maximum of 400 bulbs $\Rightarrow$ $d + t \leq 400$

Budget of £30 $\Rightarrow$ $6d + 10t \leq 3000$

cost of d daffodil bulbs

cost of t tulip bulbs

money available in pence

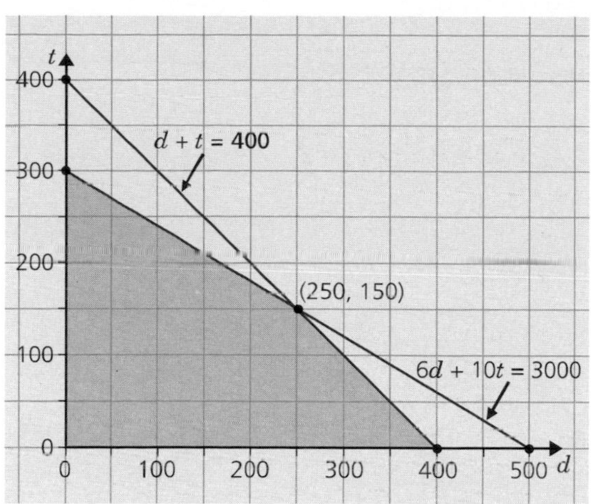

If 400 bulbs are used and a total of £30 is spent on them, the inequalities become equations:

$d + t = 400$ (1)
$6d + 10t = 3000$ (2)

The simultaneous solution of these two equations may be found graphically by finding the point of intersection of the two straight line graphs.

To use 400 bulbs and spend all the money, the gardener needs to buy 250 daffodil bulbs and 150 tulip bulbs. Given that the number of daffodil or tulip bulbs cannot be negative, i.e. $d \geq 0$, $t \geq 0$, the shaded area in the diagram represents the set of combinations that satisfy all the constraints.

Simultaneous equations – algebraic methods

The simultaneous solution of equations (1) and (2) above may be found algebraically, rather than graphically. Two methods are in common use.

Method A

$d + t = 400$ (1)
$6d + 10t = 3000$ (2)

Make the coefficient of t the same in both equations:

(1) × 10 ⇒ $10d + 10t = 4000$ (3)
(2) ⇒ $6d + 10t = 3000$ (4)

Eliminate the variable t:

(3) − (4) ⇒ $4d = 1000$ (5)

(5) ÷ 4 ⇒ $d = \frac{1000}{4} = 250$

Substitute for d in (1):

⇒ $250 + t = 400$
⇒ $t = 400 - 250 = 150$

Method B

$d + t = 400$ (1)
$6d + 10t = 3000$ (2)

Make d the subject of (1):

$d = 400 - t$

Substitute for d in (2):

$$6(400 - t) + 10t = 3000$$
$$2400 - 6t + 10t = 3000$$
$$4t = 600$$
$$t = 150$$

Substitute for t in (1):

$$d + 150 = 400$$
$$d = 400 - 150 = 250$$

Example 5.1

Solve this pair of simultaneous equations.

$3x + 4y = 29$

$2x - 5y = 4$

Illustrate your solution graphically.

Solution

Method A

$3x + 4y = 29$ (1)

$2x - 5y = 4$ (2)

Make the coefficient of x the same in both equations:

$(1) \times 2 \Rightarrow 6x + 8y = 58$ (3)

$(2) \times 3 \Rightarrow 6x - 15y = 12$ (4)

$(3) - (4) \Rightarrow 23y = 46$ (5)

$(5) \div 23 \Rightarrow y = \frac{46}{23} = 2$

Substitute for y in (2):

$$2x - 5 \times 2 = 4$$
$$\Rightarrow 2x = 14$$
$$\Rightarrow x = 7$$

Method B

$3x + 4y = 29$ (1)

$2x - 5y = 4$ (2)

Make x the subject of (2):

$$2x = 4 + 5y$$
$$x = \frac{4+5y}{2}$$

Substitute for x in (1):

$$3 \times \frac{4+5y}{2} + 4y = 29$$
$$\Rightarrow 3(4 + 5y) + 8y = 58$$
$$\Rightarrow 12 + 15y + 8y = 58$$
$$\Rightarrow 23y = 46$$
$$\Rightarrow y = \frac{46}{23} = 2$$

Substitute for y in (1):

$$3x + 4 \times 2 = 29$$
$$\Rightarrow 3x = 21$$
$$\Rightarrow x = 7$$

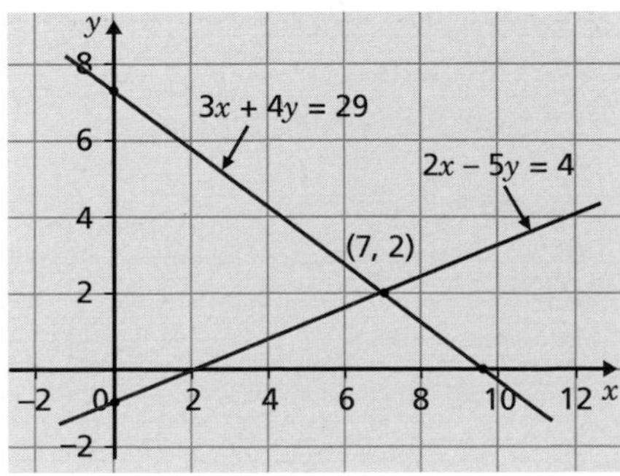

Thus $x = 7$, $y = 2$ satisfy both equations simultaneously. Graphically the point (7, 2) represents the intersection of the lines $3x + 4y = 29$ and $2x - 5y = 4$.

The line $3x + 4y = 29$ passes through $(0, 7\frac{1}{4})$ and $(9\frac{2}{3}, 0)$.

The line $2x - 5y = 4$ passes through $(0, -\frac{4}{5})$ and (2, 0).

The two lines intersect at (7, 2).

Example 5.2 *A quadrilateral has vertices A(0, 3), B(3, 4), C(5, –2) and D(–1, 0).*

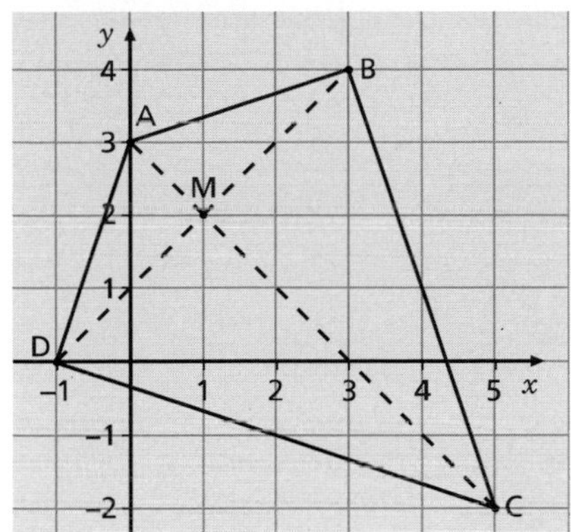

a) *Find the equations of lines AC and BD.*
b) *Show that AC bisects BD at right angles.*

Solution

Start by plotting points A, B, C and D and joining A to C and B to D. From the graph it is evident that M(1, 2) is the midpoint of BD, and AC and BD are perpendicular, i.e. AC bisects BD at right angles.

The following solution provides an algebraic proof.

a) *The equation of AC is found from:*

$$\frac{y-3}{-2-3} = \frac{x-0}{5-0}$$

$$\Rightarrow \quad \frac{y-3}{-5} = \frac{x}{5}$$

$$\Rightarrow \quad y = 3 - x$$

The equation of BD is found from:

$$\frac{y-0}{4-0} = \frac{x-(-1)}{3-(-1)}$$

$$\Rightarrow \quad \frac{y}{4} = \frac{x+1}{4}$$

$$\Rightarrow \quad y = x + 1$$

b) *Solve equations (1) and (2) simultaneously.*

$$y = 3 - x \qquad (1)$$
$$y = x + 1 \qquad (2)$$

From (1) $y = 3 - x$

Substitute for y *in (2):*

$$3 - x = x + 1$$
$$\Rightarrow \quad 2 = 2x$$
$$\Rightarrow \quad x = 1$$

Substitute for x *in (1):*

$$y = 3 - 1 = 2$$

So the coordinates of M are (1, 2)
But the midpoint of BD is $(\frac{1}{2}(-1+3), \frac{1}{2}(0+4))$ *or* $(1, 2)$.
The gradient of AC is –1 and the gradient of BD is 1, hence the product of gradients is $(-1) \times 1 = -1$.
Therefore AC bisects BD at right angles.

EXERCISES

5.1 CLASSWORK

For questions **1** to **6**, solve the pairs of simultaneous equations, illustrating your answers graphically.

1 $2x + 3y = 30$
$x + y = 12$

2 $13x + 9y = 36$
$2x + 3y = 6$

3 $5p + 3r = 41$
$p - 2r = 3$

4 $-3x + 8y = 31.1$
$5x + 3y = 3.7$

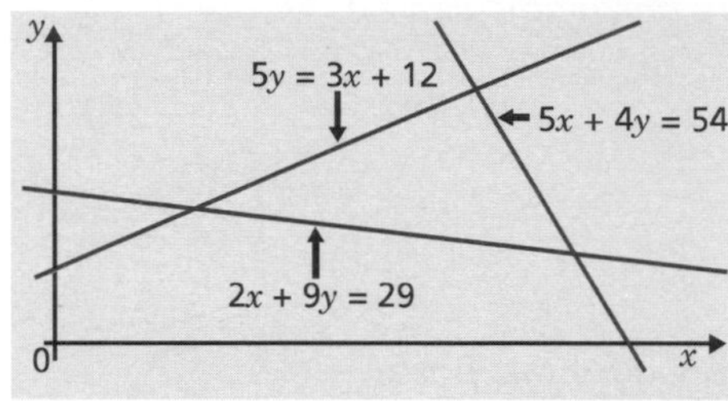

5 The three lines
$5x + 4y = 54$ $2x + 9y = 29$ $5y = 3x + 12$
make a triangle.

Find the coordinates of its vertices.

6 Show that the three lines
$2x + 7y = 42$ $y = x - 3$ $3x + y = 25$
are collinear (they meet at a single point).

7 Try to find solutions for these pairs of simultaneous equations.

a) $10x - 2y = 6$
$y = 5x - 3$

b) $6x + 3y = 20$
$y = 7 - 2x$

Give a graphical explanation for your answers.

8 Triangle EFG has vertices E(2, 5), F(–2, –2) and G(6, 0).

Show that the medians meet in a single point and find its coordinates.

9 A triangle has vertices at P(8, 0), Q(1, 1) and R(3, 5).

a) Show that the triangle is isosceles.
b) Find the equation of the straight line through P and R.
c) Find the equation of the perpendicular from Q to PR.
d) Find the coordinates of the foot of the perpendicular from Q to PR.
e) Find the area of ΔPQR in two different ways.

10 A landscape designer has £240 to spend on planting trees and shrubs to landscape an area of 1000 m^2. For a tree he plans to allow 25 m^2 and for a shrub 10 m^2. Planting a tree will cost £2 and planting a shrub will cost £4.

Let t represent the number of trees planted and s the number of shrubs planted.

Assume he spends all the money and all the area is used up.
a) Explain why $t + 2s = 120$
and $5t + 2s = 200$
b) Solve the equations in **a)** to find how many trees and how many shrubs he should buy.

EXERCISES

5.1 HOMEWORK

For questions **1** to **6**, solve the pairs of simultaneous equations, illustrating your answers graphically.

1 $5x + 4y = 9$
$6x + 2y = 2$

2 $6x - 3y = 8$
$5x + y = 4$

3 $x = 2y$
$6x + 7y = 38$

4 $8x - y - 5 = 0$
$6y - 9x + 7 = 0$

5 Find the point of intersection of the lines $y = 7x - 4$ and $3x + 5y + 1 = 0$.

6 Two of the following lines are parallel. Find which two, and find the coordinates of the points where the third line cuts the parallel lines.
$8x + 12y + 9 = 0 \qquad 6y = 3 - 9x \qquad 4x + 6y = 3$

7 Show that the three lines
$7y + 68 = 2x \qquad 9x + y = 46 \qquad 9x - 8y = 118$
all pass through a single point, and find the coordinates of that point.

8 Line l is shown on the graph on the left.

Which of the following lines is

a) parallel to **b)** equal to **c)** intersecting l?

i) $2x - 1.5y + 6 = 0$
ii) $3y = 4x + 4$
iii) $y = \frac{3}{4}x - 3$

d) For the intersecting lines, find the point of intersection.

9 Find the point where the diagonals of the quadrilateral with vertices A(2, 5), B(0, −9), C(−5, −6) and D(−3, 6) cut each other. Show that this is not the midpoint of either of the diagonals.

10 First and second class postage was introduced in 1968. First class letters weighing less than 4 oz cost 5d to post, and second class letters 4d. If 50 invitations to a party needed to be sent out at these prices, and £1 was available for postage, find how many should be sent first class and how many should be sent second class. Use all the money, so that as many can go first class as possible. £1 = 240d. Assume all the letters weighed less than 4 oz.

A QUADRATIC AND A LINEAR EQUATION

We have already seen how to find the point of intersection of two straight line graphs by solving a pair of simultaneous equations. In this section we shall discover how to find the points of intersection of a curve, such as a parabola, and a straight line.

Exploration 5.2

Lines and curves

Draw the graph of $y = x^2 - x - 2$.

■ Find where the straight lines

a) $y = 3x - 2$ **b)** $y = 3x - 6$ **c)** $y = 3x - 10$

intersect with the parabola.

Interpreting the results

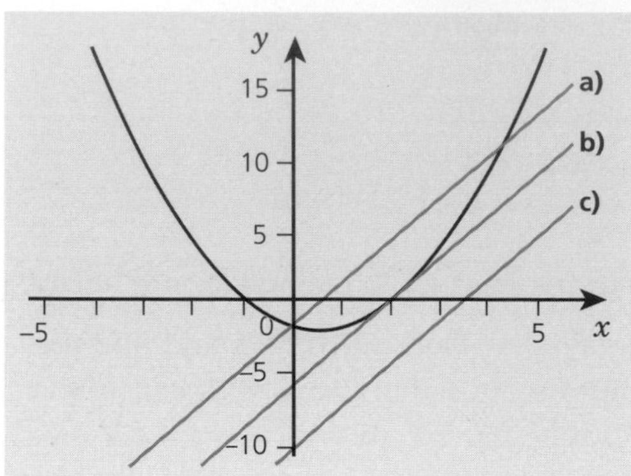

The graph is shown on the left. From it we see that:

a) $y = 3x - 2$ crosses the parabola at $(0, -2)$ and $(4, 10)$.
b) $y = 3x - 6$ touches the parabola at $(2, 0)$.
c) $y = 3x - 10$ does not intersect with the parabola at all.

In a) the points of intersection represent the pairs of (x, y) coordinates which satisfy the equations $y = x^2 - x - 2$ and $y = 3x - 2$ simultaneously.

To find these pairs algebraically, proceed as follows:

$$y = x^2 - x - 2 \qquad (1)$$
$$y = 3x - 2 \qquad (2)$$

From (2) substitute for y in (1):

$$3x - 2 = x^2 - x - 2$$

Rearrange $\Rightarrow \quad x^2 - 4x = 0$

Factorise $\Rightarrow \quad x(x - 4) = 0$

$\Rightarrow \quad x = 0$ or $x = 4$

Substitute back in (2) $\Rightarrow \quad y = -2$ or $y = 10$

The line intersects the parabola at $(0, -2)$ and $(4, 10)$.

In **b)** the points of intersection represent the pairs of (x, y) coordinates which satisfy the equations $y = x^2 - x - 2$ and $y = 3x - 6$ simultaneously. By substitution this leads to the quadratic equation:

$$x^2 - 4x + 4 = 0$$

Factorise $\Rightarrow \quad (x - 2)^2 = 0$

$\Rightarrow \quad x = 2$

Substitute back in (2) $\Rightarrow \quad y = 0$

The line touches the parabola at $(2, 0)$.

In **c)** the points of intersection represent the pairs of (x, y) coordinates which satisfy the equations $y = x^2 - x - 2$ and $y = 3x - 10$ simultaneously. By substitution this leads to the quadratic equation:

$$x^2 - 4x + 8 = 0$$

The quadratic function will not factorise. Using the discriminant from the formula, $b^2 - 4ac = (-4)^2 - 4 \times 1 \times 8 = -16$.

Therefore the quadratic equation has no real roots, which means that there are no points of intersection between the line and the parabola.

Example 5.3

A circle, centre (0, 0) and radius 5, is described by the equation $x^2 + y^2 = 25$.

Find the coordinates of the points where the line $y = 5 - 2x$ *meets the circle.*

Solution

Solving two simultaneous equations:

$x^2 + y^2 = 25$ (1)

$y = 5 - 2x$ (2)

From (2) substitute for y *in (1):*

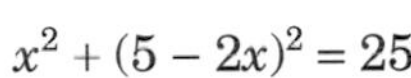

$$x^2 + (5 - 2x)^2 = 25$$

Multiply out the brackets $\Rightarrow x^2 + 25 - 20x + 4x^2 = 25$

Rearrange $\Rightarrow 5x^2 - 20x = 0$

Factorise $\Rightarrow 5x(x - 4) = 0$

$\Rightarrow x = 0$ *or* $x = 4$

Substitute back in (2) $\Rightarrow y = 5$ *or* $y = -3$

The line intersects the circle at (0, 5) and (4, −3).

EXERCISES

5.2 CLASSWORK

For the following pairs, one curve and one line, sketch them on the same axes and find the coordinates of their point(s) of intersection.

1 $y = x^2 - x - 6$
$y = x + 2$

2 $y = 4x^2 + 3x + 1$
$5x + y = 6$

Solve the following simultaneous equations, where possible.

3 $2x + 3y = 14$
$xy = 14$

4 $2x + 9y = 14$
$y(x + 1) = -2$

5 $x + 2y = 7$
$x^2 + 2y^2 = 17$

6 $x + 4y = 14$
$x^2 - y^2 = 56$

EXERCISES

5.2 HOMEWORK

For the following pairs, one curve and one line, sketch them on the same axes and find, where possible, the coordinates of their point(s) of intersection.

1 $y = 2x^2 - 3x - 1$
$y = 3x + 7$

2 $y = x^2 + 3x - 1$
$2x + 3y = 20$

Solve the following simultaneous equations, where possible.

3 $3x + 4y = 15$
$2xy = 9$

4 $y = 2x + 3$
$y(5 - x) = 20$

5 $9x^2 - 4y^2 = 576$
$3x - 2y = 12$

6 $x - y = 3$
$x^2 - y^2 = 69$

What is the significance of your answers to questions 5 and 6?

QUADRATIC INEQUALITIES

Exploration 5.3

Ranges of values

Sketch the graph of $y = x^2 + 3x - 4$.

- Find the values of x for which:

a) $x^2 + 3x - 4 = 0$ **b)** $x^2 + 3x - 4 < 0$ **c)** $x^2 + 3x - 4 > 0$

Finding the values

a) Since $x^2 + 3x - 4 = (x + 4)(x - 1)$, solve the equation by factorising:

$$x^2 + 3x - 4 = 0$$
$$\Rightarrow \quad (x + 4)(x - 1) = 0$$
$$\Rightarrow \quad x = -4 \text{ or } x = 1$$

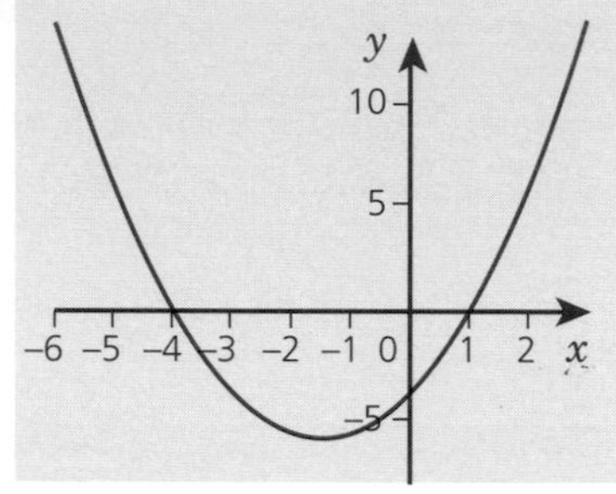

These values correspond to the x-coordinates of the points where the graph crosses the x-axis, i.e. where $y = 0$.

b) From the graph, $y < 0$ over the interval $-4 < x < 1$, so the solution to the inequality $x^2 + 3x - 4 < 0$ is a set of x-values.
The solution set is formally written $\{x: -4 < x < 1\}$.

c) Finally, notice that $y > 0$ on the graph when $x < -4$ or $x > 1$, so the solution to the inequality $x^2 + 3x - 4 > 0$ is the union of two disjoint sets of x-values.
The solution set is formally written

$$\{x: x < -4\} \cup \{x: x > 1\} \text{ or } \{x: x < -4 \text{ or } x > 1\}$$

Since $x^2 + 3x - 4 \equiv (x + 4)(x - 1)$ we can see that

$x^2 + 3x - 4 = 0$ when either factor is zero
$x^2 + 3x - 4 < 0$ when the factors have different signs
$x^2 + 3x - 4 > 0$ when the factors have the same signs.

This can be summarised as:

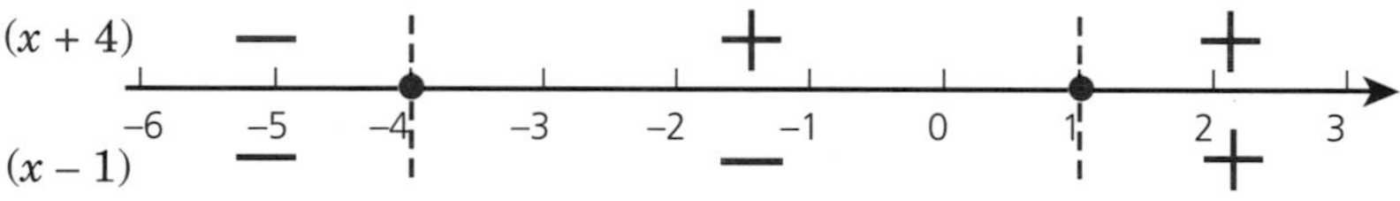

The signs are **different** for the set $\{x: -4 < x < 1\}$.

The signs are the **same** for the set $\{x: x < -4 \text{ or } x > 1\}$.

Example 5.4

Solve $15 - 4x - 4x^2 \geq 0$.

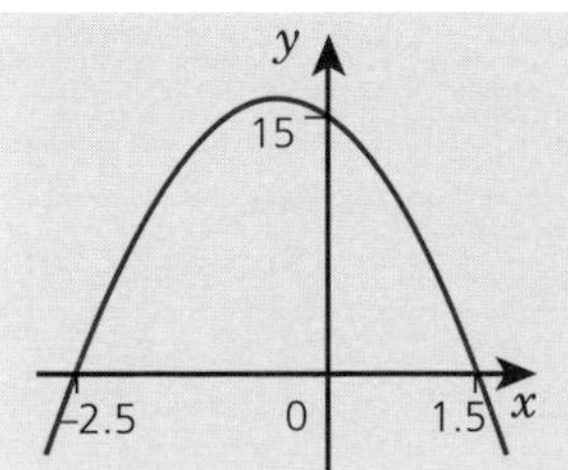

Solution

Firstly factorise the quadratic function:

$15 - 4x - 4x^2 = (5 + 2x)(3 - 2x)$
$\Rightarrow 15 - 4x - 4x^2 = 0$ *when* $x = -2.5$ or $x = 1.5$

A sketch of the graph $y = 15 - 4x - 4x^2$ *leads to the conclusion:*

$15 - 4x - 4x^2 \geq 0 \Rightarrow -2.5 \leq x \leq 1.5$

Now $15 - 4x - 4x^2 > 0 \Rightarrow$ *the factors must have the **same** sign.*

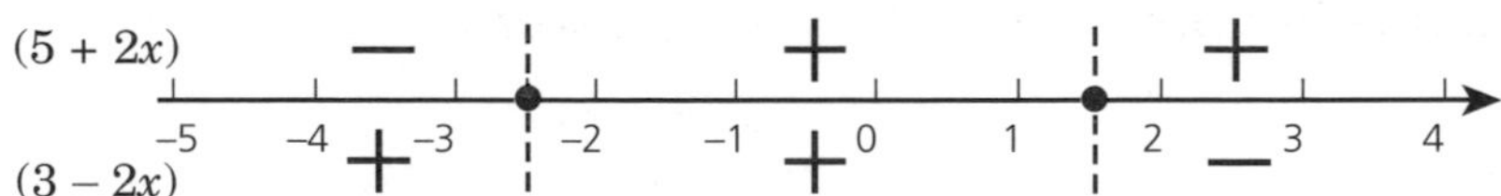

*The signs are the **same** for the set* $\{x: -2.5 < x < 1.5\}$*, which means that the solution set for the inequality is* $\{x: -2.5 \le x \le 1.5\}$.

Functions which do not factorise

For quadratic functions which do *not* factorise, we can try solving the corresponding quadratic equation (giving the **boundary** values), then solving the inequality with reference to a sketch graph. Alternatively, a formal approach is possible, which may require completing the square.

Example 5.5

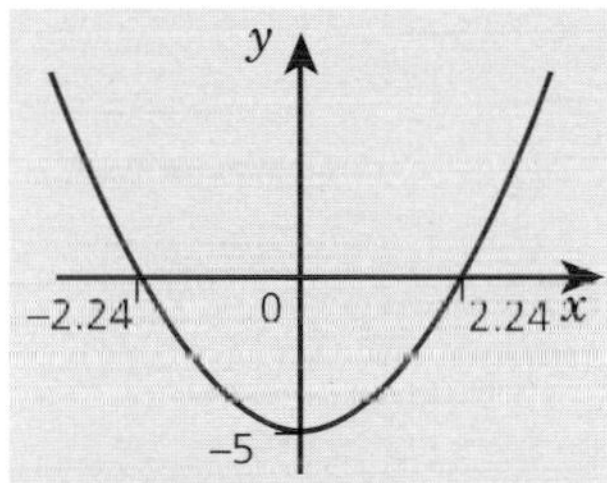

Solve the inequality $x^2 > 5$.

Solution

The equation $x^2 = 5 \Rightarrow x = \pm\sqrt{5}$.
Now $x^2 > 5 \Rightarrow x^2 - 5 > 0$ *and a sketch of the graph of* $y = x^2 - 5$ *leads to the conclusion that the* x*-values satisfying the inequality* $x^2 > 5$ *lie below* $-\sqrt{5}$ *or above* $+\sqrt{5}$.

The solution set is given by $\{x: x < -\sqrt{5} \text{ or } x > +\sqrt{5}\}$*, which is equivalent to* $\{x: |x| > \sqrt{5}\}$.

Example 5.6

Find the set of x*-values satisfying* $x^2 < 5x - 2$.

Solution

To solve the corresponding equation, use either the method of completing the square or the formula.

$$x^2 = 5x - 2$$

$$\Rightarrow \quad x^2 - 5x + 2 = 0$$

$$\Rightarrow \quad x = \frac{-(-5) \pm \sqrt{(-5)^2 - 4 \times 1 \times 2}}{2 \times 1} = \frac{5 \pm \sqrt{17}}{2}$$

$$\Rightarrow \quad x = 0.438 \text{ or } x = 4.56 \text{ (3 s.f.)}$$

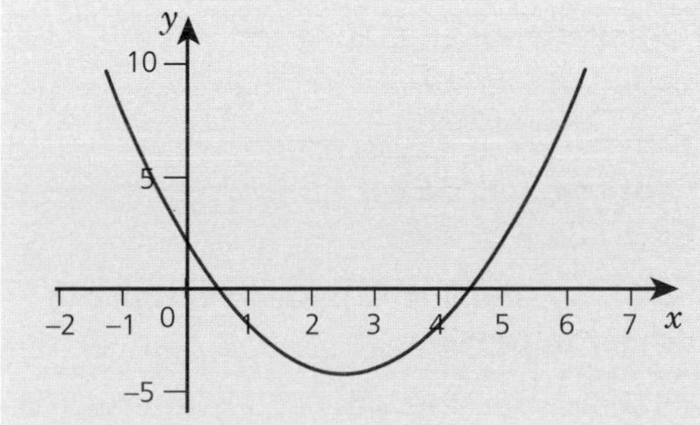

A sketch of the graph of $y = x^2 - 5x + 2$ *leads to the conclusion that the* x*-values satisfying the inequality lie between 0.438 and 4.56, i.e. the solution set is* $\{x: 0.438 < x < 4.56\}$.

A formal treatment following completion of the square gives:

$$x^2 - 5x + 2 < 0$$

Complete the square $\Rightarrow \left(x - \frac{5}{2}\right)^2 - \frac{17}{4} < 0$

Rearrange $\Rightarrow \left(x - \frac{5}{2}\right)^2 < \frac{17}{4}$

Take the square root of both sides $\Rightarrow \left|x - \frac{5}{2}\right| < \frac{\sqrt{17}}{2}$

$\Rightarrow x - \frac{5}{2} > -\frac{\sqrt{17}}{2}$ *and* $x - \frac{5}{2} < \frac{\sqrt{17}}{2}$

$\Rightarrow x > \frac{5-\sqrt{17}}{2}$ *and* $x < \frac{5+\sqrt{17}}{2}$

$\Rightarrow x > 0.438$ *and* $x < 4.56$ *(3 s.f.)*

EXERCISES

5.3 CLASSWORK

Solve the following inequalities, where possible. Illustrate your answer graphically.

1 $x^2 < \frac{1}{9}$

2 $x^2 \geq \frac{1}{9}$

3 $x^2 + \frac{1}{16} \leq 0$

4 $3x(3 - 2x) > 0$

5 $x^2 < 2x + 8$

6 $x^2 - 6x + 11 \geq 0$

7 $x^2 + 4x + 4 > 0$

8 $x^2 - 4x + 4 > 0$

9 $x^2 + 4x - 4 > 0$

10 $x^2 - 4x - 4 > 0$

EXERCISES

5.3 HOMEWORK

Solve the following inequalities, where possible. Illustrate your answer graphically.

1 $x^2 - 7 < 0$

2 $x^2 + 7 < 0$

3 $x^2 - 13 > 0$

4 $(x - 2)(x + 5) \leq 0$

5 $(x + 1)(x + 4) \leq 0$

6 $x^2 > 2x$

7 $x^2 - 4x \leq 2$

8 $x^2 + x \leq 1$

9 $3x^2 - 6x - 2 > 0$

10 $x^2 - 4x - 3 < 0$

CONSOLIDATION EXERCISES FOR CHAPTER 5

1 Solve the following pairs of simultaneous equations.

a) $x + y = 6$
$x - y = 4$

b) $4x + 3y = 1$
$5x + 4y = 2$

c) $2a + 5b = 8$
$3a + 4b = 5$

d) $5a + 4b = 22$
$3a + 5b = 21$

2 The line l has equation $2x - y - 1 = 0$. The line m passes through the point A (0, 4) and is perpendicular to the line l.

a) Find an equation of m and show that the lines l and m intersect at the point P(2, 3).

The line n passes through the point B(3, 0) and is parallel to the line m.

b) Find an equation of n and hence find the coordinates of the point Q where the lines l and n intersect.

c) Show that AP = BQ = PQ.

(ULEAC Specimen Paper, 1994)

3 The equations of the sides of a triangle ABC are:
AB $x - 2y + 11 = 0$
BC $y = 7$
AC $2x - y + 7 = 0$

a) Find the coordinates of the points A, B and C.
b) Calculate the size of each of the angles in the triangle ABC.

4 A farmer has 20 hectares available for growing barley and swedes. He has to decide how much of each to grow. The cost per hectare for barley is £30 and for swedes is £20. The farmer has budgeted £480.

a) Formulate two equations in b and s, the area planted in hectares of barley and swedes respectively.
b) Solve the equations to find the area of each crop grown.

5 **a)** Factorise the quadratic function $\mathrm{f}(x)$, where $\mathrm{f}(x) = 5x^2 - 7x - 6$.
b) Find the set of values of x for which $\mathrm{f}(x) > 0$.

6 Find the range of values for which:
a) $x > x^2 - 12$ **b)** $x(2x - 3) < x^2 - 2$
c) $2x(x - 1) < 3 - x$ **d)** $x < x^2 - 6$

7 Eliminate x from the equations
$x - 3y = 5$ and $5xy + 3x - 4y = 0$
to form a quadratic equation in y

Hence show that the two given equations are satisfied simultaneously for only **one** pair of values (x, y).

8 **a)** Factorise the quadratic function $\mathrm{f}(x) = 6x^2 - 17x + 7$.
b) Find the set of values for which $\mathrm{f}(x) > 0$
c) Solve the simultaneous equations
$y = 6x^2 - 17x + 7$ and
$y = 7 - x$.
d) Illustrate your answers to **b)** and **c)** graphically.

9 Given that $x + y = 1$ and $16x^2 + y^2 = 65$, calculate the two possible values of x.

10 Solve the simultaneous equations
$y = x + 2$ and $2x^2 - y^2 + 2x + 1 = 0$.

11 Solve the simultaneous equations
$3x + y = 7$ and $xy = -6$.

12 Find the set of values of x for which $(x - 1)(x - 4) < 2(x - 4)$.
(EDEXCEL, Question 2, Paper 1, January 1999)

13 **i)** Solve the simultaneous equations.
$y = x^2 - 3x + 2$, $y = 3x - 7$.

ii) Interpret your solution to part **i)** geometrically.

(OCR, Question 2, Specimen Paper 1 2000)

Summary

Simultaneous equations

- To solve a pair of simultaneous linear equations:
  i) eliminate x (or y) from the equations and solve the resulting equation for y (or x)
  ii) substitute back into one of the original equations to find the value of the other variable

- To solve a pair of simultaneous equations where one equation is linear and the other is quadratic:
  i) eliminate x (or y) from the equations forming a quadratic equation in y (or x)
  ii) solve the quadratic equation y (or x)
  iii) substitute back into the linear equations to find the value of the other variable

Quadratic inequalities

- To solve a quadratic inequality such as $ax^2 + bx + c > 0$:
  i) solve the quadratic equation $ax^2 + bx + c = 0$
  ii) from a sketch graph of $y = ax^2 + bx + c$ deduce the interval(s) for which the inequality holds.

Cubic and polynomial functions

In this chapter we:

- *explore the properties of cubic and polynomial functions*
- *consider the addition, subtraction and multiplication of polynomials*
- *investigate the factorisation of polynomial functions using the factor theorem*
- *solve polynomial equations and inequalities by factorisation and graph sketching.*

EXPLORING POLYNOMIALS

CALCULATOR ACTIVITY

Exploration 6.1

What is a polynomial?

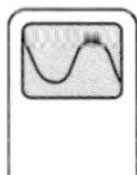

You will need a graphics calculator. By setting the range of x- and y-values appropriately, sketch the following curves.

A $y = x^3$	B $y = x^3 - 10$
C $y = 10 - x^3$	D $y = x^3 - 6x^2 + 12x - 8$
E $y = 10 - 3x - 6x^2 - x^3$	F $y = 2x^3 - 2x^2 - 12x$
G $y = x^3 + x^2 - 8x - 12$	H $y = 12 + 8x - x^2 - x^3$
I $y = x^3 + 2x^2 + 3x - 2$	J $y = 1 + 2x^2 - x^3$

- Investigate the relationship between the graphs, where possible.
- Find where the graphs intersect the axes.
- Find the coordinates of any maximum or minimum points.
- Each graph has rotational symmetry about a certain point. Find the coordinates of that point.

Interpreting the results

Having explored various properties of the ten graphs you will have noticed several things.

- The highest power of x is x^3, called 'x-cubed', which makes each curve the graph of a cubic function.
- The graphs intersect with the y-axis once, but intersect with the x-axis once, twice or three times.
- Some graphs have maximum and minimum points, some neither.

- Graphs with a positive x^3 term have this shape.

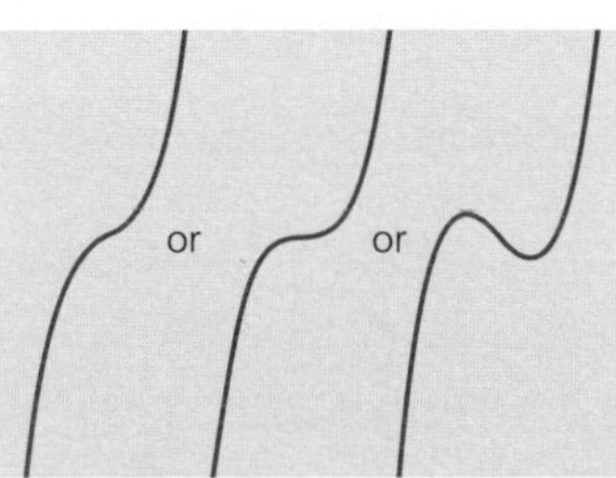

- Graphs with a negative x^3 term look like this.

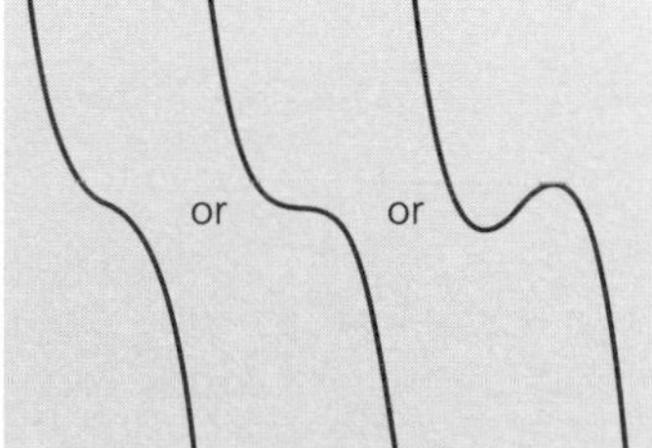

The general form of a cubic function is given by:

$f(x) = ax^3 + bx^2 + cx + d$

Both **quadratic** and **cubic** functions are examples of **polynomial** functions, where each term is a multiple of a power of x. This multiple is called a **coefficient**.

Consider the cubic function:

$f(x) = 4x^3 - 1.5x + 7$

In its fullest form it would be written: $f(x) = 4x^3 + 0x^2 - 1.5x^1 + 7x^0$

- the coefficient of x^3 is 4
- the coefficient of x^2 is 0
- the coefficient of x^1, or x, is -1.5
- the constant term 7 may be regarded as the coefficient of x^0, which itself is 1 (you met this idea in Chapter 2, *Basic algebra*).

Other polynomial functions which you will meet include:

quartic functions, e.g. $f(x) = x^4 - 3x^2 + x - 7$

quintic functions, e.g. $f(x) = 3x^5 + 2x^4 - x^2 + 8$

The **degree** of a polynomial function is the index of the highest power of x with a non-zero coefficient e.g. the cubic function $f(x) = x^3 - 2x^2 + 5x - 7$ is a polynomial of degree 3.

There is no upper limit to the degree of a polynomial. In further study you may meet polynomials with an infinite degree, but restrict your interest to terms in relatively small powers of x.

Example 6.1

Sketch graphs of the cubic functions: $y = -x^3 + 6x^2 + 15x + d$ *where:*

a) $d = -121$ ***b)*** $d = -100$ ***c)*** $d = -50$
d) $d = 8$ ***e)*** $d = 30$

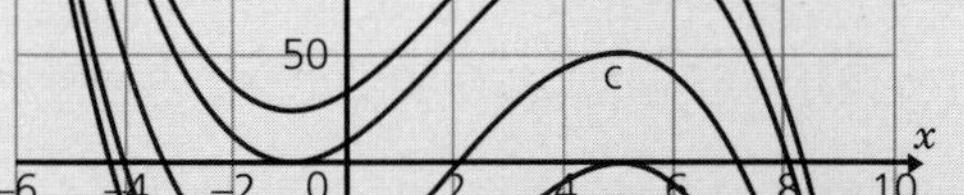

In each case find:

i) *the coordinate of the maximum and minimum points,*

ii) *the x-value(s) where the curve intersects with the x-axis, i.e. where $f(x) = 0$.*

Solution

Drawing all five graphs on one grid gives this result.

All the minimum points occur at $x = -1$ and maximum points at $x = 5$. The x-values where the curves intersect with the x-axis are either exact or can be estimated by using trace and/or zoom on a calculator. Where necessary the results are given to 3 s.f.

Curve	Minimum point	Maximum point	x-values where $f(x) = 0$
$y = -x^3 + 6x^2 + 15x - 121$	(–1, –129)	(5, –21)	–4.25
$y = -x^3 + 6x^2 + 15x - 100$	(–1, –108)	(5, 0)	–4, 5
$y = -x^3 + 6x^2 + 15x - 46$	(–1, –54)	(5, 54)	–3.20, 2, 7.20
$y = -x^3 + 6x^2 + 15x + 8$	(–1, 0)	(5, 108)	–1, 8
$y = -x^3 + 6x^2 + 15x + 30$	(–1, 22)	(5, 130)	8.26

Example 6.2

Sketch graphs of the functions $y = x^3 + cx$ where:

a) $c = -9$ ***b)*** $c = -4$ ***c)*** $c = 0$ ***d)*** $c = 4$ ***e)*** $c = 9$.

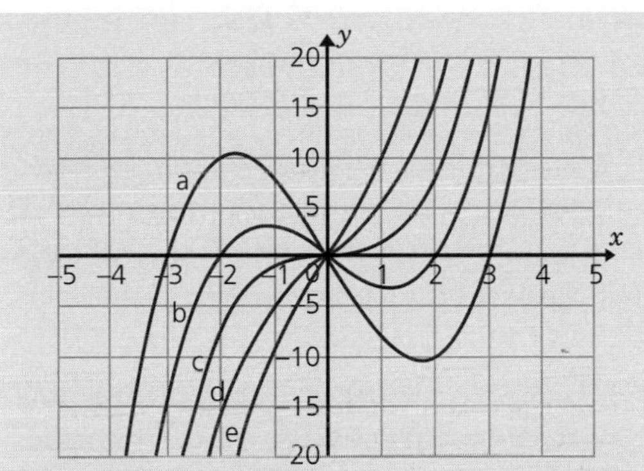

In each case find:

i) *the coordinates of the maximum and minimum points,*

ii) *the x-value(s) where $f(x) = 0$.*

Solution

Drawing all five graphs on one grid gives this result.

The x-values where $f(x) = 0$ are exact and can be read off easily. The coordinates of the maximum and minimum points, where they exist, may be estimated by using trace and/or zoom. Where necessary results are given correct to 3 s.f.

Curve	Minimum point	Maximum point	x-values where $f(x) = 0$
$y = x^3 - 9x$	(−1.73, 9.98)	(1.73, −9.98)	−3, 0, 3
$y = x^3 - 4x$	(−1.15, 3.08)	(1.15, −3.08)	−2, 0, 2
$y = x^3$	–	–	0
$y = x^3 + 4x$	–	–	0
$y = x^3 + 9x$	–	–	0

Example 6.3

Sketch the graph of the quartic function $y = 3x^4 - 15x^2 + 12$ and find the coordinates of the maximum and minimum values. Also find the x-values where $f(x) = 0$ and check your answers by calculation.

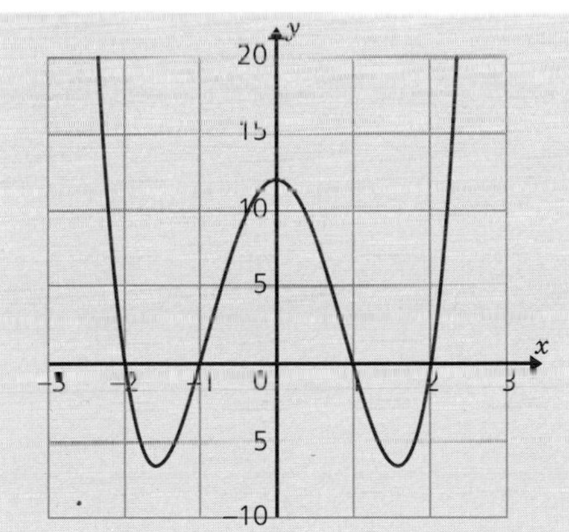

Solution

From the graph the maximum and minimum points may be read off:

maximum : (0, 12)

minimum : (−1.58, −6.75) and (1.58, −6.75)

The x-values where $f(x) = 0$ are −2, −1, 1 and 2. A check by calculation is possible since:

$$f(x) = 0 \Rightarrow 3x^4 - 15x^2 + 12 = 0$$

which is a quadratic equation in x^2.

Factorising: $3(x^4 - 5x^2 + 4) = 0$

$\Rightarrow$ $3(x^2 - 1)(x^2 - 4) = 0$

$\Rightarrow$ $x^2 - 1 = 0$ *or* $x^2 - 4 = 0$

Now $x^2 - 1 = 0 \Rightarrow (x - 1)(x + 1) = 0 \Rightarrow x = \pm 1$

$x^2 - 4 = 0 \Rightarrow (x - 2)(x + 2) = 0 \Rightarrow x = \pm 2$

CALCULATOR ACTIVITY

Exploration 6.2 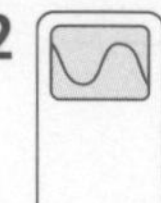

In Exploration 6.1, the graph of the cubic function $f(x) = x^3 + 2x^2 + 3x - 2$ is as shown below.

Since the graph is continuous, $f(0) = -2$ and $f(1) = 4$, there is a number a such that $0 < a < 1$ and $f(a) = 0$. From the sketch it looks as though a is about 0.5.

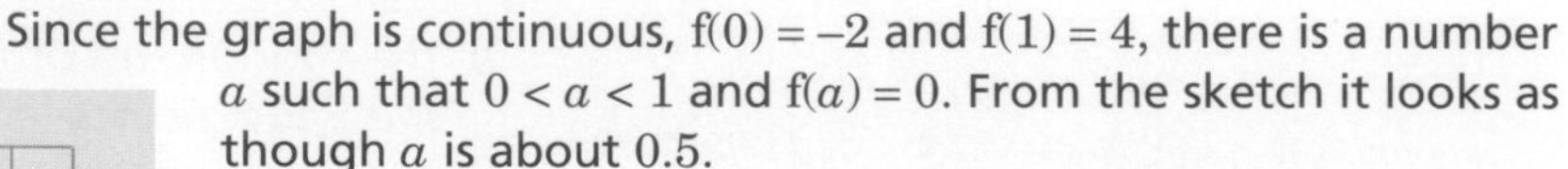

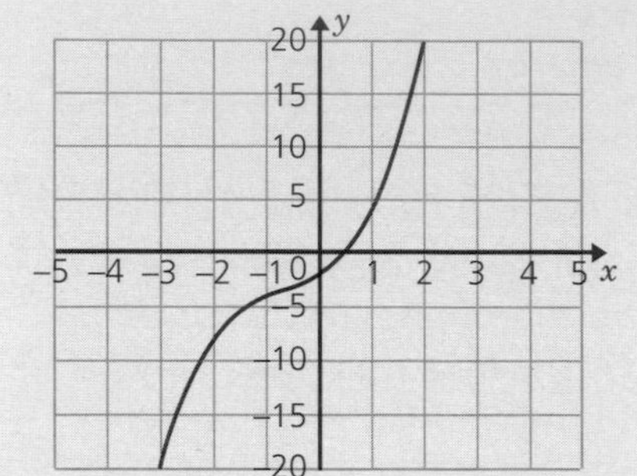

Plot the graph of $y = x^3 + 2x^2 + 3x - 2$ and zoom in to find the value of a correct to 3 d.p. Trace the curve to show that there is a change of sign of the function either side of your computed value. You should find that $a = 0.478$ (3 d.p.), i.e. $0.4775 < a < 0.4785$, since $f(0.4775) < 0$ and $f(0.4785) > 0$.

Using a calculator with a table facility or a spreadsheet will also enable you to apply a **decimal search** to find the value of a to the required degree of accuracy.

- Evaluate the function $f(x)$ between $x = 0$ and $x = 1$, in steps of 0.1: a change of sign in $f(x)$ occurs between $x = 0.4$ and $x = 0.5$.
- Evaluate $f(x)$ between $x = 0.4$ and $x = 0.5$, in steps of 0.01: a change of sign in $f(x)$ occurs between $x = 0.47$ and $x = 0.48$.
- Evaluate $f(x)$ between $x = 0.47$ and $x = 0.48$, in steps of 0.001: a change of sign in $f(x)$ occurs between $x = 0.477$ and $x = 0.478$.
- Evaluate $f(x)$ between $x = 0.477$ and $x = 0.478$, in steps of 0.0001: a change of sign in $f(x)$ occurs between $x = 0.4779$ and $x = 0.4780$.

Take the function $f(x) = 1 + 2x^2 - x^3$ from Exploration 6.1 and show that there is a number a such that $2 < a < 3$ and $f(a) = 0$. Use a graphical and/or tabular method to find the value of a correct to 3 d.p.

EXERCISES

6.1 CLASSWORK

a) Sketch the graph of each curve.
b) Find the coordinates of any maximum or minimum points.
c) Find x-values where $f(x) = 0$.

1 $y = x^3 - 7x + 6$ **2** $y = x^3 + 4x + 1$

3 $y = x^3 - 4x^2$ **4** $y = 7 - 3x + 4x^2 - x^3$

5 $y = x^4 - x^3 - 2x - 5$ **6** $y = 3 - 2x^3 - x^4$

EXERCISES

6.1 HOMEWORK

a) Sketch the graph of each curve.
b) Find the coordinates of any maximum or minimum points.
c) Find x-values where $f(x) = 0$.

1 $y = x^3 - 9x$ **2** $y = x^3 + 4x - 5$

3 $y = 2x^3 - 5x^2$ **4** $y = 2 - 8x - 7x^2 - x^3$

5 $y = x^4 - 16x^2$ **6** $y = 1 - 6x - 2x^2 + 3x^3 - x^4$

ARITHMETIC OF POLYNOMIALS

Polynomials can be added together, or one can be subtracted from another. They can be multiplied or divided by a constant, or by another polynomial. We start this section by thinking about adding and subtracting polynomial functions.

Exploration 6.3

Investigating addition and subtraction

Two polynomial functions are given by $f(x) = x^3 - 3x + 7$ and $g(x) = x^2 + 4x - 3$.

- What does $f(x) + g(x)$ mean?
- What does $f(x) - g(x)$ mean?
- How can you interpret your answers graphically?

Adding and subtracting polynomials

The polynomials $f(x)$ and $g(x)$ may be added or subtracted by collecting like terms.

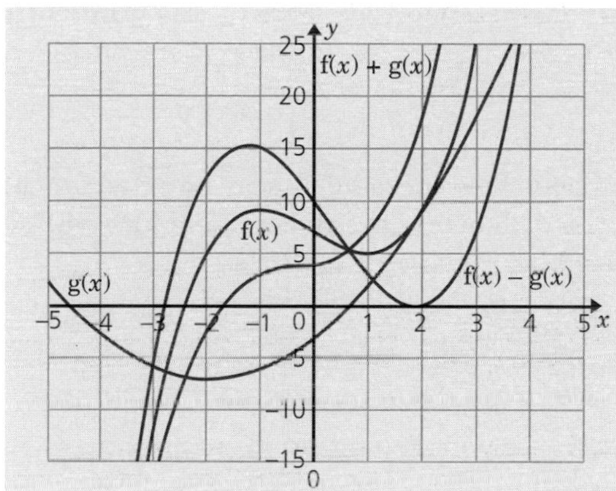

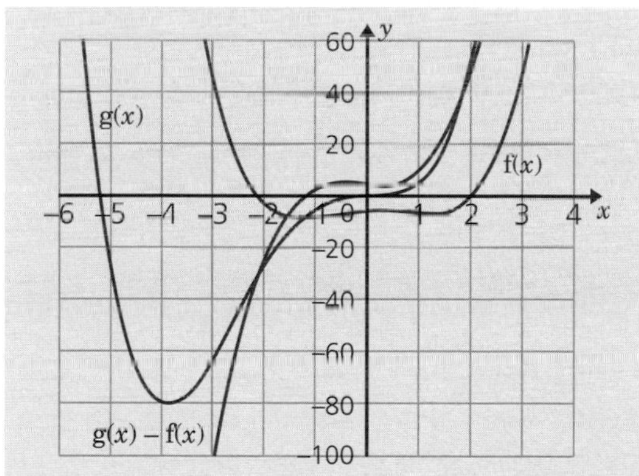

$$f(x) + g(x) = x^3 - 3x + 7 + x^2 + 4x - 3 = x^3 + x^2 + x + 4$$

$$f(x) - g(x) = x^3 - 3x + 7 - (x^2 + 4x - 3)$$
$$= x^3 - 3x + 7 - x^2 - 4x + 3 = x^3 - x^2 - 7x + 10$$

Note: The result of adding or subtracting a cubic function and a quadratic function is a cubic function. The results of the addition and subtraction may be illustrated graphically.

Note what happens when $f(x) + g(x) = 0$ and $f(x) - g(x) = 0$.

In general, if $f(x)$ is a polynomial of degree m and $g(x)$ is a polynomial of degree n, then $f(x) + g(x)$ and $f(x) - g(x)$ will both be polynomials. The degree of the resulting polynomial will be m or n, whichever is higher. The only exception is when both $f(x)$ and $g(x)$ have the same degree, n, and the coefficient of x^n is zero in the result, e.g.

$$f(x) = x^4 - 3x^2 + x - 5$$

$$g(x) = x^4 + 5x^3 - x^2$$

$$\Rightarrow\ g(x) - f(x) = 5x^3 + 2x^2 - x + 5$$

Here the result of subtracting two quartic functions is a cubic function.

Multiplying polynomials

Exploration 6.4

Investigating multiplication

How do you multiply two polynomials? This chart illustrates the multiplication of $5x + 3$ and $x^2 + 3x + 2$. Note that every term in one polynomial is multiplied by every term in the other.

	x^2	$3x$	2
$5x$	$5x^3$	$15x^2$	$10x$
3	$3x^2$	$9x$	6

- Write out $(5x + 3)(x^2 + 3x + 2)$ as a cubic polynomial.
- What different ways are there to find this product *without* the aid of a diagram?
- How is the degree of the resulting polynomial found from the degree of $5x + 3$ and $x^2 + 3x + 2$?

Multiplication without a diagram

Summing the terms in the boxes gives:

$$(5x + 3)(x^2 + 3x + 2) = 5x^3 + 15x^2 + 3x^2 + 10x + 9x + 6 = 5x^3 + 18x^2 + 19x + 6$$

Alternatively, taking the two rows separately:

$$\begin{aligned}(5x + 3)(x^2 + 3x + 2) &= 5x(x^2 + 3x + 2) + 3(x^2 + 3x + 2)\\ &= 5x^3 + 15x^2 + 10x + 3x^2 + 9x + 6\\ &= 5x^3 + 18x^2 + 19x + 6\end{aligned}$$

You should find this a convenient way of multiplying out brackets for any pair of polynomials.

Note: The degree of the product is the sum of the degrees of the parts. In the example above, the **linear** function is of degree 1, the **quadratic** function is of degree 2 and the resulting **cubic** function is of degree 3.

Polynomials of degree greater than 3

The following examples illustrate how these ideas may be extended to multiplication of higher-degree polynomials. Some of them include negative coefficients, too, so watch out for the minus signs.

Example 6.4

Find the product of $x^2 - x + 5$ *and* $x^3 - 4x^2 + 7$ *and state the degree of the resulting polynomial.*

Solution

$$\begin{aligned}&(x^2 - x + 5)(x^3 - 4x^2 + 7) = x^2(x^3 - 4x^2 + 7) - x(x^3 - 4x^2 + 7) + 5(x^3 - 4x^2 + 7)\\ &= x^5 - 4x^4 + 7x^2 - x^4 + 4x^3 - 7x + 5x^3 - 20x^2 + 35\\ &= x^5 - 5x^4 + 9x^3 - 13x^2 - 7x + 35\end{aligned}$$

The resulting product is a quintic function, a polynomial of degree 5 (= 2 + 3), the sum of the degrees of the polynomials forming the product.

Example 6.5

Simplify $(2x - 1)(2x^3 + 5x^2 - x + 3) - (x^2 - x + 3)(4x^2 - 9)$

Solution

Firstly expand each pair of brackets:

$$\begin{aligned}(2x - 1)(2x^3 + 5x^2 - x + 3) &= 2x(2x^3 + 5x^2 - x + 3) - (2x^3 + 5x^2 - x + 3)\\ &= 4x^4 + 10x^3 - 2x^2 + 6x - 2x^3 - 5x^2 + x - 3\\ &= 4x^4 + 8x^3 - 7x^2 + 7x - 3\\ (x^2 - x + 3)(4x^2 - 9) &= x^2(4x^2 - 9) - x(4x^2 - 9) + 3(4x^2 - 9)\\ &= 4x^4 - 9x^2 - 4x^3 + 9x + 12x^2 - 27\\ &= 4x^4 - 4x^3 + 3x^2 + 9x - 27\end{aligned}$$

Then subtract: $(4x^4 + 8x^3 - 7x^2 + 7x - 3) - (4x^4 - 4x^3 + 3x^2 + 9x - 27)$

$$\begin{aligned}&= 4x^4 + 8x^3 - 7x^2 + 7x - 3 - 4x^4 + 4x^3 - 3x^2 - 9x + 27\\ &= 12x^3 - 10x^2 - 2x + 24\\ &= 2(6x^3 - 5x^2 - x + 12)\end{aligned}$$

Note: Although each separate product gives a quartic function, the resulting polynomial is a cubic, since the coefficient of x^4 is 0.

When multiplying out brackets it is sometimes necessary to consider the product of three or more polynomials. In such cases a step-by-step approach is appropriate, as illustrated in the next two examples.

Example 6.6

Multiply out the brackets in $(t-3)(2t^2-t+5)(t^3+7t^2-3t-4)$.

Solution

Firstly expand the first pair of brackets.

$$\begin{aligned}(t-3)(2t^2-t+5) &= t(2t^2-t+5)-3(2t^2-t+5)\\ &= 2t^3-t^2+5t-6t^2+3t-15\\ &= 2t^3-7t^2+8t-15\end{aligned}$$

Then multiply this result by the remaining polynomial.

$$\begin{aligned}&(2t^3-7t^2+8t-15)(t^3+7t^2-3t-4)\\ &= 2t^3(t^3+7t^2-3t-4)-7t^2(t^3+7t^2-3t-4)+8t(t^3+7t^2-3t-4)\\ &\quad -15(t^3+7t^2-3t-4)\\ &= 2t^6+14t^5-6t^4-8t^3-7t^5-49t^4+21t^3+28t^2+8t^4+56t^3-24t^2\\ &\quad -32t-15t^3-105t^2+45t+60\\ &= 2t^6+7t^5-47t^4+54t^3-101t^2+13t+60\end{aligned}$$

Note: The degree of the resulting polynomial is $6 = 1 + 2 + 3$, the sum of the degrees of the polynomials in the original product.

Example 6.7

Expand $(a+bx)^4$, *where* a *and* b *are constants.*

Solution

A useful strategy is to build up the product piecewise:

$$\begin{aligned}(a+bx)^2 &= (a+bx)(a+bx) = a(a+bx)+bx(a+bx)\\ &= a^2+abx+abx+b^2x^2\\ &= a^2+2abx+b^2x^2\end{aligned}$$

$$\begin{aligned}(a+bx)^3 &= (a+bx)(a+bx)^2 = (a+bx)(a^2+2abx+b^2x^2)\\ &= a(a^2+2abx+b^2x^2)+bx(a^2+2abx+b^2x^2)\\ &= a^3+2a^2bx+ab^2x^2+a^2bx+2ab^2x^2+b^3x^3\\ &= a^3+3a^2bx+3ab^2x^2+b^3x^3\end{aligned}$$

$$\begin{aligned}(a+bx)^4 &= (a+bx)(a+bx)^3 = (a+bx)(a^3+3a^2bx+3ab^2x^2+b^3x^3)\\ &= a(a^3+3a^2bx+3ab^2x^2+b^3x^3)+bx(a^3+3a^2bx+3ab^2x^2+b^3x^3)\\ &= a^4+3a^3bx+3a^2b^2x^2+ab^3x^3+a^3bx+3a^2b^2x^2+3ab^3x^3+b^4x^4\\ &= a^4+4a^3bx+6a^2b^2x^2+4ab^3x^3+b^4x^4\end{aligned}$$

Note: This method could be extended to expand $(a+bx)^n$ for $n = 5, 6, 7, \ldots$.

An alternative approach in this example is possible by considering

$(a+bx)^4$ as $[(a+bx)^2]^2$:

$[(a+bx)^2]^2 = (a^2+2abx+b^2x^2)(a^2+2abx+b^2x^2)$

which gives the identical result when expanded.

EXERCISES

6.2 CLASSWORK

1 For each pair of polynomials $f(x)$ and $g(x)$:

i) simplify $f(x) + g(x)$ and $f(x) - g(x)$,

ii) illustrate your answers graphically.

a) $f(x) = x^2 + 5x - 8$ $\quad g(x) = x^2 - x + 5$

b) $f(x) = 2x^3 + x^2 - 4x + 9$ $\quad g(x) = 15 - x + 3x^2 - 2x^3$

c) $f(x) = 3x^4 + 5x^2 - 8$ $\quad g(x) = x^3 - 9x$

d) $f(x) = 5x^3 - x + 8$ $\quad g(x) = x^5 - x^3 + x^2 - 3$

2 Expand these, stating the degree of the resulting polynomial.

a) $(3x+2)(x^2+x+5)$ b) $(5x-1)(2x^2-3x+1)$
c) $(x^2+3x+5)(x^2+2x+8)$ d) $(t-5)(2t^3+4t^2-t+6)$
e) $(t^2+3t-5)(t^3-5t^2+2t-4)$ f) $(2x-1)(x^2-x+7)(x^2+5x+3)$

3 Simplify these.

a) $(2x-5)(3x^2-2x+7)+(x^2+x+8)(7x-1)$
b) $(3t^2+4t-2)(4t^2-5t+1)-(2t^2-5)(6t^2-3t+5)$
c) $(x+2)(4x-3)(2x+7)-(2x-5)^2(3x+2)$

4 Functions f, g and h are defined by:

$f(x)=2x+3$ $g(x)=10-x^2$ $h(x)=x^3+5x^2-3$

Simplify the following, and in each case:
i) state the degree of the resulting polynomial,
ii) give the coefficient of x^3.

a) $h(x)-g(x)+f(x)$ b) $3f(x)+2g(x)$ c) $f(x)\times g(x)$
d) $f(x)\times g(x)\times h(x)$ e) $f(x)\times h(x)-[g(x)]^2$ f) $[f(x)]^4$

EXERCISES

6.2 HOMEWORK

1 For each pair of polynomials $f(x)$ and $g(x)$:
i) simplify $f(x)+g(x)$ and $f(x)-g(x)$,
ii) illustrate your answers graphically.

a) $f(x)=2x^2+3x$ $g(x)=2x^2-4$
b) $f(x)=4-6x+2x^3$ $g(x)=x^3+x^2-4$
c) $f(x)=x^4-3x^3+6$ $g(x)=x^3-2x^2+4$
d) $f(x)=x^2+4x+4$ $g(x)=x^5-3x^2-4x+4$

2 Expand these, stating the degree of the resulting polynomial.

a) $(x^2-2)(x^2+1)$ b) $(x-3)(2x^2-4x-3)$
c) $(x^2-4x+3)(2x^2-x+2)$ d) $(2-4x-3x^3)(6x^2-3x+2)$
e) $(x^5+2x-1)(x^3-3x^2+4x)$ f) $(2x+5)(x^3-3x^2+4)(2x^2-x-2)$

3 Simplify these.

a) $(2x-1)(x^2+4)+(x-1)(x^2+1)$
b) $(2x-1)(x^2+4)-[x(2x^2-x)+4(x-1)]$
c) $(x^2+6)^2-(x+3)(x^2+2)-(x-1)$

4 Functions f, g and h are defined by:
$f(x)=3x-2$ $g(x)=x^2+9$ $h(x)=x^3+3x^2$
Simplify the following, and in each case:
i) state the degree of the resulting polynomial,
ii) give the coefficient of x^2.

a) $h(x)+g(x)$ b) $f(x)-g(x)$ c) $3h(x)-2f(x)$
d) $f(x)\times g(x)$ e) $g(x)\times 2h(x)$ f) $[h(x)]^2-[g(x)]^3$

FACTORISING AND THE FACTOR THEOREM

Exploration 6.5

Finding where the graph crosses the x-axis

Consider the function $f(x)=2x^2-11x+12$

Sketch the graph of $y=f(x)$ by considering the intersection of the curve with the axes.

Roots of an equation

The graph crosses the y-axis when $x = 0 \Rightarrow y = 12$
$\Rightarrow$ point of intersection is (0, 12).

The graph crosses the x-axis when $y = 0$, i.e. $f(x) = 0$

$2x^2 - 11x + 12 = 0$
$(2x - 3)(x - 4) = 0$ (factorising)
$x = \frac{3}{2} \Rightarrow f(\frac{3}{2}) = 0$

or $x = 4 \Rightarrow f(4) = 0$

By symmetry we deduce that the line of symmetry is given by

$$x = 2.75, \text{ since } \frac{1.5 + 4}{2} = 2.75.$$

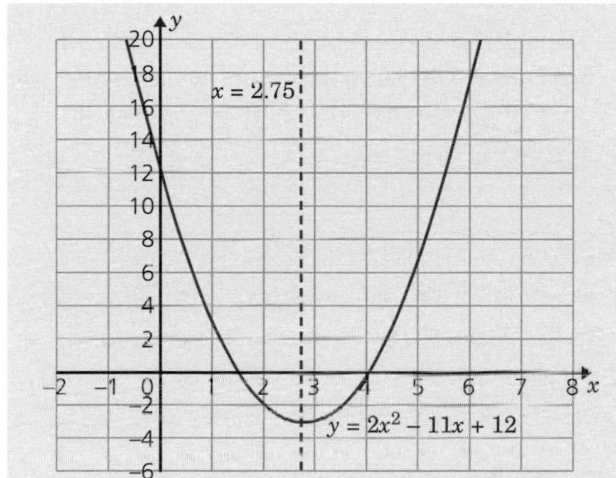

We now have sufficient information to sketch the graph of $y = f(x)$.

Reversing the above argument for finding the x-values where $f(x) = 0$:

$f(4) = 0 \Rightarrow x - 4$ is a factor of $f(x)$ and
$f(\frac{3}{2}) = 0 \Rightarrow 2x - 3$ is a factor of $f(x)$.

Looked at in this way, by locating where $f(x) = 0$ we can deduce a factor of the function $f(x)$.

This result is expressed formally as the factor theorem, which follows.

The factor theorem

For any polynomial function $f(x)$: $f(a) = 0 \Leftrightarrow x - a$ is a factor
or, more generally: $f(\frac{a}{b}) = 0 \Leftrightarrow bx - a$ is a factor

Exploration 6.6

The factor theorem

This property is especially useful when factorising polynomials of degree 3 or higher. In Exploration 6.4 we discovered that $(5x + 3)(x^2 + 3x + 2) = 5x^3 + 18x^2 + 19x + 6 = f(x)$.

- Since $5x+3$ is a factor of the cubic function, what is the value of $f(-\frac{3}{5})$?
- Can you factorise the quadratic function $x^2 + 3x + 2$?
- Find two further values of a such that $f(a) = 0$.
- Sketch the graph of $y = f(x)$.

Using the factor theorem

$f(-\frac{3}{5}) = f(-0.6) = 5 \times (-0.6)^3 + 18\,(-0.6)^2 + 19\,(-0.6) + 6 = 0$

i.e. $f(-\frac{3}{5}) = 0 \Leftrightarrow 5x + 3$ is a factor.

Factorising $x^2 + 3x + 2$ gives $(x + 1)(x + 2)$, from which we may deduce $f(-1)$ and $f(-2) = 0$

i.e. $f(-1) = 0 \Leftrightarrow x + 1$ is a factor
$f(-2) = 0 \Leftrightarrow x + 2$ is a factor.

A full factorisation of the cubic function as a product of linear factors gives:

$$f(x) = 5x^3 + 18x^2 + 19x + 6 = (5x + 3)(x + 1)(x + 2)$$

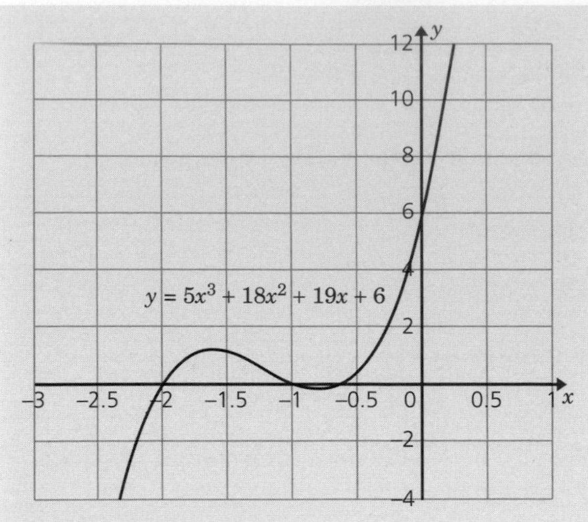

The graph of $y = f(x)$ crosses the y-axis at (0, 6) and the x-axis at (–2, 0), (–1, 0) and (–0.6, 0). This should give enough information to sketch the graph.

When attempting to factorise a polynomial of degree 3 or higher a useful strategy is:

1 By trial find a value a such that $f(a) = 0$.

2 Take $(x - a)$ out as a factor to give $f(x) = (x - a)g(x)$ where $g(x)$ is a polynomial of degree 1 less than that of $f(x)$.

3 Repeat the process on $g(x)$ if the degree of $g(x)$ is greater than 2. Otherwise factorise the remaining quadratic function, if possible, in the usual way.

Example 6.8

Factorise as fully as possible $f(x) = x^3 + 6x^2 + 3x - 10$.

Solution

By inspection $f(1) = 1^3 + 6 \times 1^2 + 3 \times 1 - 10 = 0 \Rightarrow x - 1$ *is a factor.*
Thus $f(x) = (x - 1)g(x)$ *where* $g(x)$ *is a quadratic function to be found.*

$$x^3 + 6x^2 + 3x - 10 \equiv (x - 1)(px^2 + qx + r)$$

From our experience of multiplying out polynomials we have discovered that there is only one way to produce the term in x^3.

$$x^3 + 6x^2 + 3x - 10 \equiv (x - 1)(px^2 + qx + r)$$

i.e. $x^3 \equiv x \times px^2 = px^3 \Rightarrow p = 1$

Similarly there is just one way to produce the constant term:

$$x^3 + 6x^2 + 3x - 10 \equiv (x - 1)(px^2 + qx + r)$$

i.e. $-10 \equiv -1 \times r \Rightarrow r = 10$

So far we have:

$$x^3 + 6x^2 + 3x - 10 \equiv (x - 1)(x^2 + qx + 10)$$

The term in, say, $6x^2$ *may be produced from a pair of products as shown.*

i.e. $6x^2 \equiv x \times qx - 1 \times x^2 \Rightarrow 6x^2 \equiv qx^2 - x^2 \Rightarrow q = 7$
This completes the picture.

$$\overbrace{x^3 + 6x^2 + 3x - 10}^{f(x)} \equiv (x - 1)\overbrace{(x^2 + 7x + 10)}^{g(x)}$$

The function $g(x)$ *may be factorised in the usual way, hence:*

$$x^3 + 6x^2 + 3x - 10 \equiv (x - 1)(x + 2)(x + 5)$$

Finally, check the two linear factors found from $g(x)$ *by using the factor theorem.*

$f(-2) = 0 \Leftrightarrow x + 2$ *is a factor*
$f(-5) = 0 \Leftrightarrow x + 5$ *is a factor*
$f(-2) = (-2)^3 + 6 \times (-2)^2 + 3 \times (-2) - 10 = -8 + 24 - 6 - 10 = 0$
$f(-5) = (-5)^3 + 6 \times (-5)^2 + 3 \times (-5) - 10 = -125 + 150 - 15 - 10 = 0$

Example 6.9

For the function $f(x) = x^4 - 2x^3 - 5x^2 + 6x + 8$*:*

a) *find* $f(2)$ *and so deduce a linear factor,*
b) *express* $f(x)$ *as a product of a linear and a cubic function,*
c) *factorise the cubic function as a product a linear and a quadratic function,*
d) *deduce that the quadratic function cannot be factorised and so factorise* $f(x)$ *as fully as you can.*

Solution

a) $f(2) = 2^4 - 2 \times 2^3 - 5 \times 2^2 + 6 \times 2 + 8 = 16 - 16 - 20 + 12 + 8 = 0$

$\Rightarrow$ $(x - 2)$ *is a factor of* $f(x)$

$\Rightarrow$ $f(x) \equiv (x - 2)\,g(x)$

b) *To find the exact form of* $g(x)$*, let:*

$$x^4 - 2x^3 - 5x^2 + 6x + 8 \equiv (x - 2)(px^3 + qx^2 + rx + s)$$

Comparing terms in x^4*:* $x^4 \equiv x \times px^3 = px^4 \Rightarrow p = 1.$

Comparing constants: $8 = (-2) \times s \Rightarrow s = -4$

Thus so far: $x^4 - 2x^3 - 5x^2 + 6x + 8 \equiv (x - 2)(x^3 + qx^2 + rx - 4)$

Comparing terms in x^3*:* $-2x^3 \equiv -2x^3 + qx^3 \Rightarrow q = 0$

Comparing terms in x*:* $6x \equiv -2rx - 4x \Rightarrow r = -5$

Therefore: $x^4 - 2x^3 - 5x^2 + 6x + 8 \equiv (x - 2)(x^3 - 5x - 4)$

c) *By trial,* $g(-1) = 0 \Rightarrow x + 1$ *is a factor of* $g(x)$

$\Rightarrow$ $g(x) \equiv (x + 1)h(x)$

To find the exact form of $h(x)$*, let:*

$$x^3 - 5x - 4 \equiv (x + 1)(px^2 + qx + r)$$

Comparing terms in x^3*:* $x^3 = x \times px^2 \Rightarrow p = 1$

Comparing constants: $-4 = 1 \times r \Rightarrow r = -4$

Thus, so far: $x^3 - 5x - 4 = (x + 1)(x^2 + qx - 4)$

Comparing terms in x*:* $-5x \equiv 1 \times qx - 4x \Rightarrow q = -1$

Therefore: $(x^3 - 5x - 4) \equiv (x + 1)(x^2 - x - 4)$

d) *The function* $h(x) \equiv x^2 - x^2 - 4$ *cannot be factorised, hence in fully factorised form:*

$$x^4 - 2x^3 - 5x^2 + 6x + 8 \equiv (x - 2)(x + 1)(x^2 - x - 4)$$

EXERCISES

6.3 CLASSWORK

Factorise the following functions as fully as possible.

1 $x^3 - 2x^2 - 11x + 12$

2 $2x^3 - 7x^2 - 17x + 10$

3 $x^3 - 7x + 6$

4 $x^3 - 3x^2 + 4$

5 $3x^3 + 2x^2 - 19x + 6$

6 $x^4 + 2x^3 - 13x^2 - 14x + 24$

7 $4x^4 + 4x^3 - 43x^2 - 22x + 21$

8 $5x^4 + 13x^3 - 51x^2 - 82x + 40$

EXERCISES

6.3 HOMEWORK

Factorise the following functions as fully as possible.

1 $x^3 - 6x^2 + 11x - 6$

2 $2x^3 - x^2 + 2x - 1$

3 $4x^3 + 12x^2 - x - 3$

4 $x^3 + 4x - 5$

5 $x^4 + x^3 + x + 1$

6 $3x^4 - 8x^3 + 9x^2 - 32x - 12$

POLYNOMIAL EQUATIONS AND INEQUALITIES

Exploration 6.7

Cubic functions

A cubic function is given by:

$f(x) = 2x^3 - 5x^2 - 4x + 3$

- Without using a graph plotter, find the coordinates of the points of intersection of the curve $y = f(x)$ and the axes and hence **sketch** the curve.

The factor theorem and cubic functions – and above

Identifying where the curve intersects with the y-axis is straightforward:

$f(0) = 3 \Rightarrow$ curve crosses y-axis at $(0, 3)$

To find where the curve intersects with the x-axis we need to find x-values such that $f(x) = 0$, i.e. solve the equation:

$2x^3 - 5x^2 - 4x + 3 = 0$

The first step in solving the equation is to see if $f(x)$ will factorise. By trial we see that:

$f(-1) = 2(-1)^3 - 5(-1)^2 - 4(-1) + 3 = -2 - 5 + 4 + 3 = 0$

Using the factor theorem, $(x + 1)$ must be a factor of $f(x)$, i.e. $f(x) = (x + 1)\, g(x)$ where $g(x)$ is a quadratic function.

Setting this out as before, let $g(x) = px^2 + qx + r$, then:

$2x^3 - 5x^2 - 4x + 3 \equiv (x + 1)(px^2 + qx + r)$

comparing terms in x^3: $2x^3 \equiv x \times px^2 \Rightarrow p = 2$

comparing constants: $3 \equiv 1 \times r \Rightarrow r = 3$

Substituting values for p and r gives the equivalence:

$2x^3 - 5x^2 - 4x + 3 \equiv (x + 1)(2x^2 + qx + 3)$

and comparing terms in, say, x:

$-4x \equiv 3x + qx$

$\Rightarrow -4 = 3 + q$

$\Rightarrow q = -7$

This gives:

$$\overbrace{2x^3 - 5x^2 - 4x + 3}^{f(x)} \equiv (x + 1)\overbrace{(2x^2 - 7x + 3)}^{g(x)}$$

Factorising $g(x)$ gives the complete factorisation:

$2x^3 - 5x^2 - 4x + 3 \equiv (x + 1)(2x - 1)(x - 3)$

Thus $f(x) = 0 \Rightarrow (x + 1)(2x - 1)(x - 3) = 0$

$\Rightarrow x = 1,\ x = \frac{1}{2}$ or $x = 3$

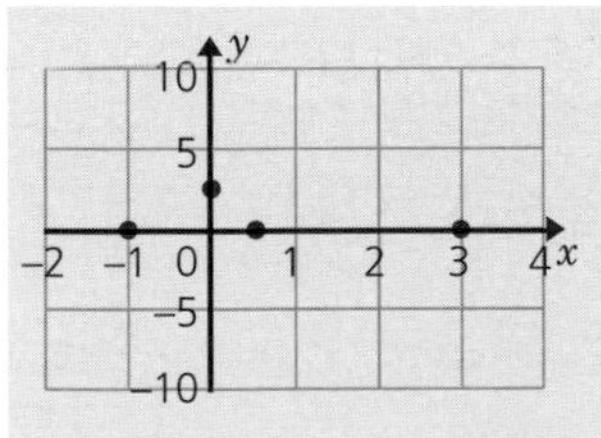

We now know that the curve $y = f(x)$ intersects the x-axis at $(-1, 0)$, $(\frac{1}{2}, 0)$ and $(3, 0)$. Taken with the fact that the curve intersects the y-axis at $(0, 3)$, four points on the curve have so far been identified.

To enable a sketch to be made it just remains to find out how the curve behaves between $(-1, 0)$ and $(\frac{1}{2}, 0)$ and between $(\frac{1}{2}, 0)$ and $(3, 0)$, and then sketch a typical cubic curve to fit the data. We already know that the graph intersects the y-axis at $(0, 3)$. By substituting in, say, $x = 1$ we can find the behaviour of the curve between $(\frac{1}{2}, 0)$ and $(3, 0)$:

$f(1) = 2(1)^3 - 5(1)^2 - 4(1) + 3 = -4$

which means that the curve also passes through $(1, -4)$.

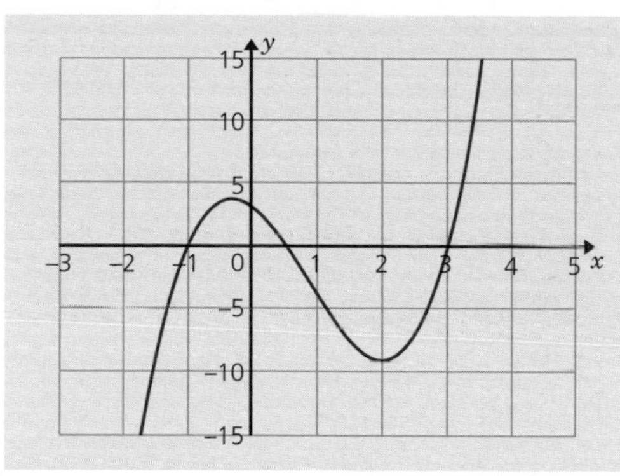

A complete picture is obtained by continuing the graph below $x = -1$ and above $x = 3$. We know roughly where the maximum and minimum points occur and that there are no more.

From the graph we may also deduce that:
$f(x) > 0$ provided $-1 < x < 0.5$ or $x > 3$ and
$f(x) < 0$ provided $x < -1$ or $0.5 < x < 3$.

By a combination of factorising and graph sketching we can now solve both equations and inequalities for suitable polynomial functions.

Example 6.10

A quartic function is given as $f(x) = x^4 + 2x^3 - 13x^2 - 14x + 24$.

a) *Solve the equation* $f(x) = 0$. **b)** *Sketch the graph of* $y = f(x)$.
c) *Solve the inequality* $f(x) \le 0$.

Solution

a) *By inspection and use of the factor theorem we may deduce that:*

$$x^4 + 2x^3 - 13x^2 - 14x + 24 \equiv (x - 1)(x + 2)(x - 3)(x + 4)$$

since $f(1) = 0$, $f(-2) = 0$, $f(3) = 0$ *and* $f(-4) = 0$.
We may find any one of the linear factors and proceed as before. Alternatively, if we spot two factors then a short-cut is possible. Suppose we find that $f(1) = 0$ *and* $f(-2) = 0$, *then not only are* $(x - 1)$ *and* $(x + 2)$ *linear factors, but also* $(x - 1)(x + 2) = x^2 + x - 2$ *is a quadratic factor, i.e.*

$$x^4 + 2x^3 - 13x^2 - 14x + 24 \equiv (x^2 + x - 2)(px^2 + qx + r)$$

Comparing terms in x^4*:* $x^4 \equiv x^2 \times px^2 \Rightarrow p = 1$
Comparing constants: $24 = -2 \times r \Rightarrow r = -12$
Thus so far we have: $x^4 + 2x^3 - 13x^2 - 14x + 24$
$\equiv (x^2 + x - 2)(x^2 + qx - 12)$
Comparing terms in x: $-14x \equiv -12x - 2qx$
$\Rightarrow -14 = -12 - 2q$
$\Rightarrow q = 1$
$\Rightarrow x^4 + 2x^3 - 13x^2 - 14x + 24$
$\equiv (x^2 + x - 2)(x^2 + x - 12)$

Since $x^2 + x - 12$ *factorises to give* $(x - 3)(x + 4)$, *in fully factorised form:*

$$f(x) = (x - 1)(x + 2)(x - 3)(x + 4)$$

Thus $f(x) = 0$ *when* $x = 1$, $x = -2$, $x = 3$ *or* $x = -4$.

b) *We now know that the curve* $y = f(x)$ *crosses the axes at (0, 24) and(–4, 0), (–2, 0), (1, 0), (3, 0). We can test some intermediate values of* $f(x)$ *to see how the graph behaves.*

$$f(-3) = (-3)^4 + 2(-3)^3 - 13(-3)^2 - 14(-3) + 24$$
$$= 81 - 54 - 117 + 42 + 24$$
$$= -24$$
$$f(0) = 24 \text{ (by inspection)}$$
$$f(2) = 2^4 + 2(2)^3 - 13(2)^2 - 14(2) + 24$$
$$= 16 + 16 - 52 - 28 + 24$$
$$= -24$$

We now have sufficient information to complete a sketch.

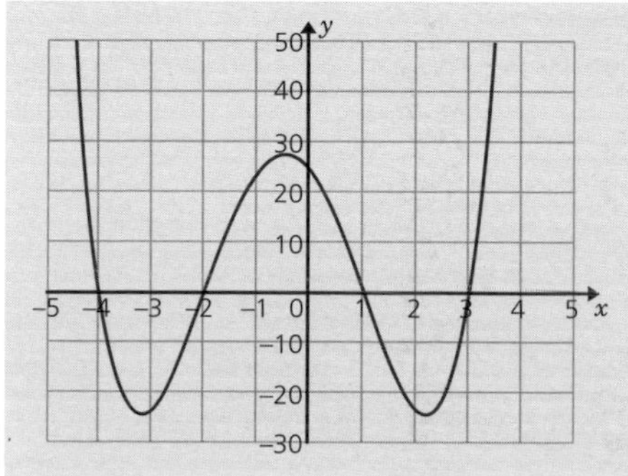

c) *The curve lies below the* x*-axis for* $-4 < x < -2$ *and* $1 < x < 3$, *hence the solution of the inequality* $f(x) \le 0$ *is* $\{x : -4 \le x \le -2 \text{ or } 1 \le x \le 3\}$.

Example 6.11

The sketch shows a cubic function $f(x)$*, which can be expressed as:*

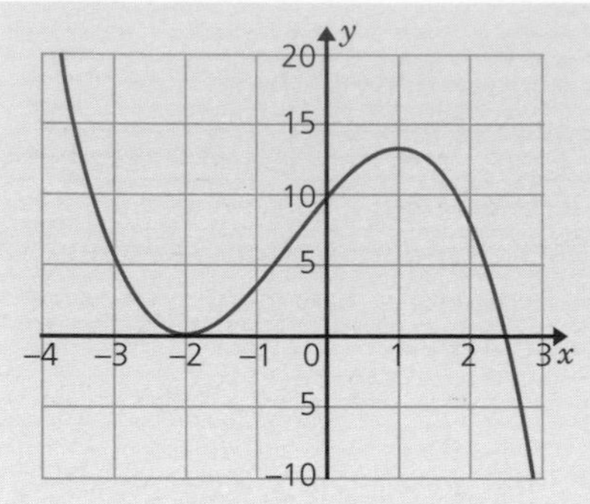

$f(x) = k(x + l)^2(mx + n)$ *where* k, l, m *and* n *are constants.*

a) *By considering the coordinates of the points where the graph meets the axes, find the values of the constants.*
b) *Express* $f(x)$ *in the form* $a + bx + cx^2 + dx^3$.
c) *Solve the inequality* $f(x) > 0$.

Solution

a) *Since the curve just touches the* x*-axis at* $x = -2$ *and crosses it at* $x = 2.5$*, the equation* $f(x) = 0$ *has a* ***repeated*** *root at* $x = -2$ *and a single root at* $x = 2.5$.
From the factor theorem:
$f(-2) = 0 \Rightarrow x + 2$ *is a factor*
$f(2.5) = 0 \Rightarrow 2x - 5$ *is a factor*

The repeated root, $x = -2$*, means that* $(x + 2)$ *is a repeated factor, therefore we can see that in the expression:*

$f(x) = k(x + l)^2(mx - n)$

$l = 2$, $m = 2$ *and* $n = 5$*, thus:* $f(x) = k(x + 2)^2(2x - 5)$

Since the curve crosses the y*-axis at (0, 10) this fact may be used to determine the value of* k.

$$\begin{aligned} f(0) = k(0 + 2)^2(2 \times 0 - 5) &= 10 \\ \Rightarrow \quad k \times 4 \times (-5) &= 10 \\ \Rightarrow \quad -20k &= 10 \\ \Rightarrow \quad k &= -0.5 \end{aligned}$$

b) *Expanding brackets:*

$$\begin{aligned} f(x) &= -0.5(x + 2)^2(2x - 5) = -0.5(x^2 + 4x + 4)(2x - 5) \\ &= -0.5(2x^3 + 3x^2 - 12x - 20) \\ &= 10 + 6x - 1.5x^2 - x^3 \end{aligned}$$

c) *The curve lies on or above the* x*-axis for* $x \le 2.5$*, so* $f(x) \ge 0$ *for* $x \le 2.5$. *However* $f(x) = 0$ *for* $x = -2$ *and* $x = 2.5$*, therefore the solution set for the inequality* $f(x) > 0$ *is* $\{x : x < 2.25;\ x \ne -2\}$.

Example 6.12

The function $f(x)$ *is given by:* $f(x) = x^3 + (3 - k)x^2 + (4 - 3k)x + 12$.

a) *Evaluate* $f(-3)$ *and hence write down a linear factor of* $f(x)$.
b) *Show that the corresponding quadratic factor is* $x^2 - kx + 4$.
c) *Solve the equation* $f(x) = 0$ *for* ***i)*** $k = 5$, ***ii)*** $k = 4$, ***iii)*** $k = 6$, ***iv)*** $k = 3$.

Solution

a) $f(-3) = (-3)^3 + (3 - k)(-3)^2 + (4 - 3k)(-3) + 12$

$$= -27 + 9(3 - k) - 3(4 - 3k) + 12 = -27 + 27 - 9k - 12 + 9k + 12$$
$$= 0$$

$\Rightarrow (x + 3)$ *is a factor of* $f(x)$.

b) *Let* $x^3 + (3 - k)x^2 + (4 - 3k)x + 12 \equiv (x + 3)(px^2 + qx + r)$

Comparing terms in x^3*:* $\quad x^3 \equiv x \times px^2 \Rightarrow p = 1$

Comparing constants: $\quad 12 \equiv 3 \times r \Rightarrow r = 4$

Thus so far we have: $\quad x^3 + (3 - k)x^2 + (4 - 3k)x + 12 \equiv (x + 3)(x^2 + qx + 4)$

Comparing terms in x^2*:* $\quad (3 - k)x^2 \equiv 3x^2 + qx^2$

$$\Rightarrow 3 - k = 3 + q$$
$$\Rightarrow q = -k$$

$\therefore$ *The quadratic factor is* $x^2 - kx + 4$.

c) $f(x) = 0 \Rightarrow (x + 3)(x^2 - kx + 4) = 0 \Rightarrow x + 3 = 0$ *or* $x^2 - kx + 4 = 0$
Thus $x = -3$ is a root, whichever value of k is chosen.

i) $k = 5 \Rightarrow x^2 - 5x + 4 = 0 \Rightarrow (x - 1)(x - 4) = 0$
$\Rightarrow x = 1$ *or* $x = 4$

ii) $k = 4 \Rightarrow x^2 - 4x + 4 = 0 \Rightarrow (x - 2)^2 = 0$
$\Rightarrow x = 2$

iii) $k = 6 \Rightarrow x^2 - 6x + 4 = 0$ *which cannot be solved by factorising.*
Using the formula: $x = \dfrac{6 \pm \sqrt{36 - 4 \times 1 \times 4}}{2} = \dfrac{6 \pm \sqrt{20}}{2}$
$\Rightarrow x = 0.76$ *or* $x = 5.24$

iv) $k = 3 \Rightarrow x^2 - 3x + 4 = 0$, *which cannot be solved by factorising.*
Using the formula: $x = \dfrac{3 \pm \sqrt{9 - 4 \times 1 \times 4}}{2} = \dfrac{3 \pm \sqrt{-7}}{2}$ *which does not give a real root.*

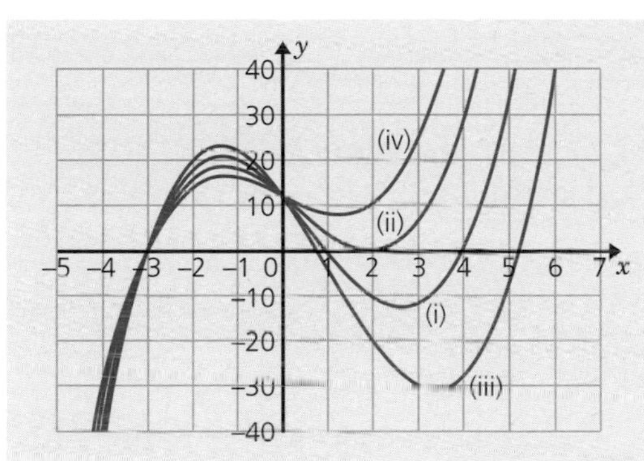

Note: Each value of k chosen above gives a different type of solution set for $f(x) = 0$:

i) $k = 5 \Rightarrow x = -3$, 1 or 4 (three distinct rational roots)
ii) $k = 4 \Rightarrow x = -3$ or 2 (three rational roots: two repeated and one distinct)
iii) $k = 6 \Rightarrow x = -3$, 0.76 or 5.24 (one rational root, two irrational roots)
iv) $k = 3 \Rightarrow x = -3$ (one rational root)

Inspecting where the various curves $y = f(x)$ intersect with the x-axis should help you appreciate the various possibilities.

EXERCISES

6.4 CLASSWORK

For each polynomial $f(x)$:

a) solve the equation $f(x) = 0$, **b)** sketch the graph of $y = f(x)$,
c) solve the inequalities $f(x) > 0$ and $f(x) \leq 0$.

1 $f(x) = (2x + 7)(x + 1)(2x - 1)(x - 3)$ **2** $f(x) = (x - 2)^3(2x + 5)$

3 $f(x) = x^3 + x^2 - 10x + 8$ **4** $f(x) = 5x^3 - 53x^2 + 155x - 75$

5 $f(x) = x^4 + 4x^3 - 20x^2 - 43x - 20$ **6** $f(x) = x^5 + 5x^4 + 2x^3 - 14x^2 - 3x + 9$

Find polynomial functions for which graphs are sketched below.

7

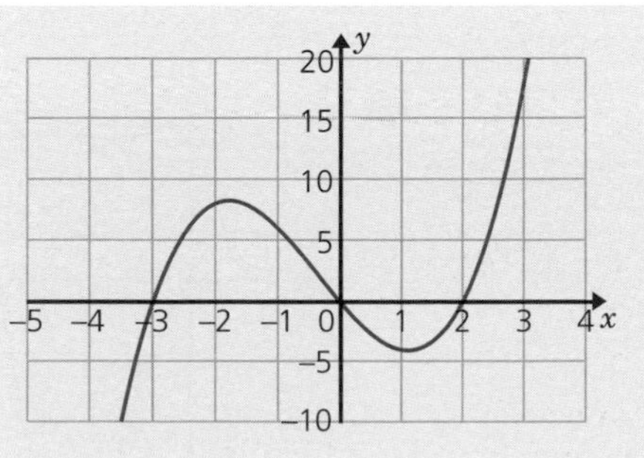

8

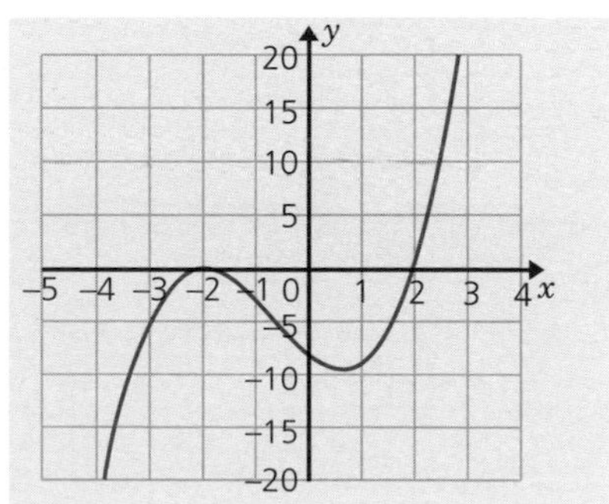

9

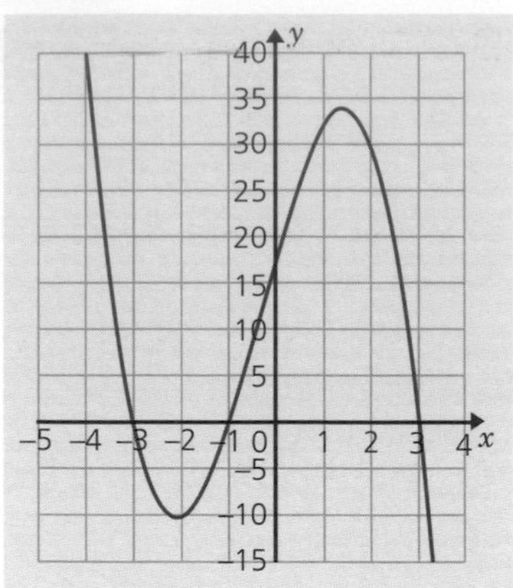

10

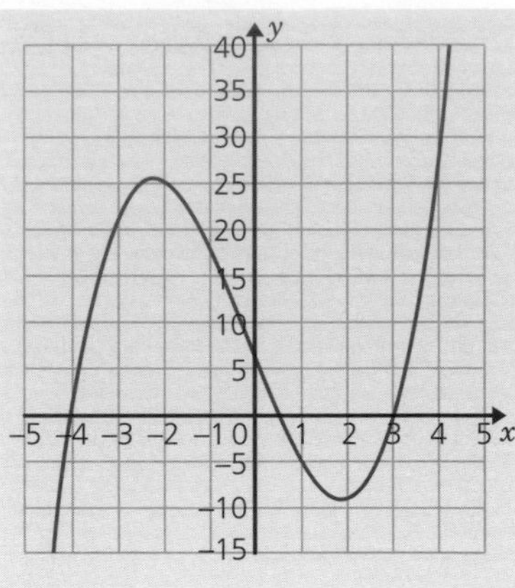

EXERCISES

6.4 HOMEWORK

For each polynomial $f(x)$:

a) solve the equation $f(x) = 0$, **b)** sketch the graph of $y = f(x)$,

c) solve the inequalities $f(x) < 0$ and $f(x) \geq 0$.

1 $f(x) = (x + 3)(2x + 3)(x - 2)$

2 $f(x) = (x + 4)(x^2 - 3x + 1)$

3 $f(x) = 3x^3 - 5x - 2$

4 $f(x) = (x + 1)(2x - 3)^3$

5 $f(x) = x^4 + 10x^3 + 35x^2 + 50x + 24$

6 $f(x) = 2x^4 + x^3 - 7x^2 - x + 5$

7 $f(x) = 6x + 6x^2 - 2x^3 - x^4 - 9$

8 $f(x) = 2x^5 + 5x^4 - 6x^3 - 19x^2 - 10x$

9 $f(x) = 3 - 7x + 5x^2 - x^3$

Find polynomial functions for which graphs are sketched below.

10

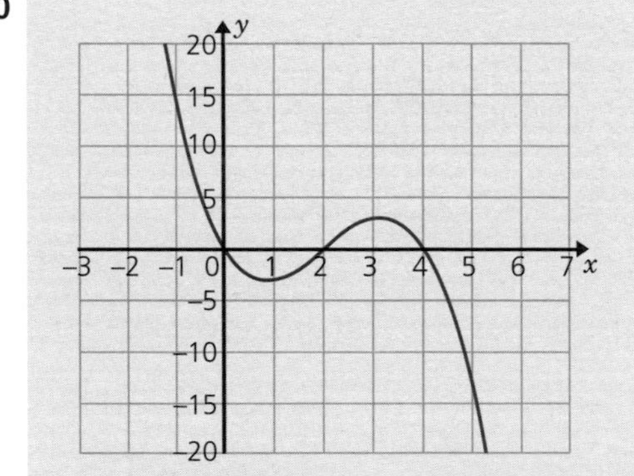

11

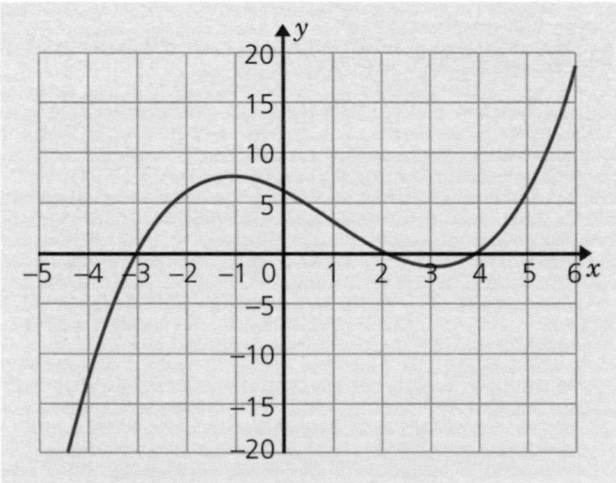

12

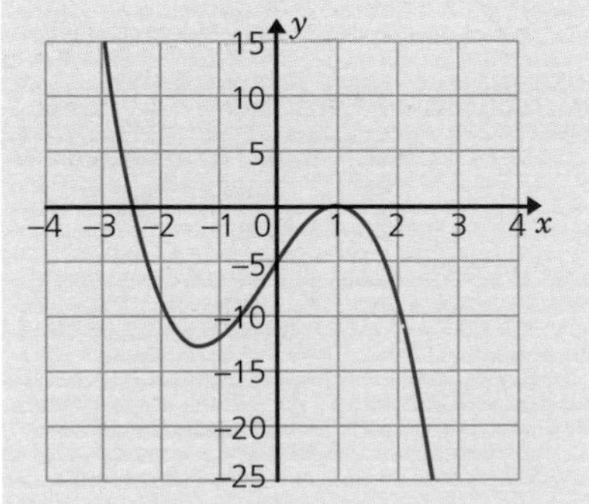

13

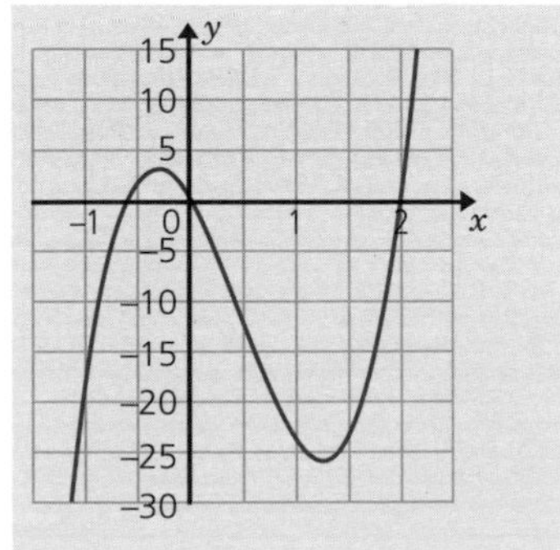

CONSOLIDATION EXERCISES FOR CHAPTER 6

1 $f(x) = x^4 + 3x^3 - 8x^2 - 22x - 24$

a) Verify that $x = 3$ and $x = -4$ are solutions of $f(x) = 0$.
b) Show that they are the only real solutions of $f(x) = 0$ and explain why.
c) Sketch the graph of $f(x)$.

2 Find a cubic polynomial, $f(x)$, such that $f(x) = 0$ at $x = 1$, $x = 2$ and $x = -1$ and the y-intercept is 10.

3 **a)** Given that $x = \frac{1}{2}$ is a root of $f(x) = 8x^3 + 4x^2 + kx + 15$, find the value of k.
b) Find all the roots of $f(x) = 0$.
c) Sketch a graph of $y = f(x)$, clearly indicating where the graph intersects the axes.

4 **a)** Write down an example of a polynomial in x of order 4.
b) In an experiment, Ama measures the value of s at different times, t. Her results are shown as the curve on the graph to the left.

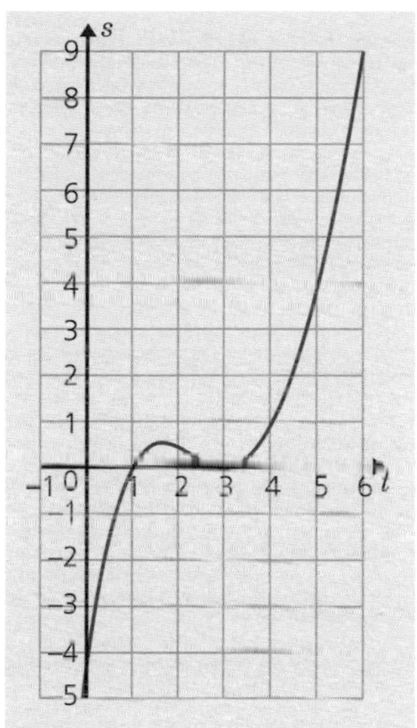

Ama believes that it is possible to model s as a polynomial in t.
i) Explain why it is reasonable to think that the order of such a polynomial might be 3.
Ama proposes a model of the form $s = a(t - p)(t - q)^2$.
ii) Write down the points where the curve meets the coordinate axes and use them to find values for p, q and a.
iii) Compare the values obtained from the model with those on the graph when $t = 2$, 4 and 5, and comment on the quality of the model.
Ama proposes a refinement to the model making it into
$s = a(t - p)(t - q)^2 (1 - ht)$.
where a, p and t have the same values as before and h is a small positive constant. Ama chooses the value of h so that the model and the graph are in agreement when $t = 5$.
iv) Find the value of h.

(MEI Specimen Paper Pure 1, 1994)

5 The function f is given by $f(x) = x^3 - 3x^2 - 2x + 6$.
a) Use the factor theorem to show that $(x - 3)$ is a factor of $f(x)$.
b) Write $f(x)$ in the form $(x - 3)(ax^2 + bx + c)$, giving the values a, b and c.
c) Hence solve $f(x) = 0$.
d) Using your solutions to $f(x) = 0$, write down the solutions of the equation $f(x + 1) = 0$.

(SMP 16–19 Specimen Paper 1, 1994)

6 Given that $(x - 2)$ and $(x + 2)$ are each factors of $x^3 + ax^2 + bx - 4$, find the values of a and b.
For these values of a and b, find the other linear factor of $x^3 + ax^2 + bx - 4$.

(UCLES (Modular) Specimen Paper, Question 5 1994)

7 Show that $(x - 2)$ is a factor of $x^3 - 9x^2 + 26x - 24$.
Find the set of values of x for which $x^3 - 9x^2 + 26x - 24 < 0$.

(AEB Specimen Paper 1, Question 7 1994)

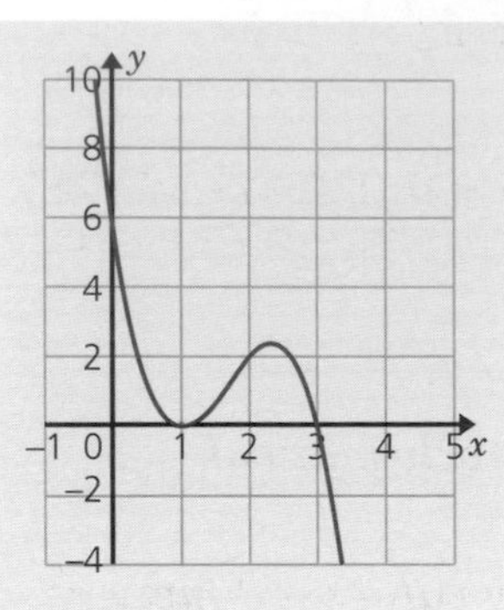

8 The graph shown left shows a curve drawn through a set of points which represents the results of several experiments. It is thought that the relationship between y and x may be modelled by a simple polynomial equation.

a) Explain, with reference to the number of turning points, why the polynomial is not a quadratic.
b) A possible form of the equation is $y = a(x - b)^2(x - c)$.
Write down the values of b and c. Substituting $x = 0$, calculate the value of a.
c) Find the values of the integers p, q, r and s when the equation is written in the form $y = px^3 + qx^2 + rx + s$.
d) A further experiment produces the result that $y = 1.9$ when $x = 2$. State, with reasons, whether you think this supports the model.

(MEI Pure 1, January 1995)

9 **a)** Show that $(x - 2)$ is a factor of $f(x) = x^3 + x^2 - 5x - 2$.
b) Hence, or otherwise, find the exact solutions of the equation $f(x) = 0$.

(EDEXCEL, Question 2, Paper 2, January 1999)

10 $f(x) \equiv 2x^3 + 5x^2 - 8x - 15$

a) Show that $(x + 3)$ is a factor of $f(x)$.
b) Hence factorise $f(x)$ as the product of a linear factor and a quadratic factor.
c) Find, to 2 decimal places, the two other values of x for which $f(x) = 0$.

(EDEXCEL, Specimen Paper P1, Question 1, 2000)

11 The cubic polynomial $3x^3 - 7x^2 - 18x - 8$ is denoted by $f(x)$. Use the factor theorem to show that $(x + 1)$ is a factor of $f(x)$.

Hence factorise $f(x)$ completely.

(OCR, Question 1, Specimen Paper 2, 2000)

Summary

Polynomial functions

- The **degree** of a polynomial function $f(x)$ is the index of the highest power of x with non-zero coefficient.
- A polynomial of degree 3 is a **cubic** function.
- The graph of a polynomial function of degree n has at most $n - 1$ maximum or minimum points.

Factorising polynomials

- Polynomial functions may be factorised using the factor theorem, which states:

  for any polynomial function $f(x)$, $f(a) = 0 \Leftrightarrow x - a$ is a factor or, more generally, $f(\frac{a}{b}) = 0 \Leftrightarrow bx - a$ is a factor.

Solving polynomial equations and inequalities

- Polynomial equations may be solved by factorising or decimal search.
- Polynomial inequalities may be solved by considering the intersection of the graph of $y = f(x)$ with the x-axis.

Differentiation 1

- *The rate of change of a function is an important concept in mathematics. The size of a rate of change tells us how quickly a quantity is changing.*

In this chapter we:

- *study differentiation, which is the mathematical representation of rate of change*
- *use differentiation to find stationary values of functions and solve optimisation problems.*

GRADIENTS AND GRADIENT FUNCTIONS

Exploration 7.1

Interpreting a distance–time graph

Alan and Bill were practising shots in ice-hockey. Alan hit the puck to Bill and Bill hit it back again.

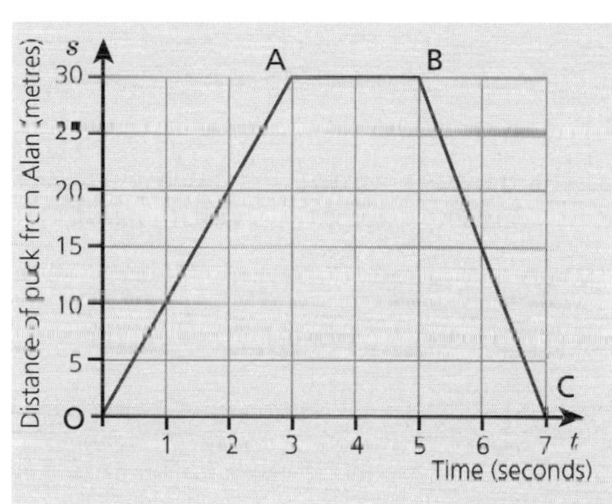

A displacement–time graph for these two shots is shown on the left (where s represents displacement in metres and t represents time in seconds).

- Who hit the puck with the greater velocity?
- How do you find the velocity of the puck for each hit?
- What happens to the puck between $t = 3$ and $t = 5$?
- What difference does the direction of slope of the lines make to:
  a) the velocity, **b)** the speed?
- What are the displacement–time equations for the three lines?

The meaning of the gradient

The velocity of the puck at any instant in time is given by the **gradient** of the displacement–time graph. Alan hit the puck to Bill with a velocity of $10\,\text{m}\,\text{s}^{-1}$ and Bill hit it back again with velocity $15\,\text{m}\,\text{s}^{-1}$. The gradient of the line for Alan's hit is **positive**, but the gradient of the line for Bill's hit is **negative**, indicating that the shots are hit in opposite directions. The gradient of the line between $t = 3$ and $t = 5$ is **zero**; the puck was at rest. It had a velocity of $0\,\text{m}\,\text{s}^{-1}$.

The gradient of a line measures **rate of change**. **Velocity** is the rate of change of **displacement** with respect to **time**. In this example all three velocities are **constant**, indicated by the straight-line graphs.

The displacement–time equations for the three lines are:

OA: $s = 10t$	AB: $s = 30$	BC: $s = 105 - 15t$
gradient = 10	gradient = 0	gradient = −15

You are more likely to meet a situation like the one in the next exploration.

Exploration 7.2

Find the velocity

Chris is a keen cricketer. He practises his fielding by throwing a cricket ball vertically upwards into the air and then catching it.

The displacement–time equation for one practice throw is given by $h = 20t - 5t^2$. By substituting for various values of t between $t = 0$ and $t = 4$ we can draw up the displacement–time graph shown here.

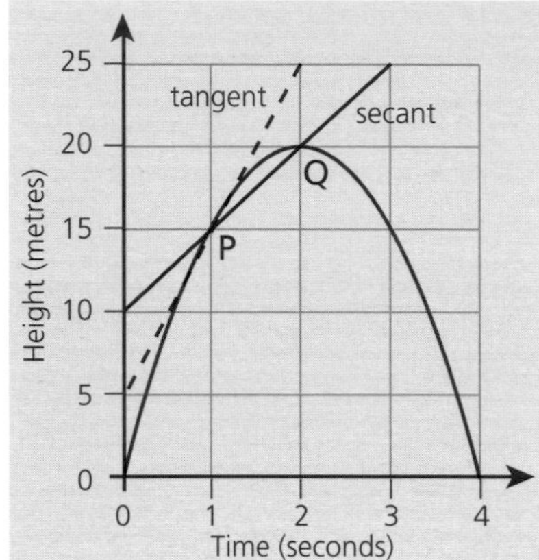

- What was the average velocity between $t = 1$ and $t = 2$?
- What was the average velocity between $t = 1$ and $t = 1.1$?
- What was the average velocity between $t = 1$ and $t = 1.01$?
- What do you think the instantaneous velocity of the ball is at $t = 1$?

Cricket ball throw

Instantaneous velocity

From the graph we can see that the average velocity of the cricket ball between $t = 1$ and $t = 2$ is given by the gradient of the **secant** passing through points P and Q: i.e. $\frac{20-15}{2-1} = 5 \text{ m s}^{-1}$.
Similarly the average velocity of the cricket ball between $t = 1$ and $t = 1.1$ is given by the gradient: $\frac{15.95-15}{1.1-1} = 9.5 \text{ m s}^{-1}$
and the average velocity of the cricket ball between $t = 1$ and $t = 1.01$ is given by the gradient: $\frac{15.0995-15}{1.01-1} = 9.95 \text{ m s}^{-1}$.

If we continue to reduce the time interval by a factor of 10 each time we find the sequence of average velocities:

between $t = 1$ and $t = 2$	average velocity = 5 m s^{-1}
between $t = 1$ and $t = 1.1$	average velocity = 9.5 m s^{-1}
between $t = 1$ and $t = 1.01$	average velocity = 9.95 m s^{-1}
between $t = 1$ and $t = 1.001$	average velocity = 9.995 m s^{-1}
between $t = 1$ and $t = 1.0001$	average velocity = 9.9995 m s^{-1}
between $t = 1$ and $t = 1.000\,01$	average velocity = $9.999\,95 \text{ m s}^{-1}$.

The **instantaneous velocity** (or just the **velocity**) of the ball at $t = 1$ is defined as the gradient of the **tangent** to the displacement–time curve at the point (1, 15). Numerically, this is the limit of the sequence of average velocities between $t = 1$ and $t = 1 + h$ as $h \to 0$.

By inspection, the limit of this sequence would seem to be 10, i.e. the velocity of the ball at $t = 1$ is 10 m s^{-1}.

By repeating this limiting process for various values of t we can build up a set of velocities, each corresponding to a different value of t.

Exploration 7.3

CALCULATOR ACTIVITY

Finding the velocity

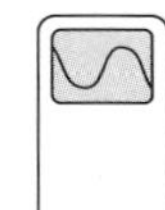

The flowchart outlines a program to find the gradient of a function as the limit of the gradient of secants.

Store X contains the value where the gradient is required.

Store G contains the gradient of the secant between X and $X + H$.

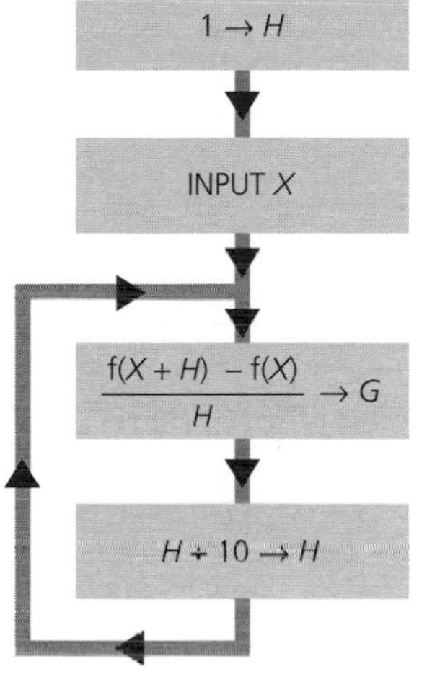

- Record values of G until a limit of the sequence is evident.

Before using the program you will need to store the function $20X - 5X^2$ as function f in the function memory.

- Use the computer program to find the velocity of the ball from $t = 0$ to $t = 4$ in steps of 0.2.
- Using suitable scales, copy the displacement–time graph and superimpose a velocity–time graph by plotting the (time, velocity) coordinates you have found.

Interpreting the results

You should obtain a graph like this.

The dotted line represents the velocity–time graph. By inspection we can find its equation. The graph is a straight line passing through (0, 20) with gradient –10. From this we deduce two important results.

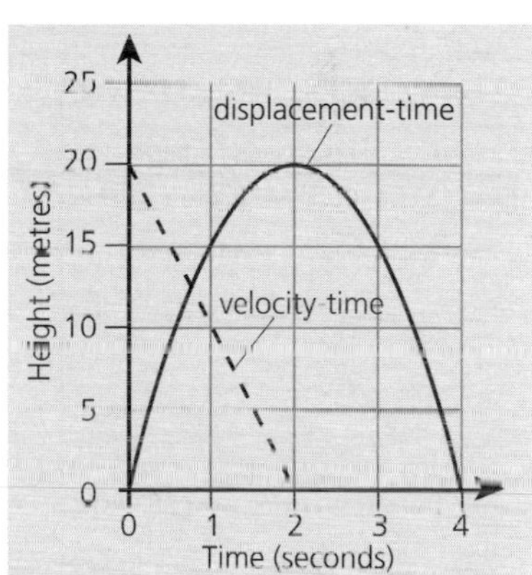

Cricket ball throw

Displacement–time equation	**Velocity–time equation**
$h = 20t - 5t^2$	$v = 20 - 10t$

So, given a displacement–time equation, we can find the corresponding velocity–time equation by plotting gradients systematically throughout a time interval.

More generally, given a function $y = f(x)$, by plotting gradients systematically over a suitable interval of x-values, we can deduce the **gradient function**, denoted by $f'(x)$, which measures the rate of change of y with respect to x.

Exploration 7.4

CALCULATOR ACTIVITY

The gradient function

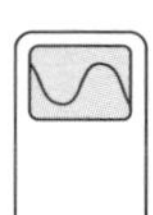

Use the Calculator activity in Exploration 7.3 to find the gradient of the function $y = x^3$ at each of the x-values –5, –4, –3, –2, –1, 0, 1, 2, 3, 4, 5.

- Firstly set function f to be x^3. Use the program repeatedly to obtain the following values.

x	$y = f(x)$	Gradient $= f'(x)$
–5	–125	75
–4	–64	48
–3	–27	27
–2	–8	12
–1	–1	3
0	0	0
1	1	3
2	8	12
3	27	27
4	64	48
5	125	75

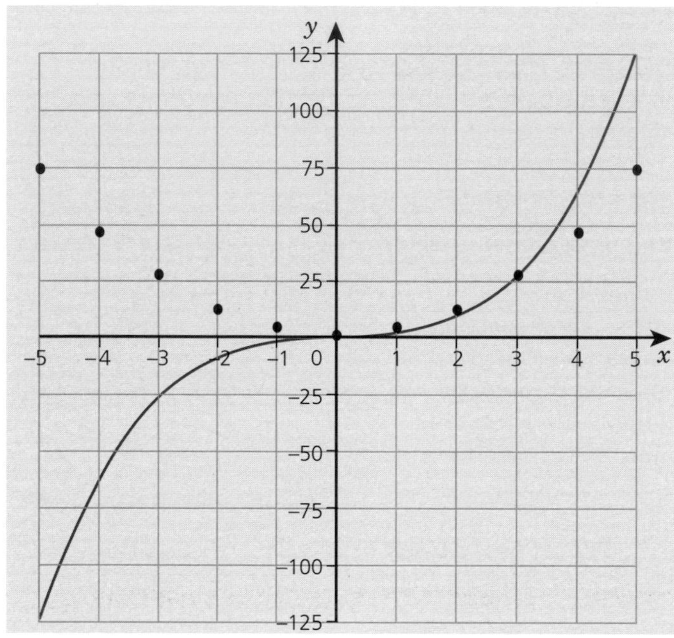

On a graphical calculator, choose a suitable range for x- and y-values.

x_{min}: –5 x_{max}: 5 x_{scl}: 1
y_{min}: –125 y_{max}: 125 y_{scl}: 25

- Draw the graph of $y = x^3$ and plot values of the gradient at each of the x-values.
- The plotted points suggest that the gradient function is a parabola through (0, 0) of the form

  $f'(x) = kx^2$

  for some constant k. By inspecting gradient values over the interval $-5 \leq x \leq 5$, deduce that $k = 3$, i.e. the gradient function for $y = x^3$ is given by $f'(x) = 3x^2$.

EXERCISES

7.1 CLASSWORK

For each of the following functions $f(x)$, adapt the Calculator activity in Exploration 7.3 to find the gradient of the function at the x-values given. Hence construct a table with headings:

x	$y = f(x)$	gradient $= f'(x)$

Complete it for the suggested values of x.

Sketch graphs of $f(x)$ and $f'(x)$ and so deduce an appropriate formula for $f'(x)$.

1 $f(x) = x^2$ $x = -3, -2, -1, 0, 1, 2, 3$

2 $f(x) = 5x^2$ $x = -3, -2, -1, 0, 1, 2, 3$

3 $f(x) = 2x^3$ $x = -3, -2, -1, 0, 1, 2, 3$

4 $f(x) = x^4$ $x = -3, -2, -1, 0, 1, 2, 3$

5 $f(x) = 3x^4$ $x = -3, -2, -1, 0, 1, 2, 3$

6 $f(x) = x^2 + x$ $x = -3, -2, -1, 0, 1, 2, 3$

7 $f(x) = x^2 + 5x$ $x = -6, -5, -4, -3, -2, -1, 0, 1$

8 $f(x) = x^3 - 3x + 2$ $x = -3, -2, -1, 0, 1, 2, 3$

7.1 HOMEWORK

For each of the following functions f(t) adapt the Calculator activity in Exploration 7.3 to find the gradient of the function at the t-values given. Hence construct a table with headings:

t	$s = f(t)$	gradient = $f'(t)$

Complete it for the suggested values of t.

1 $f(t) = t$ $t = -3, -2, -1, 0, 1, 2, 3$

2 $f(t) = -5t$ $t = -3, -2, -1, 0, 1, 2, 3$

3 $f(t) = 4t^2$ $t = -3, -2, -1, 0, 1, 2, 3$

4 $f(t) = t^5$ $t = -3, -2, -1, 0, 1, 2, 3$

5 $f(t) = t^2 - 2t + 1$ $t = -2, -1, 0, 1, 2, 3, 4$

6 $f(t) = t^2 - 3t$ $t = 0, 1, 2, 3, 4, 5, 6$

7 $f(t) = t^3 - 6t^2 + 12t - 8$ $t = -1, 0, 1, 2, 3, 4, 5$

8 $f(t) = t^2 - 8t$ $t = 5, 6, 7, 8, 9, 10, 11$

DIFFERENTIATION

The results from the previous section gave us several **gradient functions** (or **derivatives**), for example:

$f(x)$	x^2	x^3	x^4	$x^2 + 5x$	$x^2 - 7x + 10$
$f'(x)$	$2x$	$3x^2$	$4x^3$	$2x + 5$	$2x - 7$

Using these and similar results, we can see some important patterns which we can use to find a gradient function. This is called **differentiation**.

1 $f(x) = x^n \Rightarrow f'(x) = nx^{n-1}, n = 0, 1, 2, 3, 4, \ldots$

e.g. $f(x) = x^5 \Rightarrow f'(x) = 5x^4$

2 $f(x) = ax^n \Rightarrow f'(x) = anx^{n-1}$ where a is a constant

e.g. $f(x) = 5x^3 \Rightarrow f'(x) = 5 \times 3x^2 = 15x^2$

3 The derivative of a sum (or difference) is the sum (or difference) of the derivatives.

e.g. $f(x) = x^3 - 5x + 10 \Rightarrow f'(x) = 3x^2 - 5$

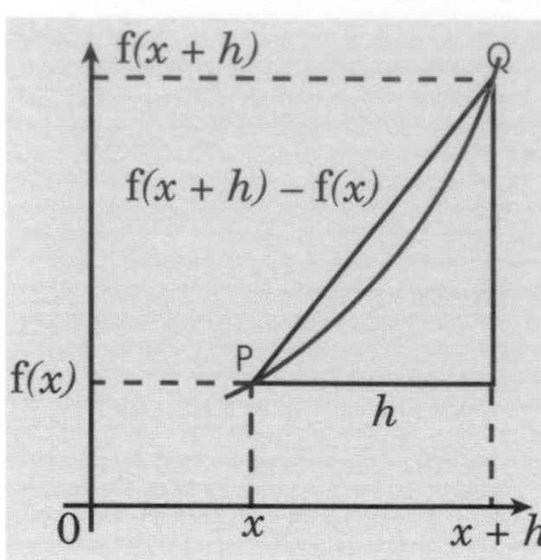

Definition

A formal definition of the gradient function $f'(x)$ is given by:

$f'(x)$ is the limit of $\dfrac{f(x+h)-f(x)}{h}$ as $h \to 0$.

Until now we have used function notation:

$f(x)$ for the original function $\qquad$ $f'(x)$ for the gradient function.

The gradient function (or derivative) is also represented by $\dfrac{dy}{dx}$, which is not a fraction, but a single quantity.

$$y = f(x) \Rightarrow \frac{dy}{dx} = f'(x)$$

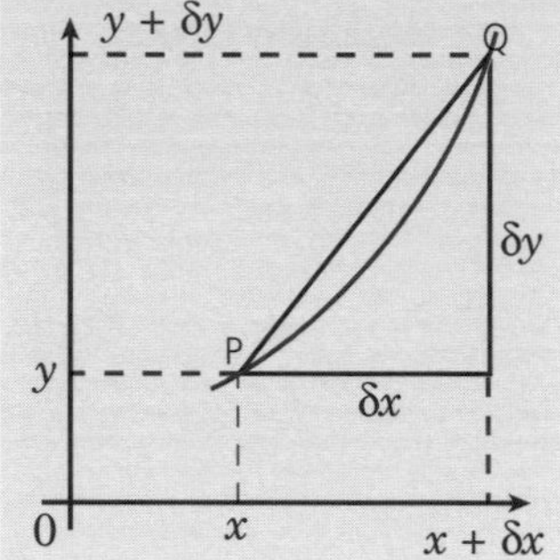

The notation $\dfrac{dy}{dx}$ comes from the idea that

the gradient is the limit of $\dfrac{\delta y}{\delta x}$ as $\delta x \to 0$.

The process is called **differentiation with respect to x.**

Exploration 7.5

The gradient function

Consider the functions **a)** $f(x) = x^2$ **b)** $f(x) = x^2 - 7x + 10$.
For each function:

- simplify $f(x + h)$
- simplify the expression $\dfrac{f(x+h)-f(x)}{h}$
- describe what happens to this expression as $h \to 0$.

Interpreting the results

In each case you should have confirmed that the formal definition of the gradient function $f'(x)$ agrees with the results from the previous section.

Example 7.1

For the function $f(x) = (x + 1)(x - 4)$, *find:*

a) $f'(1)$ $\qquad$ ***b)*** *values of* x *such that* $f'(x) = 0$.

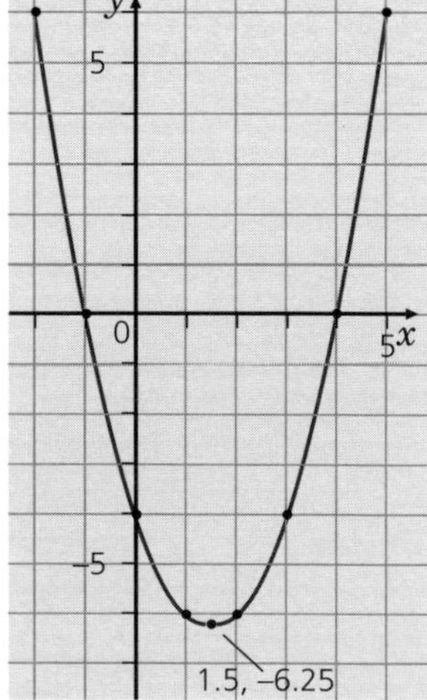

Solution

Multiplying out the brackets:

$(x+1)(x-4) \equiv x^2 - 3x - 4$

Differentiating: $f(x) = x^2 - 3x - 4$

$\Rightarrow f'(x) = 2x - 3$

a) $f'(1) = 2 \times 1 - 3 = -1$

b) $f'(x) = 0 \Rightarrow 2x - 3 = 0 \Rightarrow x = 1.5$

Differentiating with respect to any variable

The work so far has involved functions of the independent variable x. The same rule of differentiation works for other variables, for example: $f(t) = at^n \Rightarrow f'(t) = ant^{n-1}$.

This is called **differentiation with respect to t.**

Example 7.2

For the function $f(t) = 7 + 5t - t^3$*, find:*

a) $f'(1.5)$ ***b)*** *values of* t *such that* $f'(t) = 2$.

Solution

a) $f'(t) = 5 - 3t^2 \Rightarrow f'(1.5) = 5 - 3 \times (1.5)^2 = -1.75$

b) $f'(t) = 2 \Rightarrow 5 - 3t^2 = 2 \Rightarrow 3t^2 = 3 \Rightarrow t^2 = 1 \Rightarrow t = \pm 1$

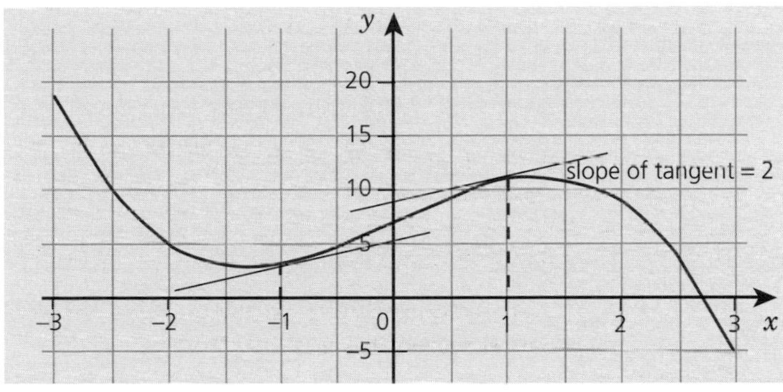

Example 7.3

Find the points on the curve $y = x^3 - 5x^2 + 5x - 3$ *where the gradient is parallel to the straight line* $y = 2x - 7$.

Solution

Differentiating: $y = x^3 - 5x^2 + 5x - 3 \Rightarrow \dfrac{dy}{dx} = 3x^2 - 10x + 5$

Since the gradient of the straight line is 2, then we look for the values of x *such that* $\dfrac{dy}{dx} = 2$.

Now: $3x^2 - 10x + 5 = 2 \Rightarrow 3x^2 - 10x + 3 = 0$

Solving the quadratic equation gives:

$(3x - 1)(x - 3) = 0 \Rightarrow x = \frac{1}{3}$ *or* $x = 3$.

Substituting for these values of x*:*

$$x = \frac{1}{3} \Rightarrow y = \left(\frac{1}{3}\right)^3 - 5\left(\frac{1}{3}\right)^2 + 5\left(\frac{1}{3}\right) - 3 = -\frac{50}{27} = -1\frac{23}{27}$$

$$x = 3 \Rightarrow y = 3^3 - 5(3)^2 + 5(3) - 3 = -6$$

Therefore the points A and B on the curve where the gradient is 2 *are* $(\frac{1}{3}, -1\frac{23}{27})$ *and* (3, −6).

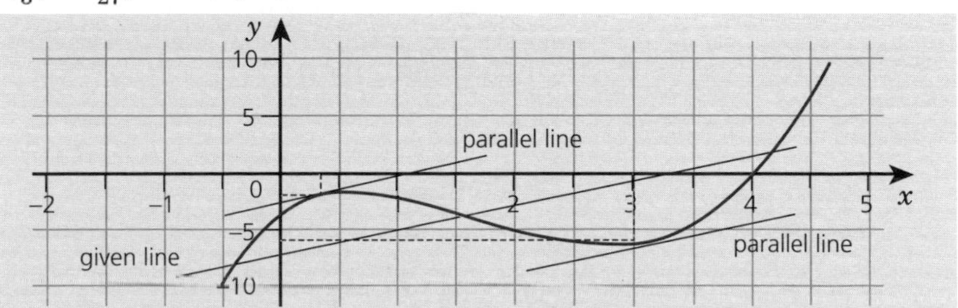

EXERCISES

7.2 CLASSWORK

Differentiate these expressions with respect to x.

1 $10x^2$

2 $12-5x$

3 x^3-2x^2+10

4 $3x^7-4x^5+2x^3$

5 $3x(x^2-4)$

6 $(x-5)(x-3)$

7 $(2x-5)(x+3)$

8 $x(x-5)(x-3)$

For each of the following, simplify the expression $\frac{f(x+h)-f(x)}{h}$ as $h \to 0$. Confirm that the limit gives the same results as the answers to questions 1–4 above.

9 $10x^2$

10 $12-5x$

11 x^3-2x^2+10

12 $3x^7-4x^5+2x^3$

Find the gradient function f'(x) and the gradient values for each of the following.

13 $f(x)=2x^2-10,\ f'(5)$

14 $f(x)=2x-x^3,\ f'(0.5)$

15 $f(x)=3x(x-7),\ f'(3.5)$

16 $f(x)=5x^2(x-2),\ f'(-1)$

Find $\frac{dy}{dx}$ and the derivatives at the points shown, for each of the following.

17 $y=2x^3-5x^2+x-8$ at (0, –8)

18 $y=x(x^2-3x+10)$ at (3, 30)

Find $\frac{ds}{dt}$ and the derivatives at the points shown.

19 $s=3+2t-4t^2$ at (1, 1)

20 $s=t(3t+2)(5t-4)$ at (–1, –9)

Find point(s) on the following curves where the gradient is as given.

21 $y=5x^2-3x+5,\ \frac{dy}{dx}=7$

22 $y=x^3-10x+5,\ \frac{dy}{dx}=17$

23 $u=x^4-2x^3,\ \frac{du}{dx}=0$

24 $y=u^3-u^2,\ \frac{dy}{du}=1$

25 $y=3x^4-4x^3-6x^2+12x-12,\ \frac{dy}{dx}=0$

26 Find the gradient of the curve $y=x^3+7x^2-x+3$ where the curve crosses the y-axis.

27 Find the gradient of the curve $y=(3x+1)(x-2)$ where the curve crosses the x-axis.

28 Find the coordinates of the points on the curve $y=4x^3-5x^2-9x+7$ where the gradient is parallel to the line $y=3x+5$. Illustrate your answer with a sketch.

7.2 HOMEWORK

Differentiate these expressions.

1 $5x^3$

2 $x^4+3x-7.5$

3 $10(1-x+x^2-x^3)$

4 $5x$

5 13

6 u^3-u^2+5u-6

7 $14x^7-10x^5$

8 $5(t-5)(3t+1)$

For each of the following, simplify the expression $\frac{f(x+h)-f(x)}{h}$ as $h \to 0$. Confirm that the limit gives the same results as the answers to questions 1–4 above.

9 $5x^3$

10 $x^4 + 3x - 7.5$

11 $10(1 - x + x^2 - x^3)$

12 $5t$

Find the gradient function $f'(x)$ and the gradient values for each of the following.

13 $f(x) = 7, f'(2)$

14 $f(x) = 7 - 5x, f'(2)$

15 $f(x) = 2x^2 - 10, f'(1)$

16 $f(x) = (2x+1)(2x-1), f'(0)$

Find $\frac{dh}{dt}$ and the derivatives at the points shown, for each of the following.

17 $h = 2t^3 + t^2 - 5t + 3$ at (–2, 1)

18 $h = t^4 - 2t^3 + 0.5t^2 - t + 1$ at (0, 1)

19 $h = \frac{1}{2}(2t - 5)^2$ at (4, 4.5)

20 $h = 3(t+1)(2t-5)^2$ at (2, 9)

Find point(s) on the following curves where the gradient is as given.

21 $y = x^4 - x^2, \frac{dy}{dx} = 0$

22 $y = (3x+4)^2, \frac{dy}{dx} = 2$

23 $s = t(t+1)(2t-5), \frac{ds}{dt} = 7$

24 $y = (x-1)(x-2)(x-3), \frac{dy}{dx} = 0$

25 The equation of a curve is $y = (3x-1)(x+2)$.

a) Find the gradient of the curve:

i) at the point (1, 6),

ii) at the point where the curve crosses the y-axis,

iii) at each point where the curve crosses the x-axis.

b) Find the coordinates of the point where $\frac{dy}{dx} = 0$.

26 The equation of a curve is $y = x^3 + 5x^2 - 4x - 20$.

a) Find the gradient of the curve:

i) at the point where the curve crosses the y-axis,

ii) at each point where the curve crosses the x-axis.

b) Find the coordinates of the points where $\frac{dy}{dx} = 0$.

27 Find the coordinates of the points on the curve $y = 2x^4 - 3x^2 + x - 7$ where the gradient is parallel to the line $y = 3x$.

28 For a certain curve, the gradient function is $\frac{dy}{dx} = 3x^2 - 1$.

Which of the following could be the equation of the curve?

a) $y = 3x^2 - x$

b) $y = x^3 - x + 4$

RATES OF CHANGE

Modelling a throw of a cricket ball, in the first section of this chapter, we found that the gradient function represented the rate of change of distance with respect to time, i.e. instantaneous **velocity**.

Using mathematical notation, this can be summarised as:

$h = f(t)$ represents height h as a function of time t

$v = \frac{dh}{dt} = f'(t)$ represents the rate of change of h with respect to t.

Similarly:

$a = \frac{dv}{dt} = f''(t)$ represents the rate of change of v with respect to t.

This rate of change of velocity with respect to time gives us the instantaneous **acceleration**. The notation $f''(t)$ means that the original function $f(t)$ has been differentiated **twice**.

Example 7.4

A particle is propelled vertically upwards from a point 6 metres above the ground. Its height, h metres, after time t seconds, is given by: $h = 6 + 13t - 5t^2$.

a) *Find its velocity after one second.*
b) *Find the time at which it reaches its greatest height, and the height above the ground at this time.*
c) *Find the time when it hits the ground and the speed with which it hits the ground.*
d) *Show that the acceleration is constant.*

Solution

a) *Velocity* $v = \frac{dh}{dt} = 13 - 10t$.

When $t = 1$, $v = 13 - 10 = 3\,\text{m s}^{-1}$.

b) *Maximum height occurs when* $v = \frac{dh}{dt} = 0 \Rightarrow 13 - 10t = 0$

$\Rightarrow \quad 10t = 13$

$\Rightarrow \quad t = 1.3$ *seconds*

c) *When the particle hits the ground,*

$h = 0 \Rightarrow \quad 6 + 13t - 5t^2 = 0$

$\Rightarrow \quad (3 - t)(2 + 5t) = 0$

$\Rightarrow \quad t = 3$ *or* $t = -0.4$

seconds

Velocity of particle after 3 seconds is $v = 13 - 10 \times 3 = -17\,\text{m s}^{-1}$.
The speed of the particle when it hits the ground is $17\,\text{m s}^{-1}$ *and the negative sign in the velocity indicates that it is travelling downwards.*

d) *The acceleration is given by* $a = \frac{dv}{dt} = -10\,\text{m s}^{-2}$, *which means that throughout its motion, the acceleration is* $10\,\text{m s}^{-2}$ *downwards.*

In general, if $y = f(x)$, then $\frac{dy}{dx} = f'(x)$ represents the rate of change of y with respect to x.

The rate of change is often with respect to time, but other situations arise.

Example 7.5

The volume, V, of a sphere in terms of its radius, r, is given by $V = \frac{4}{3}\pi r^3$.

a) *Show that the surface area is equivalent to the rate of change of volume with respect to radius.*
b) *Find the rate of change of volume with respect to radius when $r = 3$.*
c) *What is the volume of the sphere when* $\frac{dV}{dr} = 9\pi$*?*

Solution

a) $V = \frac{4}{3}\pi r^3 \;\Rightarrow\; \frac{\mathrm{d}V}{\mathrm{d}r} = \frac{4}{3}\pi \times 3r^2 = 4\pi r^2$

where $\frac{\mathrm{d}V}{\mathrm{d}r}$ *represents the rate of change of volume with respect to the radius, and the surface area of a sphere is given by* $4\pi r^2$.

b) *When* $r = 3$, $\frac{\mathrm{d}V}{\mathrm{d}r} = 4\pi \times 3^2 = 36\pi$

c) $\frac{\mathrm{d}V}{\mathrm{d}r} = 9\pi \;\Rightarrow\; 4\pi r^2 = 9\pi \;\Rightarrow\; r^2 = 2.25 \;\Rightarrow\; r = \sqrt{2.25} = 1.5$

$$\Rightarrow\; V = \tfrac{4}{3}\pi r^3 = \tfrac{4}{3}\pi \times 1.5^3 = 4.5\pi$$

EXERCISES

7.3 CLASSWORK

1 During the boost stage of a rocket launch, the height, h metres, after t seconds, is given by $h = 2t^4 - 3t^3 + 45t^2$.

a) Find the velocity v of the rocket at $t = 0$, 1, 2, 3 and 4 seconds.
b) Find the acceleration a of the rocket at $t = 0$, 1, 2, 3 and 4 seconds.
c) Sketch graphs of:
i) h against t, **ii)** v against t, **iii)** a against t,
over the interval $0 \le t \le 4$.

2 A body, which is initially at rest, is projected in a straight line from a point O. Its distance after t seconds is s metres, where $s = 10t^2 - 2t^3$.

a) Calculate the distance travelled by the body during the third second.
b) Find an expression for the velocity v in terms of t.
c) Sketch a graph of v against t for $0 \le t \le 4$.
d) Calculate the acceleration of the body when $t = 2$.
e) Find the value of t when the body is next momentarily at rest.

3 For a certain production process, the productivity p, when x machines are in use, is given by $p = 500(x + 1)^2 - 500$.

a) Determine the marginal productivity $\frac{\mathrm{d}p}{\mathrm{d}x}$, when $x = 3$.
b) How many machines are required to raise the marginal productivity to a level of 6000?

7.3 HOMEWORK

1 Fiona throws a ball straight up into the air. The height of the ball, h metres, after t seconds, is given by $h = 1.6 + 10t - 5t^2$.

a) Find the speed of the ball after one second and explain your answer in terms of the motion of the ball.
b) If Fiona catches the ball at the same height as she threw it, find the speed of the ball just before she catches it.
c) Find the acceleration of the ball.
d) For the interval $0 \le t \le 2$, sketch graphs of:
i) height against time,
ii) velocity against time,
iii) acceleration against time.

2 A yo-yo travels along a straight line, down and up. Sean models the distance, s metres, from his hand at time t seconds by $s = 24t - 3t^2$, $0 \le t \le 8$.

a) Find the speed of the yo-yo, v metres per second, at time t seconds.
b) Explain the restriction $0 \le t \le 8$.
c) What is the length of the string of the yo-yo?
d) Sketch the graphs of s and v against t and describe the motion of the yo-yo, giving its position, speed and direction of motion at t = 1, 2, 5 and 7 seconds.

3 The number of people, P, newly infected on day t of a flu epidemic is given by $P = 13t^2 - t^3$, $t \le 13$.

a) Sketch a graph of P against t.
b) Find the rate of change of P with respect to t,
i) on day 5, **ii)** on day 10. Interpret your answers.
c) Calculate the time t for which $\frac{\mathrm{d}P}{\mathrm{d}t} = 0$, the value of P at this time, and interpret your results.

STATIONARY VALUES

CALCULATOR ACTIVITY

Exploration 7.6

Zero gradient

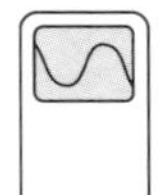

Consider the following four curves.
A $y = x^2 - 7x + 10$ B $y = 10 - x^2$ C $y = x^3$ D $y = x^3 - 12x + 3$

For each equation:

- sketch a graph of the curve,
- find the coordinates of the point(s) where the tangent to the curve is parallel to the x-axis,
- find the sign of the gradient of the curve either side of the point(s) you have found,
- describe what happens to the curve around the point(s) you have found.

Stationary points

When exploring the graphs of functions similar to those in the above Calculator activity, we find one or two points on each curve where the gradient is 0 (i.e. the tangent to the curve is parallel to the x-axis). Such points are called **stationary points**, where the function has a **stationary value**.

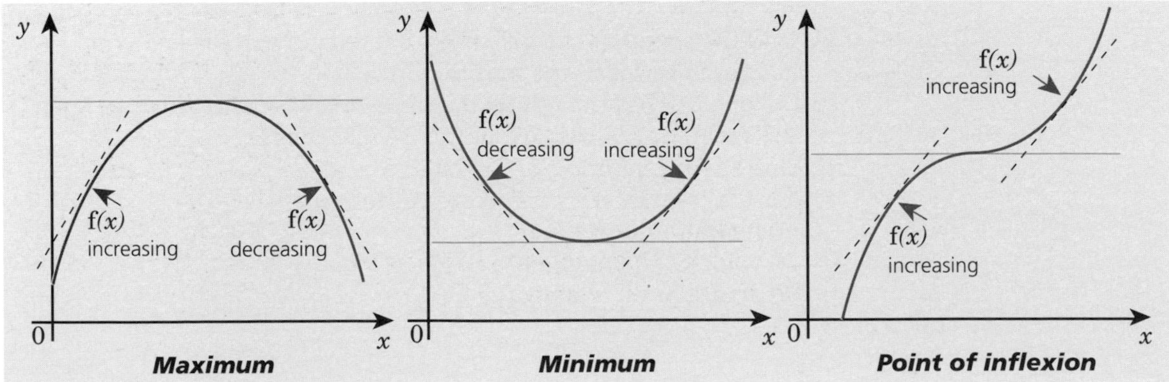

For each stationary point, the zero gradient means that $f'(x) = 0$. This means that the coordinates of a stationary point may be found by first solving the equation $f'(x) = 0$.

Once we have found the stationary point, we can classify it as a **maximum**, **minimum** or **point of inflexion** by looking at the behaviour of $f'(x)$ either side of the stationary point.

Example 7.6

Find the coordinates of the stationary point for the curve $y = x^2 - 7x + 10$ *and state which type it is.*

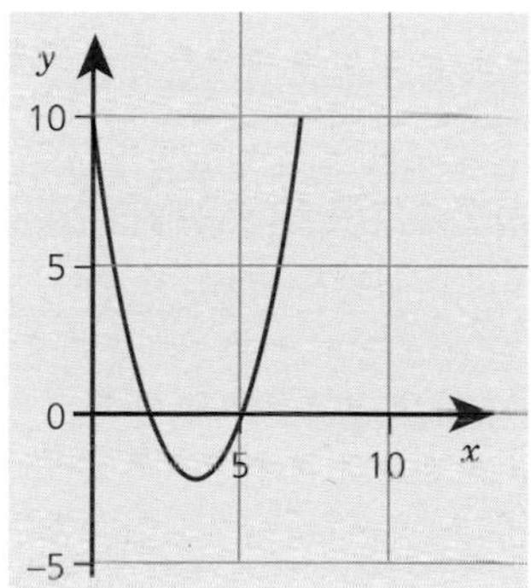

Solution

For a stationary value: $f'(x) = 2x - 7 = 0$

$\Rightarrow 2x = 7$

$\Rightarrow x = 3.5$

Since $f(3.5) = -2.25$, *the* ***only*** *stationary point is* $(3.5, -2.25)$.
Now examine the gradient function either side of $x = 3.5$, *for example:* $f'(3) = -1$ *and* $f'(4) = 1$.

A ***negative*** *gradient at* $x = 3$ *means that the function is* ***decreasing***.
A ***positive*** *gradient at* $x = 4$ *means that the function is* ***increasing***.
The conclusion is that $(3.5, -2.25)$ *is a* ***minimum*** *point.*
This should confirm the result of the exploration of curve A, in Calculator activity 7.3.

Note

For **quadratic** functions only, we can also find the stationary point by completing the square:

$$f(x) = x^2 - 7x + 10 = (x - 3.5)^2 - 12.25 + 10 = (x - 3.5)^2 - 2.25$$

from which we can deduce the minimum point $(3.5, -2.25)$.

For cubic and other polynomial functions solving the equation $f'(x) = 0$ is the best way to find stationary points for a function, as shown in the next two examples.

Example 7.7

Find the coordinates of any stationary point for the curve $y = x^3 - 12x + 3$ *and classify them.*

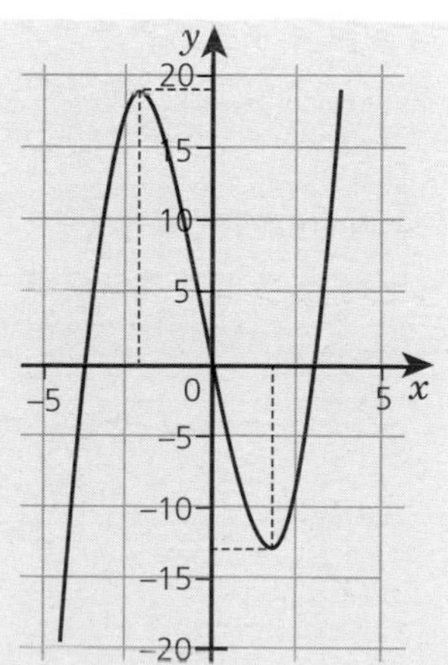

Solution

For a stationary value:

$f'(x) = 3x^2 - 12 = 0 \Rightarrow 3x^2 = 12 \Rightarrow x^2 = 4 \Rightarrow x = \pm 2$

Since

$f(-2) = (-2)^3 - 12(-2) + 3 = 19$

one stationary point is $(-2, 19)$ *and*

$f(2) = 2^3 - 12(2) + 3 = -13$

means the other one is $(2, -13)$.
Now examine the gradient function either side of the stationary points.

For $(-2, 19)$: $f'(-3) = 3(-3)^2 - 12 = 15 \Rightarrow$ *function* ***increasing***
$f'(-1) = 3(-1)^2 - 12 = -9 \Rightarrow$ *function* ***decreasing***
$\Rightarrow$ *stationary point is a* ***maximum.***
For $(2, -13)$: $f'(1) = 3(1)^2 - 12 = -9 \Rightarrow$ *function* ***decreasing***
$f'(3) = 3(3)^2 - 12 = 15 \Rightarrow$ *function* ***increasing***
$\Rightarrow$ *stationary point is a* ***minimum.***

These conclusions should confirm the exploration of curve D.

The nature of the stationary points also gives valuable information when sketching the graph by hand.

Example 7.8

Show that the curve $y = \dfrac{x^3(x-4)}{2}$ *has a point of inflexion at the origin.*
Find and classify the other stationary point.
Sketch the curve, showing clearly the stationary values and where the graph crosses the axes.

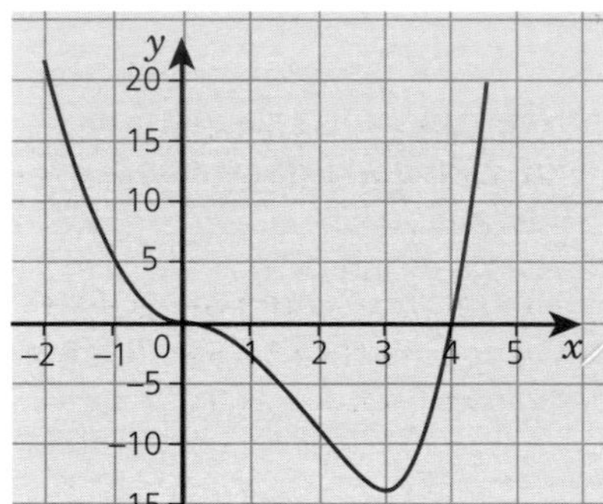

Solution

Firstly simplify the function for differentiating.

$$f(x) = \frac{x^3(x-4)}{2} = \frac{x^4 - 4x^3}{2} = 0.5x^4 - 2x^3$$

For stationary values:

$f'(x) = 2x^3 - 6x^2 = 0 \Rightarrow 2x^2(x-3) = 0 \Rightarrow x = 0 \text{ or } x = 3.$

Since $f(0) = \dfrac{0^3(0-4)}{2} = 0$, *one stationary point is* $(0, 0)$

and $f(3) = \dfrac{3^3(3-4)}{2} = -13.5$ *means the other one is* $(3, -13.5)$.

Now examine the gradient function either side of the stationary points.

For $(0, 0)$: $f'(-1) = 2(-1)^3 - 6(-1)^2 = -8 \Rightarrow$ *function* ***decreasing***
$f'(1) = 2(1)^3 - 6(1)^2 = -4 \Rightarrow$ *function* ***decreasing***
$\Rightarrow$ *stationary point is a* ***point of inflexion.***
For $(3, -13.5)$: $f'(2) = 2(2)^3 - 6(2)^2 = -8 \Rightarrow$ *function* ***decreasing***
$f'(4) = 2(4)^3 - 6(4)^2 = 32 \Rightarrow$ *function* ***increasing***
$\Rightarrow$ *stationary point is a* ***minimum.***

EXERCISES

7.4 CLASSWORK

1 A curve has equation $y = 1 + x - 2x^2$.
a) Find the gradient of the curve at the points (–2, –9) and (2, –5). Decide if the graph is increasing or decreasing at each point.
b) Find the coordinates of the point where the gradient is zero and sketch the curve.

2 A curve has equation $y = x^3 - 6x + 4$.
a) Find the gradient of the curve at the points (–3, –5), (0, 4) and (2, 0). Decide if the graph is increasing or decreasing at each point.
b) Find the coordinates of the two points where the gradient is zero and sketch the curve.

For each of the curves in questions **4** to **14**, find the stationary points and classify them as maximum, minimum or point of inflexion. Sketch a graph of the curve, clearly indicating the stationary point(s).

Check your answers on a graphics calculator.

3 $y = 14 + 5x - x^2$

4 $y = (2x - 5)^2$

5 $y = x^3 - 4x^2 + 9$

6 $y = x(3 - x)^2$

7 $y = x^3(4 - x)$

8 $y = 3 + 8x^2 - x^4$

9 $y = 3x^4 - 16x^3 + 24x^2 - 10$

7.4 HOMEWORK

1 A curve has equation $y = 12x + 3x^2 - 2x^3$.

a) Find the gradient of the curve at the points (–2, 4), (0, 0) and (3, 9). Decide if the graph is increasing or decreasing at each point.

b) Find the coordinates of the point where the gradient is zero and sketch the curve.

2 A curve has equation $s = t^2(t - 1)^2$.

a) Find the gradient of the curve at the points (–1, 4), (0, 0) and (2, 4). Decide if the graph is increasing or decreasing at each point.

b) Find the coordinates of the point(s) where the gradient is zero and sketch the curve.

For each of the curves in questions **4** to **14**, find the stationary points and classify them as maximum, minimum or point of inflexion. Sketch a graph of the curve, clearly indicating the stationary point(s).

Check your answers on a graphics calculator.

3 $y = (2 + x)(3 + x)$

4 $y = -2(x + 5)^2$

5 $y = x^3 - 3.5x^2 + 2x - 1$

6 $y = x^4 - 3x^2 - 1$

7 $s = t^3 + 6t^2 + 12t + 8$

8 $y = x^4 - 4x^3 - 2x^2 + 12x + 5$

9 $s = t^3 - t^2 + t - 1$

OPTIMISATION

In the previous section, we saw that the stationary points often represent maximum or minimum values.

For any function, stationary values can be found by setting

$$\frac{dy}{dx} = f'(x) = 0$$

and solving the resulting equation.

The method is often applied in the area of **optimisation**, where the aim is to maximise or minimise a function.

Example 7.9

A farmer wishes to create four pens with 200 metres of fencing.

a) *Assuming each pen measures x m by y m, as shown in the diagram (overleaf), express the area of the pens, A, in terms of the length, x, only.*

b) *Find the values of x and y which gives a maximum area for the pens. What is the maximum value of A?*

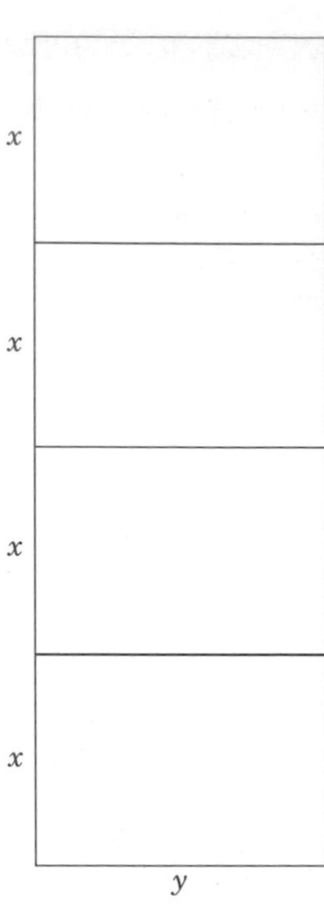

Solution

a) *The framework for the pens uses eight x-lengths plus five y-lengths. With 200 metres of fencing available, this means:*

$$8x + 5y = 200 \quad \Rightarrow 5y = 200 - 8x$$

$$\Rightarrow y = \frac{200 - 8x}{5} = 40 - 1.6x$$

$$\text{Area } A = 4x \times y = 4xy = 4x(40 - 1.6x) \Rightarrow A = 160x - 6.4x^2$$

b) *The maximum area occurs when* $\frac{dA}{dx} = 0$

$$\Rightarrow \frac{dA}{dx} = 160 - 12.8x = 0$$

$$\Rightarrow 12.8x = 160$$

$$\Rightarrow x = 160 \div 12.8 = 12.5$$

$$\Rightarrow y = \frac{200 - 8 \times 12.5}{5} = 20$$

i.e. the maximum area of pens occurs when $x = 12.5$ and $y = 20$, which gives a maximum value of A as:

$$4 \times 12.5 \times 20 = 1000.$$

The conclusion is that the maximum area enclosed is 1000 m².

Example 7.10

An open box is to be formed by cutting four squares of side x cm from the corners of a sheet of card 20 cm square.

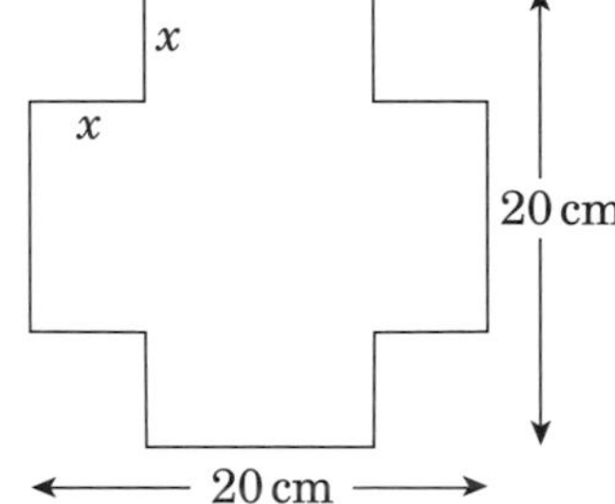

a) *Express the volume of the box, V cm³, in terms of the length, x cm.*

b) *Find the value of x which gives a maximum volume. What is the maximum volume?*

Solution

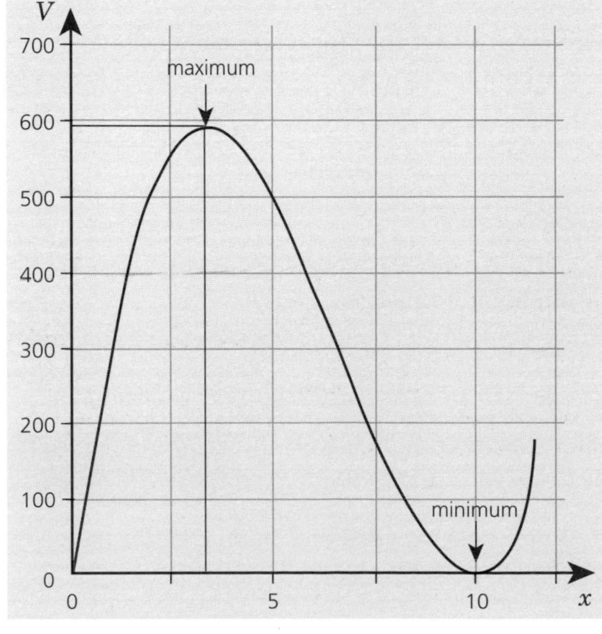

a) *Height of box* $= x$ cm $\Rightarrow$ *length and width* $= 20 - 2x$ cm.

Volume $V = x(20 - 2x)^2 = x(400 - 80x + 4x^2)$

$$\Rightarrow V = 400x - 80x^2 + 4x^3$$

b) *Maximum volume occurs when* $\frac{dV}{dx} = 0$

$$\Rightarrow \frac{dV}{dx} = 400 - 160x + 12x^2 = 0$$

$$\Rightarrow 3x^2 - 40x + 100 = 0$$

$$\Rightarrow (3x - 10)(x - 10) = 0$$

$$x = 10 \quad \Rightarrow \quad V = 10 \times (20 - 2 \times 10)^2 = 0$$

$$x = 3\tfrac{1}{3} \quad \Rightarrow \quad V = \tfrac{10}{3} \times (20 - 2 \times \tfrac{10}{3})^2 = 593$$

(3 s.f.)

Conclusion: the maximum volume of 593 cm³ occurs when $x = 3\frac{1}{3}$.

EXERCISES

7.5 CLASSWORK

x

y

1 A farmer wishes to enclose a rectangular area with a 60-metre length of fencing.

a) Explain why $2x + 2y = 60$ and rearrange this formula in the form $y = \dots$.
b) Write down a formula for the area, A, in terms of x only.
c) Find the value of x that maximises the value of A.
What is the maximum area?
What particular shape is formed in this case?
d) Sketch a graph of A against x for $0 \le x \le 30$.

2 The farmer in question **1** has alternative sites for the enclosure, one involving the use of a single existing wall (figure A) and the other involving the use of three walls (figure B).

Figure A

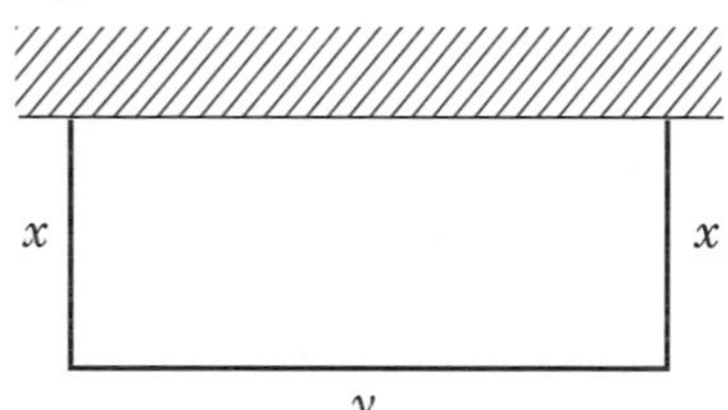

Figure B

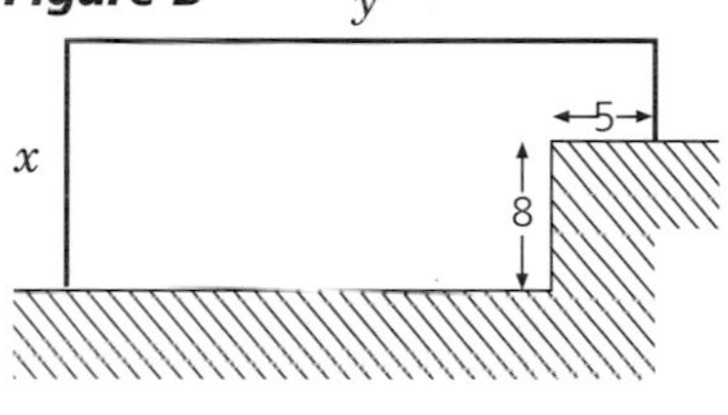

He still has only 60 metres of fencing to use. For each site:

a) write down a formula connecting x and y,
b) write down a formula for the area, A, in terms of x only,
c) find the maximum area that he can enclose, giving the dimensions of the enclosure,
d) sketch graphs of A against x for suitable values of x.

3 A farmer wishes to create six pens with 144 metres of fencing.

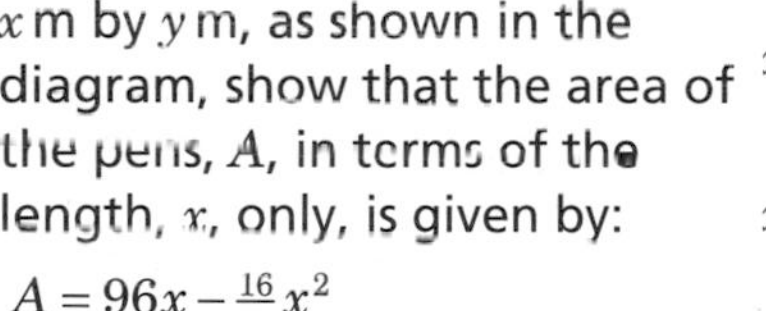

a) Assuming each pen measures x m by y m, as shown in the diagram, show that the area of the pens, A, in terms of the length, x, only, is given by:
$A = 96x - \frac{16}{3}x^2$

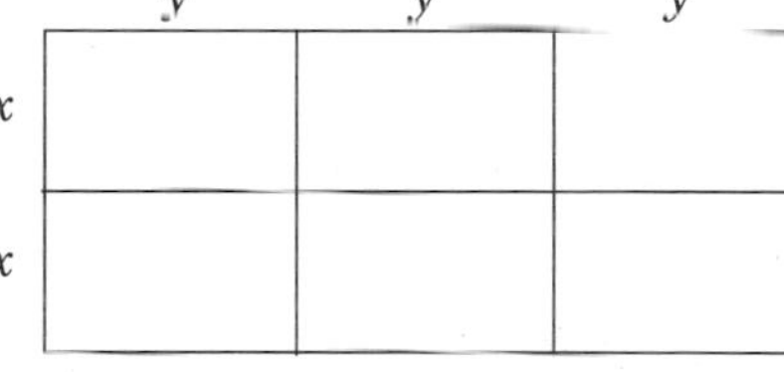

b) Find the values of x and y which give a maximum area for the pens. What is the maximum value of A?

4 Two industrial plants, 30 miles apart, are polluting a large lake. The pollution level, P parts per million, is given by:
$P = 2x^2 - 48x + 400,\ 0 \le x \le 30$
where x measures the distance from plant A towards plant B, in miles.

a) Find where, between A and B, the pollution is the least.
b) Sketch a graph of P against x for $0 \le x \le 30$ and deduce which factory pollutes the water more.

5 A cylinder is to be fitted into a sphere of radius 20 cm. The cylinder has height h cm and base radius r cm.

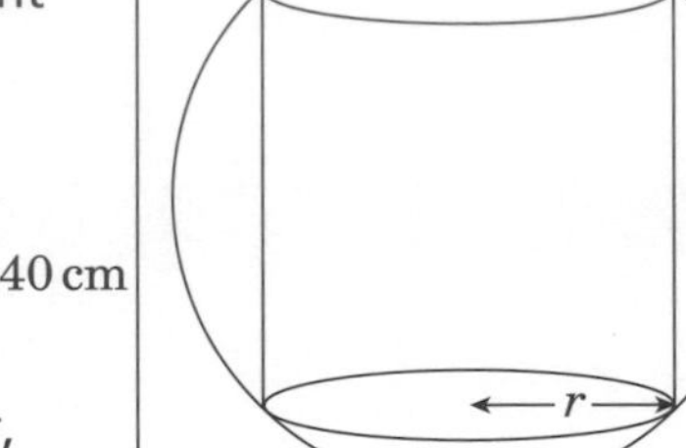

a) Use Pythagoras' theorem to show that

$$r^2 + \frac{h^2}{4} = 400$$

b) Express the volume of the cylinder, $V\,\text{cm}^3$, in terms of h only.

c) Find the value of h (and r) that maximises V. What is the maximum volume?

6 An athletics track consists of a rectangle with a semi-circle at each end, as in the diagram.

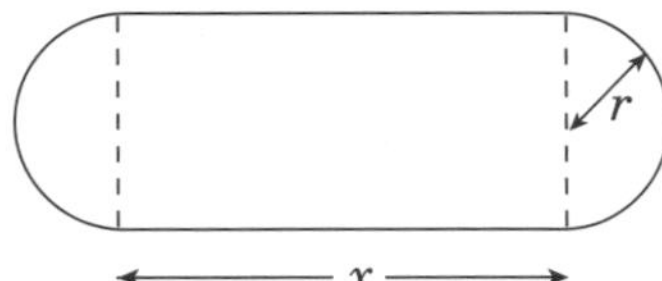

If the perimeter is to be exactly 400 metres, find the dimensions (x and r) that maximise the area of the rectangle.

7.5 HOMEWORK

1 A farmer wants to make three identical rectangular enclosures, side by side, using an existing wall as one boundary.

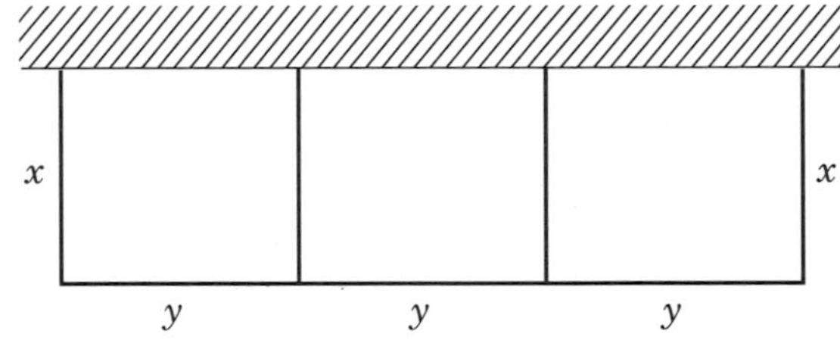

If he has 600 metres of fencing, what should be the dimensions of each enclosure if the total area is to be maximised?

2 The fuel economy E of a car, in miles per gallon, is given by:

$$E = 35 + 0.02v^2 - 3.85 \times 10^{-6}v^4,\ 5 \le v \le 70$$

where v is the speed in miles per hour.

What is the most economical speed to drive so that fuel consumption is a minimum?

3 A building contractor has 150 metres of security fencing and wishes to enclose a rectangular area. The area is divided into two parts with fencing. The areas A_1 and A_2 are such that $A_1 = 2A_2$.

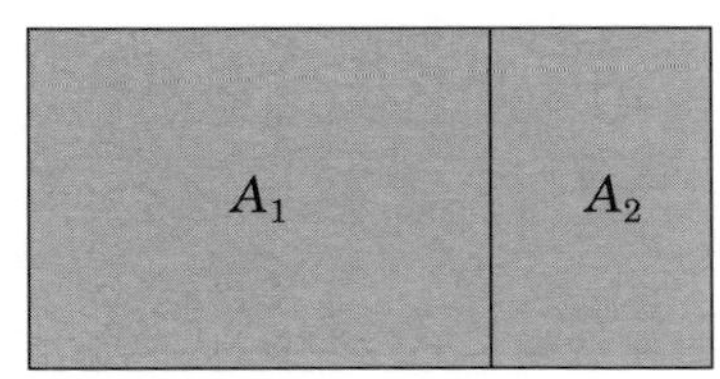

What are the dimensions of the enclosure so that the total enclosed area is a maximum?

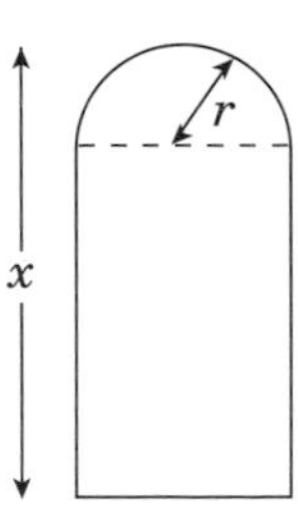

4 A Norman window has a semi-circular arch above a rectangular section. Its perimeter is to be 6 m.

a) Show that $x = 3 - \frac{1}{2}\pi r$.
b) Show that the area of the window is maximised when $r = \dfrac{6}{\pi + 4}$.
c) Find the maximum area of the window.

5 The proportion of the river's energy, E, that can be obtained from an undershot water-wheel is given by:

$$E = 2v^3 - 4v^2 + 2v,\ 0 \le v \le 1$$

where v is the speed of the water-wheel relative to the speed of the river.

Show that only about 30 per cent of the river's energy can be captured, and that this occurs when the speed of the wheel is about one-third of the speed of the river.

6 A cylindrical can without a lid is made from aluminium sheet. If A is the surface area of the sheet used and V is the volume of the can, show that $V = \frac{1}{2}(Ar - \pi r^3)$.

Show that if A is given, the volume is a maximum when the diameter of the can is twice the height of the can.

MATHEMATICAL MODELLING ACTIVITY

1 → 2 → 3
6 ← 5 ← 4
Specify the real problem

Problem statement

A manufacturer of portable telephones has designed a new model. The market research department suggests that the number sold in the first year of production will depend on the selling price in roughly the following way.

Selling price (£)	50	75	100
Number sold	10 000	8000	6000

The company would have fixed costs of £25 000 and the manufacturing cost per item is £25.

- What selling price would you recommend in order that the company:
  a) maximises its revenue, **b)** maximises its profits?

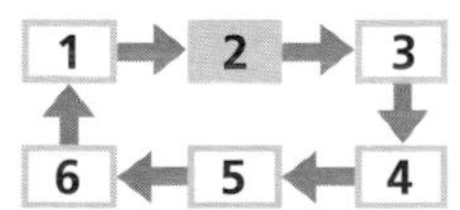

Set up a model

Set up a model

Firstly you need to identify the important variables:

- the selling price for each telephone,
- the number of telephones sold per annum,
- the revenue (receipts from sales) per annum,
- the costs involved (fixed and variable),
- the expected profit.

You will also need to make some assumptions before formulating the problem mathematically, some of which are simplistic, but necessary to tackle the problem initially:

- the relationship between number sold and price is linear,
- all telephones produced in the first year are sold.

Further refinements may be built in later.

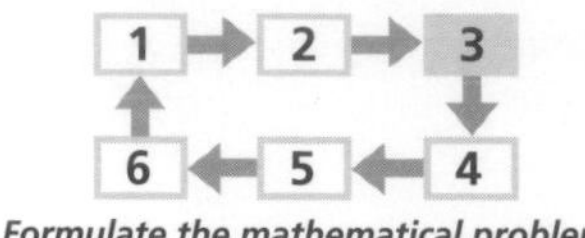

Formulate the mathematical problem

Mathematical problem

Firstly, establish the relationship between the number of telephones the company expects to sell (n) in terms of selling price (s).

The market research figures would seem to indicate a linear relationship, since for each reduction in price of £25, the company would expect to sell 20 000 more.

You should confirm that the equation connecting n and s is: $n = 14\,000 - 80s$. The revenue, R, is number sold × price = ns.

The cost of production, C, is fixed cost + variable cost = 25 000 + 25n.

The profit is the difference between revenue and cost = $R - C$.

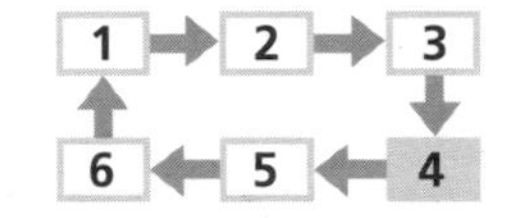

Solve the mathematical problem

Mathematical solution

Given that you need to find a selling price to:

a) maximise revenue or
b) maximise profit during the first year, you must first express both revenue, R, and profit, P, in terms of selling price, s.

Revenue function

$R = ns$ but $n = 14\,000 - 80s$
$\Rightarrow R = (14\,000 - 80s)s$
$\Rightarrow R = 14\,000s - 80s^2$

Profit function

$C = 25\,000 + 25n = 25\,000 + 25(14\,000 - 80s)$
$\quad = 25\,000 + 350\,000 - 2000s$
$\Rightarrow C = 375\,000 - 2000s$

and $P = R - C$
$\Rightarrow P = 14\,000s - 80s^2 - (375\,000 - 2000s)$
$\Rightarrow P = 16\,000s - 80s^2 - 375\,000$

Graphs of R and P in terms of s are shown below.

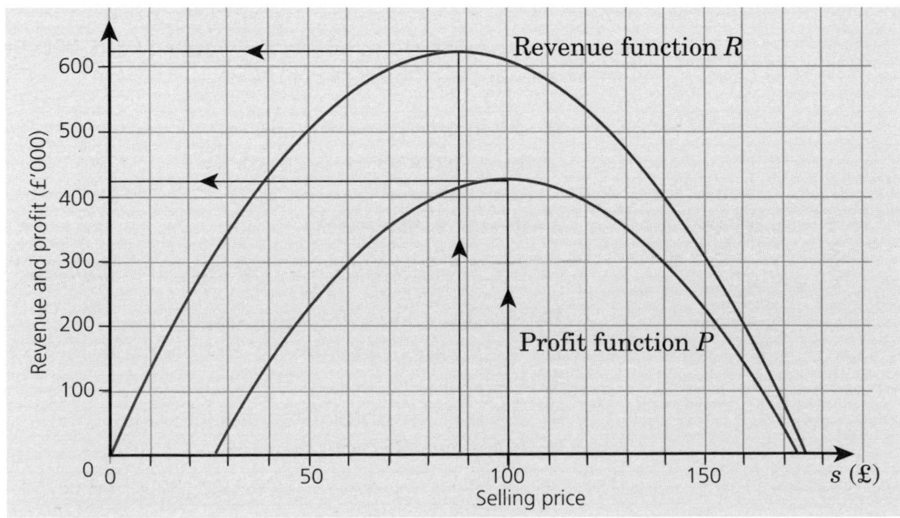

To find where R reaches a maximum:

$\dfrac{dR}{ds} = 14\,000 - 160s = 0$ for stationary values

$$\Rightarrow \quad s = \frac{14000}{160} = 87.5$$

To find where P reaches a maximum:

$\frac{dP}{ds} = 16\,000 - 160s = 0$ for stationary values

$$\Rightarrow \quad s = \frac{16000}{160} = 100$$

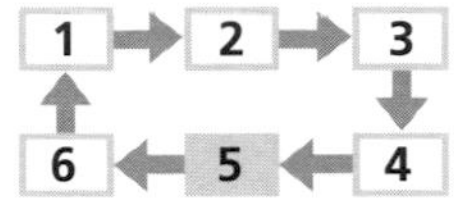

Interpret the solution

Interpretation

To maximise revenue the company should set the selling price at £87.50, but to maximise profit the price should be set at £100.

At a selling price of £87.50, the annual revenue would be £612 500, but costs of £200 000 reduce the profit to £412 500.

At a selling price of £100, the annual revenue would be reduced to £600 000, but reduced costs of £175 000, since fewer telephones are sold at a higher price, realise a profit of £425 000.

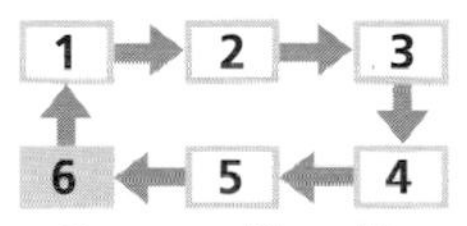

Compare with reality

Refinement of the model

Investigate the effect of:

- a change in the fixed costs,
- a change in the manufacturing cost per item,
- a different relationship between expected number sold and selling price (is a linear relationship realistic?).

CONSOLIDATION EXERCISES FOR CHAPTER 7

1 **a)** Given that $y = x^3 - x + 6$, find $\frac{dy}{dx}$.

On the curve representing y, P is the point where $x = -1$.

b) Calculate the y-coordinate of the point P.

c) Calculate the value of $\frac{dy}{dx}$ at P.

d) Find the equation of the tangent at P.

The tangent at the point Q is parallel to the tangent at P.

e) Find the coordinates of Q.

(MEI, June 1993 (part))

2 A curve has equation $y = x^3 + 3x^2 + 4x + 5$.

a) Find $\frac{dy}{dx}$.

b) Prove that the curve has no stationary points.

c) Show that the gradient function has a minimum value of 1 at $x = -1$.

d) Sketch the curve and explain why $x^3 + 3x^2 + 4x + 5 = 0$ has just one real root.

3 Functions f and g are defined by: $f(x) = -\frac{x^3}{6} + x$ and $g(x) = \frac{x^5}{120} - \frac{x^3}{6} + x$.

a) Evaluate f(0) and g(0).

b) Find $f'(x)$ and $g'(x)$ and evaluate $f'(0)$ and $g'(0)$.

c) Find the coordinates of the stationary points for:

i) $y = f(x)$, **ii)** $y = g(x)$.

d) Determine the values of x for which:

i) $f(x) = 0$, **ii)** $g(x) = 0$.

e) Sketch the curves $y = f(x)$ and $y = g(x)$ on the same axes.

4 An importer and distributor of computers has found an exclusive source of lap-top microcomputers. They will cost him £250 per machine. In addition, he will incur a cost of £5000 to adapt his distribution system to sell them, no matter how many machines he buys. The total cost of adapting his distribution system and buying n machines is £c. Express c in terms of n.

Experience suggests that the number, n, of machines is related to the selling price per machine, £s, by an equation $n = a + bs$ where a and b are constants. The importer has been informed by his market research department that if he fixes the selling price at £400 per machine he is likely to sell about 5500 machines and, if he fixes it at £500, this will fall to about 3500 machines. Find a and b based on the information supplied by the market research department.

Show that the total profit, £p, the importer will make from selling all these machines is given by $p = 18\,500s - 20s^2 - 3\,380\,000$.

Find the selling price per machine which will maximise the importer's total profit and hence find the number of machines he should purchase and his total profit on selling all the machines.

(NEAB, Specimen Paper 1)

5 This figure shows part of the curve with equation $y = 3 + 5x + x^2 - x^3$. The curve touches the x-axis at A and crosses the x-axis at C. The points A and B are stationary points on the curve.

a) Show that C has coordinates (3, 0).
Using calculus and showing all your working, find
b) the coordinates of A and B.

(EDEXCEL, Question 9, Paper 1, Jan 1999)

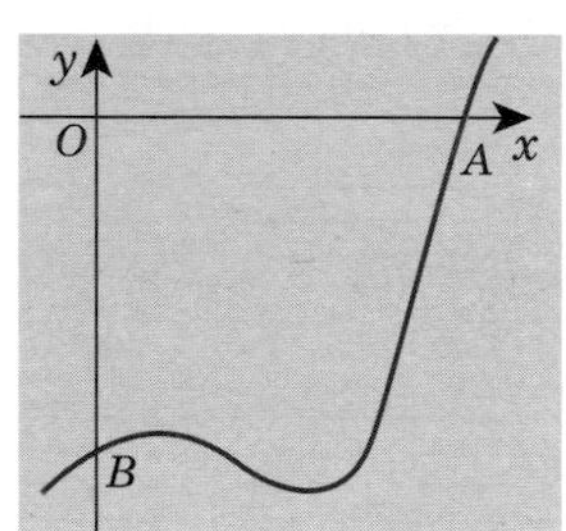

6 The curve C with equation $y = x^3 - 5x^2 + 7x - 14$ meets the x- and y-axes at the points A and B respectively, as shown in the figure.

a) State the coordinates of the point B.
b) Show that the x-coordinate of the point A lies in the interval [4, 5].
c) Determine, by calculation, the coordinates of the stationary points of the curve C.

(EDEXCEL, Question 6, Paper 1, Jan 1998)

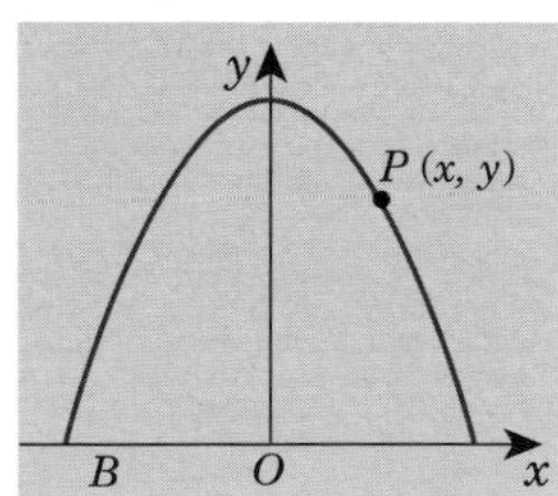

7 This figure shows the part of the curve with equation $y = 5 - \frac{1}{2}x^2$ for which $y \geq 0$. The point $\mathrm{P}(x, y)$ lies on the curve and 0 is the origin.

a) Show that $\mathrm{OP}^2 = \frac{1}{4}x^4 - 4x^2 + 25$.
Taking $\mathrm{f}(x) = \frac{1}{4}x^4 - 4x^2 + 25$,
b) find the values of x for which $\mathrm{f}'(x) = 0$.
c) Hence, or otherwise, find the minimum distance from 0 to the curve, showing that your answer is a minimum.

(EDEXCEL, Question 8, Paper 1, Jan 1997)

8 The equation of a curve is $y = 6x^2 - x^3$. Find the coordinates of the two stationary points on the curve, and determine the nature of each of these points.

Set the values for x for which $6x^2 - x^3$ is a decreasing function of x. The gradient at the point M on the curve is 12. Find the equation of the tangent to the curve at M.

(OCR, Specimen Paper 1, Question 8, 2000)

Summary

Differentiation

- *Notation:* $y = f(x) \Rightarrow \dfrac{dy}{dx} = f'(x)$

  1 $f(x) = x^n \Rightarrow f'(x) = nx^{n-1}$ for $n = 1, 2, 3, \ldots$

  2 $f(x) = ax^n \Rightarrow f'(x) = anx^{n-1}$ where a is a constant.

  3 The derivative of a sum (or difference) is the sum (or difference) of the derivatives.

Rates of change

- For any function $y = f(x)$, the **rate of change** of y with respect to x is given by $\dfrac{dy}{dx} = f'(x)$.

  In particular:

  $s = f(t)$ gives displacement s as a function of time t
  $\Rightarrow v = f'(t)$ gives velocity v as a function of time t
  $\Rightarrow a = f''(t)$ gives acceleration a as a function of time t.

Stationary values

- For any function $y = f(x)$, **stationary values** occur where $f'(x) = 0$. A stationary value may be a **maximum**, **minimum** or **point of inflexion**.

Optimisation

- Optimum values for problems may be found by formulating a function $y = f(x)$ and finding value(s) of x such that $f'(x) = 0$.

Integration 1

In this chapter we:

- *introduce the concept of integration*
- *use integration to find the area under a graph*
- *use integration to find velocity from acceleration and displacement from velocity.*

AREAS AND AREA FUNCTIONS

A velocity–time graph can be used to display a journey made by an object, but what other information can it show?

Exploration 8.1 *Velocity and distance travelled*

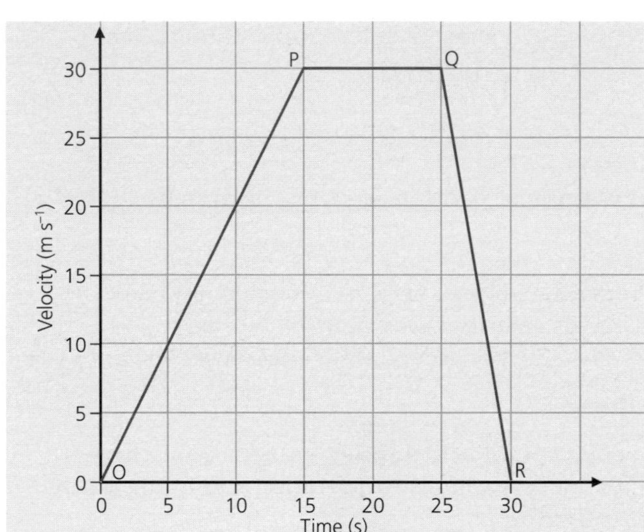

Heidi is testing the acceleration and braking power of her new car, on an open stretch of a straight road. A velocity–time graph for the motion of the car is shown on the left.

- What was the car's acceleration during the first 15 seconds?
- Describe the motion of the car during the last five seconds.
- How far did the car travel between $t = 15$ and $t = 25$?
- How far did the car travel in total?
- What are the velocity–time equations for the three lines?

The area under a velocity–time graph

The **acceleration** of the car is given by the gradient of the velocity–time graph. The car accelerates at $2\,\text{m s}^{-2}$ for the first 15 seconds, then travels at a constant velocity of $30\,\text{m s}^{-1}$ for 10 seconds before application of the brakes produces a **deceleration** (negative acceleration) of $6\,\text{m s}^{-2}$.

For the time interval $15 \leq t \leq 25$ the car is travelling at a constant speed, therefore the distance travelled between $t = 15$ and $t = 25$ is $30 \times 10 = 300$ metres.

For the time interval $0 \leq t \leq 15$ the car is accelerating, and for $25 \leq t \leq 30$ the car is decelerating, both at constant rates. To find the distance travelled between $t = 0$ and $t = 15$ we need to multiply the average velocity ($15\,\text{m s}^{-1}$) by the time of travel (15 seconds) to give a distance of $15 \times 15 = 225$ metres.

Similarly the distance travelled between $t = 25$ and $t = 30$ is $15 \times 5 = 75$ metres. Hence the total distance Heidi travels in the car is $225 + 300 + 75 = 600$ metres.

Notice that the three distances correspond to the areas of the rectangle (300 metres) and the two triangles (225 metres and 75 metres). This example illustrates an important principle:

distance travelled = area under a velocity–time graph

The velocity–time equation for line OP is $v = 2t$, since OP is a straight line through the origin with gradient 2.

The velocity–time equation for the line PQ is $v = 30$, since the car is travelling at a constant speed in a straight line.

The velocity–time equation for the line QR is of the form:

$v = mt + c$

which is a straight line equation in which:

- the gradient m is -6 (representing a deceleration of $6\,\text{m s}^{-2}$)
- the constant c may be found by substituting, say, $t = 30$ and $v = 0$ (point R on the line), from which we can deduce:
  $0 = -6 \times 30 + c \quad \Rightarrow \quad c = 180$

Hence the velocity–time equation for QR is:

$v = -6t + 180$

or $v = 180 - 6t$.

Exploration 8.2 Finding the distance

Look more closely at the motion of the car in Exploration 8.1, during the first 15 seconds.

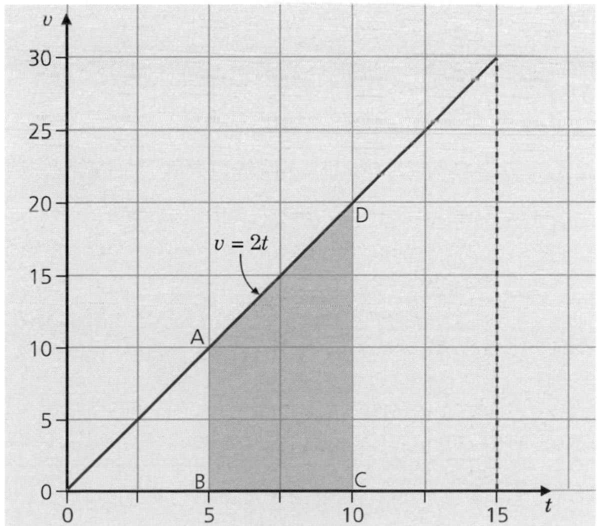

- How far does the car travel between $t = 5$ and $t = 10$?
- How far does the car travel between $t = a$ and $t = b$, where a and b are times in seconds such that $0 \leq a < b \leq 15$?

The area function

The distance travelled be the car between $t = 5$ and $t = 10$ is given by the area of the trapezium ABCD.

$$\tfrac{1}{2}(10 + 20) \times 5 = 75 \text{ metres}$$

In this case, this area is equivalent to the difference in area of triangles OCD and OAB, i.e.

$$\text{area OCD} - \text{area OAB} = \tfrac{1}{2} \times 10 \times 20 - \tfrac{1}{2} \times 5 \times 10$$
$$= 100 - 25 = 75 \text{ metres}$$

Using this idea to find the area between $t = a$ and $t = b$ a very useful generalisation emerges.

$$\text{Area of trapezium} = \tfrac{1}{2} b \times 2b - \tfrac{1}{2} a \times 2a$$
$$= b^2 - a^2$$

This is written as $\left[t^2\right]_a^b$.

$$\left[t^2\right]_a^b = (\text{area of } \Delta \text{ when } t = b) - (\text{area of } \Delta \text{ when } t = a)$$

The function $A(t) = t^2$ is called the **area function**, since:

$$\left[A(t)\right]_a^b = b^2 - a^2 = A(b) - A(a)$$

It follows that $\left[A(t)\right]_0^t = t^2 = A(t)$

which represents the displacement of the car in the first t seconds.

In general:

$f(t) = 2t$	$\Rightarrow$	$A(t) = t^2$
velocity–time equation		*displacement–time equation*

Exploration 8.3

Total distance travelled

Look again at the motion of Heidi's car, during the last five seconds.

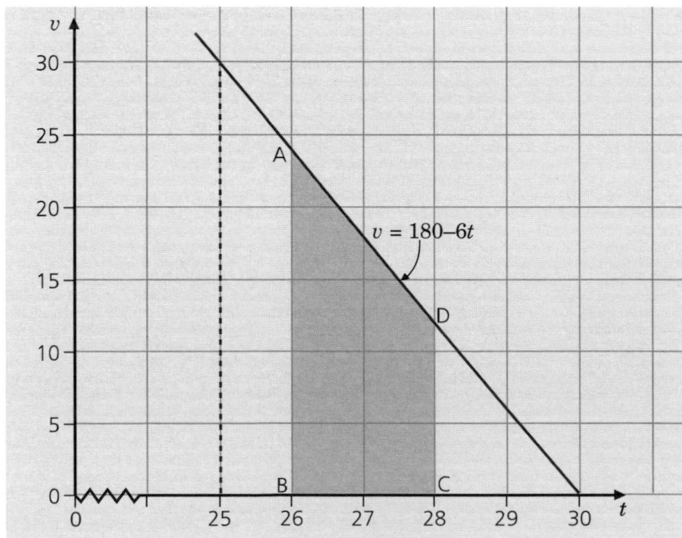

- How far does the car travel between $t = 26$ and $t = 28$?
- How far does the car travel between $t = a$ and $t = b$, where a and b are time in seconds such that $25 \le a < b \le 30$?

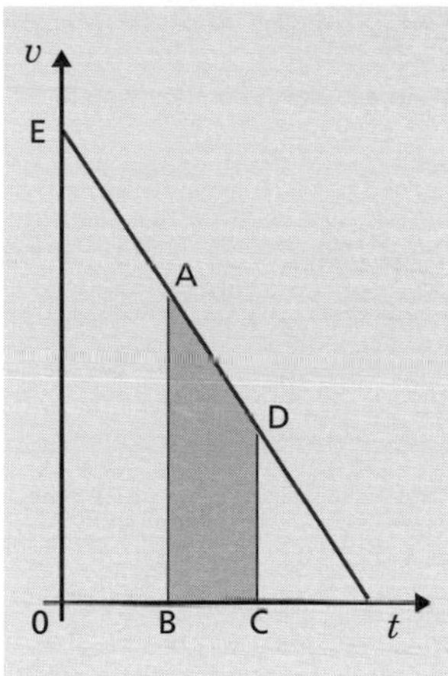

Using the area under the graph

The distance travelled by the car between $t = 26$ and $t = 28$ is given by the area of the trapezium ABCD.

$$\tfrac{1}{2}(24 + 12) \times 2 = 36 \text{ metres}$$

In this case, this is equivalent to the difference in area of the trapezia OEAB and OEDC, i.e.

$$\begin{aligned} \text{area OEDC} - \text{area OEAB} &= \tfrac{1}{2}(180 + 12) \times 28 - \tfrac{1}{2}(180 + 24) \times 26 \\ &= 2688 - 2652 = 36 \text{ metres} \end{aligned}$$

Using this idea to find the areas between $t = a$ and $t = b$, again a useful generalisation emerges.

$$\begin{aligned} \text{area OEDC} - \text{area OEAB} &= \tfrac{1}{2}(180 + 180 - 6b) \times b - \tfrac{1}{2}(180 + 180 - 6a) \times a \\ &= \left(180b - 3b^2\right) - \left(180a - 3a^2\right) \end{aligned}$$

This is written as $\left[180t - 3t^2\right]_a^b$

The function $A(t) = 180t - 3t^2$ represents the area under the graph $v = 180 - 6t$ between 0 and t.

Therefore it follows that: $f(t) = 180 - 6t \quad \Rightarrow \quad A(t) = 180t - 3t^2$

Exploration 8.4

Expressions for the area under a graph

The area under the graph of $y = mx + c$ between $x = a$ and $x = b$ is illustrated in this diagram.

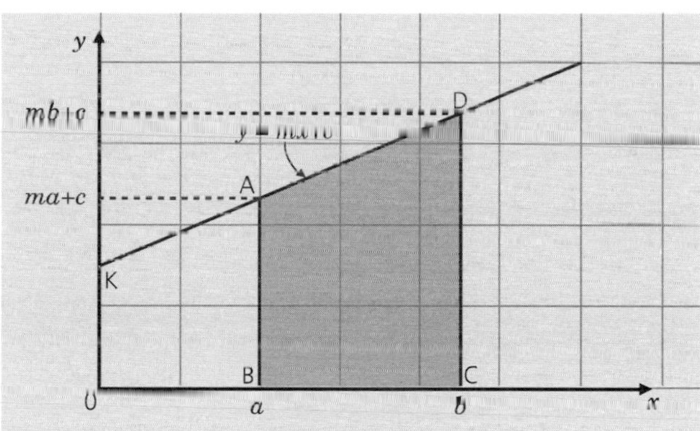

- Find an expression for the area of OBAK.
- Find an expression for the area of OCDK.
- Deduce an expression for the area of ABCD.

The integral function

The area of trapezium OBAK is $\tfrac{1}{2}(c + (ma + c))a$

The area of trapezium OCDK is $\tfrac{1}{2}(c + (mb + c))b$

Subtracting, the area of ABCD is:

$$\begin{aligned} &\tfrac{1}{2}(c + (ma + c))a - \tfrac{1}{2}(c + (mb + c))b \\ = \; &\tfrac{1}{2}(mb + 2c)b - \tfrac{1}{2}(ma + 2c)a \\ = \; &\tfrac{1}{2}mb^2 + cb - \left(\tfrac{1}{2}ma^2 + ca\right) \end{aligned}$$

This may be written as $\left[\tfrac{1}{2}mx^2 + cx\right]_a^b$.

Therefore, using f(x) for the original function and A(x) for the area function:

$$f(x) = mx + c \Rightarrow A(x) = \tfrac{1}{2}mx^2 + cx$$

Notation

The area function is also called the **integral function.**
The process of calculating the area enclosed by the graph of $y = f(x)$, the x-axis and the lines $x = a$ and $x = b$ as:

$$[A(x)]_a^b = A(b) - A(a)$$

is called **definite integration**.
We shall meet the technique again later in this chapter.
Areas *above* the x-axis result in a *positive* integral.
Areas *below* the x-axis result in a *negative* integral.

Example 8.1

Sketch the graph of $y = 10 - 4x$ for $0 \le x \le 5$ and then:

a) *find the area under the graph for $a = 1$, $b = 2$,*
b) *explain why $[A(x)]_1^4 = 0$.*

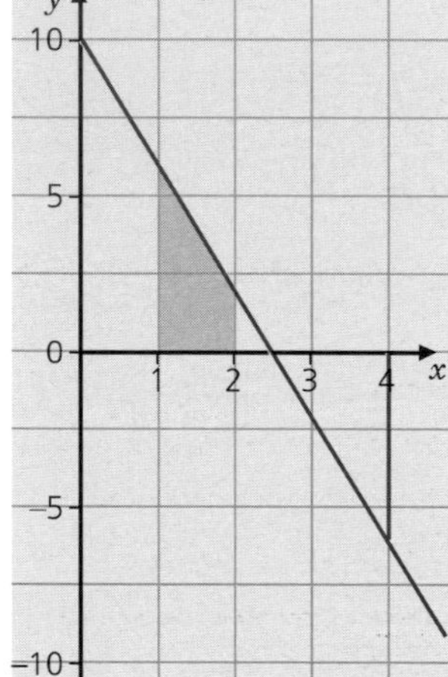

Solution
In this example $f(x) = 10 - 4x = -4x + 10$

$$A(x) = \tfrac{1}{2}(-4)x^2 + 10x = 10x - 2x^2$$

a) $a = 1, b = 2 \Rightarrow [A(x)]_1^2 = [10x - 2x^2]_1^2$
$= (10 \times 2 - 2 \times 2^2) - (10 \times 1 - 2 \times 1^2)$
$= 12 - 8 = 4$
$\Rightarrow$ *required area = 4 units*^{2}.

b) $a = 1, b = 4 \Rightarrow [A(x)]_1^4 = [10x - 2x^2]_1^4$
$= (10 \times 4 - 2 \times 4^2) - (10 \times 1 - 2 \times 1^2)$
$= 8 - 8 = 0$

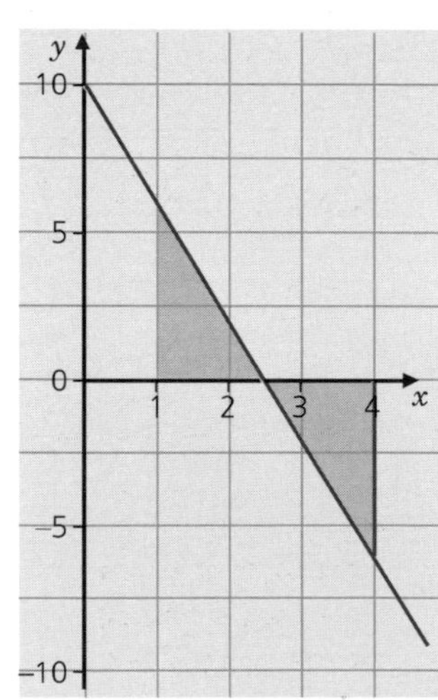

*Over the interval $1 \le t \le 4$, the graph is both positive $(1 \le t < 2.5)$ and negative $(2.5 < x \le 4)$; the area **above** the x-axis is **positive** whereas the area **below** the x-axis is **negative**.*

The two areas are equal in magnitude, but opposite in sign, which is why their sum is zero.

To find the actual area enclosed by the graph and the x-axis over the interval $1 \le t \le 4$ it is necessary to carry out two separate integrations.

$a = 1, b = 2.5 \Rightarrow [A(x)]_1^{2.5} = [10x - 2x^2]_1^{2.5}$
$= (10 \times 2.5 - 2 \times 2.5^2) - (10 \times 1 - 2 \times 1^2)$
$= 12.5 - 8 = 4.5$

$a = 2.5, b = 4 \Rightarrow [A(x)]_{2.5}^4 = [10x - 2x^2]_{2.5}^4$
$= (10 \times 4 - 2 \times 4^2) - (10 \times 2.5 - 2 \times 2.5^2)$
$= 8 - 12.5 = -4.5$

Therefore the actual area is $4.5 + |-4.5| = 9$

EXERCISES

8.1 CLASSWORK

1 For each of the following functions, find the area function $\mathrm{A}(x)$ and so calculate the area of the shaded region.

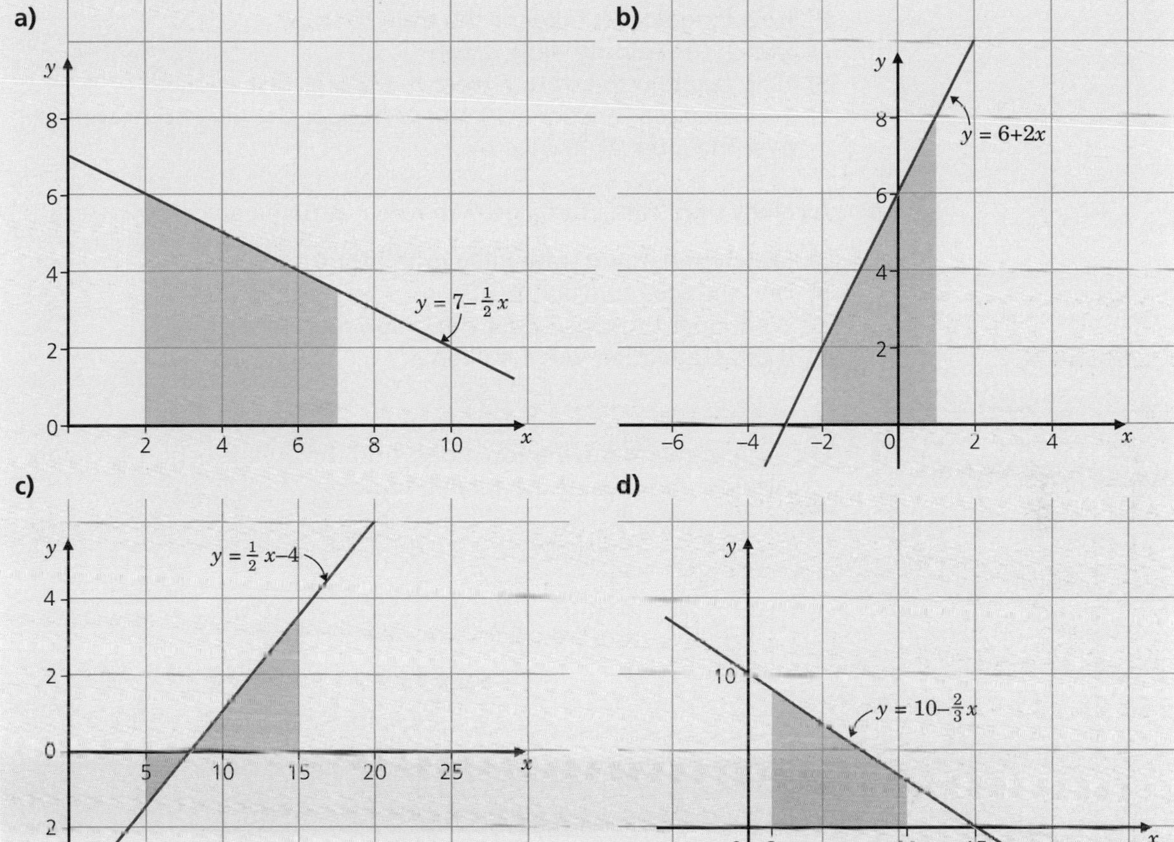

2 For each of the following functions $f(x)$, find the area function $A(x)$ and use it to find the area under the graph of $y = f(x)$ between $x = a$ and $x = b$ as given.
Illustrate your answer with a sketch.

a) $f(x) = 5x - 2$ $\quad a = 1, b = 4$
b) $f(x) = 10 - 3x$ $\quad a = -2, b = 3$
c) $f(x) = \dfrac{8 - 2x}{5}$ $\quad a = 2.8, b = 3.2$

3 For each of the following functions, sketch the graph of the function and find the x-value of the point where it crosses the x-axis. Hence find the total area between the graph and the x-axis for the given values of a and b.

a) $y = 4 - 2x$ $\quad a = 1, b = 3$
b) $y = 3x + 3$ $\quad a = -2, b = 2$
c) $y = -\frac{1}{4}x - 1$ $\quad a = -4, b = -2$

4 An engine driver applies the brakes as the train approaches a station. The train decelerates at a constant rate such that its velocity, v m s^{-1}, t seconds after applying the brakes, is given by $v = 40 - 2t$.

a) At what speed is the train travelling when the brakes are applied?
b) How long does it take for the train to stop?
c) Sketch the velocity–time graph.
d) How far from the station were the brakes first applied?
e) Find the area function $\mathrm{A}(t)$ and so deduce the distance travelled over the interval $10 \le t \le 15$.

5 A colony of bacteria has a growth rate r at time t given by $r = 0.8t + 1$.

a) Sketch the growth rate–time graph for $0 \le t \le 3$.
b) Find the area function $\mathrm{A}(t)$.
c) What does the area under the graph represent?
d) If the population was 1 million at $t = 0$, what was it at $t = 3$?

8.1 HOMEWORK

1 For each of the following functions, find the area function $\mathrm{A}(x)$ and so calculate the area of the shaded region.

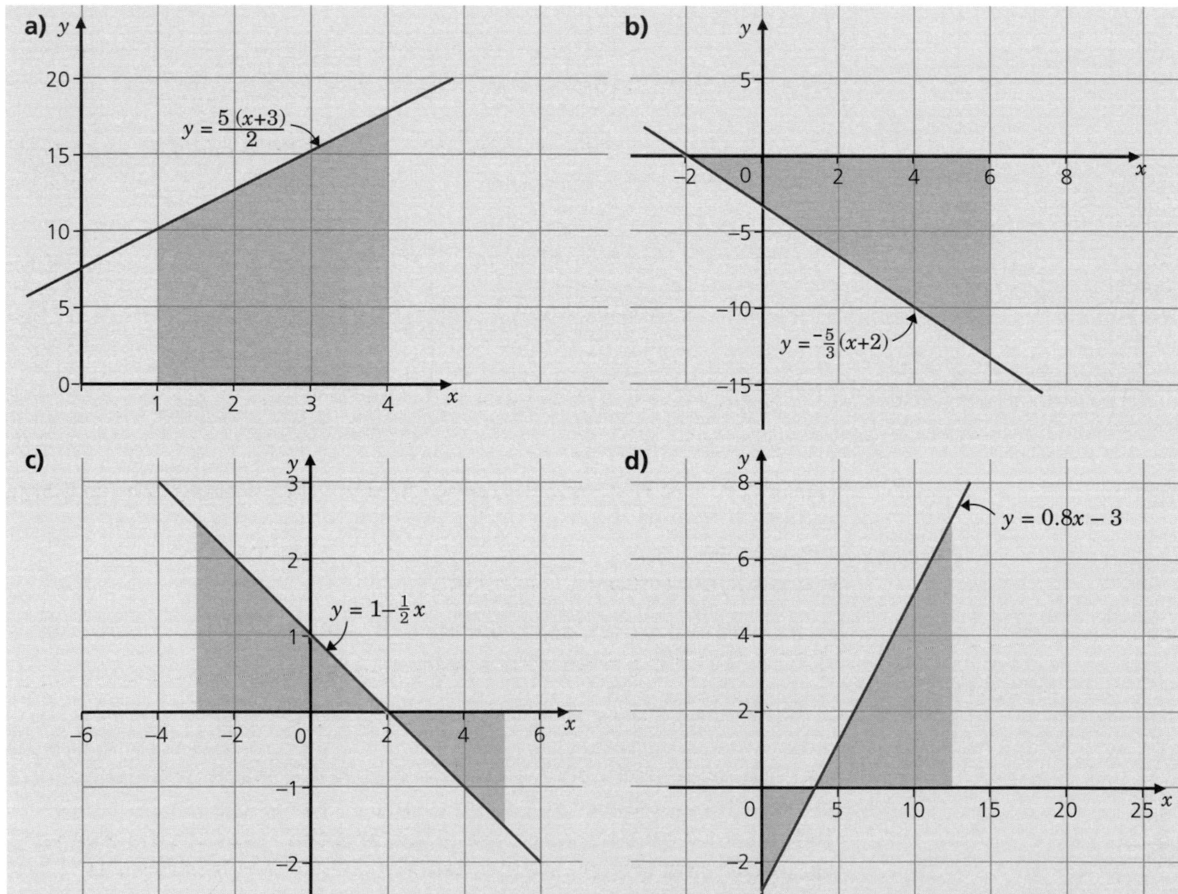

2 For each of the following functions $\mathrm{f}(x)$, find the area function $\mathrm{A}(x)$ and use it to find the area under the graph of $y = \mathrm{f}(x)$ between $x = a$ and $x = b$ as given.

Illustrate your answer with a sketch.

a) $y = 4 - 2x$ $a = -1, b = 1$ b) $y = 3x + 3$ $a = -2, b = 1$
c) $y = -\frac{1}{3}x - 1$ $a = -2, b = 3$

3 For each of the following functions, sketch the graph of the function and find the x-value of the point where it crosses the x-axis. Hence find the total area between the graph and the x-axis for the given values of a and b.

a) $f(x) = 3 - \frac{1}{2}x$ $a = 5, b = 7$ b) $f(x) = 2x - 5$ $a = 0, b = 3$
c) $f(x) = -\frac{1}{4}x - 2$ $a = -10, b = 0$

4 A driver is travelling at constant speed on a stretch of dual carriageway in a built-up area when she notices the lights change to red 50 m away. She applies the brakes in such a way that the car's velocity, v m s^{-1}, t seconds after she applies the brakes, is given by $v = 24 - 6t$.

a) At what speed is the car travelling when the brakes are applied?
b) How long does it take for the car to stop?
c) Sketch the velocity–time graph.
d) Find the area function $A(t)$ and deduce the distance from the lights when the car stops.
e) After noticing the lights, what is the maximum time delay possible, before applying the brakes, in order not to go through a red light?

5 Bob's sports bag contains a bottle of cola. When Bob throws the bag into the boot of his car, cola starts to leak from the loose cap at a rate R litres per second, given by:

$R = \frac{1}{175} + \frac{t}{1750}$ until after 50 seconds the bottle is completely empty.

a) Sketch a graph of R against t for $0 \le t \le 50$.
b) Find the area function $A(t)$.
c) What does the area under the graph actually represent?
d) How much cola was in the bottle before it started leaking?
e) After how long was the bottle half empty?

INTEGRATION: THE PROCESS

The main result from the first part of this chapter was:
$f(x) = mx + c \Rightarrow A(x) = \frac{1}{2}mx^2 + cx$

e.g. $f(x) = 5x - 2 \Rightarrow A(x) = \frac{5}{2}x^2 - 2x$

$f(x) = 1.5x + 5 \Rightarrow A(x) = 0.75x^2 + 5x$

$f(x) = 10 - 4x \Rightarrow A(x) = 10x - 2x^2$

Since the area expression $[A(x)]_0^x = A(x)$, then $A(x)$ represents the area under a curve between 0 and x.
For any function $f(x)$, the process of finding the area function $A(x)$ is called **integration**. $A(x)$ is the **integral** of $f(x)$. What is more, the inverse process, starting with $A(x)$ and finding $f(x)$ is **differentiation**, i.e. $A'(x) = f(x)$.

e.g. $A(x) = 10x - 2x^2 \Rightarrow A'(x) = 10 - 4x$

This works well as long as $f(x) = mx + c$, but what of other functions $f(x)$? Is it always true that $A'(x) = f(x)$?

Exploration 8.5

Functions and areas

The graph of the function $y = 3x^2$ is drawn on the axes below.

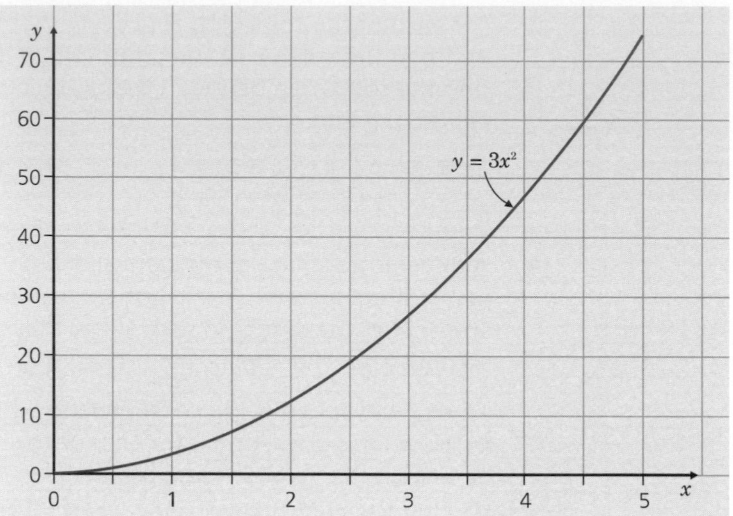

- Using a suitable numerical method, copy and complete this table.
- Find a formula for $A(x)$.
- Describe the relationship between $A(x)$ and $f(x)$.

x	$f(x) = 3x^2$	$A(x)$
0	0	0
1	3	
2	12	
3	27	
4	48	
5	75	

The inverse of differentiation

The result of the last exploration was that $A(x) = x^3$ and so once again $A'(x) = f(x)$. This is just another illustration of the general result that the process of integration is the *inverse* process to differentiation.

Notation

The integral of a function is denoted by an elongated S, i.e. $\int$.
In short:

$$A(x) = \int f(x)\mathrm{d}x$$

Integral of f(x) with respect to x

Since the derivative of a constant is 0, the integral of a function $f(x)$ *may* differ by a constant, e.g. all these statements are true:

$$\int 3x^2\mathrm{d}x = x^3$$

$$\int 3x^2\mathrm{d}x = x^3 + 5$$

$$\int 3x^2\mathrm{d}x = x^3 - 2 \quad \text{etc.}$$

In general:

$$\int 3x^2\mathrm{d}x = x^3 + c \quad \text{where } c \text{ is the constant of integration.}$$

The inclusion of a constant c other than 0 in the integral alters the left-hand boundary value a for the area function.
i.e. $A(x) = \left[A(x)\right]_0^x$ only if the constant of integration $c = 0$.

Since the process of integration is the inverse of differentiation, rules can easily be formulated, as in differentiation.

1 $f(x) = x^n \Rightarrow \int f(x)dx = \frac{1}{n+1}x^{n+1} + c$, $n = 0, 1, 2, 3, ...$

e.g. $f(x) = x^5 \Rightarrow \int f(x)dx = \frac{1}{6}x^6 + c$

2 $f(x) = ax^n \Rightarrow \int ax^n dx = a\frac{1}{n+1}x^{n+1} + c$, $n = 0, 1, 2, 3, ...$

e.g. $f(x) = 5x^3 \Rightarrow \int 5x^3 dx = 5 \times \frac{1}{4}x^4 + c = \frac{5}{4}x^4 + c$

3 The integral of a sum (or difference) is the sum (or difference) of the integrals, e.g.

$f(x) = x^3 - 5x + 10 \Rightarrow \int f(x)dx = \frac{1}{4}x^4 - \frac{5}{2}x^2 + 10x + c$

Exploration 8.6 *Areas and integrals*

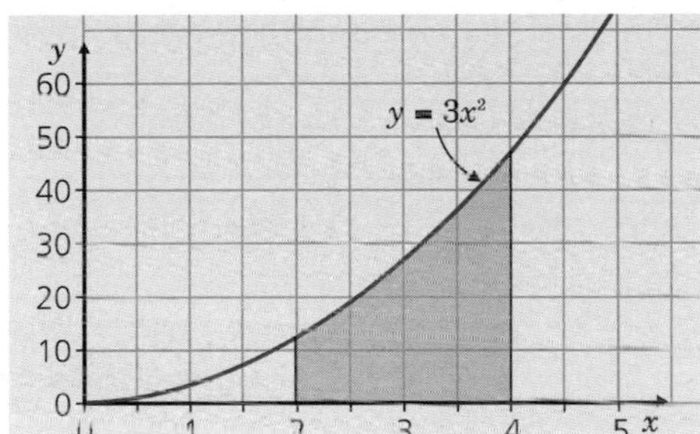

The diagram shows the graph of $f(x) = 3x^2$.

- Use the area function $A(x) = x^3$ developed in the last exploration to find the area of the shaded region.

Definite integrals

The area between $x = 0$ and $x = 4$ is given by $A(4)$.
The area between $x = 0$ and $x = 2$ is given by $A(2)$.
Area under graph between $x = 2$ and $x = 4$ is given by:
$A(4) - A(2) = 4^3 - 2^3 = 64 - 8 = 56$.

Notation

The required area is denoted by the **definite integral**:

upper limit

$$\int_2^4 3x^2 dx = \left[x^3\right]_2^4 = 4^3 - 2^3 = 56$$

lower limit

Areas can lie above the x-axis, below the x-axis or a mixture of the two.

Example 8.2

The graph shows a sketch of the graph $y = x(x^2 - 9)$.

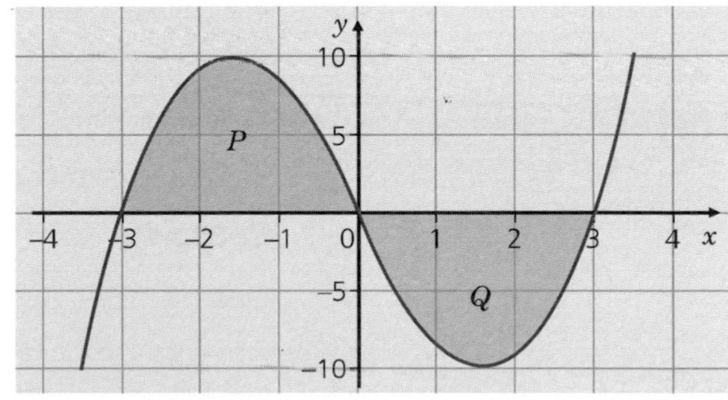

Use a definite integral to find areas P and Q.

Explain why $\int_{-3}^{3} x(x^2 - 9)\,dx = 0$.

Solution

Area P is given by $\int_{-3}^{0} x(x^2-9)\,\mathrm{d}x = \int_{-3}^{0} (x^3-9x)\,\mathrm{d}x$

$$= \left[\tfrac{1}{4}x^4 - \tfrac{9}{2}x^2\right]_{-3}^{0} = (0-0) - \left(\tfrac{1}{4}(-3)^4 - \tfrac{9}{2}(-3)^2\right)$$

$$= -\left(\tfrac{81}{4} - \tfrac{81}{2}\right) = 20.25$$

Since the function is odd, the graph has rotational symmetry of order 2 about the origin, so area $Q = 20.25$, which is confirmed by integration (the negative sign indicating area **below** the x-axis).

$$\int_{0}^{3} x(x^2-9)\,\mathrm{d}x = \int_{0}^{3} (x^3-9x)\,\mathrm{d}x = \left[\tfrac{1}{4}x^4 - \tfrac{9}{2}x^2\right]_{0}^{3}$$

$$= \left(\tfrac{1}{4}(3)^4 - \tfrac{9}{2}(3)^2\right) - (0-0) = \left(\tfrac{81}{4} - \tfrac{81}{2}\right) = -20.25$$

Finally $\int_{-3}^{3} x(x^2-9)\,\mathrm{d}x = \int_{-3}^{0} x\left(x^2-9\right)\mathrm{d}x + \int_{0}^{3} x\left(x^2-9\right)\mathrm{d}x$

$$= 20.25 + (-20.25) = 0$$

Here the zero result occurs since the positive and negative areas have 'cancelled each other out'.

Example 8.3

Find the area enclosed by the graphs of $y = 3x(5-x)$ and $y = 15 - 3x$.

Solution

Sketch the graphs and shade the required area.

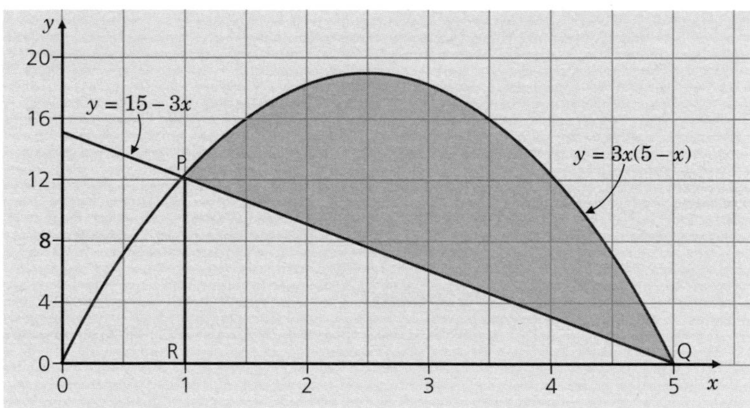

Notice that the graphs intersect at (1, 12) and (5, 0).

The required area is given by $\int_{1}^{5} 3x(5-x)\,\mathrm{d}x - \int_{1}^{5} (15-3x)\,\mathrm{d}x$

shaded area + ΔPQR area ΔPQR

There are two ways of obtaining the required answer.

Method A

Area $= \int_{1}^{5} (15x - 3x^2)\,\mathrm{d}x - \int_{1}^{5} (15-3x)\,\mathrm{d}x$

$$= \left[7.5x^2 - x^3\right]_{1}^{5} - \left[15x - 1.5x^2\right]_{1}^{5}$$

$$= \{(7.5\times 25 - 125) - (7.5\times 1 - 1)\} - \{(15\times 5 - 1.5\times 25) - (15\times 1 - 1.5\times 1)\}$$

$$= \{62.5 - 6.5\} - \{37.5 - 13.5\} = 32$$

Method B

$$\begin{aligned} \text{Area} &= \int_1^5 \{(15x - 3x^2) - (15 - 3x)\}\,dx \\ &= \int_1^5 (18x - 3x^2 - 15)\,dx \\ &= \left[9x^2 - x^3 - 15x\right]_1^5 \\ &= (9\times25 - 125 - 15\times5) - (9\times1 - 1 - 15\times1) = 32 \end{aligned}$$

EXERCISES

8.2 CLASSWORK

1 Find by definite integration the areas of the following shaded regions.

a)

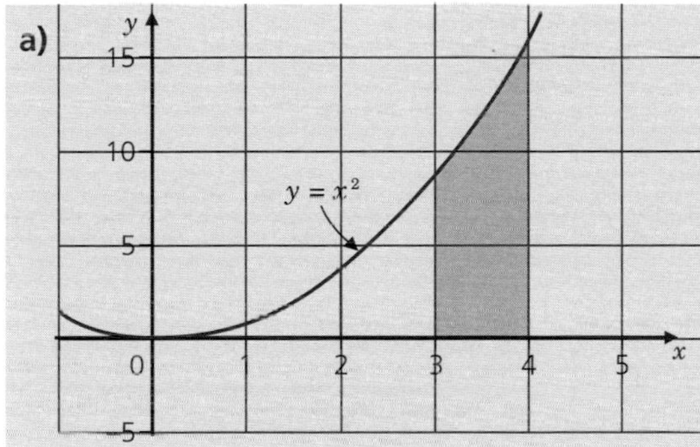

b)

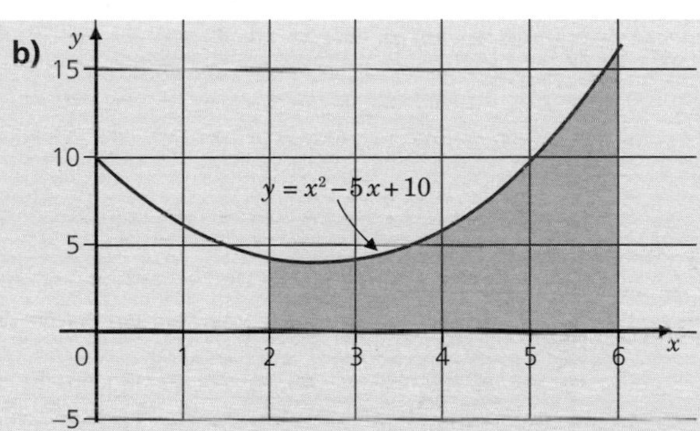

c)

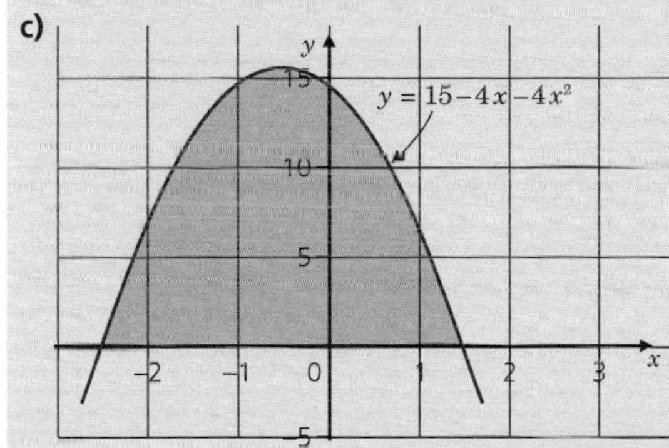

d)

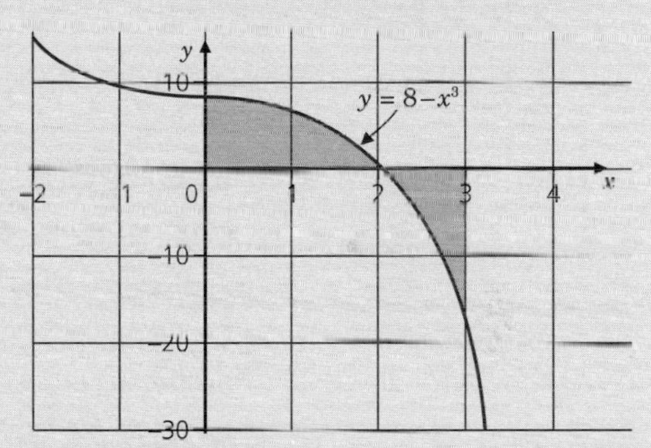

2 Find the areas represented by the following integrals. Illustrate each of your answers with a sketch.

a) $\int_1^2 x^3\,dx$ **b)** $\int_{-1}^0 (x^2 + x)\,dx$ **c)** $\int_{-2}^2 x^4\,dx$ **d)** $\int_{-3}^3 (18 - 2x^2)\,dx$

For each of questions **3** to **11** sketch a graph of the given curve(s) and find the area described.

3 The area between the curve $y = x(3 - x)$ and the x-axis from $x = 0$ to $x = 4$.

4 The area enclosed by the curve $y = (2 + x)(5 - x)$ and the x-axis.

5 The area enclosed by the curve $y = x(x - 4)^2$ and the x-axis.

6 The area bounded by the curve $y = (x - 3)(x - 4)$ and the x- and y-axis.

7 The area enclosed by the curve $y = (x - 2)^2$ and the line with equation $y = 2x - 1$.

8 The area enclosed by the curve $y = (x - 1)(x - 4)$ and the line with equation $x + y = 4$.

9 The area enclosed by the curve $y = 0.25x^3$ and the curve $y = 4x(5 - x)$.

8.2 HOMEWORK

1 Find by definite integration the areas of the following shaded regions.

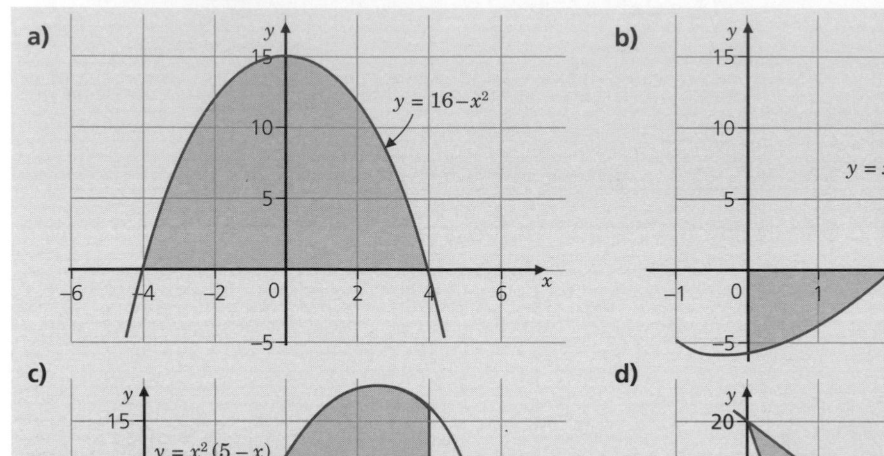

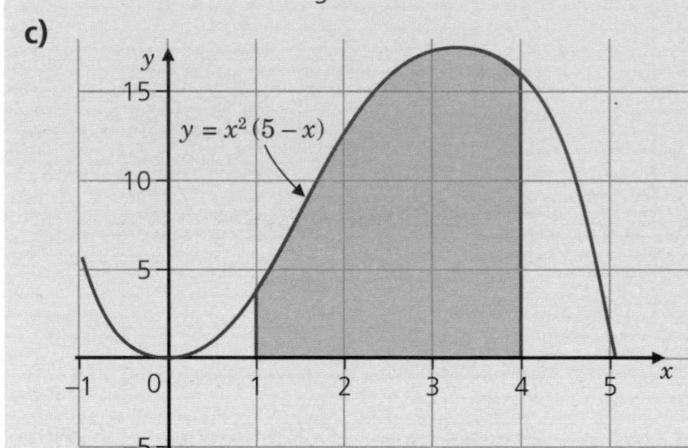

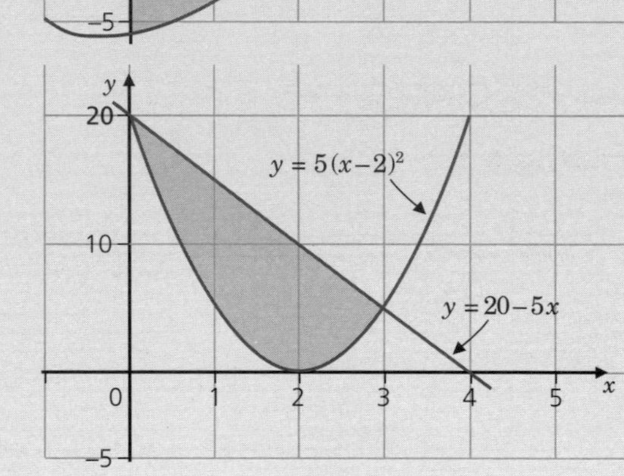

2 Find the areas represented by the following integrals. Illustrate each of your answers with a sketch.

a) $\int_1^2 3x^4 \mathrm{d}x$ **b)** $\int_{-1}^{0.5} (x^2 + x - 1)\,\mathrm{d}x$ **c)** $\int_0^4 x(4 - x)\,\mathrm{d}x$ **d)** $\int_{-4}^{4} (3x^2 - 48)\,\mathrm{d}x$

For each of questions **3** to **11** sketch a graph of the given curve(s) and find the area described.

3 The area between the curve $y = x(4 - x)$ and the x-axis from $x = 0$ to $x = 6$.

4 The area enclosed by the curve $y = (2x - 1)(2x + 1)$ and the x-axis.

5 The area enclosed by the curve $y = x(x - 1)(x - 2)$ and the x-axis.

6 The area enclosed by the curve $y = x(2 - x)$ and the line $y = \frac{1}{2}x$.

7 The area enclosed between the curve $y = x^2 - 3x - 4$ and the line $y = x + 1$.

8 The area enclosed between the curves $y = x^2 - 1$ and $y = 1 - x^2$.

9 The area enclosed between the curves $y = 4 - x^2$ and $y = x^2 - 2x + 4$.

INTEGRATION: REVERSING DIFFERENTIATION

The technique of reversing differentiation, i.e. given $\frac{\mathrm{d}y}{\mathrm{d}x} = \mathrm{f}'(x)$ finding $y = \mathrm{f}(x)$, is known as **indefinite integration**, and is written:

$$\int \mathrm{f}'(x)\mathrm{d}x = \mathrm{f}(x)$$

The function $\frac{dy}{dx} = f'(x)$ is called a **gradient function**.
Equivalently, the integral of any function $f(x)$ gives an **integral function** $F(x)$, which contains a constant of integration c.

A particular value for c may be determined by stating certain conditions for the integral function to obey.

Example 8.4

Integrate $f(x)$, *where* $f(x) = (2x - 1)(x + 3)$.

Solution

Firstly simplify the function.

$$f(x) = (2x - 1)(x + 3) = 2x^2 + 5x - 3$$

$$\Rightarrow \int f(x)\,dx = \int (2x^2 + 5x - 3)\,dx = \tfrac{2}{3}x^3 + \tfrac{5}{2}x^2 - 3x + c$$

Example 8.5

A curve has gradient function $\frac{dy}{dx} = 4x - 1$ *and passes through the point (1, 5).*
Find its equation in the form $y = f(x)$ *and illustrate your answer with a sketch.*

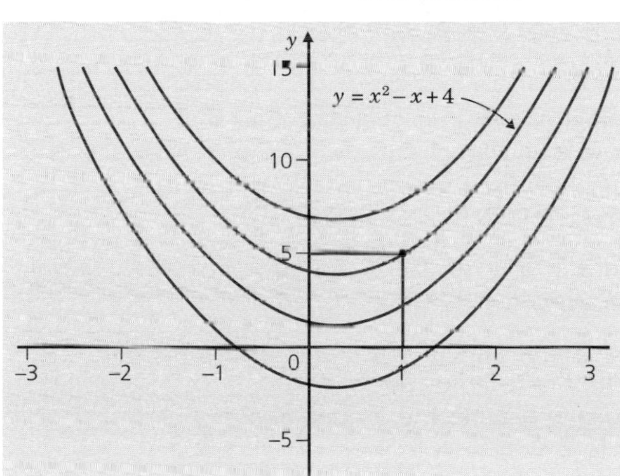

Solution

$$\frac{dy}{dx} = 4x - 1 \Rightarrow y = \int (4x - 1)\,dx = 2x^2 - x + c$$

But $y = 5$ *when* $x = 1$, *since the curve passes through* (1, 5).

$\Rightarrow 5 = 2 \times 1^2 - 1 + c$

$\Rightarrow c = 4$

Therefore the equation of the curve is
$y = 2x^2 - x + 4$.

Note

The function $2x^2 - x + c$ represents a family of curves, of which only one curve passes through (1, 5).
$y = 2x^2 - x + 4$

Example 8.6

For a function $y = f(x)$, $f'(x) = 3x^2 - 2x$ and $f(1) = 3$, find $f(x)$.

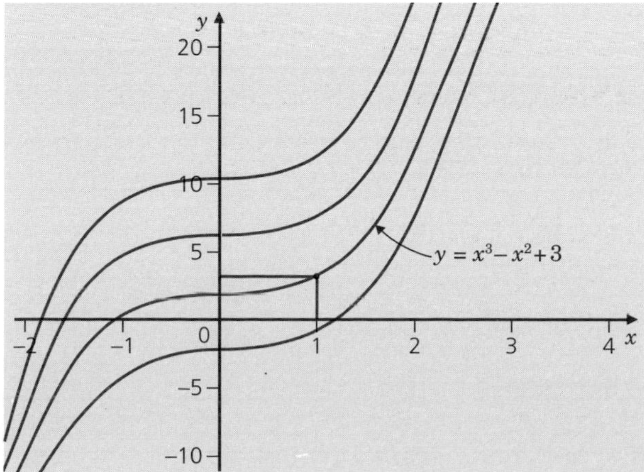

Solution

$$f(x) = \int (3x^2 - 2x)\,dx = x^3 - x^2 + c$$

But $f(1) = 3 \Rightarrow 1^3 - 1^2 + c = 3$

$\Rightarrow c = 3$

$y = f(x) = x^3 - x^2 + 3$

Note

The function $y = x^3 - x^2 + c$ represents a family of curves, of which only one curve passes through (1, 3).
$y = x^3 - x^2 + 3$.

Example 8.7

Show that $\int(x+a)^2\,dx = \frac{1}{3}(x+a)^3 + k$, where a is a constant.

Solution

Firstly simplify the function.

$(x+a)^2 = (x+a)(x+a) = x^2 + 2ax + a^2$

$$\Rightarrow \int(x^2+2ax+a^2)\,dx = \tfrac{1}{3}x^3 + \tfrac{1}{2}\times 2ax^2 + a^2x + c$$
$$= \tfrac{1}{3}\left(x^3+3ax^2+3a^2x+a^3\right)+k \quad \{\text{where } c = \tfrac{1}{3}a^3+k\}$$
$$= \tfrac{1}{3}(x+a)^3 + k$$

Displacement, velocity and acceleration

In Chapter 7, *Differentiation 1* we found that:

$s = f(t)$ gives displacement s as a function of time t

$\Rightarrow \quad v = \dfrac{ds}{dt} = f'(t)$ gives velocity v as a function of time t

$\Rightarrow \quad a = \dfrac{dv}{dt} = f''(t)$ gives acceleration a as a function of time t

Since the process of integration is the reverse of differentiation, it follows that:

$v = \int a\,dt$ and $s = \int v\,dt$

The following example illustrates how velocity–time and displacement–time equations may be deduced, by successive integration, beginning with the acceleration–time equation.

Example 8.8

A ball is thrown vertically upwards from ground level with an initial velocity of 30 m s^{-1}. Assuming a constant acceleration of –10 m s^{-2}, find:

a) *velocity–time and displacement–time equations for the ball,*
b) *the maximum height reached by the ball,*
c) *the time after which it reaches the ground again.*

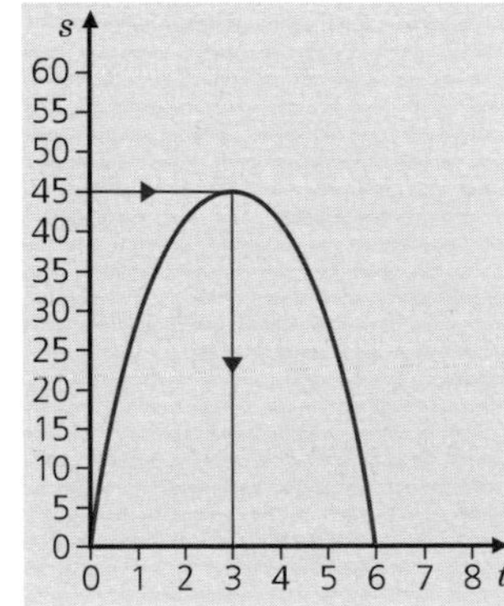

Solution

a) $a = -10 \Rightarrow v = \int a\,dt = \int -10\,dt = -10t + c$

but $v = 30$ *when* $t = 0 \Rightarrow c = 30$

hence $v = -10t + 30$

$\Rightarrow s = \int v\,dt = \int(-10t+30)\,dt = -5t^2 + 30t + c$

But $s = 0$ *when* $t = 0 \Rightarrow c = 0$

hence $s = 30t - 5t^2$.

b) *The maximum height occurs when* $\dfrac{ds}{dt} = v = 0$.

$\Rightarrow -10t + 30 = 0 \Rightarrow t = 3$

$\Rightarrow s = 30\times 3 - 5\times 3^2 = 90 - 45 = 45$

$\Rightarrow$ *The maximum height is 45 metres.*

c) *On reaching the ground again:*

$s = 0$

$\Rightarrow 30t - 5t^2 = 0 \Rightarrow 5t(6-t) = 0$

$\Rightarrow t = 0$ *or* $t = 6$

$\Rightarrow$ *The ball reaches the ground again after 6 seconds.*

EXERCISES

8.3 CLASSWORK

1 For each of the following gradient functions find $y = f(x)$.

a) $f'(x) = 7$
b) $f'(x) = 4x^3$
c) $f'(x) = 6x^2$
d) $f'(x) = x^2 - 4x + 5$
e) $f'(x) = x^7$
f) $\frac{dy}{dx} = (x+4)(x-3)$
g) $\frac{dy}{dx} = 4x^2(x-1)$
h) $\frac{dy}{dx} = (x+2)^3$

2 Find the values of the following integrals.

a) $\int (4x-7)\,dx$
b) $\int x^2(x-1)\,dx$
c) $\int 2x(x^3+4)\,dx$
d) $\int 7(2-x)^2\,dx$

3 For each of the following gradient functions, find the equation of the curve that passes through the given point and sketch the curve.

a) $f'(x) = 2x$ — $y = f(x)$ passes through (0, 3)
b) $f'(x) = 4x + 5$ — $y = f(x)$ passes through (0, 2)
c) $f'(x) = 10 - 3x^2$ — $y = f(x)$ passes through (1, 1)
d) $f'(x) = x^2(x + 1)$ — $y = f(x)$ passes through (1, 1)
e) $\frac{dy}{dx} = 2x(x-1)$ — $y = f(x)$ passes through (3, 4)
f) $\frac{dy}{dx} = (x^2-1)(3x+5)$ — $y = f(x)$ passes through (0, –3)

8.3 HOMEWORK

1 For each of the following gradient functions find $y = f(x)$.

a) $f'(x) = -3$
b) $f'(x) = 5x^4$
c) $f'(x) = 0.2x^4$
d) $f'(x) = 3.5x^6$
e) $f'(x) = x(x + 1)$
f) $\frac{dy}{dx} = (x-1)(x-2)$
g) $\frac{dy}{dx} = 3x^3(2x+7)$
h) $\frac{dy}{dx} = (3x+1)^3$

2 Find the values of the following integrals.

a) $\int (3x-4)\,dx$
b) $\int t^3(t^2-1)\,dt$
c) $\int \frac{(5-x)^2}{2}\,dx$
d) $\int x(x+1)(x+2)\,dx$

3 For each of the following gradient functions, find the equation of the curve that passes through the given point and sketch the curve.

a) $f'(x) = 0.5$ — $y = f(x)$ passes through (1, 1)
b) $f'(x) = 8x$ — $y = f(x)$ passes through (3, 4)
c) $f'(x) = 11 - 2x$ — $y = f(x)$ passes through (2, 0)
d) $f'(x) = 11 - 2x^2$ — $y = f(x)$ passes through (0, 0)
e) $\frac{dy}{dx} = x^2(x+4)$ — $y = f(x)$ passes through (3, 0)
f) $\frac{dy}{dx} = (3x-2)^3$ — $y = f(x)$ passes through (0, 0)

CONSOLIDATION EXERCISES FOR CHAPTER 8

1 Sketch the curve $y = (x - 1)(6 - x)$. Find the area enclosed between the curve and the x-axis.

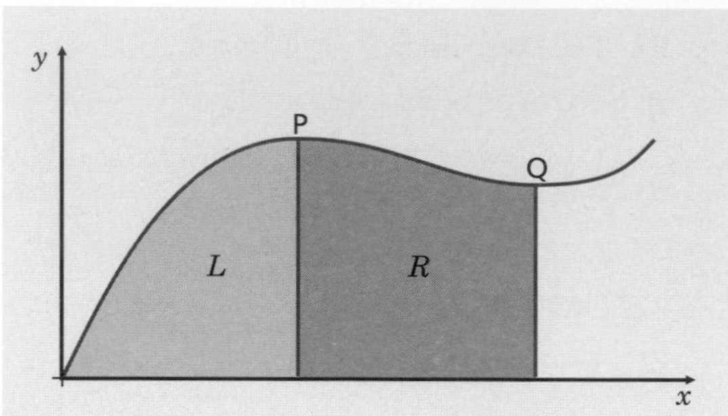

2 The diagram shows a sketch of the curve with equation $y = x^3 - 9x^2 + 24x$.

Maximum and minimum values occur at points P and Q respectively.

a) Calculate the coordinates of P and Q.
b) Show that areas L and R are in the ratio 7:9.

3 Evaluate the following integrals.

a) $\int_1^2 (x^2 + 2)^2 \, dx$ **b)** $\int_{-1}^3 (5x^2 - 2)^2 \, dx$

4 **a)** Show that the line $x + y = 4$ crosses the curve $y = \frac{1}{4}x^2 - x$ at the point A (4, 0) and find the coordinates of B, the other point of intersection.
b) Sketch the line and the curve on the same axes.
c) Evaluate these integrals.

i) $\int_{-4}^0 (\frac{1}{4}x^2 - x) \, dx$ **ii)** $\int_0^4 (\frac{1}{4}x^2 - x) \, dx$

d) Hence find the area of the region bounded by the line AB and the curve $y = \frac{1}{4}x^2 - x$.

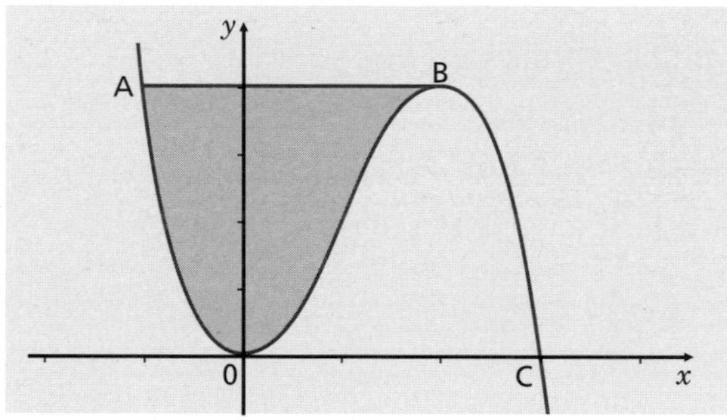

5 The diagram shows a sketch of the curve $y = x^2(3 - x)$, which crosses the x-axis at C and has stationary values at O and B.

a) Find the coordinates of A and B.
b) Calculate the area of the shaded region.
c) Prove that OABC is a parallelogram.

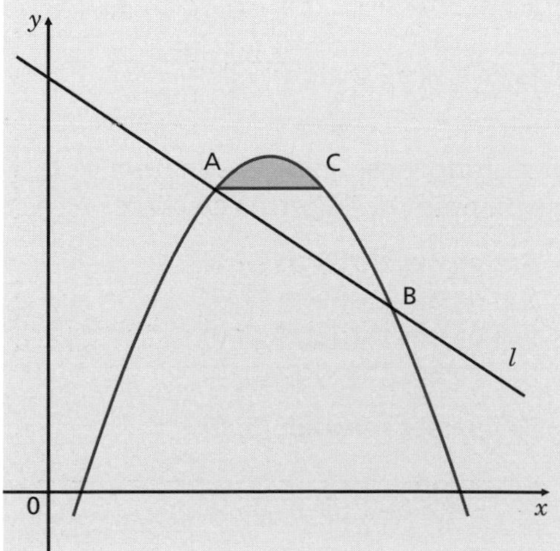

6 The figure shows part of the curve with equation $y = p + 10x - x^2$, where p is a constant, and part of the line l with equation $y = qx + 25$, where q is a constant. The line l cuts the curve at the points A and B. The x-coordinates of A and B are 4 and 8 respectively. The line through A parallel to the x-axis intersects the curve again at the point C.

a) Show that $p = -7$ and calculate the value of q.
b) Calculate the coordinates of C.

The shaded region in the figure is bounded by the curve and the line AC.

c) Using algebraic integration and showing all your working, calculate the area of the shaded region.

(EDEXCEL, Question 9, Paper 1, June 1999)

7 The diagram shows the line with equation $x + y = 4$ and the curve with equation $y = x^2 - 2x + 2$. The line and the curve intersect at the points P and Q and the minimum point on the curve is M, whose coordinates are (1, 1).

a) Find, using algebra, the coordinates of P and Q.
b) Prove that $\Delta\, MPQ$ is right-angled.

The shaded region R is bounded by the line and the curve.

c) Show that the area of the region R is $1\frac{1}{2}$ times the area of the $\Delta\, MPQ$.

(EDEXCEL, Specimen Paper 1, Question 7, 2000)

8 **i)** Evaluate $\int_0^4 x(4 - x)\mathrm{d}x$.

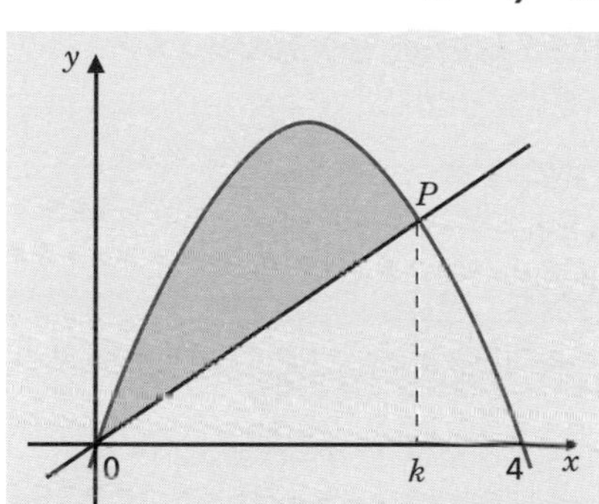

ii) The diagram shows the curve $y = x(4 - x)$, together with a straight line. This line cuts the curve at the origin O and at the point P with x-coordinate k, where $0 < k < 4$.

a) Show that the area of the shaded region, bounded by the line and the curve, is $\frac{1}{6}k^3$.
b) Find, correct to 3 decimal places, the value of k for which the area of the shaded region is half of the total area under the curve between $x = 0$ and $x = 4$.

(OCR, Question 6, Specimen Paper 1)

Summary

Integration

- The process of integration is the **inverse** of differentiation.
- The **indefinite integral** of a function f(x) with respect to x is denoted by $\int f(x)\mathrm{d}x$.

1 $f(x) = x^n \Rightarrow \int f(x)\mathrm{d}x = \dfrac{1}{n+1}x^n + c$ for $n = 0, 1, 2, 3, \ldots$

2 $f(x) = ax^n \Rightarrow \int f(x)\mathrm{d}x = \dfrac{a}{n+1}x^n + c$ for $n = 0, 1, 2, 3, \ldots$

3 The integral of a sum (or difference) is the sum (or difference) of the integrals.

Areas

- For positive functions, the area function $A(x) = \int f(x)\mathrm{d}x$ represents the area under a graph between 0 and x.
- The area under a graph between $x = a$ and $x = b$ is denoted by the **definite integral**

$$\int_a^b f(x)\mathrm{d}x = A(b) - A(a)$$

Trigonometry 1

In this chapter we:

- *investigate the sine, cosine and tangent of angles greater than 90° and explore the graphs of sine, cosine and tangent functions*
- *meet the idea of modelling periodic functions using sine and cosine*
- *introduce an alternative unit for measuring angles, called radians*
- *examine trigonometric identities which are useful for manipulating trigonometric equations*
- *solve simple trigonometric equations.*

TRIGONOMETRIC FUNCTIONS

Exploration 9.1

The position of an object moving in a circle

A big wheel at a fairground has 12 cars, equally spaced around the circumference. The radius of the wheel is 8 metres and the hub of the wheel is 9 metres above the ground.

- How high above the ground is each car?
- How far from the vertical support is each car?

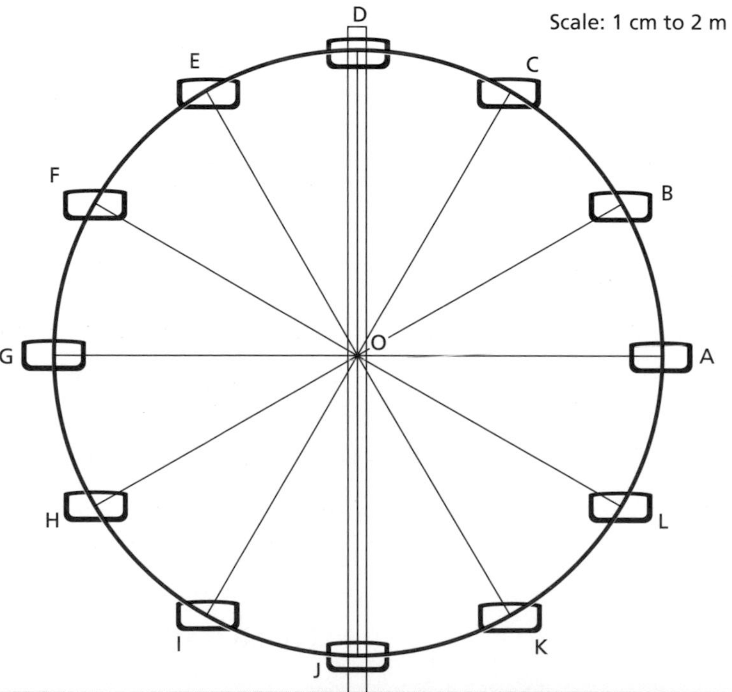

Modelling the big wheel

To model this situation, we can express the coordinates of a car, relative to O as origin, in terms of r, the radius of the wheel, and the angle AOP = θ, where P(x, y) is the position of the car.

In our 'big wheel' example, $r = 8$.

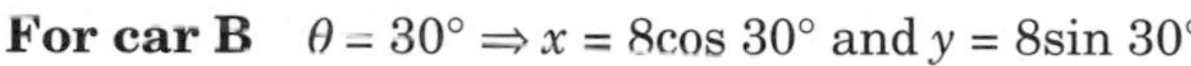

For car B $\theta = 30° \Rightarrow x = 8\cos 30°$ and $y = 8\sin 30°$

from which we can deduce:
height of car B = 9 + 8sin 30° = 13 m
distance of car B from support = 8cos 30° = 6.93 m.

For car C $\theta = 60° \Rightarrow x = 8\sin 30°$ and $y = 8\cos 30°$

from which we can deduce:
height of car C = 9 + 8sin 60° = 15.93 m
distance of car C from support = 8cos 60° = 4 m.

The positions of all the other cars, relative to O, may be deduced using similar methods, and by consideration of symmetry.

Sines and cosines of any angle

If the radius of the 'wheel' is 1 unit then $x = \cos\theta$ and $y = \sin\theta$, i.e. $\cos\theta$ is the x-coordinate of P and $\sin\theta$ is the y-coordinate of P. These definitions may be used for any angle θ, measured anticlockwise from the positive x axis. The values for cosine and sine may be found using a calculator.

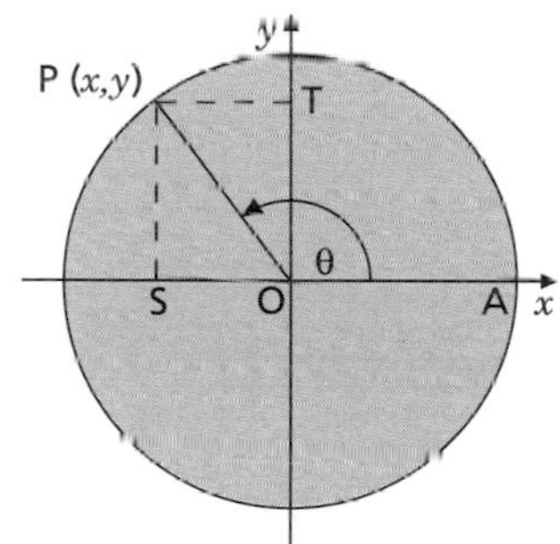

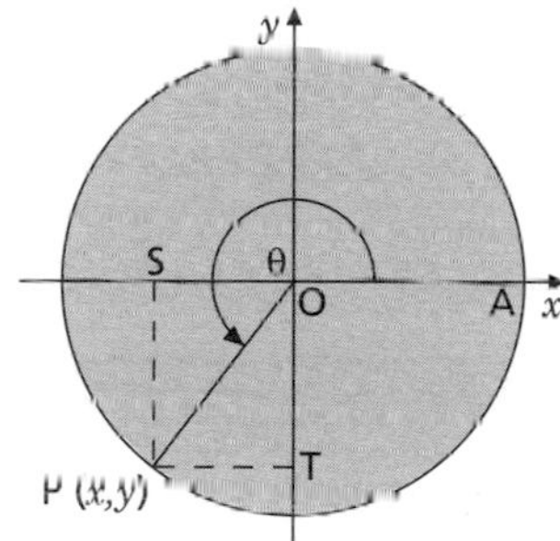

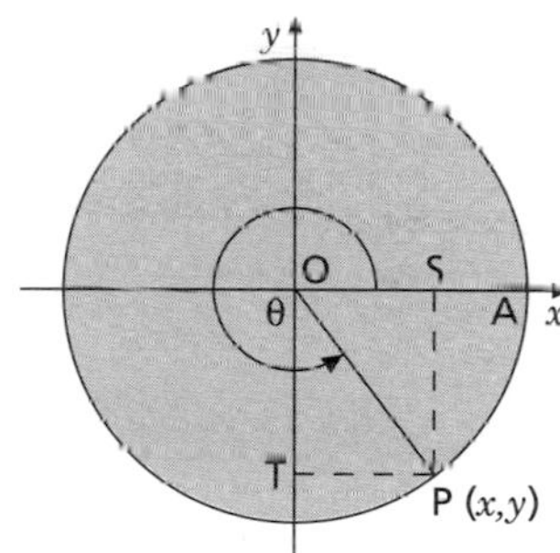

Exploration 9.2

Graphs of the sine and cosine functions

Refer again to the diagram in Exploration 9.1. Check your values for the coordinates of cars D to L relative to O using

$x = 8\cos\theta$ and $y = 8\sin\theta$.

- As θ varies from 0° to 360°, sketch graphs of both $x = \cos\theta$ and $y = \sin\theta$, with values of $\cos\theta$ and $\sin\theta$ found from your calculator.

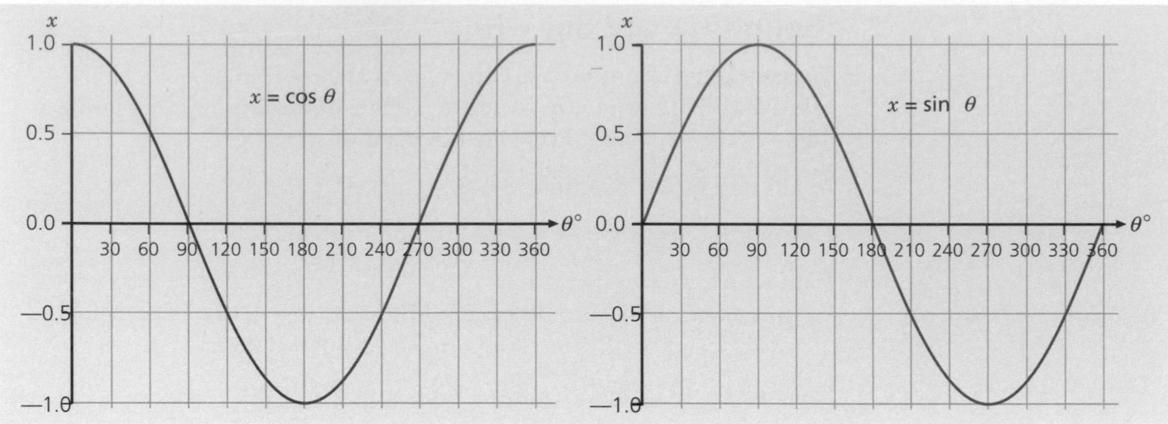

Circular functions

The definitions of x and y as $x = \cos\theta$ and $y = \sin\theta$ are derived from the coordinates of point P, as it moves round the circumference of the unit circle. Therefore they are called **circular functions**.

For either graph, plotting points at intervals of 30° and then joining them with a smooth curve is a good way to sketch it.

Remember these significant values for cosines and sines.

θ	0°	90°	180°	270°	360°
$\cos\theta$	1	0	−1	0	1
$\sin\theta$	0	1	0	−1	0

It is also useful to remember cosines and sines for angles 30° and 60°.

Exploration 9.3

Expressions for sin θ and cos θ

Draw two equilateral triangles of side 2 units, one with $\theta = 30°$ and the other with $\theta = 60°$ as indicated.

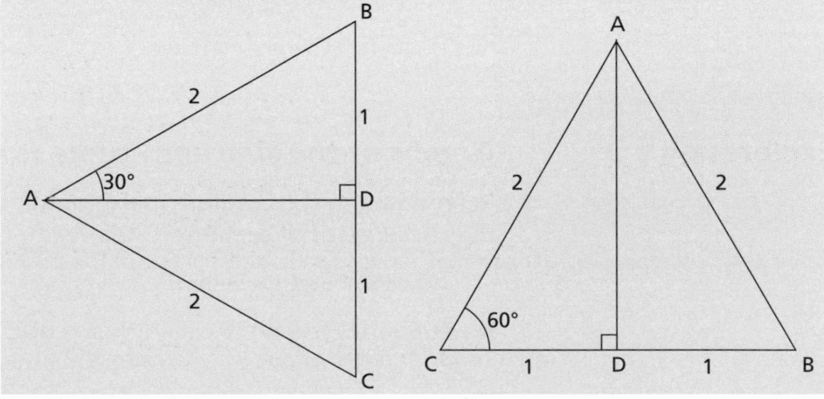

- In each case, find expressions for $\cos\theta$ and $\sin\theta$.

General results

In both diagrams, AD = √3 (by Pythagoras' theorem).

Hence:

$$\cos 30° = \frac{AD}{AB} = \frac{\sqrt{3}}{2} \approx 0.866 \text{ and } \sin 30° = \frac{BD}{AB} = \frac{1}{2} = 0.5$$

$$\cos 60° = \frac{BD}{AB} = \frac{1}{2} = 0.5 \text{ and } \sin 60° = \frac{AD}{AB} = \frac{\sqrt{3}}{2} \approx 0.866$$

These results illustrate the generalisations:

$\sin \theta = \cos (90° - \theta)$ and $\cos \theta = \sin (90° - \theta)$

By the symmetry of the cosine and sine graphs, we can also deduce:

$\cos 30° = \cos 330° = \frac{\sqrt{3}}{2} \Rightarrow \cos 150° = \cos 210° = -\frac{\sqrt{3}}{2}$

$\sin 30° = \sin 150° = \frac{1}{2} \Rightarrow \sin 210° = \sin 330° = -\frac{1}{2}$

$\cos 60° = \cos 300° = \frac{1}{2} \Rightarrow \cos 120° = \sin 240° = -\frac{1}{2}$

$\sin 60° = \sin 120° = \frac{\sqrt{3}}{2} \Rightarrow \sin 240° = \cos 300° = -\frac{\sqrt{3}}{2}$

These results illustrate some useful generalisations:

$\sin \theta = \sin (180° - \theta)$ and $\cos \theta = -\cos (180° - \theta)$ $0° \le \theta \le 180°$

$\cos \theta = \cos (360° - \theta)$ and $\sin \theta = -\sin (360° - \theta)$ $0° \le \theta < 360°$

CALCULATOR ACTIVITY

Exploration 9.4

Sine and cosine graphs

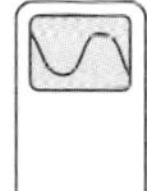

You will need a graphics calculator.

Firstly scale your axes:

$x_{min} = -360$ $x_{max} = 360$ $x_{scl} = 30$

$y_{min} = -1.5$ $y_{max} = 1.5$ $y_{scl} = 0.5$

and make sure you are in degree mode.

- Plot the graph of $y = \sin x$ and describe its properties.
- Plot the graph of $y = \cos x$ and describe its properties.
- Plot the graphs of $y = \sin x$ and $y = \cos x$.
  Identify the points where the graphs intersect.
  Describe how the two graphs are related.
- Plot the graphs of $y = \sin x$ and $y = -\sin x$.
  Describe how the two graphs are related.
- Plot the graphs of $y = \cos x$ and $y = -\cos x$.
  Describe how the two graphs are related.

Sine and cosine waves

The **sine** and **cosine** graphs (overleaf) both form **waves**. The waves **oscillate** between –1 and 1, both have an **amplitude** of 1 unit. You will note that both wave forms repeat themselves every 360°. This is the **period** of the sine and cosine graphs. Any function with a graph which exhibits a repeating pattern is **periodic**.

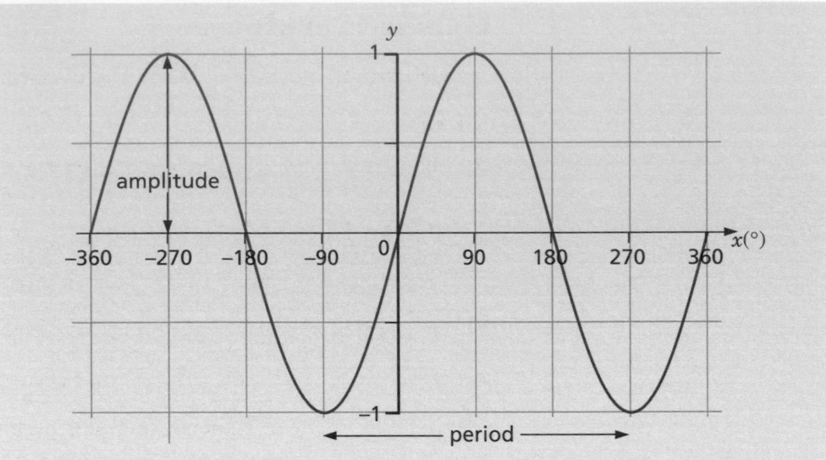

The size of angle is not restricted to the interval $-360° \leq \theta \leq 360°$. Indeed the wave form may be extended indefinitely for any angle, positive or negative.

Try some other intervals on your calculator.

Both wave forms have reflectional *and* rotational symmetry. There are an infinite number of mirror lines and centres of rotational symmetry for the infinite wave forms.

However, taking each wave over the interval $-360° \leq \theta \leq 360°$, we can see that:

- the sine curve has rotational symmetry about the origin, which makes it an **odd** function, and
- the cosine curve has reflectional symmetry in the y-axis, which makes it an **even** function.

Tangents of any angle

Following on from Explorations 9.1 and 9.2, the definitions of cosine and sine gave the coordinates (x, y) of point P as:

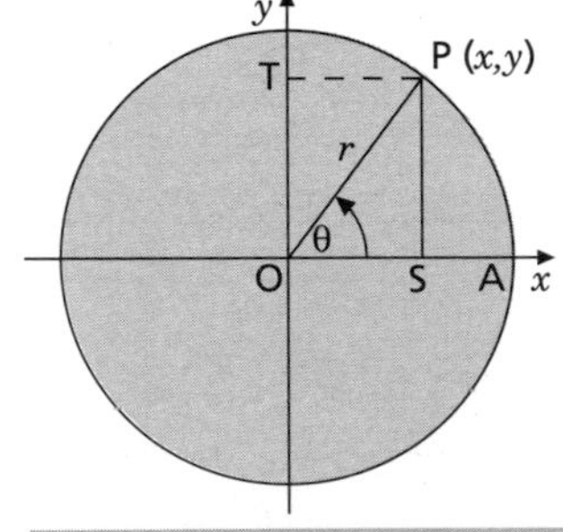

$x = r\cos\theta$ and $y = r\sin\theta$.

From the diagram:

$$\tan\theta = \frac{\text{PS}}{\text{OS}} = \frac{y}{x} = \frac{r\sin\theta}{r\cos\theta}$$

$$\Rightarrow \quad \tan\theta = \frac{\sin\theta}{\cos\theta}$$

This definition is extended to any angle θ, positive or negative.

Exploration 9.5

The graph of tan θ

- Sketch the graph of $z = \tan\,\theta$, $0° \leq \theta \leq 360°$.
- For what values of θ are these relationships true?

  a) $\tan\,\theta = 0$ **b)** $\tan\,\theta = 1$ **c)** $\tan\,\theta = -1$
- For what values of θ is $\tan\,\theta$ undefined ? Why?

- Write down values of $\tan \theta$ for:

  a) $\theta = 89°, 89.9°, 89.99°, 89.999°, 89.9999°$, etc.

  b) $\theta = 91°, 90.1°, 90.01°, 90.001°, 90.0001°$, etc.

- What happens to $\tan \theta$ as $\theta \Rightarrow 90°$ from either side of 90°?

Graph of the tangent

The **tangent graph** does not form a wave, but it does repeat itself every 180°, so it is also a periodic graph. The graph behaves in this way whatever interval for θ we take.

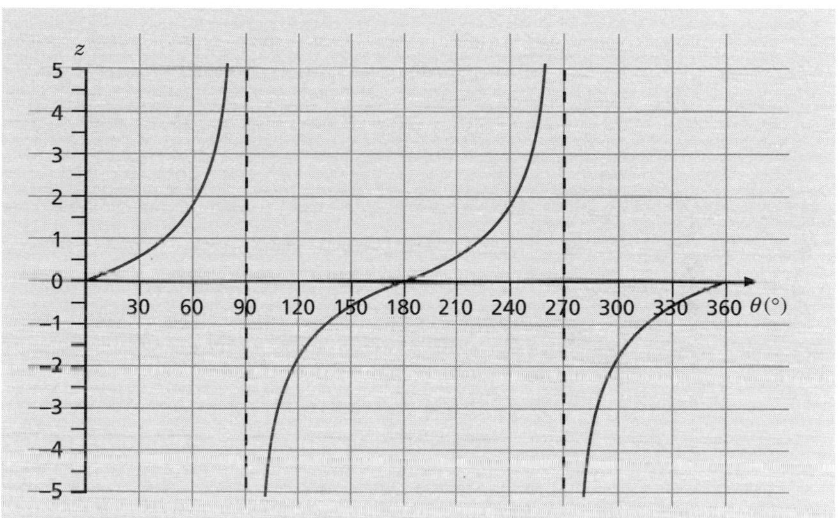

Like the sine graph, the tangent graph has rotational symmetry about the origin, which makes it an **odd** function.

The **range** of values the tangent can take is not restricted to the range −1 to 1. In fact, the range of the tangent function is infinite. We have found that by taking angles as close as we like to 90°, from below or above, we can make the value of the tangent as high, or as low, as we like.

Since the tangent of an angle is not defined for $\theta = 90°$, $\theta = 270°$, etc. the lines $\theta = 90°$, $\theta = 270°$, etc. are **asymptotes**.

EXERCISES

9.1 CLASSWORK

1 Use an isosceles right-angled triangle to find values for cos 45°, sin 45° and tan 45°. Check the decimal equivalents on your calculator.

a) What angles between −360° and 360° have cosines the same as:
  i) cos 45° **ii)** −cos 45°?

b) What angles between −360° and 360° have sines the same as:
  i) sin 45° **ii)** −sin 45°?

c) What angles between −360° and 360° have tangents the same as:
  i) tan 45° **ii)** −tan 45°?

2 Find values for tan 30° and tan 60° from the diagram on page 176 and the graphs above. Check the decimal equivalents on your calculator.

What angles between −360° and 360° have tangents the same as:
a) tan 30° **b)** tan 60° **c)** −tan 30° **d)** −tan 60°?

3 Using your calculator and the appropriate graph, find all values of θ, where $0° \leq \theta \leq 360°$, such that:

a) $\sin \theta = 0.25$ **b)** $\sin \theta = -0.866$ **c)** $\cos \theta = 0.25$
d) $\cos \theta = -0.866$ **e)** $\tan \theta = 2.5$ **f)** $\tan \theta = -1.732$.

4 Using your calculator and the appropriate graph, find all values of θ (where possible), such that $-180° \leq \theta \leq 180°$ and:

a) $\cos \theta = 0.15$ **b)** $\sin \theta = 1.25$ **c)** $\cos \theta = -0.5$ **d)** $\sin \theta = -0.33$
e) $\tan \theta = 10$ **f)** $\sin \theta = 0.866$ **g)** $\tan \theta = -0.75$ **h)** $\tan \theta = 0.577$.

5 Copy and complete the following table and comment on the results (give values of sin θ and tan θ to five decimal places).

θ	5°	4°	3°	2°	1°	0.5°	0°
$\sin \theta$							
$\tan \theta$							

9.1 HOMEWORK

1 Using a scale of 1 cm to 60° on the x-axis and 1 cm to 0.5 units on the y-axis, plot the graphs of $y = \cos x$, $y = -\cos x$ and $y = \cos(-x)$ on the same axes over the interval $-360° \leq x \leq 360°$. Comment on the graphs.

2 Using the diagrams on page 174 and the appropriate graphs, write down the sine, cosine and tangent of each of the following angles. Check the decimal equivalents using a calculator.

a) 120° **b)** 150° **c)** 210° **d)** 300°

3 Using your calculator and the appropriate graph, find all values of θ, where $0° \leq \theta \leq 360°$, such that:

a) $\sin \theta = 0.6$ **b)** $\sin \theta = -0.75$ **c)** $\cos \theta = 0.6$
d) $\cos \theta = -0.75$ **e)** $\tan \theta = 0.6$ **f)** $\tan \theta = -0.75$

4 Using your calculator and the appropriate graph, find where possible values of θ, where $-180° \leq \theta \leq 180°$, such that:

a) $\sin \theta = -0.8$ **b)** $\cos \theta = -0.35$ **c)** $\cos \theta = 50$ **d)** $\tan \theta = -0.4$
e) $\sin \theta = -1.01$ **f)** $\cos \theta = 0.94$ **g)** $\tan \theta = -100$ **h)** $\sin \theta = 0.5$

5 Choose any angle θ between 0 and 90°. Use your calculator to evaluate $(\cos \theta)^2 + (\sin \theta)^2$. Repeat for other values of θ, both inside and outside the interval $0° \leq \theta \leq 90°$. Comment on your findings.

TRIGONOMETRIC EQUATIONS

A **trigonometric equation** is an equation which contains a trigonometric function such as sine, cosine or tangent. To **solve** a trigonometric equation, we need to find values of the angle which satisfy the equation.

When using a calculator with the inverse trigonometric functions $\mathbf{sin^{-1}}$, $\mathbf{cos^{-1}}$, $\mathbf{tan^{-1}}$, the value on the display is called the **principal value** and is usually in the range $-180° \leq \theta \leq 180°$. For example,

$\cos^{-1}(-0.5) = 120°$, $\sin^{-1}(-0.5) = -30°$, $\tan^{-1}(-1) = -45°$.

If the principal value for the angle is not in the required interval, adding multiples of the period of the function (360° for sine and cosine, 180° for tangent) will give a suitable solution. Other solutions may be obtained by using symmetry properties of the graphs, etc.

Example 9.1

Find values of θ such that $0° \le \theta \le 360°$ where $4\cos\theta = 3$.

Solution

$4\cos\theta = 3 \Rightarrow \cos\theta = 0.75$

$\Rightarrow \theta = \cos^{-1}(0.75) = 41.4°$ (to 1 d.p.) (*from calculator*)

but $0° \le \theta \le 360° \Rightarrow \theta = 41.4°$ or $\theta = 360° - 41.4° = 318.6°$

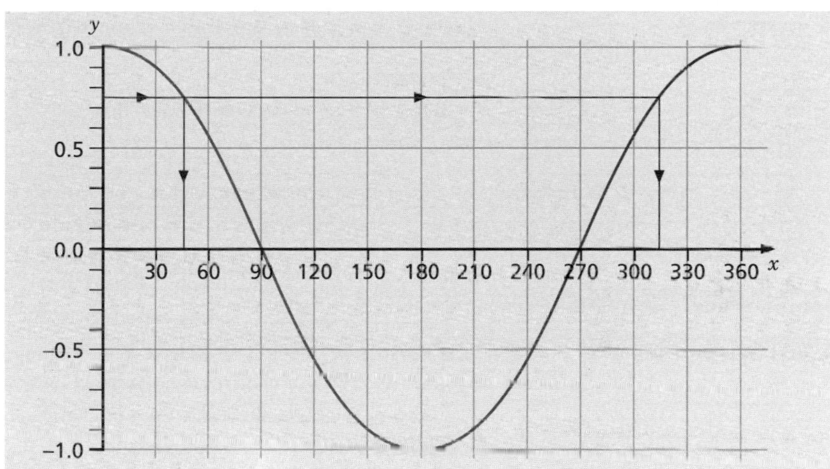

Example 9.2

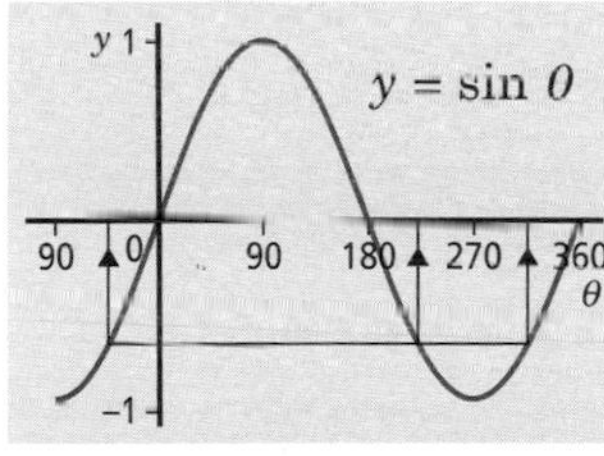

Find values of θ such that $0° \le \theta \le 360°$ where $5\sin\theta = -3$.

Solution

$5\sin\theta = -3 \Rightarrow \sin\theta = -0.6$

$\Rightarrow \theta = \sin^{-1}(-0.6) = -36.9°$ (to 1 d.p.) (*from calculator*)

but $0° \le \theta \le 360°$ *and* $\sin\theta$ has period 360°:

$\Rightarrow \theta = 180° + 36.9°$ or $\theta = 360° - 36.9°$

$\Rightarrow \theta = 216.9°$ or $\theta = 323.1°$

Example 9.3

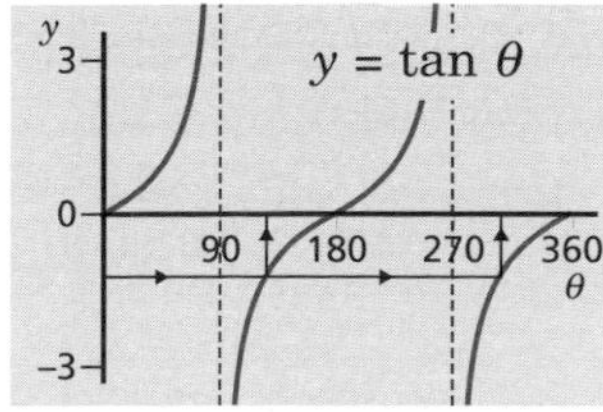

Find values of θ such that $0° \le \theta \le 360°$ where $10\tan\theta + 7 = 3$.

Solution

$10\tan\theta + 7 = 3 \Rightarrow \tan\theta = -0.4$

$\Rightarrow \theta = \tan^{-1}(-0.4) = -21.8°$ (to 1 d.p.) (*from calculator*)

but $0° \le \theta \le 360°$ *and* $\tan\theta$ has period 180°:

$\Rightarrow \theta = -21.8° + 180°$ or $\theta = -21.8° + 360°$

$\Rightarrow \theta = 158.2°$ *or* $\theta = 338.2°$

Example 9.4

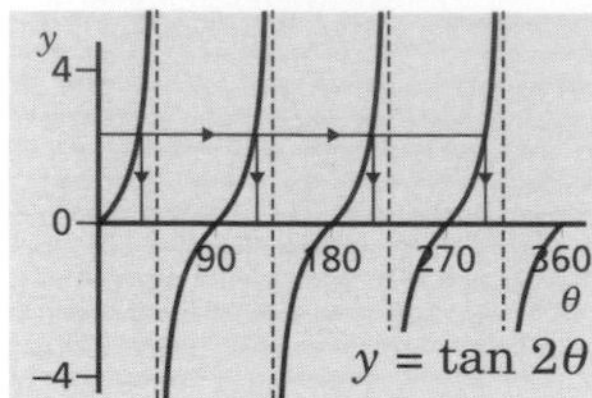

Find values of θ such that $0° \le \theta \le 360°$ where $2\tan 2\theta = 5$.

Solution

$2\tan 2\theta = 5 \Rightarrow \tan 2\theta = 2.5$

$\Rightarrow 2\theta = \tan^{-1}(2.5) = 68.2°$ (to 1 d.p.) *(from calculator)*

$\Rightarrow \theta = 68.2° \div 2 = 34.1°$ (to 1 d.p.)

but $0° \le \theta \le 360°$ *and* $\tan 2\theta$ has period 90°:

$\Rightarrow \theta = 34.1°, 34.1° + 90°, 34.1° + 180°$ or $34.1° + 270°$

$\Rightarrow \theta = 34.1, 124.1, 214.1$ or 304.1

Example 9.5

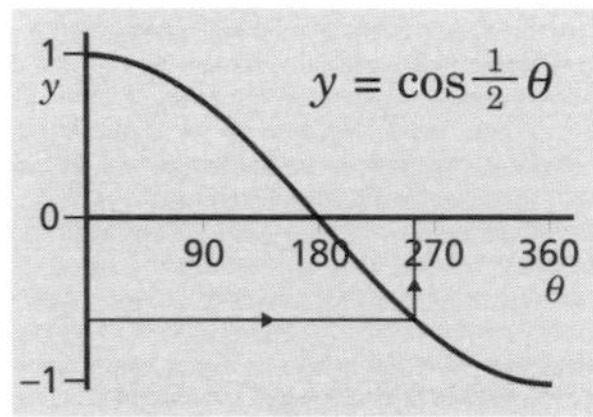

Find values of θ such that $0° \le \theta \le 360°$ where $2 + 3\cos \frac{1}{2}\theta = 0$.

Solution

$2 + 3\cos \frac{1}{2}\theta = 0 \Rightarrow \cos \frac{1}{2}\theta = -\frac{2}{3}$

$\Rightarrow \frac{1}{2}\theta = \cos^{-1}(-\frac{2}{3}) = 131.8°$ (to 1 d.p.) *(from calculator)*

$\Rightarrow \theta = 131.8° \times 2 = 263.6°$ (to 1 d.p.)

but $0° \le \theta \le 360°$ *and* $\cos\frac{1}{2}\theta$ has period 720°:

$\Rightarrow \theta = 263.6°$ is the only solution.

Example 9.6

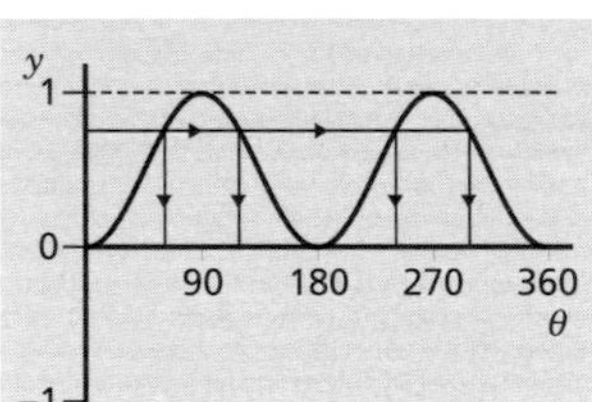

Find values of θ such that $0° \le \theta \le 360°$ where $4\sin^2 \theta = 3$. [Here $\sin^2 \theta$ means $(\sin \theta)^2$ – a commonly used shorthand.]

Solution

$4\sin^2 \theta = 3 \quad \Rightarrow \sin \theta = \pm\sqrt{\frac{3}{4}} = \pm\frac{\sqrt{3}}{2}$

Either $\sin \theta = +\frac{\sqrt{3}}{2} \quad \Rightarrow \theta = \sin^{-1}(+\frac{\sqrt{3}}{2}) = 60°$

but $0° \le \theta \le 360°$ *and* $\sin \theta$ has period 360°:

$\Rightarrow \theta = 60°$ or $\theta = 180° - 60° = 120°$

or $\sin \theta = -\frac{\sqrt{3}}{2} \quad \Rightarrow \theta = \sin^{-1}(-\frac{\sqrt{3}}{2}) = -60°$

but $0° \le \theta \le 360°$ *and* $\sin \theta$ has period 360°:

$\Rightarrow \theta = 180° + 60°$ *or* $\theta = 360° - 60°$

$\Rightarrow \theta = 240°$ *or* $\theta = 300°$

Solving trigonometric equations

The steps in solving trigonometric equations are:

1 Rearrange the equation to make sine, cosine or tangent the subject.
2 Use a calculator, where necessary, to find a principal value of the angle.
3 Using a graph, or otherwise, find other solutions to the equation in the given interval.

EXERCISES

9.2 CLASSWORK

1 Using your calculator and the appropriate graph, find all values of θ such that $0° \le \theta \le 360°$, where:

a) $5\cos \theta = 4$ **b)** $13\sin \theta = 5$ **c)** $4\tan \theta = 7$
d) $10\cos \theta = -3$ **e)** $8\sin \theta + 3 = 0$ **f)** $5\tan \theta = -12$

2 Using your calculator and the appropriate graph, find all values of θ such that $0° \leq \theta \leq 360°$, where:

a) $5\sin 2\theta = 4$ b) $9\tan 2\theta = 7$
c) $10\cos \frac{1}{2}\theta = -7$ d) $8\tan \frac{1}{2}\theta = -15$
e) $25\cos 3\theta - 7 = 0$ f) $6 - 7\tan \frac{1}{3}\theta = 30$.

3 Using your calculator and the appropriate graph, find all values of θ such that $0° \leq \theta \leq 360°$, where:

a) $13\sin^2 \theta = 5$ b) $4\tan^2 \theta = 7$
c) $16\cos^2 \theta + 6 = 15$ d) $15 - 5\tan^2 \theta = 0$.

4 Find (if possible) all values of θ such that $-180° \leq \theta \leq 180°$, where:

a) $25\tan^2 \theta = 9$ b) $14\cos (\theta + 10°) = -7$
c) $8\sin^2 \theta + 3 = 0$ d) $21 - 7\tan^2 2\theta = 0$
e) $16\cos^3\theta = 2$ f) $10 - 8\sin 5\theta = 3$
g) $5 + 2\tan(\theta - 30°) = 8$ h) $8 - 4\cos 3\theta = 3$.

9.2 HOMEWORK

1 Using your calculator and the appropriate graph, find all values of θ such that $0° \leq \theta \leq 360°$, where:

a) $10\sin \theta = 7$ b) $5\cos \theta = 2$
c) $3\tan \theta = 8$ d) $12\sin \theta = -5$
e) $8\cos \theta = -2$ f) $4 - 3\tan \theta = 11$

2 Using your calculator and the appropriate graph, find (where possible) all values of θ such that $0° \leq \theta \leq 360°$, where:

a) $10\cos 2\theta = 7$ b) $7\tan 3\theta = 8$
c) $7\cos \frac{1}{2}\theta = -4$ d) $3\tan \frac{1}{4}\theta = -4$
e) $5\sin 2\theta + 3 = 6$ f) $11 + 7\cos \frac{1}{2}\theta = 8$

3 Using your calculator and the appropriate graph, find all values of θ such that $0° \leq \theta \leq 360°$, where:

a) $9\cos^2 \theta = 4$ b) $5\sin^2 \theta = 2$
c) $8\tan^2 \theta = 5$ d) $12\cos^2 \theta - 2 = 3$

4 Find (if possible) all values of θ such that $-180° \leq \theta \leq 180°$, where:

a) $3\cos 3\theta = 4$ b) $15\sin (\theta + 14°) = -4$
c) $27\sin^3 \theta = 8$ d) $3\tan^2 \theta + 11 = 0$
e) $12 - 15\sin^2 2\theta = 0$ f) $1 + 6\cos \frac{1}{2}\theta = -2$
g) $13 - 8\cos^2 \frac{1}{2}\theta = 7$ h) $15 - \tan (2\theta + 15°) = 0$

WAVE MODELS

Back to the big wheel!

At the beginning of this chapter, we were looking at the motion of a big wheel and how the position of a car, relative to the hub, can be given in terms of the sine and cosine of the anti-clockwise angle made with the horizontal passing through the hub.

Exploration 9.6

Motion of the cars

Suppose that the wheel is now rotating at two revolutions per minute. Assume that the wheel is in the position shown in Exploration 9.1 when $t = 0$ and that it is rotating anticlockwise.

- Find an equation for the height h metres of car A after t seconds.
- Sketch a graph of h against t for $0 \le t \le 30$.
- Find the time interval for which car A is:
  a) less than 5 metres above the ground,
  b) at least 15 metres above the ground.

Repeat for car D, plotting the graph of h against t on the same axes as for car A.

When are cars A and D at the same height as each other?

Repeat for car K, plotting the graph of h against t on the same axes as for car A.

Describe the relationship between the three graphs.

Relating *h* and *t*

The wheel rotates through 360° in 30 seconds, which means that it turns through 12° in one second, or $12t°$ in t seconds, i.e. $\theta = 12t$.

For car A, relative to O, $y = 8\sin\theta \Rightarrow y = 8\sin 12t°$.

Therefore, relative to the ground, height h in terms of time t is $y = 9 + 8\sin 12t°$.

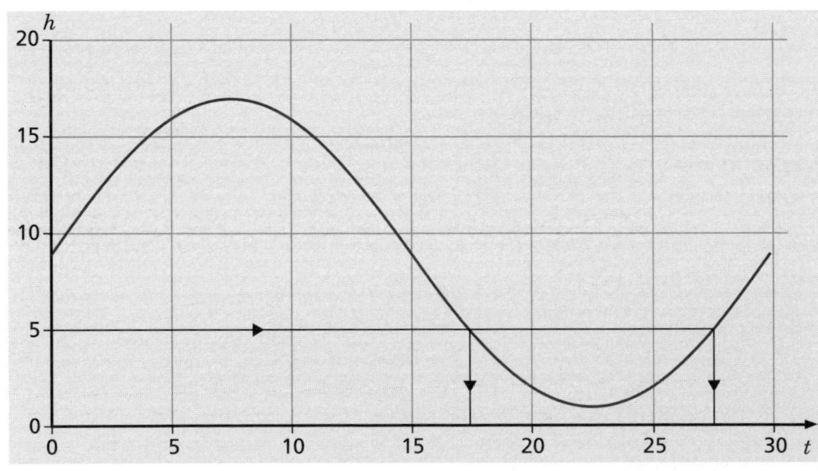

A sketch graph of h against t for car A looks like this.

From the graph it looks as though car A is less than 5 metres above the ground from $t = 17$ to $t = 28$, i.e. for about 11 seconds.

Using the techniques of the last section, the corresponding times may be found precisely by solving the equation:

$$\begin{aligned} 5 &= 9 + 8\sin 12t° \\ \Rightarrow \quad 8\sin 12t° &= -4 \\ \Rightarrow \quad \sin 12t° &= -0.5 \\ \Rightarrow \quad 12t &= 210 \text{ or } 12t = 330 \\ \Rightarrow \quad t &= 17.5 \text{ or } t = 27.5 \text{ seconds} \end{aligned}$$

Cars D and K are 'ahead' of car A, in terms of anti-clockwise position from A.

For car D $\theta = 90° + 12t°$

For car K $\theta = 210° + 12t°$.

The corresponding height functions are:

For car D $h = 9 + 8\sin(90 + 12t)°$

For car K $h = 9 + 8\sin(210 + 12t)°$

The graphs of h against t for all three cars are shown below.

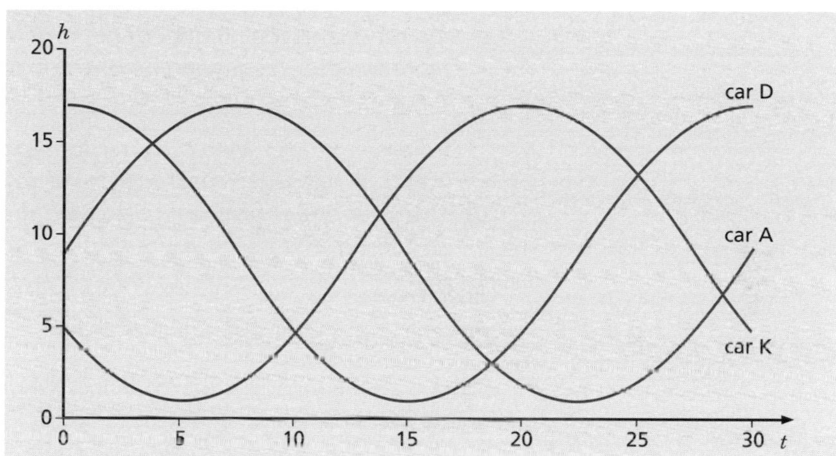

Cars A and D are at the same height after roughly 4 seconds and 19 seconds, with heights around 15 metres and 3 metres respectively.

Notice that an alternative formula for the height of car D is given by:

$h = 9 + 8\cos 12t°$

The three waves are said to be out of phase since the second and third waves may be obtained from the first one by a translation parallel to the x-axis.

CALCULATOR ACTIVITY

Exploration 9.7

Height functions

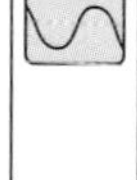

Using suitable scales, such as:

$x_{\text{min}} = 0$; $x_{\text{max}} = 30$; $x_{\text{scl}} = 2$

$y_{\text{min}} = 0$; $y_{\text{max}} = 20$; $y_{\text{scl}} = 2$.

plot the graphs for cars A, D and K.

- Check all the answers to the exploration using the trace facility.
- Think up other questions and use your calculator to solve them.

Example 9.7

The hours of daylight throughout the year for Casterton are as follows (on 21st of each month).

March	April	May	June	July	Aug.	Sept.	Oct.	Nov.	Dec.	Jan.	Feb.
12	15	17.2	18	17.2	15	12	9	6.8	6	6.8	9

a) *Plot the values on a graph and join the points with a smooth curve.*

b) *From the graph estimate:*

*   ***i)*** *the number of hours of daylight on 1st October,*
*   ***ii)*** *the period when the hours of daylight are less than 7.5 hours.*

c) *If h represents the number of hours of daylight on the 21st of a month, m, formulate an equation, to give h in terms of m, of the form:*
$h = a\sin bm^\circ + c$

where m = 0 for March, m = 1 for April, ..., m = 11 for February, and a , b and c are constants to be found.

d) *Use your equation from (c) to plot the graph on a graphical calculator and check yours results from (a) and (b).*

Solution

a)

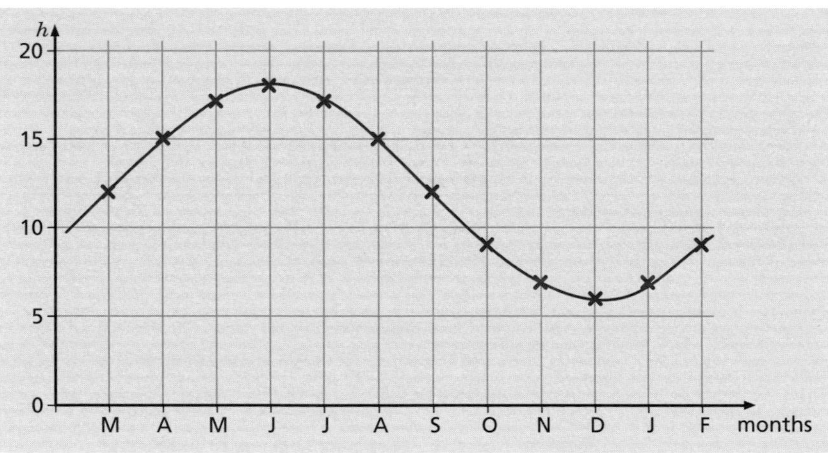

b) i) *Number of hours of daylight on 1st October ≈ 10 hours.*

ii) *There were less than 7.5 hours of daylight between early November and late January.*

c) *The range of values for h is given by $6 \le h \le 18$*
$\Rightarrow a = \frac{1}{2}(18 - 6) = 6.$

The period of the function is 12 months $\Rightarrow b = \frac{360}{12} = 30.$

The value of the constant c is given by $6 + \frac{12}{2} = 12.$
Putting these results together gives the function:
$h = 6\sin 30m^\circ + 12$

d) *Scale the axes using:*

$x_{min} = 0; \quad x_{max} = 30; \quad x_{scl} = 2$

$y_{min} = 0; \quad y_{max} = 20; \quad y_{scl} = 2.$

*and trace the curve to check your solutions to **a)** and **b)**.*
*Part **b) ii)** may be answered by solving the equation:*

$$
\begin{aligned}
& 7.5 && = 6\sin 30m^\circ + 12 \\
\Rightarrow\ & 6\sin 30m^\circ && = -4.5 \\
\Rightarrow\ & \sin 30m^\circ && = -0.75 \\
\Rightarrow\ & 30m && = 228.6 \text{ or } 311.4 \\
\Rightarrow\ & m = 7.62 \text{ or } m = 10.38 &&
\end{aligned}
$$

Therefore the model predicts that there will be less than 7.5 hours daylight between 7.62 and 10.38 months after March 21st, i.e. between November 9th and February 1st (roughly).

EXERCISES

9.3 CLASSWORK

1 The approximate depth of water in a harbour, y metres, is given by:

$y = 4\sin 30t^\circ + 7$

where t is the number of hours after midnight on a certain day.

a) Draw a graph of this function over a period of 24 hours.
b) At what times do the high and low tides occur?
c) Use your graph to estimate:
  i) the height of the tide at 07:30,
  ii) when the tide has a height of 10 metres and is falling,
  iii) how long the depth continually remains below 4.5 metres.
d) Calculate answers to **c)** to 3 s.f.

2 During a period of 13 consecutive days, referred to as days 0, 1, ..., 11, 12, the temperatures in a factory are measured, in °C, and the results are shown as plotted on this diagram.

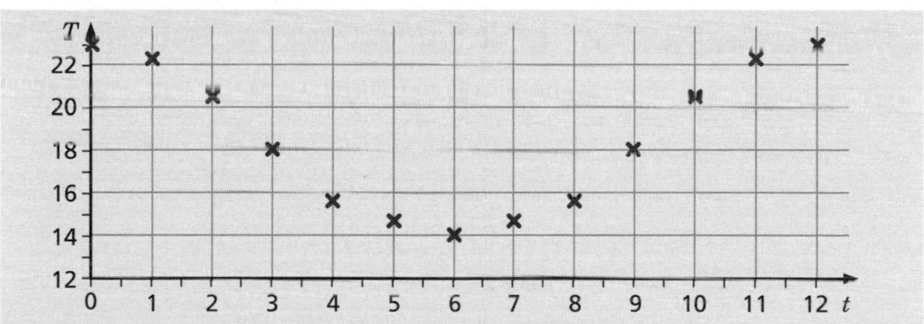

a) Given that the temperature, T°C, can be modelled as a function of time, t days, using a function of the form:
$T = a\cos bt^\circ + c$
deduce the values of the constants a, b and c.
b) From the graph find:
  i) the temperature on day 10,
  ii) the days on which the temperature was below 17.5°C.
c) Plot a graph of T against t using the definition in part **a)** and check that the curve agrees with the plotted points. Check your answers to part **b)**.

3 A mass, on the end of a spring which is hanging vertically, is pulled down and then let go. The mass begins to oscillate between 1 metre and 2 metres above the floor and completes 20 complete oscillations in one minute.

The height of the mass, h metres, above the floor after t seconds from being let go can be modelled by a function of the form:
$h = a\cos bt° + c$.

a) Find values for a and c, and explain why $b = 120$.
b) Sketch a graph of h against t for $0 \le t \le 6$.
c) Find the times, during the first minute, that the mass is:
  i) 1.25 metres above the floor,
  ii) within 15 cm of the equilibrium height (1.5 metres).

9.3 HOMEWORK

1 A mass on the end of a spring which is hanging vertically is pulled down and let go. It oscillates between 1.5 m and 2 m above the floor and completes 32 oscillations in one minute. The height, h metres, of the mass above the floor after t seconds can be modelled by a function of the form $h = a\cos bt° + c$.

a) Find values for a and b and explain why $c = 1.75$ m.
b) Sketch the graph of h against t for $0 \le t \le 5$.
c) Find the times during the first 5 seconds, when the mass is within 0.1 m of its equilibrium height.
d) Calculate the height of the mass above the ground after:
  i) 25 seconds, **ii)** 47 seconds.

2 The graph shows how an anchored buoy bobs on the waves. The difference between its highest and lowest positions is 2 metres and it returns to the same position every 15 seconds.

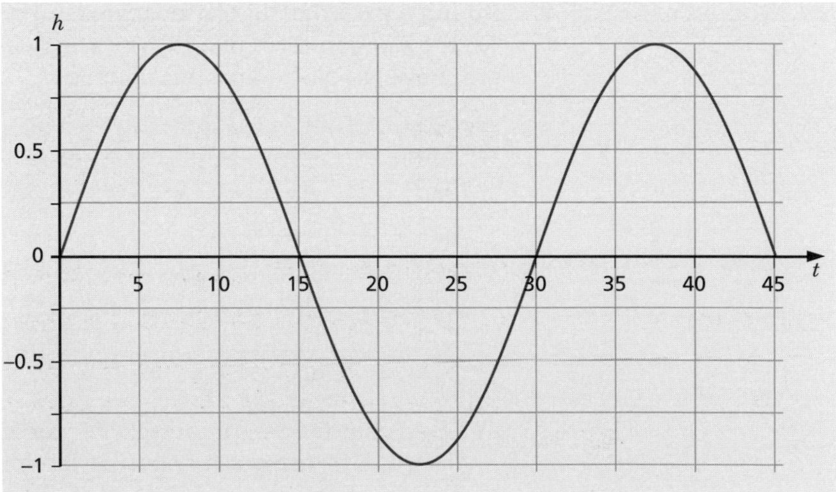

a) Write the equation for its motion.
b) If the sea-bed is 4 m below the lowest position of the buoy, write the equation for its height above the sea-bed at any time.
c) Use the equation to find the height above the sea-bed of the buoy after:
  i) 10 seconds, **ii)** 20 seconds, **iii)** 59 seconds.

3 The graphs below represent two sound wave patterns. Find the equation for each sound wave.

a)

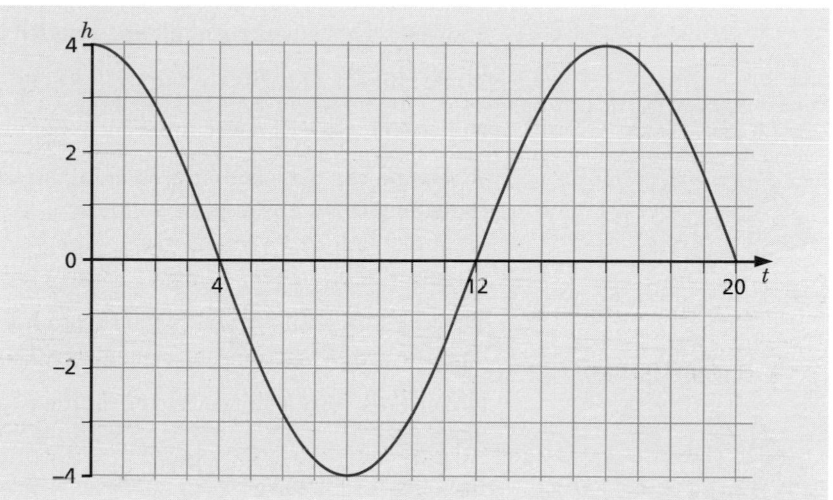

b)

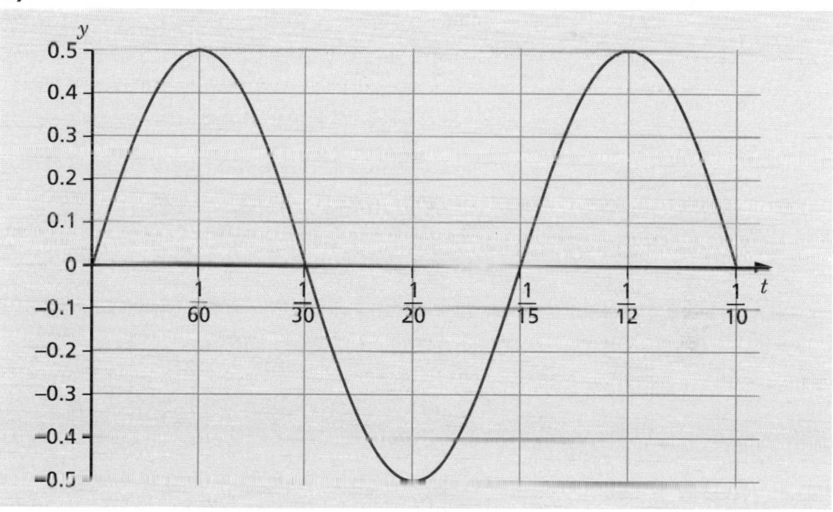

RADIANS: CIRCULAR MEASURE

Exploration 9.8

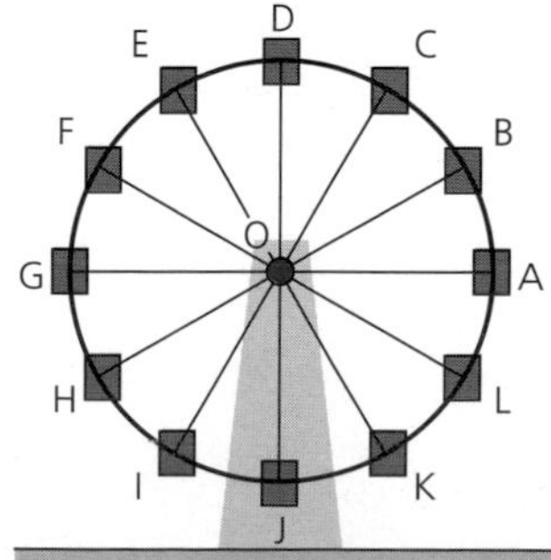

Circular motion on the big wheel

You are riding on the big wheel at a fairground. The distance of a car from the centre of the wheel is 8 metres. There are 12 cars altogether, equally spaced.

- How far do you travel in one complete revolution of the wheel?
- Assuming passengers are picked up at the bottom of the wheel, how far will you travel between pick-ups?
- Through what angle does the wheel rotate between pick-ups?
- How far will you travel when the wheel rotates through $x°$?
- Through what angle does the wheel rotate when a single car travels 8 metres?

Radians

In one revolution the car of the big wheel travels the circumference of a circle of radius 8 m, i.e. $2\pi \times 8 = 16\pi$ metres. Between pick-ups the car travels one twelfth of the circumference, i.e. $\frac{1}{12} \times 16\pi = \frac{4}{3}\pi$ metres, and the wheel turns through one-twelfth of a full turn, i.e. 30°.

When the wheel turns through $x°$, this is $\frac{1}{360}x$ of a full turn, so a car will travel $\frac{1}{360}x$ of a circumference $\frac{1}{360}x \times 16\pi$.

When the car travels 8 metres along an arc of the circle, let the angle the wheel turns through be $x°$, then:

$$\frac{x}{360} \times 16\pi = 8 \Rightarrow x = \frac{8 \times 360}{16\pi} = \frac{180}{\pi}$$

The angle that the wheel turns through when a car travels a distance equal in length to the radius is one **radian** (denoted by ^{c}).

Note: This works for a circle of radius r, for which the circumference is $2\pi r$ and:

$$\frac{x}{360} \times 2\pi r = r \Rightarrow x = \frac{180}{\pi}$$

Geometrically, the angle at the centre of a circle that subtends an arc equal in length to the radius is called a radian and is defined by:

$$1 \text{ radian} \equiv \frac{180°}{\pi} \approx 57.3°$$

Check this on your calculator.

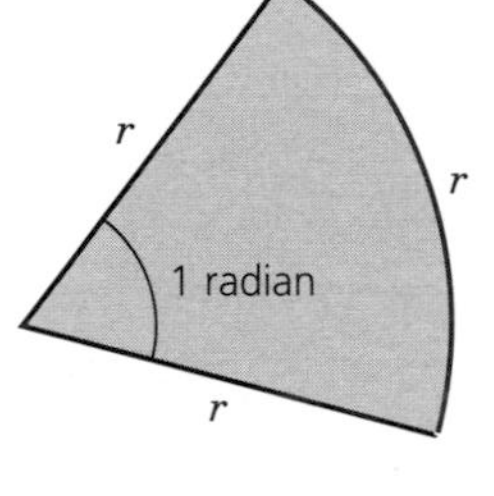

Useful equivalences may be deduced from the definition:

$$\pi \text{ radians} \equiv \pi \times \frac{180°}{\pi} = 180°$$

from which you may deduce:

$$360° \equiv 2\pi \text{ radians}$$

$$90° \equiv \tfrac{1}{2}\pi \text{ or } \frac{\pi}{2} \text{ radians}$$

$$1° \equiv \frac{\pi}{180} \text{ radians (or } \frac{\pi}{180}^c)$$

Example 9.8

Convert these angles to radians.

a) 45° ***b)*** 150°

Solution

a) $180° = \pi \text{ radians} \Rightarrow 45° = \frac{\pi}{4} \text{ radians}$

b) $180° = \pi \text{ radians} \Rightarrow 30° = \frac{\pi}{6} \Rightarrow 150° = \frac{5\pi}{6} \text{ radians}$

Example 9.9

Convert these angles to degrees.

a) $\frac{\pi}{6}$ radians ***b)*** $\frac{7\pi}{4}$ radians

Solution

a) $\pi \text{ radians} = 180° \Rightarrow \frac{\pi}{6} \text{ radians} = \frac{180°}{6} = 30°$

b) $\pi \text{ radians} = 180° \Rightarrow \frac{7\pi}{4} \text{ radians} = \frac{7 \times 180°}{4} = 315°$

Note: When an angle is expressed without any units it is assumed to be measured in radians, as in the answers in the next two examples.

Example 9.10

a) Sketch a graph of $y = \sin x$*, where* x *is measured in radians, for* $0 \le x \le 2\pi$.

b) From your graph, find, as multiples of π*, values of* x *that satisfy the following equations.*

i) $\sin x = 0$ *ii)* $\sin x = \pm 1$ *iii)* $\sin x = \frac{1}{2}$

iv) $\sin x = -\frac{1}{2}$ *v)* $\sin x = \frac{\sqrt{3}}{2}$ *vi)* $\sin x = -\frac{\sqrt{3}}{2}$

Solution

a)

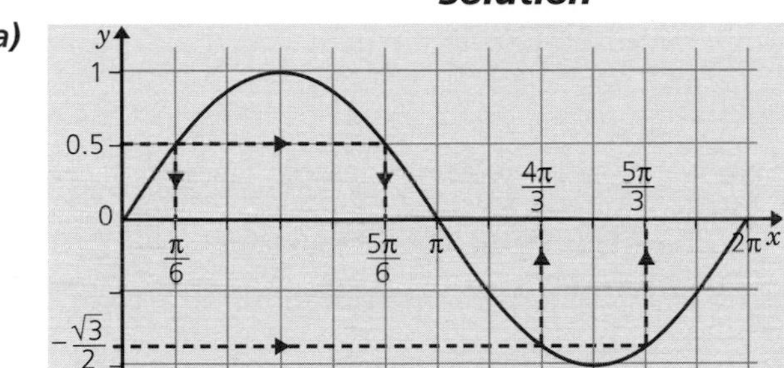

b) i) $\sin x = 0 \Rightarrow x = 0, \pi$ *or* 2π

ii) $\sin x = \pm 1 \Rightarrow x = \frac{\pi}{2}$ *or* $\frac{3\pi}{2}$

iii) $\sin x = \frac{1}{2} \Rightarrow x = \frac{\pi}{6}$ *or* $\frac{5\pi}{6}$ *(see graph)*

iv) $\sin x = -\frac{1}{2} \Rightarrow x = \frac{7\pi}{6}$ *or* $\frac{11\pi}{6}$

v) $\sin x = \frac{\sqrt{3}}{2} \Rightarrow x = \frac{\pi}{3}$ *or* $\frac{2\pi}{3}$

vi) $\sin x = -\frac{\sqrt{3}}{2} \Rightarrow x = \frac{4\pi}{3}$ *or* $\frac{5\pi}{3}$ *(see graph)*

Check these answers using your calculator in radian mode.

Example 9.11

a) Sketch a graph of $y = \cos^2 x$*, where* x *is measured in radians, for* $0 \le x \le 2\pi$. [$\cos^2 x$ *means* $(\cos x)^2$]

b) From your graph, find, as multiples of π*, values of* x *that satisfy these equations.*

i) $\cos^2 x = 0$ *ii)* $\cos^2 x = 1$ *iii)* $\cos^2 x = 0.25$ *iv)* $\cos^2 x = 0.75$

Solution

a)

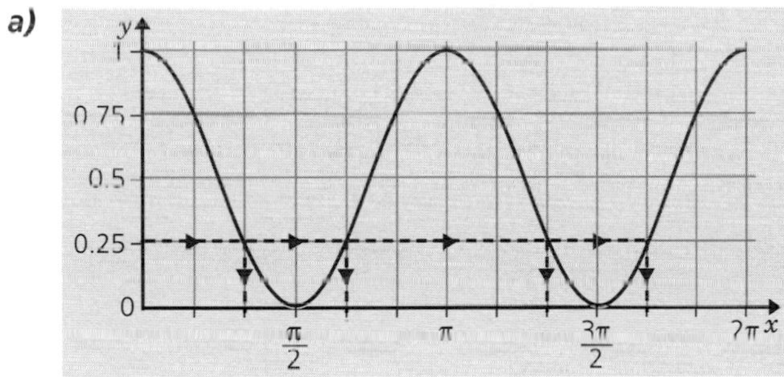

b) i) $\cos^2 x = 0 \Rightarrow x = \frac{\pi}{2}$ *or* $\frac{3\pi}{2}$

ii) $\cos^2 x = 1 \Rightarrow x = 0, \pi$ *or* 2π

iii) $\cos^2 x = \frac{1}{4} \Rightarrow x = \frac{\pi}{3}, \frac{2\pi}{3}, \frac{4\pi}{3}$ *or* $\frac{5\pi}{3}$ *(see graph)*

iv) $\cos^2 x = \frac{3}{4} \Rightarrow x = \frac{\pi}{6}, \frac{5\pi}{6}, \frac{7\pi}{6}$ *or* $\frac{11\pi}{6}$

Check these answers using your calculator in radian mode. For example, for part iii):

$$\cos^2 x = 0.25 \Rightarrow \cos x = \pm\sqrt{0.25} = \pm 0.5$$
$$\Rightarrow x = \cos^{-1}(\pm 0.5) \Rightarrow x = \frac{\pi}{3}, \frac{2\pi}{3}, \frac{4\pi}{3} \text{ or } \frac{5\pi}{3}$$

equally: $\cos\frac{\pi}{3} = 0.5 \Rightarrow \cos^2\frac{\pi}{3} = 0.5^2 = 0.25$

$\cos\frac{2\pi}{3} = -0.5 \Rightarrow \cos^2\frac{2\pi}{3} = (-0.5)^2 = 0.25$ *etc.*

EXERCISES

9.4 CLASSWORK

1 Without using a calculator, express the following angles in degrees.

a) $-\frac{2\pi}{3}$ b) $\frac{\pi}{8}$ c) $-\frac{11\pi}{6}$ d) $\frac{5\pi}{12}$ e) 1.75π

2 Copy and complete the table of equivalences.

Degrees	0°	30°		90°	120°	150°			240°	270°			360°
Radians	0		$\frac{\pi}{3}$				π	$\frac{7\pi}{6}$			$\frac{5\pi}{3}$	$\frac{11\pi}{6}$	

3 Convert the following angles in degrees to their equivalent in radians, giving answers to 3 s.f.

a) 100° b) –29° c) 307° d) –200° e) 1000°

4 Convert the following angles in radians to their equivalent in degrees, giving answers to 1 d.p.

a) 2 radians b) 0.5 radians c) 6.3 radians d) $\sqrt{3}$ radians

5 i) Sketch a graph of $y = \cos x$, where x is measured in radians, for $0 \le x \le 2\pi$.

ii) From your graph, find, in multiples of π, values of x that satisfy the following equations.

a) $\cos x = 0$ b) $\cos x = \pm 1$ c) $\cos x = \frac{\sqrt{3}}{2}$ d) $\cos^2 x = \frac{1}{2}$

Check your results using a calculator in radian mode.

6 a) Sketch a graph of $y = \sin^2 x$, where x is measured in radians, for $0 \le x \le 2\pi$.

b) From your graph, find, in multiples of π, values of x such that:

i) $\sin^2 x = 0$ ii) $\sin^2 x = 1$ iii) $\sin^2 x = 0.25$ iv) $\sin^2 x = 0.5$

Check your results using a calculator in radian mode.

EXERCISES

9.4 HOMEWORK

1 Without using a calculator, express the following angles in degrees.

a) $\frac{\pi}{4}$ b) $-\frac{\pi}{6}$ c) $\frac{5\pi}{3}$ d) $-\frac{7\pi}{12}$ e) $\frac{5\pi}{4}$

2 Use a calculator to convert the following angles in degrees to their equivalent in radians, giving answers to 3 s.f.

a) 20° b) –72° c) 400° d) –140° e) 760°

3 Convert the following angles in radians to their equivalent in degrees, giving answers to 1 d.p.

a) 1.5 radians b) 0.4 radians c) 3 radians d) 5 radians
e) 7.2 radians

4 a) Sketch a graph of $y = \sin x$, where x is measured in radians, for $0 \le x \le 2\pi$.

b) From your graph, find, in multiples of π, values of x that satisfy the following equations.
i) $\sin x = \pm 1$ ii) $\sin x = \frac{\sqrt{3}}{2}$ iii) $\sin {}^2x = \frac{1}{2}$

5 a) Sketch a graph of $y = \cos x$, where x is measured in radians, for $-\pi \le x \le \pi$.

b) Sketch a graph of $y = \cos^2 x$, where x is measured in radians, for $-\pi \le x \le \pi$.

c) From your graph, find in multiples of π, values of x that satisfy the following equations.
i) $\cos^2 x = 0$ ii) $\cos^2 x = 1$ iii) $\cos^2 x = 0.25$ iv) $\cos^2 x = 0.5$

6 a) Sketch a graph of $y = \tan x$, where x is measured in radians, for $-2\pi \le x \le 2\pi$.

b) Sketch a graph of $y = \tan^2 x$, where x is measured in radians, for $-2\pi \le x \le 2\pi$.

c) From your graph, find, in multiples of π, values of x that satisfy the following equations.

i) $\tan^2 x = 0$ **ii)** $\tan^2 x = 1$ **iii)** $\tan^2 x = 3$

iv) $\tan^2 x = \frac{1}{3}$ **v)** $\tan^2 x$ is undefined

Check your results using a calculator in radian mode.

SECTORS

Arc length

Since an angle of 1 radian subtends an arc of length r, an angle of 2π radians subtends an arc of length $2\pi r$ (the circumference) and in general an angle of θ radians subtends an arc of length

$$\frac{\theta}{2\pi} \times 2\pi r = r\theta$$

Area of a sector

Since the area of a circle, radius r, is πr^2, the area of a sector with angle at the centre θ is given by:

$$\frac{\theta}{2\pi} \times \pi r^2 = \frac{1}{2} r^2 \theta$$

Example 9.12

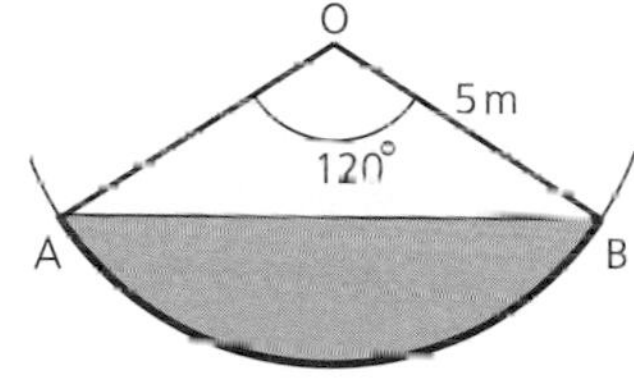

A and B are points on the circumference of a circle, centre O and radius 5 metres, and $\angle AOB = 120°$*. Calculate:*

a) *the length of arc AB,*
b) *the area of sector AOB,*
c) *the area of the shaded segment.*

Solution

Firstly convert degrees to radians: $120° \equiv \frac{2\pi}{3}$ radians.

a) *Length of arc* $AB = r\theta = 5 \times \frac{2\pi}{3} \approx 10.5$ m.

b) *Area of sector* $AOB = \frac{1}{2} r^2 \theta = \frac{1}{2} \times 25 \times \frac{2\pi}{3} \approx 26.2 \text{ m}^2$

c) *First find the area of* ΔAOB.
Area of a triangle with adjacent sides b, c *and included angle* A *is given by* $\Delta = \frac{1}{2} bc \sin A$.
In this case $b = c = r$ *and* $A = 120°$*, hence:*
area of ΔAOB *is* $\frac{1}{2} r^2 \sin 120° = \frac{1}{2} \times 25 \times \frac{\sqrt{3}}{2}$ $(\approx 10.8 \text{ m}^2)$

$\Rightarrow$ *area of shaded segment = area of sector – area of triangle*

$$= \frac{1}{2} \times 25 \times \frac{2\pi}{3} - \frac{1}{2} \times 25 \times \frac{\sqrt{3}}{2} = \frac{1}{2} \times 25 \times \left(\frac{2\pi}{3} - \frac{\sqrt{3}}{2}\right) = 15.4 \text{ m}^2$$

Example 9.13

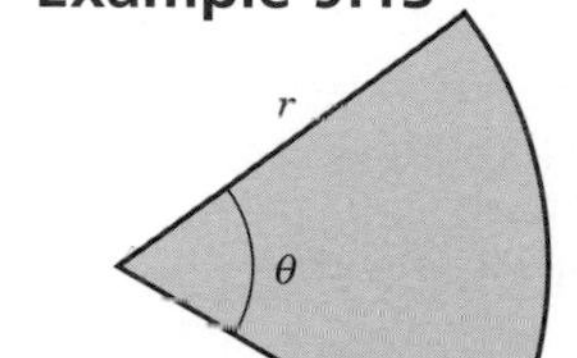

A piece of wire of length 40 cm is bent into the shape of a sector of a circle of radius r *cm and angle* θ *radians.*

a) *If* $r = 15$*, find:*
i) *the size of angle* θ*,* **ii)** *the area* A *of the sector.*
b) *Find a formula for* θ *in terms of* r *and show that* $A = 20r - r^2$.
c) *Find the value of* r *that will give the largest sector area. Write down this area, together with the corresponding value of* θ.

Solution

a) *i) Perimeter of sector* $= 40 \Rightarrow$ *arc length* $= 40 - 2 \times 15 = 10$

Arc length $= r\theta$ *and* $r = 15 \Rightarrow 15\theta = 10 \Rightarrow \theta = \frac{2}{3}$

ii) Area $A = \frac{1}{2}r^2\theta = \frac{1}{2} \times 15^2 \times \frac{2}{3} = 75 \text{ cm}^2$

b) Arc length $= r\theta = 40 - 2r \Rightarrow \theta = \dfrac{40-2r}{r}$

Area $A = \frac{1}{2}r^2\theta = \frac{1}{2}r^2 \dfrac{40-2r}{r} = \frac{1}{2}r^2 \dfrac{2(20-r))}{r} = r(20-r)$

$\Rightarrow A = 20r - r^2$

c) For maximum area:

$\dfrac{\mathrm{d}A}{\mathrm{d}r} = 0 \Rightarrow \dfrac{\mathrm{d}A}{\mathrm{d}r} = 20 - 2r = 0 \Rightarrow r = 10 \text{ cm}$

When $r = 10$ $\quad A = 20 \times 10 - 10^2 = 100 \text{ cm}^2$

$\theta = \dfrac{40 - 2 \times 10}{10} = 2 \text{ radians}$

EXERCISES

9.5 CLASSWORK

1 Find **i)** the length of the arc PQ, **ii)** the area of sector POQ, **iii)** the area of the shaded segment in these diagrams.

a)

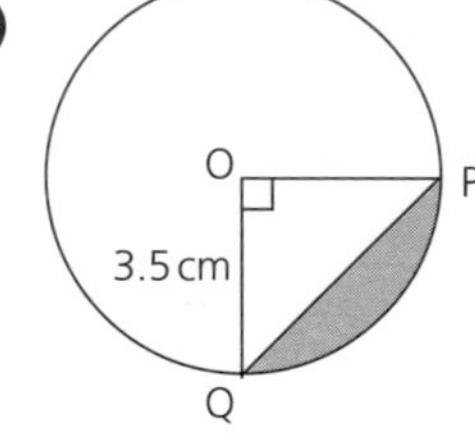

b)

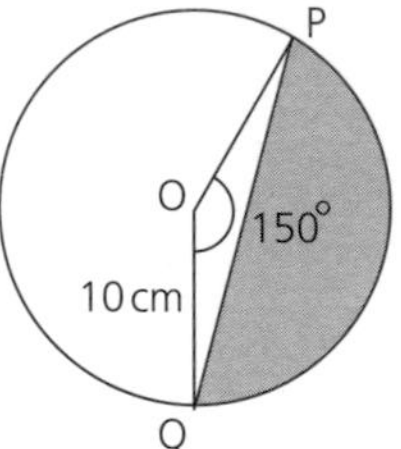

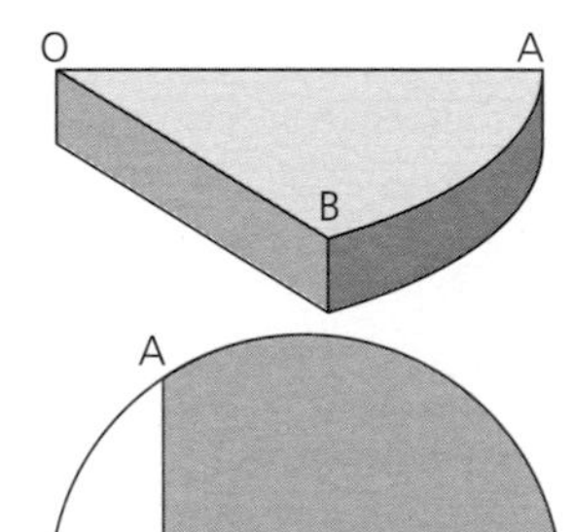

2 An angle θ subtends an arc AB of length 20 cm in a circle, centre O, diameter 30 cm. Find the value of θ and the area of sector AOB.

3 A wedge of cheese, 2 cm thick, has a cross-section which is a sector of a circle. OA = OB = 12 cm. Length of arc AB = 6 cm. Find the volume of the cheese.

4 An angle θ subtends an arc RS of length 16 cm in a circle of radius r cm. The area of the sector ROS is 50 cm^2. Formulate two equations in r and θ and so find the values of r and θ.

5 The diagram shows a circle of radius 10 cm. M is the midpoint of the chord AB and the length of MN is 2 cm. Find the perimeter and area of the shaded region.

6 A cylindrical pipe, diameter 1 metre, contains water to a depth of 0.3 m. The pipe delivers 50 litres of water per second.

a) Find the cross-sectional area of the water.

b) Find the speed with which the water is flowing through the pipe, in m s^{-1}.

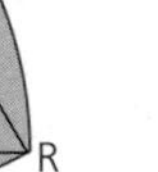

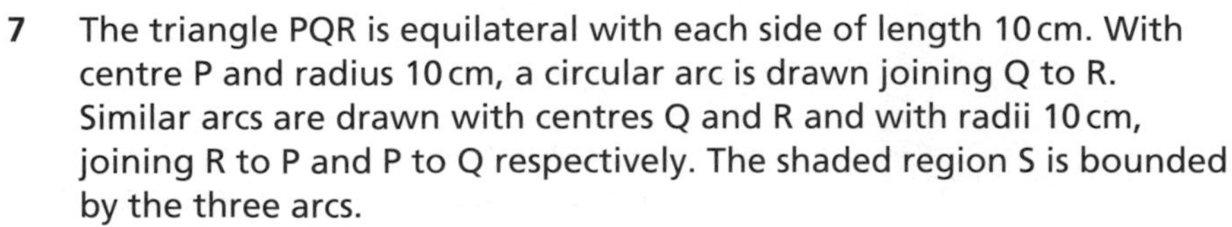

7 The triangle PQR is equilateral with each side of length 10 cm. With centre P and radius 10 cm, a circular arc is drawn joining Q to R. Similar arcs are drawn with centres Q and R and with radii 10 cm, joining R to P and P to Q respectively. The shaded region S is bounded by the three arcs.

Calculate: **a)** the area of ΔPQR, **b)** the area of S.

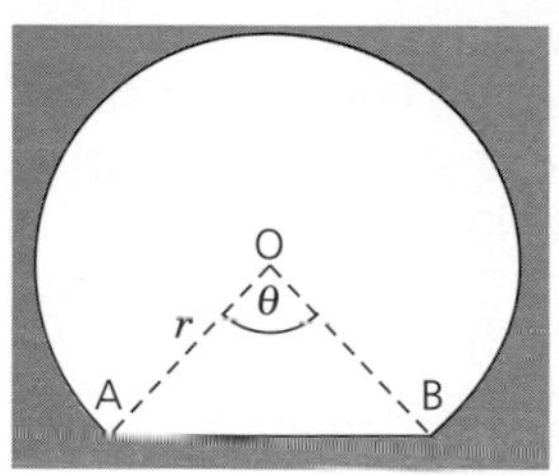

8 The diagram shows the cross-section of a tunnel. The cross-section has the shape of a major segment of a circle, and the point O is the centre of the circle. The radius is 4 m, and the size of angle AOB is 1.5 radians. Calculate the perimeter of the cross-section.

(UCLES (Linear) Specimen Paper 1, 1994)

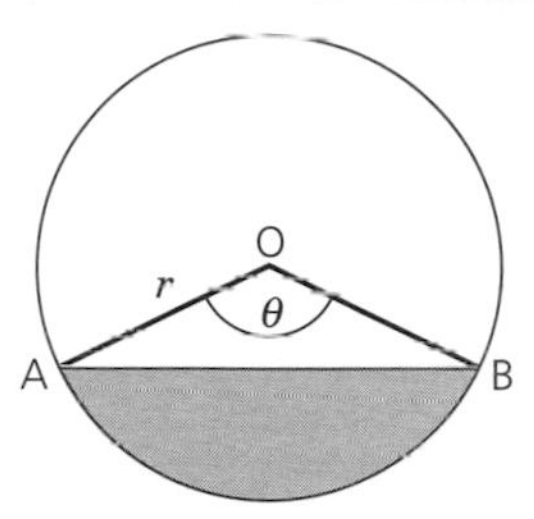

9 The diagram shows a circle with centre O and radius r, and a chord AB which subtends an angle θ radians at O. Express the area of the shaded segment bounded by the chord AB in terms of r and θ.

Given that the area of this segment is one-third of the area of the triangle OAB, show that $3\theta - 4\sin\theta = 0$.

Find the positive value of θ satisfying $3\theta - 4\sin\theta = 0$ to within 0.1 radians, by tabulating values of $3\theta - 4\sin\theta$ and searching for a sign change.

(UCLES (Modular) Specimen Paper 1, 1994)

10 A piece of wire of length l cm is bent into the shape of a sector of a circle of radius r cm and angle θ radians. Find, in terms of l, the value of r that will give the largest sector area.

Write down this area, together with the corresponding value of θ.

EXERCISES

9.5 HOMEWORK

1 Find **i)** the length of the arc PQ, **ii)** the area of sector POQ, **iii)** the area of the shaded segment in these diagrams.

a)

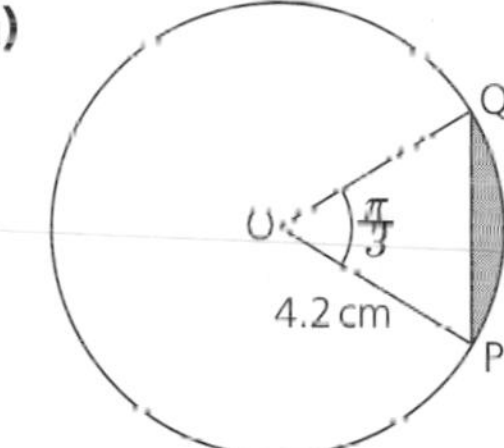

b)

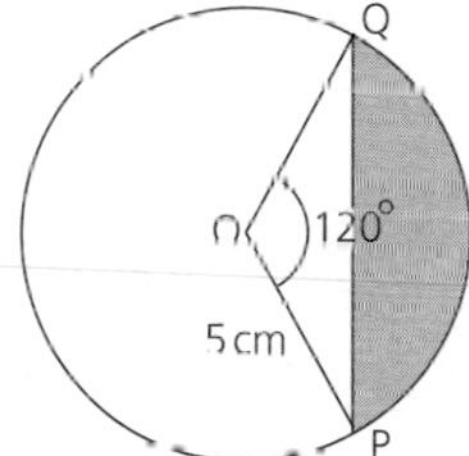

2 An angle θ subtends an arc PQ of length 15 cm in a circle, centre O, diameter 6.5 cm. Find the value of θ and the area of sector POQ.

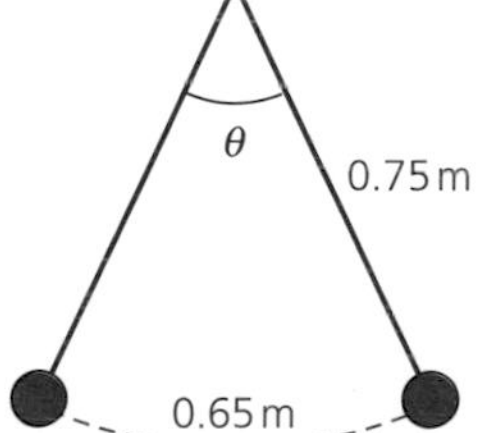

3 An angle θ subtends an arc PQ of length 25 cm in a circle of radius r cm. The area of the sector POQ is 72 cm^2. Formulate two equations in r and θ and so find the values of r and θ.

4 A cylindrical pipe of diameter 1.5 m, contains water to a depth of 0.9 m.

a) Find the cross-sectional area of water.

b) If the water is flowing at a rate of 60 litres per second, find the speed with which the water is flowing, in m s^{-1}.

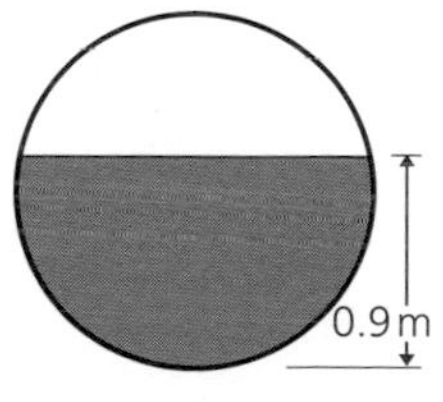

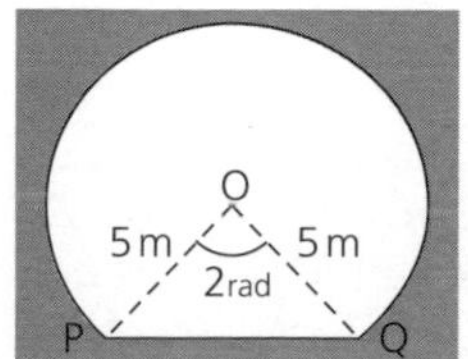

5 A railway tunnel has cross-section shaped as a major segment of a circle with diameter 10 m. The angle POQ is 2 radians. If the tunnel is 500 m long, find the area of lining material needed to line the curved surface inside the tunnel.

6 A circular cone made of card has base radius r and slant height l. If the card is unrolled it forms a circular sector. Find the angle of the sector in radians and hence show that the curved surface area of a cone is πrl.

7 The arc PQ of a circle of centre O, radius r subtends an angle α radians ($\alpha < \pi$) at O. Show that the area of triangle OPQ is $\frac{1}{2}r^2 \sin\alpha$ and hence find the area of the minor segment cut off by PQ. What can you deduce about α and $\sin\alpha$ when α is small?

8 a) Complete the table for $\sin\alpha$ (where α is in radians).

α	0.1	0.08	0.06	0.04	0.02
$\sin\alpha$	0.099 833 42				
$\alpha - \sin\alpha$	0.000 166 6				

Comment on the results. Do your comments support your deduction about α and $\sin\alpha$ in question **8**?

9 The diagram shows a triangle ABC in which AB = 5 cm, AC = BC = 3 cm. The circle, centre A, radius 3 cm, cuts AB at X; the circle, centre B, radius 3 cm, cuts AB at Y.

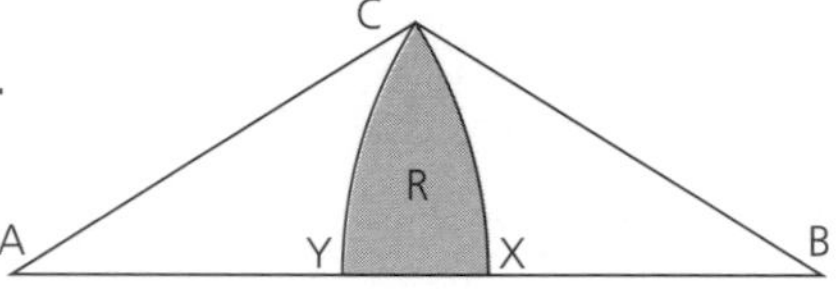

a) Determine the size of angle CAB, giving your answer in radians to four decimal places.

b) The region R, shaded in the diagram, is bounded by the arcs CX, CY and the straight line XY.
Calculate: **i)** the length of the perimeter of R,
ii) the area of the sector ACX,
iii) the area of the region R.

(Oxford, Paper 1, 1991)

TRIGONOMETRICAL IDENTITIES

CALCULATOR ACTIVITY

Exploration 9.9

Adding waves

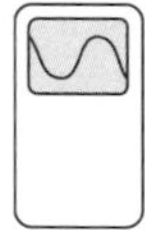

You will need a graphics calculator. Firstly scale the axes:

$x_{\min} = 0$; $x_{\max} = 360$; $x_{\text{scl}} = 30$
$y_{\min} = -0.5$; $y_{\max} = 1.5$; $y_{\text{scl}} = 0.5$.

and make sure you are in degree mode.

- On the same axes:
  plot the graphs of : $y = \sin^2 x$ Enter as $(\sin x)^2$
  $y = \cos^2 x$
  $y = \sin^2 x + \cos^2 x$
- What result does this illustrate?
- Demonstrate the result using a right-angled triangle with base angle θ and hypotenuse 1.

Results

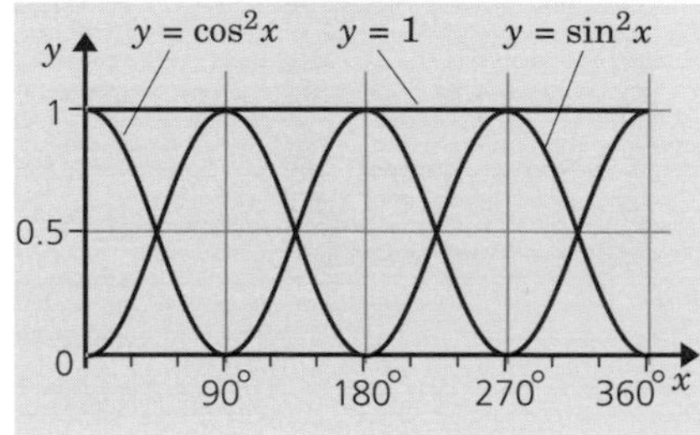

The graphs produced in the Calculator activity should look like those in the diagram.

The result of adding the two waves is always 1, i.e. for any angle:

$$\sin^2\theta + \cos^2\theta = 1$$

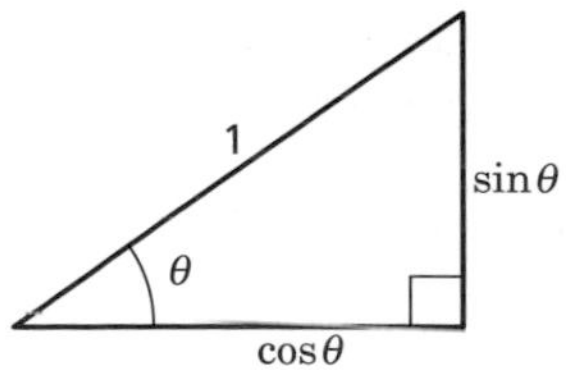

We can obtain the same result from a right-angled triangle.

The height is $\sin\theta$ and base is $\cos\theta$, using the rotating vector definitions. Using Pythagoras' theorem:

$$\sin^2\theta + \cos^2\theta \equiv 1 \qquad (1)$$

This is known as a **Pythagorean identity**.

TRIGONOMETRICAL EQUATIONS

Earlier in this chapter, we solved some simple trigonometrical equations that involved a *single* trigonometrical function. Now we can extend the idea to more complex equations, often involving two or more trigonometrical functions, which simplify to a recognisable form (e.g. a quadratic equation).

The examples below illustrate these types of equation.

Example 9.14

Solve the equation $4\sin\theta - 3\cos\theta = 0$, $0° \le \theta \le 360°$.

Solution

$$4\sin\theta - 3\cos\theta = 0 \Rightarrow 4\sin\theta = 3\cos\theta$$

$$\Rightarrow \frac{\sin\theta}{\cos\theta} = \frac{3}{4} \Rightarrow \tan\theta = 0.75$$

$$\Rightarrow \theta = \tan^{-1}0.75 = 36.9° \quad \textit{(from calculator)}$$

but $0° \le \theta \le 360°$

$$\Rightarrow \theta = 36.9° \textit{ or } 180° + 36.9° \Rightarrow \theta = 36.9° \textit{ or } 216.9°$$

Example 9.15

Solve the equation $2\cos^2\theta + \cos\theta - 1 = 0$, $0° \le \theta \le 360°$.

Solution

Treat as a quadratic equation in $\cos\theta$.

$$2\cos^2\theta + \cos\theta - 1 = 0$$

$$\Rightarrow (2\cos\theta - 1)(\cos\theta + 1) = 0$$

$$\Rightarrow 2\cos\theta - 1 = 0 \quad \textit{or} \quad \cos\theta + 1 = 0$$

$$\Rightarrow \cos\theta = 0.5 \quad \textit{or} \quad \cos\theta = -1$$

Now $\cos\theta = 0.5 \Rightarrow \theta = \cos^{-1}0.5 = 60°$ *(from calculator)*

but $0° \le \theta \le 360°$

$\Rightarrow \theta = 60°$ *or* $360° - 60° = 300°$

and $\cos\theta = -1 \Rightarrow \theta = \cos^{-1}(-1) = 180°$

Combining solutions we have:

$$\theta = 60°, 180° \textit{ or } 300°$$

Example 9.16

a) *Sketch, on the same grid, the graphs of* $y = 2\cos x$ *and* $y = 3\tan x$, *for* $-\pi \le x \le \pi$.

b) *Form and solve a quadratic equation in* $\sin x$ *to find the points of intersection of the two curves in* **a)**.

Solution

a)

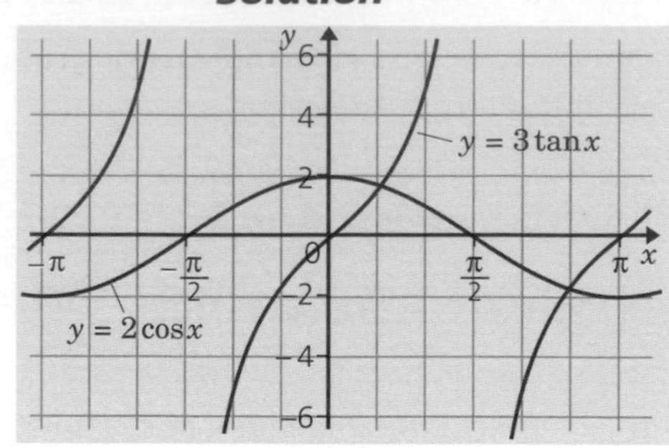

b) At the points of intersection:

$$2\cos x = 3\tan x \Rightarrow 2\cos x = 3\frac{\sin x}{\cos x}$$
$$\Rightarrow 2\cos^2 x = 3\sin x$$
$$\Rightarrow 2(1 - \sin^2 x) = 3\sin x$$
$$(\text{since } \sin^2 x + \cos^2 x = 1)$$
$$\Rightarrow 2 - 2\sin^2 x = 3\sin x$$
$$0 = 2\sin^2 x + 3\sin x - 2$$
$$= (2\sin x - 1)(\sin x + 2)$$
$$\Rightarrow 2\sin x - 1 = 0 \quad \textit{or} \quad \sin x = -2$$
$$\Rightarrow \sin x = 0.5 \quad \textit{or} \quad \sin x = -2$$

Now: $\sin x = 0.5 \Rightarrow x = \sin^{-1} 0.5 = \frac{\pi}{6}$ *(from calculator)*

but $-\pi \le x \le \pi \quad \Rightarrow \quad x = \frac{\pi}{6}$ *or* $x = \pi - \frac{\pi}{6} = \frac{5\pi}{6}$

Since $\sin x = -2$ *has no solution, the only solutions are* $x = \frac{\pi}{6}$ *or* $x = \frac{5\pi}{6}$.
To find corresponding y*-values, substitute for* x *in, say,* $y = 2\cos x$.

When $x = \frac{\pi}{6} \quad y = 2\cos\frac{\pi}{6} = 2 \times \frac{\sqrt{3}}{2} = \sqrt{3}$

When $x = \frac{5\pi}{6} \quad y = 2\cos\frac{5\pi}{6} = 2 \times -\frac{\sqrt{3}}{2} = -\sqrt{3}$

Therefore the coordinates of the points of intersection of the two curves are $\left(\frac{\pi}{6}, \sqrt{3}\right)$ *and* $\left(\frac{5\pi}{6}, -\sqrt{3}\right)$.

EXERCISES

9.6 CLASSWORK

1 Transform the following equations into equations in one trigonometrical function and solve them for the domain $0° \le \theta \le 360°$.

a) $3\sin\theta + 4\cos\theta = 0$ **b)** $\sin^2\theta - \cos^2\theta = 1$
c) $\tan^2\theta + \sec^2\theta = 9$ **d)** $1 + \cot^2\theta = 8\sin\theta$

2 Solve the following quadratic trigonometrical equations for the domain $0° \le \theta \le 360°$.

a) $4\sin^2\theta + 4\sin\theta + 1 = 0$ **b)** $4\cos^2\theta - 1 = 0$
c) $3\cos^2\theta - \cos\theta = 2$ **d)** $4\sec^2\theta - \sec\theta - 5 = 0$

3 Transform the following equations into quadratic equations in one trigonometrical function and solve for the domain $0° \le \theta \le 360°$.

a) $4 + \sin\theta = 6\cos^2\theta$ **b)** $\sin\theta = \cot\theta$
c) $\cot^2\theta = \operatorname{cosec}\theta + 11$ **d)** $2\cot\theta + \tan\theta = 2\operatorname{cosec}\theta$

4 Solve the following equations for the domain $-\pi \le x \le \pi$.

a) $\tan^2 x = \tan x + 6$ **b)** $2\sec^2 x = 5\tan x$
c) $1 + \sin^2 x = 4\sin x$ **d)** $3\cot x = \operatorname{cosec}^2 x$
e) $\tan x - 2\cot x = 3\sec x$

5 **a)** A function f is defined by: $f(s) = 4s^3 - 4s^2 - s + 1$.
Find $f(1)$ and use the factor theorem to factorise $f(s)$ fully.
b) Solve the equation $4\sin^3 x - 4\sin^2 x - \sin x + 1 = 0$ for the domain $-\pi \le x \le \pi$.

EXERCISES

9.6 HOMEWORK

1 Transform the following equations into equations in one trigonometric function and solve for the domain $0° \leq \theta \leq 360°$.

a) $\sin\theta - 2\cos\theta = 0$ **b)** $\cos^2\theta - \sin^2\theta = 0$
c) $\tan^2\theta + \sec^2\theta = 17$ **d)** $\sec^2\theta - 2\tan\theta = 0$

2 Solve the following quadratic trigonometrical equations for the domain $-180° \leq \theta \leq 180°$.

a) $6\sin^2\theta - 5\sin\theta + 1 = 0$ **b)** $9\sin^2\theta - 1 = 0$
c) $\tan^2\theta - 3\tan\theta + 2 = 0$ **d)** $4\operatorname{cosec}^2\theta - \operatorname{cosec}\theta - 5 = 0$

3 Solve the following equations for the domain $0 \leq x \leq 2\pi$.

a) $\operatorname{cosec}^2 x - 4 = 0$ **b)** $8\cos^2 x + 14\sin x = 9$
c) $3\tan x = \sec^2 x$

4 Find values of x in the range $0 \leq x \leq 2\pi$ for which $\cot^2 x + \operatorname{cosec} x = 5$.

5 **a)** A function f is defined by $f(s) = 4s^4 + 12s^3 + 7s^2 - 3s - 2$.
Find $f(-1)$ and $f(-2)$ and use the factor theorem to factorise $f(s)$ fully.
b) Solve the equation $4\sin^4\theta + 12\sin^3\theta + 7\sin^2\theta - 3\sin\theta - 2 = 0$ for the domain $0 \leq \theta \leq 2\pi$.

CONSOLIDATION EXERCISES FOR CHAPTER 9

1 Write down the maximum and minimum values of the expression $4 - 2\sin 3x$ as x varies.

Explain why the graph of $y = 4 - 2\sin 3x$ does not cut the x-axis. Sketch the graph of the curve with equation $y = 4 - 2\sin 3x$, $0° \leq x \leq 360°$, stating the values of x for which the curve has maximum and minimum values.

2 **a)** Sketch the graph of $y = \cos x$.
b) Superimpose the graph of $y = \cos 2x$.
c) Use your graphs in parts **a)** and **b)** to sketch the graph of $y = \cos x + \cos 2x$.
Where does your graph cut the x-axis?

What are the greatest and least values of the expression $\cos x + \cos 2x$?

3 State the greatest and least values of $1 + 2\cos 2\theta$ for all values of θ.

Solve the equation $1 + 2\cos 2\theta = 0$, giving all solutions in the interval $0° \leq \theta \leq 360°$.

Sketch the graph of the curve with equation $y = 1 + 2\cos 2\theta$, $0° \leq \theta \leq 360°$. *(Oxford)*

4 Using your calculator and the appropriate graph, find all values of x, such that $0° \leq x \leq 360°$, where:
$12\sin^2 x + 5 = 8$.

5 At a particular point on the earth's surface, the number n of hours of daylight x days after the start of the year is given approximately by the model: $n = 12 - 6\cos x$. (1 Jan = day 0; 365 days in total.)

a) Calculate the length of the day on May 1st, which is day 121.

b) According to the model find the dates in the year when the length of the day is longest and shortest.

c) Explain why the model is not very good and suggest an improvement.

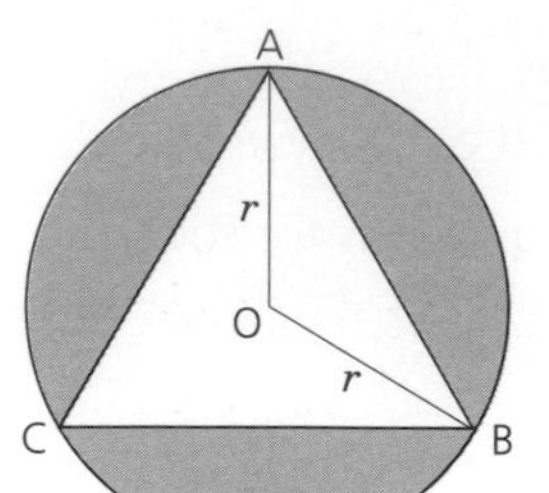

6 The diagram shows an equilateral triangle ABC whose vertices lie on a circle, centre O, of radius r.

a) Show that the length of a side of this triangle is $r\sqrt{3}$.

b) Show that the ratio of the area of the shaded region to the area of the triangle is $4\pi\sqrt{3} - 9 : 9$.

(ULEAC Question 6, Paper 1, January 1995)

7 The figure shows part of the curve C with equation $y = \mathrm{f}(x)$, where $\mathrm{f}(x) = 1.2 - \tan(2x° - \theta°)$, θ is a constant and $0 \le \theta \le 180$. The curve C intersects the y-axis at A. Given that the point with coordinates (33.75, 0.2) lies on C,

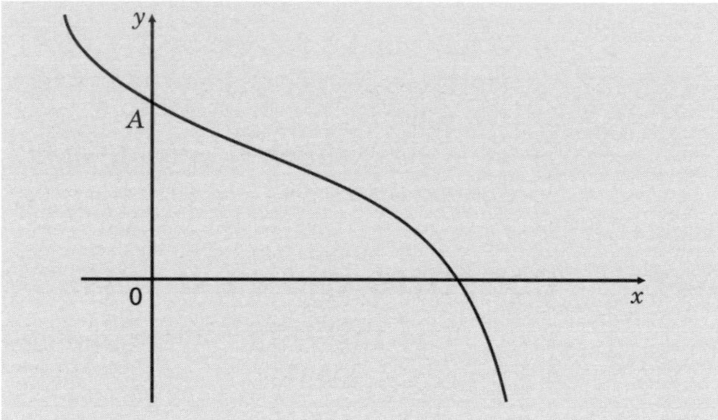

a) show that $\theta = 22.5$.

Using the value $\theta = 22.5$,

b) calculate, to 3 decimal places, the y-coordinate of A,

c) solve the equation $\mathrm{f}(x) = 0$ for $0 \le x \le 180$, giving your answers to the nearest whole number,

d) write down the period of f,

e) sketch the curve $y = \mathrm{f}(x)$ for $0 \le x \le 180$.

(EDEXCEL, Question 10, Paper 1, January 2000)

8 The figure shows an arc AB of a circle, radius r cm, which subtends an angle θ radians at the centre 0 of the circle.

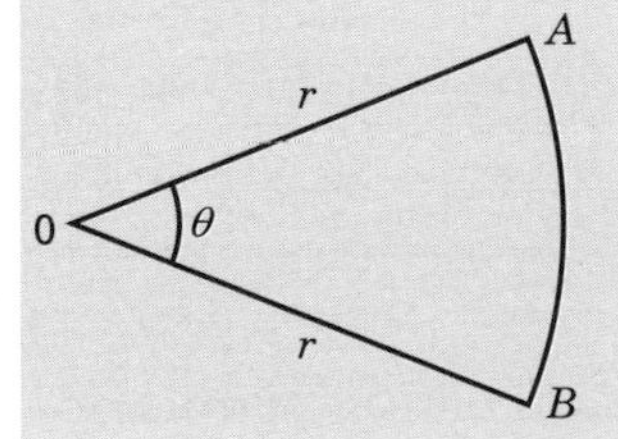

Given that $r = 9$, measured to the nearest integer, and $\theta = 1.2$, measured to1 decimal place, calculate

a) the least possible length of the arc AB of the circle.

The area of the sector of the circle bounded by the arc AB and the radii OA and OB is calculated using $r = 9$ and $\theta = 1.2$.

b) Calculate the greatest absolute error possible in this evaluation of the area.

(EDEXCEL, Question 3, Specimen Paper 1, 2000)

9 The curve with equation $y = 2 + k \sin x$ passes through the point with coordinates $(\frac{\pi}{2}, -2)$.

Find

a) the value of k, **b)** the greatest value of y,

c) the values of x in the interval $0 \leq x \leq 2\pi$ for which $y = 2 + 2\sqrt{2}$.

(EDEXCEL, Question 5, Specimen Paper 1, 2000)

10 Show that the equation $15\cos^2\theta = 13 + \sin\theta$ may be written as a quadratic equation in $\sin\theta$.

Hence solve the equation, giving all values of θ such that $0° \leq \theta \leq 360°$.

(OCR, Question 4, Specimen Paper 1, 2000)

Summary

Trigonometric functions

- The functions $\cos\theta$ and $\sin\theta$ are called **circular** functions. It is important to recognise their graphs:

i) $\cos\theta$

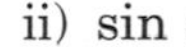

ii) $\sin\theta$

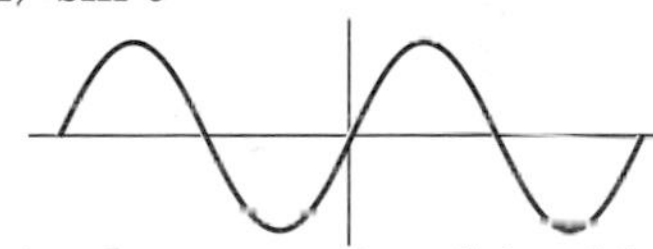

The graphs form waves, oscillating between –1 and 1, with **amplitude** 1 and **period** 360° or 2π radians. Any function with a graph which repeats itself in this way is said to be **periodic**.

Special cases

- Significant values for cosines, sines and tangents are:

θ	0°	30°	45°	60°	90°	180°	270°	360°
$\cos\theta$	1	$\frac{\sqrt{3}}{2}$	$\frac{1}{\sqrt{2}}$	$\frac{1}{2}$	0	–1	0	1
$\sin\theta$	0	$\frac{1}{2}$	$\frac{1}{\sqrt{2}}$	$\frac{\sqrt{3}}{2}$	1	0	–1	0
$\tan\theta$	0	$\frac{1}{\sqrt{3}}$	1	$\sqrt{3}$	∞	0	$-\infty$	0

Trigonometric identities

- Useful identities include:

$\sin\theta = \cos(90° - \theta)$ $\cos\theta = \sin(90° - \theta)$

$\sin\theta = \sin(180° - \theta)$ $\cos\theta = \cos(180° - \theta)$

$\sin^2\theta + \cos^2\theta = 1$

One **radian** is the angle that gives the same arc length in a sector as the radius.

$$1 \text{ radian} = \frac{180°}{\pi} = 57.3° \quad 1° = \frac{\pi}{180} \text{ radians}$$

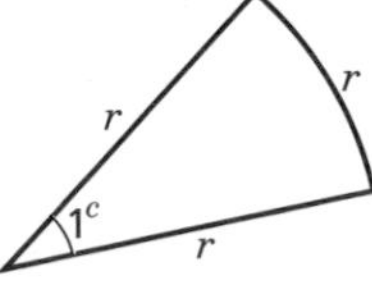

The arc length in a sector of radius r m and angle θ radians is $r\theta$ m.

The area of the sector is $\frac{1}{2}r^2\theta$ m^2

Sequences and series 1

In this chapter we:

- *explore the properties of sequences and series*
- *explore particular patterns that give rise to arithmetic and geometric sequences and series*
- *consider the convergence of a geometric series.*

SEQUENCES AND SERIES

Sequences

Exploration 10.1

Looking at sequences

Look at the following sequences of numbers.

a) 5, 10, 15, 20, 25, …
b) 2, 5, 8, 11, 14, …
c) 13, 9, 5, 1, –3, …
d) 1, 2, 4, 8, 16, …
e) 81, 27, 9, 3, 1, …
f) 1, –1.1, 1.21, –1.331, 1.461, …
g) 1, 3, 7, 15, 31, …
h) 1, 2, 6, 24, 120, …
i) 1, 4, 9, 16, 25, …
j) 1, 1, 2, 3, 5, 8, …

- What are the next three numbers in each sequence?
- For each sequence, can you find a rule for generating the number from the one before it?
- Can you find a formula that will give any number in terms of its position in the sequence?

Notation

Before analysing the results of the exploration, it is worth bringing in some notation. Each number in a sequence is called a **term**, and the terms of any sequence are often written as

$$u_1,\ u_2,\ u_3,\ u_4,\ \ldots,\ u_k,\ \ldots$$

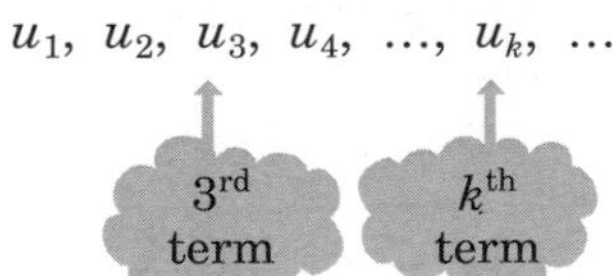

In sequences **a)**, **b)** and **c)** there is a constant difference between consecutive terms, e.g. in **b)**:

$u_1 = 2, u_2 = 5, u_3 = 8, u_4 = 11, u_5 = 14, u_6 = 17, u_7 = 20$, etc.

$\Rightarrow \quad u_2 = u_1 + 3$

$\Rightarrow \quad u_3 = u_2 + 3$

$\Rightarrow \quad u_4 = u_3 + 3$ etc.

and in general: $\quad u_{k+1} = u_k + 3$ for $k = 1, 2, 3, \ldots$

Expressing one term in terms of the term before it, and specifying the first term, is called an **inductive definition**.

A **formula** for each term, u_k, as a function of k, its position in the sequence is easily found for such sequences, e.g. in **b)**:

$u_k = 3k - 1$

In sequences **d)**, **e)** and **f)** there is a constant ratio between consecutive terms, e.g. in **e)**:
the **inductive definition** is given by:

$u_1 = 81 \quad$ and $u_{k+1} = \frac{1}{3}u_k \quad$ for $\quad k = 1, 2, 3, \ldots$

and the **formula** for u_k is given by:

$u_k = 81 \times (\frac{1}{3})^{k-1}$ or $243 \times (\frac{1}{3})^k$

Sequences **g)**, **h)**, **i)** and **j)** do not conform to either of the above patterns, but may be defined inductively and have formula definitions.

Sequence	*Inductive definition*	*Formula*
g)	$u_1 = 1$ and $u_{k+1} = 2u_k + 1$	$u_k = 2^k - 1$
h)	$u_1 = 1$ and $u_{k+1} = u_k \times (k + 1)$	$u_k = k!$
i)	$u_1 = 1$ and $u_{k+1} = u_k + (2k + 1)$	$u_k = k^2$
j)	$u_1 = 1, u_2 = 1$ and $u_{k+1} = u_k + u_{n-1}$	?

Note:
The inductive definition for sequence **j)** involves specifying *two* initial terms and the definition of a term involves the *two* previous terms. This particular pattern is called a ***Fibonacci sequence***. There is a formula for the kth term of the sequence, but it is beyond the scope of this work

Series

When terms of a sequence are added together a **series** is formed.

Exploration 10.2

Find the sum

Look at the following series of numbers, each with a different number of terms.

a) $3 + 8 + 13 + 18 + 23 + 28 + \ldots$

b) $50 + 35 + 20 + 5 - 10 - \ldots$

c) $1 + 2 + 4 + 8 + 16 + 32 + 64 + \ldots$

d) $81 + 27 + 9 + 3 + 1 + \frac{1}{3} + \ldots$

■ Find the sum of each series for the terms shown.

Notation

Before analysing the results of the exploration it is worth bringing in a little more notation.

Sums of consecutive terms are generated according to the pattern:

$S_1 = u_1$
$S_2 = u_1 + u_2$
$S_3 = u_1 + u_2 + u_3$
$S_4 = u_1 + u_2 + u_3 + u_4$

$S_n = u_1 + u_2 + u_3 + \ldots + u_n$

The terms S_1 , S_2 , S_3 , S_4 , ... are each **partial sums** of a series.

The sum $S_n = u_1 + u_2 + u_3 + \ldots + u_n$ is often written $\sum_{k=1}^{n} u_k$, which means 'the sum of u_k, for $k = 1$ to n' and Σ is the Greek letter sigma.

For **a)** $\quad u_k = 5k - 2 \Rightarrow S_6 = \sum_{k=1}^{6} u_k = \sum_{k=1}^{6} (5k-2) = 93$

For **b)** $\quad u_k = 65 - 15k \Rightarrow S_5 = \sum_{k=1}^{5} u_k = \sum_{k=1}^{5} (65-15k) = 100$

For **c)** $\quad u_k = 2^{k-1} \Rightarrow S_7 = \sum_{k=1}^{7} u_k = \sum_{k=1}^{7} 2^{k-1} = 127$

For **d)** $\quad u_k = 81\times\left(\tfrac{1}{3}\right)^{k-1} \Rightarrow S_6 = \sum_{k=1}^{6} u_k = \sum_{k=1}^{6} 81\times\left(\tfrac{1}{3}\right)^{k-1} = 121\tfrac{1}{3}$

Example 10.1

A sequence is defined by the formula $u_k = (-1)^{k+1} \times k^2$.

Write down u_1, u_2, u_3, u_4 *and* u_5 *and find* $\sum_{k=1}^{5} u_k$.

Solution

$u_1 = (-1)^2 \times 1^2 = 1$
$u_2 = (-1)^3 \times 2^2 = -4$
$u_3 = (-1)^4 \times 3^2 = 9$
$u_4 = (-1)^5 \times 4^2 = -16$
$u_5 = (-1)^6 \times 5^2 = 25$

$$\sum_{k=1}^{5} u_k = 1 - 4 + 9 - 16 + 25$$
$$= 15$$

Example 10.2

A sequence is defined inductively by $u_{k+1} = \dfrac{u_k + 3}{2}$, $u_1 = 1$.

Write down u_2, u_3, u_4, u_5 *and find a formula for* u_k.
What do you think happens as $k \to \infty$?

Solution

$u_2 = \frac{1+3}{2} = 2 \qquad u_3 = \frac{2+3}{2} = 2.5$

$u_4 = \frac{2.5+3}{2} = 2.75 \qquad u_5 = \frac{2.75+3}{2} = 2.875$

A suitable formula is $u_k = 3 - 0.5^{k-2}$. *Check this for yourself.*
As k *gets larger,* 0.5^{k-2} *gets smaller, which means that as* $k \to \infty$, $0.5^{k-2} \to 0$ *and so* $u_k \to 3$.

EXERCISES

10.1 CLASSWORK

1 For each of the following sequences, find an inductive definition and a formula.

a) 1, 5, 9, 13, … **b)** 1, –2, 4, –8, 16, …
c) 16000, 4000, 1000, 250, … **d)** 1, 8, 27, 64, …

2 Write out each of the following fully and find its value.

a) $\sum_{k=1}^{5} k^2$ **b)** $\sum_{k=0}^{4} (k+1)^2$ **c)** $\sum_{k=3}^{7} (k-2)^2$ **d)** $\sum_{k=0}^{4} (5k+2)$

3 Use the Σ notation to abbreviate (but do not evaluate) each of the following.

a) 1 + 4 + 9 + 16 + … + 625
b) (1 × 2) + (2 × 3) + (3 × 4) + … + (15 × 16)
c) $1 + \frac{1}{2} + \frac{1}{3} + \quad \ldots \quad + \frac{1}{100}$

4 For each of the inductive definitions below:

i) write down the values of $u_2, u_3, u_4, u_5, \ldots$
ii) find a formula definition for u_k,
iii) describe what happens to u_k as $k \to \infty$.

a) $u_{k+1} = \frac{u_k + 10}{3}, \quad u_1 = 2$ **b)** $u_{k+1} = \frac{2}{u_k + 1}, \quad u_1 = 0$

10.1 HOMEWORK

1 For each of the following sequences, find an inductive definition and a formula.

a) 65, 56, 47, 38, … **b)** 1, 0.9, 0.81, 0.729, …
c) 1, 3, 6, 10, 15, … **d)** $1, \frac{1}{2}, \frac{1}{3}, \frac{1}{4}, \ldots$

2 Write out each of the following fully and find its value.

a) $\sum_{k=3}^{8} \frac{1}{k}$ **b)** $\sum_{k=0}^{5} 2^k$ **c)** $\sum_{k=1}^{5} k(k+2)$ **d)** $\sum_{k=1}^{5} k^2 + 2\sum_{k=1}^{5} k$

3 Use the Σ notation to abbreviate (but do not evaluate) each of the following.

a) 2 + 16 + 54 + 128 + … + 2000
b) (2 × 5) + (3 × 6) + (4 × 7) + … + (12 × 15)
c) $1 - \frac{1}{2} + \frac{1}{3} - \quad \cdots \quad + \frac{1}{21}$

4 For each of the inductive definitions below:

i) write down the values of $u_2, u_3, u_4, u_5, \ldots$,
ii) find a formula definition for u_k,
iii) describe what happens to u_k as $k \to \infty$.

a) $u_{k+1} = \dfrac{u_k - 3}{4}, \quad u_1 = 2$ b) $u_{k+1} = \dfrac{6}{u_k + 1}, \quad u_1 = 1$

ARITHMETIC SEQUENCES AND SERIES

Exploration 10.3

Regular increases

Karen is beginning work for an engineering company. Her starting salary is £11700. Each year she can expect an increase of £850, rising to a maximum of £18500.

- How much will she earn in her fourth year with the company?
- How long will it take for her salary to rise to the maximum?
- How much will she have earned altogether by the end of the first year that she is on maximum salary?

Interpreting the results

The table shows Karen's salaries until she gets to the top of her range.

Year	Salary £
1	11 700
2	12 550
3	13 400
4	14 250
5	15 100
6	15 950
7	16 800
8	17 650
9	18 500

By inspection we can see that she will earn £14 250 in her fourth year and that it will take eight years for her salary to rise to the maximum.

By summing the second column, we find that she expects to earn a total of £135 900 over a period of nine years.

Without the aid of the table, we could deduce:

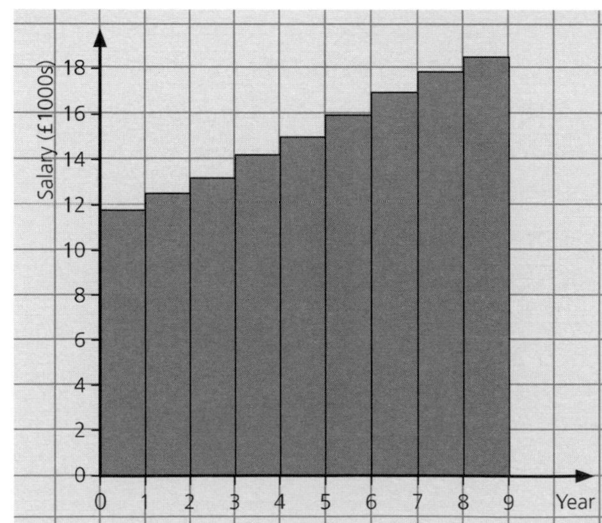

In her fourth year she will earn £11700 + 3 × £850 = £14250

Number of years taken to reach maximum salary:

$$\frac{18\,500 - 11\,700}{850} = 8$$

The salary structure could be illustrated in the following diagram.

Karen's salary in any one year is represented by the area of a rectangle. Her total earnings are represented by the total shaded area.

Taking a copy of the shaded area, rotating it through a half-turn and placing it above the original diagram gives a rectangle of width 9 (years) and height 11700 + 18500 = 30200.

The total earnings is equivalent to **half** the area of the rectangle.

$$\frac{(11\,700+18\,500)\times 9}{2}$$
$$=\frac{11\,700+18\,500}{2}\times 9$$
$$=135\,900$$

This gives an easy way of finding the total earnings:

average of first and last year's salaries × number of years

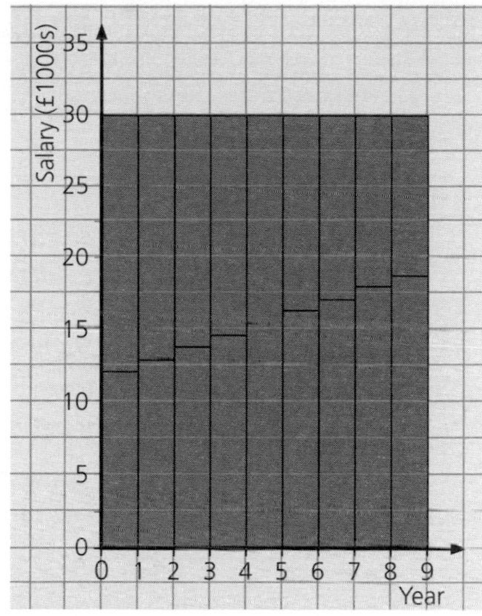

Arithmetic sequence

The pattern of salaries in Exploration 10.3: 11700, 12550, 13400, … is an example of an **arithmetic sequence** with **first term** 11700 and **common difference** 850.

In general, an arithmetic sequence with first term a and common difference d has inductive definition $u_{k+1} = u_k + d$, $u_1 = a$ and will generate the terms:

$u_2 = a + d$

$u_3 = a + 2d$

$u_4 = a + 3d$

⋮

$u_k = a + (k - 1)\,d$

⋮

i.e. the kth term is $u_k = a + (k - 1)\,d$.

The sum of the first n terms is given by:

average of first and last terms × number of terms

$$\Rightarrow \quad S_n = \frac{(a+l)}{2}\times n \equiv \frac{n}{2}\times(a+l)$$
$$\equiv \frac{n}{2}\left[a+(a+(n-1)d)\right]$$
$$\equiv \frac{n}{2}\left[2a+(n-1)d\right]$$

To prove this result we first write the sum of the first n terms as:
$S_n = a + (a + d) + (a + 2d) + (a + 3d) + \dots$ (1)

Now write the sum backwards with the last term first:
$S_n = (a + (n - 1)\,d) + (a + (n - 2)\,d) + \dots$ (2)

Adding (1) and (2) we get:
$2S_n = (2a + (n - 1)\,d) + (2a + (n - 1)\,d) + \dots$

The right-hand side has n terms, all of which are $2a + (n - 1)\,d$.
$2S_n = (2a + (n - 1)\,d)\,n$
$S_n = \frac{1}{2}(2a + (n - 1)\,d)\,n$
$S_n = \frac{1}{2}(a + a + (n - 1)\,d)\,n = \frac{1}{2}(a + l)n$

The series generated from an arithmetic sequence is called an **arithmetic progression (AP)**, so S_n is known as the **sum to *n* terms** of an arithmetic progression.

Example 10.3

The third term of an AP is 17 and the seventh term is 31. Find the common difference d, the first term a, expressions for u_k and S_n, and evaluate u_{10} and S_{10}.

Solution

$u_3 = 17 = a + 2d$ (1)

$u_7 = 31 = a + 6d$ (2)

Subtracting equation (1) from equation (2) gives:

$$14 = 4d$$
$$\Rightarrow d = 3.5$$

*Substitute for d in (**1**):*

$$17 = a + 2 \times 3.5$$
$$\Rightarrow a = 10$$

Hence $u_k = 10 + 3.5(k-1)$

$$S_n = \frac{n}{2}[2 \times 10 + 3.5(n-1)]$$

In particular:

$$u_{10} = 10 + 3.5 \times 9 = 41.55$$

$$S_{10} = \frac{10}{2}(20 + 3.5 \times 9) = 257.5$$

Example 10.4

For the AP in Example 10.3, find the value of:

a) k *if* $u_k = 59$ ***b)*** n *if* $S_n = 178$.

Solution

a) $u_k = 10 + 3.5(k-1) = 59$

$$\Rightarrow 3.5(k-1) = 49$$
$$\Rightarrow k - 1 = 14$$
$$\Rightarrow k = 15$$

b) $S_n = \frac{n}{2}[2 \times 10 + 3.5(n-1)] = 178$

$$\Rightarrow n(20 + 3.5n - 3.5) = 356$$
$$\Rightarrow n(16.5 + 3.5n) = 356$$
$$\Rightarrow 16.5n + 3.5n^2 = 356$$
$$\Rightarrow 7n^2 + 33n - 712 = 0$$
$$\Rightarrow (n-8)(7n+89) = 0$$

Since n has to be a positive integer, the solution must be $n = 8$.

In Example 10.3 the values of a and d were found by solving a pair of simultaneous equations. Another situation that gives rise to simultaneous equations is illustrated in the next example.

Example 10.5

The sum of the first n terms of a series is S_n, where $S_n = 3n^2 + n$.

a) *Show that $u_n = 6n - 2$ and find a and d.*
b) *Find $u_8 + u_9 + u_{10}$ in two different ways.*

Solution

a) *Since* $S_n = 3n^2 + n$, $S_{n-1} = 3(n-1)^2 + (n-1)$

$$\begin{aligned} \Rightarrow \quad u_n &= S_n - S_{n-1} \\ &= 3n^2 + n - 3(n-1)^2 - (n-1) \\ &= 3n^2 + n - 3(n^2 - 2n + 1) - n + 1 \\ &= 3n^2 + n - 3n^2 + 6n - 3 - n + 1 \\ &= 6n - 2 \end{aligned}$$

$a = u_1 = 6 \times 1 - 2 = 4$ *and*
$u_2 = 6 \times 2 - 2 = 10$
$\Rightarrow d = 10 - 4 = 6$

b) *Either*
$u_8 + u_9 + u_{10} = (6 \times 8 - 2) + (6 \times 9 - 2) + (6 \times 10 - 2) = 156$
or
$u_8 + u_9 + u_{10} = S_{10} - S_7 = 3 \times 10^2 + 10 - (3 \times 7^2 + 7) = 156$

EXERCISES

10.2 CLASSWORK

1 Fill in the missing terms in the following arithmetic sequences.

a) $7, -, 15$ **b)** $42, -, -, 18$
c) $20, -, -, -, -, -, -22$ **d)** $2\frac{1}{2}, -, 4, -, -, -, 7$

2 How many terms are there in the following arithmetic sequences?

a) $10, 14, 18, \ldots, 46$ **b)** $-16, \ldots, 9, 14, 19$
c) $20, 17.5, \ldots, -22.5, -25$ **d)** $p, p + q, \ldots, p + 10q$

3 For each of the following arithmetic sequences, find expressions for u_k and S_n. Find the tenth term and the sum of the first ten terms.

a) $2, 5, 8, \ldots$ **b)** $3, 2\frac{1}{4}, 1\frac{1}{2}, \ldots$
c) $-13.5, -10.5, -7.5, \ldots$ **d)** $0, x, 2x, \ldots$
e) $p, p + 2q, p + 4q, \ldots$ **f)** $p + q, p, p - q, \ldots$

4 The second term in an arithmetic progression (AP) is 5 and the sixth term is 11. Find an expression for u_k and the value of u_8.

5 In an AP, $u_5 = 13$ and $u_{12} = 27$. Find an expression for S_n and the value of S_8.

6 Find the sum of the following APs.

a) $8 + 10.25 + \ldots + 35$ **b)** $50 + 39 + \ldots - 27$
c) $-14 + \ldots + 31$ (*11 terms*) **d)** $10 + \ldots + 19$ (*13 terms*)

7 In an arithmetic sequence, the eighth term is twice the third term and the terms differ by 12. Show that $u_k = 4.8 + 2.4k$ and find S_8.

8 For the AP $20 + 17 + 14 + \ldots$, $S_n = 65$. Find the value of n.

9 A skier is skiing down a slope such that distances travelled in successive seconds form an arithmetic sequence. In the first second she travels 4 metres and after 4 seconds has travelled a distance of 25 metres.

a) How far will the skier travel in 8 seconds?
b) How long will it take her to cover a distance of 147 metres?

10.2 HOMEWORK

1 Fill in the missing terms in the following arithmetic sequences.

a) $17, -, 23$
b) $20, -, -, -, -, 5$
c) $\frac{2}{3}, -, \frac{4}{3}, -, 2$
d) $2\frac{2}{3}, -, 1\frac{2}{3}, -, \frac{2}{3}$

2 How many terms are there in the following arithmetic sequences?

a) $11, 14, 17, \ldots, 41$
b) $26, \ldots, 62, 66, 70$
c) $20, 16.5, 13, \ldots, -22$
d) $p + 5q, p + 3q, \ldots, p - 21q$

3 For each of the following arithmetic sequences, find expressions for u_k and S_n. Find the eighth term and the sum of the first eight terms.

a) $2, 4, 6, \ldots$
b) $17, 13, 9, \ldots$
c) $5, 0, -5, \ldots$
d) $30, 30 - x, 30 - 2x, \ldots$
e) $p, p - 4q, p - 8q, \ldots$
f) $p + q, 2p + 3q, 3p + 5q, \ldots$

4 The third term of an arithmetic progression (AP) is 7 and the seventh term is 15. Find an expression for u_k and the value of u_{11}.

5 In an AP, $u_6 = 21$ and $u_{13} = 56$. Find an expression for S_n and the value of S_{10}.

6 Find the sum of the following APs.

a) $13 + 17 + 21 + \ldots$ (*16 terms*)
b) $37 + 30 + 23 + \ldots$ (*12 terms*)
c) all the odd numbers between 20 and 80
d) all the even numbers between 20 and 80

7 An arithmetic sequence has 13 terms with sum 143. The fifth term is 8. Find the first term.

8 The first term of an AP is 3 and the sum of the first six terms is 4 times the sum of the first three terms. Find the common difference.

9 A major new motorway project is due to last for seven weeks. One hundred men start work on the first Monday. They are paid a flat rate of £360 for a six-day working week with Sundays off. As work progresses, every Monday for the next six weeks an additional sixty men are taken on at the same rate of pay.

How many men are employed by the end of the project and what is the total wage bill?

CALCULATOR ACTIVITY

Exploration 10.4

An arithmetic progression

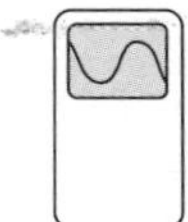

Try the following program (on a calculator or computer) which generates both the terms and the sums of an arithmetic progression. Use it to check your results from Exercises 10.2 and to investigate arithmetic progressions for various values of a and d.

Check the working of Exploration 10.3 by entering 11 700 into store A and 850 into store D. Stop the program when N (representing the year) has reached 9 and U (representing the salary) has reached 18 500.

You should be able to produce a table of values as shown.

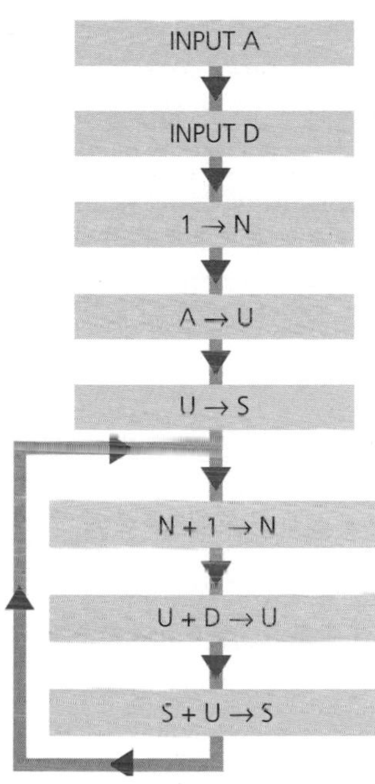

N	U	S
1	11 700	11 700
2	12 550	24 250
3	13 440	37 650
4	14 250	51 900
5	15 100	67 000
6	15 950	82 950
7	16 800	99 750
8	17 650	117 400
9	18 500	135 900

GEOMETRIC SEQUENCES AND SERIES

Exploration 10.5

Percentage increases

Stuart is starting work for a chemical firm. Like Karen (see Exploration 10.3), he is offered a salary scheme with eight annual increments. However, his initial salary is £11 500 and in each subsequent year he will be paid seven per cent more than he was paid the previous year.

- How much will he earn in his second and third years?
- How much will he earn at the top of the scale?
- How much can he be expected to earn altogether over the nine-year period?
- Compare Stuart's salary scheme with Karen's. Who is better off? Why?

Interpreting the results

In his second year with the company Stuart will earn
$£11500 \times 1.07 = £12305$

In his third year with the company Stuart will earn £12 305 × 1.07 = £11 500 × 1.07^2 = £13 166.35

Stuart will reach the top of the scale in the ninth year, during which he will earn £11 500 × 1.07^8 = £19 759.14

The table shows Stuart's salary structure over a period of nine years. By summing the second column, we can see that he expects to earn a total of £137 745.

Year	Salary (nearest £)
1	11 500
2	12 305
3	13 166
4	14 088
5	15 074
6	16 129
7	17 258
8	18 466
9	19 759

Comparing salaries for Karen and Stuart over the nine-year period, it is clear that for the first five years Karen earns more than Stuart, but from then on Stuart's salary is the greater. His cumulative earnings are £1845 more than Karen's, but his running total only exceeds Karen's for the first time after year 8.

You might argue that Stuart is better off because he will earn more than Karen altogether. However she earns more than he does for the first five years. You might think of other reasons to conclude one way or the other.

Geometric sequence

The pattern of salaries in Exploration 10.4: 11 500, 12 305, 13 166, ... is an example of a **geometric sequence** with **first term** 11 500 and **common ratio** 1.07.

In general, a geometric sequence with first term a and common ratio r has inductive definition $u_{k+1} = u_k \times r$, $u_1 = a$ and will generate the terms:

$$u_2 = ar$$
$$u_3 = ar^2$$
$$u_4 = ar^3$$
$$\vdots$$
$$u_k = ar^{k-1}$$
$$\vdots$$

i.e. the kth term is $u_k = ar^{k-1}$.

The sum of the first n terms, S_n is

$$S_n = u_1 + u_2 + u_3 + \ldots + u_n$$
$$\Rightarrow \quad S_n = a + ar + ar^2 + \ldots + ar^{n-1} \qquad (1)$$

To find a simpler form for S_n we need to carry out some algebraic manipulation.

Multiply both sides of (1) by r:

$$rS_n = ar + ar^2 + \ldots + ar^{n-1} + ar^n \qquad (2)$$

Subtracting equation (2) from equation (1) gives:

$$S_n = a + ar + ar^2 + \ldots + ar^{n-1} \qquad (1)$$
$$rS_n = \quad ar + ar^2 + \ldots + ar^{n-1} + ar^n \qquad (2)$$

$$(1)-(2):\quad S_n - rS_n = a - ar^n$$

$$\Rightarrow \quad S_n(1-r) = a(1-r^n)$$

$$\Rightarrow \quad S_n = \frac{a(1-r^n)}{1-r}$$

Equivalently, subtracting equation (1) from equation (2) gives:

$rS_n = \quad ar + ar^2 + \dots + ar^{n-1} + ar^n \qquad (2)$

$S_n = a + ar + ar^2 + \dots + ar^{n-1} \qquad (1)$

$$(2)-(1):\quad rS_n - S_n = ar^n - a$$

$$\Rightarrow \quad S_n(r-1) = a(r^n - 1)$$

$$\Rightarrow \quad S_n = \frac{a(r^n-1)}{r-1}$$

Either version of S_n is correct. We usually use whichever one gives a positive denominator. If $r < 1$ use the first one; if $r > 1$ use the second. If $r = 1$ use neither!

Exploration 10.6

Investigating the sequence

In Exploration 10.5, in the analysis of Stuart's salary, the formal approach gives:

$a = 11\,500,\ r = 1.07,\ n = 9$:

$$u_9 = 11500 \times 1.07^8 = 19\,759.14107 \approx 19759$$

$$S_9 = \frac{11500(1.07^9 - 1)}{1.07 - 1} = 137746.8707 \approx 137747$$

How do you explain the difference between S_9 and the sum of the column of salary figures for Stuart?

Note:

The series generated from a geometric sequence is called a **geometric progression (GP)**, so S_n is known as the **sum to n terms** of a geometric progression.

Example 10.6

For each of the following GPs, find expressions for u_k and S_n, evaluate u_7 and S_7 and find the least value of n such that $S_n > 1000$.

a) $a = 240, r = 0.8$

b) $5 + 7.5 + 11.25 + \dots$

c) $800 + 160 + 32 + \dots$

Solution

a) $u_k = ar^{k-1} = 240 \times 0.8^{k-1}$

$$S_n = \frac{a(1-r^n)}{1-r} = \frac{240(1-0.8^n)}{0.2} = 1200(1-0.8^n)$$

In particular: $\quad u_7 = 240 \times 0.8^6 = 62.9 \text{ (3 s.f.)}$

$$S_7 = 1200 \times (1 - 0.8^7) = 948 \text{ (3 s.f.)}$$

If $S_n > 1000$, then $1200(1 - 0.8^n) > 1000$

$$\Rightarrow \quad 1 - 0.8^n > \tfrac{5}{6}$$

$$\Rightarrow \quad \tfrac{1}{6} > 0.8^n$$

The required value of n may be found by trial and improvement using a calculator.

$0.8^7 \approx 0.210 > \frac{1}{6}$ $\quad 0.8^8 \approx 0.168 > \frac{1}{6}$ $\quad 0.8^9 \approx 0.134 < \frac{1}{6}$

So the least value of n, such that $S_n > 1000$, is $n = 9$.

b) $a = 5, \quad r = \dfrac{7.5}{5} = 1.5$

$$u_k = 5 \times 1.5^{k-1}$$

$$S_n = \frac{5(1.5^n - 1)}{1.5 - 1} = 10(1.5^n - 1)$$

In particular: $u_7 = 5 \times 1.5^6 = 57.0$ (3 s.f.)
$S_7 = 10(1.5^7 - 1) = 161$ (3 s.f.)

If $S_n > 1000$, then $10(1.5^n - 1) > 1000$
$\Rightarrow \quad 1.5^n - 1 > 100$
$\Rightarrow \quad 1.5^n > 101$
By trial and improvement:
$1.5^{10} = 57.7$ (3 s.f)
$1.5^{11} = 86.5$ (3 s.f)
$1.5^{12} = 130$ (3 s.f)
So the least value of n, such that $S_n > 1000$, is $n = 12$.

c) $a = 800 \quad r = \dfrac{160}{800} = 0.2$

$\therefore \quad u_k = 800 \times 0.2^{k-1}$

$$S_n = \frac{800(1 - 0.2^n)}{1 - 0.2} = 1000(1 - 0.2^n)$$

In particular: $u_7 = 800 \times 0.2^6 = 0.0512$
$S_7 = 1000(1 - 0.2^7) = 999.9872$

If $S_n > 1000$, then $1000(1 - 0.2^n) > 1000$

$\Rightarrow \quad 1 - 0.2^n > 1$
$\Rightarrow \quad 0.2^n < 0$

Since this is not possible (0.2^n is always positive), there is no value of n such that $S_n > 1000$.

Example 10.7

The second term of a GP is 20 and the fifth term is 2500. Find the common ratio r, the first term a, expressions for u_k and S_n, and evaluate u_{10} and S_{10}.

Solution

$u_2 = 20 = ar^1$ (1)
$u_5 = 2500 = ar^4$ (2)

(2) ÷ (1) $\Rightarrow 125 = r^3 \Rightarrow r = \sqrt[3]{125} = 5$

Substitute for r in (1): $20 = a \times 5 \Rightarrow a = 4$

Hence: $u_k = 4 \times 5^{k-1}$ and $S_n = \dfrac{4(5^n - 1)}{5 - 1} = 5^n - 1$

In particular: $u_{10} = 45 \times 5^9 = 7\,812\,500$
$S_{10} = 5^{10} - 1 = 9\,765\,624$

Example 10.8

Jenny puts £100 into a savings account on 1st January each year. Assuming a constant annual interest rate of eight per cent, how much will her savings be worth after ten years?

Solution

Value of savings after 1 year: $100 \times 1.08 = S_1$

Value of savings after 2 years: $100 \times 1.08^2 + 100 \times 1.08 = S_2$

Value of savings after 3 years: $100 \times 1.08^3 + 100 \times 1.08^2 + 100 \times 1.08 = S_3$

etc.

Rearranging S_3:

$$S_3 = 100 \times 1.08(1 + 1.08 + 1.08^2) = 100 \times 1.08\left(\frac{1.08^3 - 1}{1.08 - 1}\right)$$

From which we may deduce, for example, the value of S_{10}.

$$S_{10} = 100 \times 1.08\left(\frac{1.08^{10} - 1}{1.08 - 1}\right) = 1564.55 \text{ (2 d.p.)}$$

i.e. value of savings after ten years is £1564.55.

EXERCISES

10.3 CLASSWORK

1 Fill in the missing terms in the following geometric sequences.

a) $1, -, 25, 125, -$ **b)** $27, -, -, (-1)$

c) $20, -, 5, -, 1.25$ **d)** $2\frac{2}{3}, -, \frac{3}{8}, -, -$

e) $1, x^2, -, -, x^8, -$ **f)** $p^{13}q^7, -, -, -, -, p^3q^2, pq$

2 How many terms are there in the following geometric sequences?

a) $1, 3, 9, \ldots, 19\,683$ **b)** $1, 1.1, 1.21, \ldots, 1.610\,51$

c) $32, \ldots, \frac{1}{8}, -$ **d)** $x^{12}, x^9, \ldots, x^{-15}$

3 For each of the following geometric sequences, find expressions for u_k and S_n. Find the eighth term and the sum of the first eight terms.

a) $1, 2, 4, \ldots$ **b)** $500, 250, 125, \ldots$

c) $16, -8, 4, -2, 1, \ldots$ **d)** $1, \frac{1}{x}, \frac{1}{x^2}, \frac{1}{x^3}, \ldots$

4 In a GP, $u_2 = 3600$ and $u_3 = 4800$. Find an expression for u_k and the value of u_5.

5 In a GP, $u_3 = 3600$ and $u_5 = 1296$. Find two possible values for r and hence two possible expressions for S_n and values for S_5.

6 The second term of a GP is 48 and the sixth term is 243.

a) Find two possible values for r and a.
b) Write down the first eight terms for each pair of values of a and r.
c) Find S_n and the value of S_8 for each GP.
d) How do the two sequences differ?

7 For the GP $1 + 3 + 9 + \ldots$ find the least value of n such that $S_n > 1000$.

8 For the GP 500 + 250 + 125 + … find the least value of n such that $S_n > 999$.

9 An athlete plans a training schedule which involves running 20 km in the first week of training. In each subsequent week the distance is to be increased by ten per cent over the previous week.

a) Write down an expression for the distance to be covered in the nth week, according to this schedule.
b) Find in which week the athlete would first cover more than 100 km.
c) How far will he have run in his schedule altogether by the end of the week in part **b)**?

10.3 HOMEWORK

1 For each of the following geometric sequences, find expressions for u_k and S_n. Find the tenth term and the sum of the first ten terms.

a) $2, 6, 18, \ldots$ **b)** $27, 9, 3, \ldots$
c) $12, -6, 3, -1\frac{1}{2}, \ldots$ **d)** $\frac{\pi}{2}, \frac{\pi^2}{4}, \frac{\pi^3}{8}, \frac{\pi^4}{16}, \ldots$

2 In a GP, $u_3 = 84$ and $u_7 = 1344$. Find an expression for u_k and the value of u_9.

3 The second term of a GP is 6 and the sixth term is $\frac{2}{27}$. Find an expression for u_k and the value of u_{10}.

4 The third term of a GP is $\frac{8}{9}$ and the fifth term is $\frac{32}{81}$.

a) Find two possible values for r and the value of a.
b) Write down the first six terms for each pair of values.
c) Find S_n and the value of S_{10} for each GP.

5 **a)** Take an ordinary sheet of A4 paper and fold it in half, then fold it again and so on. You should find that the first five folds are easy, the sixth is difficult and the seventh is impossible. Assuming that the paper is 0.1 mm thick, write down the thickness of the paper after:
i) 1 fold **ii)** 2 folds **iii)** 3 folds.
b) Deduce an expression for the thickness after n folds.
c) If it were possible, how thick would the paper be after:
i) 7 folds **ii)** 10 folds **iii)** 15 folds?
d) How many folds would, in theory, be necessary to produce a thickness of at least 100 metres?

6 Modern paper sizes are designed on a mathematical principle. The largest is A0, then A1 has half the area of A0, A2 has half the area of A1 and so on.

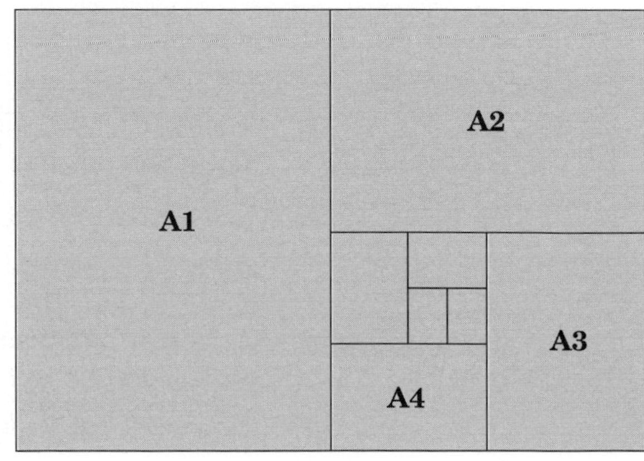

a) Measure the sides of a sheet of A4 paper to the nearest mm and calculate its area in mm^2.
b) Deduce the dimensions of A5, A3, A2, A1 and A0.
c) Deduce the area of each sheet of paper in mm^2.
d) The decreasing areas form a GP. What is its common ratio?
e) The linear dimensions also decrease in geometric progression. Write down the exact value of the common ratio.
f) In an ideal world, what do you think the area of A0 should be? Based on this estimate, estimate the ideal dimensions of a sheet of A4 in mm, correct to 3 d.p.
g) Deduce the theoretical areas and dimensions of A10 and A(–2), if these paper sizes existed.

7 A young mother takes her baby to be weighed once a week at the local clinic. For the first few months the baby gains weight at an average of four per cent per week. After how many weeks will the baby have doubled his birth weight?

8 A rubber ball is dropped onto a hard surface from a height of 2 m and bounces several times. At each bounce it rises to 60 per cent of its previous height. How many bounces will it take before it rises:

a) less than 50 cm, b) less than 10 cm?

9 You are offered a job on a short-term contract of 20 weeks and can choose one of the following two salary packages

a) £500 per week
b) one penny for the first week with salary doubling each week
Which package would you choose, and why?

CALCULATOR ACTIVITY

Exploration 10.7

A geometric progression

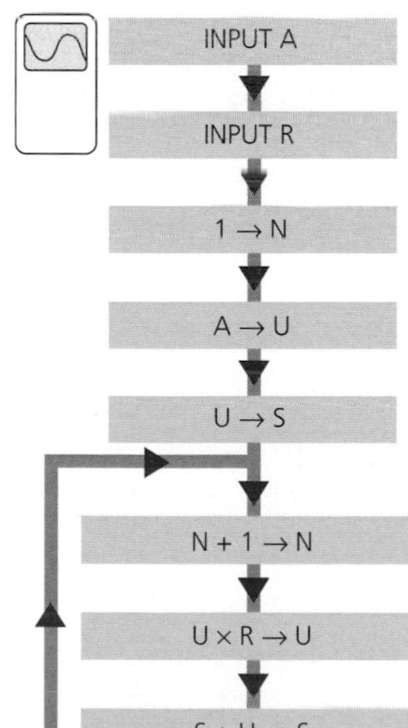

Try the following program which generates the terms and the sums of a geometric progression.

Use it to check your results from Exercises 10.3 and to investigate geometric progressions for various values of a and r.

Check the working of Explorations 10.4 and 10.5 by entering 11 500 into store A and 1.07 into store R. Stop the program when N (representing the year) has reached 9 and U (representing the salary) has reached 19759.

You should be able to produce a table of values like this.

N	U	S
1	11 500	11 500
2	12 305	23 805
3	13 166	36 971
4	14 088	51 059
5	15 074	66 133
6	16 129	82 263
7	17 258	99 521
8	18 466	117 988
9	19 759	137 747

SUM TO INFINITY OF A GEOMETRIC SERIES

Exploration 10.8

Bouncing a ball

The manufacturers of *Superbounce*, a particularly bouncy ball, claim that when the ball is dropped onto a hard surface, it will bounce back to 80 per cent of its original height.

Assuming that when left to bounce repeatedly, the ball always reaches 80 per cent of its previous height and that it is dropped initially from a height of 125 cm, find the pattern of successive heights to which the ball bounces. What happens 'in the long run'?

Consider the first n bounces:

height after the first bounce $= 0.8 \times 125 = 100$ cm

height after the second bounce $= 0.8 \times 100 = 0.8^2 \times 125 = 80$ cm

height after the third bounce $= 0.8 \times 80 = 0.8^3 \times 125 = 64$ cm

etc.

height after the nth bounce $= 0.8^n \times 125$ cm.

As n gets larger, the height of the bounce gets smaller and tends to zero, because as $n \to \infty$, $0.8^n \to 0$.

Successive heights 125, 100, 80, 64, 51.2, ... form a geometric **sequence**.

Successive partial sums 125, 225, 305, 369, 420.2, ... form a geometric **series**.

The first term $a = 125$; the common ratio $r = 0.8$.

CALCULATOR ACTIVITY

Exploration 10.9

An infinite series

Use the program from the previous Calculator activity to investigate what happens to terms in the sequence and the series for $a = 125$, $r = 0.8$ as $n \to \infty$.

- Use the formula for S_n to confirm your investigation.

Repeat this activity by keeping a fixed and varying r.

- For what range of values of r does the series converge and for what range does it diverge?

For the ball, $a = 125$ and $r = 0.8$ means that:

$$S_n = \frac{a(1-r^n)}{1-r} = \frac{125(1-0.8^n)}{0.2}$$

Substituting $n = 1, 2, 3, \ldots$ gives $S_n = 125, 225, 305, \ldots$

Running the program until n becomes large reveals that S_n is converging towards a limit, e.g.

$S_{10} = 557.891\,136$
$S_{20} = 617.794\,240\,6$
$S_{30} = 624.226\,287\,5$
$S_{40} = 624.916\,923\,3$
$S_{50} = 624.991\,079\,7$

As $n \to \infty$, $S_n \to 625$, which is confirmed by letting $n \to \infty$ in the formula for S_n.

As $n \to \infty$, $0.8^n \to \infty \quad \Rightarrow \quad S_n \to 125/0.2 = 625$

For the general geometric series, $r^n \to 0$ as $n \to \infty$, provided $-1 < r < 1$, i.e. $|r| < 1$.

This gives the general definition for the **sum to infinity** of a geometric series, S_∞.

$$S_\infty = \lim_{n \to \infty} \frac{a(1-r^n)}{1-r} = \frac{a}{1-r}$$

provided $|r| < 1$.

Note

We usually discount the trivial case $r = 0$, since this would mean that every term of a geometric sequence, after the first one, would be 0. In this case the 'sum to infinity' would just be the first term, a.

Example 10.9

For the geometric sequence 81, 27, 9, ... find expressions for S_n and S_∞. Evaluate S_5, S_{10}, S_{15} and S_∞.

Solution

First term, $a = 81$; common ratio, $r = \frac{1}{3}$.

$$\Rightarrow \quad S_n = \frac{a(1-r^n)}{1-r} = \frac{81(1-(\frac{1}{3})^n)}{1-\frac{1}{3}} = 121.5 \times (1-(\tfrac{1}{3})^n)$$

In particular: $S_5 = 121.5 \times (1-(\frac{1}{3})^5) = 121$

$$S_{10} = 121.5 \times (1-(\tfrac{1}{3})^{10}) = 121.4979424\ldots$$

$$S_{15} = 121.5 \times (1-(\tfrac{1}{3})^{15}) = 121.4989915\ldots$$

$$S_\infty = \frac{a}{1-r} = \frac{81}{1-\frac{1}{3}} = 121.5$$

Example 10.10

Express the recurring decimal 0.027 027 027... as the sum to infinity of a geometric series and so deduce its fractional equivalent in its simplest form.

Solution

0.027 027 ...= 0.027 + 0.000 027 + 0.000 000 027 + ...
which is the sum to infinity of a geometric series with $a = 0.027$, $r = 0.001$, i.e.

$$S_\infty = \frac{a}{1-r} = \frac{0.027}{1-0.001} = \frac{0.027}{0.999} = \frac{27}{999} = \frac{1}{37}$$

Example 10.11

The sum of the first two terms of a geometric sequence is 15 and the sum to infinity is 27. Find two possible geometric sequences that have this property.

Solution

Let the first term be a and the common ratio r, then:
$a + ar = 15 \qquad (1)$

and

$$\frac{a}{1-r} = 27 \qquad (2)$$

From (2): $a = 27(1 - r)$

Substitute for a *in* (1).

$$\Rightarrow \quad 27(1-r) + 27(1-r)r = 15$$
$$\Rightarrow \quad 27 - 27r + 27r - 27r^2 = 15$$
$$\Rightarrow \quad 27 - 27r^2 = 15$$
$$\Rightarrow \quad 27r^2 = 12$$
$$\Rightarrow \quad r^2 = \tfrac{4}{9}$$
$$\Rightarrow \quad r = \pm\tfrac{2}{3}$$

$$r = \tfrac{2}{3} \quad \Rightarrow \quad a = 27(1-\tfrac{2}{3}) = 9$$

$$r = -\tfrac{2}{3} \quad \Rightarrow \quad a = 27(1+\tfrac{2}{3}) = 45$$

Two possible geometric sequences are:
9, 6, 4, … and 45, –30, 20, …

EXERCISES

10.4 CLASSWORK

1 For each of the following geometric series, determine which converge to a limit and in these cases find the sum to infinity.

a) 1 + 1.1 + 1.21 + 1.331 + … **b)** 1 + 0.9 + 0.81 + 0.729 + …
c) 112 – 84 + 63 – … **d)** 1 – 4 + 8 – 16 + …

2 Express the following recurring decimals as fractions in their simplest form.

a) $0.6666\ldots = 0.\dot{6}$ **b)** $0.272\,727\ldots = 0.\dot{2}\dot{7}$ **c)** $0.0\dot{3}\dot{7}$

d) $0.\dot{1}4285\dot{7}$ **e)** $0.\dot{3}84\,61\dot{5}$ **f)** $0.\dot{0}09\dot{9}$

3 Find the sum to infinity of a geometric sequence with:

a) second term 40 and fifth term 5
b) second term –40 and fifth term 5.

4 Find the possible sums to infinity of a geometric sequence with:

a) second term –12 and fourth term $-1\tfrac{1}{3}$
b) third term 32 and fifth term 5.12

5 Write down the first five terms of a geometric sequence with first term 36 and sum to infinity 48.

6 A geometric sequence has third term 21.6 and sum to infinity 150. Find the common ratio r and first term a.

7 A rubber ball is dropped from a height of 5 m and after the first bounce rises to a height of 3 m.

a) Assuming that the heights of bounces form a geometric sequence, find the height after the third bounce.
b) Explain why the total distance travelled by the ball until it hits the ground for the second time is 5 + 2 × 3 m.
c) How far does the ball travel altogether before it stops bouncing?

10.4 HOMEWORK

1 Determine which of the following geometric series converge to a limit, and in these cases find the sum to infinity.

a) $4 + 4^2 + 4^3 + \ldots$ b) $\frac{1}{4} + (\frac{1}{4})^2 + (\frac{1}{4})^3 + \ldots$

c) $0.6^3 + 0.6^4 + 0.6^5 + \ldots$ d) $1 - 1.5 + 1.5^2 - 1.5^3 + \ldots$

2 Express the following recurring decimals as fractions in their simplest form.

a) $0.\dot{7}$ b) $1.\dot{7}$ c) $0.\dot{1}\dot{2}$ d) $0.\dot{1}2\dot{3}$

3 Find the sum to infinity of a geometric sequence with:

a) third term 135 and sixth term 5

b) second term 405 and sixth term 5.

4 A geometric sequence has first term 20 and sum to infinity 80. Find the common ratio and write down the first four terms of the sequence.

5 A geometric sequence has common ratio $\frac{11}{12}$ and its sum to infinity is 24. Find the first term and write down the first six terms of the sequence correct to 2 d.p.

6 The first term of a geometric sequence is 50, the third term is 18 and the common ratio is positive. Calculate:

a) the sum to infinity,

b) the first term of the sequence which is less than 0.01,

c) the least value of n such that the difference between S_∞ and S_n is less than 0.01.

7 a) For a certain GP, the sum to infinity is 10 times the first term. Find the common ratio.

b) Is it possible for the sum to infinity of a GP to be less than the first term? Give a reason for your answer.

MATHEMATICAL MODELLING ACTIVITY

Problem statement

1 → 2 → 3
↑ ↓
6 ← 5 ← 4

Specify the real problem

When buying a house, purchasers often pay a deposit and take out a **mortgage** (a loan over a fixed term from a bank or building society) for the rest.

- If you took out a mortgage for £40 000, what would you expect to have to repay each year so that you pay off the loan after 25 years?

Set up a model

1 → 2 → 3
↑ ↓
6 ← 5 ← 4

Set up a model

KEY SKILLS
C 3.1b

Firstly you need to identify the important variables:

- the rate of interest charged on the loan
- the amount repaid every year
- the amount owed at the beginning of each year.

You will also need to make some assumptions before formulating the problem mathematically, some of which are simplistic, but necessary to tackle the problem initially (Further refinements may be built in later.):

- the rate of interest remains constant
- the interest charged during a year depends on the amount outstanding at the beginning of the year
- a single repayment, £P, is made once a year
- there is no tax relief on interest repaid.

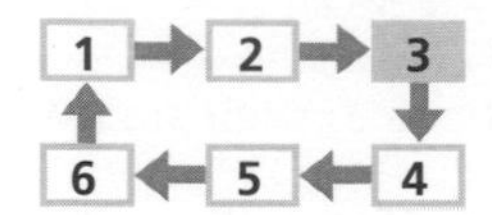
Formulate the mathematical problem

Mathematical problem

Firstly, fix the annual rate of interest at, say, 10 per cent.

Let u_n denote the amount owing to the building society (or bank) at the beginning of year n, then:

$$u_1 = 40\,000$$

and $u_{n+1} = u_n \times 1.1 - P$ for $n = 1, 2, 3, \ldots$

The multiplier of 1.1 comes from $1 + \frac{10}{100}$ assuming a rate of interest of 10 per cent.

What value of P should be chosen so that the amount outstanding *after* 25 years, i.e. u_{26}, is 0?

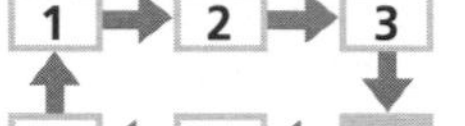
Solve the mathematical problem

Mathematical solution

Since $u_1 = 40\,000$:

$$\begin{aligned}
u_2 &= u_1 \times 1.1 - P = 40\,000 \times 1.1 - P \\
u_3 &= u_2 \times 1.1 - P \\
&= (40\,000 \times 1.1 - P) \times 1.1 - P \\
&= 40\,000 \times 1.1^2 - (P \times 1.1 + P) \\
u_4 &= u_3 \times 1.1 - P \\
&= (40\,000 \times 1.1^2 - P \times 1.1 - P) \times 1.1 - P \\
&= 40\,000 \times 1.1^3 - (P \times 1.1^2 + P \times 1.1 + P)
\end{aligned}$$

A pattern is developing which suggests that:

$$u_{26} = 40\,000 \times 1.1^{25} - (P \times 1.1^{24} + P \times 1.1^{23} + \ldots + P \times 1.1 + P)$$

The sum in brackets, reading from right to left, is the sum of the first 25 terms of a geometric series with first term P and common ratio 1.1, i.e.

$$P + P \times 1.1 + \ldots + P \times 1.1^{23} + P \times 1.1^{24} = \frac{P(1.1^{25} - 1)}{1.1 - 1}$$

Since the mortgage will be repaid after 25 years provided $u^{26} = 0$, you can deduce the value P by solving the equation:

$$0 = 40\,000 \times 1.1^{25} - \frac{P(1.1^{25} - 1)}{1.1 - 1}$$

$$\Rightarrow \quad \frac{P(1.1^{25} - 1)}{1.1 - 1} = 40\,000 \times 1.1^{25}$$

$$\Rightarrow \quad P = \frac{(40000 \times 1.1^{25}) \times 0.1}{1.1^{25} - 1} = 4406.72$$

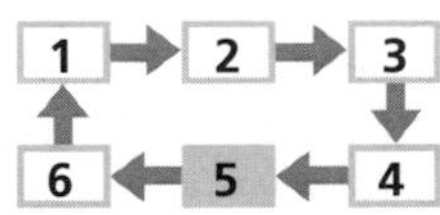
Interpret the solution

Interpretation

If you make an annual payment of just over £4400, at an annual rate of interest of 10 per cent, the mortgage will be paid off over a period of 25 years. This represents total repayments amounting to about £110 000.

Refinement of the model

Investigate the effect of:

a) a change in the rate of interest,
b) monthly repayments instead of annual repayments.

Discovery activity

Modify the flowchart for a geometric sequence, to automate the calculation of the amounts outstanding at the end of each year or each month.

Given an annual rate of interest (APR) calculate the equivalent monthly rate of interest.

CONSOLIDATION EXERCISES FOR CHAPTER 10

1 The ninth term of an arithmetic progression is 52 and the sum of the first twelve terms is 414. Find the first term and the common difference.

(AEB, Specimen Paper 1)

2 The tenth term of an arithmetic progression is 36 and the sum of the first ten terms is 180. Find the first term and the common difference.

(UCLES, Specimen Paper 2)

3 The first term of an AP is -13 and the last term is 99. The sum of all the terms is 1419.

a) Find the number of terms and the common difference.
b) Find also the sum of all the positive terms of the progression.

(AEB, Paper 1, June 1987)

4 **a)** An employer offers the following schemes of salary payments over a five year period.

Scheme X: 60 monthly payments, starting with £1000 and increasing by £6 each month (£1000, £1006, £1012, ...)
Scheme Y: five annual payments, starting with £12 000 and increasing by £d each year [£12 000, £(12 000 + d), ...].

i) Over the complete five year period, find the total salary payable under Scheme X.
ii) Find the value of d which gives the same total salary for both schemes over the complete five-year period.

b) A small ball is dropped from a height of 1 m onto a horizontal floor. Each time the ball strikes the floor it rebounds to 0.6 of the height it has just fallen.

i) Show that, when the ball strikes the floor for the third time, it has travelled a distance 2.92 m.
ii) Show that the total distance travelled by the ball cannot exceed 4 m.

(ULEAC, Paper 1, June 1992)

5 An investment of £2000 is made at the start of a year with a Finance Company. At the end of this year and at the end of each subsequent year the value of the investment is 11 per cent greater than its value at the start of that year.

a) Find, to the nearest £, the value of the investment at the end of:
i) the fifth year, **ii)** the tenth year.

A client decides to invest £2000 at the start of each year. Write down a series for which the sum is the total value of this annual investment at the end of 12 years.

b) By finding the sum of your series, determine, to the nearest £, the value of the investment at the end of 12 years.

(London, Paper 1, January 1992)

6 **a)** An arithmetic progression begins 25, 39, 53, 67, ...
i) Write down an expression for the nth term of the sequence.
ii) Find an expression for the sum of the first n terms of the sequence.

b) A group of schoolchildren decided to collect used aluminium cans to help to raise money for charity. On the first day they collected 25 cans. On each of the next three schooldays they collected 14 cans more than on the previous day (because each day more of their friends became aware that they were collecting the cans). If this pattern continues, how many cans will they collect altogether in the first ten days of their collecting period?

(O&C, Specimen Paper 1, 1994)

7 A company offers a ten-year contract to an employee. This gives a starting salary of £15 000 a year with an annual increase of eight per cent of the previous year's salary.

a) Show that the amounts of annual salary form a geometric sequence and write down its common ratio.
b) How much does the employee expect to earn in the tenth year?
c) Show that the total amount earned over the ten years is nearly £217 500.

After considering the offer, the employee asks for a different scheme of payment. This has the same starting salary of £15 000 but with a fixed annual pay rise £d.

d) Find d if the total amount paid out over ten years is to be the same under the two schemes.

(MEI, Pure 1, June 1993)

8 **a)** Timber cladding on the end of a shed roof consists of 20 narrow rectangular planks whose longest sides are in arithmetic progression. The shortest plank is 65 cm long, the longest 3.5 m. Find:
i) the difference in length between one plank and the next,
ii) the total length of all the planks.

b) For a demonstration, a 1-metre rule is cut into ten pieces whose lengths are in geometric progression. The length of the longest piece is 7.45 times the length of the shortest piece. The shortest piece is of length a cm and the common ratio is r.
i) Write down the length of the longest piece in terms of a and r.
ii) Find the values of a and r.

(MEI, Pure 1, January 1994)

9 As part of a fundraising campaign, I have been given some books of raffle tickets to sell. Each book has the same number of tickets and all the tickets I have been given are numbered in sequence. The number of the ticket on the front of the fifth book is 205 and that on the front of the 19th book is 373.

a) By writing the number of the ticket on the front of the first book as a and the number of tickets in each book as d, write down two equations involving a and d.
b) From these two equations, find how many tickets are in each book and the number on the front of the first book I have been given.
c) The last ticket I have been given is numbered 492. How many books have I been given?

(MEI, Paper 1, June 1992)

10 Prospectors are drilling for oil. The cost of drilling to a depth of 50 m is £500. To drill a further 50 m costs £640 and, hence, the total cost of drilling to a depth of 100 m is £1140. Each subsequent extra depth of 50 m costs £140 more to drill than the previous 50 m.

a) Show that the cost of drilling to a depth of 500 m is £11 300.
The total sum of money available for drilling is £76 000.
b) Find, to the nearest 50 m, the greatest depth that can be drilled.

(EDEXCEL, Question 8, Paper 1, January 2000)

11 The first three terms of a geometric series are $p(3q + 1)$, $p(2q + 2)$ and $p(2q - 1)$ respectively, where p and q are non-zero constants.

a) Use algebra to show that one possible value of q is 5 and to find the other possible value of q.
b) For each possible value of q, calculate the value of the common ratio of the series.
Given that $q = 5$ and that the sum to infinity of the geometric series is 896, calculate
c) the value of p.
d) the sum, to 2 decimal places, of the first twelve terms of the series.

(EDEXCEL, Question 7, Paper 1, June 1999)

12 The second term of a geometric series is 80 and the fifth term of the series is 5.12.

a) Show that the common ratio of the series is 0.4.
Calculate
b) the first term of the series,
c) the sum to infinity of the series, giving your answer as an exact fraction,
d) the difference between the sum to infinity of the series and the sum of the first 14 terms of the series, giving your answer in the form $a \times 10n$, where $1 \leq a < 10$ and n is an integer.

(EDEXCEL, Question 7, Paper 1, Jan 1999)

13 A competitor is running in a 25 km race. For the first 15 km, she runs at a steady rate of 12 km h^{-1}. After completing 15 km, she slows down and it is now observed that she takes 20% longer to complete each kilometre than she took to complete the previous kilometre.

a) Find the time, in hours and minutes, the competitor takes to complete the first 16 km of the race.
The time taken to complete the r th kilometre is u_r hours.
b) Show that, for $16 \leq r \leq 25$, $u_r = \frac{1}{12}(1.2)^{r-15}$.
c) Using the answer to **b)**, or otherwise, find the time, to the nearest minute, that she takes to complete the race.

(EDEXCEL, Question 8, Paper 1, June 1998)

15 **i)** A sequence of positive integers $u_1, u_2, u_3, \ldots$ Is given by
$u_1 = 2$ and $u_{n+1} = 2u_n$ for $n \geq 1$.

a) Write down the first four terms of this sequence.
b) State what type of sequence this is, and express u_n in terms of n.

ii) A sequence of positive integers $v_1, v_2, v_3, \ldots$ Is given by
$v_1 = 3$ and $v_{n+1} = 2v_n - 1$ for $n \geq 1$.

a) Show that the relation between v_{n+1} and v_n may be written in the form $v_{n+1} - 1 = 2(v_n - 1)$.
b) Hence, by using the results in part **i)**, show that $v_n = 2^n + 1$ for $n \geq 1$.

iii) The sum of the first N terms of the sequence $v_1, v_2, v_3, \ldots$ is denoted by S_N, i.e. $S_N = v_1 + v_2 + v_3 + \ldots + v_N$.
Express S_N in terms of N.

(OCR, Question 8, Specimen Paper 2, 2000)

Summary

Notation

- u_k represents the kth term of a sequence.
- S_n represents the sum of the first n terms of a series.

Arithmetic sequences and series

- For an arithmetic sequence with **first term** a and **common difference** d:

  Inductive definition: $u_{k+1} = u_k + d, \quad u_1 = a$

  Formula definition: $u_k = a + (k-1)d$

  Sum to n terms $S_n = \frac{n}{2}[2a + (n-1)d] = \frac{n}{2}(a + l)$

  where l is the last term

- The series generated from an arithmetic sequence is called an **arithmetic progression (AP)**.

Geometric sequences and series

- For a geometric sequence with **first term** a and **common ratio** r:

  Inductive definition: $u_{k+1} = ru_k, \quad u_1 = a$

  Formula definition: $u_k = ar^{k-1}$

  Sum to n terms $S_n = \frac{a(1-r^n)}{1-r}$ if $-1 < r < 1$

  $S_n = \frac{a(r^n - 1)}{r-1}$ if $r < -1$ or $r > 1$

  $S_n = na$ if $r = 1$

  Sum to infinity $S_n = \frac{a}{1-r}$ only if $-1 < r < 1$

- The series generated from an arithmetic sequence is called an **geometric progression (GP)**.

Differentiation and integration 2

In this chapter we introduce:

- *the rule for differentiation of functions with rational exponents*
- *the second derivative and show how it can be used to classify stationary points*
- *how to find the equation of the tangent and normal to a curve*
- *the rule of integration of functions with rational exponents.*

FUNCTIONS WITH RATIONAL EXPONENTS

In Chapter 7 *Differentiation 1* and Chapter 8 *Integration 1* we differentiated and integrated polynomial functions, based on the rule for powers of x:

i.e. $f(x) = x^n \Rightarrow f'(x) = nx^{n-1}, n = 0, 1, 2 \ldots$

$$\text{and } \int f(x)\,dx = \frac{x^{n+1}}{n+1}$$

In this chapter we extend these definitions for rational index n (e.g. $n = -1, n = \frac{1}{2}$)

FUNCTIONS WITH RATIONAL INDICES

Exploration 11.1

Inverse proportion

A Youth Club is organising an outing by coach. The best quotation they received for the coach hire was £240 for a 59-seater.

- How much should the Club charge each passenger to cover the cost of the coach hire?

Inverse proportion and hyperbolae

To spread the cost fairly the charge per passenger, £c, could be found by dividing the hire cost of £240 by the number of passengers, n, i.e. $c = \frac{240}{n}$.

So for 30 passengers, the coach fare would be $\frac{240}{30}$ = £8

and for 40 passengers, the coach fare would be $\frac{240}{40}$ = £6

Suppose that no one is willing to pay more than £12 each, then the minimum number of passengers is found by solving the equation:

$$12 = \frac{240}{n} \quad \Rightarrow \quad n = \frac{240}{12} = 20$$

This means the Club needs to attract at least 20 passengers to keep the cost down to £12 per head.

In this example c is **inversely proportional** to n, since $c = \dfrac{240}{n}$.
In this context the formula is only valid for whole-number values of n, which means $n = 1, 2, ..., 59$. Why?

We can draw up a table of values.

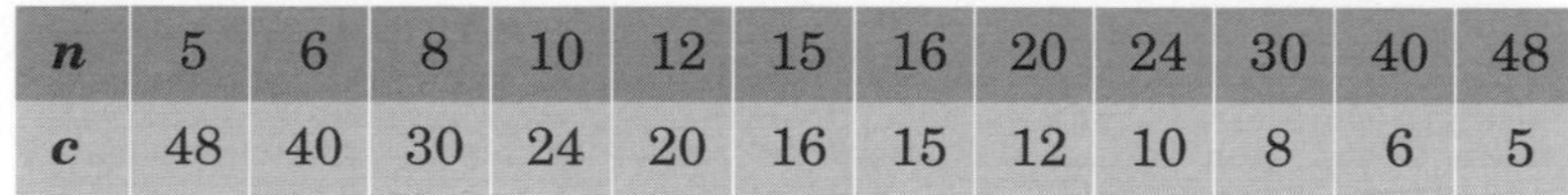

n	5	6	8	10	12	15	16	20	24	30	40	48
c	48	40	30	24	20	16	15	12	10	8	6	5

All the coordinates (x, y) lie on the curve $y = \frac{240}{x}$, although not all the points on the curve are solutions to the problem in the example.

When x *can* be any real number, except 0, the curve generated by the equation $y = \dfrac{240}{x}$ is an example of a **rectangular hyperbola**. As x gets smaller, and therefore closer to 0, from above (e.g. $x = 1, 0.1, 0.01, 0.001, ...$) y gets larger (e.g. $y = 240, 2400, 24\,000, 240\,000, ...$). Similarly as x gets closer to 0 from below (e.g. $x = -1. -0.1, -0.01,...$) y gets larger in value, although it is also negative (e.g. $y = -240, -2400, -24\,000, ...$). The y-axis is an **asymptote** to the graph. This means the curve approaches the axis but doesn't actually ever touch it.
To summarise:

as $x \to 0$ from above $y \to \infty$
as $x \to 0$ from below $y \to \infty$

The x-axis is also an asymptote, because:

as $x \to \infty$ from above $y \to 0$
as $x \to -\infty$ from below $y \to 0$.

Another way of writing $y = \dfrac{240}{x}$ is $y = 240x^{-1}$, since $\dfrac{1}{x} \equiv x^{-1}$ and $\dfrac{240}{x} = 240 \times \dfrac{1}{x}$.

Similarly $y = \dfrac{20}{x^2}$ could be written as $y = 20x^{-2}$, where y is inversely proportional to x^2.

Exploration 11.2

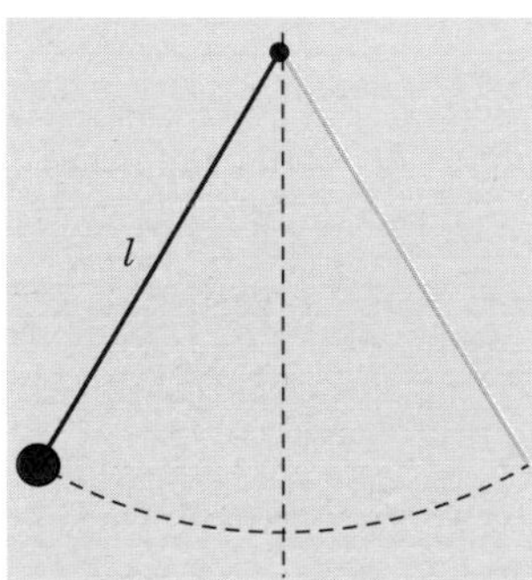

A simple pendulum

A student is trying to find the connection between the time of swing, t seconds, and length, l metres, for a simple pendulum. She obtains the following experimental results.

Length l (m)	0.5	1.0	1.5	2.0
Time t (s)	1.4	2.0	2.4	2.8

■ What is the relationship between time of swing and length?

Analysing the results

When the length is multiplied by 2, the time is multiplied by 1.4 (to 1 d.p.)

l	0.5	1.0
t	1.4	2.0

l	1.0	2.0
t	2.0	2.8

When the length is multiplied by 3, the time is multiplied by 1.7 (to 1 d.p.)

l	0.5	1.5
t	1.4	2.4

When the length is multiplied by 4, the time is multiplied by 2.0

l	0.5	2.0
t	1.4	2.8

This suggests that t is proportional to $\sqrt{l}$.

We can draw up a table to show how t varies with $\sqrt{l}$.

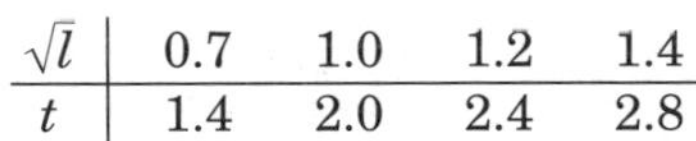

$\sqrt{l}$	0.7	1.0	1.2	1.4
t	1.4	2.0	2.4	2.8

From the table we can see that $t = 2\sqrt{l}$.

The relationship $t = 2\sqrt{l}$ may also be written as $t = 2l^{\frac{1}{2}}$.

Since l represents the length of a pendulum, $l > 0$. More generally, the equation $y = k\sqrt{x}$ is only valid for $x \geq 0$, since it is not possible to take the square root of a negative number.

Just as the equation $y = k\sqrt{x}$ may be written as $y = kx^{\frac{1}{2}}$,

the equation $y = k\sqrt[3]{x}$ may be written as $y = kx^{\frac{1}{3}}$.
This **cube root function** is valid for all real values of x.

Example 11.1

Sketch graphs of functions with the following equations. In each case describe the tangent to the curve at $x = 0$.

a) $y = x^{\frac{1}{3}}$ **b)** $y = x^{\frac{3}{4}}$

c) $y = x^{\frac{3}{2}}$ **d)** $y = x^{\frac{5}{3}}$

Solution

a)

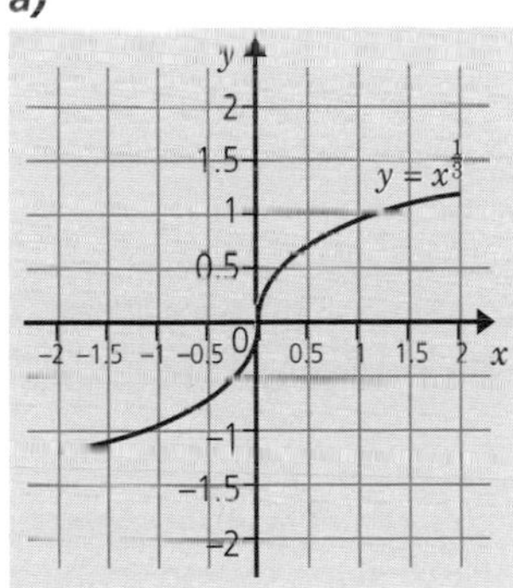

b)

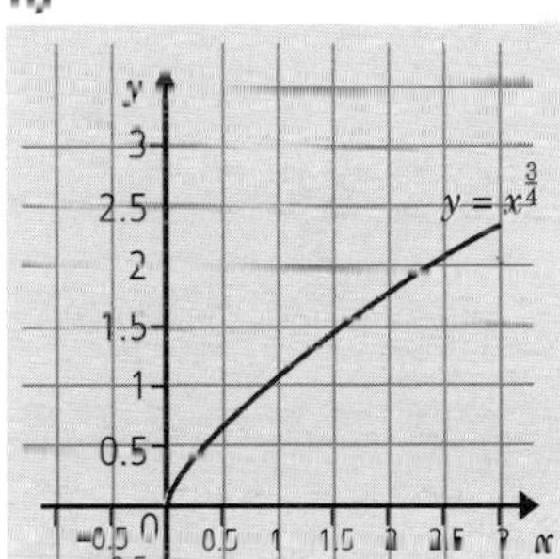

For **a)** and **b)**, the y-axis is the tangent to the curve at $x = 0$. We shall see that this is always true when we have $y = x^n$ and $n < 1$ $(n \neq 0)$.
(Note that for $y = x^{\frac{3}{4}}$, y only exists for $x \geq 0$. The curve does not exist for $x < 0$.

c)

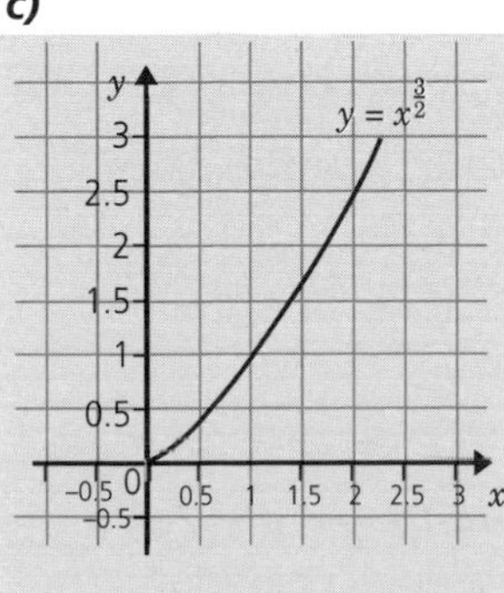

d)

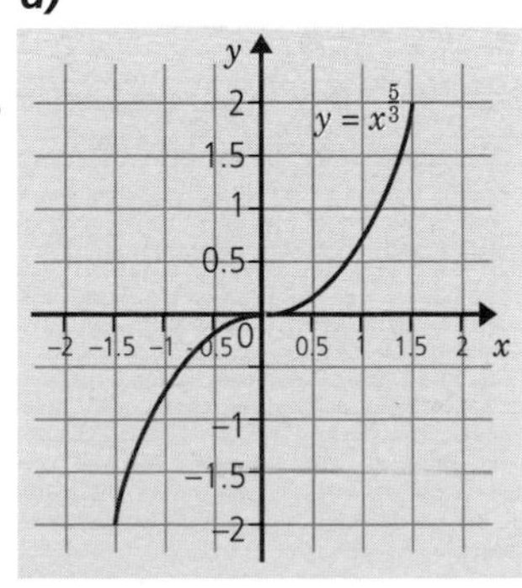

For **c)** and **d)** the x-axis is the tangent to the curve at $x = 0$. We will see that this is always true when we have $y = x^n$ and $n > 1$. Remember that when $n = 1$, $y = x \Rightarrow \frac{dy}{dx} = 1$ and when $n = 0$, $y = 1 \Rightarrow \frac{dy}{dx} = 0$ (the tangent is parallel to the x-axis). Again notice that the graph of $y = x^{\frac{3}{2}}$ only exists for $x \geq 0$.

EXERCISES

11.1 CLASSWORK

1 Sketch a graph of $y = x + \frac{1}{x}$ by considering what happens to y as:

a) $x \to 0$ from above and below, **b)** $x \to \pm\infty$.

Write down the equations for the two asymptotes. Confirm your answer using a graphics calculator. State the coordinates and nature of the two stationary points.

2 Sketch a graph of $y = x^2$ and a graph of $y = x^2 - \frac{8}{x}$ by considering what happens to y as:

a) $x \to 0$ from above and below, **b)** $x \to \pm\infty$.

Check your sketch using a graphics calculator. Write down the coordinates of the point where the graph intersects the x-axis. Check your answer algebraically. Find the coordinates of the minimum point by trial and improvement.

3 Two electrical charges attract one another with a force P units which varies inversely as the square of the distance, x units, between them. If $P = 5.4$ when $x = 6$ find P when $x = 9$.

4 A glass window consists of a rectangle with sides of length $2r$ cm and h cm and a semi-circle of radius r cm. The total area of one surface of the glass is 500 cm^2.

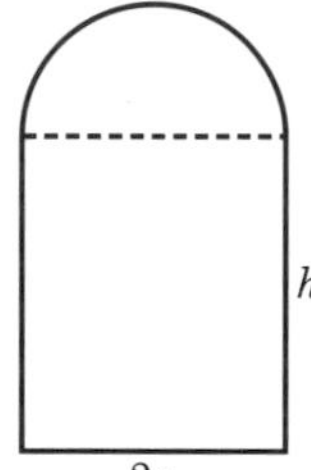

a) Write down a formula connecting h and r.

b) The perimeter of the window is p cm. By eliminating h, show that:

$$p = (2 + \tfrac{\pi}{2})r + \frac{500}{r}$$

c) Sketch a graph of perimeter against r.

d) By tracing and zooming, find the positive value of r for which p has a stationary point, giving your answer correct to one decimal place.

e) Explain the answer in words.

(AQA, Question 7, Paper 1, June 1999 parts a) and b))

EXERCISES

11.1 HOMEWORK

1 Sketch a graph of $y = x - \frac{1}{x}$ by considering what happens to y as:

a) $x \to 0$ from above and below, **b)** $x \to \pm\infty$, **c)** $y \to 0$.

Write down the equations for the two asymptotes. Confirm your answer using a graphics calculator. Are there any stationary points?

2 Sketch the graph of $y = x^3$. On the same diagram sketch a graph of $y = x^3 - \frac{16}{x}$ by considering what happens to y as:

a) $x \to 0$ from above and below, **b)** $x \to \pm\infty$.

Find where the graph cuts the x-axis. Write down any equations of any asymptotes. Confirm your answer using a graphics calculator.

3 A choir is organising a raffle to raise £300 to buy new music. The total value of the prizes will be £200. The design and print costs of producing n raffle tickets is £$(40 + 0.01n)$.

a) Write down a formula for the selling price of a single raffle ticket, as a function of n, so that the choir raises exactly £300.
b) Sketch a graph of selling price against n.
c) In a survey the choir leader finds out that the local villagers will not pay more than 50p per raffle ticket. How many raffle tickets should the choir sell to raise at least £300?

4 The frequency of an oscillation is defined as the number of complete cycles per second and is measured in hertz. Write down the formula for the frequency, for an oscillation which repeats itself every T seconds, in terms of T. The musical note middle C on a piano has the frequency 256 hertz. Calculate the interval between the oscillations for this note.

DIFFERENTIATION OF FUNCTIONS WITH RATIONAL INDICES

In Chapter 7, *Differentiation 1*, we differentiated polynomial functions, based on the rule for differentiating powers of x:

i.e. $f(x) = x^n \Rightarrow f'(x) = nx^{n-1}$, $n = 0, 1, 2, \ldots$

We can now extend this definition for any rational index n (e.g. $n = -1$, $n = \frac{1}{2}$).

Exploration 11.3

The graph of $y = f(x) = \frac{1}{x}$

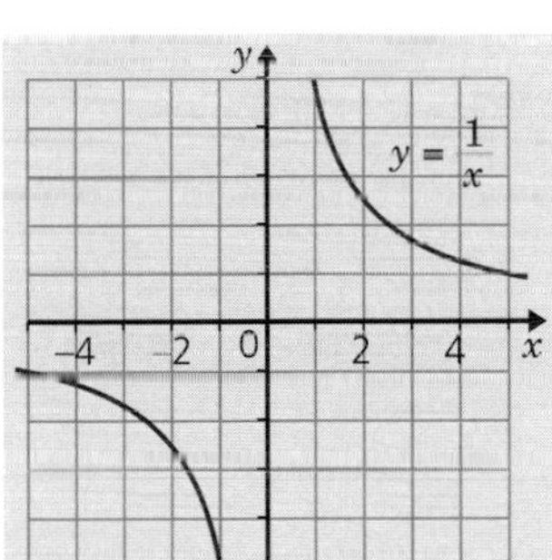

The diagram shows the graph of $y = f(x) = \frac{1}{x}$. Use a numerical method to estimate the gradient for various values of x.

- Use your numerical values to sketch a graph of the gradient function.
- Find a formula for $f'(x)$.

Using the limiting process to find the gradient

The limiting process introduced in Chapter 7, *Differentiation 1*, may be used to find the gradient at any value of x ($x \neq 0$). Consider the gradient at $x = 1$ as the limit of gradients of secants, reducing the x-interval by a factor of 10 each time:

between $x = 1$ and $x = 2$ gradient of secant $= -0.5$
between $x = 1$ and $x = 1.1$ gradient of secant $= -0.909090$
between $x = 1$ and $x = 1.01$ gradient of secant $= -0.990099$
between $x = 1$ and $x = 1.001$ gradient of secant $= -0.999000999$

So the limit of the gradient of the secant between $x = 1$ and $x = 1 + h$, as $h \to 0$, will be -1, which suggests $f'(x) = -1$.

Repeating the process for other x-values gives a table of gradient function values.

x	-5	-2	-1	-0.5	-0.2	0.2	0.5	1	2	5
$f'(x)$	-0.04	-0.25	-1	-4	-25	-25	-4	-1	-0.25	-0.04

Expressing each decimal as its fraction equivalent gives a clue as to the algebraic formula for $f'(x)$.

x	−5	−2	−1	−0.5	−0.2	0.2	0.5	1	2	5
$f'(x)$	$-\frac{1}{25}$	$-\frac{1}{4}$	−1	−4	−25	−25	−4	−1	$-\frac{1}{4}$	$-\frac{1}{25}$

We can now spot the pattern for the gradient function:

$$f'(x) = -\frac{1}{x^2}$$

If we express $f(x)$ as a power of x we see that the rule for differentiating powers of x does indeed work for $n = -1$.

$$f(x) = \frac{1}{x} = x^{-1} \Rightarrow f'(x) = -1 \times x^{-2} = -\frac{1}{x^2}$$

In fact the rule can be extended to differentiate any negative power of x,

e.g: $f(x) = \dfrac{3}{x^2} = 3x^{-2} \Rightarrow f'(x) = 3 \times (-2)x^{-3} = -\dfrac{6}{x^3}$

We can also prove the result for $f(x) = \frac{1}{x}$ formally by investigating what happens to $\frac{f(x+h)-f(x)}{h}$ as $h \to 0$.

$$f(x+h) = \frac{1}{x+h} \quad \Rightarrow \quad f(x+h) - f(x) = \frac{1}{x+h} - \frac{1}{x}$$

$$= \frac{-h}{x(x+h)}$$

$$\Rightarrow \quad \frac{f(x+h)-f(x)}{h} = \frac{-1}{x(x+h)}$$

Now as $h \to 0$ we see that $-\frac{1}{x(x+h)} \to -\frac{1}{x^2}$ proving formally that $f'(x) = -\frac{1}{x^2}$.

Exploration 11.4

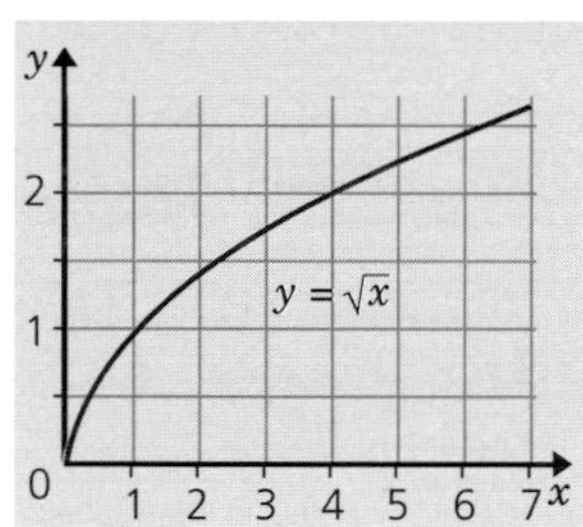

The function $y = f(x) = \sqrt{x}$

The graph of $y = f(x) = \sqrt{x}$, $x \geq 0$ is shown in the diagram.

- Use a numerical method to estimate the gradient for various values of x.
- Use your numerical values to sketch a graph of the gradient function.
- Find a formula for $f'(x)$.

Finding the gradient

Using a limiting process, we can find the gradient at any x-value ($x > 0$). Consider the gradient at $x = 1$ as the limit of gradients of secants, again reducing the x-interval by a factor of 10 each time:

between $x = 1$ and $x = 2$ gradient of secant = 0.414 213 562 4
between $x = 1$ and $x = 1.1$ gradient of secant = 0.488 088 481 7
between $x = 1$ and $x = 1.01$ gradient of secant = 0.498 756 211 2
between $x = 1$ and $x = 1.001$ gradient of secant = 0.499 875 062 4

By extending this pattern, we find that the limit of the gradient of the secant between $x = 1$ and $x = 1 + h$, as $h \to 0$, will be –0.5.

Repeating this process for other x-values gives a table of gradient function values.

x	0.01	0.04	0.0625	0.25	1	4	16	25	100
$f'(x)$	5	2.5	2	1	0.5	0.25	0.125	0.1	0.05

Again, by expressing each decimal as an equivalent fraction, we spot a pattern for the gradient function.

x	$\frac{1}{100}$	$\frac{1}{25}$	$\frac{1}{10}$	$\frac{1}{4}$	1	4	16	25	100
$f'(x)$	5	$2\frac{1}{2}$	2	1	$\frac{1}{2}$	$\frac{1}{4}$	$\frac{1}{8}$	$\frac{1}{10}$	$\frac{1}{20}$

Confirm that the gradient function is given by:

$$f'(x) = \frac{1}{2\sqrt{x}}$$

By expressing $f(x)$ as a power of x, we can see that the rule for differentiating powers of x works for $n = \frac{1}{2}$.

$$f(x) = \sqrt{x} = x^{\frac{1}{2}} \Rightarrow f'(x) = \tfrac{1}{2}x^{-\frac{1}{2}} = \frac{1}{2\sqrt{x}}$$

The rule can be extended to differentiate any functional power of x,

e.g: $f(x) = 12\sqrt[3]{x} = 12x^{\frac{1}{3}} \Rightarrow f'(x) = 12 \times \tfrac{1}{3}x^{-\frac{2}{3}} = \dfrac{4}{\sqrt[3]{x^2}}$

We have found that the rule for differentiating powers of x works for any rational index. The following examples will show how the technique can be used and applied.

Example 11.2

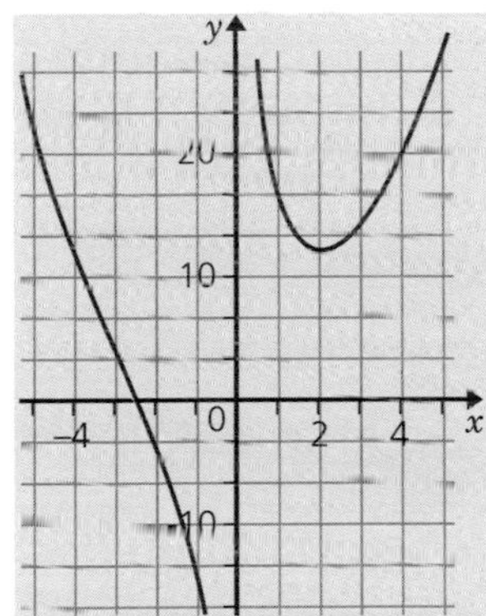

The diagram shows a sketch of $y = f(x) = x^2 + \dfrac{16}{x}$.

a) *Find* $f'(x)$ *and evaluate* $f'(-2)$.

b) *Find the coordinates of the stationary point S.*

Solution

a) $y = f(x) = x^2 + \dfrac{16}{x} = x^2 + 16x^{-1} \Rightarrow f'(x) = 2x - 16x^{-2} = 2x - \dfrac{16}{x^2}$

Hence $f'(-2) = 2 \times (-2) - \dfrac{16}{(-2)^2} = -8$

b) *For a stationary value,*

$$f'(x) = 0 \Rightarrow 2x - \frac{16}{x^2} = 0 \Rightarrow 2x^3 - 16 = 0 \Rightarrow x^3 = 8 \Rightarrow x\sqrt[3]{8} = 2$$

Now $f(2) = 2^2 + \frac{16}{2} = 12$, *which means that the coordinates of S are (2,12).*

Example 11.3

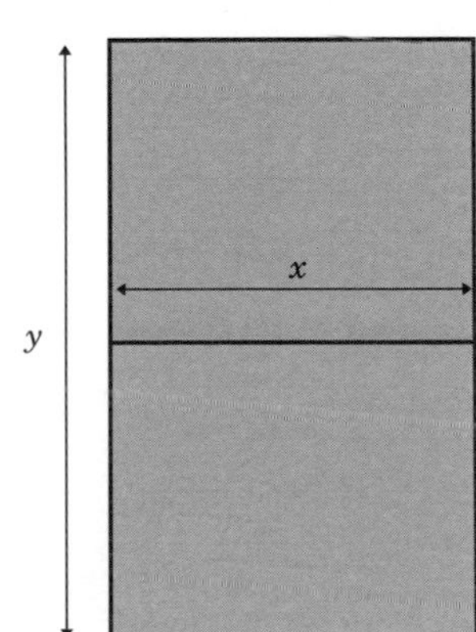

A farmer wishes to enclose a rectangular field of area 16 000 m² and to divide it in half. Fencing to enclose the field costs £3 per metre and the fencing to divide the field costs £2 per metre.

a) *Express the total cost of fencing as a function of* x*, the width of the field.*

b) *Find the dimensions and the total cost of fencing for the field that is* ***least*** *expensive to fence.*

Solution

a) *Given that the area of the field is to be 16 000 m², from the diagram we find:*

$$16\,000 = xy$$

$$y = \frac{16\,000}{x}$$

The cost of fencing the perimeter $= 3(2x + 2y) = 6x + 6y$

The cost of the dividing fence $= 2x$

Therefore the total cost of fencing is given by:

$$C = 8x + 6y = 8x + 6\times\frac{16\,000}{x} \Rightarrow C = 8x + \frac{96\,000}{x}$$

b) *To minimise C:*

$\frac{\mathrm{d}C}{\mathrm{d}x} = 8 - \frac{96\,000}{x^2} = 0$ *for stationary values.*

$\Rightarrow 8x^2 = 96\,000 \Rightarrow x^2 = 12\,000 \Rightarrow x = \sqrt{12\,000} \approx 110\text{ m}$

Substituting for x gives:

$y = \frac{16\,000}{110} \approx 145\text{ m}$

Total cost of fencing $= 8\times 110 + \frac{96\,000}{110} \approx £1750$

Example 11.4

A function is given by $y = 2\sqrt{x}(5-x)$.

a) *Find where the graph of this function intersects with the axes.*
b) *Find the value of* $\frac{\mathrm{d}y}{\mathrm{d}x}$ *at the points found in* **a)**.
c) *Find the stationary point and determine which type it is.*
d) *Use the information found in* **a)**, **b)** *and* **c)** *to sketch the graph.*

Solution

a) *The graph intersects with the x-axis when $y = 0$.*

$y = 0 \Rightarrow 2\sqrt{x}(5-x) = 0 \Rightarrow x = 0$ *or* $x = 5$

Hence the points of intersection are (0,0) and (5,0).

b) $2\sqrt{x}(5-x) = 10\sqrt{x} - 2x\sqrt{x} = 10x^{\frac{1}{2}} - 2x^{\frac{3}{2}}$

$$\Rightarrow \frac{\mathrm{d}y}{\mathrm{d}x} = 10\times\tfrac{1}{2}x^{-\frac{1}{2}} - 2\times\tfrac{3}{2}x^{\frac{1}{2}} = 5x^{-\frac{1}{2}} - 3x^{\frac{1}{2}} = \frac{5}{\sqrt{x}} - 3\sqrt{x} = \frac{5-3x}{\sqrt{x}}$$

When $x = 0$, $\frac{\mathrm{d}y}{\mathrm{d}x}$ is undefined.

When $x = 5$, $\frac{\mathrm{d}y}{\mathrm{d}x} = \frac{5-3\times 5}{\sqrt{5}} = -4.47$ *(3 s.f.)*

c) *At the stationary point,* $\frac{\mathrm{d}y}{\mathrm{d}x} = 0 \Rightarrow \frac{5-3x}{\sqrt{x}} = 0$

$\Rightarrow 5 - 3x = 0 \Rightarrow 3x = 5 \Rightarrow x = 1\tfrac{2}{3} \approx 1.67$

When $x = 1\tfrac{2}{3},\ y = 2\sqrt{1\tfrac{2}{3}}\left(5 - 1\tfrac{2}{3}\right) = 8.61$ *(3 s.f.)*

To determine which type the stationary point is, inspect the gradient at, say, $x = 1$ and $x = 2$.

$$x = 1 \Rightarrow \frac{\mathrm{d}y}{\mathrm{d}x} = \frac{5-3\times 1}{\sqrt{1}} > 0$$

$$x = 2 \Rightarrow \frac{\mathrm{d}y}{\mathrm{d}x} = \frac{5-3\times 2}{\sqrt{2}} < 0$$

Hence (1.67, 8.61) is a maximum point.

d) *Combining information from earlier parts of the question helps to sketch the graph.*

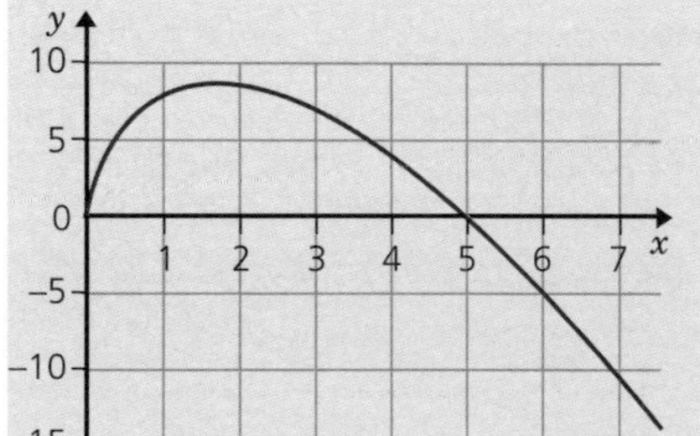

EXERCISES

11.2 CLASSWORK

1 Differentiate each of the following.

a) $\dfrac{7}{x}$ **b)** $\dfrac{-12}{x^2}$ **c)** $5x - \dfrac{16}{x^3}$ **d)** $3x\left(\dfrac{2}{x^2} - 5\right)$

e) $15\sqrt{x}$ **f)** $-\dfrac{4}{\sqrt{x}}$ **g)** $\sqrt{x}(x-8)$ **h)** $x^2\left(4+\sqrt{x}\right)$

2 For each of the following functions:
i) find where $f'(x) = 0$, **ii)** identify any stationary points,
iii) sketch a graph of the function.

a) $f(x) = x + \dfrac{1}{x}$ **b)** $f(x) = 2x - \dfrac{3}{x^2}$ **c)** $f(x) = \dfrac{x^2 - 3}{x^3}$

d) $f(x) = x\left(3 - \sqrt{x}\right)$ **e)** $f(x) = x^2\left(\sqrt{x} - 3\right)$ **f)** $f(x) = \dfrac{50}{x}\left(3 - \sqrt{x}\right)$

3 For $f(x) = \frac{1}{x^2}$ show that the limit of expression $\frac{f(x+h) - f(x)}{h}$ as $h \to 0$ gives $f'(x) = -\frac{2}{x^3}$

4 A box is to be made with a volume of 500 cm³. It is to have a square base, of side x cm.

a) Express the height, h, in terms of x.
b) Find a formula for the total surface area, A cm³, in terms of x for:
  i) an open box (i.e. a box without a lid),
  ii) a closed box
c) For each of **i)** and **ii)** in **b)** determine the dimensions to minimise the surface area A, cm³. State the corresponding values of A.

5 A cylindrical tank, open at the top and of height h m, radius r m, is to hold 2 m³.

a) Find h in terms of r.
b) Find a formula for the total surface area, A m², in terms of r.
c) Find the smallest value of A. How are r and h related in this case?

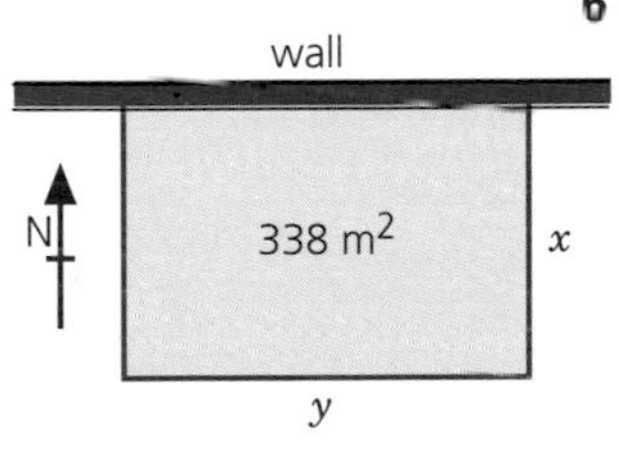

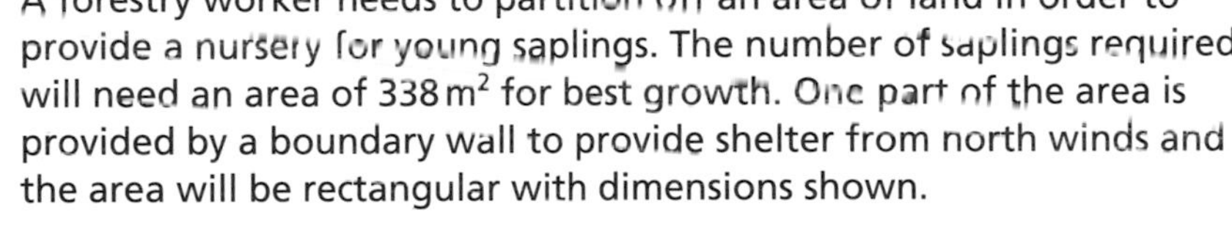

6 A forestry worker needs to partition off an area of land in order to provide a nursery for young saplings. The number of saplings required will need an area of 338 m² for best growth. One part of the area is provided by a boundary wall to provide shelter from north winds and the area will be rectangular with dimensions shown.

a) Find a formula for the total length of fencing needed, in terms of x only.
b) Find the minimum length of fencing required.
c) Use a method which shows *why* this is a minimum, not a maximum.

7 The cost per hour of operating a long-distance lorry is given by £kv^2 where v is the average speed for a journey and k is a constant. The driver works at a fixed hourly rate £C. Show that the most economical speed over a fixed distance, d, is given by:

$v^{\frac{3}{2}} = \dfrac{2C}{k}$ (independent of d).

EXERCISES

11.2 HOMEWORK

1 Differentiate each of the following , evaluating the gradient at the x-value shown.

a) $-\frac{16}{x^2}$ $(x = 2)$ **b)** $\frac{25}{2x^2}$ $(x = 5)$ **c)** $3x^4 - \frac{3}{x^4}$ $(x = 1)$

d) $\left(4x - \frac{1}{x}\right)\left(\frac{3}{x^2} + 2\right)$ $(x = -2)$ **e)** $20\sqrt{x} - \frac{6}{\sqrt{x}}$ $(x = 9)$

f) $\sqrt{x}\left(x + \sqrt{x}\right)$ $(x = 64)$ **g)** $\frac{3}{\sqrt{x}}\left(2x^2 + \sqrt{x}\right)$ $\left(x = \frac{1}{16}\right)$

2 For each of the following functions:
i) find where $f'(x) = 0$, **ii)** identify any stationary points,
iii) sketch a graph of the function.

a) $f(x) = \frac{1}{x} - 2x^2$ **b)** $f(x) = \frac{1}{x} - \frac{1}{x^2}$ **c)** $f(x) = \frac{x^2 - 5}{x^3}$

d) $f(x) = x\left(5 - 2\sqrt{x}\right)$ **e)** $f(x) = x^2\left(\sqrt{5} - \sqrt{x}\right)$ **f)** $f(x) = \frac{3}{x}\left(5 - \sqrt{x}\right)$

3 For $f(x) = \frac{1}{x^3}$ show that the limit of expression $\frac{f(x+h) - f(x)}{h}$ as $h \to 0$ gives $f'(x) = -\frac{3}{x^4}$.

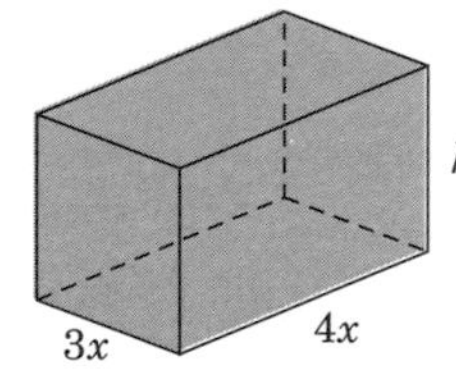

4 The rectangular block shown has a volume of 14 112 cm^3.

a) Find an expression for A, the total surface area, in terms of x only.
b) Calculate the value of x that gives A a stationary value.
c) Find this value of A and find whether it is maximum or minimum.

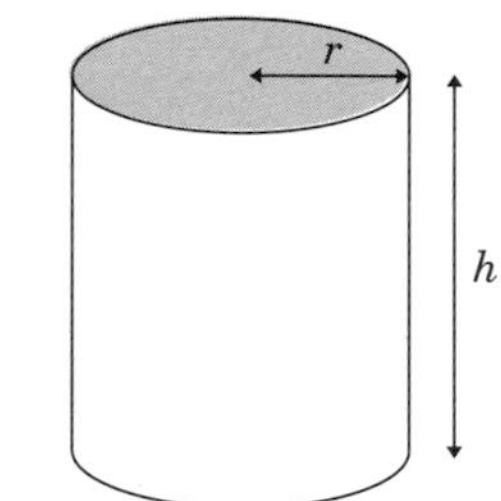

5 The closed cylindrical can shown has a volume 512π cm^3.

a) Write down expressions for the volume, V, and total surface area, S, giving your answers in terms of both r and h.
b) Eliminate h from your two equations and hence find an equation giving S in terms of r only.
c) Calculate the value of r for which S has a stationary value.
d) Does this value of r make the surface area a maximum or minimum? Give reasons for your answer.
e) Find the values of S and h for this value of r.

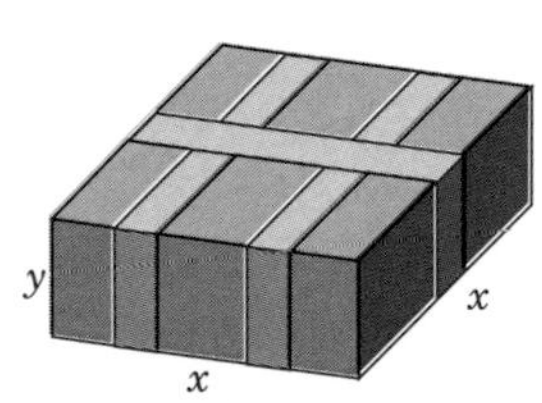

6 A regulation states that all parcels above a certain volume must be bound by at least three lengths of tape, as shown in the diagram. Given that the parcel has a square base find, to the nearest cm, the minimum length of tape required to secure a parcel of volume 8000 cm^3.

7 The velocity of a wave of length x in deep water is given by the formula: $v = k\sqrt{\frac{x}{c} + \frac{c}{x}}$, where k and c are constants.

a) Let $y = \frac{x}{c} + \frac{c}{x}$ and hence find the value of x that minimises y.

b) Deduce the minimum velocity.

SECOND DERIVATIVES

CALCULATOR ACTIVITY

Exploration 11.5

Rates of change of rates of change

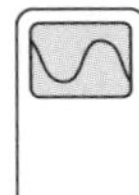

You will need a graphics calculator or computer graphing package. Scale the axes as follows.

$x_{min} = -3$; $x_{max} = 3$; $x_{scl} = 1$
$y_{min} = -5$; $y_{max} = 5$; $y_{scl} = 1$.

- Plot the graph of $y = x(x^2 - 3)$.
- Find the coordinates of the stationary points.
- Superimpose the graph of $y = 3(x^2 - 1)$. What value does it take when $x = \pm 1$?
- Superimpose the graph of $y = 6x$. What values does it take when $x = 0$ and $x = \pm 1$?
- How are the three graphs related?

Turning points

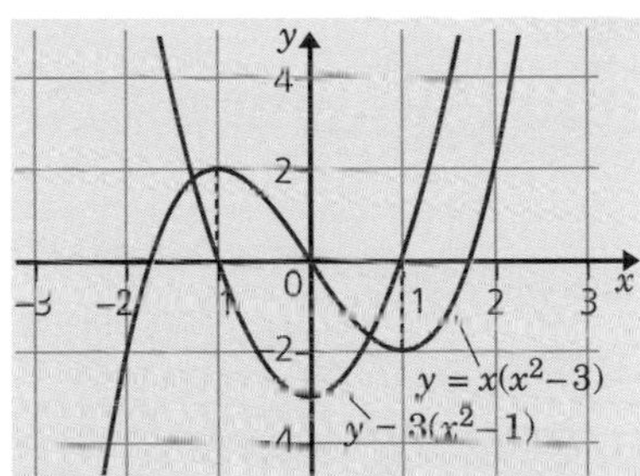

The graphs of $y = x(x^2 - 3)$ and $y = 3(x^2 - 1)$ are shown in the diagram.

Let $y = x(x^2 - 3) = x^3 - 3x$. Then $\frac{dy}{dx} = 3x^2 - 3 = 3(x^2 - 1)$

i.e. $y = 3(x^2 - 1)$ is the gradient function for $y = x(x^2 - 3)$.

Let $f(x) = x(x^2 - 3)$. Then $f'(x) = 3(x^2 - 1)$.

$f'(-1) = f'(1) = 0$, indicating that at $x = \pm 1$ the curve $y = f(x)$ has stationary values (a maximum at $(-1, 2)$ and a minimum at $(1, -2)$).

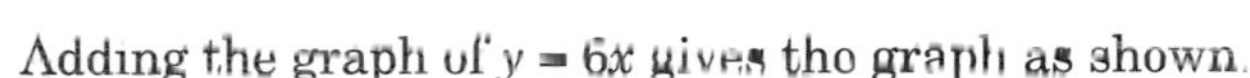

Adding the graph of $y = 6x$ gives the graph as shown.

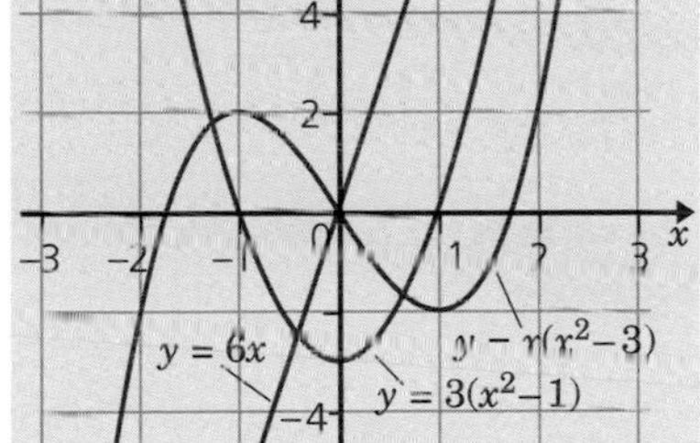

Let $y = 3(x^2 - 1) = 3x^2 - 3$, Then $\frac{dy}{dx} = 6x$

$\Rightarrow$ $y = 6x$ is the gradient function for $y = 3(x^2 - 1)$.

Since $f'(x) = 3(x^2 - 1)$ the function $f''(x) = 6x$ is called the **second derivative** of $f(x)$.

$f''(0) = 0$ indicates that at $x = 0$ the function $y = 3(x^2 - 1)$ has a stationary value and $y = x(x^2 - 3)$ has a **point of inflexion**.

$f''(-1) = -6$, i.e. $f''(-1) < 0$, which indicates that the gradient function $y = f'(x)$ is decreasing at $x = -1$; this means that the stationary point $(-1, 2)$ is a local **maximum**.

$f''(1) = 6$, i.e. $f''(1) > 0$, which indicates that the gradient function $y = f'(x)$ is increasing at $x = 1$; this means that the stationary point at $(1, -2)$ is a local **minimum**.

The results of the exploration provide two useful ideas involving second derivatives.

At stationary points $(a, f(a))$ when $f'(a) = 0$

- if $f''(a) < 0$ then $(a, f(a))$ is a local **maximum**,
- if $f''(a) > 0$ then $(a, f(a))$ is a local **minimum**.

At a point of inflexion $(b, f(b))$, $f''(b) = 0$.

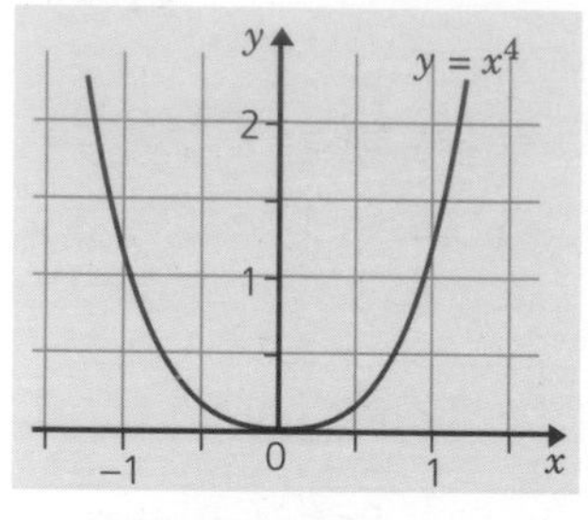

However, the converse is not always true, i.e. $f''(b) = 0$ does not always give a point of inflexion. For example:

$$y = f(x) = x^4 \Rightarrow f'(x) = 4x^3 \Rightarrow f''(x) = 12x^2$$

a local **minimum** point occurs at (0,0) even though $f''(0) = 0$.

A necessary and sufficient condition for a point of inflexion at $(b, f(b))$ is that $f''(b) = 0$ and there is a change of sign in $f''(x)$ either side of $x = b$.

Example 11.5

a) *Find and classify the stationary points of the graph of* $y = x + \frac{1}{x}$.
b) *Use your calculator to confirm the results of a).*

Solution

a) $f(x) = x + \frac{1}{x} \Rightarrow f'(x) = 1 - \frac{1}{x^2}$

For stationary values, $f'(x) = 0 \Rightarrow 1 - \frac{1}{x^2} = 0 \Rightarrow 1 = \frac{1}{x^2} \Rightarrow x = +1$ or $x = -1$

Since $f''(x) = \frac{2}{x^3}$, $f''(1) = 2 \Rightarrow$ *the stationary point is a local minimum.*

$f''(-1) = -2 \Rightarrow$ *the stationary point is a local maximum.*

b)

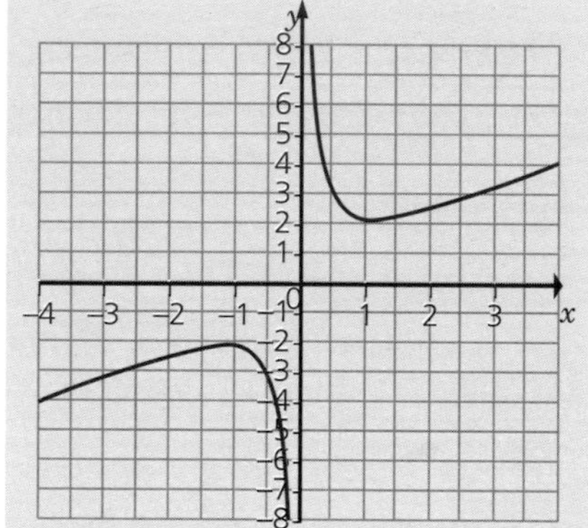

Example 11.6

Show that all cubic functions have a point of inflexion. What is the geometrical significance of the point of inflexion?

Solution

Let a general cubic function $f(x) = ax^3 + bx^2 + cx + d$, *where* a, b, c, d *are constants.*

For a point of inflexion we require $f''(x) = 0$ *and a change of sign.*

$$f(x) = ax^3 + bx^2 + cx + d \Rightarrow f'(x) = 3ax^2 + 2bx + c$$
$$\Rightarrow f''(x) = 6ax + 2b$$

Now $f''(x) = 0 \Rightarrow 6ax + 2b = 0 \Rightarrow x = -\frac{b}{3a}$

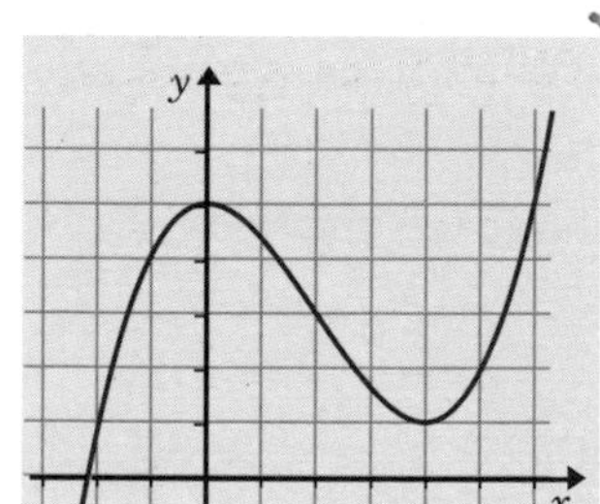

Since $y = 6ax + 2b$ *gives a straight line graph,* y *must change sign either side of* $x = -\frac{b}{3a}$, *so every cubic has a point of inflexion.*

Geometrically, all cubic graphs have rotational symmetry about the point of inflexion, e.g. for $y = x^3 - 3x^2 + 5$ *(i.e.* $a = 1, b = -3, c = 0, d = 5$*), the point of inflexion occurs when* $x = -\frac{-3}{3\times1} = 1$ *and* $y = 3$.

EXERCISES

11.3 CLASSWORK

1 For the following functions, find f″(x) and its value at the x–value given.

a) $f(x) = x^3 - 4x$, $x = 2$ **b)** $f(x) = ax^2 + bx + c$, $x = -1$

c) $f(x) = x^2 - \frac{1}{x^2}$, $x = -1$ **d)** $f(x) = \sqrt{x}(4 - x)$, $x = 4$

2 For the following functions, use f″(x) to determine the nature of any stationary points.

a) $f(x) = 2x^3 + 3x^2 - 12x + 5$ **b)** $f(x) = x + \frac{4}{x^2}$

c) $f(x) = x - \sqrt{x}$ **d)** $f(x) = 7 + 2x^2 - x^4$

3 For the following functions, find any points of inflexion.

a) $f(x) = 12 - x + 3x^2 - x^3$ **b)** $f(x) = 3x^4 - 4x^3$

c) $f(x) = 5x^3 - \frac{15}{x}$ **d)** $f(x) = x\left(x - 4\sqrt{x}\right)$

4 In the following expressions, x represents the displacement, in metres, of a particle from an origin O after t seconds, $t \geq 0$. In each case find:

i) the acceleration a at the given time t,

ii) the time at which the given acceleration a occurs.

a) $x = t^2(5 - t)$ $t = 5\text{s}$ $a = 1\,\text{m s}^{-2}$

b) $x = \frac{20}{t}$ $t = 2\text{s}$ $a = 320\,\text{m s}^{-2}$

EXERCISES

11.3 HOMEWORK

1 For the following functions, find f″(x) and its value at the x-value given.

a) $f(x) = 1 + x + \frac{x^2}{2} + \frac{x^3}{6}$, $x = 2$ **b)** $f(x) = \frac{1}{2}x^2(5 - x)$, $x = 2$

c) $f(x) = 2x^3 + \frac{3}{x}$, $x = -1$ **d)** $f(x) = 2x^2\left(3 - \sqrt{x}\right)$, $x = 5$

2 For the following functions, use f″(x) to determine the nature of any stationary points.

a) $f(x) = 10 + 3x^2 - x^3$ **b)** $f(x) = 2x^2 - \frac{5}{x}$

c) $f(x) = 2x^2(3 - \sqrt{x})$ **d)** $f(x) = 10 + 3(x - 2)^2 - (x - 2)^3$

3 For the following functions, find any points of inflexion.

a) $f(x) = x^3 - 2x^2 + 3x - 4$ **b)** $f(x) = 4x^5 - 5x^4$

c) $f(x) = 2x - \frac{5}{x}$ **d)** $f(x) = (2x - 5)^3$

4 In the following expressions, x represents the displacement, in metres, of a particle from an origin O after t seconds, $t \geq 0$. In each case find:

i) the acceleration a at the given time t,

ii) the time(s) at which the given acceleration occurs.

a) $x = \frac{1}{10}t^2(6 - t)^2$ $t = 3\,\text{s}$ $a = 1.2\,\text{m s}^{-2}$

b) $x = t - \frac{1}{6}t^3 + \frac{1}{120}t^5$ $t = 1.5\,\text{s}$ $a = 1.5\,\text{m s}^{-2}$

c) $x = t\sqrt{t}$ $t = 0.8\,\text{s}$ $a = 1\,\text{m s}^{-2}$

TANGENTS AND NORMALS

Exploration 11.6 *Equation of a tangent*

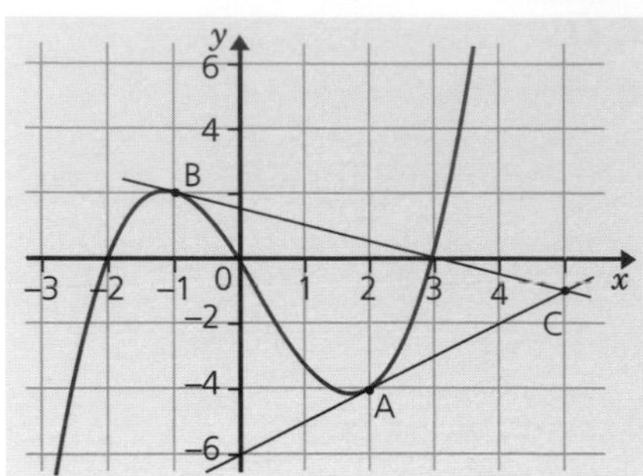

The diagram shows the graph of $y = \frac{1}{2}x(x+2)(x-3)$ with **tangents** to the curve drawn at points A and B.

- Find the equations of the two tangents.
- Find the coordinates of the point C.

Tangents

From the diagram we can see:

- for the tangent at A: gradient = 1 y-intercept = –6
  $\Rightarrow$ equation of tangent is $y = x - 6$
- for the tangent at B: gradient = –0.5 y-intercept = 1.5
  $\Rightarrow$ equation of tangent is $y = -0.5x + 1.5 \Rightarrow x + 2y = 3$
- point C, the intersection of the two tangents, has coordinates (5, –1).

All three deductions have been made from the graph. However, we must be able to complete the task more formally.

Let $y = f(x) = \frac{1}{2}x(x+2)(x-3) = \frac{1}{2}x^3 - \frac{1}{2}x^2 - 3x$

$\Rightarrow \frac{dy}{dx} = f'(x) = \frac{3}{2}x^2 - x - 3$

At A(2, –4), f(2) = 1, which enables us to find the equation of the tangent. Recall that the equation of a line with gradient m, passing through (x_1, y_1) is given by:

$$y - y_1 = m(x - x_1)$$

In this case, $x_1 = 2$, $y_1 = -4$ and $m = 1$

$\Rightarrow y - (-4) = 1(x - 2) \Rightarrow y = x - 6$ (1)

Similarly at B(–1, 2), f′(1) = –0.5

$\Rightarrow y - 2 = -0.5(x - (-1)) \Rightarrow y = -0.5x + 1.5$ or $x + 2y = 3$ (2)

Solving equations (1) and (2) simultaneously enables us to find the coordinates of C.

From (1): $y = x - 6$
Substitute in (2): $x + 2(x - 6) = 3 \Rightarrow 3x - 12 = 3 \Rightarrow x = 5$
Substitute in (1): $y = 5 - 6 = -1$
So the coordinates of C are (5, –1).

The normal

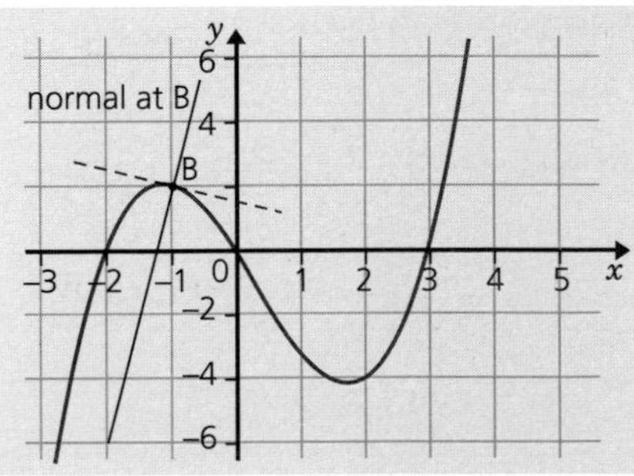

Closely related to the tangent is the **normal**, a straight line which passes through a point on a curve and is perpendicular to the tangent at that point. For perpendicular lines, the product of the gradients is –1, so the gradient of a normal can easily be deduced from the gradient of the tangent.

At B(–1, 2) the gradient of the tangent is –0.5, so the gradient of the normal is $\frac{-1}{-0.5} = 2$.

Therefore the equation of the normal through (–1, 2) is:

$$y - 2 = 2(x - (-1)) \Rightarrow y = 2x + 4$$

Example 11.7

Find the equation of the tangent and normal to the curve $y = x + \frac{1}{x}$ at the point (2, 2.5).

Solution

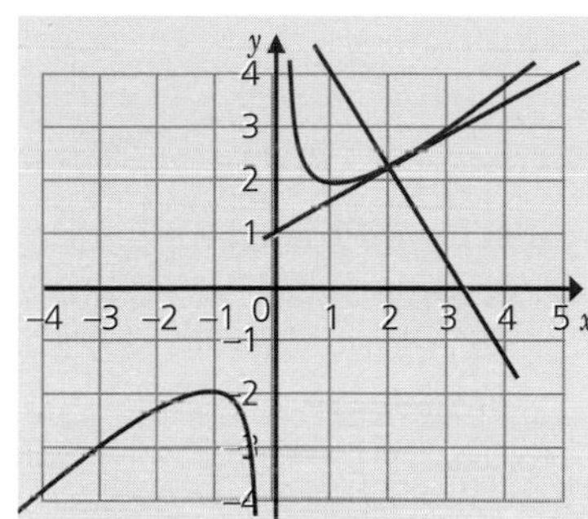

$y = x + \frac{1}{x} \Rightarrow \frac{dy}{dx} = 1 - \frac{1}{x^2}$

At A (2, 2.5) the gradient of the tangent is $\frac{dy}{dx} = 1 - \frac{1}{4} = 0.75$

The equation of the tangent through (2, 2.5) is:

$y - 2.5 = 0.75(x - 2) \Rightarrow 4y = 3x + 4$

The gradient of the normal is $\frac{-1}{0.75} = -\frac{4}{3}$

Therefore the equation of the normal through (2, 2.5) is:

$y - 2.5 = -\frac{4}{3}(x - 2) \Rightarrow 6y = -8x + 31$

EXERCISES

11.4 CLASSWORK

For questions **1** to **6**, find the gradient of the **tangent** and the gradient of the **normal** for each curve at the point given. Deduce the **equations** of the tangent and the normal passing through this point, illustrating your answer with a sketch.

1 $y = x^2 - 5$ at $(2, -1)$

2 $y = 2 - 3x - x^3$ at $(-1, 6)$

3 $y = \frac{12}{x}$ at $(-2, -6)$

4 $y = 10\sqrt{x}$ at $(9, 30)$

5 $s = t(t - 1)(t + 3)$ at $(-1, 4)$

6 $y = \frac{3}{x^2} + 1$ at $(1, 4)$

7 Find the equations of the tangents to the curve $y = 15 + 2x - x^2$ at the points where it meets the x-axis. Find the coordinates of the point where the tangents intersect.

8 Find the equations of the tangents to the curve $y = x^3 - 8x + 5$ which have a gradient 4.

9 The normals to the curve $y = x^2 + x - 12$ at (2,–6) and (p, q) are perpendicular. Find the values of p and q.

EXERCISES

11.4 HOMEWORK

For questions **1** to **6**, find the equation of the tangent and the normal to the curve through the given point. Illustrate your answer with a sketch.

1 $y = 4(x + 3)^2$, at $(-4, 4)$

2 $s = 10 + 8t - 5t^2$ at $(2, 6)$

3 $y = 5x^3 - 6x^2$ at $(1, -1)$

4 $y = 5x^2 - \frac{1}{x^2}$ at $(1, 4)$

5 $u = 3x\left(5 - \sqrt{x}\right)$ at (4, 36)

6 $y = 2x - \frac{3}{\sqrt{x}}$ at $(1, -1)$

7 Find the equations of the normals to the curve $y = (2x + 1)(2x - 5)$ at the points where it meets the x-axis. Find the coordinates of the point where the normals intersect.

8 Find the equation of the normals to the curve $y = \frac{x^3}{3} - x^2 + 2$ which have gradient $-\frac{1}{3}$.

9 Find the equations of the tangents to the curve $y = x(x - 1)(x + 3)$ at the point where it intersects with the line $y = 2x + 6$.

INTEGRATING FUNCTIONS WITH RATIONAL EXPONENTS

In Chapter 8, *Integration 1*, we integrated polynomial functions, obtaining indefinite integrals such as:

$$\int x^2 \mathrm{d}x = \frac{1}{3}x^3 + c$$

and $\frac{\mathrm{d}s}{\mathrm{d}t} = 15 - 10t \Rightarrow s = 15t - 5t^2 + k$

Earlier in this chapter we found that the rules for differentiating polynomials can be extended to differentiating functions with rational exponents, such as:

$$f(x) = \frac{3}{x} = 3x^{-1} \Rightarrow f'(x) = -3x^{-2} = -\frac{3}{x^2}$$

and $y = 10\sqrt{x} = 10x^{\frac{1}{2}} \Rightarrow \frac{\mathrm{d}y}{\mathrm{d}x} = 5x^{-\frac{1}{2}} = \frac{5}{\sqrt{x}}$

Now we can extend the rules for integrating polynomials to consider integrating functions with rational exponents.

Exploration 11.7

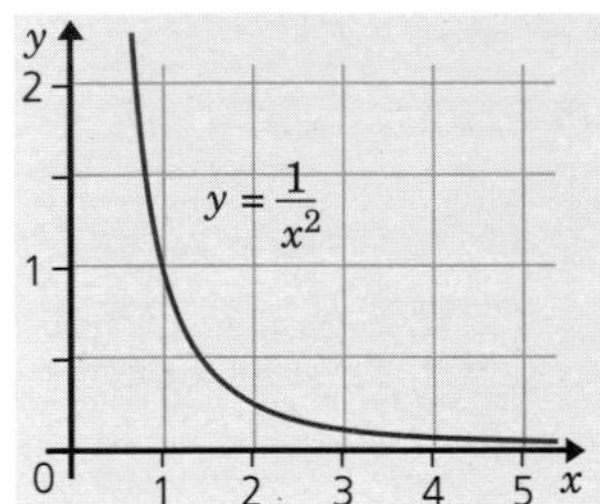

Rational exponents

The diagram shows a sketch of $f(x) = \frac{1}{x^2}$, $x \neq 0$.

- Use a numerical method to estimate areas given by $A = \int_1^a \frac{1}{x^2}\mathrm{d}x$ for $a = 2, 3, 4, 5, 10$.
- Repeat for $a = 0.5, 0.2, 0.1$.
- Use the numerical results to find the area function $A(x)$.
- Is it true that $A'(x) = f(x)$?

Numerical results

The numerical calculations should give the following results.

a	$\int_1^a \frac{1}{x^2}\mathrm{d}x$
2	0.5
3	0.67
4	0.75
5	0.8

a	$\int_1^a \frac{1}{x^2}\mathrm{d}x$
10	0.9
0.5	–1.0
0.2	–4.0
0.1	–9.0

Check that $A(x) = 1 - \frac{1}{x}$ i.e. $\int_1^a \frac{1}{x^2}\mathrm{d}x = 1 - \frac{1}{a}$

$$A(x) = 1 - \frac{1}{x} = 1 - x^{-1} \Rightarrow A'(x) = x^{-2} = \frac{1}{x^2} = f(x)$$

Since $A'(x) = f(x)$, the process of differentiation may be reversed to integrate $f(x) = \frac{1}{x^2}$,

i.e. $f(x) = \frac{1}{x^2} = x^{-2} \Rightarrow \int f(x)\,\mathrm{d}x = \frac{x^{-1}}{-1} + c = -\frac{1}{x} + c$

Note that in this case the constant of integration $c = 1$, which is determined by the lower bound of the definite integral $\int_1^a \frac{1}{x^2}\,\mathrm{d}x$.

Fractional indices

The process of integration can also be extended to fractional indices, as illustrated in the following example.

Example 11.8

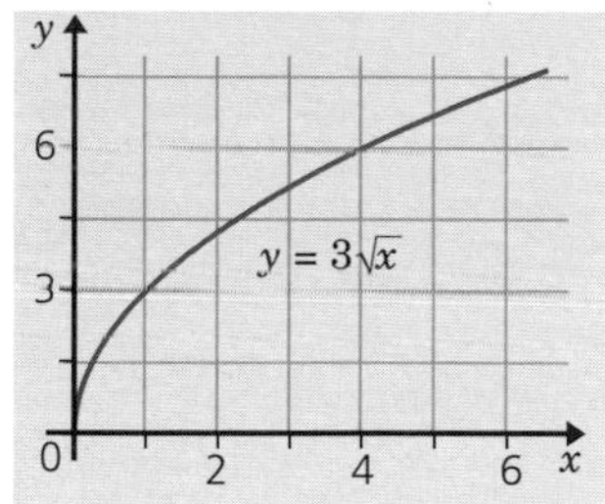

The diagram shows a sketch of $f(x) = 3\sqrt{x} \quad x \geq 0$.

a) *Use a numerical method to estimate areas given by:* $\int_0^a 3\sqrt{x}\,dx$ for $a = 1, 4, 9, 16, 25$

b) *Show that* $\int_0^a 3\sqrt{x}\,dx = \left[2\sqrt{x}^3\right]_0^a$ *is compatible with your numerical results.*

Solution

a) *Results of numerical calculations are shown in this table.*

a	1	4	9	16	25
$\int_0^a 3\sqrt{x}dx$	2	16	54	128	250

b) *Applying the integration rules to fractional indices:*

$$\int_0^a 3\sqrt{x}\,dx = \int_0^a 3x^{\frac{1}{2}}\,dx = \left[\tfrac{2}{3} \times 3x^{\frac{3}{2}}\right]_0^a = \left[2\sqrt{x}^3\right]_0^a$$

for $a = 1$: $\int_0^1 3\sqrt{x}\,dx = \left[2\sqrt{x}^3\right]_0^1 = 2 - 0 = 2$

for $a = 4$: $\int_0^4 3\sqrt{x}\,dx = \left[2\sqrt{x}^3\right]_0^4 = 16 - 0 = 16$ *etc.*

Rules for integrating rational powers

To summarise, we have found that the rules for integrating rational powers are the same as for polynomial functions.

$$\int x^n dx = \frac{1}{n+1}x^{n+1} + c \quad n \neq -1$$

This holds for all rational numbers n, except $n = -1$, since this would lead to division by 0. When $n = -1$, $f(x) = x^{-1} = \frac{1}{x}$. We shall look at this integration in Chapter 18, *Differentiation and integration 3*.

We can apply the process of integrating with rational powers to finding areas and reversing the process of differentiation, as illustrated in the next two examples.

Example 11.9

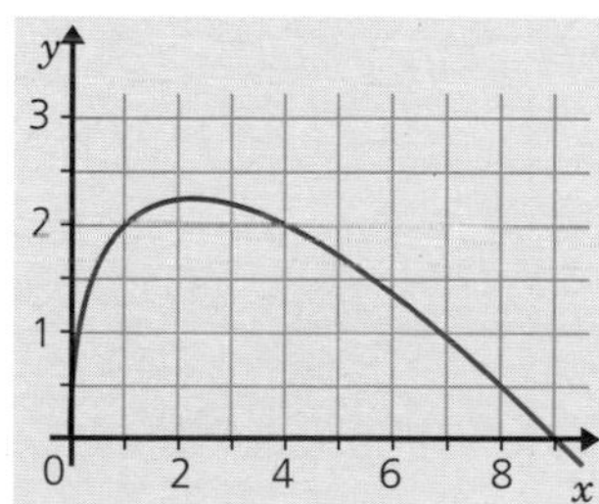

Find the area enclosed by the graph of $y = 3\sqrt{x} - x$ *and the* x*-axis.*

Solution

A sketch of $y = 3\sqrt{x} - x$ *reveals that it lies above the* x*-axis for* $0 < x < 9$ *and cuts it at* $x = 0$ *and* $x = 9$.

The points of intersection of the graph and the x*-axis occur where* $y = 0$, *so may be found algebraically.*

$$0 = 3\sqrt{x} - x \Rightarrow x = 3\sqrt{x} \Rightarrow x^2 = 9x$$

$$\Rightarrow x^2 - 9x = 0 \Rightarrow x(x - 9) = 0$$

$$\Rightarrow x = 0 \text{ or } x = 9$$

The required area is given by:

$$\int_0^9 \left(3\sqrt{x} - x\right) dx = \int_0^9 \left(3x^{\frac{1}{2}} - x\right) dx = \left[\tfrac{2}{3} \times 3x^{\frac{3}{2}} - \tfrac{1}{2}x^2\right]_0^9 = \left[2\sqrt{x}^3 - 0.5x^2\right]_0^9$$

$$= \left(2 \times \sqrt{9}^3 - 0.5 \times 9^2\right) - \left(2 \times \sqrt{0}^3 - 0.5 \times 0^2\right)$$

$$= (54 - 40.5) - 0 = 13.5$$

Example 11.10

The function $y = \mathrm{f}(x)$ *has gradient function:*

$$\mathrm{f}'(x) = \sqrt{x}(5 - x)$$

and $\mathrm{f}(1) = 3$. *Find* $\mathrm{f}(4)$.

Solution

$$\mathrm{f}'(x) = \sqrt{x}(5-x) \Rightarrow \mathrm{f}(x) = \int \sqrt{x}(5-x)\mathrm{d}x = \int \left(5\sqrt{x} - x\sqrt{x}\right)\mathrm{d}x$$

$$= \int \left(5x^{\frac{1}{2}} - x^{\frac{3}{2}}\right)\mathrm{d}x = \tfrac{2}{3} \times 5x^{\frac{3}{2}} - \tfrac{2}{5}x^{\frac{5}{2}} + c = \tfrac{10}{3}\sqrt{x}^3 - \tfrac{2}{5}\sqrt{x}^5 + c$$

Now $\mathrm{f}(1) = 3 \Rightarrow 3 = \frac{10}{3} - \frac{2}{5} + c \Rightarrow c = 3 - \frac{10}{3} + \frac{2}{5} = \frac{1}{15}$

Hence $\mathrm{f}(4) = \frac{10}{3}\sqrt{4}^3 - \frac{2}{5}\sqrt{4}^5 + \frac{1}{15} = \frac{10}{3} \times 8 - \frac{2}{5} \times 32 + \frac{1}{15} = 13\frac{14}{15}$

EXERCISES

11.5 CLASSWORK

1 Find the following integrals.

a) $\int \frac{7}{x^2}\,\mathrm{d}x$ b) $\int \frac{-12}{x^3}\,\mathrm{d}x$ c) $\int 3x\left(\frac{2}{x^3} - 5\right)\mathrm{d}x$ d) $\int 15\sqrt{x}\,\mathrm{d}x$

e) $\int \frac{-4}{\sqrt{x}}\,\mathrm{d}x$ f) $\int \sqrt{x}(x-8)\,\mathrm{d}x$ g) $\int x^2\left(4 + \sqrt{x}\right)\mathrm{d}x$ h) $\int \frac{9}{x^2}\left(1 + \sqrt{x}\right)\mathrm{d}x$

2 Evaluate the following integrals.

a) $\int_2^5 \frac{10}{x^2}\,\mathrm{d}x$ b) $\int_4^9 6\sqrt{x}\,\mathrm{d}x$ c) $\int_1^{2.25} \left(10 - 3\sqrt{x}\right)\mathrm{d}x$ d) $\int_1^2 \frac{8}{x^2}\left(1 + x^3\right)\mathrm{d}x$

e) $\int_{0.5}^{1.5} (2x+5)\sqrt{x}\,\mathrm{d}x$ f) $\int_1^4 \frac{5}{x^4}(x-1)(x+3)\,\mathrm{d}x$

3 Find the areas represented by the following integrals. Illustrate each answer with a sketch.

a) $\int_{-3}^{-1} \frac{15}{x^2}\,\mathrm{d}x$ b) $\int_1^4 \frac{-16}{x^3}\,\mathrm{d}x$ c) $\int_2^5 \left(5 - \frac{8}{x^2}\right)\mathrm{d}x$ d) $\int_0^{25} \left(x - 5\sqrt{x}\right)\mathrm{d}x$

e) $\int_0^6 \sqrt{x}(6-x)\,\mathrm{d}x$ f) $\int_0^1 \left(\sqrt{x} - \sqrt[3]{x}\right)\mathrm{d}x$ g) $\int_1^4 \left(\frac{1}{x^3} - \frac{1}{x^2}\right)\mathrm{d}x$

4 For each of the following, find the area of the shaded region.

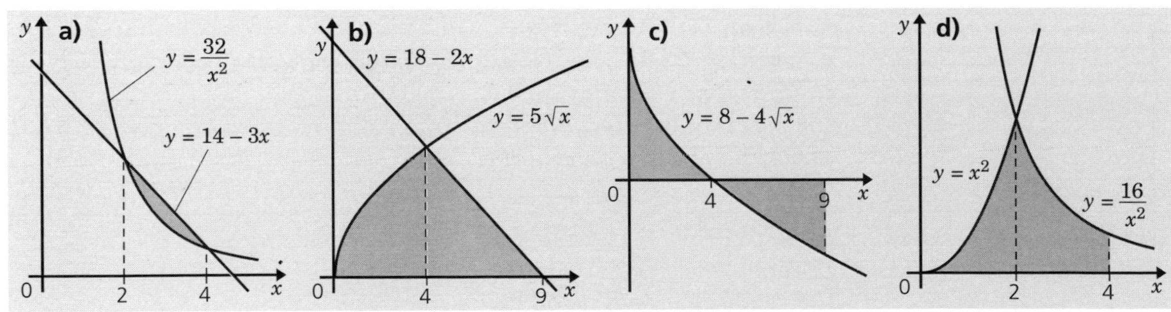

5 For each of the following gradient functions, $\mathrm{f}'(x)$, find an expression for $\mathrm{f}(x)$ and evaluate $\mathrm{f}(4)$, given the condition stated. Sketch a graph of $y = \mathrm{f}(x)$.

a) $\mathrm{f}'(x) = 5 - \frac{2}{\sqrt{x}},\ \mathrm{f}(0) = -3$ b) $\mathrm{f}'(x) = 4 - \frac{3}{x^2},\ \mathrm{f}(1) = 7$

c) $\mathrm{f}'(x) = 9\sqrt{x},\ \mathrm{f}(0) = 2$ d) $\mathrm{f}'(x) = \frac{2}{x^3} - \frac{3}{x^4},\ \mathrm{f}(1) = 2$

EXERCISES

11.5 HOMEWORK

1 Find the following integrals.

a) $\int \frac{dx}{2x^3}$ **b)** $\int \frac{-5}{x^9}\,dx$ **c)** $\int \left(3x^2 - \frac{3}{x^4}\right) dx$ **d)** $\int 11x^2\left(7 - \frac{3}{x^5}\right) dx$

e) $\int \left(\sqrt{x} + \frac{1}{\sqrt{x}}\right) dx$ **f)** $\int \frac{x-1}{\sqrt{x}}\,dx$ **g)** $\frac{1}{2}\int \left(3\sqrt{x} - \frac{1}{\sqrt{x}}\right) dx$

h) $\int x\left(\sqrt{x} - 7\right) dx$ **i)** $\int \frac{\sqrt{x}}{x^3}\,dx$ **j)** $\int \frac{(x-2)(x+2)}{\sqrt{x}}\,dx$

2 Evaluate the following integrals.

a) $\int_1^3 \frac{5}{x^3}\,dx$ **b)** $\int_0^4 3\sqrt{x}\,(1+x)\,dx$ **c)** $\int_1^2 \left(\frac{5}{\sqrt{x}} + 9\sqrt{x}\right) dx$

d) $\int_2^3 \frac{x^4 - 4}{x^3}\,dx$ **e)** $\int_0^1 (x-1)(x+1)\sqrt{x}\,dx$ **f)** $\int_{-2}^{-1} \frac{(x+2)^2}{x^4}\,dx$

3 Find the areas represented by the following integrals. Illustrate each of your answers with a sketch.

a) $\int_{-2}^{-1} \frac{3}{x^2}\,dx$ **b)** $\int_2^3 \frac{-20}{x^5}\,dx$ **c)** $\int_0^1 \left(x^2 - 2\sqrt{x}\right) dx$ **d)** $\int_0^2 \left(1 - \sqrt{x}\right)^2 dx$

e) $\int_1^2 3\left(x^2 + \frac{1}{x^2}\right) dx$ **f)** $\int_1^2 \left(\frac{1}{x} + \sqrt{x}\right)\left(x + \frac{1}{\sqrt{x}}\right) dx$

g) $\int_0^1 \left(\sqrt{x} - \sqrt[3]{x}\right)^2 dx$ **h)** $\int_1^4 \frac{x^2 + 2x + 5}{x^{\frac{3}{2}}}\,dx$

4 For each of the following, find the area of the shaded region.

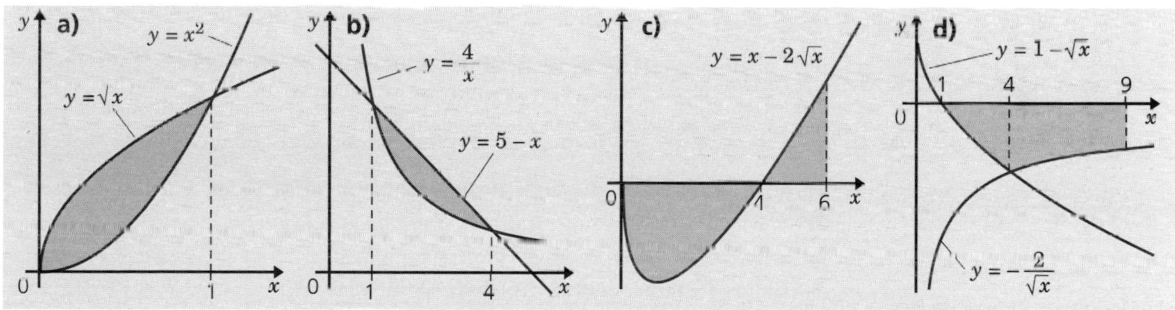

5 For each of the following gradient functions, f′(x), find an expression for f(x) and evaluate f(2), given the condition stated. Sketch a graph of y = f(x).

a) $f'(x) = \frac{3}{\sqrt{x}} - 1,\ f(1) = 2$ **b)** $f'(x) = 3 - \frac{7}{x^3},\ f\left(\frac{1}{2}\right) = 10$

c) $f'(x) = \frac{1}{\sqrt{x}} - \sqrt{x},\ f(4) = 5$ **d)** $f'(x) = \frac{3}{x^4} - \frac{4}{x^5},\ f(1) = 2$

MATHEMATICAL MODELLING ACTIVITY

Problem statement

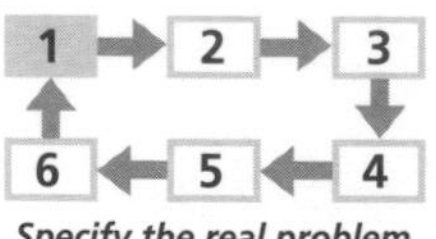

Specify the real problem

A small company that distributes books and software needs a policy for controlling levels of stock. If the company has too little stock there is a danger of orders to customers being delayed; however if stock is too high money is tied up unnecessarily and the company needs to rent storage space.

After the company has been running for one year, the following data is available for future planning.

a) Ordering costs (administration and postage) are £1.50 per order.
b) Annual cost of holding an item in stock is calculated at 20% of the item price.
c) The current price of a popular software package is £33.
d) The average number of this package sold per month is 35.

What ordering policy should the company adopt?

Set up a model

Set up a model

First you need to identify the important variables:

- how often the software packages should be ordered,
- the selling price for each package,
- the total number sold each year,
- the costs involved (fixed and variable),
- the number of packages in stock as a function of time.

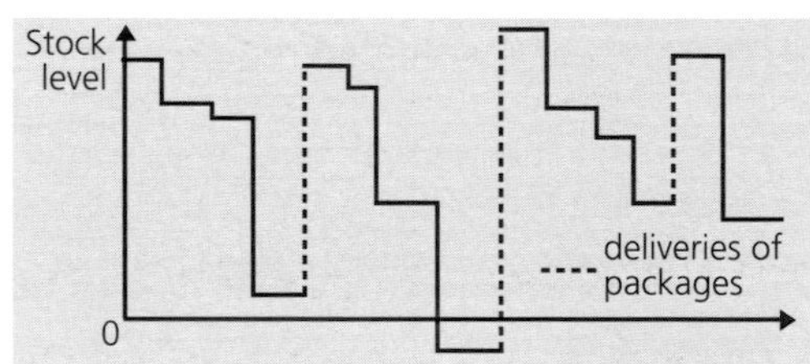

To proceed further we need to make some assumptions about stock level and time. The figure shows what has happened in the first year of running the company.

Notice that for one period there were orders from customers waiting for a delivery.

To formulate a simple model we shall assume:

- software packages will be ordered at regular intervals,
- the stock level in store reduces linearly with time,
- each order is constant,
- there are no discounts available for large orders.

Mathematical problem

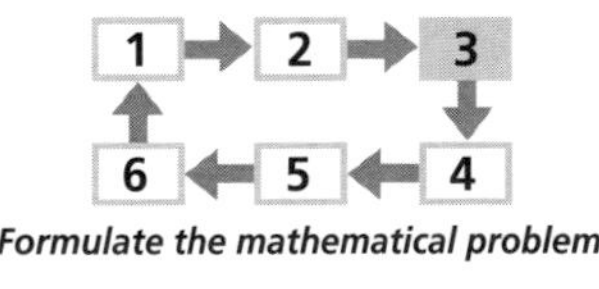

Formulate the mathematical problem

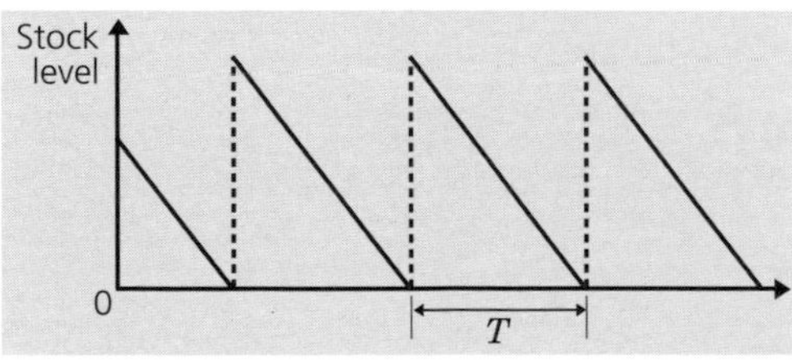

We begin by defining variables.

Let x be the number of packages ordered each T weeks, and C be the total annual costs to the company.

The annual costs are made up of two parts: the ordering costs and the storage costs.

ordering costs per year $= \dfrac{\text{total number sold}}{\text{order size}} \times \text{order costs} = \dfrac{35 \times 12 \times 1.5}{x} = \dfrac{630}{x}$

storage costs per year $= 20\%$ of average stock held $\times$ item price $= 0.2 \times \dfrac{x}{2} \times 33 = 3.3x$

$$C = \frac{630}{x} + 3.3x \qquad (1)$$

The mathematical problem is to minimise C.

Mathematical solution

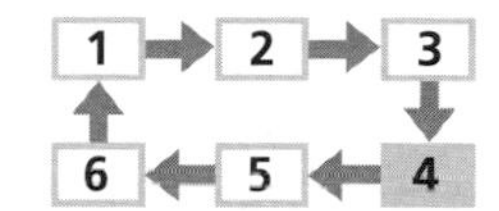

Solve the mathematical problem

Using calculus, we find that the minimum value of C occurs when $\dfrac{dC}{dx} = 0$ and $\dfrac{d^2C}{dx^2} > 0$. Differentiating (1):

$$\frac{dC}{dx} = -\frac{630}{x^2} + 3.3$$

and $\dfrac{dC}{dx} = 0$ when $x^2 = \dfrac{630}{3.3} = 190.19 \quad \Rightarrow \quad x = 13.82$

Also $\dfrac{d^2C}{dx^2} = \dfrac{1260}{x^3} > 0$ for $x = 13.82$. Hence we have a minimum.

Interpretation

Interpret the solution

Clearly we cannot order a fraction of a software package. We suggest that the company orders 14 packages. Since the total number of packages sold is 420 the company will need to make an order 30 times per year.

Refinement of the model

Compare with reality

Discuss the assumptions made and suggest other simplifying assumptions that have not been written down. Investigate the effect of changes to these assumptions.

CONSOLIDATION EXERCISES FOR CHAPTER 11

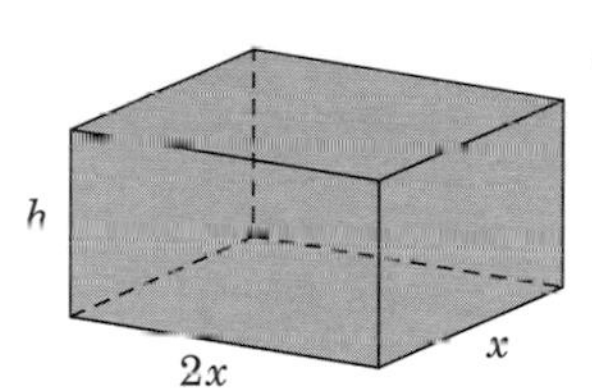

1 The diagram shows a brick in the shape of a cuboid with base x cm by $2x$ cm and height h cm. The total surface area of the brick is 300 cm^2.

a) Show that $h = \dfrac{50}{x} - \dfrac{2x}{3}$

b) The volume of the brick is V cm^3. Express V in terms of x only.

c) Given that x can vary, find the maximum value of V.

d) Explain why the value of V you have found is the maximum.

(ULEAC Question 7 Specimen Paper 1, 1995)

2 **a)** Plot the graph of $y = x - 1 + \dfrac{4}{x^2}$ for $-5 \le x \le 5$.

b) Use your graph to find:

i) the coordinates of the stationary point,

ii) the value of x such that $x + \dfrac{4}{x^2} = 1$.

c) Confirm your answer to **b) ii)** by means of a decimal search.

3 Use differentiation to find the coordinates of the stationary points on the curve: $\quad y = x + \frac{4}{x}$

and determine whether each stationary point is a maximum point or a minimum point. Find the set of values of x for which y increases as x increases.

(UCLES Modular Question 8, Specimen Paper 2, 1994)

4 Curves C_1 and C_2 have equations $y = \frac{1}{x}$ and $y = kx^2$ respectively, where k is a constant. The curves intersect at the point P, with x-coordinate $\frac{1}{2}$

a) Determine the value of k.
b) Find the gradient of C_1 at P.

(ULEAC Question 10, Paper 1, June 1994) (adapted)

5 **a)** Calculate the exact value of the area of the region bounded by the curve with equation $y = x^2 - \frac{2}{x^2}$, the x-axis and the lines $x = 2$ and $x = 3$.

b) **i)** Find the equation of the tangent to the curve with equation $y = x^2 - \frac{2}{x^2}$ at the point $P(1, -1)$.

ii) Determine the coordinates of the point where the tangent at P intersects the same curve again.

(AQA Question 8, Paper 1, June 1999) (adapted)

6 $y = 3x^{\frac{1}{2}} - 4x^{-\frac{1}{2}}$, $x > 0$

a) Find $\frac{dy}{dx}$.

b) Find $\int y dx$.

c) Hence show that $\int_1^3 y dx = A + B\sqrt{3}$ where A and B are integers to be found.

(EDEXCEL Question 7, Paper 1, January 1998)

7 **a)** Find $\int \left(x^{\frac{1}{2}} - 4\right)\left(x^{-\frac{1}{2}} - 1\right) dx$.

b) Use your answer to part **a)** to evaluate

$$\int_1^4 \left(x^{\frac{1}{2}} - 4\right)\left(x^{-\frac{1}{2}} - 1\right) dx$$

giving your answer as an exact fraction.

(EDEXCEL, Question 7, Paper 1, January 2000)

8 The diagram below shows an open tank for storing water, ABCDEF. The sides ABFE and CDEF are rectangles. The triangular ends, ADE and BCF are isosceles and ∠AED = ∠BFC = 90°. The ends ADE and BCF are vertical and EF is horizontal. Given that AD = x metres,

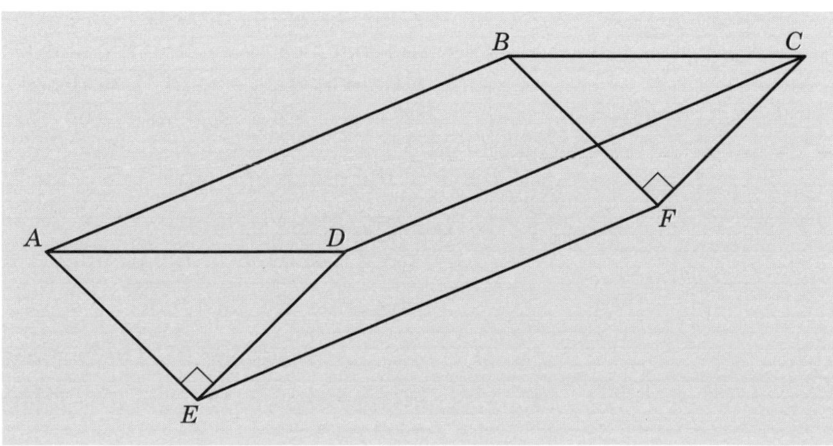

a) show that the area of Δ ADE is $\frac{1}{4}x^2$ m^2.

Given also that the capacity of the container is 4000 m^3 and that the total area of the two triangular and two rectangular sides of the container is Sm^2,

b) show that $S = \dfrac{x^2}{2} + \dfrac{16000\sqrt{2}}{x}$.

Given that x can vary,

c) use calculus to find the minimum value of S,

d) justify that the value of S you have found is a minimum.

(EDEXCEL, Question 9, Paper 1, June 1998)

9 The equation of a curve is $y = 6x^2 - x^3$. Find the coordinates of the two stationary points on the curve, and determine the nature of each of these stationary points.

State the set of values of x for which $6x^2 - x^3$ is a decreasing function of x.
The gradient at the point M on the curve is 12. Find the equation of the tangent to the curve at M.

(OCR, Question 8, Specimen Paper 1, 2000)

Summary

- The graph of $y = \dfrac{a}{x}$, where a is a constant, is called a **rectangular hyperbola**. We say that y is **inversely proportional** to x.
- $\dfrac{dx^n}{dx} = nx^{n-1}$ for any number n.
- $\int x^n dx = \dfrac{1}{(n+1)}x^{n+1} + c \quad n \neq -1$
- The second derivative of a function f(x) is the derivative of the first derivative. $f''(x) = \dfrac{d^2f}{dx^2} = \dfrac{d}{dx}\left(\dfrac{df}{dx}\right)$
- At a stationary point (a, f(a)) of a function f(x), $f'(a) = 0$:

  $f''(a) < 0 \Rightarrow (a, f(a))$ is a local maximum,
  $f''(a) > 0 \Rightarrow (a, f(a))$ is a local minimum.
- At a point of inflexion (b, f(b)), $f''(b) = 0$.

Functions

In this chapter we discuss:

- *the formal concept of a function*
- *the idea of composite functions*
- *the inverse of a function*
- *how to transform functions from the same family.*

WHAT IS A FUNCTION?

Exploration 12.1

Different functions

You have already met many different functions such as:

1	$f(x) = 2x - 3$	linear function
2	$f(x) = x^2 + 2x - 3$	quadratic function
3	$f(x) = x^3$	cubic function
4	$f(x) = \sin x$	trigonometric function

- Sketch graphs of $y = f(x)$ for each function.
- What similarities and differences are there in the graphs?
- For each function solve the equations $f(x) = 0$, $f(x) = 5$, $f(x) = -5$.

Looking at functions

Sketch graphs of the four functions listed above might look like these.

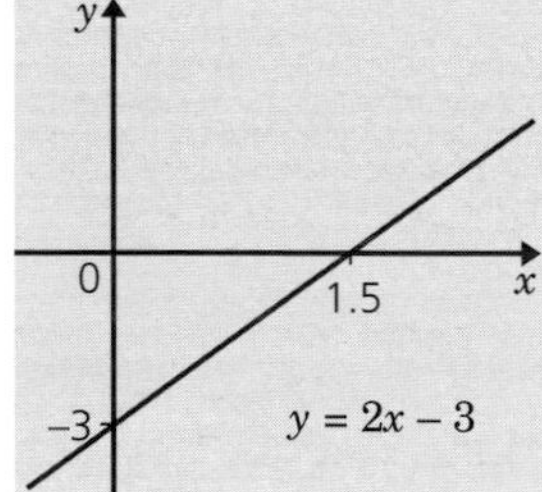

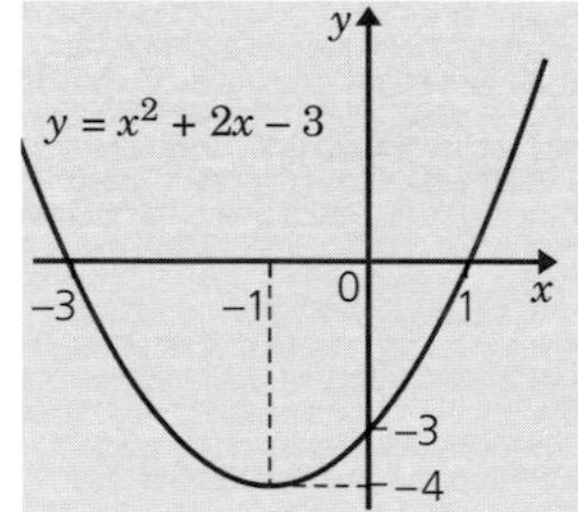

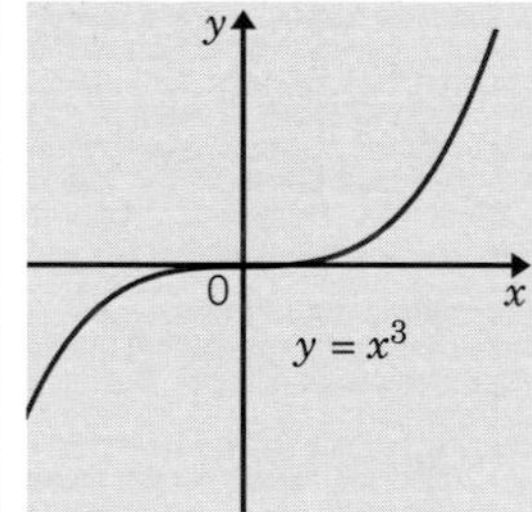

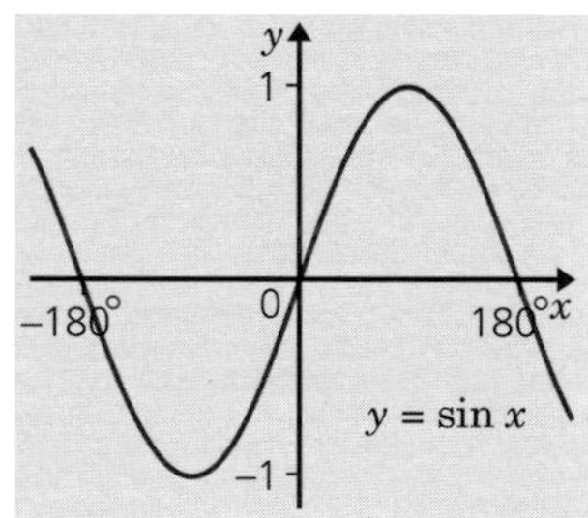

Each function may be defined for any real number x. The sketch graph can be thought of as a window through which you can see part of the graph. Plot the graphs on a graphics calculator and use the zoom facility to view the graph through different windows.

For all four functions there is a unique y-value corresponding to each x-value, found by putting $y = f(x)$. However, the reverse is only true for functions **1** (linear) and **3** (cubic). The results of solving the equations are summarised as follows.

Function	$f(x) = 0$	$f(x) = 5$	$f(x) = -5$
1 $f(x) = 2x - 3$	1.5	4	−1
2 $f(x) = x^2 + 2x - 3$	−3, 1	−4, 2	–
3 $f(x) = x^3$	0	1.71	−1.71
4 $f(x) = \sin x$	..., −180°, 0°, −180°, ...	–	–

For **2**: when $y > -4$ there are two x-values corresponding to each y-value,
when $y = -4$, $x = -1$ (vertex of parabola),
when $y < -4$ there are no x-values corresponding to each y-value.

For **4**: when $-1 \leq y \leq 1$ there is an infinite number of x-values corresponding to each y-value,
when $y < -1$ or $y > 1$ there are no x-values corresponding to each y-value.

We can now turn these observations into formal ideas by looking closely at the four functions above.

Domain and range

The set of x-values for which each function is defined as the **domain**. In all four cases the domain could be the set of real numbers, $\Re$, but we could restrict the domain to a subset of the real numbers, e.g. $\{x : -4 \leq x \leq 2\}$ or $\{x : 0, 1, 2, 3, 4\}$.

The set of y-values, corresponding to every x-value in the domain is called the **range**. Assuming the domain is $\Re$, the range in functions **1** and **3** is also $\Re$, but for **2** and **4** the range is a subset of $\Re$:

For **2**: $f(x) = x^2 + 2x - 3$ range : $\{y : y \geq -4\}$
For **4**: $f(x) = \sin x$ range : $\{y : -1 \leq y \leq 1\}$

Functions **1** and **3** are examples of **one-to-one mappings**, since for each y-value in the range there is a *unique* corresponding x-value in the domain.

Functions **2** and **4** are examples of **many-to-one mappings**, since each y-value in the range does not have a unique corresponding x-value in the domain (e.g. in **2** $y = 5 \Rightarrow x = -4$ or 2; in **4** $y = 0.5 \Rightarrow x = \ldots, -330°, -210°, 30°, 150°, 390°, \ldots$).

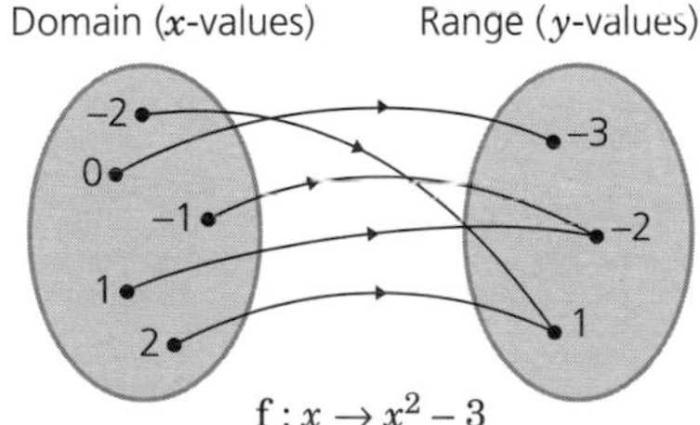

We can illustrate the idea of a mapping by a diagram, using alternative function notation. Suppose that for the domain $\{x : -2, -1, 0, 1, 2\}$ function f is defined by $f(x) = x^2 - 3$ which is equivalent to $f : x \to x^2 - 3$.

Each number in the domain is an **object** which has a corresponding **image** in the range, e.g. the image of the object 2 is 1. Note that this function is many-to-one since some y-values correspond to more than one x-value.

Example 12.1

Each of the following functions has domain $\{x : 1, 2, 3, 4\}$. For each one draw a mapping diagram, state the range and whether the mapping is one-to-one or many-to-one.

a) $f : x \to 3x - 7$ ***b)*** $f : x \to 5 - x$ ***c)*** $f : x \to (x - 2)^2$
d) $f : x \to \frac{12}{x}$ ***e)*** $f : x \to |2x - 6|$

Solution

a) Range $\{y : -4, -1, 2, 5\}$ one-to-one

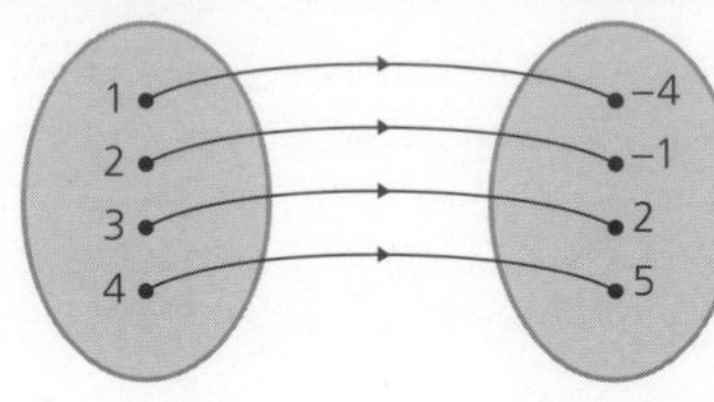

b) Range $\{y : 1, 2, 3, 4\}$ one-to-one

c) Range $\{y : 0, 1, 4\}$ many-to-one

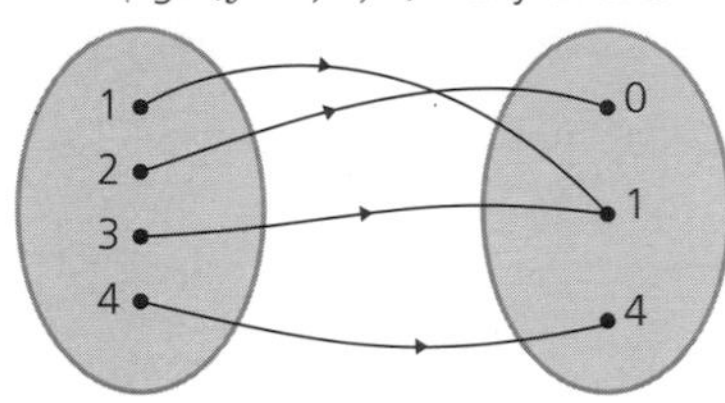

d) Range $\{y : 3, 4, 6, 12\}$ one-to-one

e) Range $\{y : 0, 2, 4\}$ many-to-one

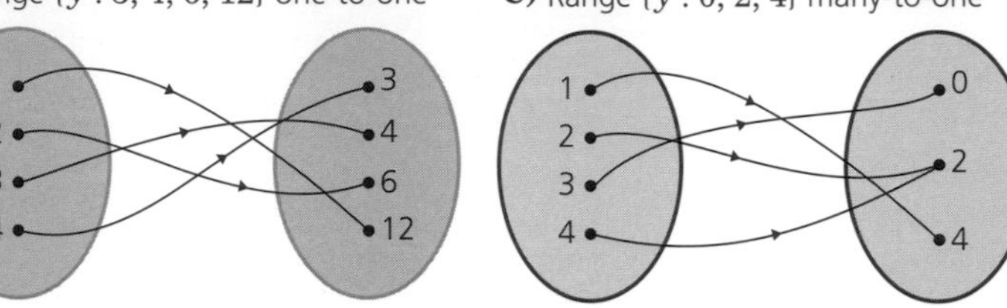

Example 12.2

For each of the following functions, restrict the domain to $\{x : -3 \leq x \leq 3\}$, sketch the graph of the function, give the range and state which type of mapping it is.

a) $f(x) = 5 - 2x$ ***b)*** $f(x) = 2x - x^2$ ***c)*** $f(x) = |3(x - 1)|$ ***d)*** $f(x) = x(x^2 - 4)$

Solution

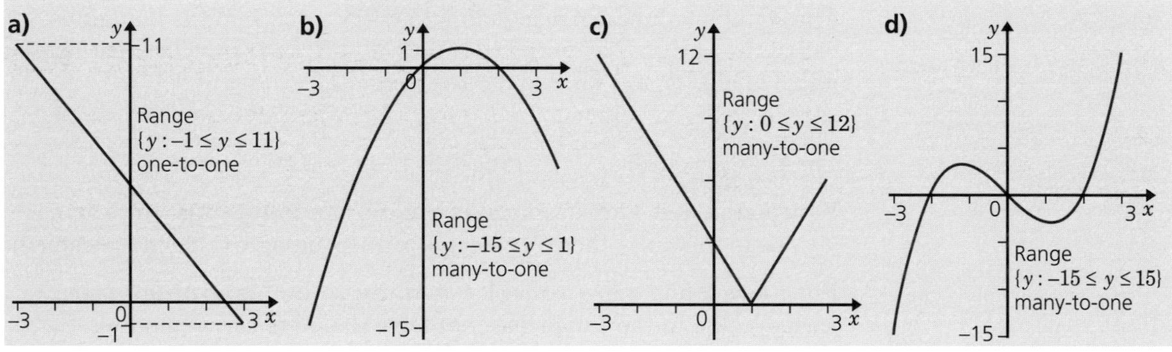

Example 12.3

For each of the following functions:

i) *give the largest possible domain,* ***ii)*** *give the corresponding range,*
iii) *sketch a suitable portion of the graph.*

a) $f : x \to 9 - x^2$ ***b)*** $f : x \to 5\sqrt{x}$ ***c)*** $f : x \to \frac{4}{x}$

Solution

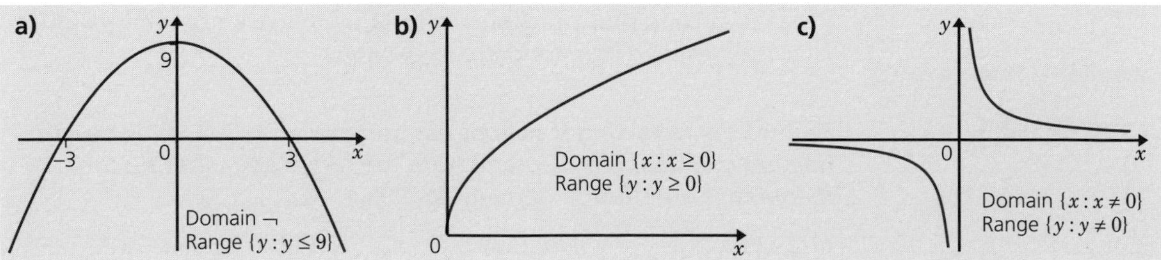

EXERCISES

12.1 CLASSWORK

1 For each of the following functions, with given domain:
   i) draw a mapping diagram,
   ii) write down the range,
   iii) state whether the mapping is one-to-one or many-to-one.

a) $f : x \to 10 - 3x$ $\{x : -2, 0, 1, 4\}$
b) $f : x \to 2x^2 - 5$ $\{x : -3, -1, 1, 3\}$
c) $f : x \to \frac{10}{x}$ $\{x : -5, -2, 2, 5\}$
d) $f : x \to |10 - 2x|$ $\{x : 2, 4, 6, 8\}$
e) $f : x \to x^3 - 9x$ $\{x : -3, 0, 3\}$

2 For each of the following functions, with given domain:
   i) sketch the graph of the function,
   ii) write down the range,
   iii) state which type of mapping it is.

a) $f(x) = \frac{1}{2}(x + 8)$ $\{x : -4 \le x \le 10\}$
b) $f(x) = 2x^2$ $\{x : -5 \le x \le 5\}$
c) $f(x) = x^2 - 3x$ $\{x : 0 \le x \le 6\}$
d) $f(x) = |2x - 5|$ $\{x : -2 \le x \le 5\}$
e) $f(x) = 20x - 5x^2$ $\Re$ (all real numbers)
f) $f(x) = 9x - x^3$ $\{x : -3 \le x \le 3\}$
g) $f(x) = \frac{12}{x}$ $\{x : x > 0\}$
h) $f(x) = \frac{5}{x^2}$ $\{x \in \Re : x \neq 0\}$

EXERCISES

12.1 HOMEWORK

1 For each of the following functions, with given domain:
   i) draw a mapping diagram,
   ii) write down the range,
   iii) state whether the mapping is one-to-one or many-to-one.

a) $f : x \to 2x + 4$ $\{x : -4, -2, 0, 1, 2\}$
b) $f : x \to 6x^2 - 5$ $\{x : -2, -1, 0, 1, 2\}$
c) $f : x \to \frac{1}{(x + 2)}$ $\{x : -1, 0, 1, 2\}$
d) $f : x \to |6 - 3x|$ $\{x : 0, 3, 4\}$
e) $f : x \to x^3 - 4x$ $\{x : -1, 0, 1\}$

2 For each of the following functions, with given domain:
   i) sketch the graph of the function,
   ii) write down the range,
   iii) state which type of mapping it is.

a) $f(x) = 3 - 2x$ $\{x : -2 \le x \le 2\}$
b) $f(x) = \frac{1}{4}(4x + 6)$ $\{x : -2 \le x \le 5\}$
c) $f(x) = \frac{1}{2}x^2$ $\{x : -5 \le x \le 5\}$
d) $f(x) = 2x^2 - x$ $\{x : -4 \le x \le 5\}$
e) $f(x) = |6 - 3x|$ $\{x : -2 \le x \le 6\}$
f) $f(x) = \frac{3}{x^2}$ $\{x \in \Re : x \neq 0\}$
g) $f(x) = -\frac{4}{x^2 + 1}$ $\{x : -3 \le x \le 3\}$
h) $f(x) = 5x - 2x^3$ $\{x : -3 \le x \le 3\}$

COMPOSITE FUNCTIONS

So far we have used f to represent a function, e.g. $f : x \to 3x - 5$, $f(x) = x^2$, $y = f(x)$, etc. When we are dealing with more than one function we shall also use g and h to represent functions, e.g. $g : x \to 2x$, $h(x) = 2x^3$, etc.

Functions we have met so far may be combined to produce **composite** functions or they may themselves be expressed as a composite of simpler functions.

Exploration 12.2

Using function machines

Three functions f, g and h are defined by:

$f(x) = x - 5 \qquad g(x) = 3x \qquad h(x) = x^2$

all with the domain $\mathfrak{R}$, the set of real numbers.

- Use function machines to illustrate:

  $f(g(x)) \quad g(f(x))$

  $g(h(x)) \quad h(g(x))$

  $h(f(x)) \quad f(h(x))$
- In each case find the range of the composite function.

The meaning of a composite function

To carry out the composite function $f(g(x))$, we first carry out function g on x, then we carry out function f on the result, e.g. 'multiply by 3' then 'subtract 5'.

$x \longrightarrow$ [×3] $\xrightarrow{g(x)}$ [−5] $\longrightarrow f(g(x)) = 3x - 5$

The composite function $f(g(x))$ is usually abbreviated to $fg(x)$ and in this case is given by $fg(x) = 3x - 5$.

To carry out the composite function $g(f(x))$, we first carry out function f on x, then we carry out function g on the result, e.g. 'subtract 5' then 'multiply by 3'.

$x \longrightarrow$ [−5] $\xrightarrow{f(x)}$ [×3] $\longrightarrow gf(x) = 3(x - 5)$

Notice that the **order** in which the functions are applied is important, since the two composites fg and gf give different functions.

You should be able to check that the other composite results simplify to:

$gh(x) = 3x^2\ (= y)$	range $\{y : y \geq 0\}$
$hg(x) = (3x)^2$	range $\{y : y \geq 0\}$
$hf(x) = (x - 5)^2$	range $\{y : y \geq 0\}$
$fh(x) = x^2 - 5$	range $\{y : y \geq -5\}$

A sketch of the graph of the composite function should help to find the range, e.g. this is the graph of $y = fh(x) = x^2 - 5$.

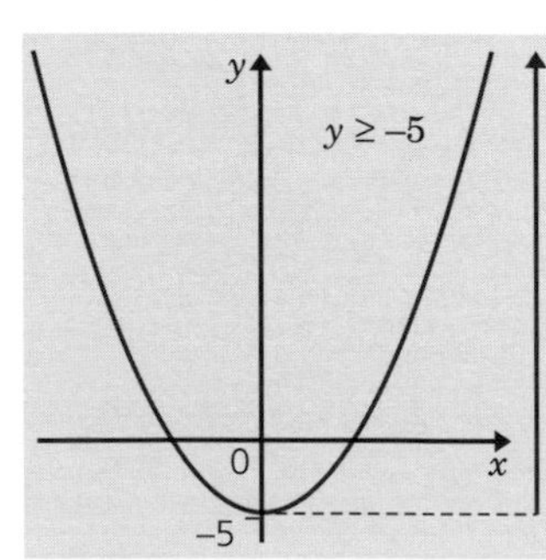

Example 12.4

Functions f, g, h *are defined by:*

$$f : x \to 8 - x$$

$$g : x \to \frac{3}{x} \quad (x \neq 0)$$

$$h : x \to 2x + 3$$

a) *Find expressions for* $gf(x)$, $hg(x)$, $fh(x)$, $hh(x)$.

b) *Show that* $ff(x) = x$ *and* $gg(x) = x$.

c) *Solve the equation* $hgf(x) = x$.

Solution

a) $gf(x) = g(f(x)) = g(8 - x) = \dfrac{3}{(8 - x)}$

$hg(x) = h(g(x)) = h\left(\dfrac{3}{x}\right) = 2\dfrac{3}{x} + 3 = \dfrac{6}{x} + 3$

$fh(x) = f(h(x)) = f(2x + 3) = 8 - (2x + 3) = 5 - 2x$

$hh(x) = h(h(x)) = h(2x + 3) = 2(2x + 3) + 3 = 4x + 9$

b) $ff(x) = f(f(x)) = f(8 - x) = 8 - (8 - x) = x$

$gg(x) = g(g(x)) = g\left(\dfrac{3}{x}\right) = \dfrac{3}{3/x} = 3 \times \dfrac{x}{3} = x$

c) $hgf(x) = h(g(f(x)))$

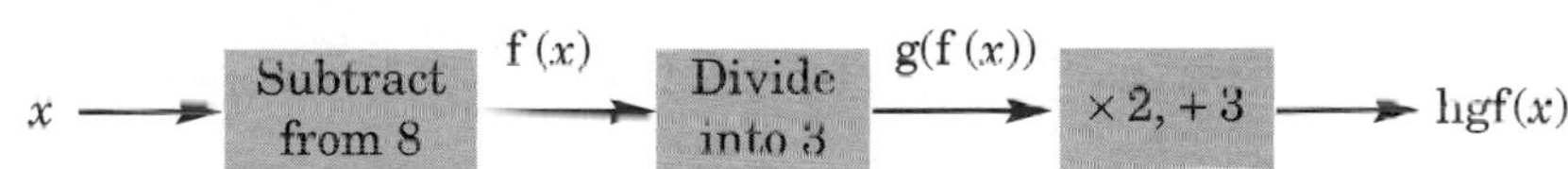

$\Rightarrow hgf(x) = h(g(8 - x)) = h\left(\dfrac{3}{8 - x}\right) = 2\dfrac{3}{(8 - x)} + 3$

Thus when $hgf(x) = x$: $\quad 2\left(\dfrac{3}{8 - x}\right) + 3 = x$

$\Rightarrow \dfrac{6}{(8 - x)} = x - 3$

$\Rightarrow 6 = (8 - x)(x - 3)$

$\Rightarrow x^2 - 11x + 30 = 0$

$\Rightarrow (x - 5)(x - 6) = 0$

$\Rightarrow x = 5$ *or* $x = 6$

EXERCISES

12.2 CLASSWORK

KEY SKILLS
N 3.2d

1 Three functions f, g and h are defined by:

$f : x \to 2x \qquad g : x \to 5 - x \qquad h : x \to x^2$

a) Find expressions for **i)** $fg(x)$, **ii)** $gh(x)$, **iii)** $hgf(x)$.

b) Evaluate: **i)** $fg(-2)$ **ii)** $gh(-2)$ **iii)** $hgf(-2)$.

c) Solve the equation $hgf(x) = 9$.

2 Functions f and g are defined by:

$f(x) = x^3 - 2x^2 - 5x + 6 \qquad g(x) = x - 1$

Show that $fg(x) = x^3 - 5x^2 + 2x + 8$.

(Scottish Higher Paper 2, 1990)

3 Functions f and g are defined by:

$f(x) = \dfrac{4}{x+3} \qquad g(x) = \dfrac{4}{x} - 3$

Find both $gf(x)$ and $fg(x)$ in their simplest form.

4 Function $f(x)$ is defined by $f(x) = \dfrac{x}{1+x}$ $(x \neq -1)$.

Find an expression for $ff(x)$.

5 Three functions f, g and h are defined by:

$f : x \to x - 3$ $\quad g : x \to x^2$ $\quad h : x \to \dfrac{12}{x}$

for suitable domains. Find each of the following functions as composites using some of f, g and h.

a) $x^2 - 3$ **b)** $\dfrac{12}{x-3}$ **c)** $\dfrac{144}{x^2}$ **d)** $x^2 - 6x + 9$ **e)** $\dfrac{3(4-x)}{x}$ **f)** x

6 Three functions f, g and h are such that:

$\text{hgf}(x) = \sqrt{25 - x^2}$

a) State a suitable domain and range so that the graph of $\text{hgf}(x)$ is a semi-circle.

b) Find expressions for functions f, g and h, stating appropriate domains and ranges for each one.

EXERCISES

12.2 HOMEWORK

1 Three functions f, g and h are defined by:

$f : x \to 3x - 4$ $\quad g : x \to x^3$

a) Find expressions for $\text{fg}(x)$ and $\text{gf}(x)$.

b) Evaluate: **i)** $\text{fg}(2)$ **ii)** $\text{gf}(2)$.

c) Solve the equation $\text{fg}(x) = 77$.

2 Let $f(x) = 2x + 4$ and $g(x) = \frac{1}{2}x - 2$.

Find: **i)** $\text{fg}(x)$ **ii)** $\text{gf}(x)$. Comment on your answer.

3 Functions f and g are defined by: $f(x) = x^2 + 1$ $\quad g(x) = 3x^2 + 2x - 4$

Show that $\text{gf}(x) = 3x^4 + 8x^2 + 1$.

4 Let $f(x) = \sqrt{1+x}$ and $g(x) = 3 - x^2$.

Determine $\text{fg}(x)$ and $\text{gf}(x)$.

5 Functions f and g are defined by: $f(x) = \dfrac{1}{x+3}$ $\quad g(x) = 5 - \dfrac{4}{x^2}$

Find $\text{fg}(x)$ and $\text{gf}(x)$ in their simplest forms.

6 Let $k(x) = \left(1 - \sqrt{x}\right)^{\frac{2}{3}}$. Find the domain of k. Find three functions $f(x)$, $g(x)$ and $h(x)$ such that $\text{fgh}(x) = k(x)$.

INVERSE FUNCTIONS

For most mathematical operations there is a corresponding operation that has the opposite or reverse effect. For example the opposite of 'add 5' is 'subtract 5'. In this case the operation of 'subtract 5' is the **inverse** operation of 'add 5', and vice-versa.

Exploration 12.3

Inverses

For each of the following operations:

- find the inverse operation,
- using a suitable domain, express the operation and its inverse as functions,
- sketch both functions on the same axes.

  a) add three **b)** subtract seven **c)** multiply by five
  d) divide by two **e)** subtract from ten **f)** divide into twenty
- What do all the sketches have in common?

Finding the inverses

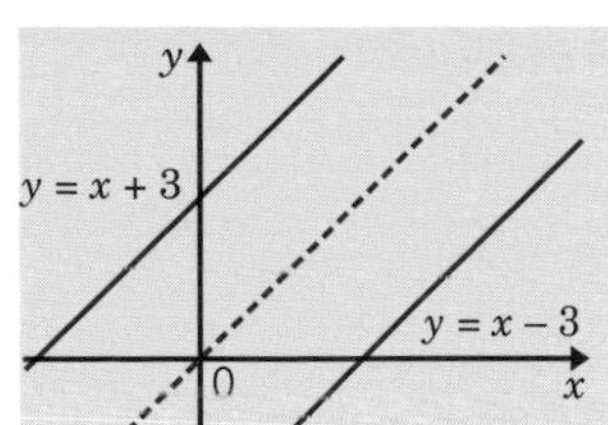

The inverse of 'add 3' is 'subtract 3'.
Formally , the function $f : x \to x + 3$ has inverse function $f^{-1} : x \to x - 3$, both valid for all values of x.

The inverse of 'subtract 7' is 'add 7'.
The inverse of $f : x \to x - 7$ is $f^{-1} : x \to x + 7$.

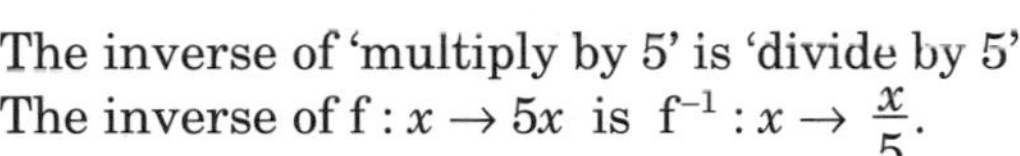

The inverse of 'multiply by 5' is 'divide by 5'.
The inverse of $f : x \to 5x$ is $f^{-1} : x \to \frac{x}{5}$.

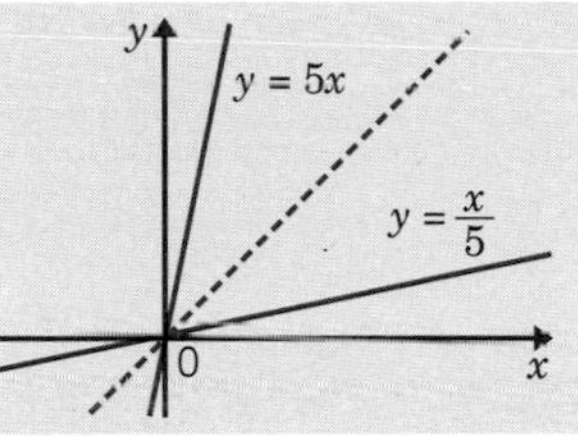

The inverse of 'divide by 2' is 'multiply by 2'.
The inverse of $f : x \to \frac{x}{2}$ is $f^{-1} : x \to 2x$.

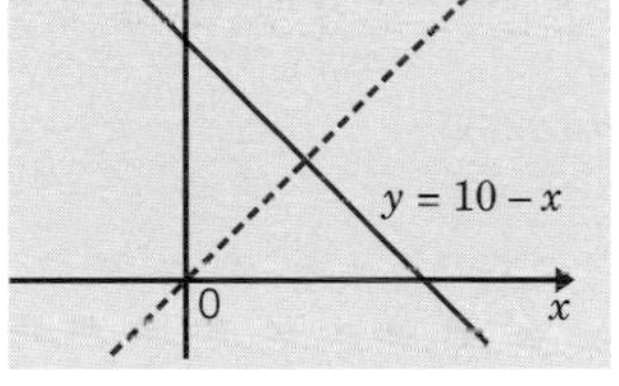

The inverse of 'subtract from 10' is 'subtract from 10'.
The inverse of $f : x \to 10 - x$ is $f^{-1} : x \to 10 - x$.
This function is **self-inverse**.

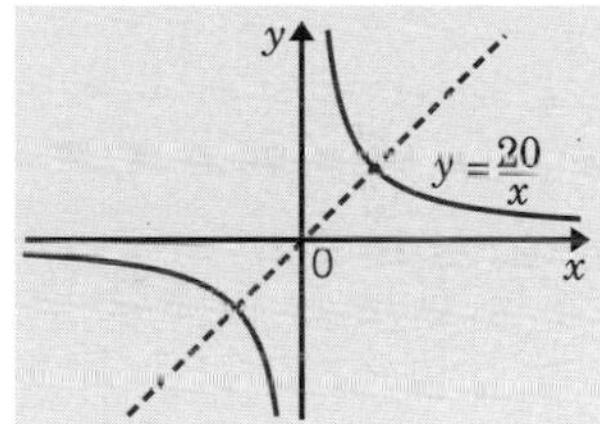

The inverse of 'divide into 20' is 'divide into 20'. The inverse of $f : x \to \frac{20}{x}$ is $f^{-1} : x \to \frac{20}{x}$.
This is another self inverse function, valid for all values of x except 0.

For each sketch the graph of the inverse function $y = f^{-1}(x)$ is the reflection of $y = f(x)$ in the line $y = x$. This property is true for any function. When the graph of a function is symmetrical about $y = x$, the function is self-inverse; operations **e)** and **f)** are examples of the two self-inverse functions:

$$f : x \to a - x \quad \text{and} \quad f : x \to \frac{a}{x}$$

where a is constant.

An important idea is that only functions which are one-to-one mappings have inverse functions. This is brought out in the following example.

Example 12.5

The function $f(x) = x^2$ has domain $\Re$. Show that the inverse relationship is not a function unless the domain of f is restricted.

Solution

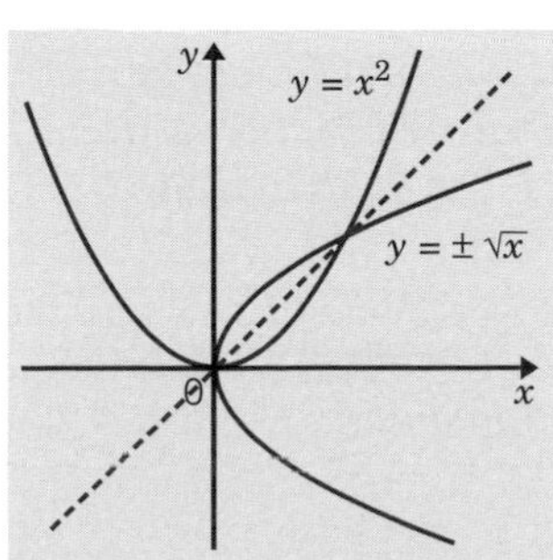

The diagram shows $y = x^2$ and its reflection in the line $y = x$. The inverse relationship may be labelled $y = \pm\sqrt{x}$. Since $f(x) = x^2$ is a many-to-one mapping, the inverse is a one-to-many mapping, which is not a function, e.g. $x = 4 \Rightarrow y = \pm 2$.

By restricting the domain of f to $\{x : x \geq 0\}$ then the reflection of $y = x^2$ is $y = \sqrt{x}$ (the positive square root) which is a function since f is now a one-to-one mapping.

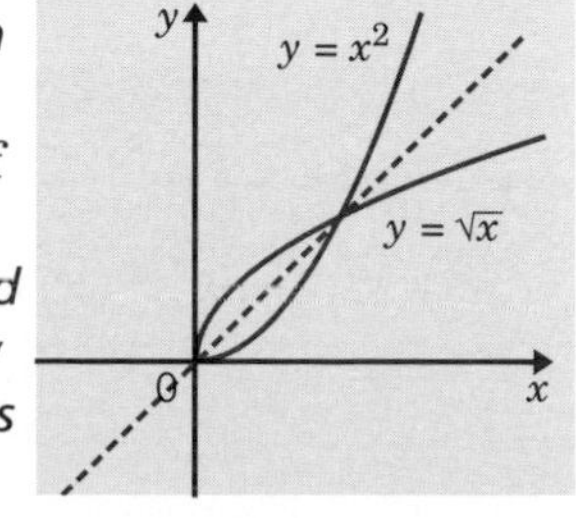

For composite functions, inverses may be found by reversing a function machine diagram or by rearranging a formula. The following examples illustrate when the methods might apply.

Example 12.6

The function $f : x \to 10 - 3x$ is defined for all real numbers. Find the inverse function f^{-1}.

Solution

Method A

Decompose the function f.

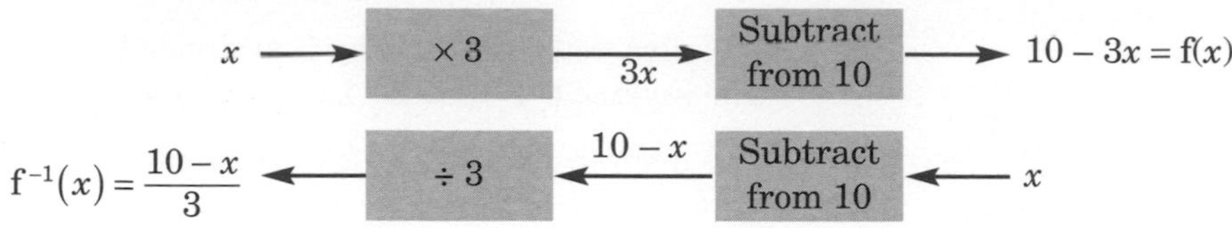

⇒ the inverse function is $f^{-1} : x \to \dfrac{10 - x}{3}$

Method B

Let $y = 10 - 3x$ and rearrange to make x the subject.

$$y = 10 - 3x \quad \Rightarrow \quad 3x = 10 - y \quad \Rightarrow \quad x = \frac{10 - y}{3}$$

Now reverse the roles of x and y to get $f^{-1} : x \to \dfrac{10 - x}{3}$

Example 12.7

By suitably restricting the domain, show that the function $f : x \to x^2 + 2x - 3$ has an inverse function f^{-1}. Sketch graphs to illustrate your answer.

Solution

First complete the square : $x^2 + 2x - 3 = (x + 1)^2 - 4$

Method A

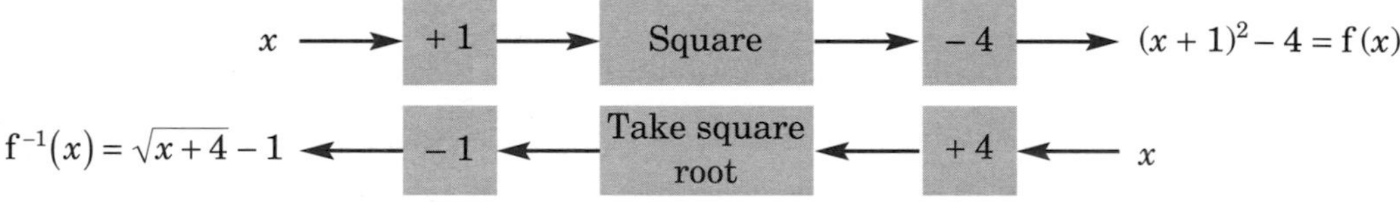

Method B

Let $y = (x + 1)^2 - 4$ and rearrange to make y the subject.

$$y = (x + 1)^2 - 4$$
$$y + 4 = (x + 1)^2$$
$$\sqrt{y + 4} = x + 1$$
$$\sqrt{y + 4} - 1 = x$$

Now reverse the roles of x and y to get $f^{-1} : x \to \sqrt{x + 4} - 1$.

***Note**: By taking the positive square root, the domain of f must be restricted to $\{x : x \geq -1\}$, which becomes the range of f^{-1}: the range of f is $\{y : y \geq -4\}$, which becomes the domain for f^{-1}. A sketch of the graphs of both functions is shown in the diagram.*

Example 12.8

Function f is defined by $f(x) = \dfrac{ax + 1}{x - 2}$ *for the domain* $\{x : x \in \Re, x \neq 2\}$.

a) *Find the inverse function, f^{-1}.*

b) *Find a value of a such that the function f is self-inverse, i.e. $f(x) = f^{-1}(x)$.*

c) *Sketch a graph of $y = f(x)$ for the value of a found in **b)**. What do you notice?*

Solution

a) *Since x appears more than once in the definition of the function, you need to use Method B, rearrangement of the formula.*

Let $y = \dfrac{ax+1}{x-2}$

$\Rightarrow y(x-2) = ax+1 \quad \Rightarrow xy - 2y = ax + 1 \quad \Rightarrow xy - ax = 2y + 1$

$\Rightarrow x(y-a) = 2y + 1 \quad \Rightarrow \quad x = \dfrac{2y+1}{y-a}$

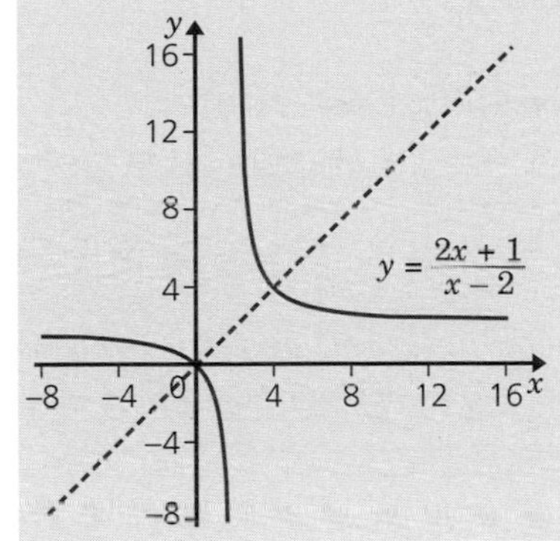

Reversing the roles of x and y : $f^{-1}(x) = \dfrac{2x+1}{x-a}$.

b) *Since* $f(x) = \dfrac{ax+1}{x-2}$ *and* $f^{-1}(x) = \dfrac{2x+1}{x-a}$, *substitution of $a = 2$ will make $f(x) = f^{-1}(x)$.*

$\Rightarrow f(x) = \dfrac{2x+1}{x-2}$ *is a self inverse function.*

c) *A sketch of the graph of* $y = \dfrac{2x+1}{x-2}$ *should reveal that it is symmetrical about $y = x$, which gives geometrical support to the idea that the function f is self-inverse.*

Since the action of an inverse function f^{-1} is to reverse the action of the function f, and vice versa, it is generally true that $f^{-1}f(x) = x$ and $ff^{-1}(x) = x$. For example:

let $f(x) = 2x - 3$, then $f^{-1}(x) = \dfrac{x+3}{2}$

$$\Rightarrow \quad f^{-1}f(x) = f^{-1}(2x-3) = \frac{(2x-3)+3}{2} = \frac{2x}{2} = x$$

and $ff^{-1}(x) = f\left(\dfrac{x+3}{2}\right) = 2\left(\dfrac{x+3}{2}\right) - 3 = x + 3 - 3 = x$

When Method A, reversing the function flow diagram, was applied in Examples 12.6 and 12.7 the functions f were seen as composite functions. The same principle is used to derive the inverse of a composite function gf.

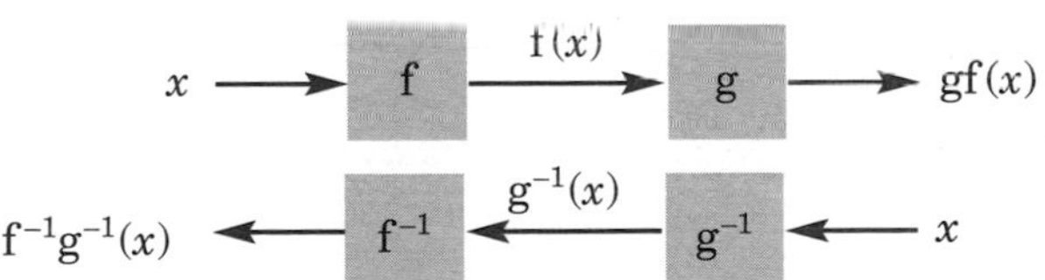

provided f^{-1} and g^{-1} exist for suitable domains:

$(gf)^{-1} \equiv f^{-1}g^{-1}$

Example 12.9

Functions f and g are defined by:

$f(x) = 16 - x^2 \quad x \in \Re \qquad\qquad g(x) = \sqrt{x} \quad \{x : x \geq 0\}$

a) *Find $f^{-1}(x)$ and $g^{-1}(x)$.*

b) *For a suitable domain, find $fg(x)$ and $(gf)^{-1}(x)$.*

Solution

a) First we find $f^{-1}(x)$.

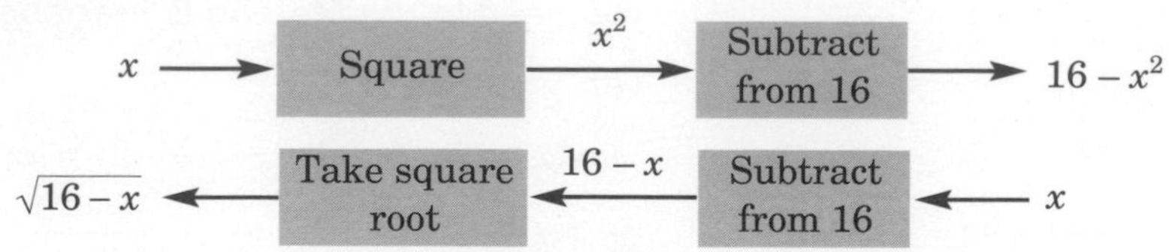

Hence $f^{-1}(x) = \sqrt{16-x}$ *with domain* $\{x : 0 \le x \le 16\}$

$g^{-1}(x) = x^2$ *with domain* $\{x : x \ge 0\}$.

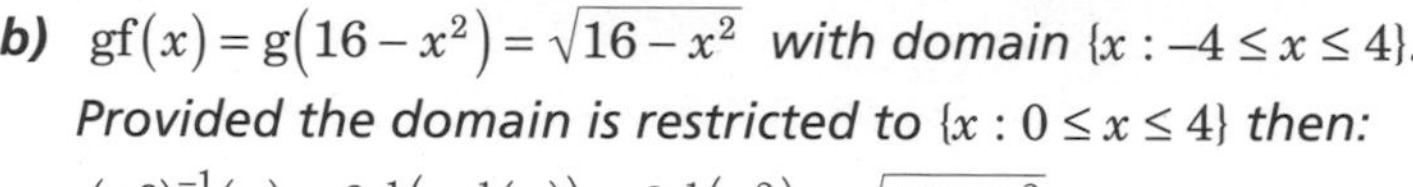

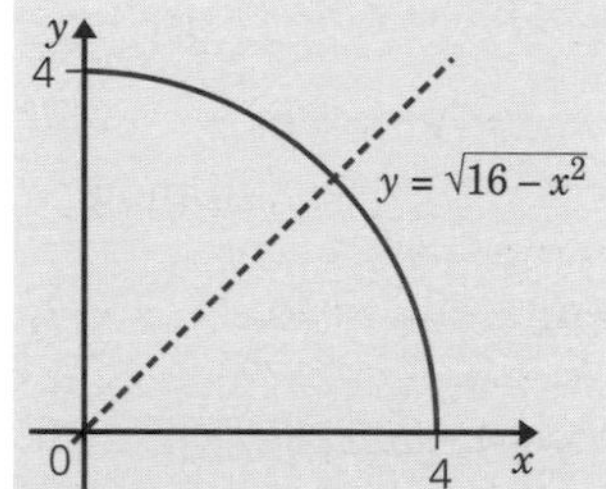

b) $gf(x) = g(16-x^2) = \sqrt{16-x^2}$ *with domain* $\{x : -4 \le x \le 4\}$.

Provided the domain is restricted to $\{x : 0 \le x \le 4\}$ *then:*

$(gf)^{-1}(x) = f^{-1}(g^{-1}(x)) = f^{-1}(x^2) = \sqrt{16-x^2}$

also with domain $\{x : 0 \le x \le 4\}$.

Note*: For the restricted domain the function* gf *is self-inverse, which is evident from the graph of* $y = gf(x)$, $0 \le x \le 4$, *which represents a quarter-circle, centre (0, 0), radius 4 units.*

EXERCISES

12.3 CLASSWORK

KEY SKILLS
N 3.2d

In questions **1–8** find the inverse function f^{-1}. Sketch graphs of $y = f(x)$ and $y = f^{-1}(x)$ on the same axes.

1 $f(x) = x - 4, x \in \Re$

2 $f(x) = 3x, x \in \Re$

3 $f(x) = 3x - 4, x \in \Re$

4 $f(x) = 7 - 2x, x \in \Re$

5 $f(x) = \frac{12}{x+1}, x \in \Re, x \ne -1$

6 $f(x) = \sqrt[3]{x-3}, x \in \Re$

7 $f(x) = 2x^2 + 5, x \in \Re, x \ge 0$

8 $f(x) = (x+2)^2, x \in \Re, x \ge 0$

9 For each of the following functions, the domain is $\{x : x \ge k\}$.

i) Find the least value of k such that f is a one-to-one mapping.
ii) For the value of k found in **i)** find the range of f.
iii) Find the inverse function f^{-1}, assuming the value of k found in **i)**.
iv) Sketch a graph showing both $y = f(x)$ and $y = f^{-1}(x)$.

a) $f : x \to x^2 + 2$ **b)** $f : x \to (x-3)^2$
c) $f : x \to 5 - (x+1)^2$ **d)** $f : x \to x^2 - 4x + 3$

10 For each of the following functions, the domain is $\{x : x \ne k\}$.

i) State the value of k.
ii) Find the inverse function f^{-1}.
iii) Write down the domain of f^{-1} and hence the range of f.

a) $f(x) = \dfrac{20}{5-x}$ **b)** $f(x) = \dfrac{5+x}{x-2}$ **c)** $f(x) = \dfrac{3x-2}{2x+5}$

11 The function f is defined by $f(x) = \dfrac{ax+b}{bx-a}$, where a and b are constants.

a) Simplify $f(x)$ when **i)** $a = 1, b = 0$, **ii)** $a = 0, b = 1$.
In both cases sketch a graph of $y = f(x)$.
b) Which value of x must be excluded from the domain when $b \ne 0$?
c) Find $f^{-1}(x)$ when $a = -1, b = 4$.
d) Show that the function f is self-inverse for all values of a and b.

EXERCISES

12.3 HOMEWORK

In questions **1–8** find the inverse function f^{-1}. Sketch graphs of $y = f(x)$ and $y = f^{-1}(x)$ on the same axes.

1 $f(x) = x - 3, x \in \Re$

2 $f(x) = 6x, x \in \Re$

3 $f(x) = 2x + 3, x \in \Re$

4 $f(x) = x^4, x \in \Re, x \geq 0$

5 $f(x) = \frac{x^3}{3}, x \in \Re$

6 $f(x) = \frac{\sqrt{x+6}}{2}, x \in \Re, x \geq 0$

7 $f(x) = \frac{4}{x+2}, x \in \Re, x \geq -2$

8 $f(x) = 3x^2 - 1, x \in \Re, x \geq 0$

9 For each of the following functions, the domain is $\{x : x \geq k\}$.

i) Find the least value of k such that f is a one-to-one mapping.
ii) For the value of k found in **i)** find the range of f.
iii) Find the inverse function f^{-1}, assuming the value of k found in **i)**.
iv) Sketch graphs of $y = f(x)$ and $y = f^{-1}(x)$ on the same axes.

a) $f : x \to 3 - x^2$
b) $f : x \to (x + 2)^2 - 5$
c) $f : x \to x^2 - 5x + 6$
d) $f : x \to 7 - (4 + x)^2$

10 For each of the following functions, the domain is $\{x : x \neq k\}$.

i) State the value of k.
ii) Find the inverse function f^{-1}.
iii) Write down the domain of f^{-1} and hence the range of f.

a) $f(x) = \frac{2}{x+5}$
b) $f(x) = \frac{2x}{5-x}$
c) $f(x) = \frac{2x+3}{x-4}$

11 A function $f : x \to px + q$ is used to convert temperatures in degrees Celsius to temperatures in degrees Fahrenheit.

a) State the values of p and q.
b) Find the inverse function f^{-1} and interpret what it does.
c) Sketch graphs of $y = f(x)$ and $y = f^{-1}(x)$ on the same axes.
d) Solve the equation $f(x) = f^{-1}(x)$. Interpret your solution.

TRANSFORMING QUADRATIC FUNCTIONS

The parabola $y = x^2$ can be transformed in various ways. In this section, we explore some of those ways. For each transformation the equation of the function will change. Start with the following explorations.

You may find a graphics calculator or computer package useful. Record your findings on sketch graphs.

Exploration 12.4

Transforming $y = x^2$

Describe geometrically the transformation of the parabola $y = x^2$ onto each of the following curves.

1 $y = x^2 - 5$

2 $y = 3x^2$

3 $y = (x - 4)^2$

4 $y = -x^2$

5 $y = 2x^2 + 3$

6 $y = 4(x + 3)^2$

7 $y = (x - 1)^2 + 4$

8 $y = (x + 2)^2 - 7$

Exploration 12.5

KEY SKILLS
IT 3.1
IT 3.2
IT 3.3

Multiple transformations

Now look at the transformation of $y = x^2$, beginning with geometrical descriptions. In each case, what is the equation of the transformed curve?

1 translation through 7 units parallel to the y-axis

2 translation through 7 units parallel to the x-axis

3 stretch, factor 2 parallel to the y-axis

4 reflection in the x-axis *followed by* translation through 5 units parallel to the y-axis

5 translation through –3 units parallel to the x-axis *followed by* translation through 4 units parallel to the y-axis

6 translation through 5 units parallel to the y-axis *followed by* a stretch, factor $\frac{1}{2}$ parallel to the y-axis.

The geometrical transformations used in the explorations may be summarised as:

	Geometrical transformation	Equation of transformed curve
1	translation through b units parallel to the x-axis	$y = (x - b)^2$
2	stretch, factor a parallel to the y-axis	$y = ax^2$
3	reflection in the x-axis	$y = -x^2$
4	translation through c units parallel to the y-axis	$y = x^2 + c$

When two or more transformations are combined the equation of the transformed curve becomes more complex, for example:

translation through b units parallel to the x-axis
followed by
translation through c units parallel to the y-axis.

The study of these transformations is important, since *any* parabola may be obtained from $y = x^2$ by a combination of one or more of the four transformations **1**, **2**, **3** and **4**, usually in that order.

Example 12.10

The parabola $y = x^2$ undergoes the following transformations:
translation through –5 units parallel to the y-axis
followed by
stretch, factor 2 parallel to the y-axis

a) *Write down the equation of the transformed curve.*
b) *If the order of the transformations was reversed, which one would have to be modified to represent the same curve?*
Explain your reasoning.

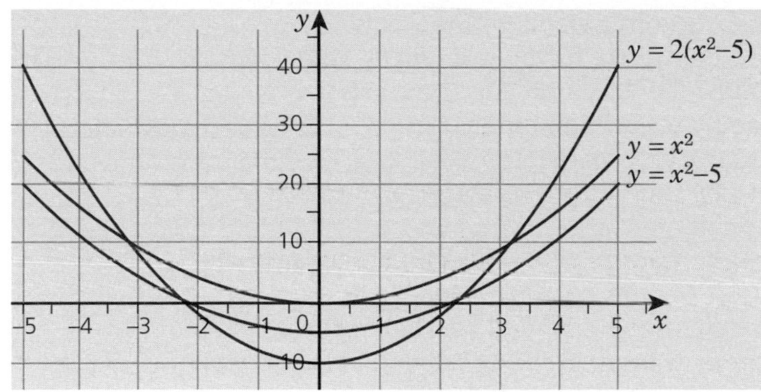

Solution

a) *The equation of the transformed curve is $y = 2(x^2 - 5)$ indicating a translation through –5 units followed by a stretch, factor 2, both parallel to the y-axis.*

b) *Multiplying out the brackets*

$\Rightarrow \quad y = 2(x^2 - 5) = 2x^2 - 10.$

Expressed in this way, we can see that the curve can be obtained by a stretch, factor 2 followed by a translation through –10 units, both parallel to the y-axis. You can see that the translation has to be modified. Try transforming $y = x^2$ using both combinations.

EXERCISES

12.4 CLASSWORK

For each of these questions, begin with the graph of $y = x^2$ and transform it using one or more transformations.

1 Write down the single geometrical transformation to obtain the following curves.

a) $y = x^2 + 3$	**b)** $y = x^2 - 7$
c) $y = (x - 2)^2$	**d)** $y = (x + 5)^2$
e) $y = 4x^2$	**f)** $y = \frac{1}{3}x^2$
g) $y = -x^2$	**h)** $y = x^2 + 6x + 9$

2 Find the equation of the curve obtained by applying the following transformations to $y = x^2$.

a) translation –5 units parallel to the y-axis
b) translation 3.5 units parallel to the y-axis
c) translation 4 units parallel to the x-axis
d) translation – 7 units parallel to the x-axis
e) stretch, factor 3 parallel to the y-axis
f) stretch, factor $\frac{1}{3}$ parallel to the y-axis.

3 Find, in a suitable order, the combination of geometrical transformations to obtain the following curves.

a) $y = 2x^2 + 6$	**b)** $y = 2(x^2 + 3)$
c) $y = \frac{1}{3}(x^2 - 5)$	**d)** $y = \frac{1}{3}x^2 - 1$
e) $y = -(x^2 - 4)$	**f)** $y = 4 - x^2$
g) $y = 3(x + 4)^2$	**h)** $y = 5(x - 1)^2$
i) $y = (x - 2)^2 + 3$	**j)** $y = (x + 5)^2 - 7$
k) $y = 2(x + 3)^2 + 5$	**l)** $y = -(x + 4)^2$
m) $y = 7 - (x + 4)^2$	**n)** $y = 0.4(x + 6)^2 - 4.4$
o) $y = 10 - 2(x - 3)^2$	**p)** $y = -(5(x + 2)^2 + 3)$

4 Find the equation of the curve obtained by applying the following transformations.

a) stretch, factor 2 parallel to the x-axis
followed by translation –5 units parallel to the y-axis
b) stretch, factor 3 parallel to the y-axis
followed by reflection in the x-axis

c) translation 3 units parallel to the x-axis
followed by stretch, factor $\frac{1}{2}$ parallel to the y-axis

d) translation –5 units parallel to the x-axis
followed by reflection in the x-axis

e) translation 2 units parallel to the x-axis
followed by translation 5 units parallel to the y-axis

f) reflection in the x-axis
followed by translation 9 units parallel to the y-axis

g) translation –4 units parallel to the x-axis
followed by stretch, factor 3 parallel to the y-axis
followed by translation –7 units parallel to the y-axis

h) translation 6 units parallel to the x-axis
followed by reflection in the x-axis
followed by translation 4 units parallel to the y-axis

EXERCISES

12.4 HOMEWORK

1 In each case make a rough sketch of $y = x^2$ and, on the same axes, make a rough sketch of the curve given to show its relationship to $y = x^2$.

a) $y = x^2 + 8$ b) $y = 2x^2$ c) $y = (x - 3)^2$
d) $y = -x^2$ e) $y = \frac{1}{4}x^2$ f) $y = -3x^2$

2 Find the equation of the curve obtained by applying the following transformations to $y = x^2$.

a) stretch, factor 6 parallel to the y-axis
b) translation 3 units parallel to the x-axis
c) translation 3 units parallel to the y-axis
d) translation $-\frac{1}{2}$ units parallel to the x-axis
e) stretch, factor 0.2 parallel to the y-axis
f) translation –8 units parallel to the y-axis

3 Find the equation of the curve obtained by applying the following transfomations to $y = x^2$.

a) translation 5 units parallel to the x-axis
followed by translation 5 units parallel to the y-axis

b) stretch, factor 7 parallel to the y-axis
followed by translation –1 unit parallel to the y-axis

c) stretch, factor 4 parallel to the y-axis
followed by reflection in the x-axis

d) translation 3 units parallel to the y-axis
followed by stretch, factor $\frac{1}{2}$ parallel to the y-axis

e) reflection in the x-axis
followed by translation –6 units parallel to the y-axis

f) translation 5 units parallel to the x-axis
followed by stretch, factor 0.7 parallel to the y-axis
followed by reflection in the x-axis

g) translation –2 units parallel to the x-axis
followed by stretch, factor 7 parallel to the y-axis
followed by translation 3 units parallel to the y-axis

h) translation 9 units parallel to the x-axis
followed by stretch, factor 2 parallel to the y-axis
followed by translation –3 units parallel to the y-axis

COMPLETING THE SQUARE

In the last section we found that we can transform the quadratic function $y = x^2$ onto another quadratic function by a combination of transformations, for example:

translation 3 units parallel to the x-axis $\quad y = (x - 3)^2$
followed by
stretch, factor 2 parallel to the y-axis $\quad y = 2(x - 3)^2$
followed by
translation –5 units parallel to the y-axis $\quad y = 2(x - 3)^2 - 5$

The transformed quadratic function may be simplified to give:

$$\begin{aligned} y &= 2(x-3)^2 - 5 \\ &= 2(x-3)(x-3) - 5 \\ &= 2(x^2 - 6x + 9) - 5 \\ \Rightarrow y &= 2x^2 - 12x + 13 \end{aligned}$$

Notice that the coefficient of x^2, i.e. 2, is the same as the stretch factor.

Any quadratic function $y = ax^2 + bx + c$ may be obtained by a combination of transformations of $y = x^2$ that gives:

$y = a(x + p)^2 + q$

where p and q are constants that depend on a, b and c. The process of expressing $y = ax^2 + bx + c$ in the form $y = a(x + p)^2 + q$ is called **completing the square** and is illustrated in the following examples.

Example 12.11

Complete the square for $y = x^2 + 10x + 8$.

Solution

Here $a = 1$, *so:*

$$\begin{aligned} & x^2 + 10x + 8 \equiv (x+p)^2 + q \\ \Rightarrow\ & x^2 + 10x + 8 \equiv (x+p)(x+p) + q \\ \Rightarrow\ & x^2 + 10x + 8 \equiv x^2 + 2px + p^2 + q \end{aligned}$$

Comparing the coefficients of x:

$$\begin{aligned} & 10 = 2p \\ \Rightarrow\ & p = 5 \end{aligned}$$

Comparing constants:

$$\begin{aligned} & 8 = p^2 + q \\ \Rightarrow\ & 8 = 25 + q \\ \Rightarrow\ & q = -17 \\ \therefore\ & y = x^2 + 10x + 8 = (x+5)^2 - 17 \end{aligned}$$

Example 12.12

Complete the square for $y = x^2 - 7x + 3$.

Solution

Here $a = 1$, *so:*

$$\begin{aligned} & x^2 - 7x + 13 \equiv (x+p)^2 + q \\ \Rightarrow\ & x^2 - 7x + 13 \equiv x^2 + 2px + p^2 + q \end{aligned}$$

Comparing the coefficients of x:

$$\begin{aligned} & -7 = 2p \\ \Rightarrow\ & p = -\tfrac{7}{2} \end{aligned}$$

Comparing constants:

$$13 = p^2 + q$$
$$\Rightarrow 13 = \tfrac{49}{4} + q$$
$$\Rightarrow \quad q = 13 - \tfrac{49}{4} = \tfrac{3}{4}$$
$$\therefore y = x^2 - 7x + 13 = (x - \tfrac{7}{2})^2 + \tfrac{3}{4}$$

Example 12.13

Complete the square for $s = 3t^2 + 12t - 10$.

Solution

Here $a = 3$*, so:*

$$3t^2 + 12t - 10 \equiv 3(t + p)^2 + q$$
$$\Rightarrow 3t^2 + 12t - 10 \equiv 3(t^2 + 2pt + p^2) + q$$
$$\Rightarrow 3t^2 + 12t - 10 \equiv 3t^2 + 6pt + 3p^2 + q$$

Comparing coefficients of t:

$$12 = 6p$$
$$\Rightarrow p = 2$$

Comparing constants:

$$-10 = 3p^2 + q$$
$$\Rightarrow -10 = 3 \times 4 + q$$
$$\Rightarrow q = -10 - 12$$
$$\Rightarrow q = -22$$
$$\therefore \quad s = 3t^2 + 12t - 10 = 3(t + 2)^2 - 22$$

Example 12.14

Express $h = 2 + 9t - 5t^2$ *in the form* $q - 5(t + p)^2$.

Solution

$$2 + 9t - 5t^2 \equiv q - 5(t + p)^2$$
$$\Rightarrow 2 + 9t - 5t^2 \equiv q - 5(t^2 + 2pt + p^2)$$
$$\Rightarrow 2 + 9t - 5t^2 \equiv q - 5p^2 - 10pt - 5t^2$$

Comparing coefficients of t:

$$9 = -\,10p$$
$$\Rightarrow p = -\,0.9$$

Comparing constants:

$$2 = q - 5p^2$$
$$\Rightarrow 2 = q - 5 \times 0.81$$
$$\Rightarrow 2 = q - 4.05$$
$$\Rightarrow q = 6.05$$
$$\therefore \quad h = 2 + 9t - 5t^2 = 6.05 - 5(t - 0.9)^2$$

Exploration 12.6

Transformations and symmetry

The parabola $y = x^2$ has a line of symmetry $x = 0$ and vertex (turning point) at (0,0).

Describe what happens to the line of symmetry and vertex of $y = x^2$ under successive transformations to give $y = a(x + p)^2 + q$.

Successive tranformations

1 translation $-p$ units parallel to the x-axis $y = (x + p)^2$
followed by

2 stretch, factor a parallel to the y-axis 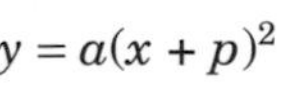

followed by

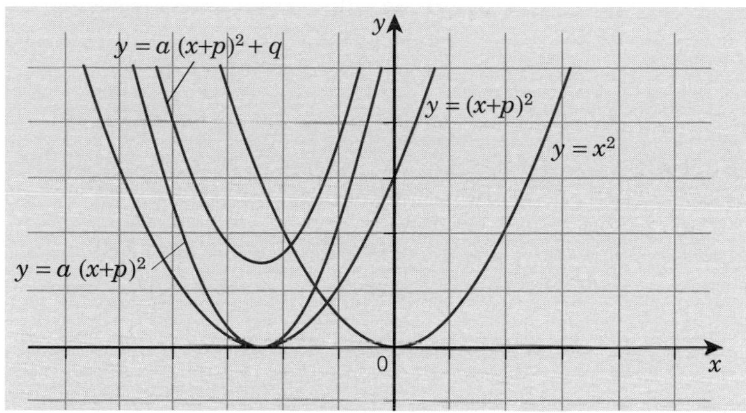

3 translation q units parallel to the y-axis $y = a(x + p)^2 + q$

As a result of successive transformations the vertex (0, 0) and line of symmetry $x = 0$ move as follows.

Transformation	*Vertex*	*Line of symmetry*
1	$(-p, 0)$	$x = -p$
2	$(-p, 0)$	$x = -p$
3	$(-p, q)$	$x = -p$

By completing the square for any quadratic function we can now read off the coordinates of the vertex and the line of symmetry, enabling us to sketch the curve. Using the results from previous worked examples:

4.4 $y = x^2 + 10x + 8 = (x + 5)^2 - 17$
$\Rightarrow \quad p = 5, q = -17$
Vertex: (–5, –17)
Line of symmetry: $x = -5$

4.7 $h = 2 + 9t - 5t^2 = 6.05 - 5(t - 0.9)^2$
$\Rightarrow \quad p = -0.9, a = 6.05$
Vertex: (0.9, 6.05)
Line of symmetry: $t = 0.9$

Example 12.15

A farmer wishes to create six pens, in the arrangement shown here, using 144 metres of fencing.

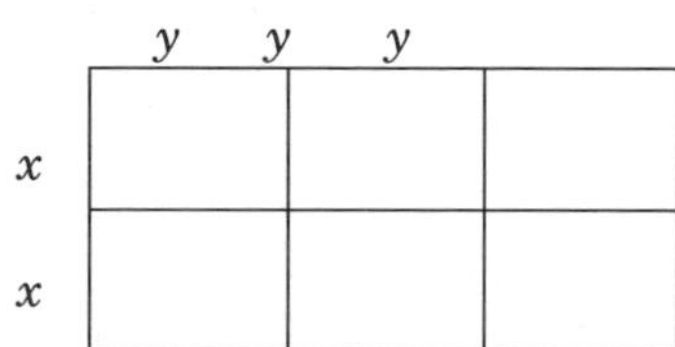

a) *Show that the area enclosed is given by* $A = 96x - \frac{16}{3}x^2$.
b) *By completing the square find the maximum area that can be enclosed and the corresponding dimensions of each pen.*

Solution

a) *The framework for the pens requires 8 x-lengths + 9 y-lengths.*

$\Rightarrow\ 8x + 9y = 144$
$\Rightarrow\ 9y = 144 - 8x$
$\Rightarrow\ y = 16 - \frac{8}{9}x$

Area $A = 2x \times 3y = 6xy = 6x(16 - \frac{8}{9}x)$
$\Rightarrow\ A = 96x - \frac{16}{3}x^2$

b) *Let* $96x - \frac{16}{3}x^2 \equiv q - \frac{16}{3}(x + p)^2$

$\Rightarrow\ 96x - \frac{16}{3}x^2 \equiv q - \frac{16}{3}x^2 - \frac{32}{3}px - \frac{16}{3}p^2$

Comparing coefficients of x:
$96 = -\frac{32}{3}p$
$\Rightarrow\ p = 96 \times (-\frac{3}{32}) = -9$

Comparing constants:
$0 = q - \frac{16}{3}p^2$
$\Rightarrow\ 0 = q - \frac{16}{3} \times 81$
$\Rightarrow\ q = 432$
$\Rightarrow\ A = 432 - \frac{16}{3}(x - 9)^2$

From this form of the equation we can see that A will be maximised when x = 9, and its value is 432.
Substituting for x gives:

$y = 16 - \frac{8}{9}x$
$= 16 - \frac{8}{9} \times 9 = 8$

The final framework is as shown here.

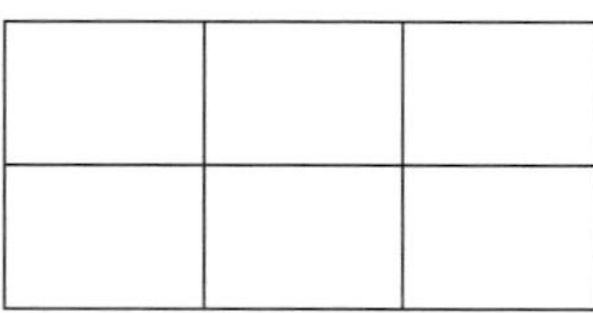

EXERCISES

12.5 CLASSWORK

1 Complete the square for each of these quadratic functions.

a) $y = x^2 + 4x + 11$ **b)** $y = x^2 - 6x + 5$ **c)** $y = x^2 - 5x - 3$
d) $y = x^2 + 3x - 8$ **e)** $y = x^2 + x + 1$ **f)** $y = x^2 - 7x$

For each of your answers, what is the quick way of finding the value of p?

2 Complete the square for each of these quadratic functions.

a) $y = 2x^2 - 8x + 5$ **b)** $y = 3x^2 + 6x - 7$
c) $y = 5x^2 - 5x + 8$ **d)** $s = 3t^2 - t + 5$
e) $d = 5t^2 + 2t - 12$ **f)** $y = 10 - 3x - x^2$
g) $y = 7 - 10x - 3x^2$ **h)** $y = 24 + 23z - 12z^2$

3 For each of the following quadratic functions, complete the square, write down the equation of the parabola's line of symmetry and the coordinates of its vertex, and illustrate your answer on a sketch graph.

a) $y = x^2 - 2x - 3$ **b)** $y = x^2 + 5x + 8$
c) $y = x^2 - 2.5x + 7$ **d)** $y = 4x^2 - 8x + 11$
e) $y = 5x^2 - 3x$ **f)** $y = 10x - x^2$
g) $y = 12 - x - x^2$ **h)** $s = 4 - 9t^2$

4 The equation of the curve taken on by a cable of a suspension bridge is $y = 0.001x^2 - x + 28$.

a) By completing the square:
  i) sketch the graph,
  ii) find the line of symmetry of the parabola,
  iii) find the coordinates of the vertex of the parabola.

b) The horizontal distance between the ends of the cable is 100 metres. Find the difference between the maximum and minimum heights of the cable.

5 A farmer wishes to create twelve pens using the arrangement shown, using 240 metres of fencing.

	y	y	y	y
x				
x				
x				

a) Show that the area enclosed is given by $A = 180x - \frac{45}{4}x^2$.

b) By completing the square:
  i) sketch the graph of A against x,
  ii) find the maximum area that can be enclosed,
  iii) find the values of x and y to give the maximum area.

EXERCISES

12.5 HOMEWORK

1 Complete the square for each of these quadratic functions.

a) $x^2 - 10x + 28$ **b)** $x^2 - 3x + 3$
c) $x^2 + 12x + 27$ **d)** $x^2 - 5x + 0.5$
e) $x^2 + 7x$ **f)** $x^2 + 7$

2 Complete the square for each of these quadratic functions.

a) $y = 2x^2 + 12x + 7$ **b)** $y = 3x^2 - 36x + 109$
c) $s = 3t^2 - 15t - 5$ **d)** $y = 8x^2 - 2x + 9$
e) $y = -x^2 + 14x - 45$ **f)** $y = 2x - 2x^2$
g) $y = 1 - 2x + 3x^2$ **h)** $y = 6x - 3 - 5x^2$

3 Give a rough sketch of each of the following parabolae, showing clearly where it crosses the y-axis and the coordinates of its vertex.

a) $y = x^2 - 4x + 7$ **b)** $y = 8 - x^2$
c) $y = x^2 + 2x - 4$ **d)** $s = t^2 + 5t + 7$
e) $y = 4x^2 - 32x + 57$ **f)** $y = 1 - x - x^2$
g) $y = 6x^2 + 8x - 5$ **h)** $h = 9t - 5t^2 - 23$

4 The Jodrell Bank radio telescope has a giant circular dish. When it is in a horizontal position, the reflecting surface has a cross-section which follows the curve given by part of the parabola

$y = 0.003\,968x^2 - 0.992x + 225$

where x is the distance from the edge of the dish in feet and y is the height above ground level in feet.

a) By completing the square, sketch the cross-section of the dish.
b) How high above the ground level is the rim of the dish?
c) How deep in the dish?
d) What is the radius of the dish?

5 A lawn is a rectangle 10 m by 15 m. It is to have two flower beds cut out of it. One will be a square flower bed and the other will be in the shape of a rectangle, twice as long as it is wide. The gardener has 13.6 m of lawn edging left to put round the flower beds to stop the grass growing into them. He wants to use up all the lawn edging, but requires to keep the lawn as large as possible in area after the flower beds have been cut out.

a) If the square bed has a side of length y metres and the rectangular bed has width x metres, show that the area of the lawn will be $A = 138.44 + 10.2x - 4.25x^2$.
b) By completing the square, find the dimensions of the flower beds so that the area of the lawn is as large as possible.

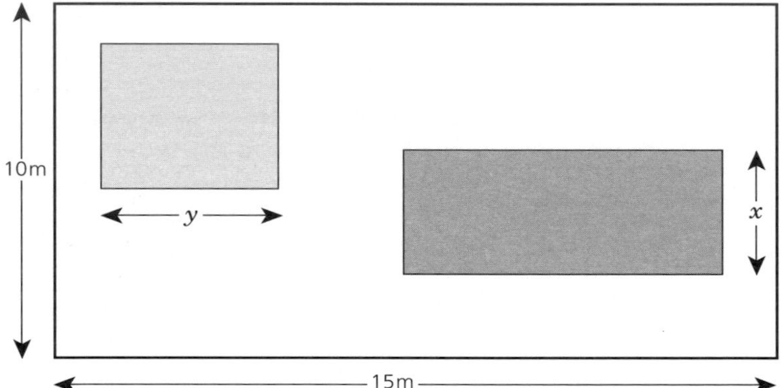

TRANSFORMATION OF TRIGONOMETRIC FUNCTIONS

The three basic trigonometric graphs, in terms of x and y:

$y = \cos x$, $y = \sin x$ and $y = \tan x$

may all be subject to simple transformations and combination of transformations.

Exploration 12.7

KEY SKILLS
IT 3.2

Transforming $y = \sin x$

Beginning with the graph of $y = \sin x$, examine the effect of each of the following transformations.

- reflection in the x-axis
- stretch parallel to the y-axis
- translation parallel to the y-axis
- stretch parallel to the x-axis
- translation parallel to the x-axis

In each case, what happens to the equation for the transformed graph?

Now try again, starting with $y = \cos x$ and then $y = \tan x$.

Combine the transformations in different ways and investigate whether the order of transformations matters.

CALCULATOR ACTIVITY

Exploration 12.8

Transformations

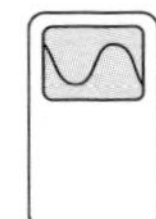

The transformation of the trigonometric functions may be illustrated using a suitable graph plotter or on a graphics calculator. Set up the axes using suitable scales, and experiment. Check the solutions of the following worked examples, but always attempt a sketch yourself before using the computer or calculator.

Example 12.16

Sketch three copies of the graph of $y = \sin x$, $0° \le x \le 360°$, $-3 \le y \le 3$.

On each sketch respectively superimpose the graphs of:

a) $y = 3\sin x$ ***b)*** $y = \sin 2x$ ***c)*** $y = 3\sin 2x$.

In each case describe the transformation from $y = \sin x$ *to a), b) or c) geometrically.*

Solution

a)

Stretch factor 3, parallel to y-axis

b)

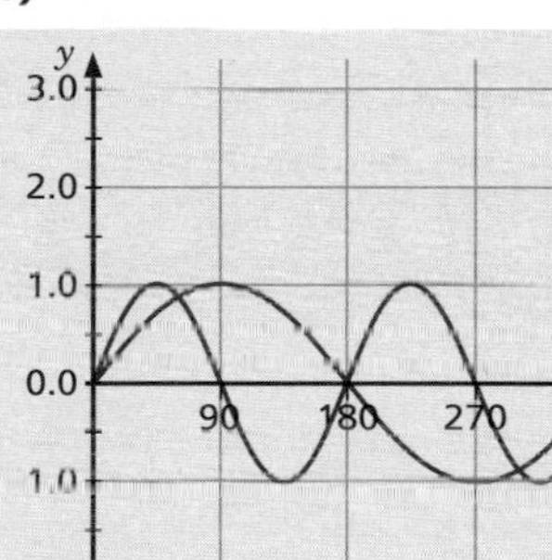

Stretch factor 0.5 parallel to x-axis

c)

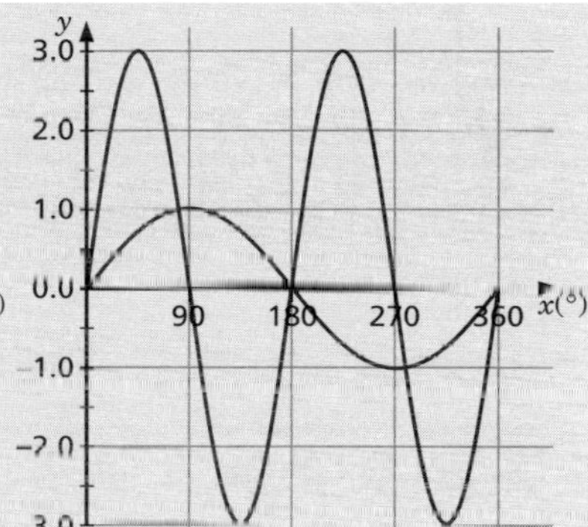

b) followed by a)

Example 12.17

Sketch three copies of the graph of $y = \cos x$, $0° \le x \le 360°$, $-1 \le y \le 3$.

On each sketch respectively show the result of transforming $y = \cos x$ *by:*

a) *translation through +2 units parallel to the* y*-axis,*

b) *translation through +90° parallel to the* x*-axis,*

c) ***b)*** *followed by* ***a)****.*

In each case give the equation of the transformed graph and state the coordinates of its stationary points.

Solution

a)

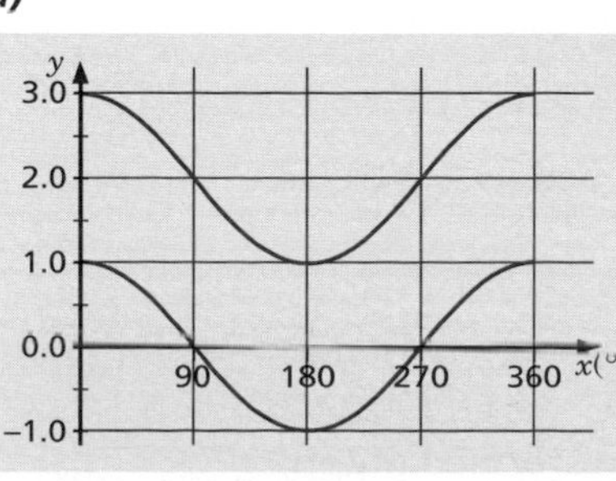

$y = \cos x + 2$

(0, 3), (180, 1), (360, 3)

b)

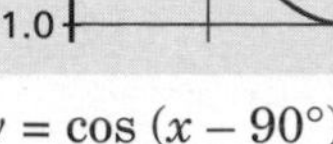

$y = \cos(x - 90°)$

(90, 1), (270, −1)

c)

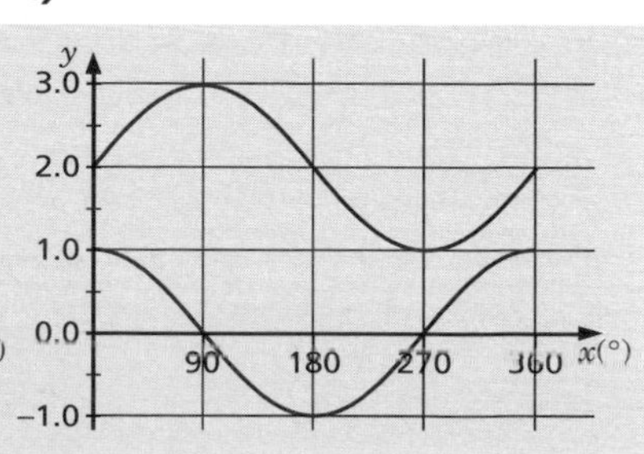

$y = \cos(x - 90°) + 2$

(90, 3), (270, 1)

Example 12.18

Sketch three copies of the graph of $y = \tan x$, $0° \le x \le 360°$, $-5 \le y \le 5$.

On each sketch respectively show the result of transforming $y = \tan x$ by:

a) *translation through –60° parallel to the x-axis,*
b) *stretch, factor 2 parallel to the y-axis,*
c) *a) followed by b).*

In each case give the equation of the transformed graph.

Solution

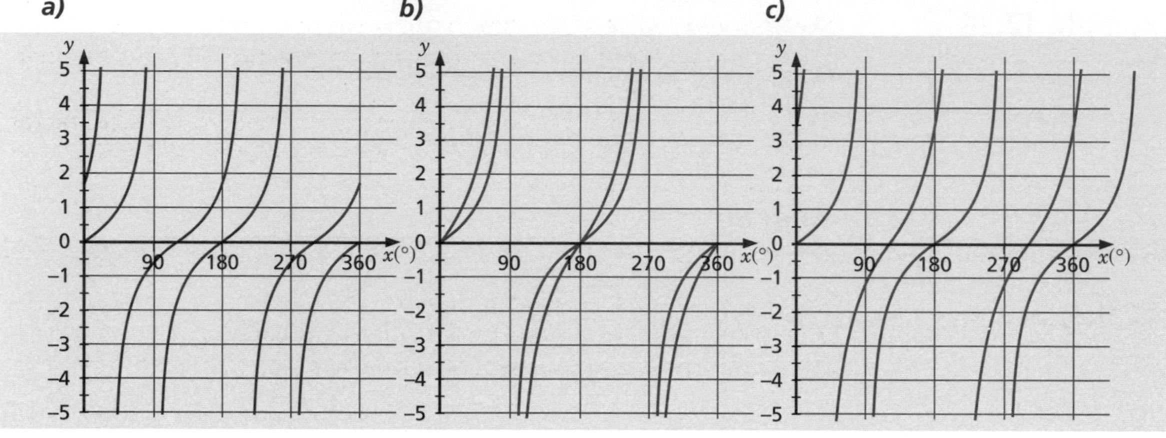

$y = \tan (x + 60°)$ $y = 2\tan x$ $y = 2\tan (x + 60°)$

EXERCISES

12.6 CLASSWORK

1 For each of the following trigonometric functions:

a) sketch the graph of the function for $0° \le x \le 360°$,
b) label the points of intersection with the axes,
c) state the range of the function in the form $a \le y \le b$.

i) $y = 3 + \sin x$ **ii)** $y = -\sin x$ **iii)** $y = 2\cos x$
iv) $y = 2 - \cos x$ **v)** $y = -3\cos x$ **vi)** $y = \cos 3x$
vii) $y = \tan 2x$ **viii)** $y = \sin (x + 90°)$ **ix)** $y = \cos (x - 60°)$

2 For each of the following trigonometric functions:

a) sketch graphs of $y = \sin x$ and the given function, for $0° \le x \le 360°$,
b) describe the geometrical transformation(s) that map(s) $y = \sin x$ onto the given function.

i) $y = \frac{1}{2}\sin x$ **ii)** $y = \sin x - 1$
iii) $y = \sin 3x$ **iv)** $y = \sin (x + 60°)$
v) $y = \frac{1}{2}\sin 3x$ **vi)** $y = \frac{1}{2}\sin x + 3$
vii) $y = \sin \frac{1}{2}x$ **viii)** $y = 5 \sin \frac{1}{2}x$
ix) $y = 3\sin (x + 60°)$ **x)** $y = \sin (x + 60°) - 5$

3 For each geometrical transformation:

a) sketch graphs of $y = \cos x$, for $0° \le x \le 360°$, and the transformation of $y = \cos x$,
b) write down the equation of the transformed graph,

c) find the coordinates of any stationary points.
   i) stretch, factor 4 parallel to the y-axis
   ii) translation –3 units parallel to the y-axis
   iii) stretch, factor 2.5 parallel to the x-axis
   iv) stretch, factor $\frac{1}{3}$ parallel to the x-axis *followed by* translation –5 units parallel to the y-axis
   v) translation –90° parallel to the x-axis *followed by* stretch, factor 4 parallel to the y-axis
   vi) translation +120° parallel to the x-axis *followed by* reflection in the x-axis
   vii) translation –45° parallel to the x-axis *followed by* stretch, factor 3 parallel to the y-axis *followed by* translation +3 units parallel to the y-axis
   viii) stretch, factor 2 parallel to the x-axis *followed by* stretch, factor 1.5 parallel to the y-axis *followed by* translation –3.5 units parallel to the y-axis

EXERCISES

12.6 HOMEWORK

1 For each of the following trigonometric functions:
   a) sketch the graph of the function for $0° \le x \le 360°$,
   b) label the points of intersection with the axes,
   c) state the range of the function in the form $a \le y \le b$.
   i) $y = 4 - \cos x$ ii) $y = 2 + \sin x$
   iii) $y = 3\cos x$ iv) $y = -2.5\sin x$
   v) $y = \tan 3x$ vi) $y = \sin (30° + x)$
   vii) $y = \sin 3x - 1$ viii) $y = \cos (30° + x) + 2$

2 For each of the following trigonometric functions:
   a) sketch graphs of $y = \cos x$ and the given function, for $0° \le x \le 360°$,
   b) describe the geometrical transformation(s) that map(s) $y = \cos x$ onto the given function.
   i) $y = \frac{1}{3}\cos x$ ii) $y = 4 + \cos x$
   iii) $y = \cos 6x$ iv) $y = \cos (90° - x)$
   v) $y = -\cos 6x$ vi) $y = \frac{1}{3}\cos 2x$
   vii) $y = \cos \frac{1}{3}x + 2$ viii) $y = 6\cos \frac{1}{3}x$

3 For each geometrical transformation:
   a) sketch the graph of $y = \sin x$ and the transformation of $y = \sin x$,
   b) write down the equation of the transformed graph.
   i) stretch, factor $\frac{1}{2}$ parallel to the y-axis
   ii) stretch, factor $\frac{1}{4}$ parallel to the x-axis
   iii) translation +60° parallel to the x-axis
   iv) stretch, factor 2 parallel to the y-axis *followed by* translation +1 unit parallel to the y-axis
   v) stretch, factor $\frac{1}{2}$ parallel to the x-axis *followed by* reflection in the x-axis
   vi) translation –30° parallel to the x-axis *followed by* translation –2 units parallel to the y-axis
   vii) translation +90° parallel to the x-axis *followed by* stretch, factor 2.5 units parallel to the y-axis *followed by* reflection in the x-axis
   viii) stretch, factor 2 parallel to the x-axis *followed by* stretch, factor –1 parallel to the y-axis *followed by* stretch, factor 0.25 parallel to the y-axis.

TRANSFORMATION OF GRAPHS

Earlier in this chapter we explored the effects on graphs of translations, stretches (scaling) and reflections. We now formalise these transformations for graphs of any functions.

CALCULATOR ACTIVITY

Exploration 12.9

Graphs of transformations

You will need a graphics calculator or graphics package.

Let $f(x) = x^2 - 4x$.

- Using suitable scales plot the graphs of:
  1 $y = f(x)$ and $y = f(x) + a = x^2 - 4x + a$
  2 $y = f(x)$ and $y = f(x + a) = (x + a)^2 - 4(x + a)$
  3 $y = f(x)$ and $y = af(x) = a(x^2 - 4x)$
  4 $y = f(x)$ and $y = f(ax) = (ax)^2 - 4ax$
  for various values of a (e.g. 5, 2, 0.5, –1, –3).
- In each case discuss the effect of a on how the graph was transformed.
- What special effect did taking $a = -1$ have in **3** and **4**?

Geometrical transformations

From your exploration of various transformations of $y = x^2 - 4x$ you may have discovered up to six geometrical transformations of the graph. The conclusions which you might have drawn are summarised below.

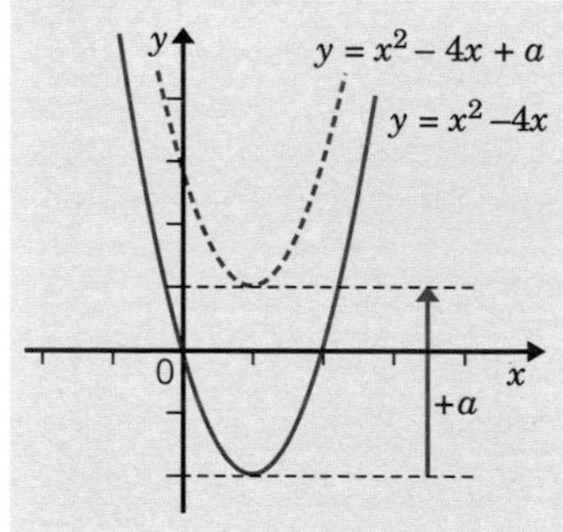

1 $y = f(x) + a$ translation of $y = f(x)$ through a units parallel to the y-axis

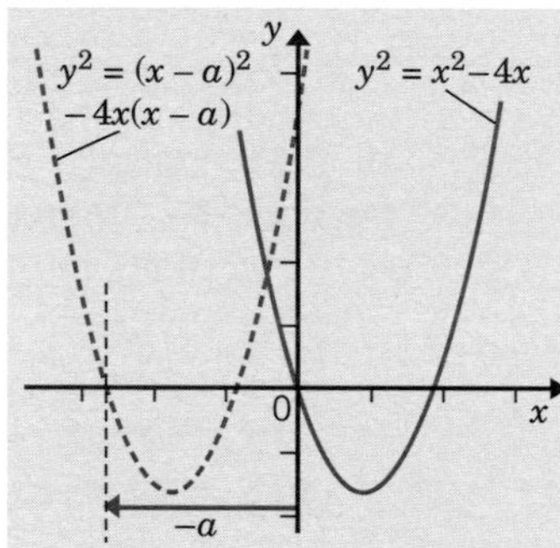

2 $y = f(x + a)$ translation of $y = f(x)$ through $-a$ units parallel to the x-axis

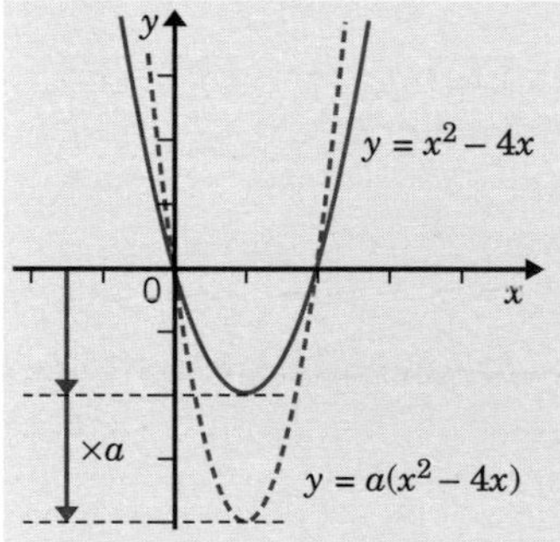

3 $y = af(x)$ stretch (scale) of $y = f(x)$, factor a, parallel to the y-axis

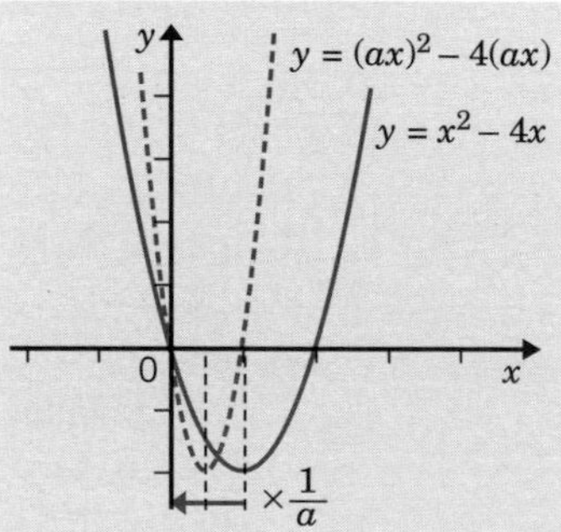

4 $y = f(ax)$ stretch (scale) of $y = f(x)$, factor $\frac{1}{a}$, parallel to the x-axis

The special case of taking $a = -1$ in **3** and **4** leads to two more geometrical transformations that are important:

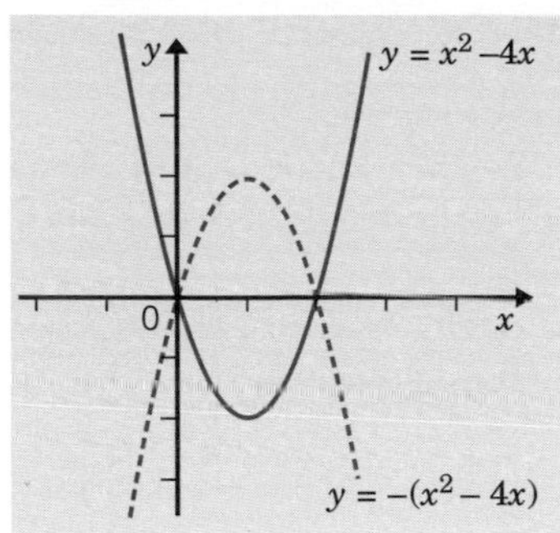

5 $y = -\mathrm{f}(x)$
reflection of $y = \mathrm{f}(x)$ in the x-axis

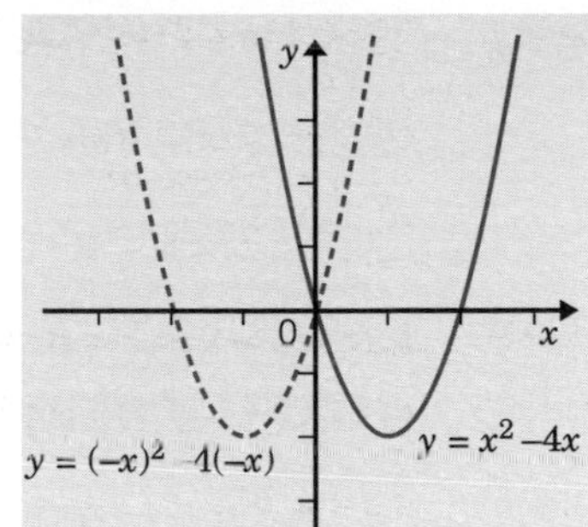

6 $y = \mathrm{f}(-x)$
reflection of $y = \mathrm{f}(x)$ in the y-axis

Combining transformations

The transformations we have met so far may be combined as before to produce graphs of composite functions, for example:

$y = b\mathrm{f}(x + a)$ represents a translation through $-a$ units parallel to the x-axis *followed by* a stretch, factor b, parallel to the y-axis

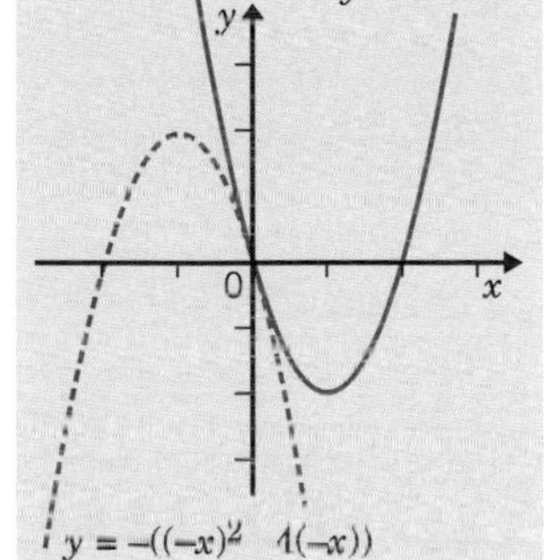

$y = -\mathrm{f}(-x)$ represents a reflection in the y-axis *followed by* a reflection in the x-axis; for $\mathrm{f}(x) = x^2 - 4x$ this produces a graph as shown.

From the diagram we see that the combined transformation may be described geometrically as a rotation through a half-turn (180°), centre (0, 0).

Note that the transformations *reflect in the x-axis* and *reflect in the y-axis* are both self-inverse, which is evident from the algebraic formulation:

i.e. $\mathrm{f}(-(-x)) = \mathrm{f}(x)$
and $-(-\mathrm{f}(x)) = \mathrm{f}(x)$

Even and odd functions

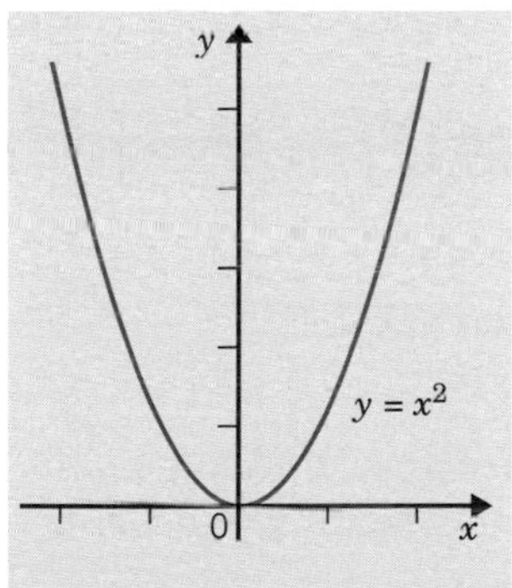

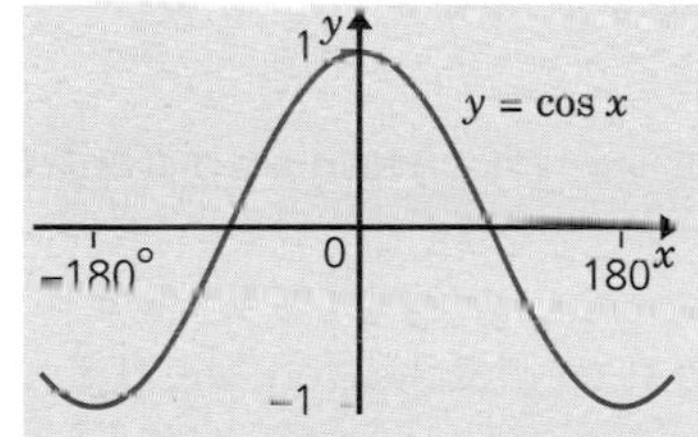

A function such as $\mathrm{f}(x) = x^2$ or $\mathrm{f}(x) = \cos x$ has the y-axis as a line of symmetry.

For these functions, reflection in the y-axis will map the graph onto itself i.e.

$$\mathrm{f}(-x) = \mathrm{f}(x)$$

Such functions are called **even functions**, since when expressed in terms of powers of x, the index or indices are even integers.

A function such as $\mathrm{f}(x) = x^3$ or $\mathrm{f}(x) = \sin x$ has half-turn rotational symmetry about (0, 0).

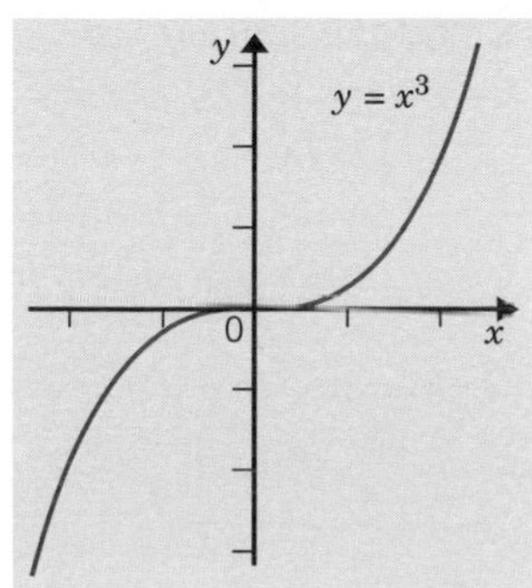

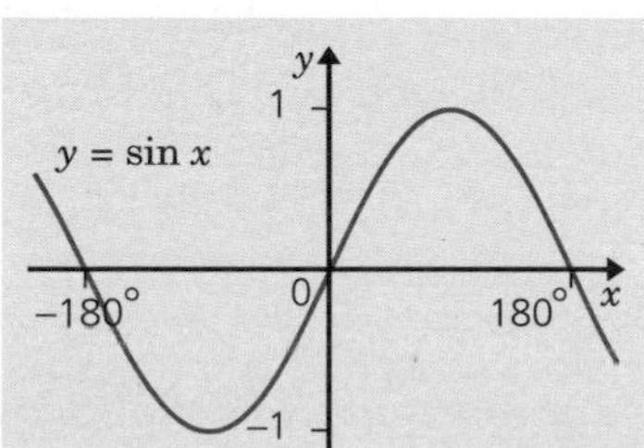

For these functions, rotation through a half-turn about (0, 0) will map the graph onto itself i.e.

$$-\mathrm{f}(-x) = \mathrm{f}(x)$$

Such functions are called **odd functions**, since when expressed in terms of powers of x, the index or indices are odd integers.

Functions which contain powers of x which are a mixture of odd and even integers are neither odd nor even.

Example 12.19

Demonstrate that the functions:

a) $f(x)=\dfrac{x^4}{24}-\dfrac{x^2}{2}+1$

b) $g(x)=\dfrac{x^5}{120}-\dfrac{x^3}{6}+x$

are even and odd respectively. Confirm your results on sketch graphs.

Solution

a) $f(-x)=\dfrac{(-x)^4}{24}-\dfrac{(-x)^2}{2}+1=\dfrac{x^4}{24}-\dfrac{x^2}{2}+1=f(x)$

Hence $f(x)$ *is even.*

b) $g(-x)=\dfrac{(-x)^5}{120}-\dfrac{(-x)^3}{6}+(-x)=-\dfrac{x^5}{120}+\dfrac{x^3}{6}-x$

$$\Rightarrow -g(-x)=-\left(\frac{(-x)^5}{120}-\frac{(-x)^3}{6}-x\right)=\frac{x^5}{120}-\frac{x^3}{6}+x=g(x)$$

Hence $g(x)$ *is odd.*

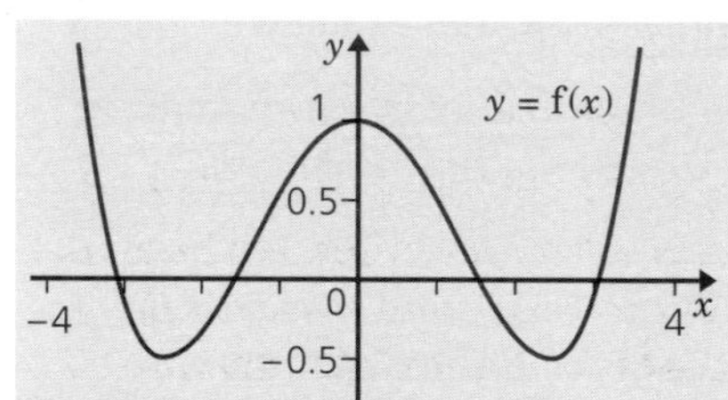

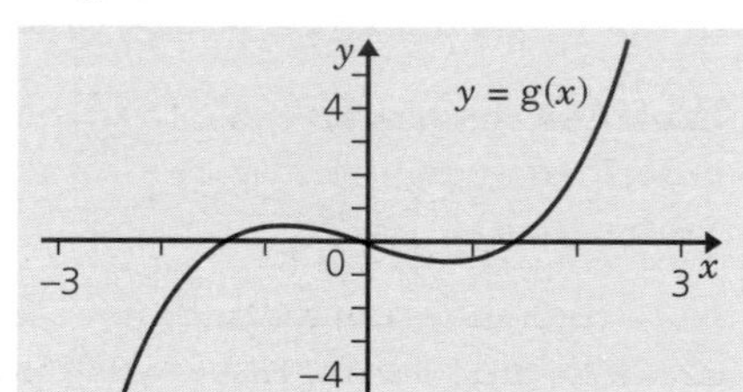

The symmetries of $f(x)$ *and* $g(x)$ *are evident from their graphs.*

Example 12.20

The function f *is defined by* $f: x \to |2x-5|$.

a) *Sketch a graph of* $y=f(x)$ *and use it to solve the inequality* $f(x)>x$.

b) *Sketch graphs of and simplify:* ***i)*** $y=2f(x-3)$ ***ii)*** $y=-f(\frac{1}{2}x)$.

Solution

a) *The graph of* $y=f(x)$ *and* $y=x$ *intersect where:*

$2x-5=x \Rightarrow x=5$

and $-(2x-5)=x \Rightarrow 3x=5 \Rightarrow x=1\frac{2}{3}$

So the points of intersection are $(1\frac{2}{3}, 1\frac{2}{3})$ *and (5, 5).*

From the graph $f(x)>x$ *when* $x<1\frac{2}{3}$ *or* $x>5$.

b) ***i)*** *Geometrically* $2f(x-3)$ *represents a translation through 3 units parallel to the* x*-axis* followed by *a stretch, factor 2, parallel to the* y*-axis, which gives the equation:*

$y=2f(x-3)=2|2(x-3)-5|=2|2x-11|=|4x-22|$

ii) *Geometrically* $f(\frac{1}{2}x)$ *represents a stretch, factor 2, parallel to the* x*-axis* followed by *a reflection in the* x*-axis, which gives the equation:*

$y=-f(\frac{1}{2}x)=-|2\times\frac{1}{2}x-5|=-|x-5|$

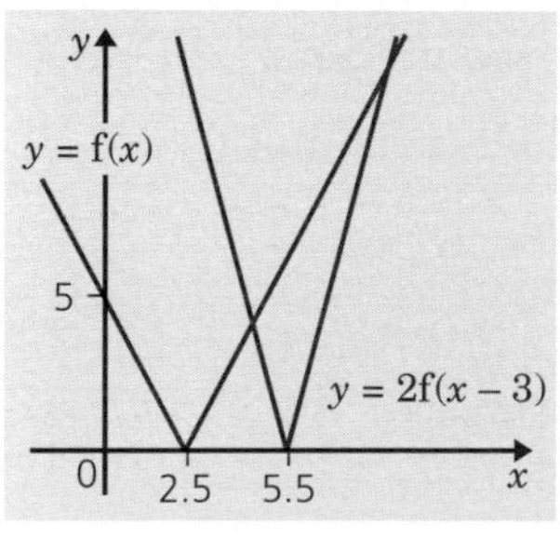

Example 12.21

Sketch graphs of functions with the following equations, in each case stating how you would transform the graph of $y=\dfrac{12}{x}$ *onto it.*

a) $y=\dfrac{12}{x}+3$ **b)** $y=\dfrac{12}{x-2}$ **c)** $y=\dfrac{-12}{x+5}$ **d)** $y=7-\dfrac{6}{x}$

Solution

a)

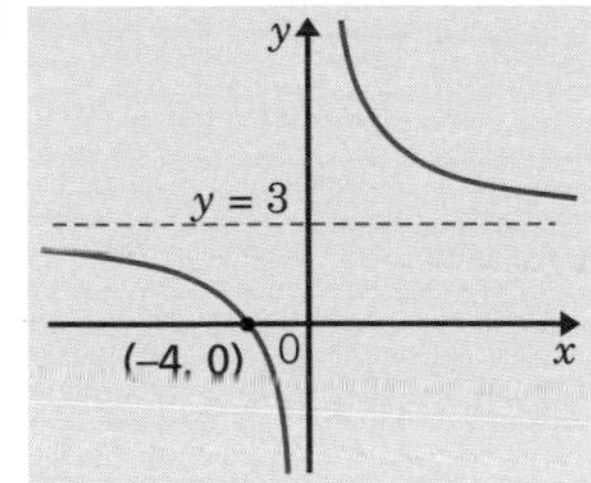

translation through 3 units parallel to the y-axis

b)

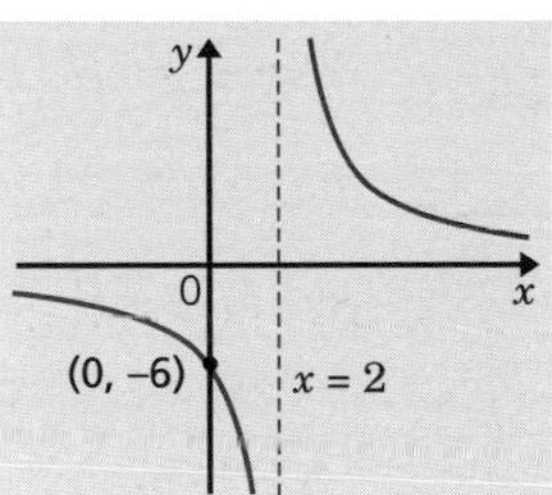

translation through 2 units parallel to the x-axis

c)

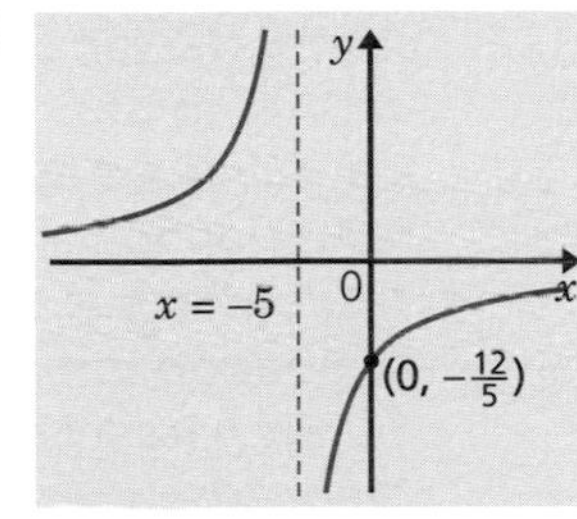

translation through −5 units parallel to the x-axis ***followed by*** *reflection in the x-axis*

d)

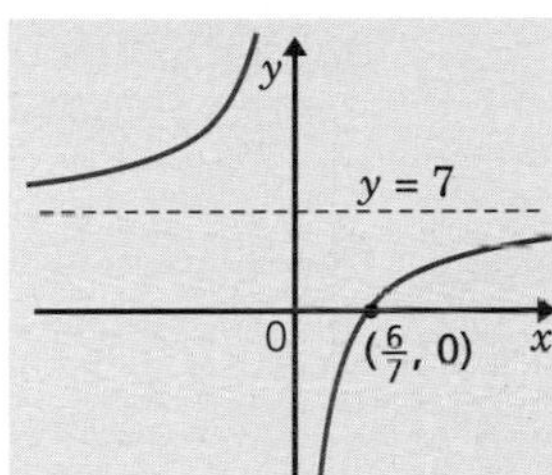

stretch, factor $\frac{1}{2}$, parallel to the y-axis ***followed by*** *reflection in the x-axis followed by translation through 7 units parallel to the y-axis*

Example 12.22

a) Sketch the graph of $y = \dfrac{20}{x^2}$.

b) Translate the graph in ***a)*** *−3 units parallel to the x-axis* ***followed by*** *−8 units parallel to the y-axis, and write down the equation of the transformed graph.*

c) Find the coordinates of the points where the transformed graph meets the axes.

Solution

a)

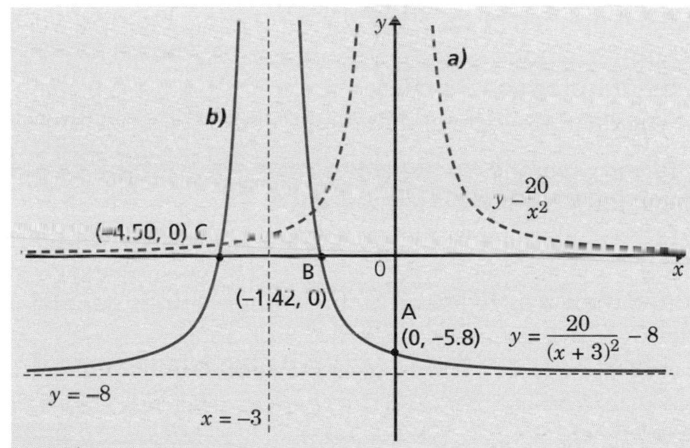

c) At A $x = 0 \Rightarrow \quad y = \dfrac{20}{3^2} - 8 = -5\frac{7}{9} \quad \Rightarrow$

A is the point $(0, -5\frac{7}{9})$.

At B and C $y = 0$

$\Rightarrow \quad \dfrac{20}{(x+3)^2} - 8 = 0$

$\Rightarrow \quad 20 = 8(x+3)^2$

$\Rightarrow \quad (x+3)^2 = 2.5$

$\Rightarrow \quad x+3 = \pm\sqrt{2.5}$

$\Rightarrow \quad x = -4.58$ or $x = -1.42$

So B is $(-1.42, 0)$ and C is $(-4.58, 0)$.

Example 12.23

Sketch graphs of functions with the following equations. In each case describe how you would transform the graph of $y = \sqrt[3]{x}$ onto it.

a) $y = \sqrt[3]{x} - 5$ **b)** $y = 4\sqrt[3]{x}$

c) $y = \sqrt[3]{x+8}$ **d)** $3 - \sqrt[3]{2x}$

Solution

a)

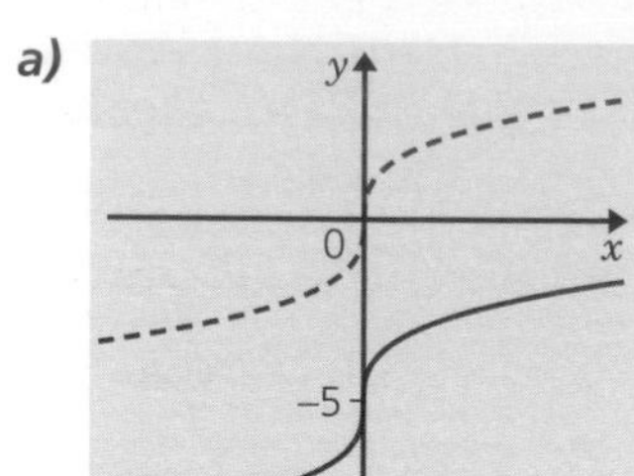

translation through –5 units parallel to the y-axis

b)

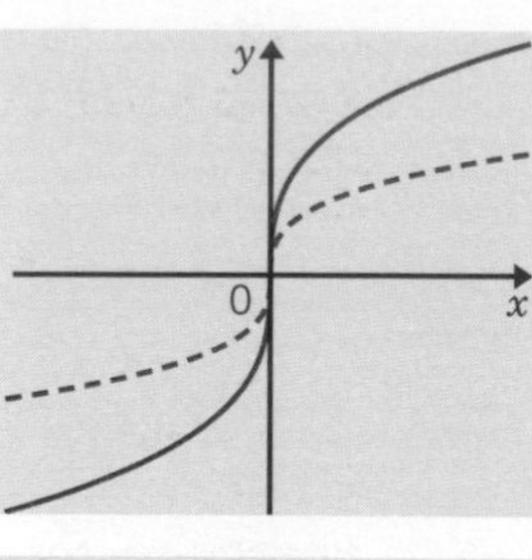

stretch, factor 4, parallel to the y-axis

c)

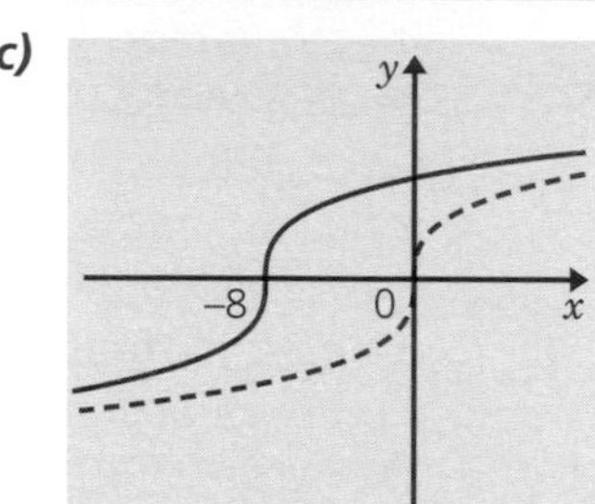

translation through –8 units parallel to the x-axis

d)

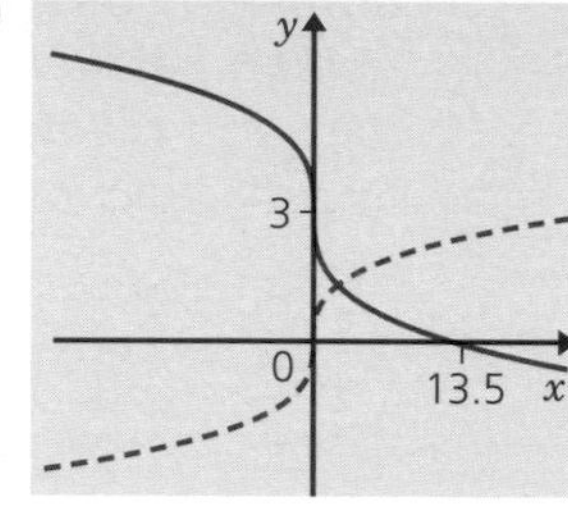

stretch, factor $\frac{1}{2}$, parallel to the x-axis ***followed by*** *reflection in the y-axis* followed by *translation through 3 units parallel to the y-axis*

EXERCISES

12.7 CLASSWORK

1 The function f is defined by $f : x \to x^3$. For each of the following transformed functions:

i) describe the transformation geometrically,
ii) sketch graphs of $y = f(x)$ and its image under the transformation.

a) $y = f(x + 3)$ **b)** $y = 2f(x)$ **c)** $y = f(\frac{1}{2}x)$ **d)** $y = \frac{1}{2}f(x) - 4$

e) $y = -f(x - 2)$ **f)** $y = 2f(\frac{1}{2}x)$ **g)** $y = f(5 - x)$ **h)** $y = 3f(2x - 1)$

2 The function g is defined by $g(x) = \frac{12}{x}, x \neq 0$. For each of the following transformations:

i) give the transformed function,
ii) sketch graphs of $y = g(x)$ and its image under the transformation.

a) stretch, factor $\frac{1}{3}$, parallel to the y-axis
b) translation –3 units parallel to the x-axis
c) stretch, factor 2, parallel to the x-axis *followed by* reflection in the x-axis
d) reflection in the y-axis *followed by* translation 4 units parallel to the y-axis
e) reflection in the y-axis *followed by* translation 4 units parallel to the x-axis
f) **b)** *followed by* **c)**

3 The function f is defined by $f : x \to \frac{3}{x^2}, x > 0$.

a) Sketch the graph of f.
b) From the graph of f sketch the graphs of these functions.

$g : x \to \frac{3}{(x-1)^2}$ $\quad h : x \to \frac{3}{(x+2)^2}$

c) State the domain and range of g and h.

4 The graph of function $g : x \to \sqrt{4 - x^2}$, $-2 \leq x \leq 2$, is a semi-circle, radius 2 units, centre (0, 0).

a) Write down a function h for which the graph is a semi-circle, radius 5 units, centre (0, 0).

b) Which two transformations, when combined, map the graph of g into the graph of h?
c) Prove your assertion in **b)** by transforming function f into function g.

5 State whether the following functions are even, odd or neither. Sketch a graph of the function, in each case, to support your answer.

a) $y = -\dfrac{1}{x}$ **b)** $y = 1 + x^2 + x^4$ **c)** $y = \dfrac{10}{x^2}$ **d)** $y = \tan x$

e) $y = \dfrac{40}{x^3} - \dfrac{12}{x}$ **f)** $y = \dfrac{40}{x^2} - 12$ **g)** $y = (x + 2)^3$ **h)** $y = (x^2 - 3)^3$

EXERCISES

12.7 HOMEWORK

1 The function f is defined by $f : x \rightarrow 2x^2$. For each of the following transformed functions:
i) describe the transformation geometrically,
ii) sketch graphs of $y = f(x)$ and its range under the transformation.

a) $y = f(x + 1)$ **b)** $y = 3f(x)$ **c)** $y = f(2x)$ **d)** $y = \frac{1}{2}f(x) + 2$
e) $y = f(x - 3)$ **f)** $y = 2f(x - 3)$ **g)** $y = f(4 - x)$ **h)** $y = 3f(2x - 1) + 4$

2 The function g is defined by $g(x) = \dfrac{3}{2x}, x \neq 0$.
For each of the following transformed functions:
i) state the transformed function,
ii) sketch the graph of $y = g(x)$ and its image under the transformation.

a) translation 3 units parallel to the x-axis
b) stretch, factor 2, parallel to the y-axis
c) stretch, factor $\frac{1}{3}$, parallel to the x-axis *followed by* translation 4 units parallel to the y-axis
d) reflection in the y-axis *followed by* translation −2 units parallel to the y-axis
e) **a)** *followed by* **c)**

3 The function f is defined by $f(x) = \sin x$.

a) **i)** Write down the transformed function following a reflection in the y-axis.
ii) Sketch $f(x)$and its image under the transformation.
b) **i)** Write down the transformed function following a reflection in the x-axis.
ii) Sketch $f(x)$ and its image under the transformation.
c) Comment on your results to **a)** and **b)**.
d) Repeat parts **a)** and **b)** for $g(x) = \cos x$ and $h(x) = \tan x$ and comment.

4 The graph of $f : x \rightarrow \sqrt{9 - x^2}, -3 \leq x \leq 3$ is a semi-circle of radius 3, centre (0, 0).

a) Describe the transformation which would map f onto a semi-circle radius 3, centre (2, 0).
b) Find the transformed function.

5 State whether the following functions are even, odd or neither. Use sketches to support your answers.

a) $f(x) = x^2 + 5$ **b)** $f(x) = x^3 + x^2 + 2$ **c)** $f(x) = x^4 - x^2$

d) $f(x) = -\dfrac{3}{2x}$ **e)** $f(x) = \dfrac{1}{x + 1}$ **f)** $f(x) = \dfrac{1}{x^2 + 1}$ **g)** $f(x) = \dfrac{x}{x^3 + 1}$

h) $f(x) = \dfrac{1}{4x^3}$ **i)** $f(x) = (x^2 + 1)^3$ **j)** $f(x) = (x^3 + 1)^2$

CONSOLIDATION EXERCISES FOR CHAPTER 12

1 The functions f and g are defined by:

$$f: x \to 3x - 1, x \in \Re \qquad g: x \to x^2 + 1, x \in \Re.$$

a) Find the range of g.
b) Determine the value of x for which $\text{gf}(x) = \text{fg}(x)$.
c) Determine the values of x for which $|\text{f}(x)| = 8$.
The function $\text{h}: x \to x^2 + 3x, x \in \Re, x \geq q$, is one-to-one.
d) Find the least value of q and sketch the graph of this function.

(ULEAC Question 9, Specimen Paper 1, 1994)

2 The function f has as its domain the set of all non-zero real numbers, and is given by $\text{f}(x) = \frac{1}{x}$ for all x in this set. On a single diagram, sketch each of the following graphs, and indicate the geometrical relationships between them.

a) $y = \text{f}(x)$ **b)** $y = \text{f}(x + 1)$ **c)** $y = \text{f}(x + 1) + 2$

Deduce, explaining your reasoning, the coordinates of the point about which the graph of $y = \frac{2x+3}{x+1}$ is symmetrical.

(UCLES Linear Question 12, Specimen Paper, 1994)

3 The diagram shows the graph of $y = x^2(3 - x)$. The coordinates of the points A and B on the graph are (2, 4) and (3, 0) respectively.

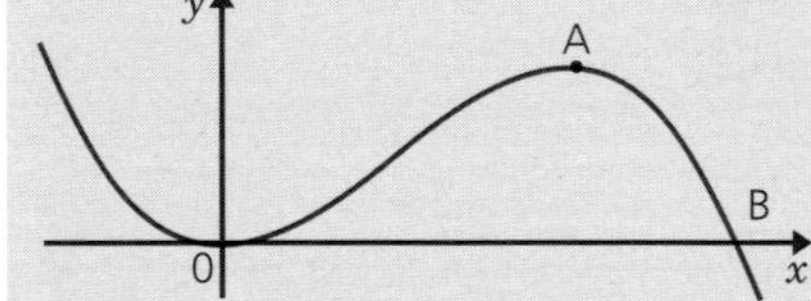

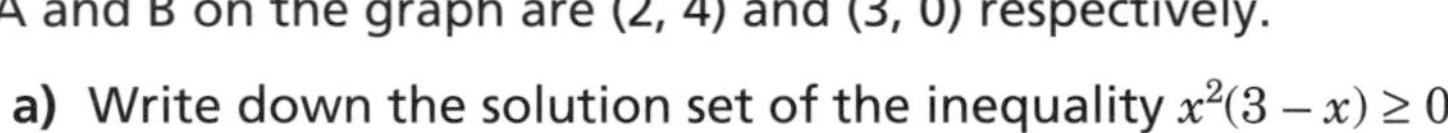

a) Write down the solution set of the inequality $x^2(3 - x) \geq 0$.
b) The equation $3x^2 - x^3 = k$ has three real solutions for x. Write down the set of possible values for k.
c) Functions f and g are defined as follows.

$$f: x \to x^2(3 - x), 0 \leq x \leq 2 \qquad g: x \to x^2(3 - x), 0 \leq x \leq 3$$

Explain why f has an inverse while g does not.
d) State the domain and the range of f^{-1}, and sketch the graph of f^{-1}.

(UCLES Modular Question 9, Specimen Paper 1, 1994)

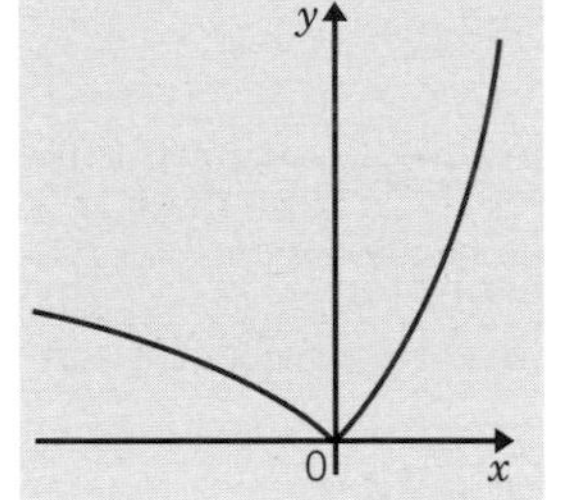

4 The diagram shows the graph of $y = |\text{f}(x)|$, for a certain function f with domain $\Re$. Sketch, on separate diagrams, two possibilities for the graph of $y = \text{f}(x)$.

(UCLES Modular Question 1, Specimen Paper 2, 1994)

5 The functions f and g are defined by:

$$f: x \to x^2 + 3, x \in \Re \qquad g: x \to 2x + 1, x \in \Re.$$

a) Find, in a similar form, the function fg.
b) Find the range of the function fg.
c) Solve the equation $\text{f}(x) = 12\text{g}^{-1}(x)$.

(ULEAC Question 3, Paper 1, January 1995)

6 The functions $\text{f}(x)$ and $\text{g}(x)$ are defined by $\text{f}(x) = x^2 + 1$ and $\text{g}(x) = x - 2$.

a) **i)** Calculate the value of $\text{g}(\text{f}(2))$.
ii) The function $\text{h}(x)$ is defined by $\text{h}(x) = \text{g}(\text{f}(x))$. Find an expression in terms of x for $\text{h}(x)$.
b) The domain and range of each of the functions $\text{f}(x)$ and $\text{g}(x)$ is the set of real numbers. Explain what is meant by this statement.
c) Only one of the functions $\text{f}(x)$ and $\text{g}(x)$ has an inverse. Write down an expression in terms of x for the inverse function.
d) The function which has no inverse does have an inverse if its domain and range are suitably restricted. Suggest suitable restrictions for the domain and range.

(Oxford Nuffield Question 5, Paper 1, 1995)

7 For the geometrical transformation stretch factor 2 parallel to the x-axis *followed by* stretch factor 2.5 parallel to the y-axis *followed by* translation –3 units parallel to the y-axis:

a) sketch graphs of $y = \cos x$, $0° \le x \le 360°$, and the transformation of $y = \cos x$,
b) write down the equation of the transformed graph,
c) find the coordinates of any stationary points.

8 Sketch the graphs of $y = \dfrac{1}{x^2}$, $y = \dfrac{1}{(x+2)^2}$, $y = \dfrac{4}{x^2}$ and $y = \dfrac{4}{(x-2)^2}$.

State how you could start from a single graph of $y = \dfrac{1}{x^2}$ and transform it to obtain the other graphs.

9 Sketch the graph of $y = \frac{10}{x^2}$. For each of the transformations, sketch the transformed curve, give its equation and write down the equations of the asymptotes.

a) translation through +3 units parallel to the x-axis
b) translation through –3 units parallel to the y-axis
c) stretch, factor 3, parallel to the y-axis
d) reflection in the x-axis *followed by* a translation through 3 units parallel to the y-axis

10 Sketch the graph of $y = \sqrt{x}$.

For each of the following equations, describe the geometrical transformation of $y = \sqrt{x}$ and then sketch the graph.

a) $y = \sqrt{x-3}$ **b)** $y = 10 - \sqrt{x}$ **c)** $y = -3\sqrt{x}$ **d)** $y = \sqrt{2x-3}$

11 The function f is defined by $f: x \to x^2 - 3x, x \in R$

a) Calculate the range of f.
The function g is defined by $g: x \to \dfrac{2}{x}, x \in R, x \neq 0.$
b) Write down an expression for $fg(x)$.
c) Calculate the coordinates of the stationary point on the curve with equation $y = fg(x)$, giving your answers as exact fractions

(EDEXCEL, Question 5, Paper 1, January 2000)

12 The function f is an odd function defined on the interval [–2, 2]. Given that $f(x) = -x, 0 \le x \le 1, f(x) = x - 2, 1 \le x \le 2,$

a) sketch the graph of f for $-2 \le x \le 2$,
b) find the values of x for which $f(x) = -\dfrac{1}{2}$

(EDEXCEL, Question 3, Paper 1, Jan 1998)

13 The curve with equation $y = f(x)$ meets the coordinate axes at the points (–1, 0), (4, 0) and (0, 3), as shown in the figure. Using a separate diagram for each, sketch the curve with equation

a) $y = f(x-1)$, **b)** $2y = -f(x)$.

On each sketch, write in the coordinates of the points at which the curve meets the coordinate axes.

(EDEXCEL, Question 2, Paper 1, June 1997)

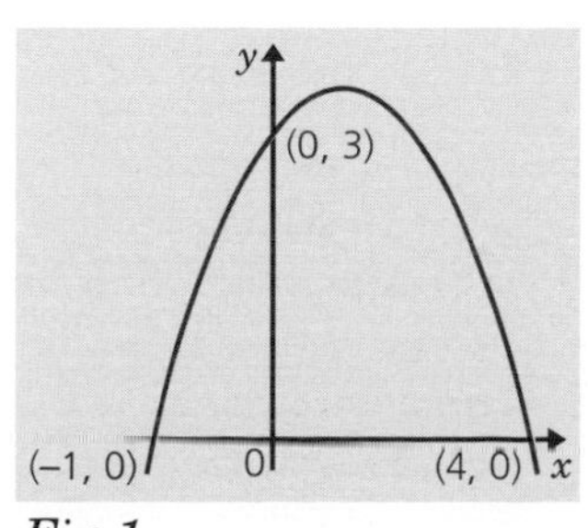

Fig.1.

14 The functions f and g are defined by

$$f : x \to 4x - 1, x \in R, g : x \to \frac{3}{2x-1}, x \in R, x \neq \frac{1}{2}$$

Find in its simplest form

a) the inverse function f^{-1},

b) the composite function gf, stating its domain.

c) Find the values of x for which $2f(x) = g(x)$, giving your answers to 3 decimal places.

(EDEXCEL, Question 5, Paper 1, June 1997)

15 The functions f and g are defined by

$$f: x \to 1 + x^{\frac{1}{2}} \qquad x \geq 0,$$

$$g: x \to x^2 \qquad x \in R$$

i) Find the domain of the inverse function f^{-1}

ii) Find an expression for $f^{-1}(x)$

iii) Find and simplify an expression for $fg(x)$ for the case where $x \geq 0$.

iv) Explain clearly why the value of $fg(-2)$ is 3.

v) Sketch the graph of $y = fg(x)$, for both positive and negative values of x, and give the equation of this graph in a simplified form.

(OCR, Question 7, Specimen Paper 2, 2000)

Summary

- A function is a one-to-one mapping from a set of values called the **domain** to a set of values called the range (or co-domain).
- A composite function is a combination of functions in which one function is followed by another e.g. $fg(x) \equiv f(g(x))$
- Given a function $f(x)$ then the inverse function $f^{-1}(x)$ is such that $f^{-1} f(x) = f f^{-1}(x) = x$.
- The transformation $y = f(-x)$ represents a reflection in the y-axis.
- The transformation $y = -f(x)$ represents a reflection in the x-axis.
- An **even** function $f(x)$ has the property $f(-x) = f(x)$.
- An **odd** function $f(x)$ has the property $-f(-x) = f(x)$.
- The transformation $y = b\, f(x + a)$ represents a translation through $-a$ units parallel to the x-axis followed by a stretch, factor b, parallel to the y-axis.

Algebra 2

In this chapter we:

- *continue to explore the properties of polynomials*
- *develop the skills of dividing polynomials*
- *manipulate rational polynomial expressions.*

POLYNOMIALS REVISITED

Exploration 13.1

Investigating polynomials

- Find the values of the positive constants a, b, c and d such that:
  $x(ax - b)^3 + cx^2 - d = 8x^4 - 12x^3 + 7x^2 - x - 1$
  for all values of x.
- Write down the degree and coefficients of the polynomial:
  $p(x) = 8x^4 - 12x^3 + 7x^2 - x - 1$

Interpreting the results

The polynomial in Exploration 13.1 has **degree** 4. The **coefficients** are the numbers 8, −12, 7, −1, −1. The degree of a polynomial is the highest power of x. Zero-degree polynomials are constants. Polynomials of degrees 1, 2 and 3 are called **linear**, **quadratic** and **cubic** polynomials respectively. Exploration 13.1 demonstrates an important property: that two polynomials are equal for all values of x if they have the same degree and their coefficients are equal. We have.

$$x(ax - b)^3 + cx^2 - d = a^3x^4 - 3a^2bx^3 + (3ab^2 + c)x^2 - b^3x - d$$
$$= 8x^4 - 12x^3 + 7x^2 - x - 1$$

For these two polynomials to be equal for all values of x:

$$a^3 = 8 \Rightarrow a = 2$$
$$-3a^2b = -12 \Rightarrow -3 \times 4 \times b = -12 \Rightarrow b = 1$$
$$3ab^2 + c = 7 \Rightarrow 3 \times 2 \times 1 + c = 7 \Rightarrow c = 1$$
$$-b^3 = -1 \Rightarrow b = 1 \text{ (as before)}$$
$$-d = -1 \Rightarrow d = 1$$

Example 13.1

Find the constants A and B such that $A(x + 1) + B(x + 2) \equiv 3x$

Solution

The left-hand side can be expanded to give:

$$Ax + A + Bx + 2B = Ax + Bx + A + 2B$$
$$= (A + B)x + (A + 2B) \equiv 3x$$

Equating the coefficients of x: $\Rightarrow A + B = 3$ *(1)*
Equating the constant terms: $\Rightarrow A + 3B = 0$ *(2)*

Now we have two simultaneous equations in A and B.
Subtract equation (1) from equation (2):

$$2B = -3 \Rightarrow B = -\tfrac{3}{2}$$

Substitute the value of B into equation (2):

$$A = -3B = \tfrac{9}{2}$$

Example 13.2

Find the constants A, B and C such that:
$A(x-1)(x+3)+B(x-1)(x+2)+C(x+2)(x+3) \equiv 4x^2+9x-1$

Solution
Expand the left-hand side as a polynomial in decreasing powers of x*:*
$A(x^2+2x-3)+B(x^2+x-2)+C(x^2+5x+6)$
$\equiv (A+B+C)x^2+(2A+B+5C)x+(-3A-2B+6C) \equiv 4x^2+9x-1$

Equating the coefficients of x^2*:* $\Rightarrow$ $A+B+C=4$ *(1)*
Equating the coefficients of x*:* $\Rightarrow$ $2A+B+5C=9$ *(2)*
Equating the constant terms: $\Rightarrow$ $-3A-2B+6C=-1$ *(3)*

$(2)-(1)$ $\Rightarrow$ $A+4C=5$ *(4)*
$(3)+2\times(1)$ $\Rightarrow$ $-A+8C=7$ *(5)*
$(4)+(5)$ $\Rightarrow$ $12C=12$ $\Rightarrow$ $C=1$
Substitute for C into equation (4) $\Rightarrow$ $A=1$
Substitute for A and C into equation (1): $\Rightarrow$ $B=2$

An alternative and often much quicker method of approach is to substitute for particular values of the variable into the identity. This approach works because the identity is true for all values of the variable. Consider the problem in Example 13.2 again.

Example 13.3

Find the constants A, B and C such that:

$A(x-1)(x+3)+B(x-1)(x+2)+C(x+2)(x+3) \equiv 4x^2+9x-1.$

Solution
We can choose any value of x *to substitute into each side of the identity, because it is true for all values of* x*. However, choosing wisely will greatly reduce the work.*
Choose $x=1$ *and then the term* $(x-1)$ *is zero.*

$A\times(0)\times(4)+B\times(0)\times(3)+C\times(3)\times(4)=4+9-1=12$
$\Rightarrow \quad 12C=12 \quad \Rightarrow \quad C=1$

Choose $x=-3$ *and then the term* $(x+3)$ *is zero.*

$A\times(-4)\times(0)+B\times(-4)\times(-1)+C\times(-1)\times(0)=36-27-1=8$
$\Rightarrow \quad 4B=8 \quad \Rightarrow \quad B=2$

Choose $x=-2$ *and then the term* $(x+2)$ *is zero.*

$A\times(-3)\times(1)+B\times(-3)\times(0)+C\times(0)\times(1)=16-18-1=-3$
$\Rightarrow \quad -3A=-3 \quad \Rightarrow \quad A=1$

This example shows that, in general, the value substitution method offers a much easier way to solve problems of this type. However, there are problems where we use a mixture of both methods.

Example 13.4

Find the constants A and B such that:

$A(x^2+1)+(x-2)(Bx+C) \equiv 3x^2-3x+4$

Solution
We begin by using the value substitution method as far as possible.
Choose $x=2$ *and then the term* $(x-2)$ *is zero.*

$A\times(5)+(0)\times(2B+C)=12-6+4=10$
$\Rightarrow \quad 5A=10 \quad \Rightarrow \quad A=2$

Choose $x = 0$ (this eliminates the constant B).

$$A \times (1) + (-2) \times C = 4$$
$$\Rightarrow \quad -2C = 4 - A$$

Substitute for A: $\Rightarrow -2C = 4 - 2 = 2$
$\Rightarrow C = -1$

For the final constant B we equate coefficients.

$$Ax^2 + A + Bx^2 - 2Bx + Cx - 2C \equiv 3x^2 - 3x + 4$$
$$(A + B)x^2 + (C - 2B)x + (A - 2C) \equiv 3x^2 - 3x + 4$$

Equate coefficients of x^2:

$$A + B = 3$$

Substitute $A = 2$: $\Rightarrow B = 1$

EXERCISES

13.1 CLASSWORK

Find the values of the constants A, B and C in the following identities.

1 $A(x + 1) + B(x + 2) \equiv 3x + 5$

2 $A(x + 5) + B(x + 3) \equiv 5x + 19$

3 $A(x + 2) + B(x - 1) \equiv 6x + 3$

4 $A(x + 2) - B(x - 4) \equiv x + 14$

5 $A(x + 1)(x - 2) + B(x - 1)(x + 3) \equiv 3x^2 + 3x - 8$

6 $A(x + 2)(x + 4) + B(x + 2)(x + 3) + C(x + 3)(x + 4) \equiv 6x^2 + 34x + 46$

7 $A(x + 1)(x + 2) + B(x + 1)(x + 3) + C(x + 2)(x + 3) \equiv 2x + 3$

8 $A(x - 1)(x + 4) + B(2x + 1)(x - 1) + C(2x + 1)(x + 4) \equiv 7x^3 + 10x - 2$

9 $(Ax + B)(x - 1) + C(x^2 + 2) \equiv x^2 + x - 5$

10 $A(x^2 + x - 1) + (Bx + C)(2x - 3) \equiv 3x^2 - 13x + 10$

11 $(Ax + B)(x + 2) + C(x^2 - 2x + 2) \equiv 5x + 5$

12 Find the values of the constants A, B and C for which:
$A(x + B)^2 + C \equiv 2 - 4x - 4x^2$
Hence find the maximum value of $2 - 4x - 4x^2$.

13 Find the values of the constants A, B and C for which:
$A(x + B)^2 + C \equiv 4x^2 - 8x + 11$
Hence find the minimum value of $4x^2 - 8x + 11$.

14 Multiply out the following polynomials.
a) $(2x^2 + 3x - 1) \times (3x - 1)$
b) $(x^2 + 5x - 2) \times (x - 3)$
c) $(2x^2 + x - 1) \times (x^2 - x + 2)$
d) $(3x^2 - 2x + 1) \times (2x^2 + x + 2)$

EXERCISES

13.1 HOMEWORK

Find the values of the constants A, B and C in the following identities.

1 $A(x - 1) + B(x + 2) \equiv -x - 5$

2 $A(x + 4) + B(x - 6) \equiv 2x - 7$

3 $A(2x - 1) + B(3x + 1) \equiv 8x + 1$

4 $(Ax + B)(x - 2) + C(x^2 + 2) \equiv 3x^2 - x - 4$

5 $A(x + 3)(x - 1) + B(x + 1)(x + 5) \equiv x^2 + 14x + 21$

6 $A(x + 2)(x + 4) + B(x + 2)(x + 3) + C(x + 3)(x + 4) \equiv -3x^2 - 24x - 44$

7 $A(x - 2)(2x + 3) + B(x - 2)(x - 4) + C(2x + 3)(x - 4) \equiv \frac{9}{2}x^2 - \frac{29}{2}x - 3$

8 $A(x - 3)(x + 4) + B(x - 3)(x - 1) + C(x - 1)(x + 4) \equiv x^2 - 3x + 7$

9 $(Ax + B)(x + 1) + C(x^2 + 3) \equiv 4x^2 - x + 3$

10 $A(x^2 - 3x - 1) + (Bx + C)(3x + 1) \equiv 6x^2 - 14x - 5$

11 $A(x - 1) + B(x - 1)^2 + C(x + 4) \equiv 3x^2 - 7x + 9$

12 Find the values of the constants A, B and C for which
$A(x + B)^2 + C \equiv -2x^2 + 6x - 5$
Hence find the maximum value of $-2x^2 + 6x - 5$.

13 Find the values of the constants A, B and C for which:
$A(x + B)^2 + C \equiv 9x^2 - 6x + 8$
Hence find the minimum value of $9x^2 - 6x + 8$.

14 Multiply out the following polynomials.
a) $(3x^2 + 2x - 4) \times (x - 1)$
b) $(x^2 - 3x - 2) \times (2x + 3)$
c) $(2x^2 + 3x - 5) \times (x^2 - 2x + 1)$
d) $(x^2 + 2x - 1) \times (3x^2 + x + 3)$

DIVISION OF POLYNOMIALS

Exploration 13.2

Remainders

- Find the remainder when 594 is divided is divided by 111.
- Find the remainder when $x^2 + 1$ is divided by x.

Interpreting the results

When we divide one positive integer by a smaller positive integer we get a whole number (called the **quotient**) and a remainder. For example:

$$\frac{594}{111} = 5 + \frac{39}{111}$$

where 5 is the quotient and 39 is the remainder. In general for any integers a, b with $|a| > |b|$:

$$\frac{a}{b} = c + \frac{r}{b}$$

where $0 \le r < b$. If $r = 0$ then b is a **factor** of a.

These ideas carry through to polynomials. For example:

$$\frac{x^2+1}{x} = x + \frac{1}{x}$$

(quotient: x; remainder: 1)

If $a(x)$ and $b(x)$ are both polynomials then $b(x)$ divides $a(x)$ provided the degree of $a(x)$ is greater than or equal to the degree of $b(x)$. The degree of the remainder is always less than the degree of $b(x)$.

$$\frac{a(x)}{b(x)} = q(x) + \frac{r(x)}{b(x)}$$

If $r(x) = 0$ then $b(x)$ is a **factor** of $a(x)$.

The method of long division is used to divide polynomials. To set the scene for the long division of polynomials, we look back at the long division process for numbers. Suppose we divide 974 by 17. It is set out like this.

Take the first two digits 97 and ask, 'How many times does 17 divide into 97?'

$$17\overline{)974}$$

The answer is 5 so write 5 above the second digit 7:

$$\begin{array}{r} 5 \\ 17\overline{)974} \end{array}$$

Then multiply 17 by 5 and put the answer under the 97. Subtract 85 from 97.

$$\begin{array}{r} 5 \\ 17\overline{)974} \\ \underline{85} \\ 12 \end{array}$$

Now bring down the 4 to join the 12. (What we have done is to say that $974 = 50 \times 17 + 124$; the next step is to divide 124 by 17.)

$$\begin{array}{r} 5 \\ 17\overline{)974} \\ \underline{85} \\ 124 \end{array}$$

Now ask the question, 'How many times does 17 go into 124?" and the answer is 7. So write 7 next to the 5 and multiply 17 by 7.

$$\begin{array}{rl} 57 & \\ 17\overline{)974} & \\ \underline{85} & \\ 124 & \\ \underline{119} & \leftarrow \text{Multiply 17 by 7} \\ 5 & \leftarrow \text{Subtract 119 from 124} \end{array}$$

Thus 5 is the remainder and we have:

$$\frac{974}{17} = 57\frac{5}{17}$$

Example 13.5

Divide $6x^3 + x^2 + 7x + 4$ by $2x - 1$.

Solution

Set up the long division of $6x^3 + x^2 + 7x + 4$ by $2x - 1$ *like this.*

$$2x - 1\overline{)6x^3 + x^2 + 7x + 4}$$

Take the first term, i.e. $6x^3$, *'under the bridge' and ask, 'How many times does* $2x$ *go into* $6x^3$*?' The answer is* $3x^2$ *(with a remainder). Multiply* $2x - 1$ *by* $3x^2$.

$$\begin{array}{r} 3x^2\phantom{{}+7x+4} \\ 2x - 1\overline{)6x^3 + x^2 + 7x + 4} \\ \underline{6x^3 - 3x^2}\phantom{{}+7x+4} \\ 4x^2 + 7x + 4 \end{array}$$

Subtract $6x^3 - 3x^2$ *from* $6x^3 + x^2 + 7x + 4$.

Now repeat the process. 'How many times does $2x$ *go into the leading term* $4x^2$*?'*
The answer is $2x$ *(with a remainder).*
Multiply $2x - 1$ *by* $2x$.

$$\begin{array}{rl} 3x^2 + 2x\phantom{{}+4} & \\ 2x - 1\overline{)6x^3 + x^2 + 7x + 4} & \\ \underline{6x^3 - 3x^2}\phantom{{}+7x+4} & \\ 4x^2 + 7x + 4 & \\ \underline{4x^2 - 2x}\phantom{{}+4} & \leftarrow \textit{Multiply } 2x - 1 \textit{ by } 2x. \\ 9x + 4 & \leftarrow \textit{Subtract } 4x^2 - 2x \textit{ from } 4x^2 + 7x + 4. \end{array}$$

Repeat the process one more time.

$$
\begin{array}{r}
3x^2 + 2x + \\
2x - 1\overline{)6x^3 + x^2 + 7x + 4} \\
\underline{6x^3 - 3x^2} \\
4x^2 + 7x + 4 \\
\underline{4x^2 - 2x} \\
9x + 4 \\
\underline{9x - \tfrac{9}{2}} \\
\tfrac{17}{2}
\end{array}
$$

Multiply $2x - 1$ *by* $\frac{9}{2}$.

Subtract $9x - \frac{9}{2}$ *from* $9x + 4$.

The quotient is $3x^2 + 2x + \frac{9}{2}$ *and the remainder is* $\frac{17}{2}$.

Example 13.6

Find the quotient and remainder when $6x^4 + 7x^3 - 3x^2 + 8x - 12$ *is divided by* $2x^2 + x - 1$.

Solution

Set up the long division of $6x^4 + 7x^3 - 3x^2 + 8x - 12$ *by* $2x^2 + x - 1$.

$$2x^2 + x - 1\overline{)6x^4 + 7x^3 - 3x^2 + 8x - 12}$$

We need to ask, 'How many times does $2x^2$ *go into* $6x^4$*?'*

Divide $6x^4$ *by* $2x^2$ *to give* $3x^2$ *and write:*

$$
\begin{array}{r}
3x^2 \\
2x^2 + x - 1\overline{)6x^4 + 7x^3 - 3x^2 + 8x - 12} \\
\underline{6x^4 + 3x^3 - 3x^2} \\
4x^3 + 8x - 12
\end{array}
$$

Multiply $2x^2 + x - 1$ *by* $3x^2$.

Subtract $6x^4 + 3x^3 - 3x^2$. *from* $6x^4 + 7x^3 - 3x^2 + 8x - 12$.

Divide $4x^3$ *by* $2x^2$ *to give* $2x$.

$$
\begin{array}{r}
3x^2 + 2x \\
2x^2 + x - 1\overline{)6x^4 + 7x^3 - 3x^2 + 8x - 12} \\
\underline{6x^4 + 3x^3 - 3x^2} \\
4x^3 + 8x - 12 \\
\underline{4x^3 + 2x^2 - 2x} \\
-2x^2 + 10x - 12
\end{array}
$$

Multiply $2x^2 + x - 1$ *by* $2x$.

Subtract $4x^3 + 2x^2 - 2x$ *from* $4x^3 + 8x - 12$.

Divide $-2x^2$ *by* $2x^2$ *to give* -1.

$$
\begin{array}{r}
3x^2 + 2x - 1 \\
2x^2 + x - 1\overline{)6x^4 + 7x^3 - 3x^2 + 8x - 12} \\
\underline{6x^4 + 3x^3 - 3x^2} \\
4x^3 + 8x - 12 \\
\underline{4x^3 + 2x^2 - 2x} \\
-2x^2 + 10x - 12 \\
\underline{-2x^2 - x + 1} \\
11x - 13
\end{array}
$$

Multiply $2x^2 + x - 1$ *by* -1.

Subtract $-2x^2 - x + 1$ *from* $-2x^2 + 10x - 12$.

Finally we write:

$$\frac{6x^4 + 7x^3 - 3x^2 + 8x - 12}{2x^2 + x - 1} = 3x^2 + 2x - 1 + \frac{11x - 13}{2x^2 + x - 1}$$

The quotient is $3x^2 + 2x - 1$ *and the remainder is* $11x - 13$.

EXERCISES

13.2 CLASSWORK

Divide:

1 $2x^2 - 7x - 1$ by $x - 3$

2 $2x^3 - 11x^2 + 12x - 37$ by $x - 5$

3 $x^5 + x^4 - x^3 + 2x - 1$ by $x^2 + x + 1$

4 $4x^3 + 1$ by $(x - 1)^2$

5 $x^4 - x^2 - 2x + 2$ by $(x - 1)^2$

6 $x^5 + 3x^4 - 2x^3 - 5x^2 + 6x - 2$ by $x^3 + x^2 - x + 1$

EXERCISES

13.2 HOMEWORK

Divide:

1 $x^3 - 5x^2 - 2x + 24$ by $x + 2$

2 $-18x^3 + 3x^2 - 27x + 10$ by $-3x + 2$

3 $x^5 - x^4 + 3x^3 + 2x + 5$ by $x^2 - x + 2$

4 $x^4 + 3x^2 + 1$ by $x^2 + x + 1$

5 $6x^5 + 4x^4 - 7x^3 + 3x^2 + x - 2$ by $2x^2 + 1$

6 $x^4 + (2 + a)x^3 + (3a + 1)x^2 + 3ax + 1$ by $(x + 1)^2$

ALGEBRAIC FRACTIONS

Exploration 13.3

Simplifying fractions

Simplify: ■ $\frac{4}{3} \div \frac{5}{9} + \frac{2}{7}$ ■ $\frac{a^2}{3b} \div \frac{ab}{c} + \frac{4}{a}$

Manipulating fractions

The process of simplifying algebraic fractions obeys the same rules as manipulating numbers in numerical expressions.

For $\frac{4}{3} \div \frac{5}{9} + \frac{2}{7}$ we first simplify the division $\frac{4}{3} \div \frac{5}{9} = \frac{4 \times \not{9}^{3}}{\not{3}_{1} \times 5} \times 5 = \frac{12}{5}$

To add $\frac{12}{5}$ and $\frac{2}{7}$ we first find the lowest common denominator which in this case is $7 \times 5 = 35$.

$$\frac{12}{5} + \frac{2}{7} = \frac{12 \times 7 + 2 \times 5}{35} = \frac{84 + 10}{35} = \frac{94}{35}$$

For the second expression we follow similar steps.

$$\frac{a^2}{3b} \div \frac{ab}{c} = \frac{{}^{a}\not{a}^2 \times c}{3b \times \not{a}b} = \frac{ac}{3b^2}$$

$$\frac{ac}{3b^2} + \frac{4}{a} = \frac{ac \times a + 4 \times 3b^2}{3ab^2} = \frac{a^2c + 12b^2}{3ab^2}$$

common denominator

Example 13.7

Multiplying fractions

Simplify: $\frac{7}{x^2 - 4} \times \frac{x + 2}{14}$

Solution

The first step is to look for factors in the polynomials.

$x^2 - 4 \equiv (x - 2)(x + 2)$

$$\Rightarrow \frac{7}{x^2 - 4} \times \frac{x + 2}{14} = \frac{7}{(x - 2)(x + 2)} \times \frac{x + 2}{14}$$
$$= \frac{1 \times 1}{(x - 2) \times 2}$$
$$= \frac{1}{2\,(x - 2)}$$

Cancel numerator and denominator by 7.
Cancel numerator and denominator by $(x + 2)$.

Example 13.8

Dividing fractions

Simplify: $\frac{3x^2}{x^2 - 1} \div \frac{4x}{x^2 - 3x + 2}$

Solution

Factorise: $x^2 - 1$ *to give* $(x - 1)(x + 1)$.
Factorise: $x^2 - 3x + 2$ *to give* $(x - 1)(x - 2)$.

$$\frac{3x^2}{x^2 - 1} \div \frac{4x}{x^2 - 3x + 2} = \frac{3x^2}{(x - 1)(x + 1)} \div \frac{4x}{(x - 1)(x - 2)}$$
$$= \frac{3x^2}{(x - 1)(x + 1)} \times \frac{(x - 1)(x - 2)}{4x}$$
$$= \frac{3x \times (x - 2)}{(x + 1) \times 4}$$
$$= \frac{3x\,(x - 2)}{4(x + 1)}$$

Cancel by x.
Cancel by $(x - 1)$.

Example 13.9

Adding and subtracting fractions

Write $\frac{3}{x - 1} + \frac{7}{x^2 - 1} - \frac{1}{x + 2}$ *as a single fraction.*

Solution

Factorise $x^2 - 1 = (x - 1)(x + 1)$

$$\frac{3}{x - 1} + \frac{7}{(x - 1)(x + 1)} - \frac{1}{x + 2}$$

The common denominator is $(x - 1)(x + 1)(x + 2)$ *so we write each fraction over the common denominator.*

$$\frac{3(x + 1)(x + 2)}{(x - 1)(x + 1)(x + 2)} + \frac{7(x + 2)}{(x - 1)(x + 1)(x + 2)} - \frac{(x - 1)(x + 1)}{(x - 1)(x + 1)(x + 2)}$$

$$= \frac{3(x^2 + 3x + 2) + 7x + 14 - (x^2 - 1)}{(x - 1)(x + 1)(x + 2)} = \frac{2x^2 + 16x + 21}{(x - 1)(x + 1)(x + 2)}$$

Example 13.10

Write $\frac{(x+1)(x-2)}{(x+3)(x+1)} - \frac{3(x-1)}{(x+3)} + \frac{2x+1}{(x+1)}$ *as a single fraction.*

Solution

The common denominator is $(x+3)(x+1)$. *Write each expression in terms of the common denominator.*

$$\frac{(x+1)(x-2)}{(x+3)(x+1)} - \frac{3(x-1)(x+1)}{(x+3)(x+1)} + \frac{(2x+1)(x+3)}{(x+3)(x+1)}$$

$$= \frac{x^2-x-2}{(x+3)(x+1)} - \frac{3x^2-3}{(x+3)(x+1)} + \frac{2x^2+7x+3}{(x+3)(x+1)}$$

$$= \frac{x^2-x-2-3x^2+3+2x^2+7x+3}{(x+3)(x+1)}$$

$$= \frac{6x+4}{(x+3)(x+1)} = \frac{2(3x+2)}{(x+3)(x+1)}$$

EXERCISES

13.3 CLASSWORK

Express each of the following in the simplest form.

1 $\frac{(x+1)^2}{3x^2} \div \frac{2(x+1)(x-1)}{5x}$

2 $\frac{x^2-9}{x^2-4} \div \frac{5(x-3)}{2x^2(x+2)}$

3 $\frac{1+\frac{3}{x}}{\frac{3}{x}-1}$

4 $\frac{2}{1-x^2} \div \left(\frac{1}{1-x} - \frac{1}{1+x}\right)$

5 $\frac{x^2+3x+2}{x^2-3x+2} \div \frac{x^2+5x+4}{2x^2-3x+1}$

6 $\frac{2}{3x-1} - \frac{1}{2-5x}$

7 $\frac{2}{(x+3)(x-1)} + \frac{1}{(x-1)(x+1)}$

8 $\frac{2x+1}{x^2-9} - \frac{x+2}{x^2-2x-3}$

9 $\frac{5}{x-3} + \frac{x+2}{x^2+4x-21} - \frac{2x-3}{2x^2+13x-7}$

10 $\frac{(x+1)(x+2)}{(x+3)(x-1)} + \frac{2x}{x+3} - \frac{4x-1}{x-1}$

EXERCISES

13.3 HOMEWORK

Express each of the following in the simplest form.

1 $\frac{(x+2)(x-3)}{x+1} \div \frac{4x(x+2)}{x^2-1}$

2 $\frac{1-x^2}{4x(x+7)} \div \frac{3+x-2x^2}{6x^2}$

3 $\frac{\frac{2}{1+x} - \frac{1}{1-x}}{1-x^2}$

4 $\frac{2}{1-x^2} + \frac{1}{1-x} - \frac{1}{1+x}$

5 $\frac{2(x+3)^2}{x^2(x-1)} \div \frac{10(x^2-9)}{2x^2+x-3}$

6 $\frac{1}{2x+1} - \frac{2}{x+3}$

7 $\frac{3}{(x+1)(x-2)} + \frac{2}{x^2+3}$

8 $\frac{2}{x^2+4x+3} - \frac{3}{2x-1}$

9 $\frac{2}{x+1} + \frac{2x+1}{x^2+8x+15} - \frac{x-1}{x^2+4x+3}$

10 $\frac{2(x+3)(2x-3)}{(2x-1)(x+7)} - \frac{4x-1}{2x-1} + \frac{x+1}{x+7}$

CONSOLIDATION EXERCISES FOR CHAPTER 13

1 The constants a, b, c and d are chosen so that the following identity is true for all values of x:

$$(ax + b)(x^2 - 4x + 5) \equiv 2x^3 + cx^2 + dx + 5$$

Find the values of a, b, c and d.

2 Find the values of A, B and C for which:

$$2x^2 - 4x + 5 \equiv A(x + B)^2 + C$$

Hence find the minimum value of $2x^2 - 4x + 5$.

3 Find the values of the constants A, B and C for which:

$$A(x^2 + 5) + (Bx + C)(x - 3) \equiv 3x^2 + 5x + 28$$

4 Use long division of polynomials to verify that $x^2 + x + 2$ is a factor of $f(x) = 2x^4 - x^3 + 5x^2 - 2x + 8$. Hence deduce that $f(x) = 0$ has no real roots.

5 What is the remainder when $x^4 + 2x^3 - x^2 + x - 4$ is divided by $(x^2 + 2)$?

6 Express $\frac{5(x-3)(x+1)}{2(x-2)(x+3)} - \frac{3(x+1)}{x-2} + \frac{2(x-3)}{(x+3)}$ as a single fraction in its simplest form.

(Edexcel Question 2, Specimen Paper 2 2000)

7 Express $\frac{3x+1}{x^2+x+1} + \frac{2}{(x-1)} - \frac{3}{x+3}$ as a single fraction in its simplest form.

8 Use a graphic calculator to find the real roots of the polynomial $f(x) = 2x^4 + 3x^3 - 2x - 3$ and hence factorise $f(x)$.

9 Find the quotient and remainder when $f(x) = x^4 - ax^2 + (2a - 4)x + (3 - a)$ is divided by $(x - 1)^2$. Hence prove that the zeros of $f(x)$ are real if $a \geq 2$.

Summary

- Two polynomials are equal for all values of x if they have the same degree and their coefficients are equal.
- If $a(x)$ and $b(x)$ are both polynomials then $b(x)$ divides $a(x)$ provided the degree of $a(x)$ is greater than or equal to the degree of $b(x)$. The remainder is a polynomial $r(x)$ with degree less than the degree of $b(x)$.

  $$\frac{a(x)}{b(x)} = 9x + \frac{r(x)}{b(x)}$$
- If $r(x) = 0$ then $b(x)$ is a factor of $a(x)$.
- The method of long division is used to divide polynomials.

Sequences and series 2: Binomial expansions

In this chapter we introduce:

- *the binomial theorem expansion of $(a + b)^n$ for integer n*
- *the binomial series expansion of $(1 + x)^n$ for integer, negative and fractional values of n.*

THE BINOMIAL THEOREM

In this section we shall develop the ideas introduced in Chapter 10, *Sequences and series 1*, and examine the binomial theorem and series.

Exploration 14.1

Pascal's triangle

This pattern of numbers is called **Pascal's triangle**.

1							
1	1						
1	2	1					
1	3	3	1				
1	4	6	4	1			
1	5	10	10	5	1		
•	•	•	•	•	•	•	
•	•	•	•	•	•	•	•
etc.							

- Continue the pattern for the next four rows.
- What properties can you find?

Patterns in Pascal's triangle

There are several interesting features of Pascal's triangle, for example:

- for any row, the sum of two adjacent numbers gives the number in the next row underneath the second number.

  e.g.

1	2		6	4		5	10
	3			10			15

- the sum of the numbers in each row is a power of 2.
  e.g. $1 + 4 + 6 + 4 + 1 = 16 = 2^4$

- the third column gives the triangle numbers.
  1, 3, 6, 10, 15, ...

Notation

We can refer to any number in Pascal's triangle by specifying its row (n) and column (r), denoting the number by $\binom{n}{r}$.

Both n and r begin at 0, e.g. $\binom{5}{3} = 10$, since 10 is the entry in row 5, column 3.

n \ r	0	1	2	**3**	4	5	6	7
0	1							
1	1	1						
2	1	2	1					
3	1	3	3	1				
4	1	4	6	4	1			
5	1	5	10	**10**	5	1		
6	1	6	15	20	15	6	1	
7	1	7	21	35	35	21	7	1

We have seen that, for example,

$$\binom{6}{4} + \binom{6}{5} = \binom{7}{5} \qquad \text{i.e. } 15 + 6 = 21$$

In general, this gives rise to: $\binom{n}{r} + \binom{n}{r+1} = \binom{n+1}{r+1}$

This is an **inductive** definition, giving one number in the triangle as the sum of two others in the previous row. This is fine for small values of n and r but what of $\binom{15}{4}$? Do we need to extend the triangle to row 15 before we can find its value?

Exploration 14.2

Continuing patterns

Continue the pattern in these expansions.

$$\begin{aligned}
(a+b)^1 &= a + b \\
(a+b)^2 &= a^2 + 2ab + b^2 \\
(a+b)^3 &= a^3 + 3a^2b + 3ab^2 + b^3 \\
(a+b)^4 &= a^4 + 4a^3b + \ldots \\
\ldots &= \ldots \\
\ldots &= \ldots
\end{aligned}$$

- What patterns do the coefficients form?
- What patterns do the powers of a and b form?
- How can you generate the expansion of $(a + b)^n$?

Coefficients and Pascal's triangle

The coefficients in the expansion of $(a + b)^n$ form the nth row of Pascal's triangle:

$$(a+b)^4 = \mathbf{1}a^4 + \mathbf{4}a^3b + \mathbf{6}a^2b^2 + \mathbf{4}ab^3 + \mathbf{1}b^4$$

Just as the fourth row of the triangle can be generated from the third row, so $(a + b)^4$ can be generated from $(a + b)^3$.

$$\begin{aligned}
(a+b)^4 &= (a+b)^3(a+b) \\
&= (a^3 + 3a^2b + 3ab^2 + b^3)(a+b) \\
&= a^4 + 4a^3b + 6a^2b^2 + 4ab^3 + b^4
\end{aligned}$$

Note that in the expansion of $(a+b)^4$, reading from left to right, the powers of a descend from 4 to 0, the powers of b ascend from 0 to 4 and for any term, the sum of the indices is 4. This can be extended to $(a+b)^n$.

A formula for $\binom{n}{r}$ arises from a consideration of the expansion of $(a+b)^n$ from first principles.
Look again at $(a+b)^4$.

$$(a+b)^4 = (a+b)(a+b)(a+b)(a+b)$$

The term in a^3b is formed by combining a from three brackets and b from one bracket. This may be done in four ways.

$$\left.\begin{aligned} aaab &= a^3b \quad + \\ aaba &= a^3b \quad + \\ abaa &= a^3b \quad + \\ baaa &= a^3b \end{aligned}\right\} = 4a^3b$$

These four ways are related to the number of ways of choosing one bracket from four to generate the b, the rest generating an a. The number of ways of choosing one object from four is:

$${}^4C_1 = \frac{4!}{1!3!} = 4 \text{ thus } \binom{4}{1} = {}^4C_1$$

Similarly, the term in a^2b^2 is formed by choosing b from two brackets and a from the rest, which can be done in six ways.

$$\binom{4}{2} = {}^4C_2 = \frac{4!}{2!2!} = 6$$

In the expansion of $(a+b)^n$, the term in, say, $a^{n-3}b^3$ is formed by choosing b from three brackets and a from the rest, which gives the coefficient.

$$\binom{n}{3} = {}^nC_3 = \frac{n!}{3!(n-3)!}$$

In general, then, the coefficient of $a^{n-r}b^r$ is formed by choosing b from r brackets and a from the rest, which can be done in

$$\binom{n}{r} = {}^nC_r = \frac{n!}{r!(n-r)!} \text{ ways.}$$

This leads to the general statement of the **binomial theorem**.

$$(a+b)^n = \binom{n}{0}a^n + \binom{n}{1}a^{n-1}b + \binom{n}{2}a^{n-2}b^2 + \ldots + \binom{n}{r}a^{n-r}b^r + \ldots + \binom{n}{n-1}ab^{n-1} + \binom{n}{n}b^n$$

Example 14.1

For the expression $(a+b)^{10}$:

a) *find the coefficient of a^3b^7,*

b) *write down the first four terms in descending powers of a.*

Solution

a) *The coefficient of a^3b^7 is* $\binom{10}{7} = {}^{10}C_7 = \frac{10!}{7!3!} = 120$

b) $(a+b)^{10} = \binom{10}{0}a^{10} + \binom{10}{1}a^9b + \binom{10}{2}a^8b^2 + \binom{10}{3}a^7b^3 + \ldots$

$= a^{10} + 10a^9b + 45a^8b^2 + 120a^7b^3 + \ldots$

Example 14.2

For the expression $(2p - q)^7$:

a) *find the term in* p^2,
b) *write down the first three terms in ascending powers of* q.

Solution
Firstly treat $(2p - q)^7$ *as* $(2p + (-q))^7$, *i.e.*
$a = 2p$, $b = -q$ *and* $n = 7$.

a) *The term in* $p^2 \equiv$ *term in* q^5, *which is:*
$^7C_5(2p)^2(-q)^5 = 21 \times 4p^2 \times (-q^5) = -84p^2q^5$

b)
$$(2p-q)^7 = \binom{7}{0}(2p)^7 + \binom{7}{1}(2p)^6(-q) + \binom{7}{2}(2p)^5(-q)^2 + \ldots$$
$$= 2^7p^7 + 7 \times 2^6p^6(-q) + 21 \times 2^5p^5(-q)^2 + \ldots$$
$$= 128p^7 - 448p^6q + 672p^5q^2 + \ldots$$

Example 14.3

Find the term in x^3 *in the expansion of* $(1 - x)(2 + x)^5$.

Solution
$$(2+x)^5 = \binom{5}{0}2^5 + \binom{5}{1}2^4x + \binom{5}{2}2^3x^2 + \binom{5}{3}2^2x^3 + \binom{5}{4}2x^4 + \binom{5}{5}x^5$$
$$= 32 + 80x + 80x^2 + 40x^3 + 10x^4 + x^5$$

$\Rightarrow$ *the term in* x^3 *for*

$$(1-x)(2+x)^5 \equiv (1-x)(32 + 80x + 80x^2 + 40x^3 + 10x^4 + x^5)$$

is $1 \times 40x^3 - x \times 80x^2 = 40x^3 - 80x^3 = -40x^3$

EXERCISES

14.1 CLASSWORK

1 Use Pascal's triangle to expand the following.

a) $(a + b)^6$ **b)** $(p - q)^5$ **c)** $(3r + 5)^8$

2 For the expression $(a + b)^{12}$:

a) find the coefficient of a^4b^8,
b) write down the first four terms in descending powers of a.

3 Use the binomial theorem to expand the following expressions.

a) $(x + 3y)^4$ **b)** $(2f + 3g)^5$ **c)** $(3x - 2y)^8$

4 Find the coefficients of the stated terms in the following.

a) b^3 in $(a + b)^9$ **b)** z^2 in $(2z + 1)^{10}$ **c)** q^5 in $(2p - q)^8$
d) g^7 in $(5f + 2g)^{12}$ **e)** x^{13} in $(1 - x)^{20}$ **f)** x^r in $(1 - x)^{20}$

5 Find the term in x^3 in each of the following expansions.

a) $(2 + x)(3 + x)^4$ **b)** $(3 - x)(1 + x)^7$ **c)** $(2 + x)^2(3 + x)^{10}$

EXERCISES

14.1 HOMEWORK

1 Use Pascal's triangle to expand the following expressions.

a) $(m+n)^5$ **b)** $(3-a)^7$ **c)** $(2x+3)^4$

2 For the expression $(x-y)^{10}$:

a) find the coefficient of x^5y^5,
b) write down the first four terms in descending powers of x.

3 Use the binomial theorem to expand the following expressions.

a) $(a+2b)^5$ **b)** $(4a-2b)^7$ **c)** $(\frac{1}{2}m-2n)^6$

4 Find the coefficients of the stated terms in the following.

a) a^3 in $(a+b)^4$ **b)** x^4 in $(2x+3)^{13}$ **c)** q^2 in $(p-4q)^{12}$
d) a^5 in $(9a+3b)^7$ **e)** x^5 in $(1-2x)^6$ **f)** x^n in $(2+x)^8$

5 Find the term in x^3 in each of the following expansions.

a) $(3+x)(5+x)^5$ **b)** $(1+x)(x-3)^9$ **c)** $(5-x^2)(7-x)^6$

BINOMIAL SERIES

A special case of the binomial theorem arises when $a = 1$ and $b = x$. It can be very useful, as we shall see.

$$(1+x)^n = \binom{n}{0} + \binom{n}{1}x + \binom{n}{2}x^2 + \ldots + \binom{n}{r}x^r + \ldots + \binom{n}{n-1}x^{n-1} + \binom{n}{n}x^n$$

But:

$$\binom{n}{0} = 1,\ \binom{n}{1} = n,\ \binom{n}{2} = \frac{n(n-1)}{2!},\ \ldots,\ \binom{n}{r} = \frac{n(n-1)\ldots(n-r+1)}{r!},\ \ldots,\ \binom{n}{n-1} = n,\ \binom{n}{n} = 1$$

hence:

$$(1+x)^n = 1 + nx + \frac{n(n-1)}{2!}x^2 + \ldots + \frac{n(n-1)(n-2)\ldots(n-r+1)}{r!}x^r + \ldots + nx^{n-1} + x^n$$

This form of expansion is called the **binomial series**, valid for any positive integer n.

Example 14.4

Expand the following in ascending powers of x, up to and including the term in x^4.

a) $(1+2x)^7$ ***b)*** $(1-x)^8$ ***c)*** $(1+x^2)^5$

Solution

a) $(1+2x)^7$

$$\equiv 1 + 7\times 2x + \frac{7\times 6}{2!}\times(2x)^2 + \frac{7\times 6\times 5}{3!}\times(2x)^3 + \frac{7\times 6\times 5\times 4}{4!}\times(2x)^4 + \ldots$$
$$= 1 + 14x + 84x^2 + 280x^3 + 560x^4 + \ldots$$

b) $(1-x)^8$

$$\equiv 1 + 8(-x) + \frac{8\times 7}{2!}\times(-x)^2 + \frac{8\times 7\times 6}{3!}\times(-x)^3 + \frac{8\times 7\times 6\times 5}{4!}\times(-x)^4 + \ldots$$
$$= 1 - 8x + 28x^2 - 56x^3 + 70x^4 + \ldots$$

c) $(1+x^2)^5 \equiv 1 + 5x^2 + \frac{5\times 4}{2!}\times(x^2)^2 + \ldots$

$$= 1 + 5x^2 + 10x^4 + \ldots$$

Example 14.5

Use the binomial series to find the first four terms of $(5+x)(1-3x)^7$.

Solution

$$(1-3x)^7 \equiv 1+7(-3x)+\frac{7\times 6}{2!}(-3x)^2+\frac{7\times 6\times 5}{3!}(-3x)^3+...$$
$$=1-21x+189x^2-945x^3+...$$
$$\Rightarrow (5+x)(1-3x)^7 \equiv (5+x)(1-21x+189x^2-945x^3+...)$$
$$=5-104x+924x^2-4536x^3+...$$

Example 14.6

The coefficient of x in the expansion of $(1-4x)(1+cx)^6$ is 8. Find the coefficient of x^2.

Solution

$$(1+cx)^6 \equiv 1+6cx+15c^2x^2+...$$
$$\Rightarrow (1-4x)(1+cx)^6 \equiv (1-4x)(1+6cx+15c^2x^2+...)$$
$$\equiv 1+(6c-4)x+(15c^2-24c)x^2+...$$

Coefficient of x is 8 $\Rightarrow 6c-4=8 \Rightarrow 6c=12 \Rightarrow c=2$

$\Rightarrow$ *Coefficient of x^2 is* $15c^2-24c=15\times 4-24\times 2=12$

Approximating powers

It is often appropriate to use the binomial series to approximate powers of numbers *without using a calculator*. This is illustrated in the next example.

Example 14.7

Approximate all of the following numbers, correct to three significant figures.

a) 1.01^4 ***b)*** 0.97^{10} ***c)*** 10.5^6

Solution

a) $1.01^4=(1+0.01)^4$

$$=1+4\times 0.01+\frac{4\times 3}{2!}\times(0.01)^2+4\times(0.01)^3+(0.01)^4$$
$$=1+0.04+6\times 0.0001+4\times 0.000001+0.00000001$$

Only the first two terms are required to give an answer correct to 3 s.f., i.e.

$1.01^4\approx 1.04$

b) $0.97^{10}=(1-0.03)^{10}$

$$=1+10\times(-0.03)+\frac{10\times 9}{2!}\times(-0.03)^2+\frac{10\times 9\times 8}{3!}\times(-0.03)^3+...$$
$$=1-0.3+45\times 0.0009-120\times 0.000027+...$$
$$=1-0.3+0.0405-0.00324+...$$

Only the first four terms are required to give accuracy to 3 s.f., i.e.

$0.97^{10}\approx 0.737$

c) $10.5^6=(10\times 1.05)^6=10^6\times(1.05)^6=10^6\times(1+0.05)^6$

$$=10^6\times\left(1+6\times 0.05+\frac{6\times 5}{2!}\times 0.05^2+\frac{6\times 5\times 4}{3!}\times 0.05^3+...\right)$$
$$=10^6\times(1+0.3+15\times 0.0025+20\times 0.000125+...)$$
$$=10^6\times(1+0.3+0.0375+0.0025+...)$$

Only the first four terms are required to give accuracy to 3 s.f., i.e.

$10.5^6\approx 10^6\times 1.34=1340000$

Exploration 14.3

Approximations and significant figures

Part **a)** of Example 14.7 gave: $(1.01)^4 = (1 + 0.01)^4 \approx 1 + 4 \times 0.01 = 1.04$
i.e. $(1.01)^4 = 1.04$ to 3 s.f.

Which of the following approximations are correct to three significant figures?

$(1.02)^4 = (1 + 0.02)^4 \approx 1 + 4 \times 0.02 = 1.08$
$(1.03)^4 = (1 + 0.03)^4 \approx 1 + 4 \times 0.03 = 1.12$
$(0.99)^4 = (1 - 0.01)^4 \approx 1 - 4 \times 0.01 = 0.96$
$(0.98)^4 = (1 - 0.02)^4 \approx 1 - 4 \times 0.02 = 0.92$
$(0.97)^4 = (1 - 0.03)^4 \approx 1 - 4 \times 0.03 = 0.88$

- For what range of values of x will it be true that $(1 + x)^4 = 1 + 4x$ to 3 s.f?
- For what range of values of x will approximating $(1 + x)^4$ by $1 + 4x$ produce an error of less than 1%?
- Choose different values of n and investigate the ranges of x values for which the error in approximating $(1 + x)^n$ by $1 + nx$ is less than 1%.

Errors

The error in approximating $(1 + x)^4$ by $1 + 4x$ is less than 1% provided $-0.0382 \le x \le 0.0438$ (to 3 s.f.). We can check this by working out the percentage error for the boundary values. (Try it. You will notice that the smaller $|x|$ is, the smaller the percentage error.) As n gets larger, the range of values of x which give a percentage error less than 1%, when approximating $(1 + x)^n$ by $1 + nx$, becomes narrower.

A general principle arising from the exploration is: $(1 + x)^n \approx 1 + nx$
i.e. terms in x^2, x^3 etc. may be neglected provided $|x|$ is small.

Example 14.8

The equation $5x^3 + 12x - 18 = 0$ has a root close to 1. Use the substitution $x = 1 + h$ and the approximation $(1 + h)^3 \approx 1 + 3h$ to find the root to 3 s.f.

Solution

$5x^3 + 12x - 18 = 0$
$\Rightarrow 5(1 + h)^3 + 12(1 + h) - 18 = 0$
from which we deduce the approximation
$5(1 + 3h) + 12(1 + h) - 18 = 0$
$\Rightarrow 5 + 15h + 12 + 12h - 18 = 0$
$\Rightarrow 27h = 1$
$\Rightarrow h = \frac{1}{27} \approx 0.037$

Therefore the root close to 1 is $1 + h = 1 + \frac{1}{27} = 1.04$ (3 s.f.)

EXERCISES

14.2 CLASSWORK

1 Use the binomial series to expand the following in ascending powers of x, up to and including the term in x^4.

a) $(1+x)^{10}$ **b)** $(1-x)^7$ **c)** $(1+3x)^4$
d) $(1+\frac{1}{2}x)^{12}$ **e)** $(1-\frac{1}{3}x)^6$ **f)** $(1+ax)^8$

2 Find the first four terms, in ascending powers of x, of each of the following expressions.

a) $(1 + 3x)(1 - x)^6$ **b)** $(1 - x)(1 + 2x)^{10}$
c) $(3 + x)(1 - 3x)^5$ **d)** $(5 - x)(1 + \frac{1}{5}x)^8$

3 The first three terms in the expansion of $(1 + ax)^n$ are $1 + 10x + 40x^2$. Find the values of a and n.

4 The expansion of $(1 + ax)(1 + bx)^8$, in ascending powers of x, begins: $1 - 4x - 4x^2 + \ldots$ Find the values for a and b assuming:

a) a and b are integers, **b)** a and b are rational.
Hint: Form a quadratic equation in b. It has two roots, one of which is an integer, the other being a rational number.

5 Expand $(1 - x)^{10}$ in ascending powers of x up to the term in x^3. Hence approximate 0.98^{10} to 3 s.f.

6 Expand $(1 + \frac{1}{2}x)^8$ in ascending powers of x up to the term in x^2. Hence approximate 2.02^8 to 3 s.f.

7 Use binomial expansions to calculate the following to 5 s.f.

a) $(1.001)^{12}$ **b)** $(3.006)^{10}$ **c)** $(3.996)^7$

8 The equation $x^4 + 0.5x - 1.45 = 0$ has a root close to 1. Use the substitution $x = 1 - h$ and a suitable approximation for $(1 - h)^4$ to find the root to 3 s.f.

EXERCISES

14.2 HOMEWORK

1 Use the binomial series to expand the following in ascending powers of x, up to and including the term in x^4.

a) $(1 + x)^{15}$ **b)** $(1 - x)^9$ **c)** $(1 + 5x)^7$
d) $(1 + \frac{1}{3}x)^{12}$ **e)** $(1 - \frac{2}{3}x)^5$ **f)** $(1 - ax)^{10}$

2 Find the first four terms, in ascending powers of x, of each of the following expressions.

a) $(1 + 2x)(1 + x)^7$ **b)** $(1 - 5x)(1 - 2x)^6$
c) $(x + 3)(1 - 9x)^8$ **d)** $(8 - x)(1 + \frac{1}{4}x)^{12}$

3 The first three terms in the expansion of $(1 + ax)^n$ are $1 - 54x + 1296x^2$. Find the values of a and n.

4 The expansion of $(1 + ax)(1 + bx)^6$, in ascending powers of x, begins $1 + 9x + 24x^2 + \ldots$. Find the values for a and b.

5 When $(1 - x)(1 + \frac{1}{2}x)^n$ is expanded in ascending powers of x, the term in x^2 is $\frac{25}{4}x^2$. Find the value of n, given that it is a positive integer.

6 Expand $(1 - 2x)^{17}$ in ascending powers of x up to the term in x^3, and hence approximate 0.98^{17} to 3 s.f.

7 Use a binomial expansion to calculate $(2.006)^9$ to 5 s.f.

8 Use the binomial theorem to write down the expansion of $(1 + x)^4$. Explain why, if δ is sufficiently small, $(1 + \delta)^4 \approx 1 + 4\delta$.

You are given that the equation $x^4 - 0.7x - 0.32 = 0$ has a solution very close to $x = 1$.

By writing this solution in the form $x = 1 + \delta$ and substituting in the equation, use the approximation above to obtain a further estimate for the solution.

(MEI Pure 1, Question 4, June 1991)

BINOMIAL SERIES FOR RATIONAL INDICES

In the previous section we found that, provided $|x|$ is small:

$$(1+x)^n \approx 1+nx \qquad n = 1, 2, 3, 4, 5, \ldots$$

We shall verify that both the binomial expansion and this approximation are valid for all rational numbers, including **fractions** and **negative numbers**.

Exploration 14.4

Fractional indices

- Choose several values of x close to 0 (positive and negative), e.g. 0.01, –0.02, etc. and find values for $\sqrt{1+x}$. Compare your results, when rounded to 2 d.p. and derive a suitable approximation without the use of a calculator.
- Repeat the process, this time for $\sqrt[3]{1+x}$. Again compare your results and find a suitable approximation.

Approximations

The approximation $(1+x)^n \approx 1+nx$, for small values of x, works for rational values of n.

$$\sqrt{1+0.02} = (1+0.02)^{\frac{1}{2}} = 1.009950494 \approx 1.01 = 1+\tfrac{1}{2}\times 0.02$$

$$\sqrt[3]{1+0.03} = (1+0.03)^{\frac{1}{3}} = 1.009901634 \approx 1.01 = 1+\tfrac{1}{3}\times 0.03$$

This is called a **first-order approximation**. A second-order approximation of the form:

$$(1+x)^n \approx 1+nx+\frac{n(n-1)}{2}x^2$$

should give an even better approximation.

When $n = \frac{1}{2}$ and $x = 0.02$, $\sqrt{1.02} \approx 1+\frac{1}{2}\times 0.02 - \frac{1}{8}\times 0.02^2 = 1.00995$

When $n = \frac{1}{3}$ and $x = 0.03$, $\sqrt[3]{1.03} \approx 1+\frac{1}{3}\times 0.03 - \frac{1}{9}\times 0.03^2 = 1.0099$

Try first-order and second-order approximations to $\sqrt[4]{1.04}$

Exploration 14.5

Negative indices

- Choose several values of x close to 0 (positive and negative) and find values for $\dfrac{1}{1+x}$. Compare your results, rounded to 2 d.p. and derive a suitable approximation which does not require a calculator.
- Repeat the process, this time for $\dfrac{1}{(1+x)^2}$. Again working to 2 d.p. find a suitable approximation.

Approximations

The first-order approximation $(1+x)^n \approx 1+nx$, for small values of x, works for negative values of n:

$$\frac{1}{1+0.02} = (1+0.02)^{-1} = 0.9803921\ldots \approx 0.98 = 1-0.02$$

$$\frac{1}{(1-0.01)^2} = (1-0.01)^{-2} = 1.0203040\ldots \approx 1.02 = 1+0.02$$

Second-order approximations of the form:

$$(1+x)^n \approx 1+nx+\frac{n(n-1)}{2}x^2$$

give even better approximations.

When $n = -1$, $x = 0.02$: $\dfrac{1}{1+0.02} \approx 1 - 0.02 + 0.0004 = 0.9804$

When $n = -2$, $x = -0.01$: $\dfrac{1}{(1-0.01)^2} \approx 1 + 0.02 - 0.0003 = 1.0197$

For both rational and negative indices n, ${}^nC_r$ has no meaning since the definition:

$${}^nC_r = \frac{n!}{r!(n-r)!}$$

only applies when n and r are **natural numbers** (non-negative integers). However, the alternative version:

$${}^nC_r = \frac{n(n-1)(n-2)...(n-r+1)}{r(r-1)(r-2)...3\times 2\times 1}$$

can be evaluated for rational and negative n (r is always a natural number).

If n is **not** a natural number, then $(n - 1)$, $(n - 2)$, $(n - 3)$, etc. always give a non-zero result. Therefore the binomial expansion of $(1 + x)^n$ has no last term; it produces an **infinite series**.

$$(1+x)^n = 1 + nx + \frac{n(n-1)}{2!}x^2 + ... + \frac{n(n-1)(n-2)...(n-r+1)}{r!}x^r + ...$$

CALCULATOR ACTIVITY

Exploration 14.6

Polynomial approximations

KEY SKILLS
IT 3.1
IT 3.2
IT 3.3

You will need a graphics calculator or graph-drawing package. Scale your axes:

$x_{min} = -3$; $x_{max} = 5$; $x_{scl} = 1$
$y_{min} = -1$; $y_{max} = 5$; $y_{scl} = 1$.

- Plot the graph of $y = \sqrt{1+x}$.
- Superimpose the first-order and second-order polynomial approximations given by the binomial series expansion.
- How closely do the approximations fit the original curve?
- What do all three curves have in common when $x = 0$?
- Repeat for different values of n, e.g. $y = \dfrac{1}{1+x} \Rightarrow n = -1$.
- Repeat for the expansion of $(1 - x)^n$.
- What happens if n is a positive integer?
- Consider higher order approximations – do they always give a better fit to the original curve?

Expected results

For the function $y = \sqrt{1+x} = (1+x)^{\frac{1}{2}}$, the first and second order approximations are given by:

$$y = 1 + \tfrac{1}{2}x \text{ and } y = 1 + \tfrac{1}{2}x - \tfrac{1}{8}x^2.$$

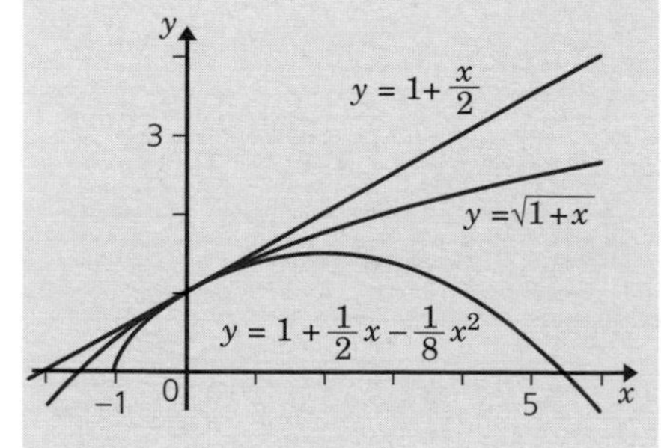

The diagram shows the original curve and the two approximations. All three curves pass through (0, 1).

The first-order and second-order approximations are a close fit to the original graph provided $|x|$ is small, with the quadratic approximation fitting better around $x = 0$. It is also important to note that all three curves have the same **gradient** when $x = 0$, i.e. the line $y = 1 + \frac{1}{2}x$ is a **tangent** to the original graph at the point (0, 1) and to any higher order approximation.

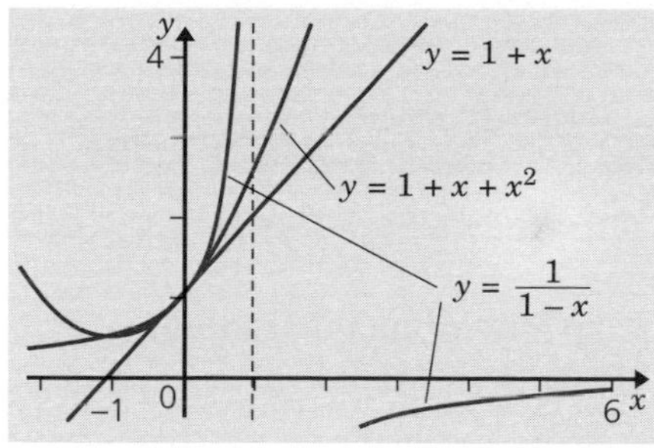

Similar patterns emerge for other values of n and for approximations to $y = (1 - x)^n$, e.g. the graph of

$y = \frac{1}{1-x} (\equiv (1-x)^{-1})$ has first-order and second-order approximations:

$$y = 1 + x \text{ and } y = 1 + x + x^2$$

which are illustrated in the diagram.

CALCULATOR ACTIVITY

Exploration 14.7

Partial sums

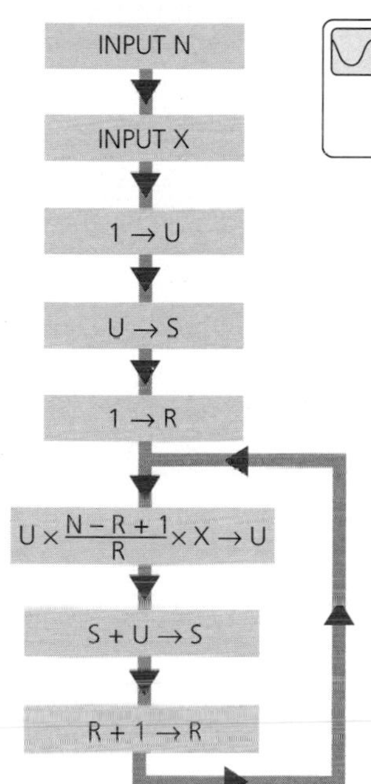

Try the program, outlined by this flowchart, which produces the sum of the first 1, 2, 3, 4, ... terms of a binomial series and will work for any value of n and x.

Run the program with different values of n and x and describe what happens 'in the long run'. Classify the sequence of partial sums as convergent or divergent, oscillating or non-oscillating;

Expected results

You probably chose various values of n and x in the last Calculator activity. Here are some examples showing what you might have found.

1 $n = 0.5$, $x = 0.1$ produces:

1.05, 1.04875, 1.0488125, 1.048808594, 1.048808867, 1.048808847, 1.048808848, ...

This is an **oscillating convergent** sequence, the limit of which is $\sqrt{1+0.1} = 1.048808848...$

2 $n = -2$, $x = 3$ produces:

−5, 22, −86, 319, −1139, 3964, −13532, 45517, −151313, 498226, ...

This is an **oscillating divergent** sequence, which has no limit.

3 $n = -3$, $x = -2$ produces:

7, 31, 11, 351, 1023, 2815, 7423, 18943, 47103, 114687, 274431, ...

This is a **non-oscillating divergent** sequence, which has no limit.

4 $n = -0.5$, $x = -0.2$ produces:

1.1, 1.115, 1.1175, 1.1179375, 1.11801625, 1.118030688, ...

This is a **non-oscillating convergent** sequence, the limit of which is

$$\frac{1}{\sqrt{1-0.2}} = 1.118033989...$$

Your investigations should confirm the following summary of the behaviour of successive partial sums for the expansion of $(1 + x)^n$.

	$x < -1$	$-1 < x < 0$	$0 < x < 1$	$x > 1$
$n \in N$	oscillating	oscillating	non -oscillating	non -oscillating
$n \notin N$	non-oscillating divergent	non-oscillating convergent	oscillating convergent	oscillating divergent

When $x = 1$, the series for $(1 + x)^n$ converges to $2n$ provided $n > -1$.
When $x = -1$, the series for $(1 + x)^n$ has interesting patterns!

Results

The **binomial expansion** of $(1 + x)^n$ for any rational n, **converges** provided $-1 < x < 1$, i.e. $|x| < 1$.

Similarly, the **binomial expansion** of $(1 + ax)^n$ for any rational n, **converges** provided $-1 < ax < 1$, i.e. $|x| < \frac{1}{a}$.

Example 14.9

Find the first four terms in the expansion of $(1 + 2x)^{-3}$ and state the range of values of x for which the expansion converges. Use the expansion to estimate $\frac{1}{1.02^3}$ to 3 s.f.

Solution

$$(1+2x)^{-3} = 1+(-3)\times 2x + \frac{(-3)\times(-4)}{2!}\times(2x)^2 + \frac{(-3)\times(-4)\times(-5)}{3!}\times(2x)^3 + \ldots$$
$$= 1 - 6x + 24x^2 - 80x^3 + \ldots$$

The series converges provided $-1 < 2x < 1 \Rightarrow -\frac{1}{2} < x < \frac{1}{2}$ *or* $|x| < \frac{1}{2}$.

Substituting $x = 0.01$*:*

$$\frac{1}{1.02^3} = (1+2\times 0.01)^{-3} = 1 - 6\times 0.01 + 24\times 0.01^2 - 80\times 0.01^3 + \ldots$$
$$= 1 - 0.06 + 0.0024 - 0.000080 + \ldots$$
$$= 0.942 \quad (3 \text{ s.f.})$$

Example 14.10

Find a quadratic function that approximates $(4 + x)^{\frac{1}{2}}$ for small values of x. Use it to approximate $\sqrt{3.97}$ to 6 s.f.

Solution

$$(4+x)^{\frac{1}{2}} = \left(4(1+\tfrac{1}{4}x)\right)^{\frac{1}{2}} = 4^{\frac{1}{2}}(1+\tfrac{1}{4}x)^{\frac{1}{2}} = 2(1+\tfrac{1}{4}x)^{\frac{1}{2}}$$

Now:

$$(1+\tfrac{1}{4}x)^{\frac{1}{2}} = 1+\tfrac{1}{2}\left(\tfrac{1}{4}x\right) + \frac{\left(\frac{1}{2}\right)\left(-\frac{1}{2}\right)}{2!}\left(\tfrac{1}{4}x\right)^2 + \cdots$$
$$= 1 + \tfrac{1}{8}x - \tfrac{1}{128}x^2 + \ldots$$

$$\Rightarrow \quad 2(1+\tfrac{1}{4}x)^{\frac{1}{2}} = 2 + \tfrac{1}{4}x - \tfrac{1}{64}x^2 + \ldots$$

which converges provided $-1 < \frac{1}{4}x < 1$
$\Rightarrow -4 < x < 4$ *or* $|x| < 4$.
$\Rightarrow$ *the approximating quadratic function is* $2 + \frac{1}{4}x - \frac{1}{64}x^2$.

To approximate $\sqrt{3.97}$ *let* $x = -0.03$

$$\Rightarrow \quad \sqrt{3.97} \approx 2 + \tfrac{1}{4}\times(-0.03) - \tfrac{1}{64}\times(-0.03)^2$$
$$= 1.99249 \quad (6 \text{ s.f.})$$

Check the answer using a calculator.

Example 14.11

Expand $\frac{(3+x)}{(1-x)^2}$ in ascending powers of x as far as the term in x^4.

Solution

$$\frac{(3+x)}{(1-x)^2} \equiv (3+x)(1-x)^{-2}$$

Now

$$(1-x)^{-2} \equiv 1+(-2)(-x)+\frac{(-2)(-3)}{2!}(-x)^2+\frac{(-2)(-3)(-4)}{3!}(-x)^3 +\frac{(-2)(-3)(-4)(-5)}{4!}(-x)^4+\dots$$

$$= 1+2x+3x^2+4x^3+5x^4+\dots$$

$$\Rightarrow \quad (3+x)(1-x)^{-2} = (3+x)(1+2x+3x^2+4x^3+5x^4+\dots)$$

$$= 3+(6+1)x+(9+2)x^2+(12+3)x^3+(15+4)x^4+\dots$$

$$= 3+7x+11x^2+15x^3+19x^4+\dots$$

EXERCISES

14.3 CLASSWORK

1 For each of the following expressions, write down the first five terms of its binomial expansion. In each case state the range of values of x for which the series converges.

a) $(1+x)^{-1}$ **b)** $(1+3x)^{\frac{1}{2}}$ **c)** $(1-\frac{1}{3}x)^{-2}$ **d)** $\sqrt[3]{8+x}$

2 Use appropriate binomial expansions to approximate each of the following to 3 s.f.

a) $\sqrt{1.04}$ **b)** $\sqrt{96}$ **c)** $\sqrt[3]{8.32}$

3 Expand $\frac{(1-x)}{(1+x)}$ in ascending powers of x, up to and including the term in x^3.

4 Show that $\sqrt{\frac{(1-x)}{(1+x)}} \equiv (1-x)^{\frac{1}{2}}(1+x)^{-\frac{1}{2}}$.

Using suitable binomial expansions show that:

$$\sqrt{\frac{(1-x)}{(1+x)}} \approx 1-x+\tfrac{1}{2}x^2-\tfrac{1}{2}x^3$$

Using a suitable value of x, estimate $\sqrt{\frac{2}{3}}$ to 3 s.f.

5 When $(1+ax)^{-2}$ is expanded in ascending powers of x, the first four terms are $1+Px+Qx^2-\frac{1}{2}x^3$. Find a and then P and Q.

6 The first three terms of the expansion of $(1+rx)^n$ are $1-\frac{3}{2}x+\frac{27}{4}x^2$. Find the values of r and n, and the range of values of x for which the series converges.

EXERCISES

14.3 HOMEWORK

1 For each of the following expressions, write down the first four terms of its binomial expansion. In each case state the range of values of x for which the series converges.

a) $(1+2x)^{-3}$ **b)** $\left(1-\frac{x}{5}\right)^{-1}$ **c)** $\sqrt[3]{27+x}$ **d)** $(1+7x)^{\frac{1}{2}}$

2 Use appropriate binomial expansions to approximate each of the following to 3 s.f.

a) $\sqrt{0.95}$ **b)** $\sqrt{140}$ **c)** $(16.12)^{\frac{1}{4}}$

3 Expand $\frac{(1+x)}{\sqrt{1-x}}$ in ascending powers of x, up to and including the term in x^4.

4 The first three terms in the expansion of $(a-3x)^{\frac{1}{2}}$, in ascending powers of x, are $2-\frac{3}{4}x+bx^2$ where a and b are constants. Find the values of a and b.

5 Expand $(1 + x + x^2)^{\frac{1}{2}}$ as a series in ascending powers of x up to and including the term in x^4. Find the values of x for which the series is valid.

6 Expand $\left(1 - \frac{8}{x}\right)^{\frac{1}{3}}$ as a series in ascending powers of $\frac{1}{x}$ up to and including the term in $\frac{1}{x^3}$. State the set of values of x for which the expansion is valid.

MATHEMATICAL MODELLING ACTIVITY

Problem statement

Specify the real problem

The map shows part of the city of Venice in Northern Italy. It's a beautiful city and each street has old buildings worth viewing. As the map shows the streets and canals are laid out in a roughly rectangular grid. (This layout for roads is typical of many cities around the world especially in America.) With so much to see, there are many different routes between two specific points such as St Mark's Square and the Rialto Bridge. Formulate a model for finding the number of routes between two points in a city made up of rectangular grids.

Rialto Br.

St Mark's Sq.

Set up a model

Set up (another) model

The streets in Venice are of different lengths and do not form an exact grid system so we must start with some simplifying assumptions.

- Assume that the city streets form a rectangular grid orientated with horizontal and vertical lines.
- Assume that the distance between adjacent junctions horizontally is a constant h.
- Assume that the distance between adjacent junctions vertically is a constant v.

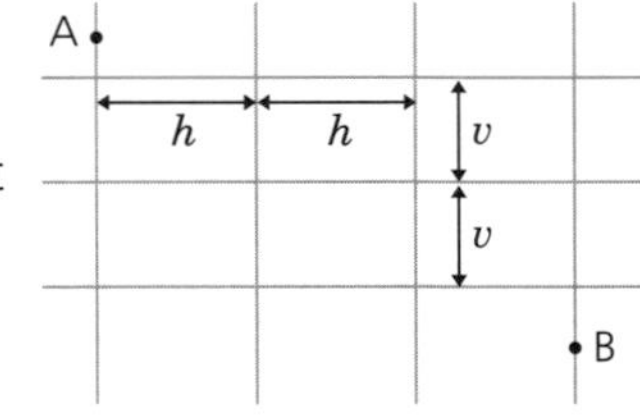

The problem is: how many 'routes of shortest distance' are there between two junctions A and B?

Consider some simple examples. How many routes are there in the following diagrams? (One possible route is shown for each case.)

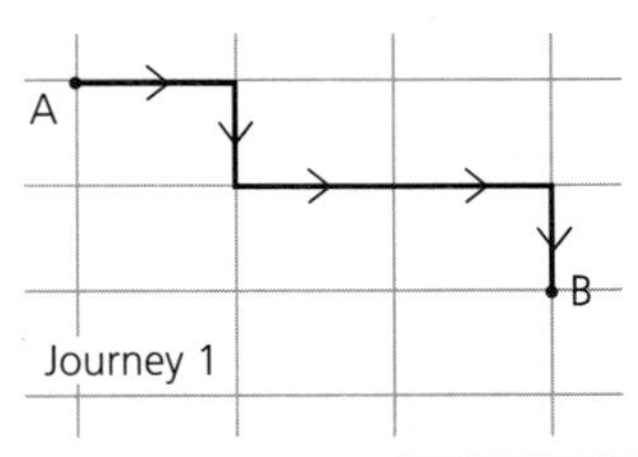

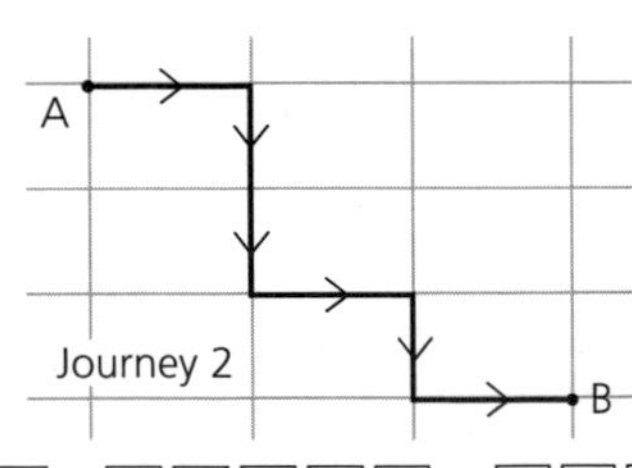

For Journey 1 the shortest distance is $3h + 2v$ and you should have found ten different routes between A and B. Each possible path can be written in the form of a table. The ten possible routes of shortest distance are shown below.

H	H	H	V	V
H	H	V	H	V
H	H	V	V	H
H	V	H	H	V
H	V	V	H	H
H	V	H	V	H
V	H	H	H	V
V	H	H	V	H
V	H	V	H	H
V	V	H	H	H

The total number of routes is the same as the number of ways of putting three Hs and two Vs in the five boxes in the table. We can show that this is the coefficient of h^3v^2 in the expansion of $(h + v)^5$.

Mathematical problem

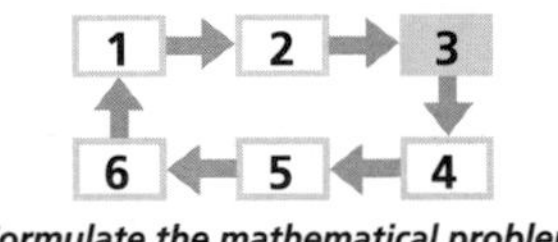

Formulate the mathematical problem

For Journey 2 the shortest distance is $3h + 3v$ and the number of different routes is 20. This is the coefficient of h^3v^3 in $(h + v)^6$.

Confirm these results by expanding $(h + v)^5$ and $(h + v)^6$.

We can propose a model. Let $nh + mv$ be the shortest distance between two junctions made up of n horizontal steps and m vertical steps. Then the number of different routes is the coefficient of $h^n v^m$ in the binomial expansion of $(h + v)^{n+m}$.

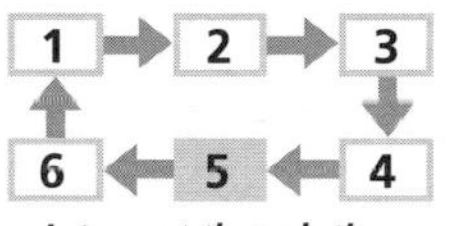

Interpret the solution

Validation of the model

Choose journeys between different junctions and check that the model works for each of your journeys.

Discuss the appropriateness of the model for the streets of Venice.

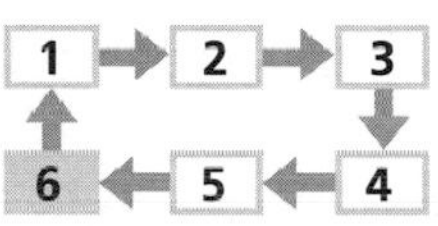

Compare with reality

Refinement of the model

Investigate the effects of:

- applying the model to Venice,
- applying the model to other cities with grid road systems,
- revising the model for cities whose roads almost form exact rectangular grids.

CONSOLIDATION EXERCISES FOR CHAPTER 14

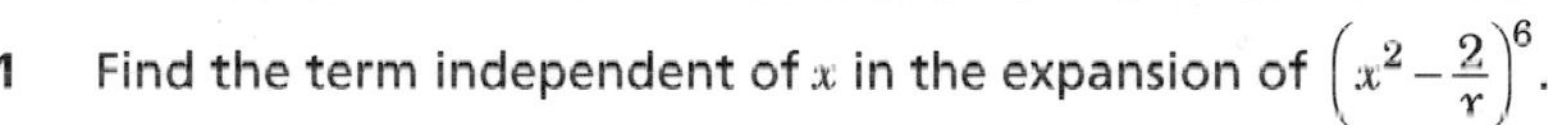

1 Find the term independent of x in the expansion of $\left(x^2 - \frac{2}{x}\right)^6$.

(UCLES Modular Question 1, Specimen Paper P3, 1994)

2 A shelf support is made of wood, with its cross-section in the shape below. The top and bottom edges of the support are horizontal.

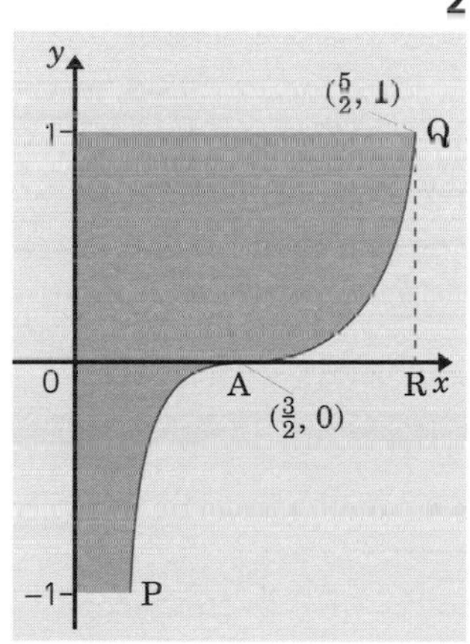

The shape of the curved edge of the shelf support is modelled by the equation:

$$8y = (2x - 3)^3 \quad \text{for} \quad -1 \le y \le 1.$$

a) Find the coordinates of the point P.

b) Using Pascal's triangle, or otherwise, write down the expansion of $(2x - 3)^3$.

c) Write down the integral which should be calculated in order to find the area AQR between the curve and the x-axis.

d) Carry out the integration to find this area.

e) Hence or otherwise calculate the area of the cross-section of the shelf support.

(MEI Question 5, Paper 1, January 1995)

3 **a)** Use the formula for solving a quadratic equation to write down the two roots of the equation $x^2 + x + p = 0$, where p is a constant.

b) Find the values of A, B and C for which:

$$1 + Ap + Bp^2 + Cp^3$$

is equal to the first four terms in the binomial expansion of $\sqrt{1-4p}$. State the condition for which the expansion is valid.

c) Use your expansion to find approximations to the two roots of the equation, assuming that terms in p^4 and higher powers of p are so small that they may be neglected.

d) Use your answer to part **c)** to find the approximate values of the two roots of the equation $10x^2 + 10x + 1 = 0$.

(MEI Question 1, Paper 2, June 1993)

4 In the binomial expansion of $(2k + x)^n$, where k is a constant and n is a positive integer, the coefficient of x^2 is equal to the coefficient of x^3.

a) Prove that $n = 6k + 2$.

Given also that $k = \frac{2}{3}$,

b) expand $(2k + x)^n$ in ascending powers of x up to and including the term in x^3, giving each coefficient as an exact fraction in its simplest form.

(EDEXCEL, Question 5, Paper 2, Jan 2000)

5 **a)** Expand $(1 + 2x)^{12}$ in ascending powers of x up to and including the term in x^3, simplifying each coefficient.

b) By substituting a suitable value for x, which must be stated, into your answer to part **a)**, calculate an approximate value of $(1.02)^{12}$.

c) Use your calculator, writing down all the digits in your display, to find a more exact value of $(1.02)^{12}$. (1 mark)

d) Calculate, to 3 significant figures, the percentage error of the approximation found in part **b)**.

(EDEXCEL, Question 5, Paper 2, June 1999)

6 The coefficient of x^2 in the binomial expansion of $[1 + \frac{x}{2}]^n$, where n is a positive integer, is 7.

a) Find the value of n.

b) Using the value of n found in **a)**, find the coefficient of x^4.

(EDEXCEL, Question 3, Paper 2, June 1998)

7 Expand $(1 + x)^5$ in ascending powers of x, simplifying the coefficients. Hence, by letting $x = y + y^2$, find the coefficient of y^4 in the expansion of $(1 + y + y^2)^5$ in powers of y.

(OCR, Question 3, Specimen Paper 2, 2000)

8 Expand $(1 - 2x)^{-\frac{1}{2}}$ in ascending powers of x, up to and including the term in x^2.
State the set of values of x for which the expansion is valid.

(OCR, Question 1, Specimen Paper 3, 2000)

Summary

- The binomial theorem is the expansion of $(a + b)^n$ in the form:

$$(a + b)^n = \binom{n}{0}a^n + \binom{n}{1}a^{n-1}b + \binom{n}{2}a^{n-2}b^2 + \ldots + \binom{n}{r}a^{n-r}b^r + \ldots + \binom{n}{n-1}ab^{n-1} + \binom{n}{n}ab^n$$

where n is a positive integer.

- The binomial series is a special case of the binomial theorem when $a = 1$ and $b = x$ and is usually written

$$(1+x)^n = 1 + nx + \frac{n(n-1)}{2!}x^2 + \ldots + \frac{n(n-1)\ldots(n-r+1)}{r!}x^r + \ldots + nx^{n-1} + x^n$$

- For negative and fractional values of n the binomial series gives an infinite number of terms. It converges provided $|x| < 1$.

Trigonometry 2

In this chapter we shall introduce:

- *compound-angle formulae, or expansions for expressions such as* $\sin(\theta+\varphi)$, $\cos(\theta+\varphi)$
- *double-angle expansions*
- *the use of these expansions to model waves*
- *reciprocal trigonometric functions.*

COMPOUND-ANGLE FORMULAE

In studying trigonometry we have discovered various relationships between trigonometric functions such as:

$$\tan\theta \equiv \frac{\sin\theta}{\cos\theta} \qquad \cos(90^\circ-\theta)\equiv\sin\theta \qquad \cos^2\theta+\sin^2\theta\equiv 1$$

In each case the expressions contain trigonometric functions of a single variable, θ. In this chapter we shall find other useful relationships involving trigonometric functions of two variables, say θ and φ. We begin with an exploration.

Exploration 15.1

Coordinates and angles

The diagram shows three points, O, P and Q where O is the origin and P and Q are in the first quadrant such that OP = OQ = 1. OP makes an angle φ with the x-axis, OQ makes an angle θ with the x-axis and $\theta > \varphi$.

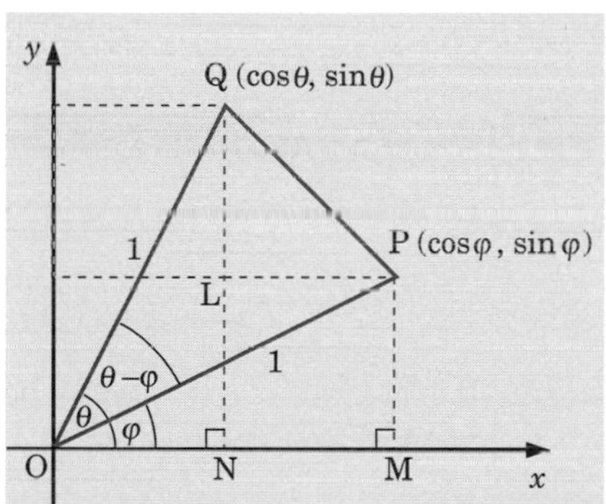

- Explain why the coordinates of P and Q are $(\cos\varphi, \sin\varphi)$ and $(\cos\theta, \sin\theta)$ respectively.
- Find an expression for PQ^2.
- Use the cosine rule on ΔOPQ to derive a formula for $\cos(\theta-\varphi)$.

Interpreting the results

The lines OP and OQ are hypotenuses of right-angled triangles OPM and OQN respectively. Since OP = 1, OM = $\cos\varphi$ and PM = $\sin\varphi$. Similarly we can see that ON = $\cos\theta$ and QN = $\sin\theta$.

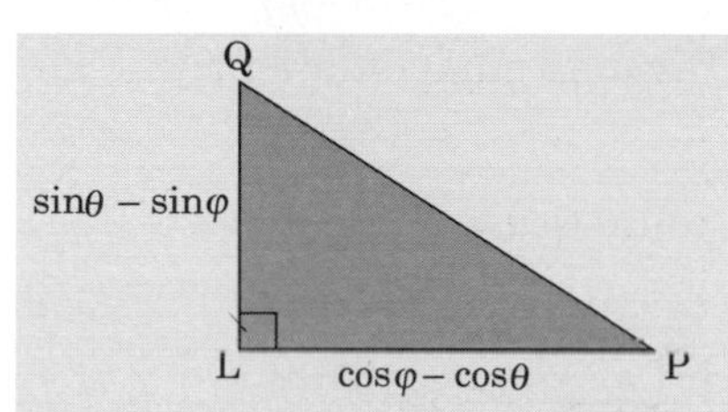

Treating PQ as the hypotenuse of ΔPQL, by Pythagoras' theorem:

$$
\begin{aligned}
PQ^2 &= PL^2 + QL^2 \\
&= (\cos\varphi - \cos\theta)^2 + (\sin\theta - \sin\varphi)^2 \\
&= \left(\cos^2\varphi - 2\cos\varphi\cos\theta + \cos^2\theta\right) + \left(\sin^2\theta - 2\sin\theta\sin\varphi + \sin^2\varphi\right) \\
&= \left(\cos^2\theta + \sin^2\theta\right) + \left(\cos^2\varphi + \sin^2\varphi\right) - 2\cos\theta\cos\varphi - 2\sin\theta\sin\varphi \\
&= 2 - 2(\cos\theta\cos\varphi + \sin\theta\sin\varphi)
\end{aligned}
$$

Using the cosine rule on ΔOPQ:

$$
\begin{aligned}
PQ^2 &\equiv OP^2 + OQ^2 - 2 \times OP \times OQ \times \cos(\theta - \varphi) \\
&\equiv 1 + 1 - 2 \times 1 \times 1 \times \cos(\theta - \varphi)
\end{aligned}
$$

$$\Rightarrow 2 - 2(\cos\theta\cos\varphi + \sin\theta\sin\varphi) \equiv 2 - 2\cos(\theta - \varphi)$$

$$\Rightarrow \cos(\theta - \varphi) = \cos\theta\cos\varphi + \sin\theta\sin\varphi$$

Check the equivalence by inserting values for θ and φ and showing the two sides balance, e.g. with $\theta = 70°$ and $\varphi = 10°$, show that both sides equal 0.5, i.e:

$$\cos 60° = \cos 70° \cos 10° + \sin 70° \sin 10°$$

We have used a geometrical argument to develop our first compound-angle formula. Now we can use various properties of trigonometrical functions to develop five more formulae.

Replacing φ by $-\theta$ gives:

$$
\begin{aligned}
&\cos\left(\theta - (-\varphi)\right) \equiv \cos\theta\cos(-\varphi) + \sin\theta\sin(-\varphi) \\
&\Rightarrow \cos(\theta + \varphi) \equiv \cos\theta\cos\varphi - \sin\theta\sin\varphi
\end{aligned}
$$

Compound-angle formulae for $\sin(\theta + \varphi)$ and $\sin(\theta - \varphi)$ can be developed from the respective formulae for $\cos(\theta + \varphi)$ and $\cos(\theta - \varphi)$:

$$
\begin{aligned}
\sin(\theta + \varphi) &\equiv \cos\left(90° - (\theta + \varphi)\right) \\
&\equiv \cos\left((90° - \theta) - \varphi\right) \\
&\equiv \cos(90° - \theta)\cos\varphi + \sin(90° - \theta)\sin\varphi
\end{aligned}
$$

$$\Rightarrow \sin(\theta + \varphi) \equiv \sin\theta\cos\varphi + \cos\theta\sin\varphi$$

$$
\begin{aligned}
\sin(\theta - \varphi) &\equiv \cos\left(90° - (\theta - \varphi)\right) \\
&\equiv \cos\left((90° - \theta) + \varphi\right) \\
&\equiv \cos(90° - \theta)\cos\varphi - \sin(90° - \theta)\sin\varphi
\end{aligned}
$$

$$\Rightarrow \sin(\theta + \varphi) \equiv \sin\theta\cos\varphi + \cos\theta\sin\varphi$$

Finally, compound-angle formulae for $\tan(\theta + \varphi)$ and $\tan(\theta - \varphi)$ may be deduced from the definition of tangent in terms of sine and cosine:

$$\tan(\theta + \varphi) \equiv \frac{\sin(\theta + \varphi)}{\cos(\theta + \varphi)} \equiv \frac{\sin\theta\cos\varphi + \cos\theta\sin\varphi}{\cos\theta\cos\varphi - \sin\theta\sin\varphi}$$

Dividing numerator and denominator by $\cos\theta\cos\varphi$ gives:

$$\tan(\theta + \varphi) \equiv \frac{\dfrac{\sin\theta\cos\varphi}{\cos\theta\cos\varphi} + \dfrac{\cos\theta\sin\varphi}{\cos\theta\cos\varphi}}{\dfrac{\cos\theta\cos\varphi}{\cos\theta\cos\varphi} - \dfrac{\sin\theta\sin\varphi}{\cos\theta\cos\varphi}}$$

$$\equiv \frac{\dfrac{\sin\theta}{\cos\theta} + \dfrac{\sin\varphi}{\cos\varphi}}{1 - \dfrac{\sin\theta}{\cos\theta} \times \dfrac{\sin\varphi}{\cos\varphi}}$$

$$\Rightarrow \tan(\theta + \varphi) \equiv \frac{\tan\theta + \tan\varphi}{1 - \tan\theta\tan\varphi}$$

Similar reasoning, or replacing φ by $-\varphi$ gives:

$$\tan(\theta + (-\varphi)) \equiv \frac{\tan\theta + \tan(-\varphi)}{1 - \tan\theta\tan(-\varphi)}$$

$$\Rightarrow \tan(\theta - \varphi) \equiv \frac{\tan\theta - \tan\varphi}{1 + \tan\theta\tan\varphi}$$

The following examples illustrate some of the ways in which the compound-angle formula may be used.

Example 15.1

Without using a calculator, find the value of:

a) sin 15° *b) tan 105°.*

Solution

a) $\sin 15° = \sin(45° - 30°) = \sin 45° \cos 30° - \cos 45° \sin 30°$

$$= \frac{1}{\sqrt{2}} \times \frac{\sqrt{3}}{2} - \frac{1}{\sqrt{2}} \times \frac{1}{2} = \frac{\sqrt{3} - 1}{2\sqrt{2}} = \frac{\sqrt{2}(\sqrt{3} - 1)}{4}$$

b) $\tan 105° = \tan(60° + 45°) = \frac{\tan 60° + \tan 45°}{1 - \tan 60° \tan 45°}$

$$= \frac{\sqrt{3} + 1}{1 - \sqrt{3}}$$

$$= \frac{-(1 + \sqrt{3})^2}{2}$$

Example 15.2

Without using a calculator, find the exact value of:

a) $\cos(\alpha + \beta)$ *b)* $\tan(\alpha - \beta)$

given that α *and* β *and are both acute angles and* $\tan\alpha = \frac{4}{3}$ *and* $\sin\beta = \frac{5}{13}$.

Solution

First, deduce values for $\sin\alpha$, $\cos\alpha$, $\cos\beta$, $\tan\beta$ *from right angled triangles.*

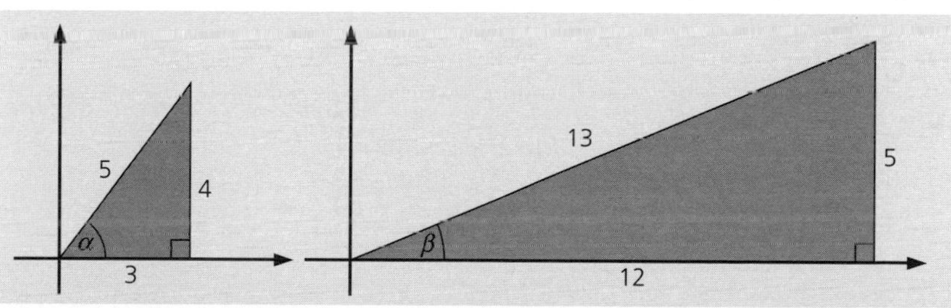

$\sin\alpha = \frac{4}{5}, \cos\alpha = \frac{3}{5}$ *and* $\cos\beta = \frac{12}{13}, \tan\beta = \frac{5}{12}$

a) $\cos(\alpha + \beta) = \cos\alpha\cos\beta - \sin\alpha\sin\beta = \frac{3}{5} \times \frac{12}{13} - \frac{4}{5} \times \frac{5}{13}$

$$= \frac{36 - 20}{65} = \frac{16}{65}$$

b) $\tan(\alpha - \beta) = \frac{\tan\alpha - \tan\beta}{1 + \tan\alpha\tan\beta} = \frac{\frac{4}{3} - \frac{5}{12}}{1 + \frac{4}{3} \times \frac{5}{12}} = \frac{\frac{11}{12}}{\frac{14}{9}} = \frac{11}{56}$

Example 15.3

Show that $\sin(A+B)\sin(A-B) \equiv (\sin A + \sin B)(\sin A - \sin B)$.

Solution

$$\begin{aligned}
LHS &\equiv \sin(A+B)\sin(A-B) \\
&\equiv (\sin A\cos B + \cos A\sin B)(\sin A\cos B - \cos A\sin B) \\
&\equiv \sin^2 A\cos^2 B + \cos A\sin B\sin A\cos B - \cos A\sin B\sin A\cos B \\
&\quad - \cos^2 A\sin^2 B \\
&\equiv \sin^2 A\left(1-\sin^2 B\right) - \left(1-\sin^2 A\right)\sin^2 B \\
&\equiv \sin^2 A - \sin^2 A\sin^2 B - \sin^2 B + \sin^2 A\sin^2 B \\
&\equiv \sin^2 A - \sin^2 B \\
&\equiv (\sin A + \sin B)(\sin A - \sin B) \equiv RHS
\end{aligned}$$

Example 15.4

The diagram shows graphs of $y = -2\cos x$ *and* $y = \sin(x + 45°)$, $0 \le x \le 360°$. *Find the coordinates of points A and B, where the graphs intersect.*

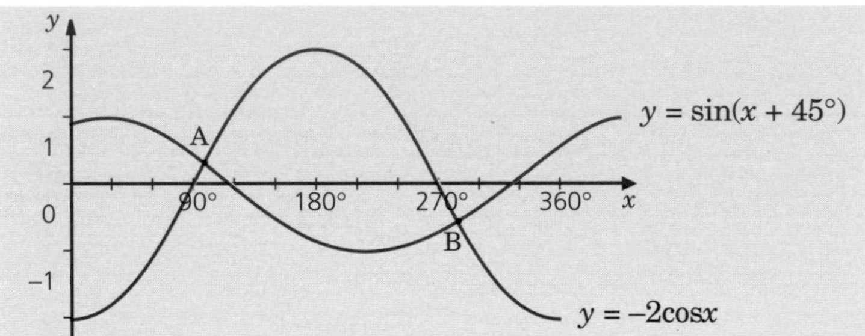

Solution

At the point of intersection:

$\sin(x+45°) = -2\cos x$

$\Rightarrow \sin x\ \cos 45° + \cos x\ \sin 45° = -2\cos x$

$\Rightarrow \dfrac{\sin x}{\cos x}\cos 45° + \dfrac{\cos x}{\cos x}\sin 45° = -\dfrac{2\cos x}{\cos x}$

$\Rightarrow \tan x \times \dfrac{1}{\sqrt{2}} + \dfrac{1}{\sqrt{2}} = -2$

$\Rightarrow \tan x + 1 = -2\sqrt{2}$

$\Rightarrow \quad \tan x = -1 - 2\sqrt{2} \approx -3.83$

$\Rightarrow \quad x = -75.4°$ *(from calculator)*

But $0 \le x \le 360°$

$\Rightarrow\ x = 180° - 75.4° = 104.6°$

or $x = 360° - 75.4° = 284.6°$

EXERCISES

15.1 CLASSWORK

1 Use compound-angle formulae to find the following.

a) cos 15° **b)** tan 15° **c)** sin 75°
d) tan 75° **e)** cos 105° **f)** sin 165°

2 Without using a calculator, find the values of the following.

a) $\sin 52°\cos 22° - \cos 52°\sin 22°$

b) $\cos 17°\cos 43° - \sin 17°\sin 43°$

c) $\dfrac{\tan 73° - \tan 13°}{1 + \tan 73°\tan 13°}$

3 Acute angles α and β are such that $\tan\alpha = \frac{15}{8}$ and $\sin\beta = \frac{12}{13}$. Find the exact value of each of the following.
a) $\sin(\alpha+\beta)$ **b)** $\cos(\alpha-\beta)$ **c)** $\tan(\alpha+\beta)$

4 Obtuse angles α and β are such that $\sin\alpha = \frac{7}{25}$ and $\cos\beta = -\frac{4}{5}$. Find the exact value of each of the following.
a) $\sin(\alpha-\beta)$ **b)** $\cos(\alpha+\beta)$ **c)** $\tan(\alpha-\beta)$

5 Find algebraically the exact value of $\sin\theta° + \sin(\theta+120)° + \cos(\theta+150)°$.

6 If A and B are acute angles such that $\tan A = \frac{1}{2}$ and $\tan B = \frac{1}{3}$ show that $A + B = 45°$.

7 Triangle PQR has vertices P(3, 7), Q(1, 2), R(–4, –8). Find:
a) the gradient of the line PQ,
b) the gradient of the line QR,
c) the angle PQR.

8 Find the acute angle between the lines $y = 2x - 1$ and $2y = x + 1$.

9 Write down an expression for tan (60° + 30°). What can you deduce about tan 90°?

10 If $\tan(x + 45°) = 2$, find the smallest positive value of x.

11 If $\tan P = \frac{1}{3}$ and $\tan Q = \frac{1}{2}$, and $R = P + Q$, find possible values for R such that $0 \le R \le 360°$.

12 Show that:
a) $\sin(A+B)+\sin(A-B) \equiv 2\sin A\cos B$
b) $\cos(A-B)\cos(A+B) \equiv (\cos A - \cos B)(\cos A + \cos B)$.

13 Show that $\tan A + \tan B = \dfrac{\sin(A+B)}{\cos A\cos B}$

14 If $\sin(x-\alpha) = k\sin(x+\alpha)$,
a) express $\tan x$ in terms of k and $\tan\alpha$,
b) determine possible values of x when $k = \frac{1}{2}$, $\alpha = 30°$, such that $0 \le x \le 360°$.

15 Solve the equation $\sin(x+60°) = \cos x$, $0 \le x \le 360°$.

16 Solve the equation $2\cos(x-20°) + \cos x = 0$, $-180° \le x \le 180°$.

17 Sketch the graphs of $y = 2\sin x$ and $y = \sin(x-30°)$, $0 \le x \le 360°$.

Find the coordinates of their points of intersection, P and Q.

EXERCISES

15.1 HOMEWORK

1 By calculating each side separately, verify the identity $\sin(A+B) \equiv \sin A\cos B + \cos A\sin B$ for the following pairs of angles.
a) A = 30°, B = 135° **b)** A = 23°, B = 211°
c) A = 0.765 radians, B = 3.468 radians

2 Repeat question 1 for the identity $\cos(A+B) \equiv \cos A\cos B - \sin A\sin B$.

3 Repeat question 1 for the identity $\tan(A+B) \equiv \dfrac{\tan A + \tan B}{1 - \tan A\tan B}$.

4 Rewrite the following expressions as single sines or cosines.
a) $\sin 53°\cos 51° + \cos 53°\sin 51°$ **b)** $\sin 24°\cos 20° - \cos 24°\sin 20°$
c) $\cos 57°\cos 17° + \sin 57°\sin 17°$ **d)** $\sin 41°\sin 19° - \cos 41°\cos 19°$

e) $\sin\frac{5\pi}{12}\cos\frac{\pi}{12}+\cos\frac{5\pi}{12}\sin\frac{\pi}{12}$ f) $\sin 2x\cos x-\cos 2x\sin x$

g) $\cos^2 x-\sin^2 x$ h) $\sin(x+y)\cos y-\cos(x+y)\sin y$

5 If $\sin\frac{\pi}{4}=\frac{\sqrt{2}}{2}$, $\sin\frac{\pi}{6}=\frac{1}{2}$ and $\sin\frac{\pi}{3}=\frac{\sqrt{3}}{2}$, evaluate each of the following, without using a calculator.

a) $\sin\left(\frac{\pi}{4}+\frac{\pi}{6}\right)$ b) $\cos\left(\frac{\pi}{4}+\frac{\pi}{6}\right)$ c) $\tan\left(\frac{\pi}{4}+\frac{\pi}{6}\right)$

6 Use the compound-angle identities to verify the following.

a) $\sin(x+180°)=-\sin x$ b) $\cos(x+180°)=-\cos x$

c) $\sin(x+360°)=\sin x$ d) $\cos(x+360°)=\cos x$

7 This question should be attempted without using a calculator.

If $\cos A=\frac{3}{5}$, $\cos B=\frac{12}{13}$ and both A and B are acute angles:

a) find sin A, tan A, sin B and tan B,

b) use the compound-angle formulae to find sin (A + B), sin (A – B), cos (A + B), cos (A – B), tan (A + B) and tan (A – B).

8 If A is the acute angle with sine $\frac{3}{5}$ and B is the obtuse angle with sine $\frac{5}{13}$, find cos (A + B) and tan (A – B), without using a calculator.

9 Prove the following identities.

$\sin(X+Y)\sin(X-Y)\equiv\sin^2 X-\sin^2 Y$

$\cos(X+Y)\cos(X-Y)\equiv\cos^2 X-\sin^2 Y$

Hence, without using a calculator, evaluate $\sin 75°\sin 15°$, $\cos 75°\cos 15°$, $\sin 105°\sin 15°$ and $\cos 105°\cos 15°$.

10 Show that $\cos(x+45°)=\frac{\sqrt{2}}{2}(\cos x-\sin x)$ and

$\sin(x+45°)=\frac{\sqrt{2}}{2}(\cos x+\sin x)$.

Hence find the exact values of $\cos 75°$, $\sin 75°$, $\cos 105°$ and $\sin 105°$.

11 The diagram shows two straight lines, gradients m_1 and m_2, which intersect at P. The angle between the lines is θ, as shown.

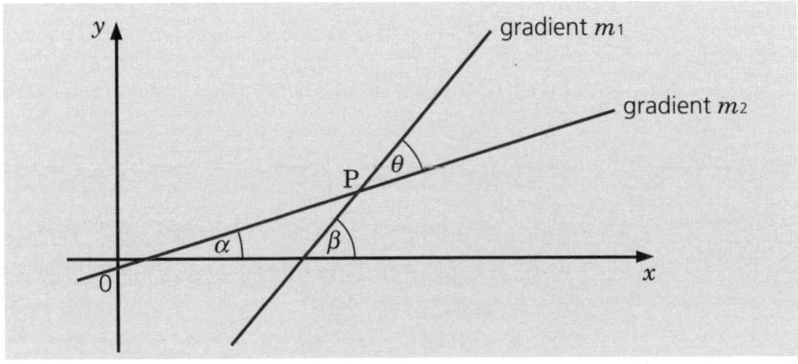

a) Find the relationship between θ, α and β.

b) Hence show that $\tan\theta=\frac{m_1-m_2}{1+m_1m_2}$.

c) Find the angle between the lines $y = 3x + 2$ and $y = 2x + 3$.

12 Use the compound-angle identities to verify the following.

a) $\tan(x + 180°) = \tan x$ **b)** $\tan(180° - x) = \tan x$

c) $\sin(90° + x) = \cos x$ **d)** $\cos(90° - x) = \sin x$

13 Show that $\tan(x + 45°) \equiv \dfrac{1 + \tan x}{1 - \tan x}$ and $\tan(x - 45°) \equiv \dfrac{\tan x - 1}{\tan x + 1}$.

14 Prove the identity $\sin(x + y) + \cos(x - y) \equiv (\sin x + \cos x)(\sin y + \cos y)$.

15 Given that $2\sin(\theta + 60°) = \cos(\theta + 60°)$ show that $\tan\theta = \sqrt{3}a + b$ where a and b are integers.

DOUBLE-ANGLE FORMULAE

In the first section of this chapter we discovered six compound-angle formulae. A very useful *particular* case occurs when $\theta = \varphi$ in the trigonometric formulae for the sum of two angles.

Let $\theta = \varphi$, then we have:

$$\sin(\theta + \theta) = \sin\theta\cos\theta + \cos\theta\sin\theta$$
$$\Rightarrow \sin 2\theta = 2\sin\theta\cos\theta$$
$$\cos(\theta + \theta) = \cos\theta\cos\theta - \sin\theta\sin\theta$$
$$\Rightarrow \cos 2\theta = \cos^2\theta - \sin^2\theta$$

Since $\cos^2\theta + \sin^2\theta = 1$, there are two useful alternative forms for $\cos 2\theta$:

$$\cos 2\theta = \cos^2\theta - \left(1 - \cos^2\theta\right)$$
$$= 2\cos^2\theta - 1$$

and:

$$\cos 2\theta = (1 - \sin^2\theta) - \sin^2\theta$$
$$= 1 - 2\sin^2\theta$$

Finally:

$$\tan(\theta + \theta) = \frac{\tan\theta + \tan\theta}{1 - \tan\theta\tan\theta}$$
$$\Rightarrow \tan 2\theta = \frac{2\tan\theta}{1 - \tan^2\theta}$$

Note that letting $\theta = \varphi$ in the trigonometrical formulae for the difference of the two angles gives two obvious and one interesting result.

$$\sin(\theta - \theta) = \sin\theta\cos\theta - \cos\theta\sin\theta$$
$$\Rightarrow \sin 0 = 0$$
$$\tan(\theta - \theta) = \frac{\tan\theta - \tan\theta}{1 + \tan^2\theta}$$
$$\Rightarrow \tan 0 = 0$$
$$\cos(\theta - \theta) = \cos\theta\cos\theta + \sin\theta\sin\theta$$
$$\Rightarrow \quad 1 = \cos^2\theta + \sin^2\theta$$

which is the basic Pythagorean identity.

The examples that follow illustrate some useful applications of the double-angle formulae.

Example 15.5

Given that $\cos\theta = 0.96$ *and* θ *is acute, find the value of each of the following.*

a) $\sin\theta$ ***b)*** $\sin 2\theta$ ***c)*** $\cos 2\theta$ ***d)*** $\tan 2\theta$

Solution

a) $\sin^2\theta = 1-\cos^2\theta \Rightarrow \sin\theta = \sqrt{1-\cos^2\theta} = \sqrt{1-0.96^2}$
$= \sqrt{0.0784}$
$= 0.28$

b) $\sin 2\theta = 2\sin\theta\cos\theta = 2\times 0.28\times 0.96 = 0.5376$

c) $\cos 2\theta = \cos^2\theta - \sin^2\theta = 0.96^2 - 0.28^2 = 0.8432$

d) $\tan\theta = \dfrac{\sin\theta}{\cos\theta} = \dfrac{0.28}{0.96} = \dfrac{7}{24} \Rightarrow \tan 2\theta = \dfrac{2\tan\theta}{1-\tan^2\theta}$

$= \dfrac{2\times\frac{7}{24}}{1-\left(\frac{7}{24}\right)^2} = \dfrac{336}{527} \approx 0.6376$ (correct to four decimal places)

Example 15.6

Show that $\dfrac{1-\cos 2A+\sin 2A}{1+\cos 2A+\sin 2A} \equiv \tan A.$

Solution

$$\frac{1-\cos 2A+\sin 2A}{1+\cos 2A+\sin 2A} \equiv \frac{2\sin^2 A+2\sin A\cos A}{2\cos^2 A+2\sin A\cos A}$$
$$\equiv \frac{2\sin A(\sin A+\cos A)}{2\cos A(\cos A+\sin A)} \equiv \tan A$$

Example 15.7

The diagram shows the graphs of $y = 5\cos 2x$ *and* $y = 3\cos x - 4$ *for* $0 \le x \le 360°$. *Find the coordinates of the points of intersection.*

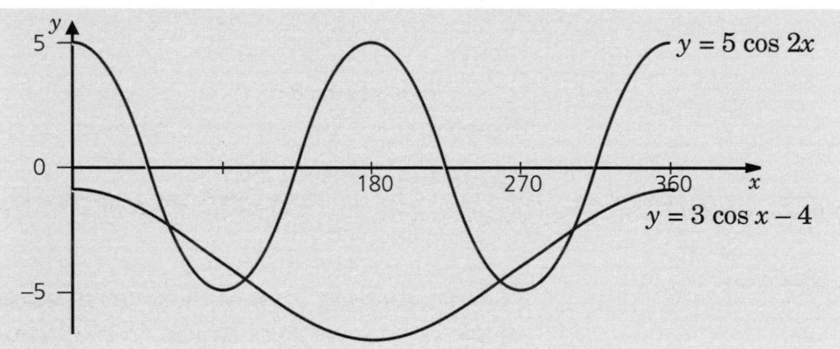

Solution

At the points of intersection:

$5\cos 2x = 3\cos x - 4$

$\Rightarrow 5\left(2\cos^2 x - 1\right) = 3\cos x - 4$

$\Rightarrow 10\cos^2 x - 5 = 3\cos x - 4$

$\Rightarrow 10\cos^2 x - 3\cos x - 1 = 0$

$\Rightarrow (2\cos x - 1)(5\cos x + 1) = 0$

$\Rightarrow 2\cos x - 1 = 0 \quad \Rightarrow \cos x = \frac{1}{2}$

or $5\cos x + 1 = 0 \quad \Rightarrow \cos x = -\frac{1}{5}$

$\cos x = \frac{1}{2} \quad \Rightarrow x = 60°$ or $x = 300°$

$\cos x = -\frac{1}{5} \Rightarrow x = 101.5°$ or $x = 258.5°$

The points of intersection are (60°, –2.5), (101.5°, –4.6), (258.5°, –4.6) and (300°, –2.5).

EXERCISES

15.2 CLASSWORK

1 Given that θ is acute and $\tan\theta = \frac{3}{4}$, find the values of the following.
a) $\sin \theta$ **b)** $\cos \theta$ **c)** $\sin 2\theta$
d) $\cos 2\theta$ **e)** $\tan 2\theta$

2 Given that $\sin\theta = 0.8$ and $\frac{\pi}{2} < \theta < \pi$, find the values of the following.
a) $\sin 2\theta$ **b)** $\cos 2\theta$ **c)** $\sin 4\theta$

3 Given that $25\cos\theta + 7 = 0$ and θ is obtuse, find the exact values of the following.
a) $\cos 2\theta$ **b)** $\sin 2\theta$ **c)** $\tan 2\theta$

4 Show that the following identities are true.
a) $\dfrac{\sin 2\theta}{1+\cos 2\theta} = \tan\theta$ **b)** $\dfrac{1-\cos 2\theta}{\sin 2\theta} = \tan\theta$

5 Show that the following identities are true.
a) $\sin 2\theta \equiv \dfrac{2\tan\theta}{1+\tan^2\theta}$ **b)** $\cos 2\theta \equiv \dfrac{1-\tan^2\theta}{1+\tan^2\theta}$

6 Show that the following identities are true.
a) $\cos^4\theta - \sin^4\theta = \cos 2\theta$ **b)** $\cos 4\theta = 8\cos^4\theta - 8\cos^2\theta + 1$

7 Show that $\cos 3\theta = 4\cos^3\theta - 3\cos\theta$.
Find the value of $\cos 3\theta$ if:
a) $\cos\theta = \frac{2}{\sqrt{5}}$ and θ is acute, **b)** $\sin^2\theta = 0.51$ and θ is obtuse.

8 Solve these equations for $0 \le x \le 2\pi$.
a) $\sin 2x + \cos x = 0$ **b)** $\cos^2 x - \sin 2x = 0$

9 Solve these equations for $0 \le x \le 360°$.
a) $\cos x + \cos 2x = 0$ **b)** $\cos 2x + 4\sin x = 3$

EXERCISES

15.2 HOMEWORK

1 On the same axes, draw the graphs of the functions $y = \cos 2x$ and $y = 2\cos^2 x$ for the domain $-2\pi \le x \le 2\pi$. What is the transformation that maps $y = \cos 2x$ onto $y = 2\cos^2 x$? Deduce the relationship between the two functions.

2 Use the appropriate double-angle formula in each case to evaluate the following, without using a calculator.
a) $2\sin 30°\cos 30°$ **b)** $2\cos^2 22.5° - 1$ **c)** $1 - 2\sin^2 15°$
d) $\cos^2 45° - \sin^2 45°$ **e)** $\dfrac{2\tan\frac{\pi}{6}}{1-\tan^2\frac{\pi}{6}}$

3 **a)** If $\cos x = \frac{3}{4}$ and x is in the first quadrant, find the value of the following, without using a calculator.
i) $\sin x$ **ii)** $\sin 2x$ **iii)** $\cos 2x$ **iv)** $\tan 2x$
b) The double-angle formulae work for all angles. Use the values of $\sin 2x$, $\cos 2x$ and $\tan 2x$ that you found in part **a)**, together with the appropriate formula, to find $\sin 4x$, $\cos 4x$ and $\tan 4x$.

4 **a)** If $\sin x = -\frac{1}{\sqrt{5}}$ and x is in the fourth quadrant, find the values of the following, without using a calculator.
i) $\cos x$ **ii)** $\sin 2x$ **iii)** $\cos 2x$ **iv)** $\tan 2x$

b) Use the values of $\sin 2x$, $\cos 2x$ and $\tan 2x$ that you found in part **a)**, together with the appropriate formula, to find $\sin 4x$, $\cos 4x$ and $\tan 4x$.

5 By writing cos $3x$ as $\cos(2x + x)$, express $\cos 3x$ in terms of $\cos x$ only.

6 **a)** Prove that $\sin 4x \equiv 4\sin x \cos x \cos 2x$.
b) Hence, without using a calculator, find the value of $\sin 4x$ when $\sin x = \frac{3}{5}$.

7 Solve the following equations for all values in the range $0 < x < 360°$.
a) $2\cos 2x + 4\cos x - 1 = 0$ **b)** $4\cos 2x + 2\sin x = 3$

8 Simplify the following expression.

$$\sqrt{\frac{1-\cos\theta}{1+\cos\theta}}$$

COMBINING WAVES

Exploration 15.2

Adding waves

You will need a graphics calculator or equivalent computer program. Set the range of values as follows.

$x_{min} = 0$; $x_{max} = 360$; $x_{scl} = 30$
$y_{min} = -5$; $y_{max} = 5$; $y_{scl} = 1$

Make sure you – and your calculator – are working in degree mode.

- Draw the graphs of $y = 3\cos x$, $y = 4\sin x$ and $y = 3\cos x + 4\sin x$ on the same axes.
- What is the result of adding the two waves?
- What is the amplitude and the period of the resultant wave?
- How would you transform:
  a) $y = \cos x$, **b)** $y = \sin x$
  to produce the same graph as $y = 3\cos x + 4\sin x$?
- For what values of x does $3\cos x + 4\sin x = 0$?

Interpreting the results

The diagram shows the three graphs.

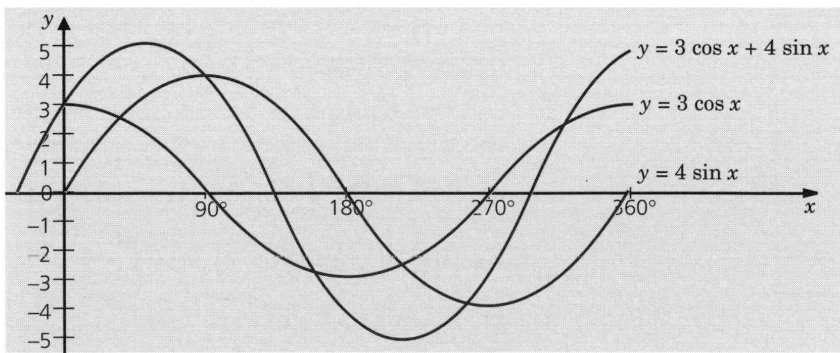

The graph of $y = 3\cos x + 4\sin x$ is a wave with period 360° and amplitude 5. The functions $y = 5\cos x$ and $y = 5\sin x$ both have this property, but need to be translated parallel to the x-axis to fit the graph if $y = 3\cos x + 4\sin x$.

Exploration 15.2 *(continued)*

Now clear the screen and draw the graph of $y = 3\cos x + 4\sin x$. Try to find a value for α such that $y = 5\sin(x + \alpha)$ gives the same curve.

When you have found a suitable value for α, repeat the exercise, but this time attempt to fit $y = 5\sin(x + \alpha)$ to the graph of $y = 3\cos x + 4\sin x$.

Which values of α fit the functions best?

Interpreting the results

In the first case $y = 5\cos(x - 53°)$ fits the graph of $y = 3\cos x + 4\sin x$ well. Alternatively, $y = 5\sin(x + 37°)$ also provides a good fit.

By zooming in on the points of intersection of $y = 3\cos x + 4\sin x$ and the x-axis, you should find that solutions of the equation $3\cos x + 4\sin x = 0$ are as shown in this diagram.

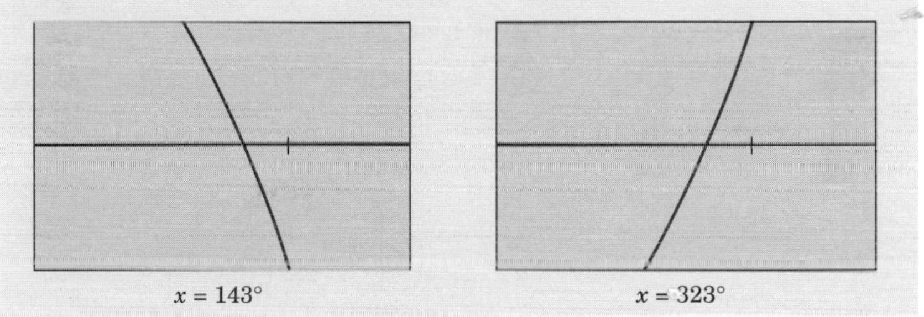

Use the trace function to find each solution correct to the nearest degree.

Knowing alternative expressions for $3\cos x + 4\sin x$ enables us to find the solutions directly, for example:
$3\cos x + 4\sin x = 0 \Rightarrow 5\cos(x - 53°) = 0$

which means that:
either $x - 53° = 90° \Rightarrow x = 143°$
or $x - 53° = 270° \Rightarrow x = 323°$

We shall now formalise this idea.

An alternative form for $a\cos x + b\sin x$ enables us to solve equations of the type $a\cos x + b\sin x = c$.

From our exploration the single wave would seem to have the form $r\cos(x - \alpha)$, where r and α are constants, or $r\sin(x - \alpha)$. We shall deal with each in turn.

Using the compound-angle formula for $\cos(x - \alpha)$:

$$r\cos(x-\alpha) \equiv r(\cos x\cos\alpha + \sin x\sin\alpha)$$
$$\equiv r\cos\alpha\cos x + r\sin\alpha\sin x$$

If this is equivalent to:
$a\cos x + b\sin x$

then:

$$a = r\cos\alpha \quad \text{and} \quad b = r\sin\alpha$$
$$\Rightarrow a^2 = r^2\cos^2\alpha \quad \text{and} \quad b^2 = r^2\sin^2\alpha$$
$$\Rightarrow a^2 + b^2 = r^2\cos^2\alpha + r^2\sin^2\alpha$$
$$= r^2(\cos^2\alpha + \sin^2\alpha)$$
$$= r^2$$
$$r = \sqrt{a^2 + b^2}$$

In our example, $a = 3$, $b = 4 \Rightarrow r = \sqrt{3^2 + 4^2} = 5$

Now substitute for r to find α:

$$a = r\cos\alpha \Rightarrow \cos\alpha = \tfrac{a}{r} \quad \Rightarrow \alpha = \cos^{-1}\left(\tfrac{a}{r}\right)$$
$$b = r\sin\alpha \Rightarrow \sin\alpha = \tfrac{b}{r} \quad \Rightarrow \alpha = \sin^{-1}\left(\tfrac{b}{r}\right)$$

In our example:

$$\alpha = \cos^{-1}\left(\tfrac{3}{5}\right) = 53.1° \text{ or } \alpha = \sin^{-1}\left(\tfrac{4}{5}\right) = 53.1°$$

Putting both results together:

$$3\cos x + 4\sin x \equiv 5\cos(x - 53.1°)$$

Since α is acute, both principal values from the calculator will be the same and consistent, so either one may be used.

Note also that $\dfrac{r\sin\alpha}{r\cos\alpha} = \dfrac{b}{a} \Rightarrow \tan\alpha = \dfrac{b}{a}$

$$\Rightarrow \alpha = \tan^{-1}\left(\frac{b}{a}\right).$$

In our example, $\alpha = \tan^{-1}\left(\tfrac{4}{3}\right) = 53.1°$

For any expression of the type $a\cos x + b\sin x$ we could also use $r\sin(x + \alpha)$ as the equivalent single wave function.

$$r\sin(x + \alpha) \equiv r(\sin x\cos\alpha + \cos x\sin\alpha)$$
$$\equiv r\sin\alpha\cos x + r\cos\alpha\sin x$$
$$\Rightarrow a = r\sin\alpha \quad \text{and} \quad b = r\cos\alpha$$
$$\Rightarrow r = \sqrt{a^2 + b^2} \quad \text{and} \quad \alpha = \tan^{-1}\left(\tfrac{a}{b}\right)$$

For our example $r = 5$ and $\alpha = \tan^{-1}\left(\tfrac{3}{4}\right) = 36.9°$

$$\Rightarrow 3\cos x + 4\sin x \equiv 5\sin(x + 36.9)°$$

If either a or b is negative, the same approach may be taken, but care must be taken over the choice of α, since the principal value might not be suitable.

Example 15.8

Express $5\cos x - 12\sin x$ *in the form* $r\sin(x + \alpha)$.

Solution

$$r\sin(x + \alpha) \equiv r\sin\alpha\cos x + r\cos\alpha\sin x$$
$$\Rightarrow 5 = r\sin\alpha \quad \text{and} \quad -12 = r\cos\alpha$$
$$\Rightarrow r = \sqrt{5^2 + (-12)^2} \text{ and } \alpha = \tan^{-1}\left(\tfrac{-5}{12}\right)$$

Now $r = \sqrt{169} = 13$ *and the principal value of* α *is –22.6°.*

However:

$5 = 13\sin\alpha \Rightarrow \alpha = \sin^{-1}\left(\frac{5}{13}\right) = 22.6°$

$-12 = 13\cos\alpha \Rightarrow \alpha = \cos^{-1}\left(-\frac{12}{13}\right) = 157.4°$

The only value of α compatible with all three requirements is $\alpha = 157.4°$.

$\Rightarrow 5\cos x - 12\sin x = 13\sin(x + 157.4°)$

Using the wave form $r\cos(x \pm \alpha)$ may prove easier, as in the following example.

Example 15.9

a) Find a single wave function equivalent to $f(x) = \sqrt{3}\cos x - \sin x$.

b) Solve the equation $f(x) = 0, -180° \le x \le 180°$.

c) Determine maximum and minimum values of $f(x)$ and the values of x at which they occur for the domain $-180° \le x \le 180°$.

Solution

a) A suitable compound formula is $\cos(x + \alpha)$, since:

$r\cos(x + \alpha) \equiv r\cos\alpha\cos x - r\sin\alpha\sin x$

Matching this to $\sqrt{3}\cos x - \sin x$, take $a = \sqrt{3}$ and $b = 1$.

$\Rightarrow r\cos\alpha = \sqrt{3}$ and $r\sin\alpha = 1$

From this we can deduce:

$r^2 = \sqrt{3}^2 + 1^2 = 4$

$\Rightarrow r = 2$

and:

$\alpha = \cos^{-1}\left(\frac{\sqrt{3}}{2}\right) = 30°$ *or* $\alpha = \sin^{-1}\left(\frac{1}{2}\right) = 30°$.

Therefore $f(x) = \sqrt{3}\cos x - \sin x \equiv 2\cos(x + 30)°$

b) $f(x) = 0 \Rightarrow 2\cos(x + 30)° = 0$

$\Rightarrow x + 30° = 90° \Rightarrow x = 60°$

or $x + 30° = -90° \Rightarrow x = -120°$

c) The maximum value of $f(x)$ is 2 (i.e. when $\cos x = 1$), which occurs when $x + 30° = 0 \Rightarrow x = -30°$.

The minimum value of $f(x)$ is –2 (i.e. when $\cos x = -1$), which occurs when $x + 30° = 180° \Rightarrow x = 150°$.

The single wave form is useful for solving equations of the form $a\cos x + b\sin x = c$. This is illustrated in the following example.

Example 15.10

Solve the equation $2\sin x - 3\cos x = 1, 0 < x < 2\pi$.

Solution

First rearrange into an appropriate form.

$3\cos x - 2\sin x = -1$

Now express the left-hand side in a suitable form.

$3\cos x - 2\sin x = r\cos(x + \alpha)$

$\Rightarrow r = \sqrt{3^2 + 2^2} = \sqrt{13}$

$\alpha = \tan^{-1}\left(\frac{2}{3}\right) = 0.588$

Hence $\sqrt{13}\cos(x+0.588)=-1$

$\Rightarrow x+0.588=\cos^{-1}\left(-\frac{1}{\sqrt{13}}\right)$

$\Rightarrow\ x+0.588=1.852$
or $x+0.588=4.431$

$x=1.264$ *or* $x=3.843$

EXERCISES

15.3 CLASSWORK

1 On the same axes, plot carefully graphs of the functions $y=3\cos x+4\sin x$, $y=5\sin x$ and $y=5\cos x$, using sufficient values of x chosen from the domain $-360°\le x\le 360°$.

a) Describe the transformation that maps $y=3\cos x+4\sin x$ onto $y=5\sin x$ and hence write $y=3\cos x+4\sin x$ in a form involving just one trigonometric function.
b) Describe the transformation that maps $y=3\cos x+4\sin x$ onto $y=5\sin x$ and hence write $y=3\cos x+4\sin x$ in another form involving just one trigonometric function.

2 Express the following in the form given, where R_1 and R_2 are positive and both α and β are in degrees.

a) $5\cos x-12\sin x$ as $R_1\cos(x-\alpha)$ and $R_2\sin(x+\beta)$

b) $7\cos x-24\sin x$ as $R_1\cos(x+\alpha)$ and $R_2\sin(x-\beta)$
In each case, verify that $R_1=R_2$.

3 Rewrite each of the following expressions in the form $R\cos(x-\alpha)$.

a) $\sin x+\cos x$ **b)** $4\cos x+3\sin x$

4 Rewrite each of the following expressions in the form $R\cos(x+\alpha)$.

a) $4\sin x-3\cos x$ **b)** $12\cos x-5\sin x$

5 Rewrite each of the following expressions in the form $R\sin(x-\alpha)$.

a) $2\sin x-\cos x$ **b)** $\sqrt{3}\sin x-3\cos x$

6 Rewrite each of the following expressions in the form $R\sin(x+\alpha)$.

a) $4\sin x+5\cos x$ **b)** $\sqrt{2}\cos x+\sin x$

7 Express $8\sin x-15\cos x$ in the form $R\sin(x-\alpha)$, where α is an acute angle and hence find the greatest and least values of the following.

a) $8\sin x-15\cos x$ **b)** $\dfrac{1}{8\sin x-15\cos x}$

8 Find the maximum and minimum values of the following functions in the domain $0\le x\le 360°$. In each case, sketch the graph and find the values of x in the domain $0\le x\le 360°$ at which the turning points occur.

a) $\sqrt{3}\cos x-\sin x$ **b)** $8\cos x-15\sin x+3$

c) $\dfrac{1}{\cos x+\sin x}$ **d)** $(5\cos x+12\sin x)^2$

If you have a graphics calculator, use it to sketch the graphs in each case.

EXERCISES

15.3 HOMEWORK

1 On the same axes, plot carefully drawn graphs of the functions $y = 5\sin x + 12\cos x$, $y = 13\sin x$ and $y = 13\cos x$, using sufficient values of x chosen from the domain $-360° \le x \le 360°$.

a) Describe the transformation that maps $y = 5\sin x + 12\cos x$ onto $y = 13\sin x$ and hence write $y = 5\sin x + 12\cos x$ in a form involving just one trigonometric function.
b) Describe the transformation that maps $y = 5\sin x + 12\cos x$ onto $y = 13\cos x$ and hence write $y = 5\sin x + 12\cos x$ in another form involving just one trigonometric function.

2 Express the following in the form given, where R_1 and R_2 are positive and both α and β are in degrees.

a) $3\cos x - 4\sin x$ as $R_1 \cos(x - \alpha)$ and $R_2 \sin(x + \beta)$
b) $8\cos x - 15\sin x$ as $R_1 \cos(x + \alpha)$ and $R_2 \sin(x - \beta)$
In each case, verify that $R_1 = R_2$.

3 Rewrite each of the following expressions in the form $R\cos(x - \alpha)$.
a) $\sqrt{2}\cos x + \sin x$ **b)** $3\cos x + \sin x$

4 Rewrite each of the following expressions in the form $R\cos(x + \alpha)$.
a) $\cos x - \sqrt{3}\sin x$ **b)** $4\cos x - 3\sin x$

5 Rewrite each of the following expressions in the form $R\sin(x - \alpha)$.
a) $3\sin x - 4\cos x$ **b)** $\cos x - \sin x$

6 Rewrite each of the following expressions in the form $R\sin(x + \alpha)$.
a) $7\cos x + 2\sin x$ **b)** $3\cos x + 11\sin x$

7 Express $7\cos x + 24\sin x$ in the form $R\cos(x - \alpha)$, where α is an acute angle and hence find the greatest and least values of the following.
a) $7\cos x + 24\sin x$ **b)** $\dfrac{1}{7\cos x + 24\sin x}$

8 Find the maximum and minimum values of the following functions in the domain $0 \le x \le 360°$. In each case, sketch the graph and find the values of x in the domain $0 \le x \le 360°$ at which the turning points occur.
a) $2\sin x - 3\cos x$ **b)** $3\cos x - 7\sin x + 2$
c) $\dfrac{1}{\sqrt{2}\cos x - \sin x}$ **d)** $(2\cos x + 3\sin x)^2$
If you have a graphics calculator, use it to sketch the graphs in each case.

RECIPROCAL TRIGONOMETRIC FUNCTIONS

We have already studied the graphs of $\sin x$, $\cos x$ and $\tan x$, all of which can have domain as the set of real numbers except for $\tan x$, which is not valid for $x = \ldots, -270°, -90°, 90°, 270°, \ldots$ (or $x = \ldots, \frac{-3\pi}{2}, \frac{-\pi}{2}, \frac{\pi}{2}, \frac{3\pi}{2}, \ldots$ in radians)

Each one is a periodic function:
- $\sin x$ is an odd function with period $360°$ (or 2π)
- $\cos x$ is an even function with period $360°$ (or 2π)
- $\tan x$ is an odd function with period $180°$ (or π)

We can now introduce three new trigonometrical functions, all of which are reciprocals of the three above.

$$\operatorname{cosec} x = \frac{1}{\sin x} \quad \sec x = \frac{1}{\cos x} \quad \cot x = \frac{1}{\tan x}$$

Exploration 15.3

Graphs of functions

Using a scale of $-360° \le x \le 360°$ [or $-2\pi \le x \le 2\pi$ if working in radian mode] and $-3 \le y \le 3$, use a graphics calculator or computer package to plot the following pairs of graphs separately.

a) $y = \sin x$ and $y = \operatorname{cosec} x$ ($\frac{1}{\sin x}$)

b) $y = \cos x$ and $y = \sec x$ ($\frac{1}{\cos x}$)

c) $y = \tan x$ and $y = \cot x$ ($\frac{1}{\tan x}$)

Study each pair of graphs in turn.

- Describe what happens to one curve as the other curve crosses the x-axis. Why does this happen?
- Describe the nature of any stationary points.
- How are the graphs of $\operatorname{cosec} x$ and $\sec x$ related?
- How are the graphs of $\tan x$ and $\cot x$ related?

These new trigonometrical functions may not be supplied on your calculator but using their definitions, you can find values and solve equations, as shown in the following examples.

Example 15.11

Find: ***a)*** $\operatorname{cosec} 30°$ ***b)*** $\sec^2 135°$ ***c)*** $5\cot(-\frac{2\pi}{3})$

Solution

a) $\operatorname{cosec} 30° = \dfrac{1}{\sin 30°} = \dfrac{1}{0.5} = 2$ ***b)*** $\sec^2 135° = \dfrac{1}{\cos^2 135°} = \dfrac{1}{0.5} = 2$

c) $5\cot(-\frac{2\pi}{3}) = 5 \times \dfrac{1}{\tan(-\frac{2\pi}{3})} = 5 \times \dfrac{1}{1.732} = 2.89$ (3 s.f.)

Example 15.12

Find values of θ such that $0° \le \theta \le 360°$, where:

a) $\operatorname{cosec}\theta = -5$ ***b)*** $\sec 2\theta = 3$ ***c)*** $\cot^2\theta = 3$

Solution

a) $\operatorname{cosec}\theta = -5 \Rightarrow \dfrac{1}{\sin\theta} = -5 \Rightarrow \sin\theta = -0.2$

$\Rightarrow \theta = \sin^{-1}(-0.2) = -11.5°$ *(from calculator)*

but $0° \le \theta \le 360°$*:*
$\Rightarrow \theta = 180° + 11.5°$ *or* $360° - 11.5°$
$\Rightarrow \theta = 191.5°$ *or* $\theta = 348.5°$

b) $\sec 2\theta = 3 \Rightarrow \dfrac{1}{\cos 2\theta} = 3 \Rightarrow \cos 2\theta = \frac{1}{3}$

$\Rightarrow 2\theta = \cos^{-1}\frac{2}{3} = 70.53°$

but $0° \le \theta \le 360° \Rightarrow 0° \le 2\theta \le 720°$
$\Rightarrow 2\theta = 70.53°, 360° - 70.53°, 360° + 70.53°$ *or* $720° - 70.53°$
$\Rightarrow 2\theta = 70.53°, 289.47°, 430.53°$ *or* $649.47°$
$\Rightarrow \theta = 35.3°, 144.7°, 215.3°$ *or* $324.7°$

c) $\cot^2\theta = 3 \Rightarrow \cot\theta = \pm\sqrt{3} \Rightarrow \dfrac{1}{\tan\theta} = \pm\sqrt{3} \Rightarrow \tan\theta = \pm\dfrac{1}{\sqrt{3}}$

Either $\tan\theta = +\dfrac{1}{\sqrt{3}} \Rightarrow \theta = \tan^{-1}(+\dfrac{1}{\sqrt{3}}) = 30°$ *(from calculator)*

but $0° \le \theta \le 360° \Rightarrow \theta = 30°$ *or* $180° + 30° \Rightarrow \theta = 30°$ *or* $210°$

or $\tan\theta = -\frac{1}{\sqrt{3}} \Rightarrow \theta = \tan^{-1}(-\frac{1}{\sqrt{3}}) = -30°$ *(from calculator)*

but $0° \leq \theta \leq 360° \Rightarrow \theta = 180° - 30°$ *or* $360° - 30° \Rightarrow \theta = 150°$ *or* $330°$

EXERCISES

15.4 CLASSWORK

1 Find (where possible) the values of the following.

a) $\sec 60°$ **b)** $\operatorname{cosec} 100°$ **c)** $\cot -70°$ **d)** $5\cot 270°$
e) $\sec^2 45°$ **f)** $1 + \tan^2 45°$ **g)** $\operatorname{cosec}^2 60°$ **h)** $\cot^2 60° + 1$

What do you notice about your answers to parts **e)** and **f)** and to parts **g)** and **h)**?

2 Find (where possible) the values of the following.

a) $\sec\frac{5\pi}{3}$ **b)** $\operatorname{cosec}\frac{3\pi}{2}$ **c)** $\cot -\frac{\pi}{4}$
d) $7\sec\frac{\pi}{2}$ **e)** $\frac{1}{2}\operatorname{cosec}\frac{7\pi}{6}$ **f)** $-3\cot\frac{\pi}{10}$

3 Find (if possible) values of θ such that $0° \leq \theta \leq 360°$ which satisfy these equations.

a) $\sec\theta = 2$ **b)** $\operatorname{cosec}\theta = -5$ **c)** $\operatorname{cosec} 2\theta = 3$ **d)** $5\sec 2\theta = 8$
e) $\cot\frac{1}{2}\theta = -2.5$ **f)** $5\operatorname{cosec}^2\theta = 2$ **g)** $\cot^2 2\theta = \frac{1}{3}$ **h)** $1 + \cot^2\frac{1}{2}\theta = 5$

4 Find (if possible) values of θ such that $0 \leq \theta \leq 2\pi$, which satisfy the following equations.

a) $\sec\theta = -1$ **b)** $\operatorname{cosec}\theta = 4$ **c)** $2\cot\theta = 5$ **d)** $\operatorname{cosec} 2\theta = \frac{2}{\sqrt{3}}$
e) $2\sec 2\theta = 3$ **f)** $\cot 3\theta = -2$ **g)** $4\sec^2\theta = 1$ **h)** $\operatorname{cosec}^2\theta = 2$

EXERCISES

15.4 HOMEWORK

1 Find (where possible) the values of the following.

a) $\sec 20°$ **b)** $\operatorname{cosec} -50°$ **c)** $\cot 270°$ **d)** $5\sec^2 90°$
e) $1 + \tan^2 30°$ **f)** $\sec^2 30°$ **g)** $\frac{\cos 40°}{\sin 40°}$ **h)** $\cot 40°$

What do you notice about your answers to parts **g)** and **h)**? Can you explain this?

2 Find, where possible, the values of the following.

a) $\cot\frac{\pi}{3}$ **b)** $\operatorname{cosec}\frac{\pi}{4}$ **c)** $\sec\left(-\frac{\pi}{6}\right)$
d) $2\sec\frac{3\pi}{2}$ **e)** $\cot^2\pi$ **f)** $-4\operatorname{cosec}\frac{8\pi}{5}$

3 **a)** Complete the table to show the signs of the reciprocal trigonometric functions (their graphs may help you).

	$0 < \theta < \frac{\pi}{2}$	$\frac{\pi}{2} < \theta < \pi$	$\pi < \theta < \frac{3\pi}{2}$	$\frac{3\pi}{2} < \theta < 2\pi$
$\operatorname{cosec}\theta$	+			
$\sec\theta$		–		
$\cot\theta$			+	

b) State values of θ for which the following are not defined.
i) $\operatorname{cosec}\theta$ **ii)** $\sec\theta$ **iii)** $\cot\theta$

4 Find (if possible) values of θ such that $0 \le \theta \le 2\pi$ which satisfy the following equations.

a) $\cot\theta = \sqrt{3}$ **b)** $\operatorname{cosec}\theta = -2$ **c)** $\sec^2\theta = \frac{3}{4}$
d) $\cot 2\theta = -5$ **e)** $4\sec 3\theta = 6$ **f)** $\operatorname{cosec} 4\theta = 0.7$
g) $5\cot 2\theta = -2$ **h)** $1 - \operatorname{cosec} 2\theta = 0.5$

CALCULATOR ACTIVITY

Exploration 15.4

Adding more waves

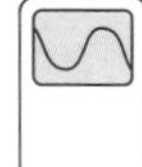

Use a graphics calculator. Rescale the axes to:

$x_{\min} = 0 \quad x_{\max} = 360 \quad x_{\text{scl}} = 30$
$y_{\min} = 0 \quad y_{\max} = 1.5 \quad y_{\text{scl}} = 1$

and make sure you are in degree mode.

- On the same axes:
  plot the graphs of : $y = \sec^2 x$
  $y = \tan^2 x$
  $y = \sec^2 x - \tan^2 x$
- What result does this illustrate?
- How could you manipulate identity (1) above to get this result?

Results

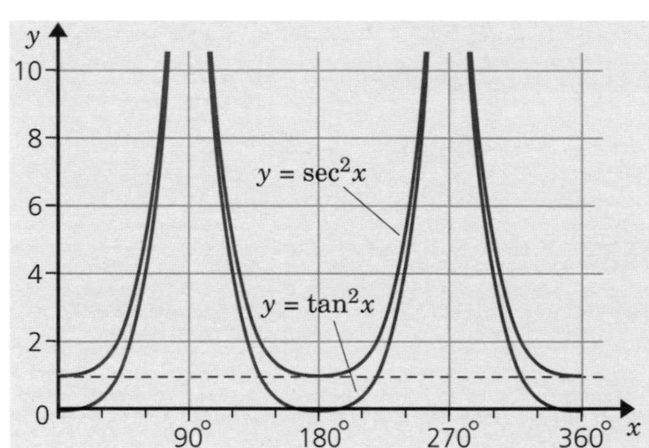

The graphs produced should look like these.

The difference between the two waves is always 1, i.e. for any angle:

$$\sec^2\theta - \tan^2\theta \equiv 1$$

$$\Rightarrow \quad \sec^2\theta \equiv 1 + \tan^2\theta \qquad (2)$$

We can derive this result from identity (1) by dividing throughout by $\cos^2\theta$.

$$\frac{\sin^2\theta}{\cos^2\theta} + \frac{\cos^2\theta}{\cos^2\theta} \equiv \frac{1}{\cos^2\theta}$$

$$\Rightarrow \tan^2\theta + 1 \equiv \sec^2\theta$$

A third identity may be derived by dividing (1) throughout by $\sin^2\theta$.

$$\frac{\sin^2\theta}{\sin^2\theta} + \frac{\cos^2\theta}{\sin^2\theta} \equiv \frac{1}{\sin^2\theta}$$

$$\Rightarrow 1 + \cot^2\theta \equiv \operatorname{cosec}^2\theta \qquad (3)$$

Using the Pythagorean identities

The three identities:

$$\sin^2\theta + \cos^2\theta \equiv 1$$

$$1 + \tan^2\theta \equiv \sec^2\theta$$

$$1 + \cot^2\theta \equiv \operatorname{cosec}^2\theta$$

are useful for simplifying trigonometrical expressions and establishing further identities, as shown in the following examples.

Example 15.13

Simplify $\dfrac{\sin x}{\sqrt{1 - \sin^2 x}}$.

Solution

$$\frac{\sin x}{\sqrt{1-\sin^2 x}} \equiv \frac{\sin x}{\sqrt{\cos^2 x}} \equiv \frac{\sin x}{\cos x} \equiv \tan x$$

Example 15.14

Prove the following identity.

$$\tan\theta + \cot\theta \equiv \sec\theta \operatorname{cosec}\theta$$

Solution

$$\text{LHS} = \tan\theta + \cot\theta = \frac{\sin\theta}{\cos\theta} + \frac{\cos\theta}{\sin\theta} \equiv \frac{\sin^2\theta + \cos^2\theta}{\cos\theta\sin\theta} \equiv \frac{1}{\cos\theta\sin\theta}$$

$$\equiv \frac{1}{\cos\theta} \times \frac{1}{\sin\theta} \equiv \sec\theta\operatorname{cosec}\theta = \text{RHS}$$

Note: Expressing $\tan\theta$ and $\cot\theta$ in terms of $\sin\theta$ and $\cos\theta$, and then simplifying, enables the identity to be proved.

Example 15.15

Prove this identity.

$$(\sec\theta - \cos\theta)(\sec\theta + \cos\theta) \equiv \tan^2\theta + \sin^2\theta$$

Solution

$$\text{LHS} = (\sec\theta - \cos\theta)(\sec\theta + \cos\theta) \equiv \sec^2\theta - \cos\theta\sec\theta + \cos\theta\sec\theta - \cos^2\theta$$

$$\equiv 1 + \tan^2\theta - (1 - \sin^2\theta) \equiv \tan^2\theta + \sin^2\theta = \text{RHS}$$

EXERCISES

15.5 CLASSWORK

1 Simplify the following trigonometrical expressions.

a) $\tan\theta\operatorname{cosec}\theta$ b) $\sqrt{(1+\cos\theta)(1-\cos\theta)}$ c) $\dfrac{\sin\theta}{1-\cos^2\theta}$

d) $\dfrac{1-\sec^2\theta}{1-\operatorname{cosec}^2\theta}$ e) $\sqrt[3]{\dfrac{\sin\theta}{1+\cot^2\theta}}$ f) $\sec\theta\sqrt{1-\sin^2\theta}$

2 Prove the following identities.

a) $\operatorname{cosec}\theta - \sin\theta \equiv \cos\theta\cot\theta$ b) $(1+\sec\theta)(1-\cos\theta) \equiv \tan\theta\sin\theta$

c) $\dfrac{\operatorname{cosec}\theta}{\operatorname{cosec}\theta - \sin\theta} \equiv \sec^2\theta$ d) $(1+\cos\theta+\sin\theta)^2 \equiv 2(1+\cos\theta)(1+\sin\theta)$

e) $(\sin\theta+\cos\theta)^2 + (\sin\theta-\cos\theta)^2 \equiv 2$

f) $(\sin\theta+\operatorname{cosec}\theta)^2 \equiv \cot^2\theta - \cos^2\theta + 4$

g) $\dfrac{\sin\theta}{1+\cos\theta} \equiv \dfrac{1-\cos\theta}{\sin\theta}$ Hint: multiply LHS by $\dfrac{1-\cos\theta}{1-\cos\theta}$

EXERCISES

15.5 HOMEWORK

1 Simplify the following trigonometrical expressions.

a) $\sin\theta\cot\theta$ b) $\dfrac{\sin\theta}{1+\cot^2\theta}$ c) $\dfrac{1}{\cos\theta\sqrt{(1+\cot^2\theta)}}$ d) $\sqrt{\dfrac{1-\cos^2\theta}{4\sec^2\theta-4}}$

2 Prove the following identities.

a) $\cot\theta + \tan\theta \equiv \sec\theta\operatorname{cosec}\theta$ b) $(\sin\theta+1)^2 \equiv 2(1+\sin\theta) - \cos^2\theta$

c) $(1-\cos^2\theta)(1+\cot^2\theta) \equiv 1$ d) $\dfrac{1}{\tan\theta+\cot\theta} \equiv \sin\theta\cos\theta$

e) $(\cos\theta - \sin\theta)^2 \equiv 1 - 2\cos\theta\sin\theta$ **f)** $\dfrac{2}{\sin\theta + 1} - \dfrac{2}{\sin\theta - 1} \equiv 4\sec^2\theta$

g) $\sec^2\theta + \operatorname{cosec}^2\theta \equiv \sec^2\theta\operatorname{cosec}^2\theta$

Comment on the last result.

MATHEMATICAL MODELLING ACTIVITY

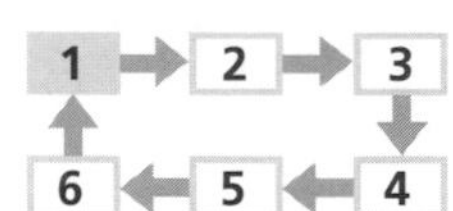

Specify the real problem

Problem statement

When two musical instruments are being played together it is important that they are in tune otherwise the sound is not very good. For example, if you pluck the strings on two guitars which are *almost* in tune (i.e. they almost play the same note), the sound appears to arrive in pulses getting louder then softer, a phenomenon called **beats**. This is, in fact, a useful method of tuning two instruments. By adjusting the note produced by one instrument to a standard note, then tuning the second instrument until the beats disappear, a constant pure sound is heard.

The task is to formulate a model to describe this phenomenon.

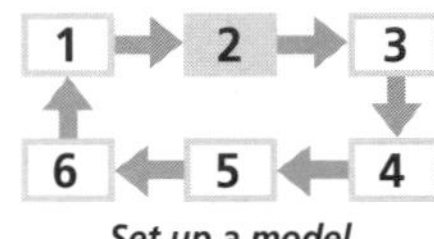

Set up a model

Set up a model

First you need to identify the simplifying assumptions and the important variables to describe the sound waves from the two musical instruments.

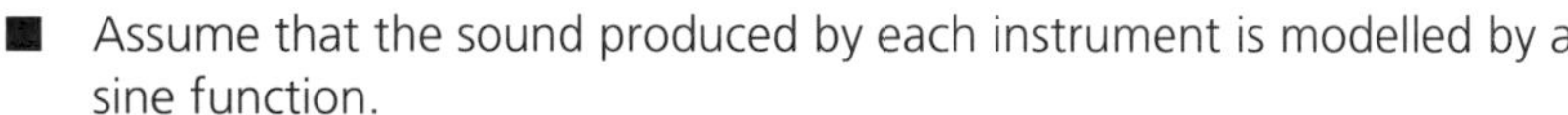

- Assume that the sound produced by each instrument is modelled by a sine function.
- Assume that the amplitude of each sound wave is the same.
- Assume that the frequency of each sound wave is slightly different.
- Let the amplitude of each sine function be a.
- Let the frequencies of the two sine functions be ω_1 and ω_2 where $\omega_1 - \omega_2$ is small.

Formulate the mathematical problem

Mathematical problem

Firstly, establish a function to describe the sound wave from each musical instrument. Using the assumptions and variables, confirm that a simple model of each sound wave is $x_1 = a\sin\omega_1 t$ and $x_2 = a\sin\omega_2 t$.

The problem is to combine the sine functions to find the combined sound wave produced when two musical notes are produced simultaneously.

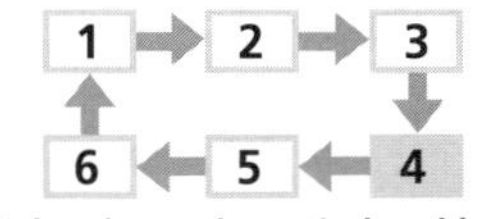

Solve the mathematical problem

Mathematical solution

The resultant sound wave has equation:

$x = x_1 + x_2 = a\sin\omega_1 t + a\sin\omega_2 t$

$= 2a\sin[\tfrac{1}{2}(\omega_1 + \omega_2)t]\cos[\tfrac{1}{2}(\omega_1 - \omega_2)t].$

Check that this is correct by expanding these formulae.

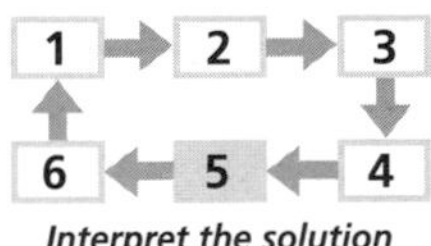

Interpret the solution

Interpret the solution

To interpret the mathematical solution, choose values for ω_1 and ω_2. Suppose that the standard note is chosen as middle C on the piano with frequency 256 hertz. Let $\omega_1 = 256$ and suppose that $\omega_2 = 276$. Then:

$x = 2a\sin 266t\cos 10t$

A graph of this resultant wave is shown in the diagram.

$x = 2\sin 266t \cos 10t$

$x = \pm\, 2 \cos 10t$

The amplitude of the wave grows to double the original amplitude a and then decays to zero. This process is then repeated. The mathematical model describes the physical phenomenon of beats.

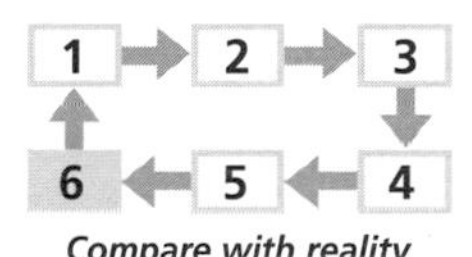

Compare with reality

Refinement of the model

Investigate the effects of:

- changes to ω_2 so that $|\omega_2 - \omega_1|$ increases in size,
- changes to the chosen standard note.

Is it easier to tune notes of high or low frequency?

CONSOLIDATION EXERCISES FOR CHAPTER 15

1 Expand the LHS of the equation $\sin(x + 45°) = 2\cos x$ using the appropriate addition theorem and hence:
a) show that $\tan x = 2\sqrt{2} - 1$,
b) find all values of x from 0 to 360°

2 Using the addition theorems, show that the equation $\sin\left(x + \dfrac{\pi}{4}\right) - \cos x + \cos\left(x + \dfrac{\pi}{4}\right)$ is equivalent to the equation $\tan x = \frac{\sqrt{2}}{2}$ and hence find the general solution of the original equation, giving your answer in radians.

3 Solve the equation $\cos(x + 30°) = 2\sin(x + 60°)$ in the domain $0 \le x \le 360°$, by first showing that $\tan x = -\frac{\sqrt{3}}{3}$.

4 Use a method similar to those above to solve the equation $2\cos x = \sin\left(x + \dfrac{\pi}{6}\right)$, giving the general solution, in radians.

5 Given that $\tan x \tan(x + 45°) = 3$, by expanding $\tan(x + 45°)$ and letting $t = \tan x$, show that $t^2 + 4t - 3 = 0$. Solve this equation to find the two possible values of t and hence find *all* the values of x that satisfy the original equation.

6 Draw an accurate graph of the function $y = \sin x - \sin 2x$ using values of x = 0°, 30°, 45°, 60°, 90°, 120°, 135°, 150° and 180°. Use your graphs to solve the equation $\sin x = \sin 2x$ giving answers to one decimal place.
Confirm your result by use of the identity $\sin 2x = 2\sin x \cos x$.
If you have a graphics calculator, use it to confirm this result.

7 Draw an accurate graph of the function $y = \sin x - \cos 2x$ using values of $x = 0°, 30°, 45°, 60°, 90°, 120°, 135°, 150°$ and $180°$. On the same axes, draw the lines $y = 1$ and $y = -1$. Use your graphs to solve these equations.
a) $\sin x = \cos 2x$ **b)** $\sin x = \cos 2x + 1$ **c)** $\sin x = \cos 2x - 1$
Confirm your results by solving the equations using, in each case, an appropriate identity for $\cos 2x$. If you have a graphics calculator, use it to confirm these results.

8 Find the values of x between 0 and 2π radians satisfying $\cos 2x = 2 \sin x$. Illustrate your answer by sketching the graphs of $\cos 2x$ and $2 \sin x$ on the same axes. If you have a graphics calculator, use it to help you sketch the graphs.

9 Solve the following equations for $0 \le x \le 360°$.
a) $\sin 2x + \cos x = 0$ **b)** $\sin 2x + 3\sin x = 0$
c) $\cos 2x = 1 + 2\sin x$ **d)** $\cos 2x + \sin x - 1 = 0$
e) $3\cos 2x = -\sin^2 x - 2\sin x$ **f)** $\cos 2x + 2\sin^2 x = 4\cos^2 x$

10 The double-angle formulae can be used for any angle and its double, for example, $\sin 4x \equiv 2\sin 2x \cos 2x$. Write down the three corresponding formulae for $\cos 4x$. Use an appropriate one of these, in each case, to solve the equations:
a) $\cos 4x - 3\cos 2x + 2 = 0$ **b)** $2\cos 4x + 4\sin 2x + 1 = 0$
giving all solutions between 0 and 180°.

11 Solve the equation $\sin 2x \equiv \tan x$ in the domain $0 \le x \le 2\pi$.

12 By using the identity for $\tan 2x$ and letting $\tan x = t$, solve the following equations for values of x between 0 and 360°.
a) $\tan 2x = \tan x$ **b)** $\tan 2x = 4\cot x$ **c)** $\tan x \tan 2x = 2$

13 Find a positive number R and an acute angle α such that $8\sin x - 15\cos x = R\sin(x - \alpha)$.
Hence find all solutions of the equation $8\sin x - 15\cos x = 17$ that lie between −360° and 360°.

14 By writing the LHS in the form indicated, where R is a positive number and α is an acute angle, solve the following equations for values of x in the domain $0 \le x \le 360°$.
a) $3\sin x + 4\cos x = 2$, $R\sin(x + \alpha)$
b) $2\cos x - \sin x = 0.5$, $R\cos(x + \alpha)$
c) $\cos x + \sin x = 1$, $R\cos(x - \alpha)$
d) $3\sin x - 4\cos x = 4$, $R\sin(x - \alpha)$

15 Find the general solutions of the following equations, in degrees.
a) $5\sin x + 12\cos x = 6.5$ **b)** $\sqrt{2}\sin x + \cos x = 1$
c) $\cos x + \sin x = \sqrt{2}$ **d)** $\cos x - 3\sin x = 1$

16 Find the general solutions of the following equations, in radians.
a) $6\cos x + 8\sin x = 9$ **b)** $4\cos x + \sin x = 3$
c) $5\cos x - 12\sin x = 6.5$ **d)** $\sec x = 1 - \sqrt{3}\tan x$

17 Find the general solution of the equation $7\cos x + 24\sin x = 12.5$ and hence find all solutions in the domain $0 \le x \le 360°$. Deduce the solutions of the equations:
a) $7\cos\frac{x}{2} + 24\sin\frac{x}{2} = 12.5$ **b)** $7\cos 2x + 24\sin 2x = 12.5$
lying in the same domain.

18 Rewrite $2\sin x + \cos x$ in the form $R\sin(x+\alpha)$ and hence solve the equation $2\sin x + \cos x = 1$ giving values of x between 0 and 360°. Deduce the solutions, in the same domain, of these equations.

a) $2\sin\frac{x}{2} + \cos\frac{x}{2} = 1$ **b)** $2\sin 3x + \cos 3x = 1$

19 Show that $(\cos x + \sin x)^2 = 1 + \sin 2x$.
Sketch the graph of $y = (\cos x + \sin x)^2$ for $0 \le x \le 2\pi$, indicating clearly the value of x for which $y = 0$.
Deduce the exact values of x in this interval for which $(\cos x + \sin x)^2 = 1.5$.

(NEAB Question 6, Specimen Paper 2, 1994)

20 **a)** Express the function $3\cos x + 4\sin x$ in the form $R\sin(x+\alpha)$, stating the values of R and α.
b) Write down the maximum value of $3\cos x + 4\sin x$.
c) Solve the equation $3\cos x + 4\sin x = 0$ for $0 \le x \le 360°$.

(SMP 16–19 Question 8, Specimen Paper, 1994)

21 Show that $\tan\theta + \cot\theta = \dfrac{2}{\sin 2\theta}$.
Hence, or otherwise, solve the equation $\tan\theta + \cot\theta = 4$, giving all the values of θ between 0 and 360°.

(UCLES Linear Question 10, Specimen Paper 1, 1994)

22 Prove that $\sin 3\theta = 3\sin\theta - 4\sin^3\theta$.
Hence find all values of θ, for $0 \le \theta \le 360°$, which satisfy the equation $\sin 3\theta = 2\sin\theta$.

(UCLES (Modular) Question 7, Specimen Paper P3, 1994)

23 The diagram shows a fixed semicircle, with centre O and radius r, and an inscribed rectangle ABCD. The vertices A and B of the rectangle lie on the circumference of the semicircle, and C and D lie on the diameter. The size of angle BOC is θ radians.

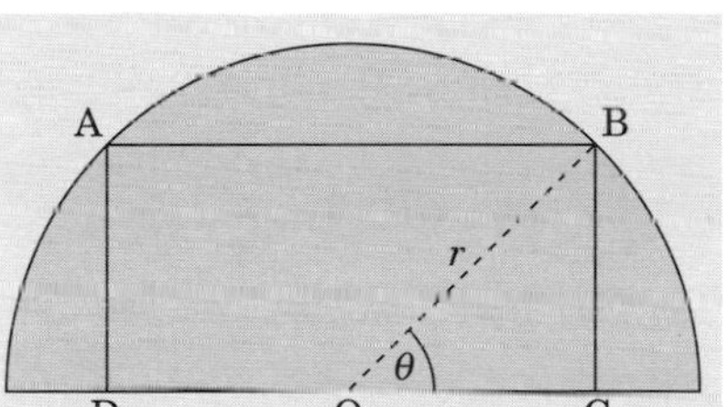

a) Express the perimeter, p, of the rectangle in terms of r and θ, and show that the area, a, may be expressed in the form $a = r^2\sin 2\theta$.
b) Find the maximum value of a as θ varies, and show that when a has its maximum value, $p = 3r\sqrt{2}$.
c) Find, in terms of r, the area of the rectangle which has maximum perimeter.

(UCLES (Modular) Question 8, Specimen Paper P3, 1994)

24 **a)** Write $f(x) = \sin x + 2\sin(x + 60°)$ in the form $f(x) = a\sin x + b\cos x$, where a and b are numbers.
b) Hence write $f(x)$ in the form $r\sin(x + c)$ where r is a positive number and c is an acute angle (in degrees).
c) For what values of x in the domain $0 \le x \le 90°$ does $f(x)$ take:
i) its greatest value, **ii)** its smallest value?

(Oxford and Cambridge Question 2, Specimen Paper 2, 1994)

25 **a)** Use a trigonometrical formula to expand $\cos(x+\alpha)$.
b) Express $y = 2\cos x - 5\sin x$ in the form $r\cos(x+\alpha)$, giving the positive value of r and the smallest positive value of α.
c) State the maximum and minimum values of y and the corresponding values of x for $0 \le x \le 360°$.
d) Solve the equation $2\cos x - 5\sin x = 3$ for $0 \le x \le 360°$.

(MEI Question 2, Paper 2, June 1994)

26 $8\cos x - 15\sin x \equiv R\cos(x + A)$

a) Find the positive constant R.

b) Find the acute angle A, giving your answer in degrees to 1 decimal place.

c) Hence, or otherwise, find the maximum value of $8\cos x - 15\sin x$.

d) Find the value of x, in the range $0 \le x \le 360°$, which will give the maximum value, giving your answer in degrees to 1 decimal place.

(ULEAC Question 6, Paper 2, January 1994)

27 **a)** Show that $7\cos x - 4\sin x$ may be expressed in the form $R\cos(x + \alpha)$, where R is $\sqrt{65}$ and $\tan \alpha = \frac{4}{7}$.

b) Find, in radians to 2 decimal places, the smallest positive value of x for which $7\cos x - 4\sin x$ takes its maximum value.

c) Find, in radians to 2 decimal places, the two smallest positive values of x for which $7\cos x - 4\sin x = 4.88$.
The curve C has equation $y = (7\cos x - 4\sin x + 4)^{\frac{1}{2}}$.

d) Take corresponding values of y at $x = 0$, $\frac{\pi}{6}$, $\frac{\pi}{3}$ and $\frac{\pi}{2}$ for the curve C and use the trapezium rule to find an estimate for the area of the finite region bounded by the curve C, the y-axis and the x-axis for $0 \le x \le \frac{\pi}{2}$ giving your answer to 1 decimal place.

(ULEAC Question 9, Paper 2, June 1993)

28 **a)** Express $3\cos x + \sin x$ in the form $R\cos(x - \alpha)$, giving the value of R and the smallest positive value of α.

b) Use your answer to part **a)** to solve the equation $3\cos x + \sin x = 1$, for $0 \le x \le 360°$.

c) Solve the equation $(3\cos x)^2 = (1 - \sin x)^2$ by substituting $\cos^2 x$ in terms of $\sin x$ and solving the resulting quadratic equation in $\sin x$.

d) Explain why the answers to **b)** and **c)** are not the same.

(MEI Question 5, Paper 2, January 1995)

29 Prove the identity $\sin(x + 30°) + \sqrt{3}\cos(x + 30°) = 2\cos x$, where x is measured in degrees.
Hence express cos 15° in surd form.

(OCR, Question 2, Specimen Paper 3)

30 Given that $\sin(x + \alpha) = \sqrt{2}\cos(x - \alpha)$, where $\cos x \cos \alpha \ne 0$,

a) prove that $\tan x = \dfrac{\sqrt{2} - \tan\alpha}{1 - \sqrt{2}\tan\alpha}$.

b) Hence, or otherwise, find the solutions in the interval $0 < x < 2\pi$ of $\sin\left(x + \frac{\pi}{6}\right) = \sqrt{2}\cos\left(x - \frac{\pi}{6}\right)$ giving your answers in radians to 3 decimal places.

(EDEXCEL, Question 3, Paper 2, January 2000)

31 Solve, giving your answers in terms of π, $\cos 2x + 3\sin x = 2$, $0 \le x < 2\pi$.

(EDEXCEL, Question 1, Paper 2, June 1999)

32 Find, to the nearest integer, the values of x in the interval $0° \le x < 180°$ for which $3\sin^2 3x - 7\cos 3x - 5 = 0$.

(EDEXCEL, Question 2, Paper 2, June 1998)

Summary

- **Compound-angle formulae**

  $\sin(\theta + \varphi) \equiv \sin\theta\cos\varphi + \cos\theta\sin\varphi$ $\quad \sin(\theta - \varphi) = \sin\theta\cos\varphi - \cos\theta\sin\varphi$

  $\cos(\theta + \varphi) \equiv \cos\theta\cos\varphi - \sin\theta\sin\varphi$ $\quad \cos(\theta - \varphi) = \cos\theta\cos\varphi + \sin\theta\sin\varphi$

  $\tan(\theta + \varphi) \equiv \dfrac{\tan\theta + \tan\varphi}{1 - \tan\theta\tan\varphi}$ $\quad \tan(\theta - \varphi) = \dfrac{\tan\theta - \tan\varphi}{1 + \tan\theta\tan\varphi}$

- **Double-angle formulae**

  $\sin 2\theta \equiv 2\sin\theta\cos\theta$

  $\cos 2\theta \equiv \cos^2\theta - \sin^2\theta \equiv 2\cos^2\theta - 1 \equiv 1 - 2\sin^2\theta$

  $\tan 2\theta \equiv \dfrac{2\tan\theta}{1 - \tan^2\theta}$

- To solve equations of the form $a\cos x + b\sin x = c$ we first write the left-hand side as $R\cos(x - \alpha)$ or $R\sin(x + \alpha)$ and then find the appropriate values of R and α.

- The reciprocal trigonometric functions are

  $\operatorname{cosec} x = \dfrac{1}{\sin x}$ $\quad \sec x = \dfrac{1}{\cos x}$ $\quad \cot x = \dfrac{1}{\tan x}$

  Three important trigonometric identities are

  $\sin^2\theta + \cos^2\theta = 1$

  $1 + \tan^2\theta = \sec^2\theta$

  $1 + \cot^2\theta = \operatorname{cosec}^2\theta$

Exponentials and logarithms

In this chapter we introduce:

- *exponential functions of the form $f(x) = a^x$*
- *their inverse functions which are called logarithms.*

EXPONENTIAL FUNCTIONS

When we studied population growth in bacteria at the beginning of Chapter 2 *Basic algebra*, we met a function of the form $y = a^x$. Functions of this type are **exponential functions**, and their curves always take the same general shape.

Exploration 16.1

The shape of an exponential curve

The general form of the function for bacteria population growth is $y = 2^x$, illustrated in the diagram.

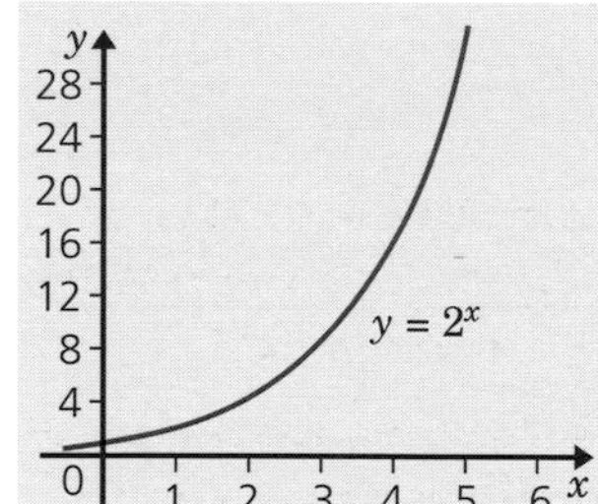

- What happens to y as $x \to \infty$?
- What happens to y as $x \to -\infty$?
- Why is y always positive?
- Estimate the gradient at various points on the curve.
- Describe what happens to the gradient as $x \to \pm\infty$.

The exponential curve

As x gets larger, 2^x gets large (at an increasing rate) so $y \to \infty$ as $x \to \infty$. As x gets smaller, 2^x gets smaller (at a decreasing rate) so $y \to 0$ from above as $x \to -\infty$. [In future work we shall need to use the idea that $2^{-\infty} = 0$]. Since the graph lies entirely above the x-axis y is always positive.

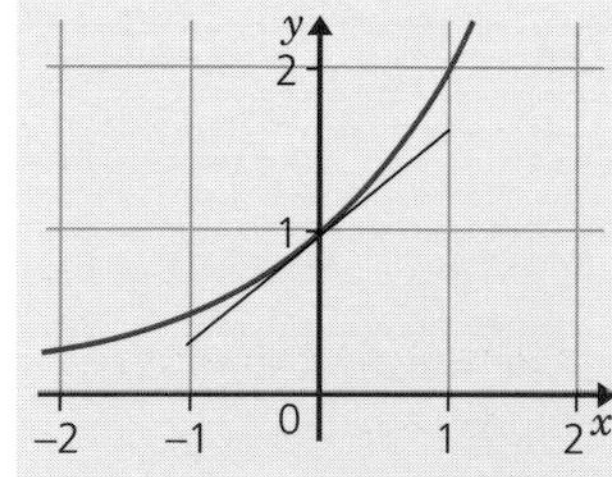

We can find estimates of the gradient at points on the curve, by drawing and measuring the gradient of tangents or by numerical approximation. For example, to estimate the gradient at $x = 0$ we can draw the tangent, as in the diagram. Then we can see that the gradient of the tangent is 0.7.

Numerically, we consider the gradient of the chord PQ, where P and Q have coordinates $(-0.01, 2^{-0.01})$ and $(0.01, 2^{0.01})$ respectively.

$$\text{Gradient of PQ} = \frac{2^{0.01} - 2^{-0.01}}{0.01-(-0.01)} \approx 0.693$$

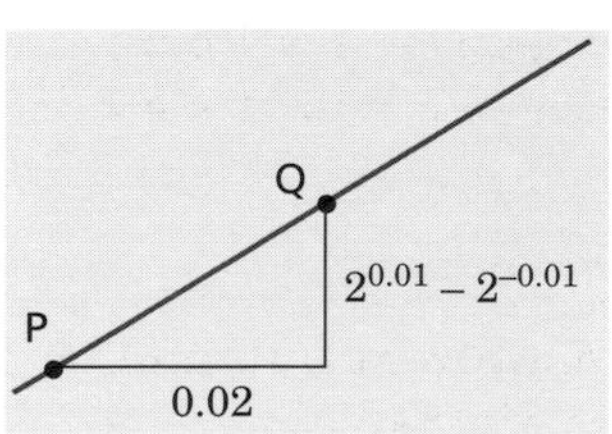

Since P and Q are so close together, the gradient of chord PQ is a close approximation to the gradient of the tangent at (0, 1).

Gradients at points around the origin are listed in this table.

x	−3	−2	−1	0	1	2	3
y	0.125	0.25	0.5	1	2	4	8
gradient	0.087	0.173	0.347	0.693	1.387	2.773	5.545

We can see that as x gets larger, the gradient gets larger (at an increasing rate) and as x gets smaller the gradient gets smaller (at a decreasing rate). The gradient is always positive.

Note that the gradient is always about 0.69 times the y-value, which suggests the following relationships.

$$f(x) = 2^x \Rightarrow f'(x) \approx 0.69 \times 2^x$$

There is a more formal treatment of gradients of exponential functions in Chapter 17, *The exponential and the natural logarithmic functions*.

Example 16.1

The diagram shows graphs of $y = 2^x$, $y = 2^{x-1}$ and $y = 2^{x+1}$. Identify which is which and describe geometrically the transformation of $y = 2^x$ onto $y = 2^{x-1}$ and $y = 2^x$ onto $y = 2^{x+1}$ in each of two ways.

a)

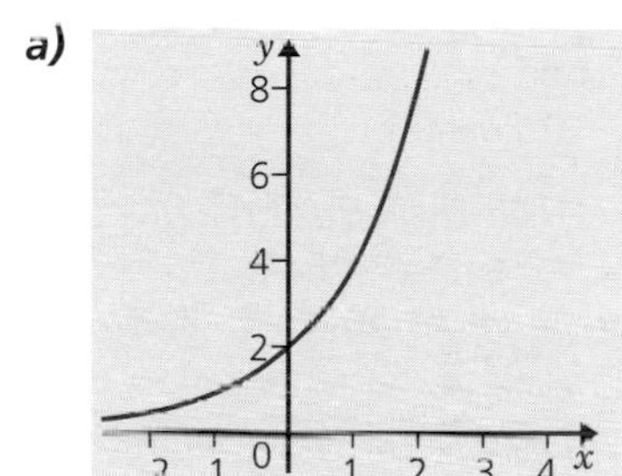

b)

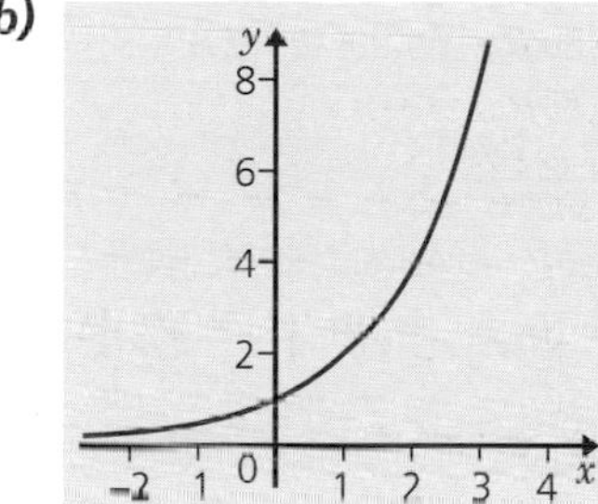

c)

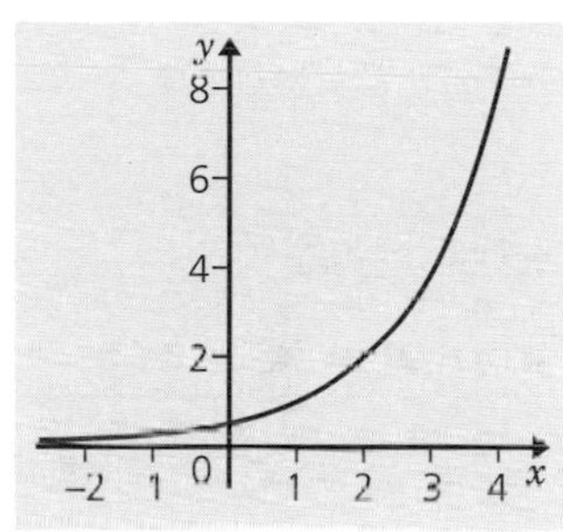

Solution

The graphs illustrated are:

a) $y = 2^{x+1}$ ***b)*** $y = 2^x$ ***c)*** $y = 2^{x-1}$.

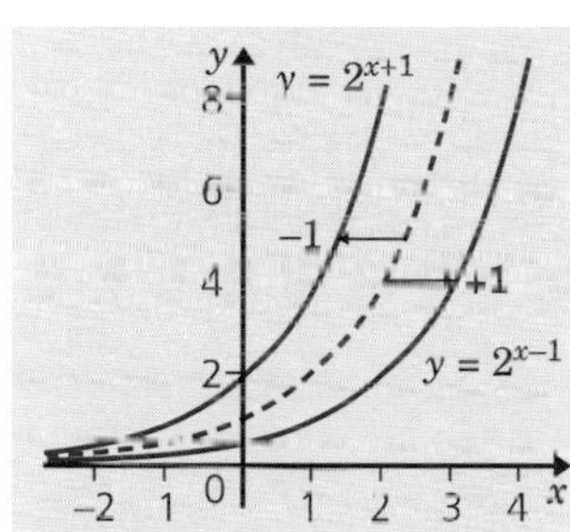

One way of transforming the graph of $y = 2^x$ onto the graph of $y = 2^{x+1}$ is by a translation of −1 unit parallel to the x-axis. Similarly, a translation of +1 unit parallel to the x-axis transforms $y = 2^x$ onto $y = 2^{x-1}$.

Alternatively a stretch, factor 2, parallel to the y-axis transforms $y = 2^x$ onto $y = 2^{x+1}$ and stretch, factor $\frac{1}{2}$, parallel to the y-axis transforms $y = 2^x$ onto $y = 2^{x-1}$.

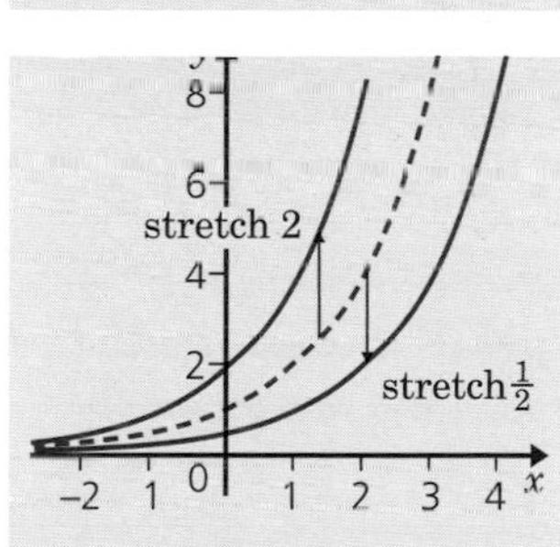

The reasons for these alternative descriptions are explained by the rules of indices.

$$2^{x+1} = 2^x \times 2^1 = 2 \times 2^x$$
$$2^{x-1} = 2^x \div 2^1 = \tfrac{1}{2} \times 2^x$$

Standard form

A useful exponential function which appears on scientific calculators is 10^x. A common use of the function 10^x is the expression of numbers in standard form, where any number can be expressed as a number between 0 and 1, multiplied by an integer power of 10. In general, a number in standard form is expressed as $a \times 10^b$, $0 < a < 1$, b is an integer.

e.g. $93\,000\,000 = 9.3 \times 10^7$ $\quad 0.000\,032\,8 = 3.28 \times 10^{-5}$

When x is a real number, then $f(x) = 10^x$ is a **continuous** function, and values for it may be found using the appropriate key on a calculator. Equations involving 10^x may be solved by a numerical method such as **decimal search**.

Example 16.2

Find values of x, correct to 3 s.f., which satisfy these equations.
a) $10^{-x} = 378$ ***b)*** $15 + 6x = 10^x$

Solution

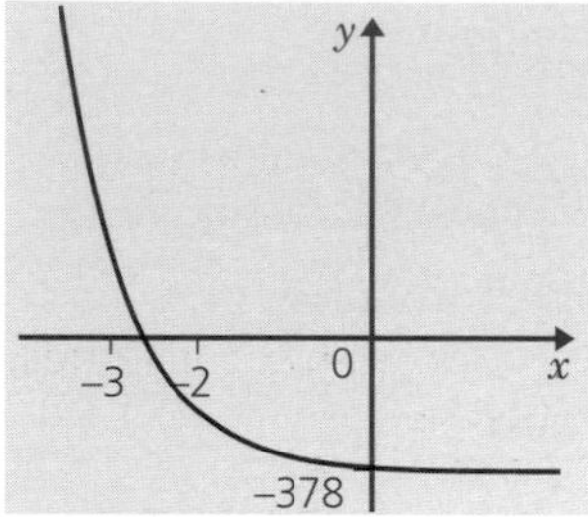

a) $10^{-x} = 378 \Rightarrow 10^{-x} - 378 = 0$
A sketch of $y = 10^{-x} - 378$ shows that the equation has a root between $x = -3$ and $x = -2$, i.e. if α is the root then $-3 < \alpha < -2$.
Using a decimal search with successive refinements, we find that:
$-2.6 < \alpha < -2.5$
$-2.58 < \alpha < -2.57$
$-2.578 < \alpha < -2.577$
This is sufficient to show that $\alpha = -2.58$ (to 3 s.f.). Accuracy to 3 s.f. is confirmed by noting that:
when $x = -2.585$ $y = 6.5918$
when $x = -2.575$ $y = -2.1626$

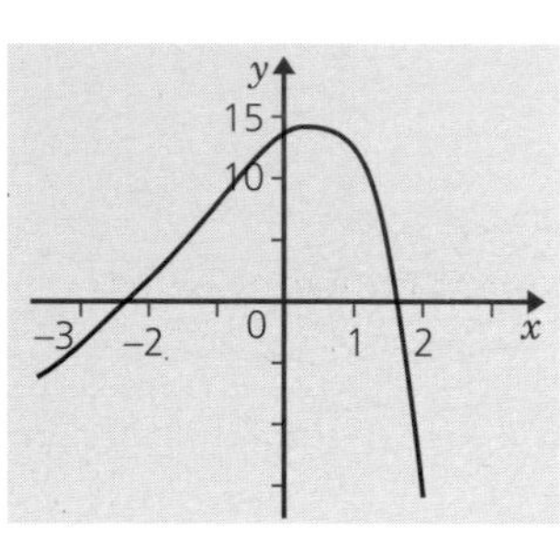

b) $15 + 6x = 10^x \Rightarrow 15 + 6x - 10^x = 0$
A sketch of $y = 15 + 6x - 10^x$ shows that the equation has two roots, α and β, such that: $-3 < \alpha < -2$ and $1 < \beta < 2$
Using a decimal search with successive refinements, we find that:
$-2.5 < \alpha < -2.4$ $1.3 < \beta < 1,4$
$-2.50 < \alpha < -2.49$ $1.36 < \beta < 1.37$
$-2.500 < \alpha < -2.499$ $1.365 < \beta < 1.366$
This is sufficient to show that $\alpha = -2.50$ and $\beta = 1.37$ (to 3 s.f.).
Note that when $x = -2.5$, $y = 15 + 6(-2.5) - 10^{-2.5}$
$= 15 - 15 - 0.003\,16 = -0.003\,16$
Since the term in 10^x is relatively small when $x = -2.5$, then a good approximation to the lower root will be found by solving the equation:
$15 + 6x = 0 \Rightarrow x = -2.5$
and this confirms that $\alpha = -2.50$ (to 3 s.f.).

Modelling problems

The ability to solve equations involving exponential functions is a useful tool in modelling problems, as shown in the next example.

Example 16.3

*The radioactivity of a substance decays by 10 per cent over a period of a year. Its initial level of radioactivity is 200. Find the time taken for the level to fall to 100, i.e. find its **half-life**.*

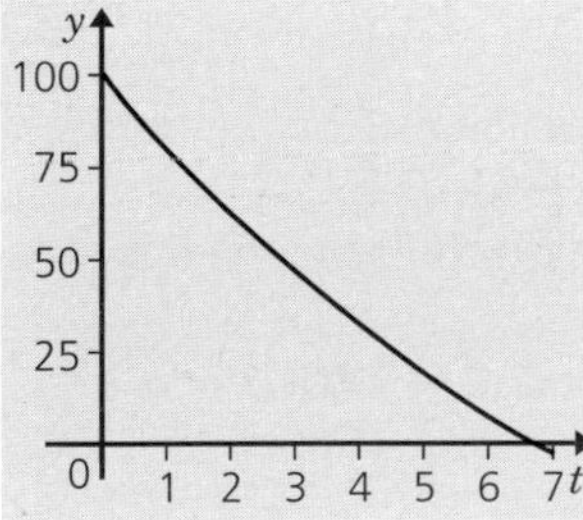

Solution

If R is the level of radioactivity after t years, then:
$R = 200 \times 0.9^t$
When $R = 100$:
$100 = 200 \times 0.9^t \Rightarrow 200 \times 0.9^t - 100 = 0$
A sketch graph shows that the equation has a root, α and $6 < \alpha < 7$.
Using a decimal search with successive refinements, we find that:
$6.5 < \alpha < 6.6$
$6.57 < \alpha < 6.58$
$6.578 < \alpha < 6.579$
Therefore $\alpha = 6.58$ (to 3 s.f.), so the half-life of the substance is 6.58 years, which is approximately 6 years 7 months.

EXERCISES

16.1 CLASSWORK

1 **a)** Copy and complete this table for the function $y = 3^x$.
b) Using suitable scales, plot a graph of $y = 3^x$ for $-3 \le x \le 3$.
c) Use your graph to solve the equation $3^x = 20$.
d) Draw tangents to the curve for each point in the table and estimate the gradient at that point.

x	-3	-2	-1	0	1	2	3
y							

2 **a)** Use a decimal search to solve the equation $3^x - 20 = 0$, giving your answer correct to 3 s.f.
b) Use a numerical method to demonstrate that $\mathrm{f}(x) = 3^x \Rightarrow$ $\mathrm{f}'(x) \approx 1.1 \times 3^x$ for $x = -2, -1, 0, 1, 2$. Compare your numerical values with the gradient estimates you found in question **1**.

3 **a)** Use a decimal search to solve the equation $2^{-x} = 3$, giving your answer correct to 3 s.f.
b) Use a numerical method to demonstrate that $\mathrm{f}(x) = 5 \times 2^{-x} \Rightarrow$ $\mathrm{f}'(x) \approx 3.5 \times 2^{-x}$ for $x = -2, -1, 0, 1, 2$.

4 On the same axes sketch graphs of:

a) $y = 4^x$ **b)** $y - 4^{-x}$ **c)** $y = 4^{\frac{1}{2}-x}$

For parts **b)** and **c)**, describe the geometrical transformations which map the graph of $y = 4^x$ onto the curve.

5 On the same axes sketch graphs of $k \times 10^x$ for $k = 2, 1, 0.5, 0.5, 1, 2$.

6 **a)** Sketch a graph of $y = 2^x - 9x + 5$ for $-1 \le x \le 7$.
b) Use your graph to show that the equation $2^x - 9x - 5$ has roots α and β such that $0 < \alpha < 1$ and $5 < \beta < 6$.
c) Use a decimal search to find values for α and β correct to 3 s.f.

7 The population of a country, currently 2 million, is growing at a rate of two per cent per annum.

a) Show that the expected population, P millions, in t years time, is given by $P = 2 \times 1.02^t$.
b) Sketch a graph of P against t for $0 \le t \le 100$.
c) Use your graph to estimate:
i) the size of the population in 35 years' time,
ii) the time taken for P to reach 10 million.

8 The concentration of a drug in a patient's bloodstream is C milligrams per millilitre after t hours, where $C = ka^{-t}$.

For drug A, $k = 2, a = 1.2$ For drug B, $k = 3, a = 1.4$

a) On the same axes, sketch graphs of C against t for both drugs.
b) Which drug will have the greater concentration after:
i) 2 hours, **ii)** 3 hours?
c) After what period of time would the concentration levels be the same for both drugs?

EXERCISES

16.1 HOMEWORK

x	-3	-2	-1	0	1	2	3
y							

1 **a)** Copy and complete this table for the function $y = 5^x$.
b) Using suitable scales, plot a graph of $y = 5^x$ for $-3 \le x \le 3$.
c) Use your graph to solve the equation $5^x = 15$.
d) Draw tangents to the curve for each point in the table and estimate the gradient at the solution point of $5^x = 15$.

2 **a)** Use a decimal search to solve the equation $5^x - 15 = 0$, giving your answer correct to 3 s.f.
b) Use a numerical method to demonstrate that $f(x) = 5^x \Rightarrow f'(x) \approx 1.6 \times 5^x$ for $x = -2, -1, 0, 1, 2$. Compare your numerical values with the gradient estimates you found in question **1**.

3 **a)** Use a decimal search to solve the equation $3^{-x} = 8$, giving your answer correct to 3 s.f.
b) Use a numerical method to demonstrate that $f(x) = 4 \times 3^{-x} \Rightarrow f'(x) \approx -4.4 \times 3^{-x}$ for $x = -2, -1, 0, 1, 2$.

4 On the same axes, sketch graphs of:

a) $y = 5^x$ **b)** $y = 5^{-x}$ **c)** $y = 5^{x+1}$ **d)** $y = 5^{x-1}$

For parts **b), c)** and **d)** describe the geometrical transformations which maps the graph of $y = 5^x$ onto the curve.

5 On the same axes, sketch graphs of $y = a^x$ for $a = -2, -1, -\frac{1}{2}, 1, 2$.

6 Sketch a graph of $y = 2^{-x}$ and $y = x^2 - 1$.

a) Use your graph to show that the equation $2^{-x} = x^2 - 1$ has two solutions, α and β, such that $1 < \alpha < 2$ and β is a negative integer.
b) Use a decimal search to find a value for α correct to 3 s.f.

7 During the first five years after the opening of a theme park in Dorset, the number of visitors increased by 30 per cent per annum. In the first year there were 6000 visitors.

a) Show that the number of visitors, P, after t years is given by:
$P = 6000 \times 1.3^{t-1}$ $1 \le t \le 5$.
b) Sketch a graph of P against t for $1 \le t \le 5$.
c) If the number of visitors continues to grow at 30 per cent per annum how many people will visit the theme park in the tenth year after opening?
d) The maximum number of visitors per year is to be restricted to 300 000. Use your graph to predict when this will occur.

8 The solar system consists of the sun and the nine planets together with many smaller bodies such as the comets and the meteorites. The nine planets are, in order of distance from the sun, Mercury, Venus, Earth, Mars, Jupiter, Saturn, Uranus, Neptune and Pluto. Between Mars and Jupiter are many very small bodies called the minor planets or asteroids and nearly all of them are too small to be seen by the naked eye from the Earth.

This problem is about Bode's law, developed in the 18th century, that relates the distance of a planet from the sun to a number representing the planet.

Data for Bode's law

The table below gives the average distance of the planets from the sun and the ratio of these distances to the Earth's distance from the sun.

Planet	Distance from the sun R (10^6 km)	Ratio $\frac{R}{R_e}$ where R_e is the Earth's distance from the sun
Mercury	57.9	0.39
Venus	108.2	0.72
Earth	149.6	1.00
Mars	227.9	1.52
Asteroids	433.8	2.9
Jupiter	778.3	5.20
Saturn	1427	9.54
Uranus	2870	19.2
Neptune	4497	30.1
Pluto	5907	38.5

Ignoring Mercury, we assign a number to each planet:

- for Venus, $n = 0$
- for Earth, $n = 1$
-
- for Pluto, $n = 8$

Use the data to find a model relating $\frac{R}{R_e}$ and n. What value of n should you give to Mercury so that it, too, fits the model?

DEFINITION AND LAWS OF LOGARITHMS

Exploration 16.2

Drawing graphs of exponential functions

- On graph paper draw graphs of $y = 2^x$ and $y = x$ for $-5 < x < 5$.
- Draw the reflection of the graph of $y = 2^x$ in the line $y = x$.

Repeat the activity for $y = 3^x$ and $y = 5^x$.

Graphs of exponentials

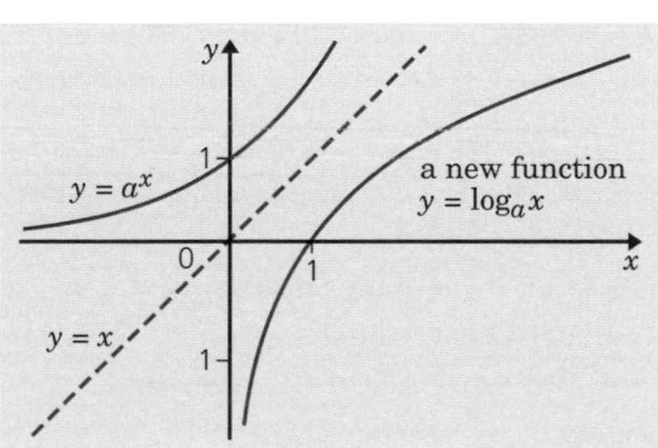

The graphs drawn in Exploration 16.2 had the general shape as shown in the diagram.

In Chapter 12, *Functions*, this idea was used to draw the graphs of inverse functions. For a function $y = f(x)$ the graph of the inverse function $y = f^{-1}(x)$ is a reflection, in the line $y = x$, of the original function $y = f(x)$.

The reflections drawn in Exploration 16.2 are the inverse functions of $y = 2^x$, $y = 3^x$ and $y = 5^x$. They are examples of **logarithmic functions**.

The logarithm of x to base a is defined as the inverse function of a^x in the following way.

If $a^m = b$ then $m = \log_a b$.

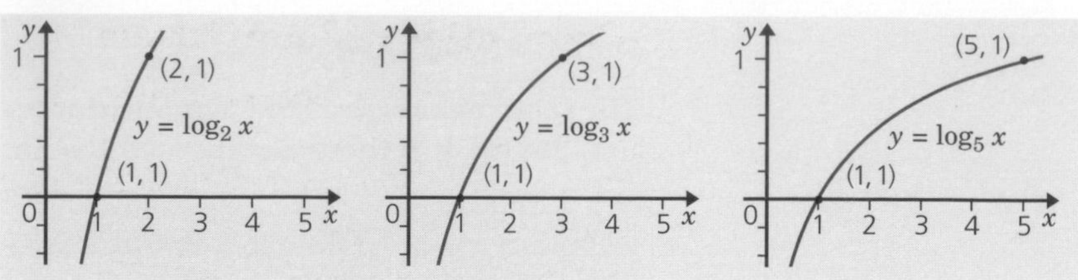

Exploration 16.2 involved graphs of $y = \log_2 x$, $y = \log_3 x$ and $y = \log_5 x$.

In each case the graph passes through the point (1, 0). One important property of logarithms is that:

$\log_a 1 = 0$ for any base a.

This result can be obtained from the definition by letting $b = 1$.

$a^m = 1 \Rightarrow m = 0 \Rightarrow \log_a 1 = 0.$

Example 16.4

Write each of the following in index form.

a) $\log_2 32 = 5$ ***b)*** $\log_3 81 = 4$ ***c)*** $\log_a 5 = b$

Solution

a) *If* $\log_2 32 = 5$ *then the base and index is 2.*

$\log_2 32 = 5 \Rightarrow 32 = 2^5$

b) *Similarly* $\log_3 81 = 4 \Rightarrow 81 = 3^4$

c) *In this case the base and index is* a.

$\log_a 5 = b \Rightarrow 5 = a^b$.

Example 16.5

Write each of the following in logarithmic form.

a) $5^2 = 25$ ***b)*** $x^y = 3$

Solution

a) *The index is 5 and so the base of the logarithm is 5.*

$5^2 = 25 \Rightarrow \log_5 25 = 2$

b) *The index is* x *and so the base of the logarithm is* x.

$x^y = 3 \Rightarrow \log_x 3 = y$

Common logarithms

Although logarithms may be expressed in terms of any base, there are two that are generally used. One of these is base 10. Logarithms to base 10 are called **common logarithms** and are often written as $\log b$, i.e. without including the base number 10. Find the common logarithm key on your calculator. It will be labelled log (or maybe $\log_{10}$). It is usually on the same key as 10^x, showing that the functions are related.

Use your calculator to check the following values.

$\log_{10} 10 = 1$	$\log_{10} 100 = 2$	$\log_{10} 1000 = 3$
$\log_{10} 20 = 1.30103$	$\log_{10} 0.5 = -0.30103$	$\log_{10} 1 = 0$
$\log_{10} 5.73 = 0.75815$	$\log_{10} 0.12 = -0.92082$	$\log_{10}(-2)$ gives error

Two important properties can be seen from these values.

- If $x < 1$ then $\log_{10} x < 0$.
- If $x < 0$ then $\log_{10} x$ is not defined.

These properties are true for logarithms to any base.

Properties of logarithms

An important property of logarithms is:

$\log_a a = 1$

for any $a \neq 0$. This can be deduced from the definition of logarithms with $b = a$.

If $a^m = a$ then $m = 1 \Rightarrow \log_a a = 1$.

Exploration 16.3

Logarithms of powers of ten

- Write the following numbers as powers of 10.
  100 1000 10 000 100 000 0.1 0.01 0.001
- Use your calculator to find the log of each number to base 10.
- Deduce a law for simplifying $\log_{10} 10^r$.

Developing the properties of logarithms

You will have found that $\log_{10} 10^r = r$. This is a special case of one of the properties of logarithms that we will now show.

Consider $x = \log_a b$ and $y = \log_a c$

$\Rightarrow$ $b = a^x$ and $c = a^y$

now $bc = (a^x)(a^y) = a^{x+y}$ *using properties of indices*

$\Rightarrow$ $x + y = \log_a bc$

$\Rightarrow$ $\log_a b + \log_a c = \log_a bc$

The logarithm of a **product** of numbers is the **sum** of the logarithms.

If we divide b by c we have:

$$\frac{b}{c} = \frac{a^x}{a^y} = a^{x-y} \Rightarrow x - y = \log_a \frac{b}{c} \Rightarrow \log_a b - \log_a c = \log_a \frac{b}{c}$$

The logarithm of a **quotient** of numbers is the **difference** between the logarithms.

From this property we deduce that: $\log_a \frac{1}{c} = \log_a 1 - \log_a c = -\log_a c$

The third general law concerns powers of numbers.

$$b^r = (a^x)^r = a^{xr} \Rightarrow xr = \log_a b^r \Rightarrow r\log_a b = \log_a b^r$$

With this last result we can see why the result of Exploration 16.3 works.

$\log_{10} 10^r = r \log_{10} 10 = r$

Since $\log_{10} 10 = 1$.

Example 16.6

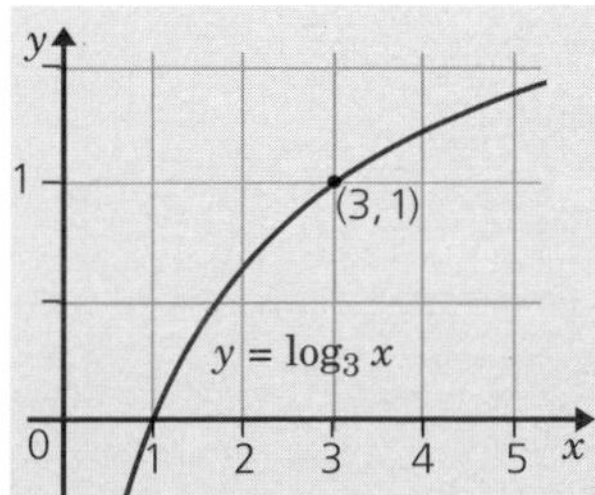

The diagram shows a sketch of the graph of $y = \log_3 x$.

Sketch a graph of $y = \log_3 2x$.

Solution

The rule for the logarithm of a product gives:

$y = \log_3 2x = \log_3 2 + \log_3 x$

The graph of $y = \log_3 2x$ is a translation of $\log_3 x$ of $\log_3 2$ parallel to the y-axis.

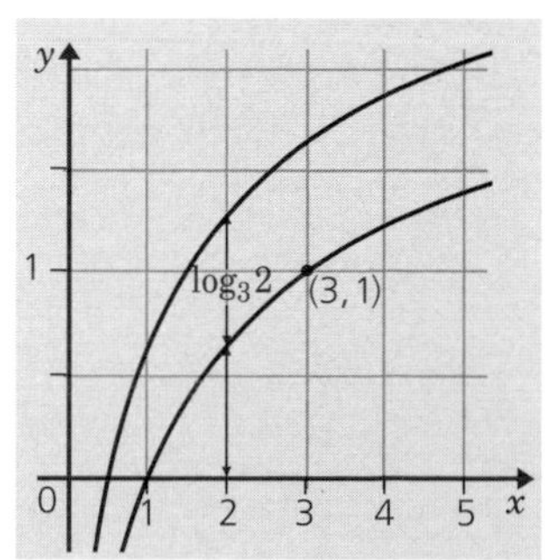

Example 16.7

Write each of the following as a single logarithm.

a) $\log_2 9 - \log_2 16 + \log_2 3$ ***b)*** $3\log_5 2 - 2\log_5 3$
c) $2\log x + 3\log y - \log xy$

Solution

a) $\log_2 9 - \log_2 16 + \log_2 3 = \log_2 \frac{9\times 3}{16} = \log_2 \frac{27}{16}$

b) $3\log_5 2 - 2\log_5 3 = \log_5 2^3 - \log_5 3^2 = \log_5 \frac{2^3}{3^2} = \log_5 \frac{8}{9}$

c) $2\log x + 3\log y - \log xy = \log x^2 + \log y^3 - \log xy$
$= \log\left(\frac{x^2y^3}{xy}\right) = \log\left(xy^2\right)$

Example 16.8

Expand the following in terms of $\log x$, $\log y$ *and* $\log z$.

a) $\log_3 xy$ ***b)*** $\log_2\left(\frac{x^2y^3}{z^4}\right)$

Solution

a) $\log_3 xy = \log_3 x + \log_3 y$

b) $\log_2\left(\frac{x^2y^3}{z^4}\right) = \log_2 x^2 + \log_2 y^3 - \log_2 z^4 = 2\log_2 x + 3\log_2 y - 4\log_2 z$

Example 16.9

Solve the following equations for x *to 4 d.p.*

a) $10^x = 13$ ***b)*** $\log_{10} x = 2.1$

Solution

a) $10^x = 13 \Rightarrow x = \log_{10} 13 = 1.1139$
b) $\log_{10} x = 2.1 \Rightarrow x = 10^{2.1} = 125.8925$

EXERCISES

16.2 CLASSWORK

1 Sketch the graph of $y = \log_{10} x$ for $0 < x \le 10$.

a) Explain why the graph does not intersect the line $y = x$.
b) From your graph, sketch the graphs of $\log_{10}(x-2)$ and $\log_{10} 3x$.

2 Sketch the graph of $y = \log_{10}\frac{1}{x}$ for $0 < x \le 10$.

Use your graph to sketch graphs of $y = \log_{10}\frac{2}{x}$ and $y = \log_{10}\frac{1}{x-2}$.

3 Write each of the following in index form.

a) $\log_2 8 = 3$ **b)** $\log_{10} 100\,000 = 5$ **c)** $\log_a 3 = b$
d) $\log_a x = 5$ **e)** $\log_a 1 = 0$ **f)** $\log_p q = y$

4 Write each of the following in logarithmic form.

a) $3^2 = 9$ **b)** $11^0 = 1$ **c)** $8^{\frac{1}{3}} = 2$
d) $m = n^2$ **e)** $x^y = 2$ **f)** $10^p = q$

5 Solve the following equations using the log key on your calculator.

a) $10^x = 150$ **b)** $10^{-x} = 0.2$ **c)** $10^{2x} = 72$
d) $10^{2x-1} = 25$ **e)** $10^{0.1x} = 5$ **f)** $10^{0.2x+1} = 18$

6 Solve the following equations using the 10^x key on your calculator.

a) $\log_{10} x = 2.1$ **b)** $\log_{10} x = 4.2$ **c)** $\log_{10} 3x = 1.4$
d) $\log_{10} 5x = 3.5$ **e)** $\log_{10}(2x - 1) = 0.6$ **f)** $\log_{10}(2x + 1) = -0.5$
g) $\log_{10} x + \log_{10}(x + 1) = 0.5$ **h)** $\log_{10}(x + 1) + \log_{10}(x - 1) = 1.2$
i) $2\log_{10} x - \log_{10}(2x - 1) = 0.1$

7 Write each of the following as a single logarithm in its simplest form.

a) $\log_a 7 + 2\log_a 3 - 3\log_a 5$ **b)** $\log_2 p + 2\log_2 q + 3$
c) $2\log r + 3\log s - 4\log t - 2$ **d)** $\frac{1}{2}\log_a x + \frac{1}{3}\log_a y$
e) $\log_a(x^2 - 3x + 2) - \log_a(x - 1) + \log_a(x - 2)$
f) $\log_2(x^2 - 1) - \log_2(x - 1) + \log_2(x + 1)$

8 Expand the following in terms of $\log u$, $\log v$ and $\log w$.

a) $\log_2 uv$ **b)** $\log_3 u^2v^3$ **c)** $\log \dfrac{u^a v^b}{w}$ **d)** $\log_a u^{\frac{1}{2}} v^2 w^{\frac{1}{3}}$
e) $\log \sqrt{u^3 w^5}$ **f)** $\log_{10}(100\, v^3)$ **g)** $\log_a \left(\dfrac{1}{w^2}\right)$ **h)** $\log \left(\dfrac{(u-1)(v+1)}{(w-2)}\right)$

EXERCISES

16.2 HOMEWORK

1 Sketch the graph of $y = \log_{10} x$ for $0 < x \leq 10$.

a) Use your graph to show that $\log_{10} 10 = 1$ and $\log_{10} 1 = 0$.
b) From your graph, sketch the graphs of $\log_{10}(x + 2)$ and $\log_{10} 5x$.

2 Sketch the graph of $y = \log_{10} \dfrac{1}{x}$ for $0 < x \leq 10$.

Use your graph to sketch graphs of these functions.

a) $y = \log_{10} \dfrac{3}{x}$ **b)** $y = \log_{10} \dfrac{1}{x+2}$

3 Write each of the following in index form.

a) $\log_2 128 = 7$ **b)** $\log_{10} 1\,000\,000 = 6$ **c)** $\log_a 7 = b$
d) $\log_a x = 31$ **e)** $\log_a 1 = 0$ **f)** $\log_r s = p$

4 Write each of the following in logarithmic form.

a) $7^2 = 49$ **b)** $130^0 = 1$ **c)** $16^{\frac{1}{2}} = 4$
d) $10^{-2} = 0.01$ **e)** $p = r^3$ **f)** $10^{-p} = q$

5 Solve the following equations using the log key on your calculator.

a) $10^x = 169$ **b)** $10^{-x} = 0.3$ **c)** $10^{3x} = 90$
d) $10^{2x+1} = 36$ **e)** $10^{0.1x} = 7$ **f)** $10^{0.4x-1} = 240$

6 Solve the following equations using the 10^x key on your calculator.

a) $\log_{10} x = 1.1$ **b)** $\log_{10} x = 2.5$ **c)** $\log_{10} 5x = 1.5$
d) $\log_{10} 14x = 0.14$ **e)** $\log_{10} 0.2x = 1$ **f)** $\log_{10}(3x + 1) = 0$
g) $\log_{10}(0.1x - 3) = -0.2$ **h)** $\log_{10} x + \log_{10}(x - 1) = 0.1$

7 Write each of the following as a single logarithm in its simplest form.

a) $\log_a 9 + 2\log_a 2 - 3\log_a 3$ **b)** $\log_3 r + 2\log_3 s - 2$
c) $\log x + 2\log y - 5\log t + 1$ **d)** $\frac{1}{4}\log r - \frac{1}{8}\log s$
e) $\log_a(x^2 + 5x + 6) - \log_a(x + 2) + \log_a(x + 3)$ **f)** $\log_5(x^3 - 1) - \log_5(x - 1)$

8 Expand the following in terms of $\log r$, $\log s$ and $\log t$.

a) $\log_3 rs$ b) $\log_4 s^4 t$ c) $\log r^m s^n t^p$

d) $\log_a\left(\frac{\sqrt{r}}{s^3}\right)$ e) $\log\sqrt[3]{s^4 t^5}$ f) $\log_{10}(0.01\, r^2)$

g) $\log_a\left(\frac{1}{rst}\right)$ h) $\log\left(\frac{(2r+1)(3s-2)}{t+3}\right)$

MODELLING WITH LOGARITHMS

KEY SKILLS
N 3.1
IT 3.1

The Richter scale

Greece rocked by earthquake

A POWERFUL EARTHQUAKE rocked central and northern Greece, badly damaging the towns of Larissa and Kozani. Fifteen people were hurt. It was the second earthquake to hit Greece this month. It measured 6.6 on the Richter scale.

A sudden rupture in the solid crust of the Earth causes vibrations in the body of the Earth, called **seismic waves**, When these vibrations reach the surface of the Earth they cause the ground to tremble and we call this an **earthquake**. During an earthquake a very large amount of energy is dissipated. For example, the devastating San Francisco earthquake of 1906 had an estimated 10^{17} joules of energy. Physical phenomena which involve such large numbers are usually described in terms of common logarithms to base ten.

Exploration 16.4

The Richter scale

The strength of an earthquake, M, is expressed by the **Richter magnitude scale** – a logarithmic scale.

$$M = 0.67\log_{10}E - 2.9$$

where E is the energy of the earthquake in joules.

- What was the magnitude of the San Francisco earthquake in 1906?
- How strong, in joules, was the earthquake in Greece in May 1995?
- Approximately how much stronger was the San Francisco earthquake compared with the earthquake in Greece?

KEY SKILLS
IT 3.1

Comparing the strength

You should have found that:

- for the San Francisco earthquake $M = 8.5$
- for the Greek earthquake $E = 10^{14}$.

This means that the earthquake in San Francisco had approximately 1000 times more energy than that in Greece. The use of common logarithms allows us to describe physical phenomena with 'sensible numbers' that non-mathematicians can understand.

KEY SKILLS
IT 3.1

Noise levels

The intensity of sound is usually measured on a logarithmic scale called the **intensity level**. The formula for measuring sound intensity is:

$$L = 10\log_{10}\frac{I}{I_0}$$

where L is the level of sound in decibels (dB) and I is the observed sound intensity. (The definition of I_0 is $L = 0$ dB when $I_0 = 0.468 \times 10^{-12}\,\mathrm{W\,m^{-2}}$). The sound intensity for the threshold of our hearing is $1.2 \times 10^{-12}\,\mathrm{W\,m^{-2}}$ and for the threshold of pain it is $1\,\mathrm{W\,m^{-2}}$. Notice that for sound levels we are dealing with very small numbers, whereas for earthquakes we have very large numbers.

Example 16.10

Find the level of sound in decibels for the following.

a) *threshold of our hearing*
b) *threshold of pain*
c) *heavy rock music for which* $I = 0.15\,\mathrm{W\,m^{-2}}$

Find the sound intensity I for a background noise of 50 dB.

Solution

In each case $I_0 = 0.468 \times 10^{-12}$.

a) *For the threshold of hearing* $I = 1.2 \times 10^{-12}$

$$\Rightarrow\ L = 10\log_{10}\left(\frac{1.2\times10^{-12}}{0.468\times10^{-12}}\right) = 4\text{dB}$$

b) *For the threshold of pain* $I = 1$

$$\Rightarrow\ L = 10\log_{10}\left(\frac{1}{0.468\times10^{-12}}\right) = 123\text{dB}$$

c) *For heavy rock music* $I = 0.15$

$$\Rightarrow\ L = 10\log_{10}\left(\frac{0.15}{0.468\times10^{-12}}\right) = 115\text{ dB}$$

For a background noise of 50 dB we have:

$$50 = 10\log_{10}\left(\frac{I}{0.468\times10^{-12}}\right)$$

$$\Rightarrow\ 5 = \log_{10}\left(\frac{I}{0.468\times10^{-12}}\right)$$

$$\Rightarrow\ 10^5 = \frac{I}{0.468\times10^{-12}}$$

$$\Rightarrow I = 10^5 \times 0.468 \times 10^{-12} = 0.468 \times 10^{-7}\,\mathrm{W\,m^{-2}}$$

We see that heavy rock music produces a sound intensity which is close to the threshold of pain and can cause serious damage to hearing if sustained over a long period of time. On the logarithmic scale a sound intensity 100 times as large as I_0 corresponds to 20 dB; an intensity 1000 times as large corresponds to 30 dB, and so on. This tends to agree with our subjective feeling of sound in that we underestimate very large sounds.

EXERCISES

16.3 CLASSWORK

1 By what factor is the energy in the seismic waves of an earthquake of magnitude 8.0 on the Richter scale larger than in those of an earthquake of magnitude 4.0?

2 The great earthquake in Lisbon, Portugal, in 1755 had an estimated magnitude of 9 on the Richter scale. What was the energy associated with this earthquake?

3 An office has a general sound level of 60 dB. A new photocopier is introduced into the office that doubles the sound intensity. What is the new sound level in dB?

4 An obvious feature of the stars in the night sky is that they appear to shine with different brightness. Over 2000 years ago the Greek astronomer Hipparcus divided the stars into classes of brightness. The brightest stars were classified as first magnitude and the very faintest that could be seen with the naked eye were classified as sixth magnitude. This classification leads to a logarithmic scale for star brightness:

$$m = -2.5 \log_{10} S$$

where m is the apparent magnitude of a star and S is the apparent brightness of the star. This formula is used for comparing star magnitudes. For this formula the brightest star, Sirius has an apparent magnitude of –1.4.

a) By what factor do the brightness of stars of first ($m = 1$) and sixth ($m = 6$) magnitude differ? This is the brightness ratio between the brightest and faintest stars S_1/S_6.

b) On this scale the sun and moon have apparent magnitudes of –26.8 and –12.6 respectively. What is the brightness ratio for the sun and moon?

c) The faintest observed objects have an apparent magnitude of +28. What is the brightness ratio for this object and the brightest star, Sirius?

EXERCISES

16.3 HOMEWORK

1 What is the energy associated with an earthquake that measures 5.8 on the Richter scale? By what factor is this earthquake stronger than an earthquake that measures 4.8 on the Richter scale?

2 The Richter scale number for the Italian earthquake in November 1980 was 6.8 and for the San Francisco earthquake in 1989 it was 6.1. Show that the Italian earthquake was roughly ten times more intense than the San Francisco earthquake.

3 One noise has a sound intensity of $I_1\,\mathrm{W\,m^{-2}}$ and associated sound level of $L_1\,\mathrm{dB}$. A second noise has a sound intensity of $I_2\,\mathrm{W\,m^{-2}}$ and associated sound level of $L_2\,\mathrm{dB}$. Show that:

$$L_2 - L_1 = 10\log_{10}\left(\frac{I_2}{I_1}\right)$$

Deduce that if the sound intensity increases by a factor 10^s then the intensity level changes by $10s$ dB.

4 In chemistry, the acidity or alkalinity of a solution is measured by its pH factor defined by

$$\mathrm{pH} = -\log_{10}[\mathrm{H^+}]$$

where $[\mathrm{H^+}]$ is the quantity of hydrogen ions present in the solution. A pH of 7.0 indicates neutral solution for which $[\mathrm{H^+}] = 10^{-7}$ moles per litre. If $\mathrm{pH} < 7.0$ the solution is acidic.

a) What is the pH for a hair shampoo of strength 1.1×10^{-8} moles per litre? Is the shampoo acidic or alkaline?
b) What is the concentration of hydrogen ions for apple juice with a pH value of 5?

SOLUTION OF EQUATIONS OF THE FORM $a^x = b$

Exploration 16.5

Solving an equation

Take the equation $10^{-x} = 378$.

- Draw a graph of $y = 10^{-x} - 378$ and use it to estimate a solution of the equation $10^{-x} = 378$ correct to 1 d.p.
- Use logarithms as the inverse function of 10^{-x} to find x to 4 d.p.

Using common logarithms

The equation in Exploration 16.5 was solved in Example 16.2 on page 334 by a decimal search method, giving $x = -2.58$. From your graph you probably obtained $x = -2.6$ to one decimal place.

From $10^{-x} = 378$ we have $-x = \log_{10}378 = 2.5775 \Rightarrow x = -2.5775$ correct to four decimal places.

This exploration shows how equations of the form $10^x = b$ can be solved using common logarithms. Will it work for other values of a?

Consider $2^x = 20$. The inverse function of 2^x is $\log_2$ so in this case $x = \log_2 20$. Calculators do not use logs to base 2.

Start again but take logs of each side to base 10, since these are available on calculators.

$$2^x = 20 \Rightarrow \log_{10}2^x = \log_{10}20 \Rightarrow x\log_{10}2 = \log_{10}20$$

$$\Rightarrow x = \frac{\log_{10}20}{\log_{10}2} = 4.3219 \text{ to 4 d.p.}$$

This effectively provides a method of solving any exponential equation.

$$a^x = b$$

Take logs to base 10 of both sides.

$$\log_{10}a^x = \log_{10}b \Rightarrow x\log_{10}a = \log_{10}b \Rightarrow x = \frac{\log_{10}b}{\log_{10}a}$$

Example 16.11

Solve these equations.

a) $5^{3x} = 26$ ***b)*** $3^{-0.1t} = 0.2$

Solution

a) $5^{3x} = 26$

Take logs to base 10.

$$\log_{10}5^{3x} = \log_{10}26 \Rightarrow 3x\log_{10}5 = \log_{10}26 \Rightarrow x = \frac{1}{3}\frac{\log_{10}26}{\log_{10}5} = 0.6748$$

b) $3^{-0.1t} = 0.2$

Take logs to base 10.

$$\log_{10}3^{-0.1t} = \log_{10}0.2 \Rightarrow -0.1t\log_{10}3 = \log_{10}0.2$$

$$\Rightarrow t = -10\frac{\log_{10}0.2}{\log_{10}3} = 14.6497$$

EXERCISES

16.4 CLASSWORK

1 Solve the following equations giving your answers correct to 4 d.p.

a) $10^x = 132$ **b)** $10^{-x} = 67$ **c)** $10^{2x} = 27$ **d)** $10^{-3x} = 620$
e) $10^{0.1t} = 14.1$ **f)** $4^{-x} = 0.8$ **g)** $5^{2t} = 32$ **h)** $3^{2x-1} = 7$

2 Use logs to base 10 to solve the following equations correct to 4 d.p. Compare your answers with those obtained graphically and by decimal search in Exercise 16.1A.

a) $3^x = 20$ **b)** $2^{-x} = 3$

3 Solve these equations.

a) $5^{2x} - 5^{2x+1} + 6 = 0$ (**Hint:** let $y = 5^x$) **b)** $3^{2x} = 8^{x+1}$
c) $7^{2x} - 3(7^x) + 2 = 0$ **d)** $\dfrac{10^{x-1}}{3^x} = 7^{2x+1}$

4 Find the least value of the integer n for which $0.9^n < 0.001$.

EXERCISES

16.4 HOMEWORK

1 Solve the following equations giving your answers correct to 4 d.p.

a) $10^x = 1740$ **b)** $10^{-x} = 5$ **c)** $10^{-2t} = 2.6$ **d)** $10^{-5y} = 0.02$
e) $10^{0.3u} = 16$ **f)** $7^x = 40$ **g)** $3^{-0.5t} = 10$ **h)** $5^{-0.1x+1} = 3$

2 Use logs to base 10 to solve the following equations correct to 4 d.p. Compare your answers with those obtained graphically and by decimal search in Exercise 16.1B.

a) $5^x = 15$ **b)** $3^{-x} = 8$

3 Solve these equations.

a) $2^{2x} - 7(2^x) + 12 = 0$ **b)** $5^{3t} = 7^{t-2}$
c) $3^{2p} - 3^{2p+1} + 10 = 0$ **d)** $\dfrac{10^{x-1}}{9^{x-1}} = 8^x$

4 Find the least value of the integer n for which $1.5^n > 32$.

REDUCTION TO LINEAR FORM

Exploration 16.6

Equations from graphs

- Draw graphs of the following data.
- Find the equation of each curve.

Data set A

x	0.0	0.5	1.0	1.5	2.0	2.5
y	0.0	0.125	1.0	3.975	8.0	15.625

Data set B

x	0.0	0.5	1.0	1.5	2.0	2.5
y	1.0	1.732	3.0	5.196	9.0	15.58

Try to find the equation of the graph of the following data.

Data set C

x	0.0	0.5	1.0	1.5	2.0	2.5
y	0.0	0.4061	1.0	1.694	2.462	3.29

Working with equations

You probably found the equations for data sets A and B quite easily. The curve from set A has equation $y = x^3$ and the curve from set B has equation $y = 3^x$. You may even have spotted the equation from the data before drawing the graph.

For data set C the equation is not so obvious. Its equation is $y = x^{1.3}$ and you should not worry if you did not find it.

Logarithms can be used to help us find equations relating sets of data by transforming the graph of the data from a curve into a straight line.

Case 1: The power law $y = ax^b$

Take the equation $y = ax^b$ where a and b are constants. Take logs of both sides (using $\log_{10}$).

$$\log_{10}y = \log_{10}(ax^b) = \log_{10}a + \log_{10}x^b \Rightarrow \log_{10}y = \log_{10}a + b\log_{10}x$$

Compare this with the equation of a straight line $Y = mX + c$.

If data satisfies a power law $y = ax^b$ then a graph of $Y = \log_{10}y$ against $X = \log_{10}x$ will be a straight line with slope $m = b$ and intercept $c = \log_{10}a$.

Example 16.12

Find the equation of the graph for data set C.

x	0.0	0.5	1.0	1.5	2.0	2.5
y	0.0	0.4061	1	1.694	2.462	3.29

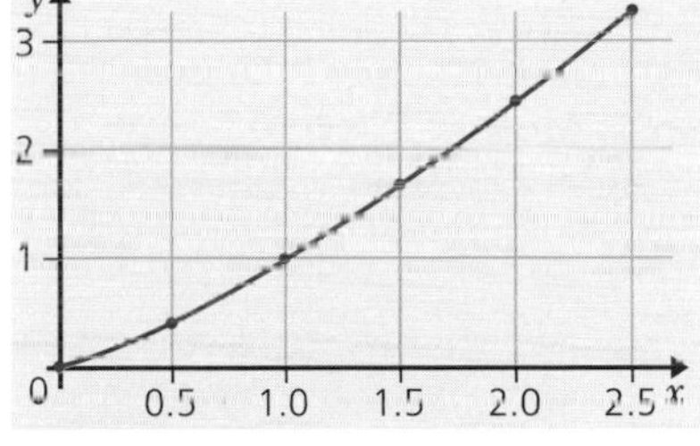

Solution

The graph of y against x is a curve through the origin.
Take logs of x and y, avoiding (0, 0).

$\log_{10}x$	−0.30	0	0.18	0.30	0.40
$\log_{10}y$	−0.39	0	0.23	0.39	0.53

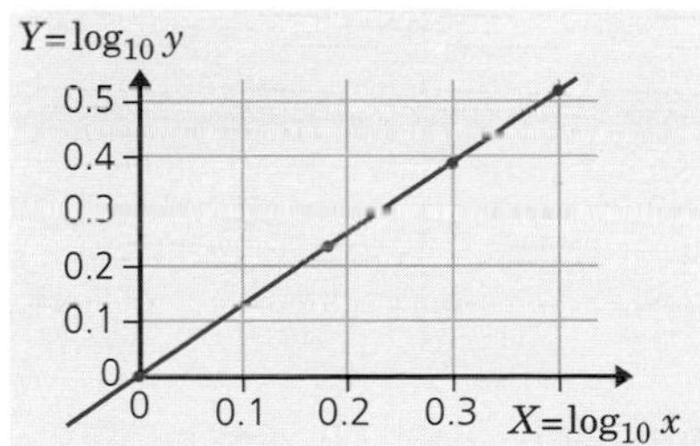

A graph of $\log_{10}y$ against $\log_{10}x$ is a straight line. In this case the points lie very close to the line which passes through the origin.

The slope of the line is 1.3 and the intercept is 0.
The equation of the line is:

$$\log_{10}y = 0 + 1.3\log_{10}x$$

we see that $\log_{10}a = 0 \Rightarrow a = 1$ and $b = 1.3$. The law relating x and y is $y = x^{1.3}$.

Case 2: The exponential law $y = ab^x$

Take the equation $y = ab^x$ and take logs of both sides.

$$\log_{10}y = \log_{10}ab^x = \log_{10}a + \log_{10}b^x \Rightarrow \log_{10}y = \log_{10}a + x\log_{10}b$$

Compare this with the equation of a straight line $Y = mX + c$.

If the data satisfies an exponential law $y = ab^x$ then a graph of $Y = \log_{10}y$ against $X = x$ will be a straight line with slope $m = \log_{10}b$ and intercept $c = \log_{10}a$.

Example 16.13

Find the equation of the graph for this data set.

x	0.0	0.5	1.0	1.5	2.0	2.5
y	3.0	3.911	5.1	6.649	8.67	11.30

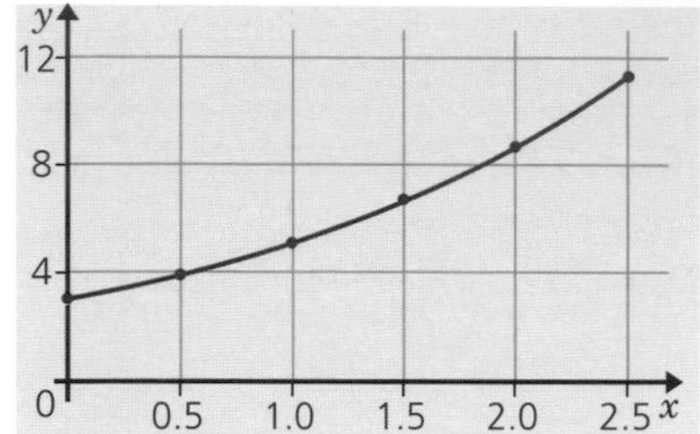

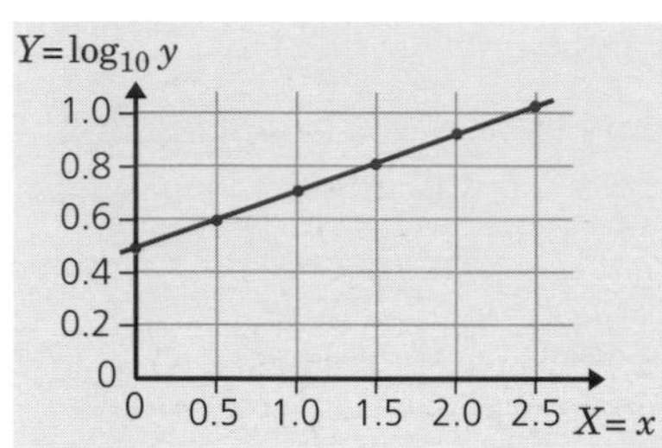

Solution

A graph of y against x is a curve through the point (0, 3).
Take logs of y.

x	0.0	0.5	1.0	1.5	2.0	2.5
$\log_{10}y$	0.48	0.59	0.71	0.82	0.94	1.05

A graph of $\log_{10}y$ against x is a straight line.
The slope of the line is 0.228 and the intercept is (0, 0.48).
The equation of the line is:

$$\log_{10}y = 0.48 + 0.228x$$

We see that $\log_{10}a = 0.48 \Rightarrow a = 10^{0.48} = 3$ *and* $\log_{10}b = 0.228$
$\Rightarrow b = 10^{0.228} = 1.69.$

The law relating x and y is $y = 3(1.69)^x$.

Which graph to draw?

When given a set of data the first problem is to decide which graph to draw, **a)** $\log_{10}y$ against $\log_{10}x$ or **b)** $\log_{10}y$ against x. We could draw both graphs; if one of the graphs is a straight line then we should know which model to choose.

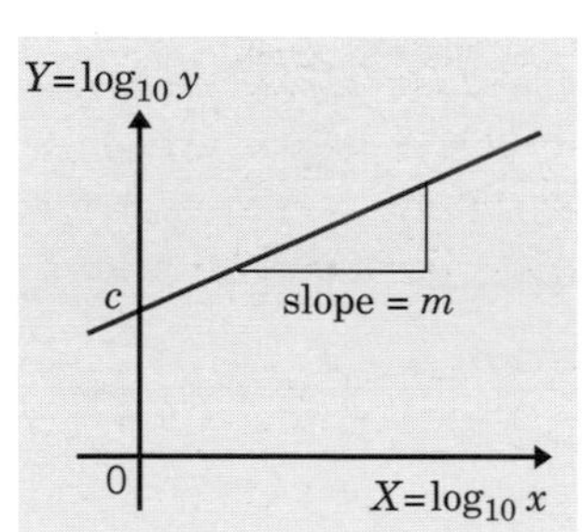

$\Rightarrow y = ax^b$
$b \equiv$ slope of line m
$c \equiv \log_{10}a \Rightarrow a = 10^c$

$\Rightarrow y = ab^x$
$\log_{10}b \equiv$ slope of line m
$\Rightarrow b = 10^m$
$c \equiv \log_{10}a \Rightarrow a = 10^c$

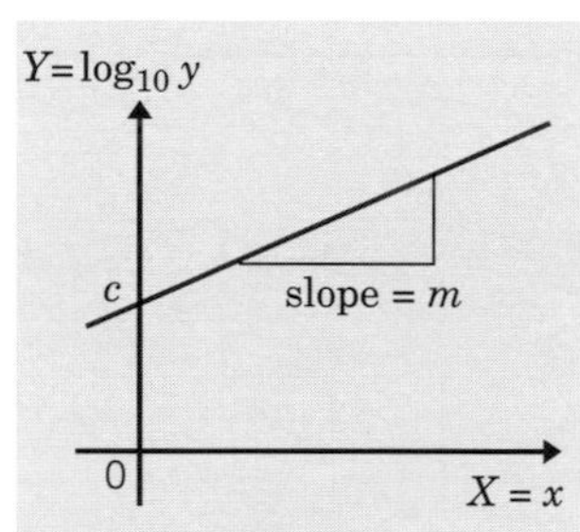

If neither graph is a straight line then the data does not obey a power law or an exponential law.

In some examples we can save time and effort by looking at a graph of the original data. If it passes through the origin, the law is likely to be a power law $y = ax^b$. For example, data set A is a power law because $y = 0$ when $x = 0$.

Exploration 16.7

Finding equations using logs

Take data sets A and B from Exploration 16.6.

- Draw graphs of $\log_{10}y$ against $\log_{10}x$ and $\log_{10}y$ against x for each data set.

- Which data sets give straight lines?
- Use the equations of the straight lines to find the equations relating x and y for each data set.

Confirming the results

You should have confirmed that set A obeys the power law $y = x^3$ with a straight line graph of $\log_{10} y$ against $\log_{10} x$ and set B obeys the exponential law $y = 3^x$ with a straight line graph of $\log_{10} y$ against x.

For examples where reading the $\log_{10} y$ intercept is not a practical proposition, then the rule of thumb, given in Chapter 3, *Linear functions* for lines of best fit, is to fit a straight line through the mean $(\bar{X}, \bar{Y})$ giving the equation:

$$Y - \bar{Y} = m(X - \bar{X})$$

This method is used in the following mathematical modelling activity.

EXERCISES

16.5 CLASSWORK

In problems **1–4** use logs to straighten the curves of the data and hence find the equation for each data set.

1

x	0.0	0.2	0.4	0.6	0.8	1.0
y	0.0	1.78	2.53	3.09	3.58	4.0

2

x	0.0	0.4	0.8	1.2	1.6	2.0
y	5.0	5.88	6.92	8.13	9.57	11.25

3

x	0.5	0.7	0.9	1.1	1.3	1.5
w	16.97	7.32	3.90	2.36	1.56	1.09

4

t	1	2	3	4	5	6
u	2.5	7.58	14.50	22.97	32.83	43.95

5 Experimental values of the pressure P of a given mass of gas corresponding to various values of the volume V are given in a table. According to thermodynamic principles a relationship having the form $P = CV^{-\lambda}$ where λ and C are constants, should exist between the variables.

a) Find the values of λ and C.
b) Write the equation connecting P and V. Estimate P when $V = 100.0$.

Volume V	54.3	61.8	72.4	88.7	118.6	194.0
Pressure P	61.2	49.5	37.6	28.4	19.2	10.1

6 A census of the population of the United States each decade during 1840–1960 is shown in the following table.

Year	1840	1850	1860	1870	1880	1890	1900
Population (in millions)	17.1	23.2	31.4	39.8	50.2	62.9	76.0

Year	1910	1920	1930	1940	1950	1960
Population (in millions)	92.0	105.7	122.8	131.7	151.1	179.3

Formulate a mathematical model to describe the population as a function of time.

7 Burning fossil fuels such as coal and oil adds carbon dioxide to the atmosphere around the Earth. This may be partly removed by biological reactions, but the concentration of carbon dioxide is gradually increasing. This increase leads to a rise in the average temperature of the Earth. The table on the left shows this temperature rise over the 100-year period up to 1980.

Year	Temperature rise of the Earth above the 1860 figure (°C)
1880	0.01
1890	0.02
1900	0.03
1910	0.04
1920	0.06
1930	0.08
1940	0.10
1950	0.13
1960	0.18
1970	0.24
1980	0.32

If the average temperature of the Earth rises by about another 6°C from the 1980 value this would have a dramatic effect on the polar ice caps, winter temperatures etc. As the polar ice caps melt, there could be massive floods and a lot of land mass would be submerged. The UK would disappear except for the tops of the mountains!

a) Find a model of the given data and use it to predict when the Earth's temperature will be 7°C above its 1860 value.

b) Discuss how seriously you should take the prediction in **a)**.

EXERCISES

16.5 HOMEWORK

In problems **1–4** use logs to straighten the curves of the data and hence find the equation for each data set.

1

x	1	2	3	4	5	6
y	3.4	22.1	66.0	143.6	262.2	429.0

2

t	0	1	2	3	4	5
x	0.3	1.23	5.04	20.67	84.77	347.5

3

t	0	1	2	3	4	5
p	1.5	4.08	11.08	30.12	81.90	222.6

4

t	0.1	0.4	0.7	1.0	1.3	1.6
p	0.01	0.22	0.71	1.50	2.60	4.02

5 In a fishing competition on the River Dart in Devon the following data was collected for the mass of each fish and its length.

Length l (cm)	37	32	44	45	36	41	34
Mass M (kg)	0.77	0.48	1.16	1.39	0.65	1.02	0.58

a) Formulate a mathematical model relating mass and length of the fish for this data.

b) Explain how the model makes sense from theoretical arguments.

6 The viscosity of a liquid is a measure of its resistance to flow. Its value is often found experimentally using a quantity of the liquid between two moving parallel plates and measuring the friction force on one plate. In such an experiment, values of the coefficient of viscosity of lubricating oil against temperature were measured and are shown in the following table. Show that a power law relation of the form $\mu = AT^m$ exists between the variables, and find values of the constants A and m.

Temperature T (°C)	20	40	60	80	100
Viscosity μ ($\text{kg m}^{-1}\text{s}^{-1}$)	0.0986	0.0241	0.0110	0.0055	0.0036

7 The heat of combustion H (joule mol^{-1}) for a petroleum hydrocarbon of molecular mass M is given in the following table.

H	213	373	530	688	845	1002	1159
M	16	30	44	58	72	86	100

Show, using logarithms and a suitable graph, that a relationship of the form $H = kM^n$ exists between H and M where k and n are constants. From your graph determine values for k and n and find the value of H when $M = 50$.

MATHEMATICAL MODELLING ACTIVITY

Problem statement

In the early 17th century the German astronomer, Johannes Kepler formulated three laws for the motion of the planets around the sun. These are known as **Kepler's laws**.

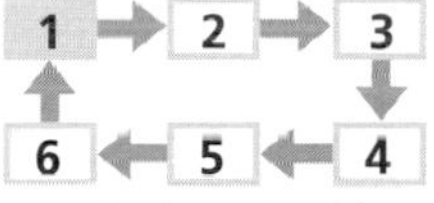

Specify the real problem

1 Each planet moves in an ellipse with the sun at one focus.
2 For each planet, the line from the sun to the planet sweeps out equal areas in equal times.
3 The squares of the orbital periods of the planets vary as the cubes of their mean distance from the sun.

Kepler formulated the first two laws after studying the motion of the planet Mars. It took a further ten years for him to verify these laws and he formulated the third law in 1619 after studying other planets.

The following table shows the average distance from the sun, R, and the period of revolution around the sun, T, for each planet.

Planet	Distance from the sun R ($\times 10^6$ km)	Period of revolution around the sun T (days)
Mercury	57.9	88
Venus	108.2	225
Earth	149.6	365
Mars	227.9	687
Jupiter	778.3	4329
Saturn	1427	10753
Uranus	2870	30660
Neptune	4497	60150
Pluto	5907	90670

Note that the planets outside Saturn were not known to Kepler. Show that Kepler's third law is a good model by fitting an appropriate graph to the data.

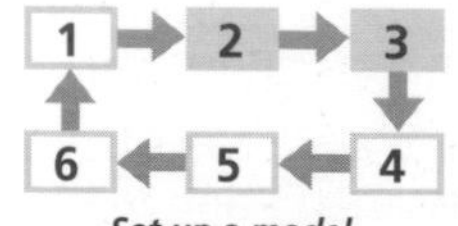

Set up a model

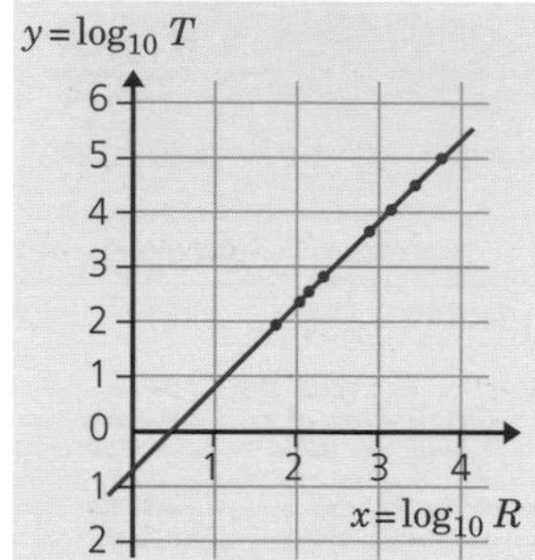

Set up a model

This is an empirical modelling activity obtained from a graph. Kepler's third law suggest a power law of the form:

$$T = KR^{\alpha}$$

where K and α are constants. Taking logs of each side:

$$\log_{10} T = \log_{10} K + \alpha \log_{10} R$$

Thus if Kepler's third law holds true, a plot of $\log_{10} T$ against $\log_{10} R$ should be a straight line. The following table and graph show $\log_{10} T$ and $\log_{10} R$.

$y = \log_{10} T$	$x = \log_{10} R$
1.94	1.76
2.35	2.03
2.56	2.17
2.84	2.36
3.64	2.89
4.03	3.15
4.49	3.46
4.78	3.65
4.96	3.77

1 → 2 → 3
6 ← 5 ← 4

Interpret the solution

Interpret the model

From the graph, the slope is approximately 1.5. The mean values of $\log_{10}R$ and $\log_{10}T$ are (2.80, 3.51) so the equation of the line of best fit is:

$$y - 3.51 = 1.5(x - 2.80)$$

$$\Rightarrow \; y = 1.5x - 0.69$$

Comparing this with the general model:

$$\log_{10}T = \alpha \log_{10} R + \log_{10} K$$

we see that $\alpha = 1.5$ and $\log_{10} K = -0.69 \Rightarrow k = 10^{-0.69} = 0.50$

The empirical model gives:

$$T = 0.5R^{1.5}$$

Squaring both sides gives $T^2 = 0.25R^3$ which agrees well with Kepler's third law.

CONSOLIDATION EXERCISES FOR CHAPTER 16

1 **a)** Copy and complete this table for the function $y = 1.5 \times 2^x$.

b) Using suitable scales, plot a graph of $y = 1.5 \times 2^x$ for $-3 \le x \le 3$.

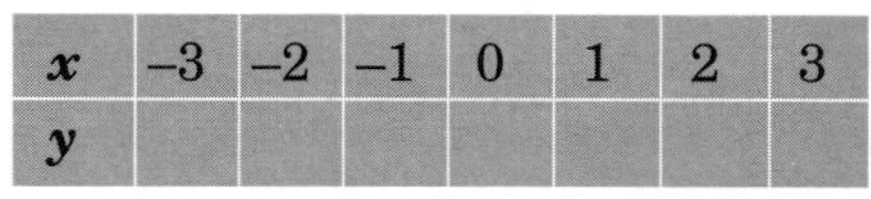

x	-3	-2	-1	0	1	2	3
y							

c) Use your graph to solve the equation $2^x = 5$.

d) Draw tangents to the curve for each point in the table and estimate the gradient at that point.

2 **a)** Use a decimal search to solve the equation $2^x - 5 = 0$, giving your answer correct to 3 s.f.

b) Use a numerical method to demonstrate that $f(x) = 1.5 \times 2^x \Rightarrow f'(x) \approx 1.04 \times 2^x$ for $x = -2, -1, 0, 1, 2$.

3 The giant Amazon water lily grows exponentially. Over a period of 25 weeks, its diameter d cm after t weeks is given by $d = 10 \times 2^{\frac{1}{5}t}$.

a) Draw a graph of d against t for $0 \le t \le 25$.

b) Use your graph to find:

i) the diameter of the lily after $12\frac{1}{2}$ weeks,

ii) the time it takes for the diameter to reach 2 metres.

c) Confirm your answer to **b) ii)** by a decimal search.

4 The diagram shows the graphs of $y = 2^x$ and $y = 2^{x+1}$. Describe two different geometrical transformations which map the graph of $y = 2^x$ onto the graph of $y = 2^{x+1}$.

(UCLES Modular Specimen Paper P2, Question 5(Part))

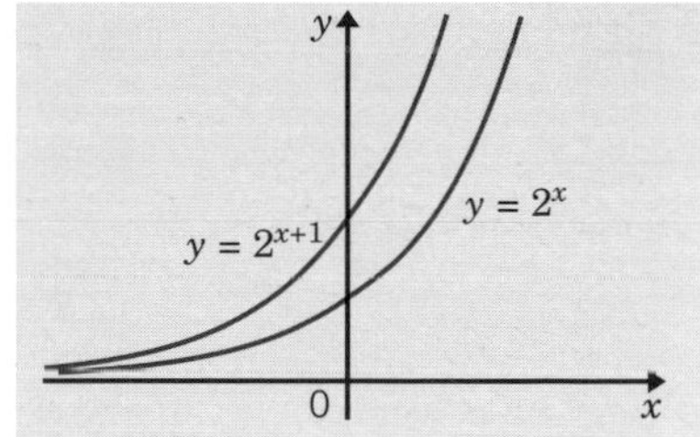

5 **a)** Sketch the graph of $y = \dfrac{x^2}{2^x}$ for $x \geq 0$.

b) The graph has a local maximum. Use graphical methods to find its coordinates.

(Oxford Nuffield, Paper 1, 1995)

6 The curve with equation $ky = a^x$ passes through the points with coordinates (7, 12) and (12, 7). Find, to 2 significant figures, the values of the constants k and a.
Using your values of k and a, find the value of $\dfrac{dy}{dx}$ at $x = 20$, giving your answer to 1 decimal place.

(EDEXCEL, Question 6, Specimen Paper 2, 2000)

7 The concentration of a drug in a patient's bloodstream is C milligrams per millilitre after t hours where $C = Ka^{-t}$.

For drug A, $K = 2$ and $a = 1.2$

For drug B, $K = 3$ and $a = 1.4$

Show that the concentration levels are the same for both drugs when

$2(1.2^{-t}) = 3(1.4^{-t})$

and use logs to solve this equation for t.

8 The following table shows three sets of experimental data. One pair of variables satisfies a power law, one pair satisfies an exponential law and the other pair does not satisfy either of these laws. Use appropriate graphs to find the relationships.

x	0.1	0.4	0.7	1.0	1.3	1.6
y	2.010	0.606	0.182	0.055	0.017	0.005

u	0.1	0.3	0.6	0.9	1.2	1.5
v	1.00	0.96	0.83	0.62	0.36	0.07

t	0.1	0.5	0.9	1.3	1.7	2.1
s	0.084	1.293	3.511	6.561	10.35	14.83

9 A controlled experiment was concerned with estimating the number of microbes, N, present in a culture at time T days after the start of the experiment. Some results from the experiment are shown in the table below.

Time T (days)	3	5	10	15	20
Number of microbes N	900	2000	5000	9000	16 000

By plotting values of $\log N$ against the corresponding values of $\log T$, draw a graph using all the data in the table.

Explain why the graph that you have obtained supports the belief that N and T are related by an equation of the form:

$N = AT^B$
where A and B are constants.

Use your graph to find an estimate for A, giving your answer to 1 significant figure, and an estimate for B, giving your answer to 2 significant figures. *(ULEAC Question 6, Paper 2, January 1993)*

10 The table shows experimental values of two quantities x and y which are known to satisfy the equation $yx^n = k$, where n and k are constants.

x	2	3	4	5	6	7
y	39	32	28	25	22.5	20.8

a) Draw a graph of $\log y$ against $\log x$.
b) Use your graph to estimate values for n and k, giving your answers to 2 significant figures. *(ULEAC Question 8, Paper 2, January 1994)*

11 It is believed that the relationship between the variables x and y is of the form $y = Ax^n$

In an experiment the following data are obtained.

x	3	6	10	15	20
y	10.4	29.4	63.2	116.2	178.9

In order to estimate the constants A and n, $\log_{10} y$ is plotted against $\log_{10} x$.

a) Complete the table of values of $\log_{10} x$ and $\log_{10} y$, and draw the graph of $\log_{10} y$ against $\log_{10} x$.
b) Explain and justify how the shape of your graph enables you to decide whether the relationship is indeed of the form $y = Ax^n$.
c) Estimate the values of A and n. *(MEI Question 5, Paper1, June 1993)*

12 The following table gives the number of people in a particular area who own shares in a public company.

Year	1987	1988	1989	1990	1991
Number of years after 1987, x	0	1	2	3	4
Number of people who own shares, y	12	17	25	37	53

a) Plot the points (x, y) on a the graph. Join the points with a smooth curve.

It is thought that there may be a relationship connecting x and y which is of the form $y = ab^x$.

b) Explain how, by using logarithms (to base 10), the curve given by plotting y against x can be transformed into a straight line.
State the gradient of this straight line and its intercept with the vertical axis, in terms of a and b.
c) Form a table of x and $\log_{10} y$. Plot the points $(x, \log_{10} y)$ on a graph and draw a 'best fit' line through the points and use it to estimate the values of a and b. *(MEI Paper 1, Question 5, June 1994)*

13 **a)** The variables x, y are thought to satisfy an equation of the form

$$y = ab^x$$

where a, b are unknown constants. To estimate a and b, y is measured when $x = 2.2$ and $x = 3.6$. The respective values of y are 4.21 and 6.22.

Find the values of a and b.
Hence find the value of x when $y = 5$.

b) Six pairs of measurements (x_1, y_1); (x_2, y_2); (x_3, y_3); (x_4, y_4); (x_5, y_5); (x_6, y_6) are now made on x and y. Explain briefly how you would use these values to plot a graph which could be used to investigate whether or not x and y do in fact satisfy the above relationship. How could you use your graph to estimate a and b?

(WJEC, Specimen Paper A1, Question 11)

Summary

Functions of the type $f(x) = a^x$ are called **exponential functions**, where the constant a is called the **base**.

The logarithm is defined from the exponential function a^x in the following way.

$$y = a^x \Rightarrow x = \log_a y$$

This is called the logarithm to base a.

Logarithms obey the following rules.

- $\log_a 1 = 0$
- $\log_a a = 1$
- $\log_a(xy) = \log_a x + \log_a y$
- $\log_a \left(\frac{x}{y}\right) = \log_a x - \log_a y$
- $\log_a x^r = r$ lo

Logarithms to base 10 are found on scientific calculators and are usually written as $\log x$ i.e. omitting the base 10 ($\log_{10} x = \log x$). These logarithms are used in scientific scales and in straightening curves to model data.

- If $y = ax^b$ then a graph of $\log y$ against $\log x$ is a straight line.
- if $y = ab^x$ then a graph of $\log y$ against x is a straight line.

The exponential and the natural logarithmic functions

In this chapter we study two special functions for mathematics, science and engineering:

- *the exponential function*
- *the natural logarithmic function.*

CALCULATOR ACTIVITY

Exploration 17.1

Exponential growth

$1 \rightarrow N$

$\left(1 + \frac{1}{N}\right)^N \rightarrow Y$

$N \times 10 \rightarrow N$

$N \leq 10^{12}$?

yes

no

STOP

- Use this flowchart to create a program that allows you to complete the table.
- Describe what happens to the sequence of values in the right-hand column as n gets larger.

n	$\left(1+\frac{1}{n}\right)^n$
1	2
10	2.593 742 46
100	

Limits of the function

As n gets larger, the value of $\left(1 + \frac{1}{n}\right)^n$ converges towards a limit 2.718 28... which is an irrational number known as e. It has such an important role to play in mathematics that the values of the **exponential function** e^x may be obtained directly from your calculator (show that $e^1 = 2.718\ 28...$).

Exploration 17.2

APR

Imagine you have £100 to invest for one year at a nominal annual rate of interest of 8%.

- How much would your investment be worth after one year if interest is compounded:
  a) annually, **b)** quarterly, **c)** monthly, **d)** weekly, **e)** daily?
- What are the corresponding **annual percentage rates** (APRs)?
- What is the APR which corresponds to continuous compounding?

Summarising the results

The results of each computation are summarised in the table overleaf.

The quarterly, monthly, etc. rates of interest are found by dividing the nominal annual rate by 4, 12 etc. The APR, the rate that would provide the same growth if compounded once per year, may be deduced from the corresponding investment values. These values form a convergent sequence as the number of compoundings increases.

	Number of compoundings	Value of investment after 1 year	APR
a)	1	$100\times(1+0.08)=£108$	8.00%
b)	4	$100\times\left(1+\frac{0.08}{4}\right)^4=100\times1.02^4=£108.24$	8.24%
c)	12	$100\times\left(1+\frac{0.08}{12}\right)^{12}=100\times1.0067^{12}=£108.30$	8.30%
d)	52	$100\times\left(1+\frac{0.08}{52}\right)^{52}=100\times1.0015^{52}=£108.32$	8.32%
e)	365	$100\times\left(1+\frac{0.08}{365}\right)^{365}=100\times1.0002^{365}=£108.33$	8.33%

Even hourly compounding (8760 times a year) has no effect on the investment value, to the nearest penny, also giving an APR of 8.33%.

Continuous compounding, corresponding to continuous growth, occurs as the number of compoundings per year **tends to infinity**.

Suppose there are n compoundings per year, then the value of the investment of £100 after one year is given by:

$$A=100\times\left(1+\frac{0.08}{n}\right)^n$$

Let $k=\frac{1}{0.08}n$, then $n=0.08k$, which gives:

$$A=100\times\left(1+\frac{1}{k}\right)^{0.08k}=100\times\left[\left(1+\frac{1}{k}\right)^k\right]^{0.08}$$

As $n\to\infty$, $k\to\infty$, and from the last Calculator activity you will have discovered that as $k\to\infty$, $(1+\frac{1}{k})^k\to \mathrm{e}$ (2.718 28), which means that the limiting value of A is $100\times \mathrm{e}^{0.08}=108.33$ (2 d.p.), which also gives an APR of 8.33%.

The results of Exploration 17.1 may be generalised as follows.

An amount £P is invested at a nominal annual rate of interest R%, with n compoundings per year. The value of the investment £A after one year is given by:

$$A=P\times\left(1+\frac{R}{100n}\right)^n$$

Let $k=\dfrac{100n}{R}$, then $n=\dfrac{Rk}{100}$, which gives:

$$A=P\times\left[\left(1+\frac{1}{k}\right)^k\right]^{\frac{R}{100}}$$

As $n\to\infty$, $k\to\infty\Rightarrow A=P\mathrm{e}^{\frac{R}{100}}$.

The APR corresponding to continuous compounding is given by:

$$\frac{A-P}{P}\times100=\frac{P\mathrm{e}^{\frac{R}{100}}-P}{P}\times100=100\left(\mathrm{e}^{\frac{R}{100}}-1\right)$$

The corresponding formulae for the value of the investment after t years are:

$$A = P \times \left(1 + \frac{1}{k}\right)^{kt} \text{ and } A = P e^{\frac{Rt}{100}}$$

CALCULATOR ACTIVITY

Exploration 17.3

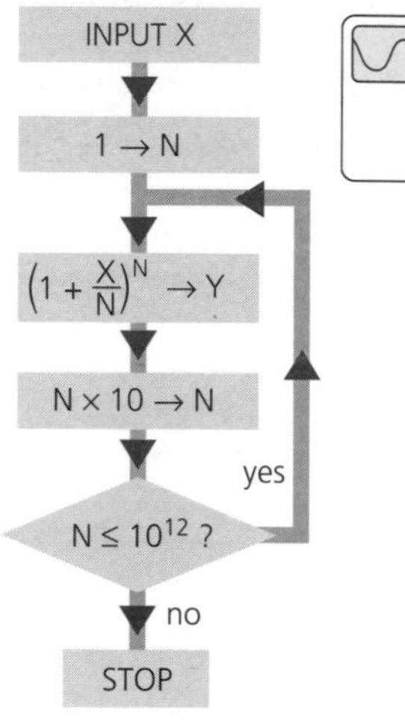

Finding a limit

- Use the flowchart to create a program to find the limit of the sequence $\left(1 + \frac{x}{n}\right)^n$ as $n \to \infty$ for various values of x.
- In each case compare the limiting value with e^x from your calculator.

The limit of the sequence

You will have seen that the limit of the sequence as $n \to \infty$ is equivalent to e^x, i.e.

$$\lim_{n \to \infty} \left(1 + \frac{x}{n}\right)^n = e^x$$

Using the binomial theorem:

$$\left(1 + \frac{x}{n}\right)^n = 1 + \frac{nx}{n} + \frac{n(n-1)}{2!}\frac{x^2}{n^2} + \frac{n(n-1)(n-2)}{3!}\frac{x^3}{n^3} + \ldots + \ldots + \frac{x^n}{n^n}$$

As $n \to \infty$ $\frac{n-1}{n}$, $\frac{n-2}{n}$, etc. $\to 1$, in which case:

$$\lim_{n \to \infty} \left(1 + \frac{x}{n}\right)^n = 1 + x + \frac{x^2}{2!} + \frac{x^3}{3!} + \frac{x^4}{4!} + \ldots..$$

You have found two ways of expressing the limit of $\left(1 + \frac{x}{n}\right)^n$ as $n \to \infty$; equating them gives:

$$e^x \equiv 1 + x + \frac{x^2}{2!} + \frac{x^3}{3!} + \frac{x^4}{4!} + \ldots$$

The series expansion of e^x is valid for all values of x since it is derived from a binomial expansion with a positive integer power (n). Since we are using the limiting case as $n \to \infty$, the expansion has an infinite number of terms but is convergent for any real value of x.

Example 17.1

Expand the series to find e correct to 3 d.p.

Solution

$$e^x = 1 + x + \frac{x^2}{2!} + \frac{x^3}{3!} + \frac{x^4}{4!} + \ldots$$

$$\Rightarrow \quad e^1 = 1 + 1 + \frac{1}{2!} + \frac{1}{3!} + \frac{1}{4!} + \ldots$$

$$= 1 + 1 + 0.5 + 0.166\,666\,666\,7 + 0.041\,666\,666\,7 + 0.008\,333\,333\,3 + 0.000\,198\,412\,7 + \ldots$$

Accuracy to 3 d.p. is achieved after eight terms, the sum of which is 2.718 253 968 (10 s.f.), giving e = *2.718 (3 d.p.).*

CALCULATOR ACTIVITY

Exploration 17.4

Expansion of e^x

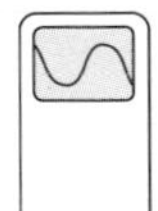

The process of finding the series expansion for e^x, up to any number of terms, may be programmed using this flowchart.

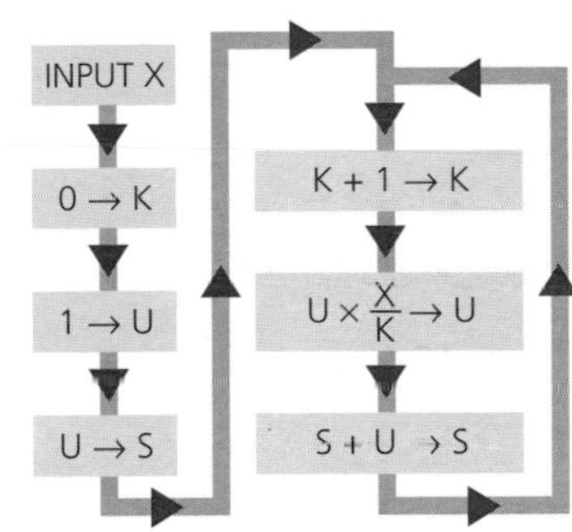

Check that the series is convergent for a variety of x-values. For which range of values does the series oscillate?

EXERCISES

17.1 CLASSWORK

1 A sum of £2000 is invested at a nominal interest rate of 12%. Calculate its value:

a) after one year if compounding is quarterly,
b) after one year if compounding is monthly,
c) after four years if compounding occurs every six months.

2 Find the APR that is equivalent to:

a) 6% nominal rate compounded semi annually,
b) 8% nominal rate compounded quarterly,
c) 10% nominal rate compounded weekly.

3 Find the value of each of the following investments, each compounded continuously.

a) £5000 for three years at a nominal annual rate of 6%
b) £2000 for five years at a nominal annual rate of 8%
c) £1000 for six years at a nominal annual rate of 10%

4 An investment is compounded continuously at a nominal rate of 8% per annum. How long does it take the investment to:

a) double in value, **b)** triple in value?

5 Use the series expansion for e^x to find each of the following to 3 d.p. Check your answers using your calculator function.

a) e^3 **b)** $\sqrt[3]{e}$ **c)** $\frac{1}{e^2}$ **d)** $\sqrt[3]{e^2}$

6 Bank A pays 8.1% compounded quarterly on its savings accounts. Bank B offers 7.8% but compounded daily. Where would you invest your money?

7 You have £500 to invest and you are attracted by two five-year savings schemes. The first offers 12.5% p.a. nominal interest compounded twice yearly and the second just 12.25% nominal interest rate but compounded monthly.

a) Calculate the APR in each case, correct to 2 d.p.
b) Which is worth more after five years and by how much?

EXERCISES

17.1 HOMEWORK

1 £3500 is invested at a nominal interest rate of 12.5%. Calculate its value to the nearest penny:

a) after one year if compounding is monthly,
b) after one year if compounding is weekly,
c) after five years with monthly compounding.

2 Find the APR that is equivalent to:

a) 5% nominal rate compounded quarterly,
b) 11% nominal rate compounded monthly,
c) 9% nominal rate compounded daily (in a non-leap-year).

3 Find the value of the following continuously compounded investments.

a) £1500 for four years at a nominal annual rate of 5%
b) £850 for seven years at a nominal annual rate of 7.5%
c) £2400 for ten years at a nominal annual rate of 12%

4 An investment is compounded continuously at a nominal rate of 12.5% per annum. How long does it take for the investment to

a) double in value, **b)** triple in value, **c)** quadruple in value?

Give your answers to the nearest month.

5 Suppose that in the year 1800, one of your wise old ancestors invested £1 in a bank at 5% interest compounded quarterly. You will inherit this investment in the year 2000. How much will you inherit? How much was it worth in the year 1900?

6 Building Society A pays 5.75% compounded quarterly on its savings accounts. Society B offers just 5.5% but compounded daily. Where would you invest your money?

7 Use the series expansion for e^x to find each of the following correct to 3 d.p. Check your answers using your calculator function.

a) e^2 **b)** $\frac{1}{e}$ **c)** $\sqrt{e}$ **d)** $\frac{1}{\sqrt{e}}$

In each case describe the series as oscillating or non-oscillating.

THE EXPONENTIAL FUNCTION

Exploration 17.5

Exponential graphs

On the same axes draw accurately graphs of:

a) $y = e^x$ **b)** $y = -e^x$ **c)** $y = e^{-x}$ **d)** $y = -e^{-x}$

for the domain $\{x: -2 \leq x \leq 2\}$.

- Describe geometrically how each graph is related to each of the others.
- Estimate the gradient of the curve $y = e^x$ at:
  i) $x = 0$ **ii)** $x = 1$ **iii)** $x = -1$.
  What do you notice?
- Use these gradient values to estimate the gradients at the corresponding x-values on the other three curves.

Interpreting the graphs

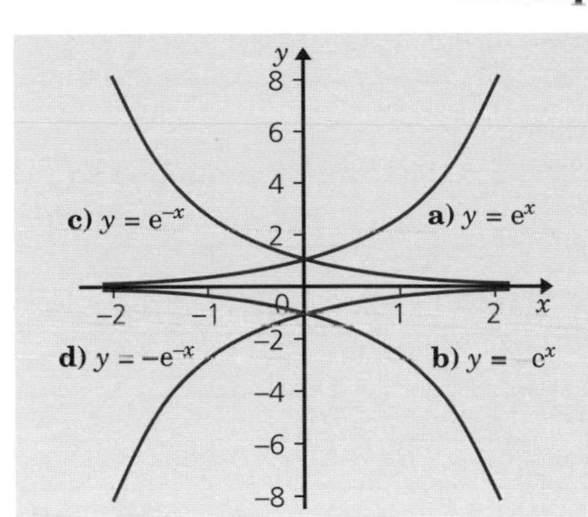

You should obtain the graphs shown below.

Graph **b)** is a reflection of graph **a)** in the x-axis.
Graph **c)** is a reflection of graph **a)** in the y-axis.
Graph **d)** is a rotation through 180° of graph **a)**, centre (0, 0).

Similar relationships exist between other pairs of graphs.

For the curve $y = e^x$, you should have found the following gradients.

i) at (0, 1) gradient = 1
ii) at (1, 2.718) gradient ≈ 2.7
iii) at (−1, 0.368) gradient ≈ 0.4.

It looks as though the gradient equals the function value on each occasion. This is true for any x-value, a property that is brought out in Chapter 18, *Differentiation and integration 3*.

Example 17.2

On separate grids sketch a graph of $y = e^x$ and each of the following equations. In each case describe the geometrical transformation(s) which map(s) $y = e^x$ onto the given equation.

a) $y = 3e^x$ ***b)*** $y = e^{2x}$ ***c)*** $y = 10 - e^x$ ***d)*** $y = 0.5e^{-x}$

Solution

Stretch, factor 3, parallel to the y-axis

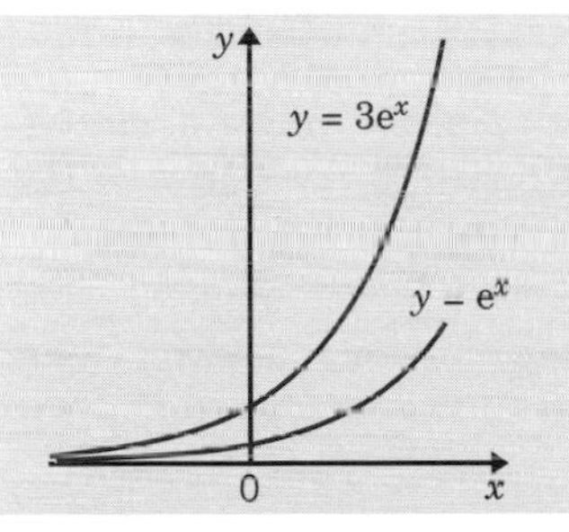

Stretch, factor 0.5, parallel to the x-axis

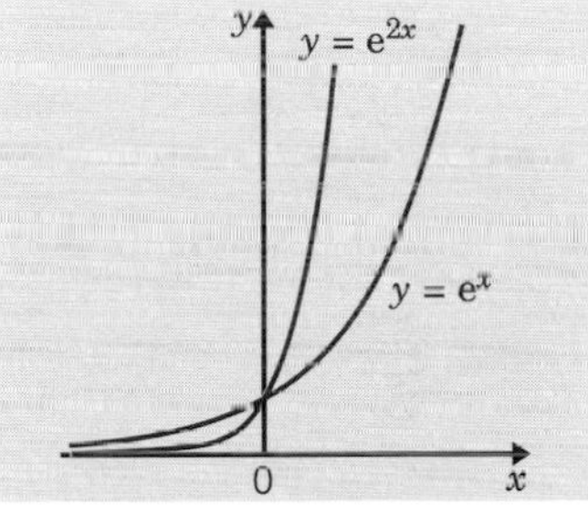

Reflection in the x-axis

followed by

translation 10 units parallel to y-axis

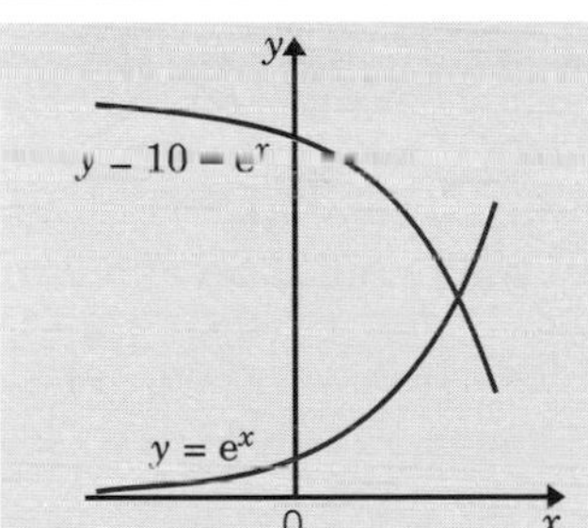

Reflection in the y-axis

followed by

stretch factor 0.5 parallel to the y-axis

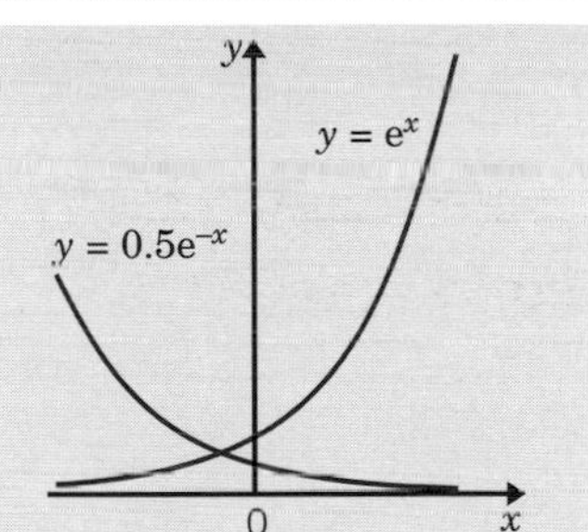

Example 17.3

The population, P, of a certain country is found to be given in millions by the formula:

$P = 10e^{0.03t}$ *where t is time in years since 1980.*

a) *What was the population in 1980?*
b) *Predict the population in the year 2000.*
c) *Draw a graph of P against t for $0 \le t \le 30$.*
d) *Use your graph to estimate when the population will be double its size in 1980.*

e) Show that the annual percentage growth rate is constant. State its value.

Solution

a) In 1980 $t = 0 \Rightarrow P = 10e^0 = 10$ million.

b) In 2000 $t = 20 \Rightarrow P = 10e^{0.03 \times 20} = 10e^{0.6} = 18.2$ million *(3 s.f.)*

c)

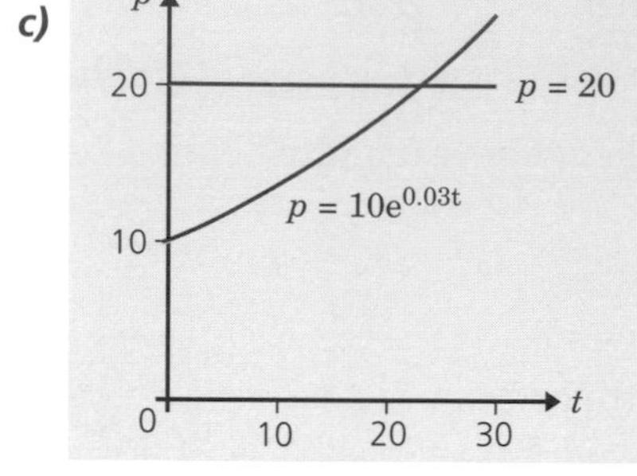

d) From the graph, when $P = 20$, $t \approx 23$, *i.e. population should double by the year 2003.*

e) When $t = n$, $P = 10e^{0.03n}$ *and when* $t = n + 1$, $P = 10e^{0.03(n+1)}$.
The increase in population between $t = n$ *and* $t = n + 1$ *is:*

$$10e^{0.03(n+1)} - 10e^{0.03n} = 10e^{0.03n}(e^{0.03} - 1)$$

$$\Rightarrow \text{percentage increase} = \frac{10e^{0.03n}\left(e^{0.03} - 1\right)}{10e^{0.03n}} \times 100$$

$$= 100(e^{0.03} - 1) = 3.05\% \text{ (3 s.f.)}$$

EXERCISES

17.2 CLASSWORK

1 Given $f(x) = e^x$, show that each of these relations is true.

a) $f(0) = 1$ **b)** $f(x + y) = f(x)f(y)$ **c)** $\frac{f(x)}{f(y)} = f(x-y)$ **d)** $\left[f(x)\right]^n = f(nx)$

2 Draw accurate graphs for the following functions for $-3 \leq x \leq 3$.
Use your graph to estimate:

i) the x-value of the given y-value,
ii) the gradient of the curve when $x = 1$.

a) $y = 0.3e^x$; $y = 2$ **b)** $y = e^{x-2}$; $y = 4$ **c)** $y = 2e^{-x}$; $y = 3.5$
d) $y = 5 + 1.5e^x$; $y = 5.3$ **e)** $y = 8 - e^{0.5x}$; $y = -2$ **f)** $y = e^{-x^2}$; $y = 0.9$

3 On separate grids sketch a graph of $y = e^x$ and each of the following equations. In each case describe the geometrical transformation(s) which map(s) $y = e^x$ onto the given equation.

a) $y = -2e^x$ **b)** $y = 10 - e^{-x}$ **c)** $y = e^{\frac{1}{2}x}$ **d)** $y = e^{2x} - 5$

4 The population, P, of a certain city at time t (measured in years) is given by the formula:

$P = 50\,000\, e^{0.05t}$

Draw an accurate graph of P against t for the domain $0 \leq t \leq 20$.
Use your graph to estimate:

a) the time it takes for the population to double,
b) the rate of growth of the population at $t = 10$.

5 A machine is purchased for £10 000 and depreciates continuously from the date of purchase. Its value, V, after t years is given by the formula:

$V = 10\,000\, e^{-0.2t}$

a) Draw a graph of V against t for the domain $0 \leq t \leq 10$.
b) From your graph estimate:
i) the value of the machine after eight years,
ii) the time it takes for its value to fall by £6000.
c) Calculate the percentage decline in value each year.

EXERCISES

17.2 HOMEWORK

1 Given $f(x) = e^{-x}$, show that each of these relations is true.

a) $f(0) = 1$ **b)** $f(x+y) = f(x)f(y)$ **c)** $f(x-y) = \frac{f(x)}{f(y)}$ **d)** $[f(x)]^n = f(nx)$

2 Draw accurate graphs of the following functions for the domain $-2 \le x \le 2$.

Use your graph to estimate:

i) the x-value for the given y-value,

ii) the gradient of the curve when $x = -1$.

a) $y = 2e^{-x}$; $y = 0.75$ **b)** $y = 3e^{2x}$; $y = 3$ **c)** $y = 2 - e^{3x}$; $y = -18$

d) $y = e^{x+4}$; $y = 20$ **e)** $y = 2e^{x^2}$; $y = 4$

3 On separate grids sketch a graph of $y = e^x$ and each of the following equations. In each case describe the geometrical transformation(s) which map(s) $y = e^x$ onto the given equation.

a) $y = \frac{1}{5}e^x$ **b)** $y = e^{x+1}$ **c)** $y = e^{2x-3}$ **d)** $y = 2.5e^{-2x}$ **e)** $y = 4 - 4e^{-x}$

4 In a simple population model, the number of individual members of the population, N, at time t is given by:

$N = N_0 e^{(B-D)t}$

where N_0 is the initial size of the population, B is the number of births per 1000 per year and D is the number of deaths per 1000 per year.

a) What happens if: **i)** $B > D$, **ii)** $B < D$, **iii)** $B = D$?

b) If, in a certain population, $B = 25$, $D = 15$ and $N_0 = 10\,000$ estimate the size of the population in: **i)** 5 years, **ii)** 10 years, **iii)** 50 years.

c) Explain why, in the real world, your answer to **b) iii)** is probably unrealistic.

5 A patient is injected with a certain drug which gradually diffuses from the bloodstream such that the quantity left in the bloodstream (in milligrams) after t hours is given by:

$Q = Q_0 e^{-0.2t}$

where Q_0 is the initial amount injected.

a) If the patient is given an initial dose of 10 milligrams, draw a graph of Q against t for the domain $0 \le t \le 12$.

b) From your graph estimate:

i) the amount present after 5 hours,

ii) how long (to the nearest 15 minutes) it takes for 9 milligrams to diffuse,

iii) the rate of diffusion after 5 hours.

THE NATURAL LOGARITHM FUNCTION

In Chapter 16, *Exponentials and logarithms*, we saw that each exponential function had an inverse function, e.g.

$f(x) = 10^x \Rightarrow f^{-1}(x) = \log_{10} x$

$f(x) = 2^x \Rightarrow f^{-1}(x) = \log_2 x$

Similarly, if $f(x) = e^x$ then $f^{-1}(x) = \log_e x$.

Logarithms to the base e are so important in mathematics that they are often called the **natural logarithms** and denoted by $\ln x$.

Exploration 17.6

Graphing natural logarithms

Using axes with the same scales, draw graphs of $y = e^x$ and $y = \ln x$.

- Describe the behaviour of each curve geometrically.
- How are the two curves related geometrically?

The graphs of natural logs

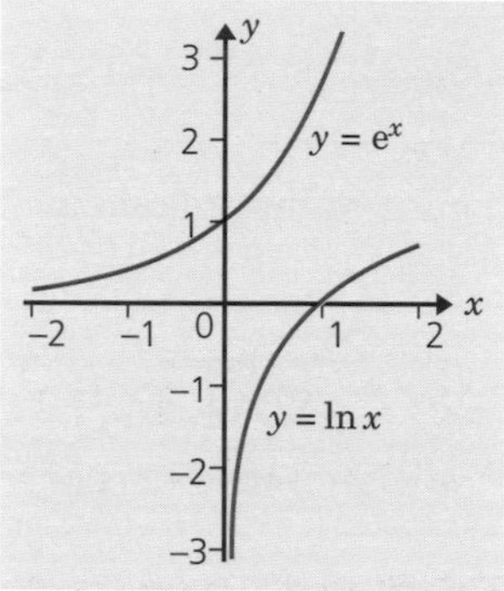

The graphs of $y = e^x$ and $y = \ln x$ are shown below.

The graph of $y = e^x$ passes through (0, 1). As $x \to -\infty$, $y \to 0$, i.e. the negative x-axis is an asymptote to the curve; as $x \to +\infty$, $y \to +\infty$. The gradient of the curve is always positive and gets steeper as x increases.

The graph of $y = \ln x$ passes through (1, 0). As $x \to 0$, $y \to -\infty$, i.e. the negative y-axis is an asymptote to the curve; as $x \to +\infty$, $y \to +\infty$. The gradient of the curve is always positive and gets shallower as x increases.

As with all inverse functions, the two graphs are reflections of each other in the line $y = x$.

$$f^{-1}f(x) = x \Rightarrow \ln e^x = x \text{ and } e^{\ln x} = x$$

Exploration 17.7

Domain of the logarithmic function

On the same axes draw accurately graphs of:

a) $y = \ln x$ **b)** $y = \ln(-x)$ **c)** $y = -\ln x$ **d)** $y = -\ln(-x)$

for suitable domains.

- Write down the largest possible domain for each graph.
- Describe how the graph of $y = \ln x$ may be transformed onto each of the other graphs.

Transforming the graphs

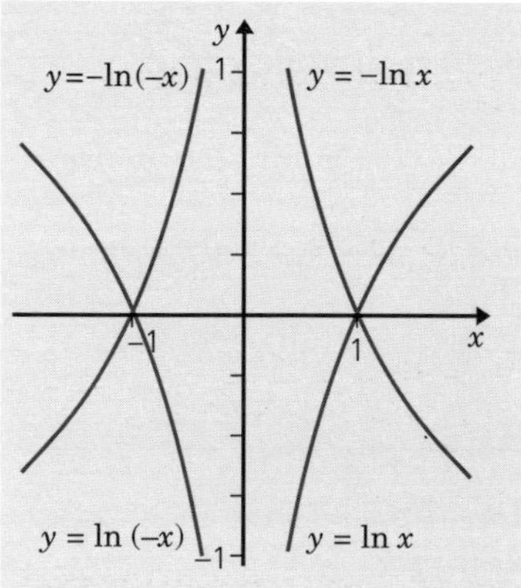

The largest possible domain for $y = \ln x$ and $y = -\ln x$ is $\{x: x > 0\}$ and for $y = \ln(-x)$ and $y = -\ln(-x)$ is $\{x: x < 0\}$.

$y = \ln(-x)$ is a reflection of $y = \ln x$ in the y-axis.
$y = -\ln(x)$ is a reflection of $y = \ln x$ in the x-axis.
$y = -\ln(-x)$ is a rotation of $y = \ln x$ about (0, 0) through 180°.

Note that $y = -\ln x$ is also the result of composite reflections in two different ways. Describe them for yourself.

The laws of logarithms established in Chapter 16, *Logarithms*, apply to natural logarithms.

$$\ln(ab) = \ln a + \ln b$$
$$\ln\left(\tfrac{a}{b}\right) = \ln a - \ln b$$
$$\ln a^n = n \ln a$$

They are demonstrated in the following example and in the exercises.

Example 17.4

On the same axes sketch the graphs of the following.

a) $\ln x$ ***b)*** $\ln(3x)$ ***c)*** $\ln(3x) - \ln x$

*Use the law of logarithms to explain your graph for **c)** and so describe how the graph for **a)** may be transformed onto the graph for **b)** using a translation.*

Solution

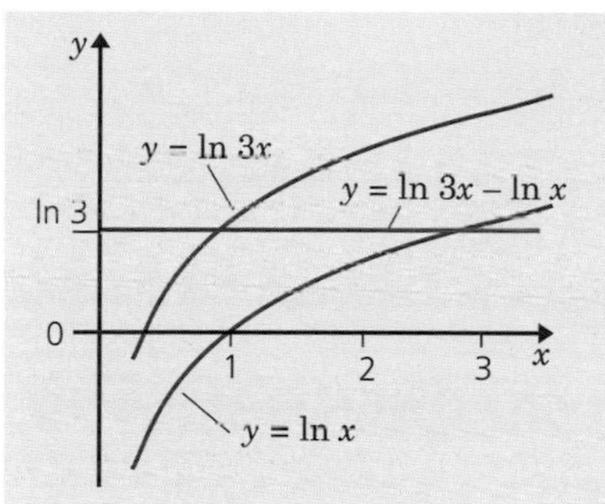

Since $\ln(3x) - \ln x = \ln\left(\frac{3x}{x}\right) = \ln 3$*, the graph of* $y = \ln(3x) - \ln x = \ln 3$ *is a line parallel to the* x*-axis.*
The graph of $y = \ln(3x)$ *is therefore a translation of* $y = \ln x$ *through* $\ln 3$ *units parallel to the* y*-axis.*

$$\ln(3x) = \ln x + \ln 3$$

Note: *The graph of* $y = \ln(3x)$ *is also a stretch, factor* $\frac{1}{3}$ *of* $y = \ln x$ *parallel to the* x*-axis, since for any function* $f(x)$*,* $f(ax)$ *represents a stretch factor* $\frac{1}{a}$ *of* $f(x)$ *parallel to the* x*-axis.*

EXERCISES

17.3 CLASSWORK

1 Use the laws of logarithms to express each of these as a single logarithm.

a) $\ln 3 + \ln 7$ **b)** $\frac{1}{2}\ln 25 + \frac{1}{3}\ln 27$ **c)** $n\ln a + \ln b$

2 Simplify these expressions.

a) $5\ln e^2$ **b)** $\ln\sqrt{e}$ **c)** $3\ln e^{n} - 12\ln\sqrt[3]{e}$ **d)** $\ln e^x$ **e)** $\dfrac{\ln e^{4\sin x}}{\ln e^{5\cos x}}$

3 **a)** On the same axes sketch the graphs of $y = \frac{1}{2}e^x$ and $y = \ln 2x$.
b) Explain why $f(x) = \frac{1}{2}e^x \Rightarrow f^{-1}(x) = \ln 2x$.

4 **a)** On the same axes sketch the graphs of $y = \ln x$ and $y = \ln\left(\frac{1}{5}\right)$.
b) Describe how the graph of $y = \ln x$ may be transformed onto the graph of $y = \ln\left(\frac{1}{5}x\right)$ in *two* different ways.

5 **a)** On the same axes sketch the graphs of $y = \ln x$, $y = \ln x^2$ and $y = \ln\sqrt{x}$.
b) Describe how the graph of $y = \ln x$ may be transformed onto:
i) the graph of $y = \ln x^2$,
ii) the graph of $\ln\sqrt{x}$.

c) Find inverse functions for $y = \ln x^2$ and $y = \ln\sqrt{x}$ for suitable domains.

6 **a)** On the same axes sketch graphs of $y = \ln x$ and $y = \ln\left(\frac{1}{x}\right)$.
b) Describe the geometrical transformation suggested in part **a)**.
c) Use the laws of logarithms to justify your conclusion in part **b)**.
d) Write down the inverse function of $y = \ln\left(\frac{1}{x}\right)$.

EXERCISES

17.3 HOMEWORK

1 Express each of these as a single logarithm.

a) $\ln 4 + \ln 6$ **b)** $3\ln 10 - 2\ln 5$ **c)** $\frac{1}{3}\ln 125 + \frac{1}{2}\ln 25$

2 Simplify each of these.

a) $\frac{1}{3}\ln e^3$ **b)** $6\ln\sqrt[3]{e}$ **c)** $7\ln e^4 - 6\ln\sqrt{e}$ **d)** $e^{4\ln x}$

3 Given that $\ln a = 5$ and $\ln b = 7$ express the following as simple exponentials.

a) ab **b)** $a + b$ **c)** $\frac{a}{b}$

4 **a)** On the same axes sketch the graphs of $y = \frac{1}{3}e^{-x}$ and $y = -\ln 3x$.
b) Explain why $f(x) = \frac{1}{3}e^{-x} \Rightarrow f^{-1}(x) = -\ln 3x$.

5 **a)** On the same axes sketch the graphs of $y = \ln x$ and $y = \ln 5x$.
b) Describe how the graph of $y = \ln x$ may be transformed onto the graph of $y = \ln 5x$ in *two* different ways.

6 **a)** On the same axes sketch the graphs of $y = \ln x$, $y = \ln x^3$ and $y = \ln \sqrt[3]{x}$.
b) Describe how the graph of $y = \ln x$ may be transformed onto: **i)** the graph of $y = \ln x^3$, **ii)** the graph of $\ln \sqrt[3]{x}$.
c) Find inverse functions for $y = \ln x^3$ and $y = \ln \sqrt[3]{x}$ for suitable domains.

SOLVING EQUATIONS WITH EXPONENTIALS AND LOGARITHMS

Exploration 17.8

Radioactive decay

A radioactive substance has a **half-life** of five years, i.e. it takes five years for the level of radioactivity to decay to half its original level.

- After how many years will the level of radioactivity be one-quarter of its original level?
- The radioactive substance is deemed to be 'safe' when the level of radioactivity is 1% of its original level. How long will this take?

A suitable model

A suitable model for the decaying process is: $A = A_0e^{-kt}$

where A represents the amount of radioactivity after t years and A_0 and k are constants to be found. When $t = 0$, $A = A_0e^0 = A_0$, i.e. A_0 represents the original level of radioactivity.

When $t = 5$, the level of radioactivity has halved. Substituting $t = 5$ and $A = \frac{1}{2}A_0$ gives:

$$\frac{1}{2}A_0 = A_0e^{-5k}$$
$$\Rightarrow \frac{1}{2} = e^{-5k}$$

Taking the natural logarithm of both sides gives:

$$\ln\tfrac{1}{2} = \ln e^{-5k}$$
$$\Rightarrow \ln\tfrac{1}{2} = -5k$$
$$\Rightarrow k = \frac{\ln\frac{1}{2}}{-5} = 0.139 \text{ (3 s.f.)}$$

so the radioactive decay is modelled by the equation:

$$A = A_0e^{-0.139t}$$

When at one-quarter of its original level $A = \frac{1}{4}A_0$

$$\Rightarrow 0.25A_0 = A_0e^{-0.139t}$$

which you can solve for t.

$$0.25 = e^{-0.139t} \Rightarrow \ln 0.25 = \ln e^{-0.139t} \Rightarrow \ln 0.25 = -0.139t$$
$$\Rightarrow t = \frac{\ln 0.25}{-0.139} = 10$$

For the safety level $A = 0.01A_0$

$\Rightarrow\ 0.01A_0 = A_0 e^{-0.139t} \Rightarrow 0.01 = e^{-0.139t} \Rightarrow \ln 0.01 = -0.139t$

$\Rightarrow\ t = \dfrac{\ln 0.01}{-0.139} = 33.2\ \text{(3 s.f.)}$

i.e. the level of radioactivity will have reached a safe level after a little more than 33 years.

The property that the exponential and logarithm functions are inverses of each other can be used in any problem where one of the functions needs to be reversed.

Example 17.5

The growth of a population is modelled by the logistic equation:

$$P(t) = \frac{30}{1+5e^{-0.1t}}$$

where t is time in years and $P(t)$ is the population in millions.

a) *Find the initial population size.*

b) *Describe what happens to $P(t)$ as $t \to \infty$.*

c) *Sketch a graph of the function for $0 \le t \le 100$.*

d) *By what time will the population have grown to 25 million?*

Solution

a) *Initially $t = 0 \Rightarrow P(0) = \dfrac{30}{1+5e^0} = 5$ million*

b) *As $t \to \infty$ $e^{-0.1t} \to 0 \Rightarrow P(t) \to 30$, i.e. the limiting population size is 30 million.*

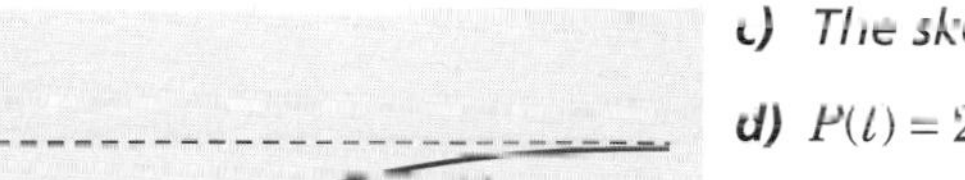

c) *The sketch graph shows a typical logistic curve*

d) $P(t) = 25 \Rightarrow 25 = \dfrac{30}{1+5e^{-0.1t}}$

$\Rightarrow 25(1 + 5e^{-0.1t}) = 30 \Rightarrow 5(1 + 5e^{-0.1t}) = 6$

$\Rightarrow 5 + 25e^{-0.1t} = 6 \Rightarrow 25e^{-0.1t} = 1 \Rightarrow e^{-0.1t} = 0.04$

$\Rightarrow \ln e^{-0.1t} = \ln 0.04 \Rightarrow -0.1t = \ln 0.04$

$\Rightarrow t = \dfrac{\ln 0.04}{-0.1} \Rightarrow t = 32.2$ *(3 s.f.)*

i.e. the population reaches 25 million after 32.2 years.

Example 17.6

Solve this equation. $e^{4x} + e^{2x} - 6 = 0$

Solution

Let $u = e^{2x}$, then $e^{4x} = (e^{2x})^2 = u^2$

$\Rightarrow u^2 + u - 6 = 0 \Rightarrow (u-2)(u+3) = 0 \Rightarrow u = 2$ *or* $u = -3$

$u = 2 \Rightarrow e^{2x} = 2 \Rightarrow \ln e^{2x} = \ln 2 \Rightarrow 2x = \ln 2 \Rightarrow x = \dfrac{\ln 2}{2} = 0.347$ *(3 s.f.)*

$u = -3 \Rightarrow e^{2x} = -3$

which is not possible, since $e^{2x} > 0$ for any real value of x.

So the only solution is $x = 0.347$ (3 s.f.).

Example 17.7

Solve the equation $a^x = e^5$ given that $\ln a = 2$.

Solution

Start with $a^x = e^5$ and take natural logarithms of each side.

$\ln a^x = \ln e^5 \Rightarrow x \ln a = 5 \ln e = 5$

since $\ln e = 1$. Substituting for $\ln a = 2$ gives the solution $x = \frac{5}{2}$.

EXERCISES

17.4 CLASSWORK

1 Solve these equations.

a) $e^x = 10$ **b)** $2e^{5t} = 30$ **c)** $8e^{2x} = 5$ **d)** $4e^{-x} = 15$ **e)** $10 = 7e^{-3t}$

2 Solve these equations.

a) $\ln x = 3$ **b)** $5 + 2\ln x = 0$ **c)** $5\ln x^2 - 3\ln x = 2.1$
d) $\ln 2x + \ln 3x = 20$ **e)** $\ln(x^2 - 6) - \ln x = 0$

3 Solve these equations, where possible.

a) $e^{2x} - 7e^x + 12 = 0$ **b)** $e^{5t} - 2e^{3t} = 0$ **c)** $3e^{4x} + 10e^{2x} + 3 = 0$

4 The population of a certain country is given by: $P = 15e^{0.02t}$ where P is the population in millions and t is the time in years measured from 1980. When will the population reach 25 million, assuming the formula continues to hold?

5 The decay constant for C^{14} (carbon-14) is 1.24×10^{-4}, when t is measured in years.

a) Calculate the percentage of the original specimen that remains after 2000 years and 10 000 years.
b) Find the half-life of C^{14}.

6 When cancer cells are subjected to radiation treatment, the proportion, P, of cells that survive the treatment is given by: $P = P_0e^{-kr}$ where r is the radiation level and k a constant. It is found that 40% of the cancer cells survive when $r = 500$. What should the radiation level be in order to allow only 1% to survive?

7 A cup of coffee, at temperature T °C cools down according to the formula:

$$T = 70e^{-kt} + 20$$

where t is the time in seconds after the cup of coffee was made.

a) What is the initial temperature of the coffee?
b) The coffee cools by 20°C after the first minute. Find the value of k.
c) How long will it take for the temperature to drop to 50°C?

8 A learning curve is given by:

$$y = A(1 - e^{-kt})$$

where y is a measure of efficiency in terms of time t, and A and k are constants. When $t = 1$, $y = 10$ and when $t = 2$, $y = 15$.

a) Find values of A and k. **b)** Find the value of y when $t = 3$.
c) How long will it take for y to reach 19?

9 The spread of information through a population is modelled by the logistic equation:

$$p = \frac{1}{1 + Ce^{-kt}}$$

where p represents the proportion of the population that is aware of the information after time t, and C and k are constants.

At $t = 0$, 10% of all stockbrokers have heard about the impending financial collapse of a company. Two hours later 25% have heard about it.

a) Show that $C = 9$ and $k = \frac{1}{2}\ln 3$.
b) How long will it be before 75% have heard about it?

EXERCISES

17.4 HOMEWORK

1 Solve these equations.

a) $e^x = 5$ **b)** $3e^{4x} = 7$ **c)** $2e^{-x} = 3$ **d)** $4 - 3e^x = 1$ **e)** $2e^x = 3e^2$

2 Solve these equations.

a) $\ln x = 7$ **b)** $3 - 4\ln x = 0$ **c)** $3\ln x^3 + 4\ln x = 9$
d) $\ln 7x + \ln 5x = 1$ **e)** $\ln(2x - 3) - \ln x = 0$

3 Solve these equations, where possible;

a) $e^{2x} - 7e^x + 10 = 0$ **b)** $e^{6x} - e^{3x} - 2 = 0$ **c)** $e^{4x} + 4e^{2x} + 5 = 0$
d) $e^{2x} + 7e^x + 12 = 0$ **e)** $\dfrac{e^x + e^{-x}}{2} = 2$

(**Hint:** in **e)** multiply both sides by $2e^x$ and rearrange as quadratics.)

4 The decay of a radioactive isotope is modelled by the law $M = M_0e^{-kt}$ where M is the mass remaining (in g) after t days.

A certain isotope has a half-life of 10 days and after this time 40 g remain.

a) How much of the isotope was present initially? (i.e. what is M_0?)
b) Find the value of the decay constant, k.
c) How much will remain after: **i)** 20 days, **ii)** 50 days?
d) When will 90% have decayed (to nearest day)?

5 **a)** 90% of the original amount of a radioactive isotope remains after five days. Find the half-life in days.
b) For a longer lived substance, it takes 1 year for 5% to decay. Find the half-life in years.
c) Certain substances are very short-lived. If a substance loses 99% of its mass in $\frac{1}{100}$ of a second, find the half-life.

6 A culture is grown in a Petri dish in a biology lab under controlled conditions. The number (N) of bacteria grows from 100 to 500 in 24 hours and obeys the law $N = N_0e^{kt}$ where N_0 is the initial number of bacteria and k is a constant.

a) Find the time taken, to the nearest minute, for the number of bacteria to double.
b) Assuming conditions remain the same, how many bacteria do you predict after 48 hours.
c) Would you expect to be able to predict how many bacteria there would be after one week? Explain your reasoning carefully.

7 Bacteria are growing rapidly according to the law $N = N_0e^{kt}$ where N is the number of bacteria present at time t hours and N_0 and k are constants.

If 200 000 bacteria grow to 300 000 in five hours, how many bacteria do you predict after ten hours?

8 The population of Great Britain at the time of the Queen's Coronation in 1953 was approximately 52 million. In 1993, this figure had grown to close on 60 million. Assuming a law of the form $N = N_0e^{kt}$, no major wars, plagues, etc, estimate the population of Great Britain, to the nearest hundred thousand, in the year:

a) 2000 **b)** 2001 **c)** 2050. (**Hint:** take 1953 as year zero)

9 Atmospheric pressure, P, at height x feet above sea level can be modelled by the formula:

$$P = P_0 e^{-kx}$$

The pressure is measured in millibars (mbar) and at sea level the pressure is approximately 1000 mbar on average, at 15°C. At 1000 feet the pressure is approximately 967 mbar.

a) What is the atmospheric pressure:

i) on top of High Willhays (Dartmoor) at 2038 feet,

ii) on top of Snowdon (3559 feet),

iii) on top of Ben Nevis (4406 feet)?

b) At what height would you expect atmospheric pressure to be 1 mbar?

MATHEMATICAL MODELLING ACTIVITY

Carbon dating

Background

The molecular structure of living things is based on the element carbon. There are two types or **isotopes** of carbon, carbon-14 and carbon-12, labelled C^{14} and C^{12} respectively. A molecule of C^{14} is heavier than a molecule of C^{12} and C^{14} is radioactive.

Whilst a plant is alive it takes in carbon dioxide from the air and converts it into useful products. The process of conversion does not distinguish between carbon dioxide containing C^{12} and carbon dioxide containing C^{14}. Hence the ratio of $C^{14} : C^{12}$ in living tissue is approximately the same as the ratio of $C^{14} : C^{12}$ in the carbon dioxide in the air.

However, when a plant or animal dies it no longer takes in carbon dioxide. The amount of C^{12} remains constant but the radioactive carbon-14, C^{14} decays exponentially with a half-life of 5760 years. By measuring the ratio of $C^{14} : C^{12}$ it is possible to estimate the length of time that has elapsed since the plant or animal died.

This provides a method for archaeologists to estimate the age of fossil remains and other antiquities.

Problem statement

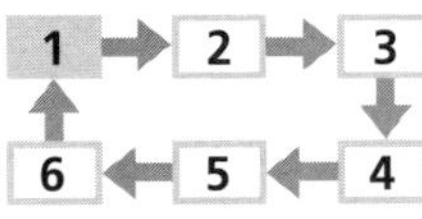

Specify the real problem

In fossilised seeds found recently the residual C^{14} was only 0.5% of the amount present in the air today.

How old were the fossils?

Before the findings, the site was thought to be at least 60 000 years old.

What percentage of C^{14} had been expected prior to finding the seeds?

Set up a model

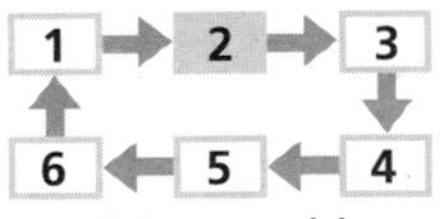

Set up a model

The important variables in this problem are the percentage of C^{14} remaining, $c(t)$ after time t years. In an experiment $c(t)$ could be measured by comparing the amount of C^{14} with the amount of C^{12} present at the present time.

You will need to make some assumptions before formulating the mathematical problem to solve. Here we assume:

- the amount of C^{12} remains constant in dead material,
- when the seeds were living the ratio of $C^{12} : C^{14}$ in the seeds was the same as the ratio at the present day,
- the C^{14} decays exponentially with time,
- environmental conditions have not changed over the last 60 000 years.

Mathematical problem

1 → 2 → 3 / 6 ← 5 ← 4

Formulate the mathematical problem

The three assumptions lead to the model.

$$c = c_0 e^{-kt}$$

where c_0 is the percentage of C^{14} initially present in the seeds when they were alive. We take $c_0 = 100$.

The mathematical problem is to use the background information to find a value for k then:

a) to find t when $c = 0.5\%$,
b) to find c when $t = 60\,000$ years.

Mathematical solution

1 → 2 → 3 / 6 ← 5 ← 4

Solve the mathematical problem

The background information gives a half-life for C^{14} as 5760 years.

Hence $c = 50\%$ when $t = 5760 \quad \Rightarrow 50 = 100e^{-5760k}$

$$\Rightarrow k = \frac{\ln 2}{5760} = 0.000\,12 \text{ (to 2 s.f.)}$$

The model for carbon dating is $c = 100e^{-0.000\,12t}$

When $c = 0.5$, $t = -\dfrac{1}{0.000\,12}\ln\left(\dfrac{0.5}{100}\right) = 44\,000$ (to 2 s.f.)

When $t = 60\,000$, $c = 100e^{-0.000\,12 \times 600\,00} = 0.075$

Interpretation

1 → 2 → 3 / 6 ← 5 ← 4

Interpret the solution

The data for the fossilised seeds suggests that the site where they were found is 44 000 years old (to 2 s.f.). If the site was 60 000 years old then the percentage of C^{14} would be expected to be 0.075% (to 2 s.f.).

Criticism

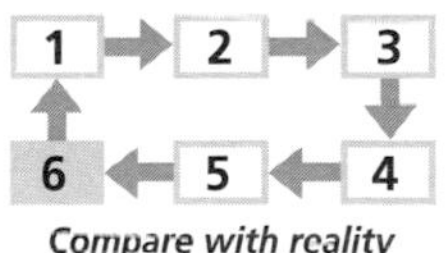

Compare with reality

There are several sources of error in our modelling, in particular:

- the assumption of exponential decay for radioactive decay needs validating with appropriate data,
- the measurement of the residual C^{14} is very small and may be inaccurate,
- the assumption about the environment is important; in recent years the C^{14} levels in the atmosphere have increased because of atmospheric testing of nuclear weapons so it will not be possible to use carbon dating for plants and animals that have died in the past fifty years. This will lead to an imbalance of C^{12} and C^{14} in living material.

CONSOLIDATION EXERCISES FOR CHAPTER 17

1 Find the APR (annual percentage rate) that is equivalent to:

a) 10% nominal rate compounded monthly,
b) 8% nominal rate compounded every three months,
c) 12% nominal rate compounded continuously.

2 The following graphs represent the functions:

A: $y = e^{-x}$ B: $y = e^{-2x}$ C: $y = e^{x}$
D: $y = e^{2x}$ E: $y = 2e^{-x}$ F: $y = 2e^{x}$

Without using a graphics calculator or graph-drawing software, label each graph with its function.

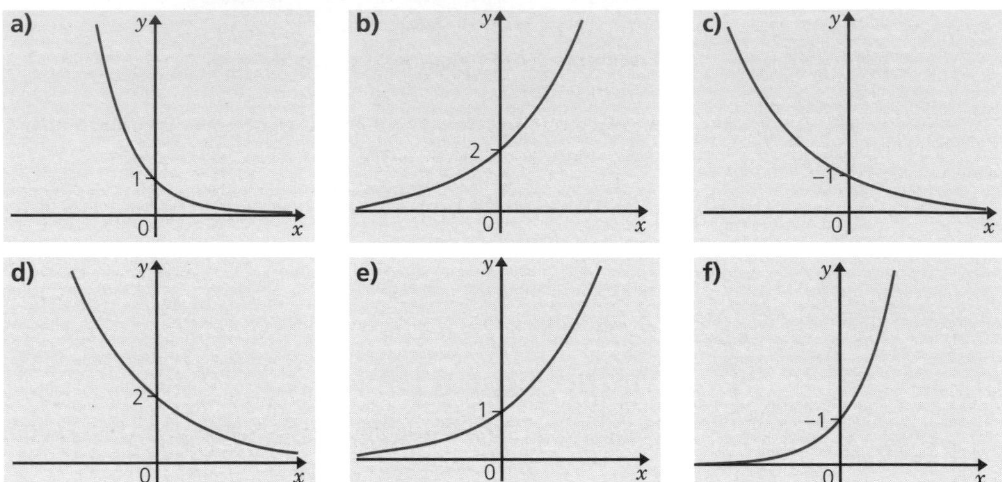

3 In Winchester Guildhall there is a round table that legend says belonged to King Arthur, who was alive in the fifth century AD. When the table was analysed for its carbon content archaeologists found the table to contain 91% of residual C^{14}.

a) Find an approximate age for the round table. Could it have belonged to King Arthur?

b) The method of measuring residual C^{14} is not very accurate. Suppose that there is an error of ± 6% in the measurement. Is it possible that the table could be King Arthur's?

4 A culture of bacteria grows in the laboratory so that its mass M, in mg, after t days satisfies the logistic model:

$$M = \frac{L}{1 + De^{-at}}$$

Initially the amount of culture was 10 mg. After 1 day the mass was 14 mg and after 2 days the mass was 18 mg.

a) Find the values of the constants L, D and a.

b) After how many days is the mass of culture equal to 25 mg?

c) Draw a graph of M against t.

d) What is the limiting amount of mass of culture?

5 A microbiologist measures the population of a certain type of bacterium. He starts the experiment at time $t = 0$. The population, n at time t hours is given by the formula: $n = A(1 - e^{-Bt})$ where A and B are positive constants.

a) Sketch a graph of n against t.

When $t = 2$, $n = 10\,000$ and when $t = 4$, $n = 15\,000$.

b) Show that $2e^{-4B} - 3e^{-2B} + 1 = 0$.

c) Use the substitution $y = e^{-2B}$ to show that $2y^2 - 3y + 1 = 0$.
d) Solve this equation for y and hence show that $B = 0.347$ to 3 significant figures.
e) Determine, to the nearest 100, the maximum population size.

(Oxford Question 9, Specimen Paper 1, 1994)

6 a) For a particular radioactive substance, the mass m (in grams) at time t (in years) is given by $m = m_0 e^{-0.02t}$ where m_0 is the original mass. If the original mass is 500 grams, find the mass after ten years.
b) The half-life of any material is the time taken for half of the mass to decay. Find the half-life of this substance.
c) Illustrate all of the above information on a graph.

(Scottish Higher Question 4, Paper 2, 1992)

7 A medical technician obtains this print out of a wave from generated by an oscilloscope. The technician knows that the equation of the first branch of the graph (for $0 \le x \le 3$) should be of the form $y = ae^{kx}$.

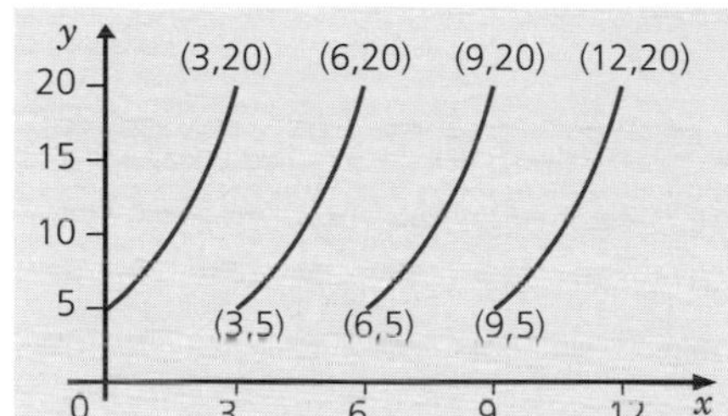

a) Find the values of a and k.
b) Find the equation of the second branch of the curve (i.e. for $3 \le x \le 6$).

(Scottish Highers Question 15, Paper 1, 1993)

8 The function f is defined by $f(x) = e^x - 5x, x \in \mathbb{R}$.

a) Determine $f'(x)$.
b) Find the value of x for which $f'(x) = 0$, giving your answer to 2 decimal places.
c) Show, by calculation, that there is a root a of the equation $f(x) = 0$ such that $0.2 < a < 0.3$,
d) Determine the integer p such that the other root b of the equation $f(x) = 0$ lies in the interval $\frac{p}{10} < b < \frac{p+1}{10}$.

(EDEXCEL, Question 8, Specimen Paper 1, 2000)

9 The function f is defined by $f : x \rightarrow \ln(5x - 2), x > \frac{2}{5}$.

a) Find an expression for $f^{-1}(x)$.
b) Write down the domain of f^{-1}.
c) Solve, giving your answer to 3 decimal places, $\ln(5x - 2) = 2$.

(EDEXCEL, Question 2, Paper 1, June 1999)

10 A formula used to calculate the power gain of an amplifier has the form $G = h \ln [\frac{P_2}{P_1}]$. Given that $G = 16$, $h = 4.3$ and $p_1 = 8$,

a) calculate, to the nearest whole number, the value of p_2.

(EDEXCEL, Question 3, Paper 1, January 1999)

11 The figure shows a brick in the shape of a cuboid with base x cm by $2x$ cm and height h cm. The total surface area of the brick is 300 cm^2.

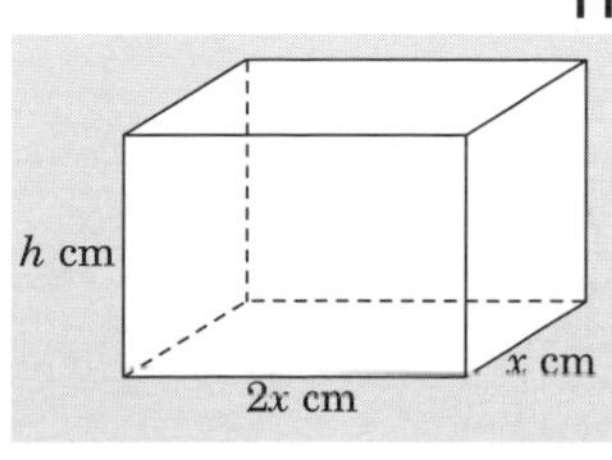

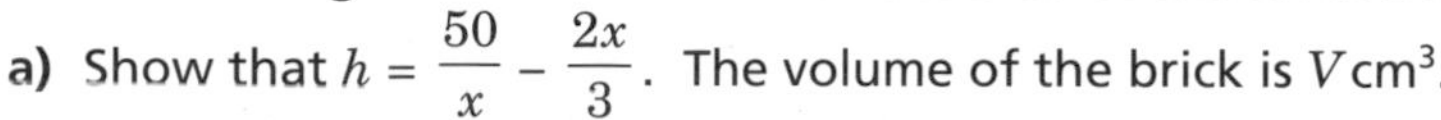
a) Show that $h = \frac{50}{x} - \frac{2x}{3}$. The volume of the brick is V cm^3.
b) Express V in terms of x only. Given that x can vary,
c) find the maximum value of V.
d) Explain why the value of V you have found is the maximum.

(EDEXCEL, Question 7, Specimen Paper 1, 2000)

12 At time t minutes after an oven is switched on, its temperature θ°C is given by $\theta = 200 - 180e^{-0.1t}$.

i) State the value which the oven's temperature approaches after a long time.

ii) Find the time taken for the oven's temperature to reach 150°C.

iii) Find the rate at which the temperature is increasing at the instant when the temperature reaches 150°C.

(OCR, Question 5, Specimen Paper 2, 2000)

Summary

- The exponential function e^x is defined in two equivalent ways:

$$e^x = \lim_{n \to \infty} \left(1 + \frac{x}{n}\right)^n$$

$$e^x = 1 + x + \frac{x^2}{2!} + \frac{x^3}{3!} + \frac{x^4}{4!} + \ldots$$

- The natural logarithm function $\ln x$ is the inverse function of e^x, that is, if $y = e^x$ then $x = \ln y$.

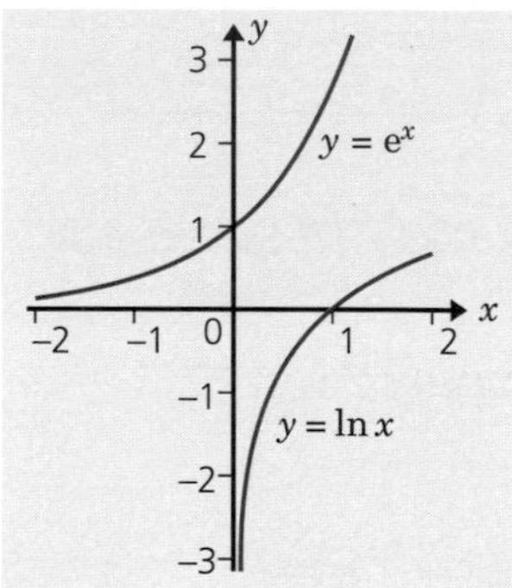

- The function $y = e^{kx}$ models exponential growth if $k > 0$ and exponential decay if $k < 0$.

- Graphs of $y = e^{kx}$ for $k > 0$ and $k < 0$ are shown on the right.

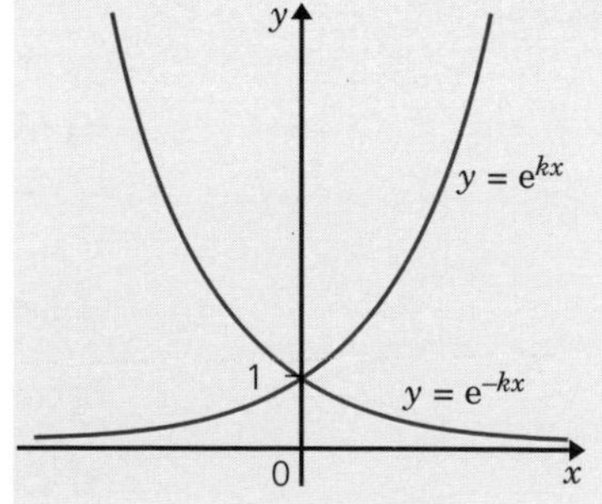

Differentiation and integration 3

In this chapter we introduce:

- *the rules for differentiation of exponential and logarithmic functions*
- *the rules for integration of exponential functions and* $f(x) = \frac{1}{x}$
- *the method of finding volumes of revolution.*

In Chapter 7, *Differentiation 1*, and Chapter 8, *Integration 1*, we differentiated and integrated polynomial functions, based on the rule for powers of x:

i.e. $f(x) = x^n \Rightarrow f'(x) = nx^{n-1}$ and $\int f(x)dx = \frac{x^{n+1}}{n+1}$ $n \neq -1$

and in Chapter 11, *Differentiation and Integration 2*, we extended the rules for rational index n. In this chapter we investigate the calculus of exponential functions and complete the story for $\int x^n dx$ when $n = -1$

DIFFERENTIATION OF EXPONENTIAL AND LOGARITHMIC FUNCTIONS

Exploration 18.1

Differentiating $f(x) = e^{kx}$

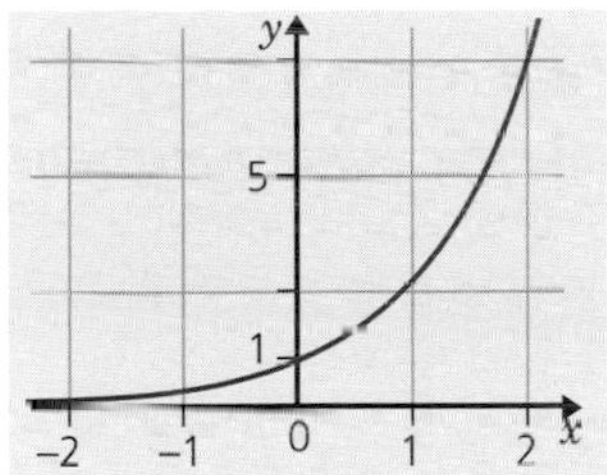

The diagram shows a graph of $y = f(x) = e^x$.

- Use a numerical method to estimate values of the gradient function $f'(x)$ for $x = -2, -1, 0, 1$ and 2.
- What is the connection between $f(x)$ and $f'(x)$?
- Repeat the activities for the functions:

  $f(x) = e^{2x}$ $\quad$ $f(x) = e^{\frac{1}{2}x}$ $\quad$ $f(x) = e^{-x}$

Values of the gradient function

Values of $f(x)$ and $f'(x)$ for the function $f(x) = e^x$, to 3 d.p, are shown in this table.

x	−2	−1	0	1	2
$f(x)$	0.135	0.368	1.000	2.718	7.389
$f'(x)$	0.135	0.368	1.000	2.718	7.389

The gradient function takes the same values as $f(x)$, i.e.

$$f(x) = e^x \Rightarrow f'(x) = e^x$$

or $\quad y = e^x \Rightarrow \frac{dy}{dx} = e^x$

Finding numerical gradients for the other functions reveals different, but consistent patterns.

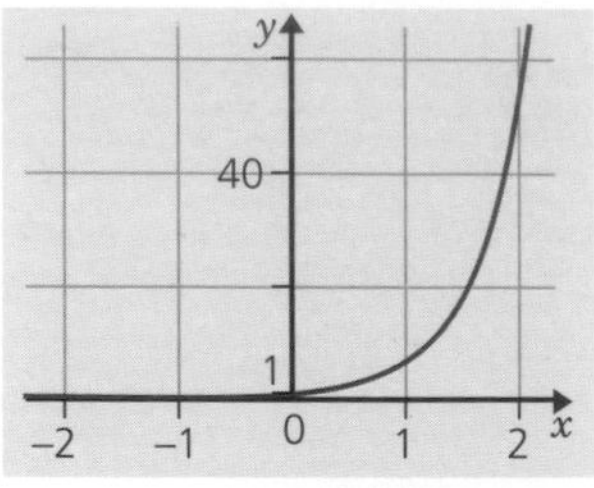

$f(x) = e^{2x}$

x	-2	-1	0	1	2
$f(x)$	0.018	0.135	1.000	7.389	54.598
$f'(x)$	0.037	0.271	2.000	14.778	109.196

Conclusion: $f(x) = e^{2x} \quad \Rightarrow \quad f'(x) = 2e^{2x}$

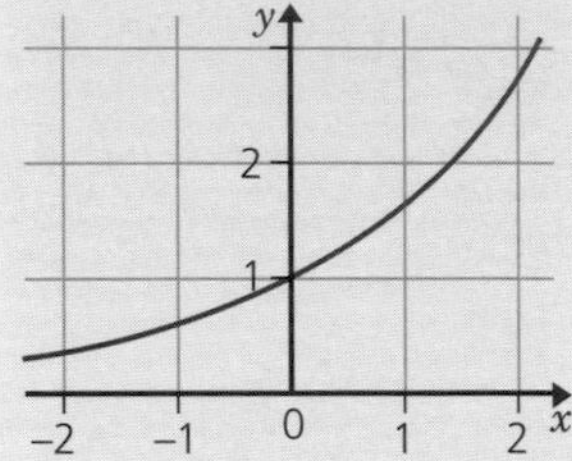

$f(x) = e^{\frac{1}{2}x}$

x	-2	-1	0	1	2
$f(x)$	0.368	0.607	1.000	1.649	2.718
$f'(x)$	0.184	0.303	0.500	0.824	1.359

Conclusion: $f(x) = e^{\frac{1}{2}x} \quad \Rightarrow \quad f'(x) = \frac{1}{2}e^{\frac{1}{2}x}$

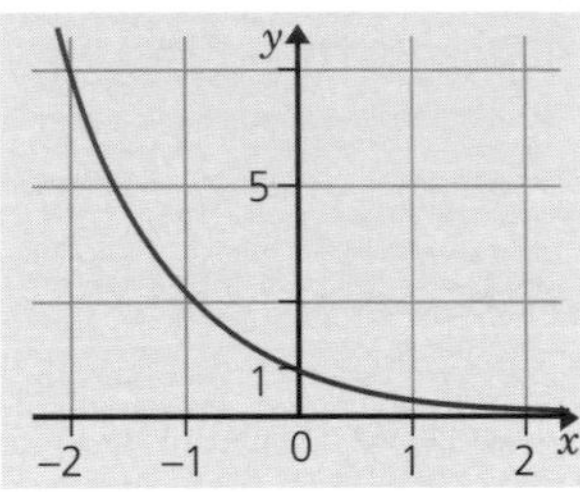

$f(x) = e^{-x}$

x	-2	-1	0	1	2
$f(x)$	7.389	2.718	1	0.368	0.135
$f'(x)$	-7.389	-2.718	-1	-0.368	-0.135

Conclusion: $f(x) = e^{-x} \quad \Rightarrow \quad f'(x) = -e^{-x}$

From the exploration we see that a rule emerges for differentiating exponential functions of the form e^{kx}.

$$f(x) = e^{kx} \quad \Rightarrow \quad f'(x) = ke^{kx}$$

for any rational number k.

Exploration 18.2

An alternative way of differentiating e^{kx}

In Chapter 17, *The exponential and the natural logarithmic functions*, we introduced the series expansion for e^x:

$$e^x \equiv 1 + x + \frac{x^2}{2!} + \frac{x^3}{3!} + \frac{x^4}{4!} + \dots$$

which is true for all values of x.

- Differentiate the exponential series to show that $\frac{d}{dx}e^x = e^x$, i.e. the derivative of e^x is e^x.
- Write down the series expansion for e^{2x} and so find $\frac{d}{dx}e^{2x}$.
- Use a similar method to find $\frac{d}{dx}e^{kx}$ for other values of k, e.g. $k = 3$, $k = -1$, $k = \frac{1}{2}$.

Examining the results

$$\frac{d}{dx}e^x = \frac{d}{dx}\left(1 + x + \frac{x^2}{2!} + \frac{x^3}{3!} + \frac{x^4}{4!} + \dots\right) = 0 + 1 + \frac{2x}{2!} + \frac{3x^2}{3!} + \frac{4x^3}{4!} + \dots = 1 + x + \frac{x^2}{2!} + \frac{x^3}{3!} + \dots = e^x$$

Replacing x by $2x$ in the series expansion gives:

$$e^{2x} \equiv 1 + 2x + \frac{(2x)^2}{2!} + \frac{(2x)^3}{3!} + \frac{(2x)^4}{4!} + \dots \equiv 1 + 2x + \frac{4x^2}{2!} + \frac{8x^3}{3!} + \frac{16x^4}{4!} \dots$$

Differentiating with respect to x:

$$\frac{d}{dx}\left(1+2x+\frac{4x^2}{2!}+\frac{8x^3}{3!}+\frac{16x^4}{4!}\ldots\right)=0+2+\frac{4(2x)}{2!}+\frac{8(3x^2)}{3!}+\frac{16(4x^3)}{4!}+\ldots$$

$$=2+4x+\frac{8x^2}{2!}+\frac{16x^3}{3!}+\ldots=2\left(1+2x+\frac{4x^2}{2!}+\frac{8x^3}{3!}+\ldots\right)$$

$$\Rightarrow \frac{d}{dx}e^{2x}=2e^{2x}$$

Replacing x with $3x$, $\frac{1}{2}x$, $-x$ etc. in the series expansion enables us to demonstrate the general result.

$$\frac{d}{dx}e^{kx}=ke^{kx}$$

Example 18.1

The diagram shows a sketch of $y=f(x)=e^{0.5x}-4x+5$.

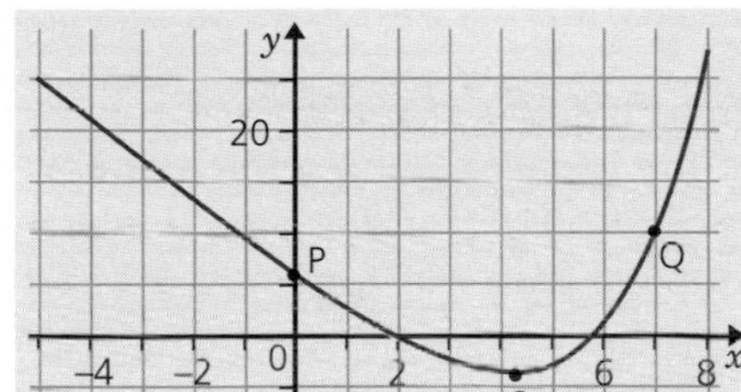

a) *Find the coordinates of points P and Q.*

b) *Find the gradient of the curve at P and Q.*

c) *Find the coordinates of point S, the minimum point.*

Solution

a) *At P,* $x=0\Rightarrow f(0)=e^0-4\times 0+5=6$, *hence point P has coordinates (0, 6).*
At Q, $x=7\Rightarrow f(7)=e^{3.5}-4\times 7+5=10.115$, *hence point Q has coordinates (7, 10.115).*

b) $f'(x)=0.5e^{0.5x}-4$, *hence:*
at point P $f'(0)=0.5e^0-4=-3.5$
at point Q $f'(7)=0.5e^{3.5}-4=12.558$

c) *For a stationary value* $f'(x)=0$
$\Rightarrow 0.5e^{0.5x}-4=0 \Rightarrow e^{0.5x}=8 \Rightarrow \ln e^{0.5x}=\ln 8 \Rightarrow 0.5x=\ln 8$
$\Rightarrow x=2\ln 8=4.16$ *(3 s.f.)*
Since $f(4.16)=-3.64$ *(3 s.f.), the coordinates of S are (4.16, –3.64).*

Example 18.2

A population is growing according to the formula:

$$P=20e^{0.02t}$$

where P *is the population in millions and* t *is the time in years measured from 1990.*

a) *When will the population reach 25 million?*

b) *At what rate will the population be growing at that time?*

Solution

a) *When* $P=25$,

$$25=20e^{0.02t}\Rightarrow 1.25=e^{0.02t}\Rightarrow \ln e^{0.02t}=\ln 1.25\Rightarrow 0.02t=\ln 1.25$$
$$\Rightarrow t=50\ln 1.25=11.2 \quad (3\text{ s.f.})$$

i.e. the population will reach 25 million during the year 2001.

b) $P=20e^{0.02t}\Rightarrow \dfrac{dP}{dt}=0.4e^{0.02t}$

$t=11.2\Rightarrow 0.02t=\ln 1.25$

$\Rightarrow \dfrac{dP}{dt}=0.4e^{\ln 1.25}=0.4\times 1.25=0.5$

i.e. when the population reaches 25 million it is increasing at a rate of 0.5 million per year.

Differentiating a constant raised to a power

We have seen that $f(x) = e^x \Rightarrow f'(x) = e^x$, but can we deduce anything about the derivative of a^x, where a is a constant?

Since the functions e^x and $\ln x$ are inverse functions of each other:

$$a \equiv e^{\ln a}$$
$$\Rightarrow a^x = \left(e^{\ln a}\right)^x = e^{x \ln a}$$

This important equivalence enables us to differentiate a^x:

$$f(x) = a^x = e^{x \ln a}$$
$$\Rightarrow \quad f'(x) = \ln a \times e^{x \ln a}$$
$$\text{e.g. } f(x) = 2^x \quad \Rightarrow \quad f'(x) = \ln 2 \times 2^x$$

We now know how to compute rates of change for any exponential function, as illustrated in the following example.

Example 18.3

The alcohol level in a person's blood at time t is given by $A = 0.35 \times 0.5^t$, where A is measured in mg per ml and t is the number of hours after consuming four units of alcohol. Find the rate at which the alcohol level is falling after 1 hour.

Solution

$$A = 0.3 \times 0.5^t \Rightarrow \frac{dA}{dt} = 0.3 \times \ln 0.5 \times 0.5^t$$

when $t = 1$, $\dfrac{dA}{dt} = 0.3 \times \ln 0.5 \times 0.5 = -0.104 \quad (3\text{ s.f.})$

i.e. the alcohol level is falling at 0.104 mg/ml per hour.

The derivative of the inverse function

Having explored the derivative of $f(x) = e^x$, we now look at the derivative of the inverse function $f^{-1}(x) = \ln x$.

Exploration 18.3

Differentiating $g(x) = \ln x$

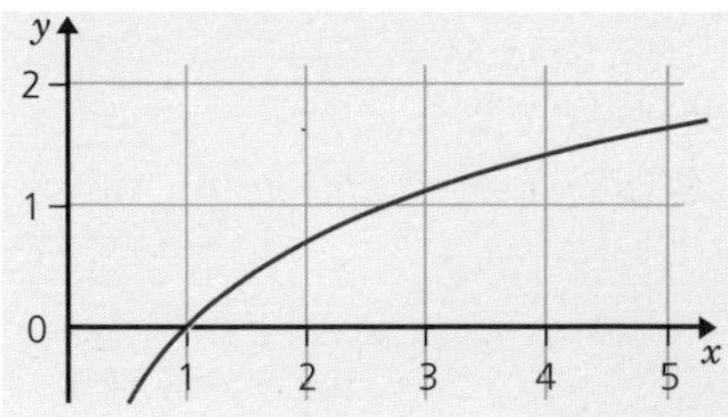

The diagram shows a graph of $y = g(x) = \ln x$.

- Use a numerical method to estimate values of the gradient function $g'(x)$ for $x = 0.5, 1, 2, 3, 4, 5$.
- What is the connection between x and $g'(x)$?
- Repeat these activities for these functions.
  $g(x) = \ln 2x \qquad g(x) = \ln 0.5x$

The gradient function

Values of $g(x)$ and $g'(x)$, to 3 d.p, for the function $g(x) = \ln x$ are given in this table.

x	0.5	1	2	3	4	5
$g(x)$	−0.693	0.000	0.693	1.099	1.386	1.609
$g'(x)$	2.000	1.000	0.500	0.333	0.250	0.200

The gradient function takes the same values as $\frac{1}{x}$.

i.e. $g(x) = \ln x \Rightarrow g'(x) = \dfrac{1}{x}$

or $\quad y = \ln x \Rightarrow \dfrac{dy}{dx} = \dfrac{1}{x}$

Finding numerical gradients for the other functions reveals similar patterns, which leads to the generalisation:

$$g(x) = \ln kx \Rightarrow g'(x) = \frac{1}{x}$$

for any positive constant k.

Example 18.4

A function f is given by $f(x) = x^2 - 8\ln 0.5x,\ x > 0$.

a) *Sketch a graph of* $y = x^2 - 8\ln 0.5x$.

b) *Show that it has a minimum point at (2,4).*

Solution

a) *A sketch of* $y = f(x)$ *shows the curve's stationary point is a minimum.*

b) $f(x) = x^2 - 8\ln 0.5x \Rightarrow f'(x) = 2x - 8 \times \dfrac{1}{x}$

For a stationary point:

$$f'(x) = 0 \Rightarrow 2x - \frac{8}{x} = 0 \Rightarrow 2x^2 - 8 = 0 \Rightarrow x^2 = 4$$

$\Rightarrow x = 2$ *(function only defined for* $x > 0$*)*

Since $f(2) = 2^2 - 8\ln 1 = 4$, *the curve has a stationary point at (2, 4). By examining the gradient either side of* $x = 2$ *we can show that it is a minimum point.*

Check that $f'(1.9) = -0.411$ *(3 s.f.) and* $f'(2.1) = 0.390$ *(3 s.f.).*

Example 18.5

Find the equation of the normal at a point on the curve $y = e^{2x} - 0.5x$ *where the gradient is 5.*

Solution

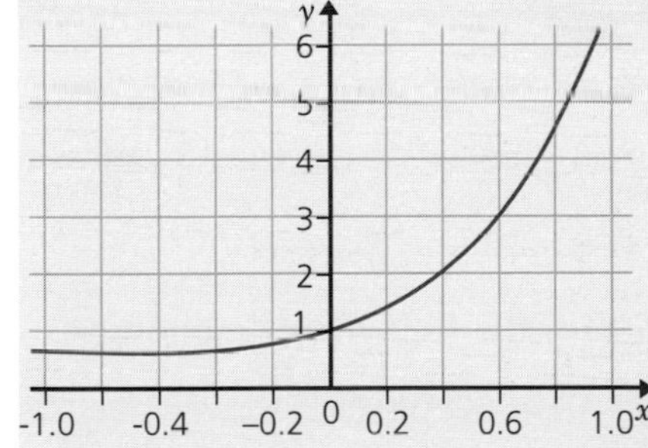

$$y = e^{2x} - 0.5x \Rightarrow \frac{dy}{dx} = 2e^{2x} - 0.5$$

If the gradient of the curve is 5 then:

$$2e^{2x} - 0.5 = 5 \Rightarrow 2e^{2x} = 5.5 \Rightarrow e^{2x} = 2.75$$

$$\Rightarrow \ln e^{2x} = \ln 2.75 \Rightarrow 2x = 1.0116 \Rightarrow x = 0.5058$$

When $x = 0.5058,\ y = e^{1.0116} - 0.5 \times 0.5058 = 2.4971$

Gradient of tangent $= 5 \ \Rightarrow$ *gradient of normal* $= -\frac{1}{5} = -0.2$.

Therefore the equation of the normal through (0.5058, 2.4971) is:

$y - 2.4971 = -0.2(x - 0.5058) \Rightarrow y = -0.2x + 2.5983$ *or* $x + 5y = 12.99$

Example 18.6

a) *Find and classify the stationary point of the graph of* $y = e^x - x$.

b) *Show that* $y = e^x - x^2$ *has a point of inflexion, but no stationary points.*

c) *Use your calculator and a numerical method to find stationary points and points of inflexion for the graph of* $y = e^x - x^3$.

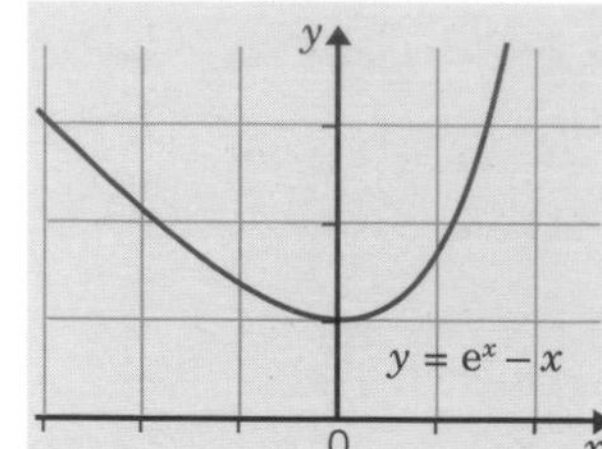

Solution

a) $\mathrm{f}(x) = \mathrm{e}^x - x \;\Rightarrow\; \mathrm{f}'(x) = \mathrm{e}^x - 1$

For stationary values, $\mathrm{f}'(x) = 0 \Rightarrow \mathrm{e}^x - 1 = 0 \Rightarrow \mathrm{e}^x = 1 \Rightarrow x = \ln 1 = 0$

Since $\mathrm{f}(0) = 1 - 0 = 1$, $y = \mathrm{e}^x - x$ *has a stationary point at (0, 1).*

Since $\mathrm{f}''(x) = \mathrm{e}^x$, $\mathrm{f}''(0) = 1 \Rightarrow$ *the stationary point is a local minimum.*

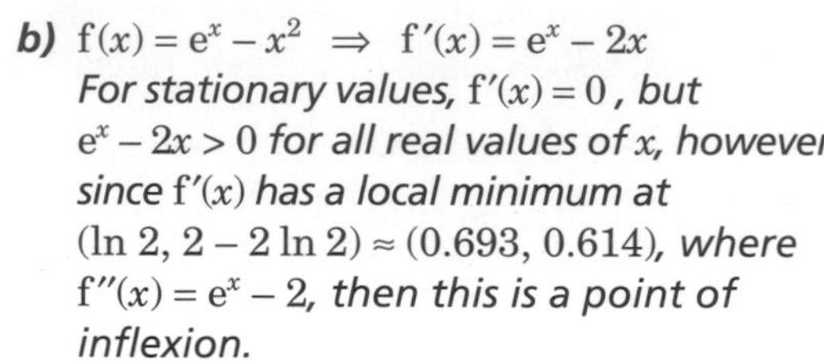

b) $\mathrm{f}(x) = \mathrm{e}^x - x^2 \;\Rightarrow\; \mathrm{f}'(x) = \mathrm{e}^x - 2x$

For stationary values, $\mathrm{f}'(x) = 0$, *but* $\mathrm{e}^x - 2x > 0$ *for all real values of* x*, however since* $\mathrm{f}'(x)$ *has a local minimum at* $(\ln 2, 2 - 2\ln 2) \approx (0.693, 0.614)$*, where* $\mathrm{f}''(x) = \mathrm{e}^x - 2$*, then this is a point of inflexion.*

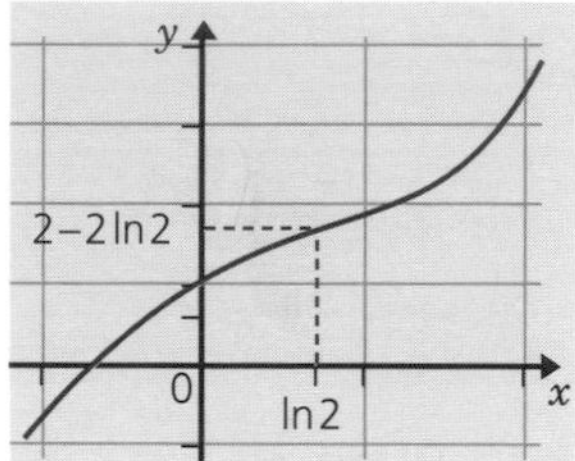

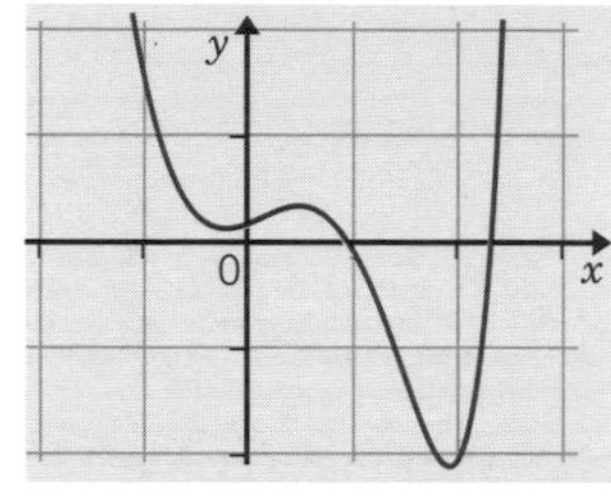

c) $\mathrm{f}(x) = \mathrm{e}^x - x^3 \;\Rightarrow\; \mathrm{f}'(x) = \mathrm{e}^x - 3x^2$

For stationary values, $\mathrm{f}'(x) = 0 \Rightarrow \mathrm{e}^x - 3x^2 = 0$

Since this equation cannot be solved analytically, a graphical or decimal search reveals three stationary values (figures to 3 s.f.), at (–0.459, 0.729), (0.910, 1.73) and (3.73, –10.2).

EXERCISES

18.1 CLASSWORK

1 Differentiate the following functions and evaluate the derivative at the value shown.

a) $\mathrm{f}(x) = \mathrm{e}^{0.5x}, x = 2.5$ **b)** $\mathrm{f}(x) = 2\mathrm{e}^{5x}, x = -1$

c) $\mathrm{f}(x) = \mathrm{e}^{-x}, x = -0.3$ **d)** $g(x) = \dfrac{10}{\mathrm{e}^{4x}}, x = 0.2$

e) $\mathrm{f}(t) = 5\mathrm{e}^t + \dfrac{3}{\mathrm{e}^{2t}}, t = 1.5$ **f)** $g(x) = 5^x, x = -1.2$

g) $g(t) = 0.02 \times 3^t, t = 2.1$ **h)** $h(x) = -2 \times 0.3^{2x}, x = 0$

i) $f(x) = 5\ln x, x = 8$ **j)** $g(x) = -\ln 2x, x = 5$

k) $f(t) = 2\ln t^3, t = 0.8$ **l)** $g(x) = \ln x\,\mathrm{e}^x, x = 1$

2 For each of the following functions, find:
i) $\mathrm{f}'(x)$ **ii)** the values of x for which the derivative is given.

a) $f(x) = \mathrm{e}^{2x} - 0.5x, f'(x) = 5$ **b)** $f(x) = 0.25\mathrm{e}^{-0.8x} - 3, f'(x) = -10$

c) $f(x) = 10 - 4^{-x}, f'(x) = \ln 2$ **d)** $f(x) = 2\ln\dfrac{7}{x}, f'(x) = -0.75$

3 Find and classify the stationary points for the following functions.

a) $f(x) = \mathrm{e}^x - 2x$ **b)** $f(x) = 5x - \mathrm{e}^{1.2x} + 10$ **c)** $g(x) = 2x - 3\ln x$

d) $g(x) = 12\ln x^2 - x^3$ **e)** $g(x) = 7\ln\dfrac{1}{x} + 4x$

4 A car is purchased for £10 000 and depreciates continuously from the date of purchase. Its value, £V, after t years is given by the formula $V = 10\,000\mathrm{e}^{-0.3t}$. Find:

a) the rate of depreciation after two years,
b) the time by which the rate of depreciation has fallen to £600 per year.

5 The number of bacteria in a certain culture doubles every three hours. After six hours the estimated number of bacteria present is 10 000.

a) Find f(t), the number of bacteria present after t hours (known as the population function).
b) Find f′(t), the rate at which the population is growing after t hours.
c) After how many hours will the population reach 15 000?

6 For the following functions, find f″(x) and its value at the given x-value.

a) $f(x) = e^x,\ x = 0$ b) $f(x) = 2\ln(x),\ x = 1$

c) $f(x) = 2^x,\ x = 3$ d) $f(x) = 10x - e^{2x},\ x = 1$

7 For the following functions, find the equation of the tangent and the equation of the normal passing through the given point.

a) $y = 2e^{-x}$ at $(0, 2)$ b) $y = 10x - e^x$ at $(0, -1)$

c) $y = 4 - \ln(x)$ at $(1, 4)$ d) $y = 3x^2 + 2\ln(x)$ at $(1, 3)$

EXERCISES

18.1 HOMEWORK

1 Differentiate the following functions and evaluate the derivative at the value shown.

a) $f(x) = e^{0.25x},\ x = 4$ b) $f(x) = 3e^{7x},\ x = 2$ c) $f(x) = -e^{-x},\ x = -6$

d) $h(x) = \dfrac{7}{e^{0.5x}},\ x = 0$ e) $g(t) = 3e^{2t} - \dfrac{3}{e^{2t}},\ t = 3$

f) $g(u) = 3e^{-2u} + 7u^3,\ u = 2$ g) $f(x) = 7^x,\ x = 5$

h) $g(t) = 10\,000 \times 5^{-2t},\ t = 0.5$ i) $f(p) = -\frac{2}{3} \times 0.12^{\frac{3}{2}p},\ p = 1$

j) $f(t) = 7\ln 2t,\ t = 5$ k) $f(t) = \ln t^3 - \ln t^2,\ t = 2$

l) $h(x) = 2\ln\dfrac{1}{\sqrt{x}},\ x = 9$ m) $h(x) = \ln\left(x^2 e^{3x}\right),\ x = 3$

2 For each of the following functions, find:
I) $f'(x)$ II) the values of x for which the derivative is given.

a) $f(x) = \frac{1}{2}\left(e^x + e^{-x}\right),\ f'(x) = 0$ b) $f(x) = x - \ln x,\ f'(x) = \frac{2}{3}$

c) $f(x) = \sqrt{x} - \ln\sqrt{x},\ f'(x) = 0$ d) $f(x) = \frac{1}{2}\left(e^x - e^{-x}\right),\ f'(x) = \sqrt{5}$

3 Find and classify the stationary points for the following functions.

a) $f(x) = \sqrt{e^x} - x$ b) $f(x) = 3x^2 - \frac{1}{2}\ln x$ c) $f(x) = e^{2x} + 2e^x - 12x$

d) $f(x) = 4^x - 2^x$ e) $f(x) = \ln\left(x^2 e^{-2x}\right)$

4 The concentration of a medical drug injected into the bloodstream can be modelled by the function:

$$c(t) = k\left(e^{-at} - e^{-bt}\right)$$

where a, b and k are all constants (> 0).

a) Show that $c(t) \to 0$ as $t \to \infty$.
b) Find $c'(t)$ and explain its significance.
c) Find the time when $c'(t) = 0$.
d) Does this give a maximum or minimum value of $c(t)$?

5 A bacterial culture starts with 2000 bacteria. After one hour the count is 8000.

a) Find the doubling period.
b) Find the population function.
c) Evaluate the growth rate after one hour and after two hours.

6 For the following functions, find $f''(x)$ and its value at the given x-value.

a) $f(x) = 4e^{\frac{1}{2}x}, x = -1$ b) $f(x) = 9 - \ln(x^2), x = 3$

c) $f(x) = 5 \times 3^{-x}, x = 0.5$ d) $f(x) = 3^x - 2^x, x = -1$

7 For the following functions, find the equation of the tangent and the equation of the normal passing through the given point.

a) $y = e^{0.25x}$ at $(4, e^1)$ b) $y = 7\ln(2t)$ at $(0.5, 0)$

c) $y = e^x - 12x$ at $(0, 1)$ d) $y = x^5 + \ln(x^2)$ at $(1, 1)$

INTEGRATING EXPONENTIAL FUNCTIONS AND $\frac{1}{x}$

Earlier in this chapter, we found that certain rules applied to differentiating exponential and logarithmic functions.

- $f(x) = e^x \Rightarrow f'(x) = e^x$
- $f(x) = \ln x \Rightarrow f'(x) = \frac{1}{x}$

Reversing the process of differentiation suggests the following indefinite integrals.

- $f(x) = e^x \Rightarrow \int f(x)\,dx = e^x + c$
- $f(x) = \frac{1}{x} \Rightarrow \int f(x)\,dx = \ln x + c$

How are these results related to finding areas under graphs?

Exploration 18.4

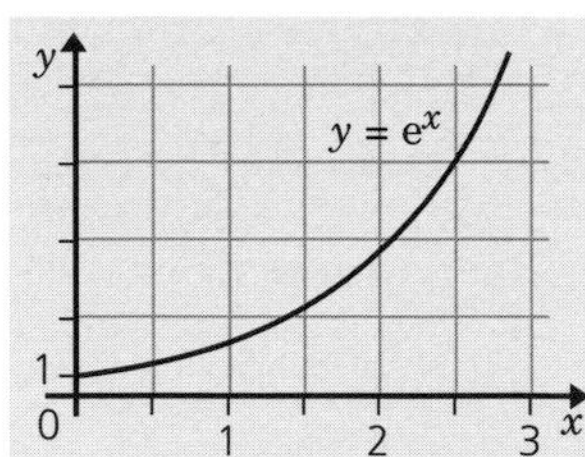

Areas under graphs

The diagram shows a sketch of $f(x) = e^x$.

- Use a numerical method to estimate areas given by $\int_0^a e^x\,dx$ for $a = 1, 2, 3, 4, 5$.
- Use the numerical results to find the area function $A(x)$.
- Is it true that $A'(x) = f(x)$?

Analysing the results

Results of numerical calculations should give you the following results (given to 3 d.p.).

a	1	2	3	4	5
$\int_0^a e^x\,dx$	1.718	6.389	19.086	53.598	147.413

Check that $A(x) = e^x - 1$, i.e. $\int_0^a e^x\,dx = e^a - 1$

$$A(x) = e^x - 1 \Rightarrow A'(x) = e^x = f(x)$$

i.e. the process of differentiation may be reversed to integrate e^x.

Exploration 18.5

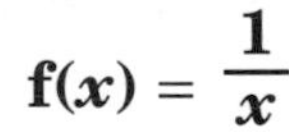

$$f(x) = \frac{1}{x}$$

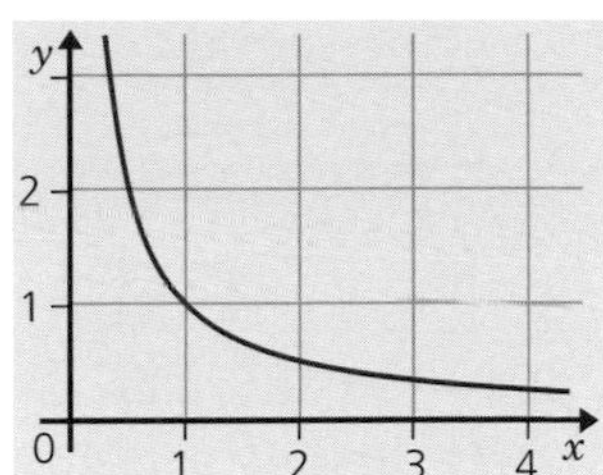

The diagram shows a sketch of $f(x) = \frac{1}{x}$.

- Use a numerical method to estimate areas given by $\int_1^a \frac{1}{x} \mathrm{d}x$ for $a = 2, 3, 4, 5, 10$.
- Repeat for $a = 0.5, 0.2, 0.1$.
- Use the numerical results to find the area function $A(x)$.
- Is it true that $A'(x) = f(x)$?

Analysing the results

Results of numerical calculations should give you the following (given to 3 d.p.).

a	2	3	4	5	10	0.5	0.2	0.1
$\int_1^a \frac{1}{x}\mathrm{d}x$	0.693	1.099	1.386	1.609	2.303	–0.693	–1.609	–2.303

Check that $A(x) = \ln x$ i.e. $\int_1^a \frac{1}{x}\mathrm{d}x = \ln a$

$$A(x) = \ln x \Rightarrow A'(x) = \tfrac{1}{x} = f(x)$$

i.e. the process of differentiation may be reversed to integrate $\frac{1}{x}$.

Having seen that $\int e^x \,\mathrm{d}x = e^x + c$ and $\int \frac{1}{x}\mathrm{d}x = \ln x + c$ we can also reverse associated results for differentiation.

$$\int e^{kx}\,\mathrm{d}x = \frac{1}{k}e^{kx} + c \qquad \text{e.g. } \int e^{3x}\,\mathrm{d}x = \frac{1}{3}e^{3x} + c$$

$$\int a^x\,\mathrm{d}x = \frac{1}{\ln a}a^x + c \qquad \text{e.g. } \int 10^x\,\mathrm{d}x = \frac{1}{\ln 10}10^x + c$$

$$\int a^{kx}\,\mathrm{d}x = \frac{1}{k\ln a}a^{kx} + c \quad \text{e.g. } \int 2^{5x}\,\mathrm{d}x = \frac{1}{5\ln 2}2^{5x} + c$$

Example 18.7

Evaluate these definite integrals.

a) $\int_0^3 5e^{-x}\,\mathrm{d}x$ **b)** $\int_0^2 \left(2^x - 0.5x^3\right)\mathrm{d}x$ **c)** $\int_1^5 \frac{9-x^2}{x}\mathrm{d}x$

Solution

a) $\int_0^3 5e^{-x}\,\mathrm{d}x = \left[-5e^{-x}\right]_0^3 = \left(-5e^{-3}\right) - \left(-5e^0\right) = -0.2489 + 5 = 4.75$ *to 3 s.f*

b) $\int_0^2 \left(2^x - 0.5x^3\right)\mathrm{d}x = \left[\frac{1}{\ln 2}2^x - 0.125x^4\right]_0^2$

$$= \left(\frac{1}{\ln 2}2^2 - 0.125\times 2^4\right) - \left(\frac{1}{\ln 2}2^0 - 0.125\times 0^4\right)$$

$= 3.7708 - 1.4427 = 2.33$ *to 3 s.f.*

c) $\int_1^5 \frac{9-x^2}{x}\mathrm{d}x = \int_1^5 \left(\frac{9}{x} - x\right)\mathrm{d}x = \left[9\ln x - 0.5x^2\right]_1^5$

$$= \left(9\ln 5 - 0.5\times 5^2\right) - \left(9\ln 1 - 0.5\times 1^2\right)$$

$= 1.9849 - (-0.5) = 2.48$ *to 3 s.f.*

Example 18.8

Find the area enclosed by the graphs $y = \frac{2}{x}$ and $2x + y = 5$.

Solution

A sketch graph reveals that $y = \frac{2}{x}$ and $2x + y = 5$ intersect at (0.5, 4) and (2, 1).

The shaded area is given by:

$$\int_{0.5}^{2} (5-2x)\,\mathrm{d}x - \int_{0.5}^{2} \frac{2}{x}\,\mathrm{d}x = \int_{0.5}^{2} \left(5 - 2x - \frac{2}{x}\right)\mathrm{d}x = \left[5x - x^2 - 2\ln x\right]_{0.5}^{2}$$

$$= (10 - 4 - 2\ln 2) - (2.5 - 0.25 - 2\ln 0.5)$$

$$= 4.6137 - 3.6363 = 0.977 \text{ to 3 s.f.}$$

EXERCISES

18.2 CLASSWORK

1 Find the following integrals.

a) $\int 4e^x\,\mathrm{d}x$ **b)** $\int e^{-x}\,\mathrm{d}x$ **c)** $\int 6e^{2x}\,\mathrm{d}x$ **d)** $\int 2e^{-3x}\,\mathrm{d}x$

e) $\int 2^x\,\mathrm{d}x$ **f)** $\int 0.5^{2x}\,\mathrm{d}x$ **g)** $\int 3^{-x}\,\mathrm{d}x$ **h)** $\int 5^{-2x}\,\mathrm{d}x$

2 Find the following integrals.

a) $\int \frac{4}{x}\,\mathrm{d}x$ **b)** $\int -\frac{3}{x}\,\mathrm{d}x$ **c)** $\int \frac{x^2-9}{x}\,\mathrm{d}x$ **d)** $\int \frac{2x-5}{x^2}\,\mathrm{d}x$

3 Evaluate the following definite integrals.

a) $\int_0^2 0.5e^x\,\mathrm{d}x$ **b)** $\int_{-\infty}^{0} 4e^x\,\mathrm{d}x$ **c)** $\int_{-1}^{1} 3^x\,\mathrm{d}x$ **d)** $\int_1^6 \frac{12}{x}\,\mathrm{d}x$

e) $\int_1^3 \left(10x - e^x\right)\mathrm{d}x$ **f)** $\int_0^5 \left(e^{-x} + \frac{x^2}{4}\right)\mathrm{d}x$ **g)** $\int_2^6 \left(\frac{x^2-16}{x}\right)\mathrm{d}x$ **h)** $\int_{-3}^{1} 2^{-x}\,\mathrm{d}x$

4 Find the areas of the shaded regions.

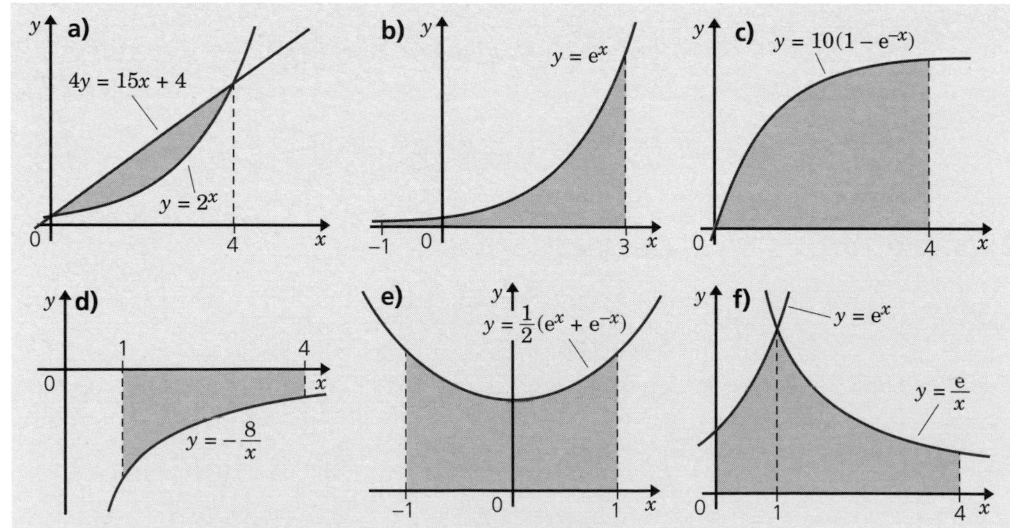

5 **a)** By writing e^{2x+3} as $e^{2x}e^3$, find $\int e^{2x+3}\,\mathrm{d}x$.

b) Using a similar method, find $\int e^{4x-7}\,\mathrm{d}x$.

c) Deduce $\int e^{ax+b}\,\mathrm{d}x$ where a and b are constants.

d) Use your result to evaluate these integrals.

i) $\int_0^{0.5} e^{5x-1}\,\mathrm{d}x$ **ii)** $\int_2^4 e^{3-x}\,\mathrm{d}x$ **iii)** $\int_{-2}^{2} \sqrt{e^x}\,\mathrm{d}x$

6 Find the area of the shaded region in the diagram on the right.

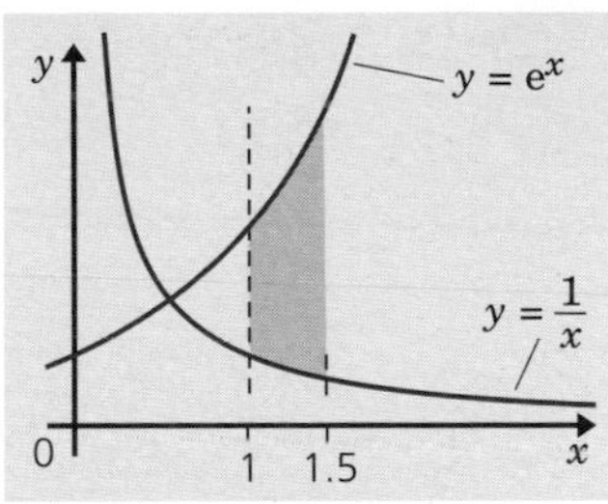

EXERCISES

18.2 HOMEWORK

1 Find the following integrals.

a) $\int 7e^{3x}\,dx$ **b)** $\int e^{-2x}\,dx$ **c)** $\int 12e^{-3x}\,dx$ **d)** $\int (9e^{-3x} + 15e^{-5x})\,dx$

e) $\int 5^x\,dx$ **f)** $\int 0.25^{-x}\,dx$ **g)** $\int 7^{3x}\,dx$ **h)** $\int 8^{-4x}\,dx$

2 Find the following integrals.

a) $\int \frac{11}{x}\,dx$ **b)** $\int -\frac{17}{x}\,dx$ **c)** $\int \frac{13 - x^2}{x}\,dx$ **d)** $\int \frac{7x^2 + 15x - 1}{x^3}\,dx$

3 Evaluate the following definite integrals.

a) $\int_0^{1.5} 1.3e^x\,dx$ **b)** $\int_{-\infty}^{0} \frac{e^x}{4}\,dx$ **c)** $\int_{-0.5}^{0.5} 5^x\,dx$ **d)** $\int_1^4 \frac{1}{3x}\,dx$

e) $\int_4^3 (x^2 - 2^x)\,dx$ **f)** $\int_0^5 \left(e^{-3x} - \frac{x^3}{3}\right)dx$ **g)** $\int_4^6 \frac{x^2 - 25}{x}\,dx$ **h)** $\int_{-1}^{2} 5^{-x}\,dx$

4 Find the areas of the shaded regions.

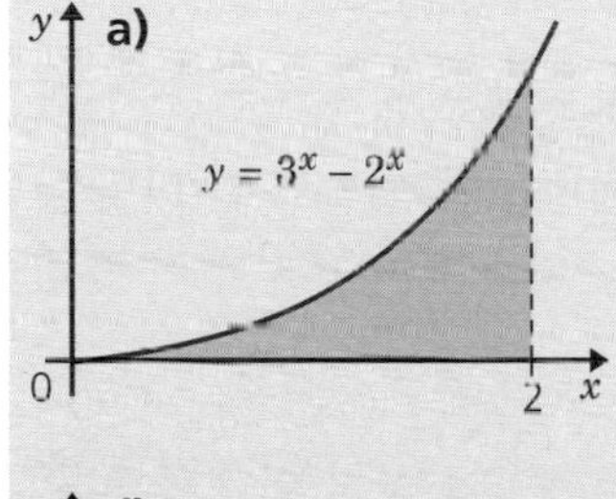

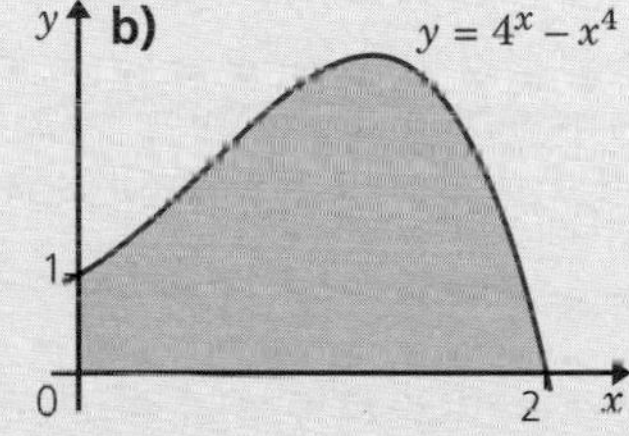

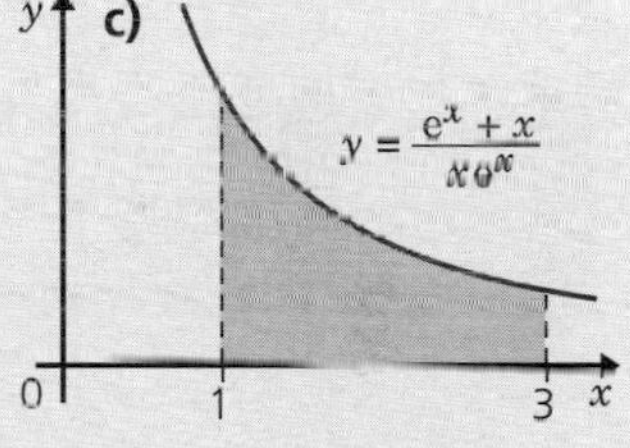

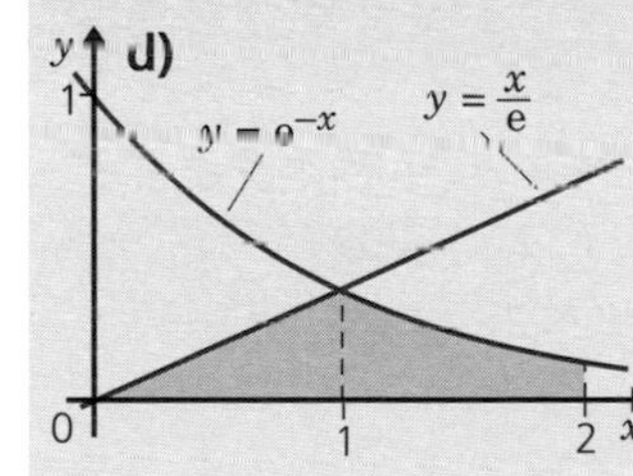

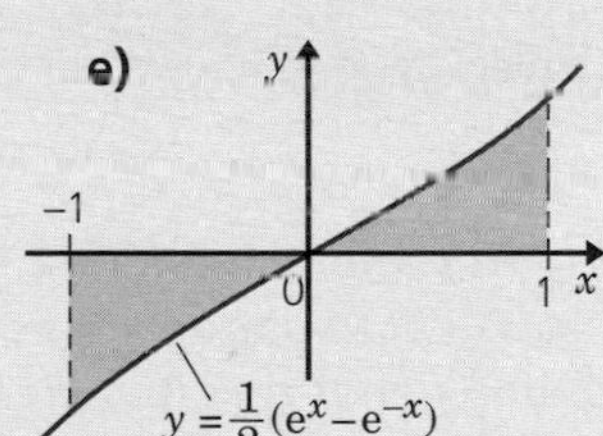

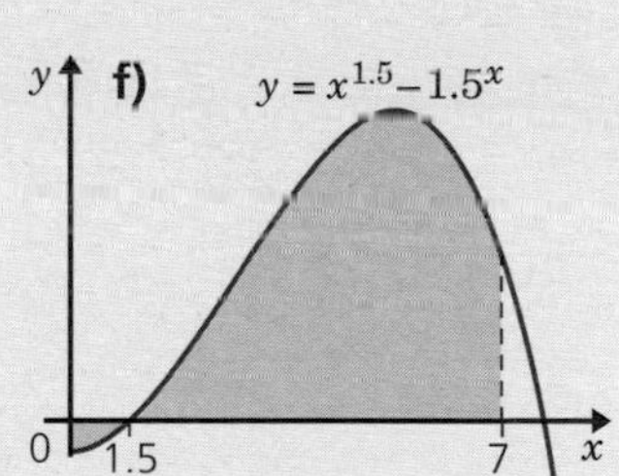

5 **a)** By writing e^{3x+5} as $e^{3x}e^5$, differentiate e^{3x+5} and use your result to find $\int e^{3x+5}\,dx$.

b) Similarly, differentiate e^{4x-11} and use your result to find $\int e^{4x-11}\,dx$.

c) Deduce $\int e^{ax+b}\,dx$ where a and b are constants.

d) Use your general result to evaluate these integrals.

i) $\int_1^2 e^{1-2x}\,dx$ **ii)** $\int_{-2}^{0} \frac{1}{e^{x+1}}\,dx$ **iii)** $\int_2^4 \frac{1}{\sqrt{e^x}}\,dx$

6 Find the area of the shaded region in the diagram on the right.

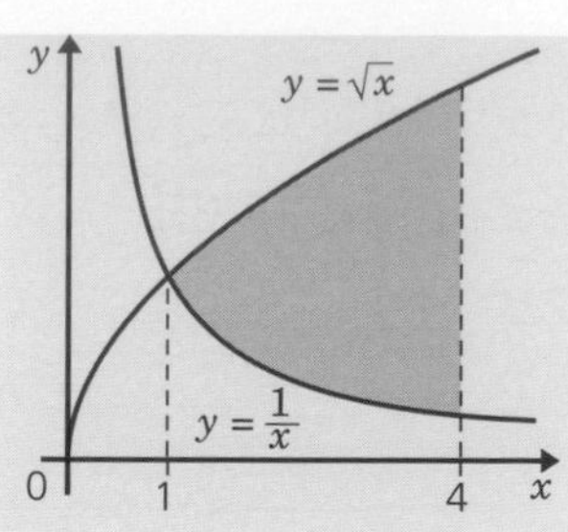

VOLUMES OF REVOLUTION

Exploration 18.6

Strips and slices

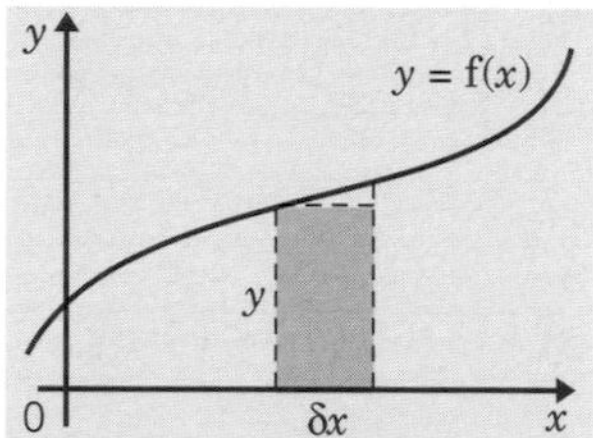

The diagram shows a rectangular strip under a curve $y = f(x)$, with length y and width δx.

- What is the area of the strip?
- If the strip is rotated through 360° about the x-axis, what solid is traced out?
- What is the volume of this shape?

Discs

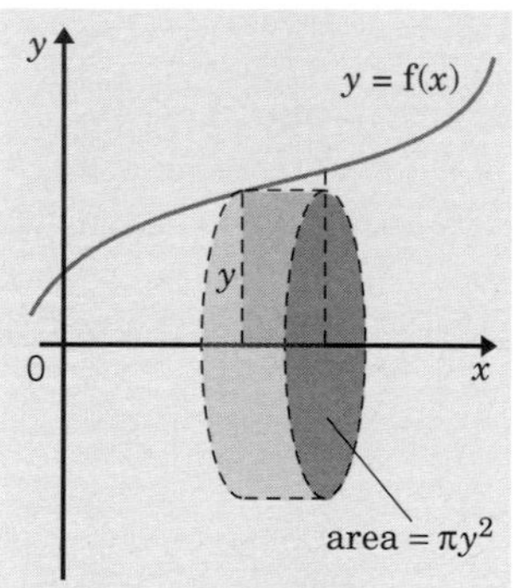

The area of the rectangular strip is $y\delta x$. When it is rotated through 360° about the x-axis a cylindrical disc is traced out with cross-sectional area πy^2 and thickness δx.

If many such strips are considered, then the integral $\int_a^b y\,dx$ can be found as the limit of the sum of such strips as $\delta x \to 0$ and the number of strips tends to infinity. This represents the area under the graph over the interval $a \le x \le b$. Similarly, if many such discs are considered, then the integral $\int_a^b \pi y^2\,dx$ can be found as the limit of the sum of such discs as $\delta x \to 0$ and represents the **volume of the solid of revolution** found by rotating the curve through 360° about the x-axis over the interval $a \le x \le b$.

By considerations of symmetry, when a curve is rotated about the y-axis over the interval $c \le y \le d$, then the volume of solid of revolution is given by $\int_c^d \pi x^2\,dy$.

Example 18.9

Find the volume generated when the curve $y = 2x(x - 3)$ is rotated through 360° about the x-axis over the interval $0 \le x \le 3$. Illustrate the volume generated in a sketch.

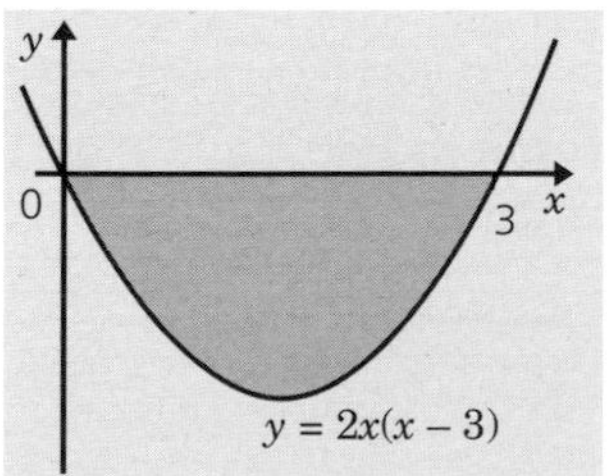

Solution

The volume generated $= \int_0^3 \pi y^2\,dx$

$$= \int_0^3 \pi\left(2x(x-3)\right)^2 dx = 4\pi\int_0^3 x^2(x-3)^2\,dx$$
$$= 4\pi\int_0^3\left(x^4 - 6x^3 + 9x^2\right)dx$$
$$= 4\pi\left[\tfrac{1}{5}x^5 - \tfrac{3}{2}x^4 + 3x^3\right]_0^3$$
$$= 4\pi\left\{\left(\tfrac{1}{5}\times 3^5 - \tfrac{3}{2}\times 3^4 + 3\times 3^3\right) - (0 - 0 + 0)\right\}$$
$$= 32.4\pi$$

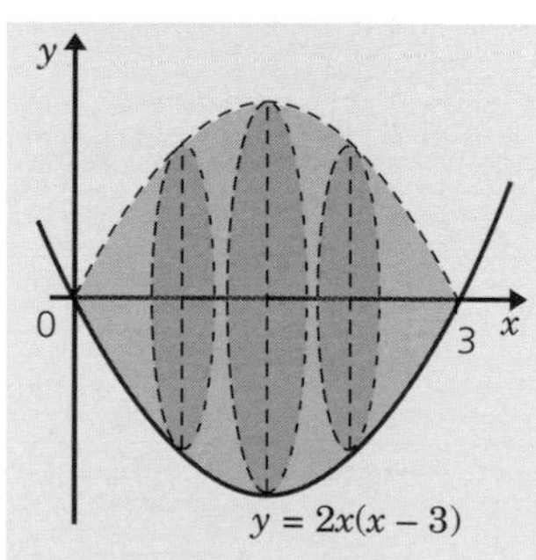

Example 18.10

Find the volume generated when the area enclosed by the graphs of $y = \frac{2}{x}$ and $2x + y = 5$ are rotated:

***a)** about the x-axis,* ***b)** about the y-axis.*

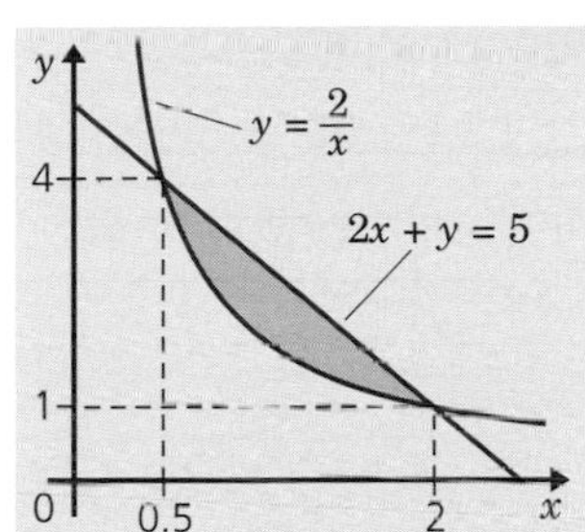

Solution

a) *Volume generated* $= \int_{0.5}^{2} \pi(5-2x)^2\,\mathrm{d}x - \int_{0.5}^{2} \pi\left(\frac{2}{x}\right)^2 \mathrm{d}x$

$$= \pi\int_{0.5}^{2} \left\{(5-2x)^2 - \frac{4}{x^2}\right\}\mathrm{d}x = \pi\int_{0.5}^{2}\left(25 - 20x + 4x^2 - \frac{4}{x^2}\right)\mathrm{d}x$$

$$= \pi\left[25x - 10x^2 + \frac{4}{3}x^3 + \frac{4}{x}\right]_{0.5}^{2}$$

$$= \pi\left\{\left(25\times2 - 10\times2^2 + \frac{4}{3}\times2^3 + \frac{4}{2}\right) - \left(25\times0.5 - 10\times0.5^2 + \frac{4}{3}\times0.5^3 + \frac{4}{0.5}\right)\right\}$$

$$= \pi\left(22\tfrac{2}{3} - 18\tfrac{1}{6}\right) = 4\tfrac{1}{2}\pi$$

b) *For the line $2x + y = 5$, rearrange to give $x = \frac{1}{2}(5-y)$ and for the curve $y = \frac{2}{x}$, rearrange to give $x = \frac{2}{y}$.*

Volume generated $= \int_1^4 \pi\left(\frac{1}{2}(5-y)\right)^2 \mathrm{d}y - \int_1^4 \pi\left(\frac{2}{y}\right)^2 \mathrm{d}y$

$$= \pi\int_1^4\left\{\left(\frac{1}{2}(5-y)\right)^2 - \frac{4}{y^2}\right\}\mathrm{d}y = \pi\int_1^4\left(\frac{1}{4}\left(25 - 10y + y^2\right) - 4y^{-2}\right)\mathrm{d}y$$

$$= \pi\left[\frac{1}{4}\left(25y - 5y^2 + \frac{1}{3}y^3\right) + \frac{4}{y}\right]_1^4$$

$$= \pi\left\{\left(\frac{1}{4}\left(25\times4 - 5\times4^2 + \frac{1}{3}\times4^3\right) + \frac{4}{4}\right) - \left(\frac{1}{4}\left(25\times1 - 5\times1^2 + \frac{1}{3}\times1^3\right) + \frac{4}{1}\right)\right\}$$

$$= \pi\left(11\tfrac{1}{3} - 9\tfrac{1}{12}\right) = 2\tfrac{1}{4}\pi$$

Exploration 18.7

CALCULATOR ACTIVITY

Checking a specification

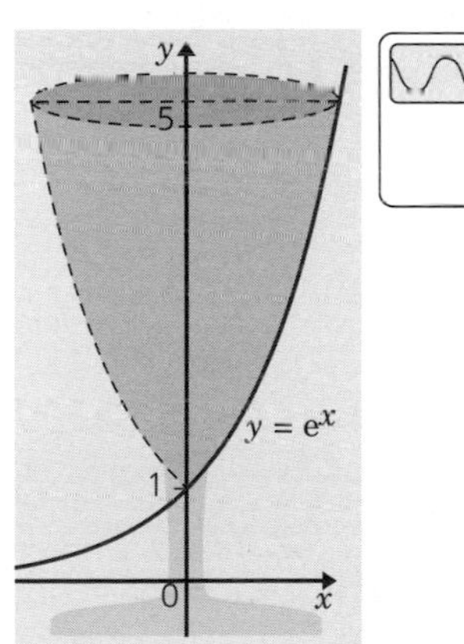

A wine glass is to be modelled by rotating the graph of $y = e^x$ about the y-axis over the interval $1 \le y \le 5$, where 1 unit represents 1 cm.

- A standard 75 cl bottle of wine is to be shared equally among six people, using glasses of the type proposed in the model. Are the specifications suitable?

The volume generated = $\int_1^5 \pi x^2 \mathrm{d}y$

since $y = e^x$, $x = \ln y \Rightarrow$ volume = $\int_1^5 \pi(\ln y)^2\,\mathrm{d}y$

The integral cannot be found analytically without employing techniques which we have not yet met. Use a numerical method (e.g. the trapezium rule) to evaluate the integral correct to 3 s.f.

Analysing the results

Since each glass needs to hold at least $12.5\,\mathrm{cm}^3$, the volume of the glass is just under $15.3\,\mathrm{cm}^3$, so the specifications are suitable.

EXERCISES

18.3 CLASSWORK

1 Find the volumes generated when the following are rotated about the x-axis, between the bounds given. In each case draw a sketch of the resulting volume of revolution.

a) $y = 2x$ from $x = 0$ to $x = 3$ **b)** $y = 2\sqrt{x}$ from $x = 0$ to $x = 4$

c) $y = x^2$ from $x = 0$ to $x = 2$ **d)** $y = 2^x$ from $x = 2$ to $x = 3$

e) $y = 10(1 - e^{-x})$ from $x = 0$ to $x = 2$

2 Find the volumes generated when the following are rotated about the y-axis, between the bounds given. In each case draw a sketch of the resulting volume of revolution.

a) $y = 16 - x$ from $y = 0$ to $y = 16$ **b)** $y = \sqrt{x - 2}$ from $y = 0$ to $y = \sqrt{3}$
c) $y = x^{\frac{2}{3}}$ from $y = 0$ to $y = 2$

3 For each of the following curves:
i) find the x-coordinates of the points where the curve cuts the x-axis,
ii) sketch the curve between these values of x,
iii) find the volume generated when the region between the curve and the x-axis is rotated about that axis.

a) $y = x(6 - x)$ **b)** $y = \sqrt{x}(3 - x)$

4 Find the volumes generated when the shaded areas are rotated about the x-axis.

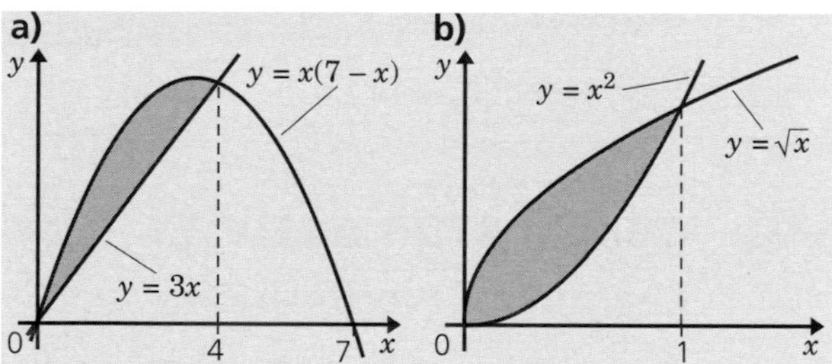

5 Find:
a) the area of the region bounded by the curve $y = \dfrac{6}{x^2}$, the x-axis and the lines $x = 1$ and $x = 2$,
b) the volume generated when this region is rotated through 360° about the x-axis.

6 When the straight line shown in the diagram is rotated about the x-axis, it forms a cone of base radius a and height h.

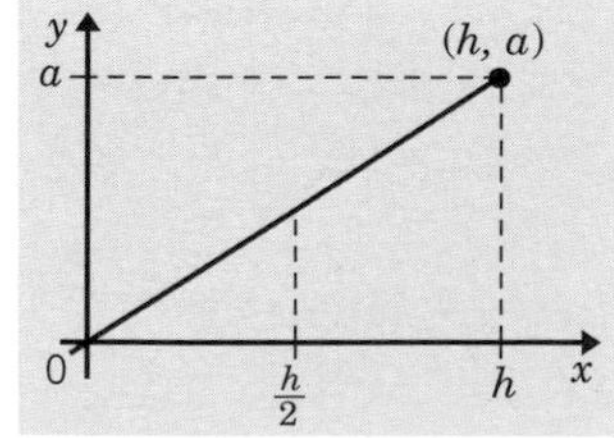

a) Find the equation of the line.
b) Show, by integration, that the volume of a cone is $\frac{1}{3}\pi a^2 h$.
c) If the region between the line, the x-axis and the lines $x = \frac{1}{2}h$ and $x = h$ is rotated about the x-axis, it generates a bucket-shaped object (known as a frustum). Show that the volume of this frustum is $\frac{7}{24}\pi a^2 h$.
d) Repeat part **c)** for a more general vertical line $x = b$.

EXERCISES

18.3 HOMEWORK

1 Find the volumes generated when the following are rotated about the x-axis, between the bounds given. In each case draw a sketch of the resulting volume of revolution.

a) $y = 16 - x$ from $x = -4$ to $x = +4$ **b)** $y = \sqrt{x-2}$ from $x = 2$ to $x = 5$

c) $y = x^{\frac{2}{3}}$ from $x = 0$ to $x = 8$ **d)** $y = 3^x$ from $x = 0$ to $x = 2$

e) $y = 2 - e^x$ from $x = 0$ to $x = \ln 2$

2 Find the volumes generated when the following are rotated about the y-axis, between the bounds given. In each case draw a sketch of the resulting volume of revolution.

a) $y = 2x$ from $y = 0$ to $y = 3$ **b)** $y = 2\sqrt{x}$ from $y = 0$ to $y = 6$
c) $y = x^2$ from $y = 0$ to $y = 4$

3 For each of the following curves:
i) find the x-coordinates of the points where the curve cuts the x-axis,
ii) sketch the curve between these values of x,
iii) find the volume generated when the region between the curve and the x-axis is rotated about that axis.

a) $y = x(x - 5)$ **b)** $y = \sqrt{x}\left(2\sqrt{x} - x\right)$

4 Find the volumes generated when the shaded areas are rotated about the x-axis.

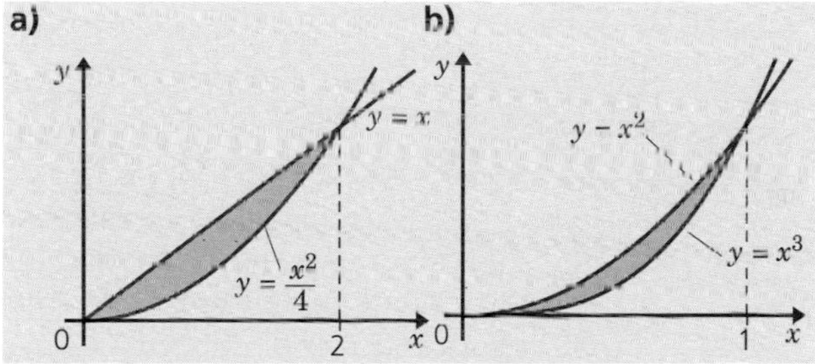

5 Find:
a) the area of the region bounded by the curve $y = 2 + \frac{3}{x}$, the x-axis and the lines $x = 3$ and $x = 6$.
b) the volume generated when this region is rotated through 360° about the x-axis.

6 When the semi-circle shown in the diagram is rotated about the x-axis, it forms a sphere of radius a.

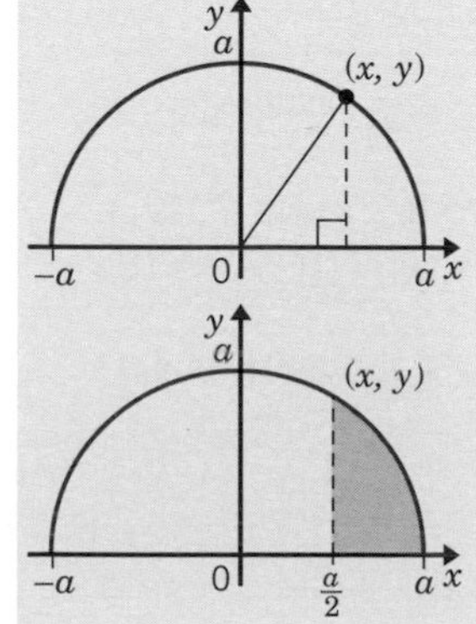

a) Using Pythagoras' theorem, verify that all points on the semi-circle satisfy the equation $y = \sqrt{a^2 - x^2}$.

b) Show, by integration, that the volume of a sphere is $\frac{4}{3}\pi a^3$.

c) If the region between the curve, the x-axis and the line $x = \frac{1}{2}a$ (on the RHS of the line) is rotated about the x-axis, show that it generates a cap-shaped object of volume $\frac{5}{24}\pi a^3$.
d) Repeat part **c)** for a more general vertical line $x = b$.

CONSOLIDATION EXERCISES FOR CHAPTER 18

1 The curve with equation $ky = a^x$ passes through the points with coordinates (7, 12) and (12, 7). Find, to 2 significant figures, the values of the constants k and a.

Using your values of k and a, find the value of $\frac{dy}{dx}$ at $x = 20$, giving your answer to 1 decimal place.

(ULEAC Question 6, Specimen Paper 2, 1995)

2 A forest fire spreads so that the number of hectares burnt after t hours is given by $h = 30(1.65)^t$.

a) By what constant factor is the burnt area multiplied from time $t = N$ to time $t = N + 1$? Express this as a percentage increase.

b) 1.65 can be written as e^K. Find the value of K.

c) Hence show that $\frac{dh}{dt} = 15e^{Kt}$.

d) This shows that $\frac{dh}{dt}$ is proportional to h. Find the constant of proportionality.

(Oxford & Cambridge Question 1, Specimen Paper 2, 1994)

3 Find the volumes generated when the following regions are rotated about the given axes.

a) $y = 2x + 1$ about the x-axis for $1 \le x \le 4$

b) $y = \frac{6}{x}$ about the x-axis from $x = 1$ to $x = 3$

c) $y = e^x$ about the x-axis from $x = 0$ to $x = 2.5$

d) $y = \frac{8}{\sqrt{x}}$ about the x-axis between $x = 2$ and $x = 16$

e) $y = \ln x$ about the y-axis from $y = 0$ to $y = 1$

f) $y = \frac{\sqrt{x+1}}{x^{\frac{3}{2}}}$ $1 \le x \le 2$, about the x-axis

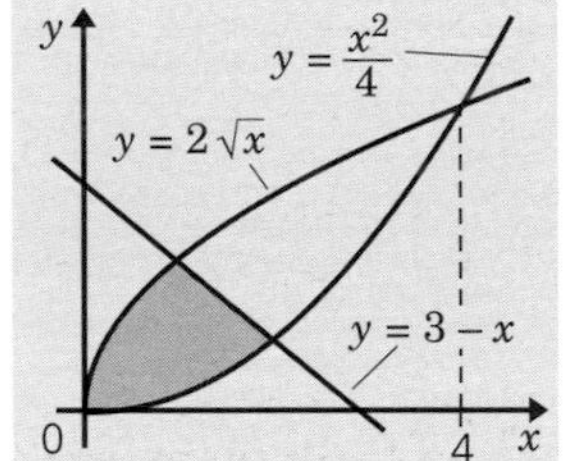

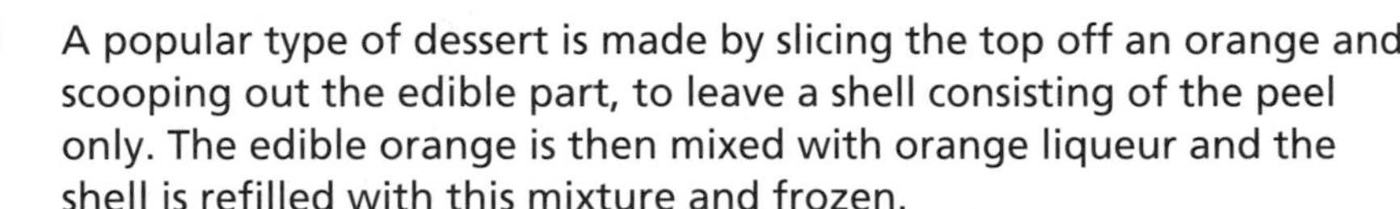

4 **a)** Find the area of the region shaded in the diagram.

b) Find the volume generated when this region is rotated through 360° about the x-axis.

5 A popular type of dessert is made by slicing the top off an orange and scooping out the edible part, to leave a shell consisting of the peel only. The edible orange is then mixed with orange liqueur and the shell is refilled with this mixture and frozen.

Assuming you have a perfectly spherical orange of radius 5 cm and a slice of depth is 1 cm removed, this dessert can be modelled by rotating a portion of the circle shown in the diagram about the y-axis. The surface of the dessert is level with the line $y = 4$.

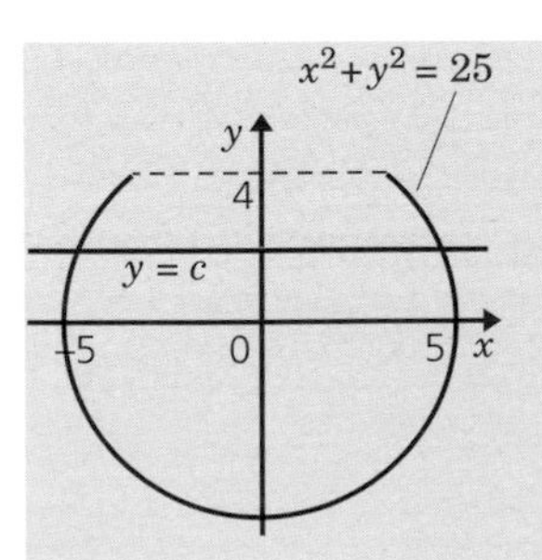

a) Use integration to find the volume of the dessert, leaving your answer in terms of π.

b) Assuming someone eating the dessert tries to keep the surface horizontal, find, in terms of π, the volume remaining when the **depth** of dessert has been halved.

c) When one-third of the dessert has been eaten, the horizontal surface is level with $y = c$ as shown in the diagram. Show that c satisfies the equation:

$$c^3 - 75c + 74 = 0$$

Use the factor theorem to find the only sensible value of c and hence the depth of dessert remaining.

d) Find a similar cubic equation that is satisfied when two-thirds of the dessert have been eaten. Using trial and improvement or an iterative method, show that c is now negative and find the depth of dessert remaining in this case, to 3 d.p.

6 Curves C_1 and C_2 have equations $y = \frac{1}{x}$ and $y = kx^2$ respectively, where k is a constant. The curves intersect at the point P, with x-coordinate $\frac{1}{2}$.

a) Determine the value of k.
b) Find the gradient of C_1 at P.
c) Calculate the area of the finite region bounded by C_1, C_2, the x-axis and the line $x = 2$, giving your answer to 2 decimal places.

(ULEAC Question 10, Specimen Paper 1, 1994)

7 The figure shows part of the curve with equation $y = f(x)$, where $f(x) = e^{0.5x} + \dfrac{1}{x}$, $x > 0$. The curve has a stationary point at $x = \alpha$.

a) Find $f'(x)$.
b) Hence calculate $f'(1.05)$ and $f'(1.10)$ and deduce that $1.05 < \alpha < 1.10$.
c) Find $\int f(x)\,dx$.
The shaded region R is bounded by the curve, the x-axis and the lines $x = 2$ and $x = 4$.
d) Find, to 2 decimal places, the area of R.

(EDEXCEL, Question 9, Paper 1, January 2000)

8 A curve has equation $y = f(x)$ and passes through the point with coordinates $(0, -1)$. Given that $f'(x) = \frac{1}{2}e^{2x} - 6x$, use integration to obtain an expression for $f(x)$.

(EDEXCEL, Question 4, Paper 1, Jan 1999)

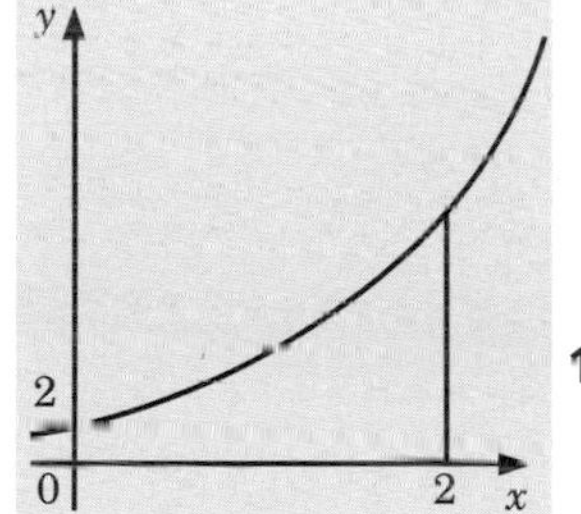

9 The figure shows part of the curve with equation $y = 3e^{2x} - 1$. Find, giving your answer in terms of e, the area of the finite region bounded by the curve with equation $y = 3e^{2x} - 1$, the x-axis and the lines with equations $x = 0$ and $x = 2$.

(EDEXCEL, Question 3, Paper 1, June 1998)

10 The area, p mm^2, of a bacterial culture is recorded at time t hours after the culture was created. The pairs of values of t and p obtained are shown in this table.

t	2	4	6	8	10
p	64	81	103	131	166

a) Draw a graph of $ln\ p$ against t.
b) Show that the pairs of values given in Table 1 are consistent with a law,of the form $p = ae^{kt}$.
c) Use your graph to estimate, to 2 significant figures, the value of a and the value of k.
d) Use the value of a and the value of k found in **c)** to estimate the rate of change of the area with respect to time, in $\text{mm}^2\ h^{-1}$, when $t = 5$.

(EDEXCEL, Question 8, Paper 2, June 1998)

Summary

- The following table shows the derivative of the functions introduced so far.

$f(x)$	x^n	e^{kx}	a^x	$\ln x$
$f'(x)$	nx^{n-1}	ke^{kx}	$a^x \ln a$	$\frac{1}{x}$

(for any number n)

- $\int x^n \mathrm{d}x = \frac{1}{(n+1)} x^{n+1} + c \quad n \neq -1$

This result holds for all rational numbers except $n = -1$, in this case

- $\int \frac{1}{x} \mathrm{d}x = \ln x + c$
- $\int e^{kx} \mathrm{d}x = \frac{1}{k} e^{kx} + c$
- The **volume of revolution** about the x-axis of the area bounded by $y = f(x)$, $x = a$, $x = b$ and the x-axis is given by $V = \int_a^b \pi y^2 \mathrm{d}x$

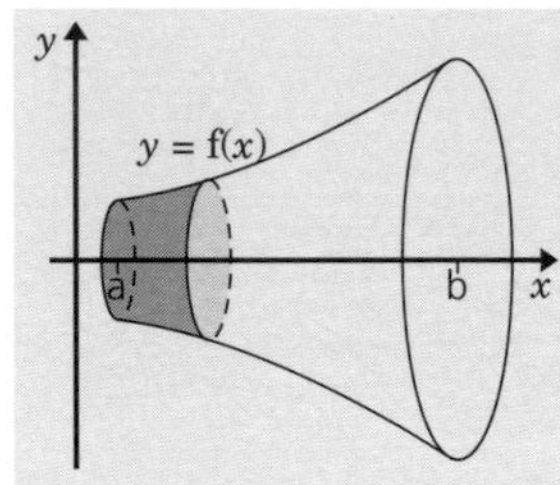

Numerical methods

In this chapter we shall solve equations numerically using:

- *the method of interval bisection*
- *fixed point iteration*
- *Newton–Raphson iteration*
- *approximate definite integrals using the trapezium rule.*

INTERVAL BISECTION

In earlier chapters we have solved various kinds of equations analytically. This means that there is an analytical method by which equations can be solved by algebraic manipulation. Examples of such analytical methods are:

- **quadratic equations**

  $2x^2 - 5x + 1 = 0 \Rightarrow x = 2.28$ or 0.219 (3 s.f.)

  solved by using the quadratic formula

- **exponential equations**

$$\begin{aligned} 5\mathrm{e}^{0.2t} = 18 &\Rightarrow \mathrm{e}^{0.2t} = 3.6 \\ &\Rightarrow 0.2t = \ln 3.6 \\ &\Rightarrow t = 6.40 \text{ (3 s.f.)} \end{aligned}$$

However, there are many equations for which there is no easy analytical method available, so a **numerical** method needs to be developed to find solutions to any desired degree of accuracy.

In the first exploration we use a graphical approach to solving a general cubic equation. We shall then develop three different numerical methods and compare then using this cubic equation.

We have already used the idea of finding a solution by **decimal search** in earlier chapters. The three techniques studied in this chapter may be compared amongst themselves and with the method of decimal search.

Exploration 19.1

Solving equations graphically

Find solutions to these equations.

a) $x^3 - 7x + 6 = 0$

b) $x^3 - 7x + 3 = 0$

Illustrate your solutions graphically.

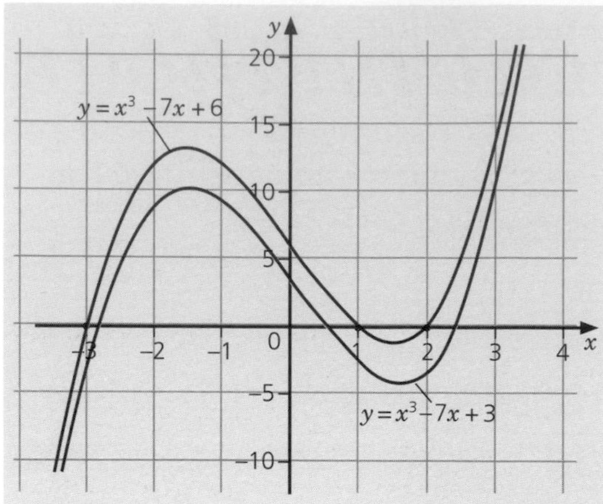

Conclusions

In **a)** the LHS factorises:

$$x^3 - 7x + 6 = 0 \Rightarrow (x + 3)(x - 1)(x - 2) = 0$$
$$\Rightarrow x = -3,\ x = 1 \text{ or } x = 2$$

(three **rational** roots)

In **b)** the LHS will not factorise, but the equation has three **irrational** roots, which can be seen from the graphical illustration for the equations.

Unlike the general quadratic equation it is not easy to develop an **analytical method** for cubic equations which do not factorise. Plotting the graph $y = x^3 - 7x + 3$ and zooming in to where the curve crosses the x-axis gives:

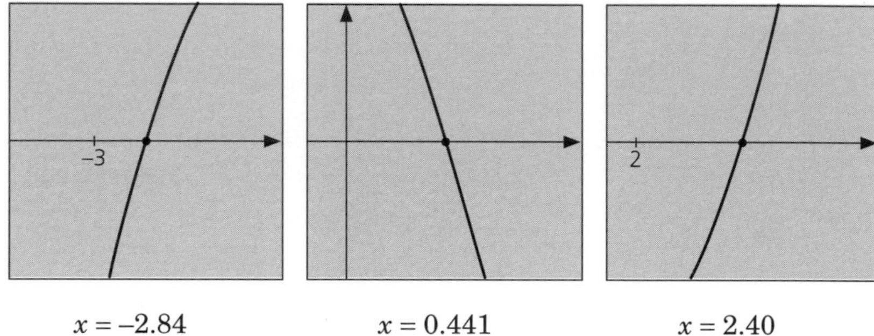

$x = -2.84$ $x = 0.441$ $x = 2.40$

where each root is given correct to three significant figures.

This **graphical method** gives reasonable accuracy after two or three applications of the zoom function on a graphical calculator. However, several **numerical methods** have been devised to enable us systematically to find closer and closer approximations to the roots of an equation. If one approximation can be guaranteed to give a closer approximation than the previous one, then a systematic search will eventually produce an approximation as close to the true value as we want to take it. Such a search method is called an **iteration**.

Exploration 19.2

Interval bisection

The upper root of the equation $x^3 - 7x + 3 = 0$ lies between 2 and 3.

- Find f(2.5), where $f(x) = x^3 - 7x + 3$, and deduce that the upper root lies between $x = 2$ and $x = 2.5$.
- Find f(2.25) and deduce that this root lies between $x = 2.25$ and $x = 2.5$.
- Continue this process of bisecting intervals until you have isolated the root between x-values which differ by less than 0.001.

Conclusions

Since $f(2) = -3$ and $f(3) = 9$, the sign of $f(x)$ changes in the interval [2, 3] which means there is an x-value in this interval such that $f(x) = 0$.
Since $f(2.5) = 1.125$, $f(x)$ changes sign in the interval [2, 2.5], i.e. the upper root lies in this interval.
Since $f(2.25) = -1.359$, $f(x)$ changes sign in the interval [2.25, 2.5], i.e. the upper root lies in this interval.

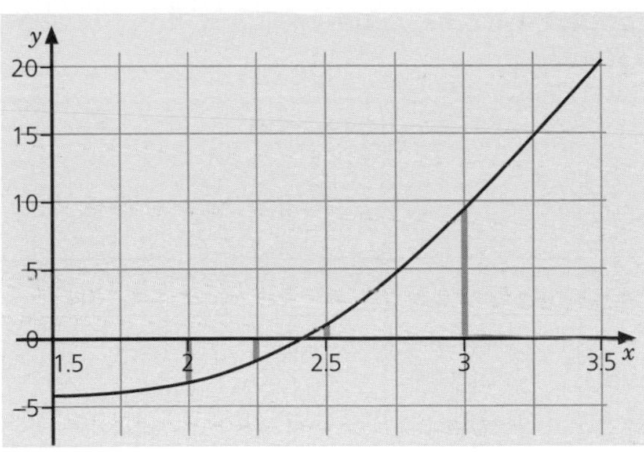

Continuing this process of interval bisection eventually gives a change of sign in the interval [2.396 484 375, 2.398 437 5] which guarantees accuracy to three significant figures. We know this since all x-values in this interval round to 2.40, and the one we are looking for is in this interval, $f(2.396\ 484\ 375) \approx -0.012\ 05$ and $f(2.398\ 437\ 5) \approx 0.007\ 96$.

Successive evaluations of the function, taking the midpoint of the previous interval, leads us to deduce in which half of the current interval the root lies, by comparing values of the function at an end point and the mid-point. The interval is bisected to give a new interval to test. By repeating this process as many times as we wish, we can narrow down the interval within which the root lies indefinitely.

A formal algorithm for interval bisection

Find an interval $[a, b]$ such that $f(a)$ and $f(b)$ have opposite signs.

Let $c = \dfrac{(a+b)}{2}$ and compare $f(a)$ and $f(c)$. If $f(a)$ and $f(c)$ have opposite signs then c becomes the new b, otherwise c becomes the new a. Repeat this process until the interval $[a, b]$ is narrow enough to ensure the required degree of accuracy.

Example 19.1

Find the middle root of the equation $x^3 - 7x + 3 = 0$ by interval bisection, giving your answer correct to three significant figures.

Solution

Inspecting the graph from the exploration, we see that the middle root lies in the interval $[0, 1]$. *Taking* $a = 0$ *and* $b = 1$, $c = 0.5$.
Since $f(0) = 3$ *and* $f(0.5) = -0.375$, $f(a)$ *and* $f(c)$ *have opposite signs,* c *becomes the new* b.
Taking $a = 0$ *and* $b = 0.5$, $c = 0.25$.
Since $f(0) = 3$ *and* $f(0.25) = 1.265\ 625$, $f(a)$ *and* $f(c)$ *have the same sign,* c *becomes the new* a.
Taking $a = 0.25$ *and* $b = 0.5$, $c = 0.375$.
Since $f(0.25) = 1.265\ 625$ *and* $f(0.375) = 0.427\ 734$, $f(a)$ *and* $f(c)$ *have the same sign,* c *becomes the new* a.

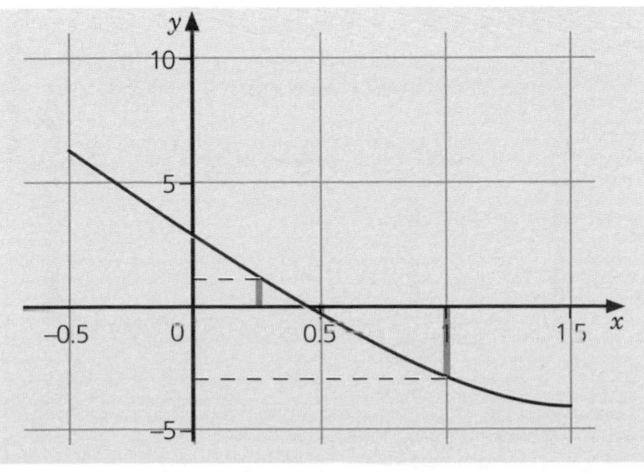

The process continues until the interval $[a, b]$ *within which the root lies is narrow enough to give the desired degree of accuracy. After thirteen steps, we find the root lies in the interval* $[0.440\ 674, 0.440\ 918]$ *which means that the middle root is* 0.441 *correct to three significant figures.*

The table shows a spreadsheet with the values of a, b, c, $f(a)$, $f(b)$ and $f(c)$ for the first thirteen steps.

n	a	b	c	$f(a)$	$f(b)$	$f(c)$
1	0	1	0.5	3	–3	–0.375
2	0	0.5	0.25	3	–0.375	1.265625
3	0.25	0.5	0.375	1.265625	–0.375	0.427734
4	0.375	0.5	0.4375	0.427734	–0.375	0.02124
5	0.4375	0.5	0.46875	0.02124	–0.375	–0.17825
6	0.4375	0.46875	0.453125	0.02124	–0.17825	–0.07884
7	0.4375	0.453125	0.445313	0.02124	–0.07884	–0.02888
8	0.4375	0.445313	0.441406	0.02124	–0.02888	–0.00384
9	0.4375	0.441406	0.439453	0.02124	–0.00384	0.008695
10	0.439453	0.441406	0.44043	0.008695	–0.00384	0.002426
11	0.44043	0.441406	0.440918	0.002426	–0.00384	–0.00071
12	0.44043	0.440918	0.440674	0.002426	0.00071	0.000859
13	0.440674	0.440918	0.440796	0.000859	–0.00071	0.000076

The way in which the root is trapped in successively narrower intervals is illustrated in the diagram.

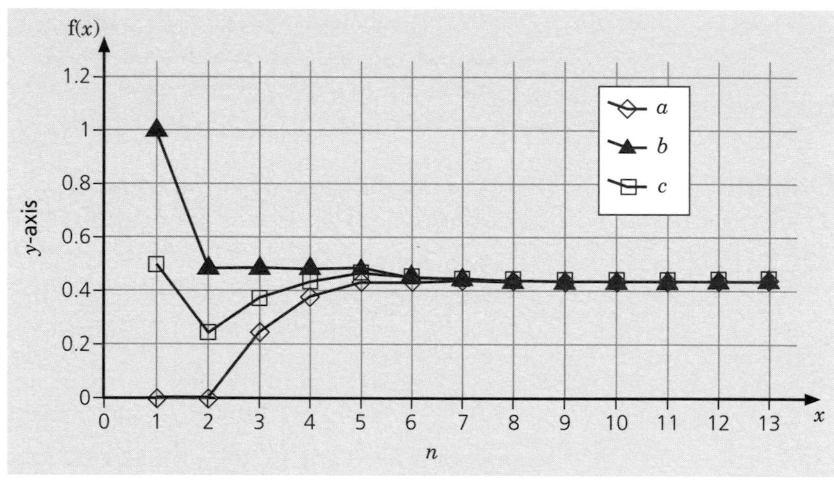

CALCULATOR ACTIVITY

Exploration 19.3

Interval bisection

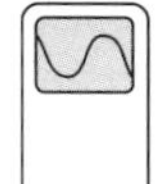

The output on the spreadsheet was produced by automating the algorithm according to this flowchart.

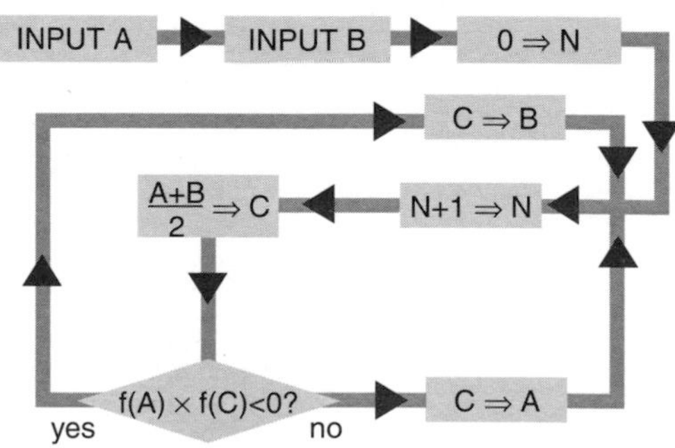

Use the flowchart to write a program for the method of interval bisection and test it by finding all three roots of the equation $x^3 - 7x + 3 = 0$.

EXERCISES

19.1 CLASSWORK

For questions **1–4**, study the function $f(x)$ and then:

a) sketch the graph of $y = f(x)$,
b) find the interval(s) $[a, b]$ within which the root(s) of $f(x) = 0$ lie, where a and b are consecutive integers,
c) use the method of interval bisection to find the root(s) of $f(x) = 0$, correct to three significant figures.

1 $f(x) = x^3 + 5x - 9$

2 $f(x) = x^3 + 5x^2 - 9$

3 $f(x) = e^x - x - 5$

4 $f(x) = x^4 + x^3 - 4x^2 - 3x + 4$

5 The equation $x^4 + x^3 - 4x^2 - 3x + 4 = 0$ has just two roots (see question **4**), but the equation $x^4 + x^3 - 4x^2 - 3x + 3 = 0$ has four roots.
a) Explain, with the aid of a sketch, why the procedure for finding the negative roots needs to be modified.
b) Find the negative roots correct to three significant figures.

6 **a)** Sketch a graph of $y = 8 + 2x - x^2 - x^4$.
b) Find $\dfrac{dy}{dx}$.
c) Use interval bisection to find the coordinates of the graph's only stationary point.

7 **a)** Sketch a graph of $y = x^4 - 4x^2 + 4$.
b) Solve the equation $x^4 - 4x^2 + 4 = 0$ analytically.
c) Explain why the method of interval bisection would fail to produce the roots in **b)**.

8 **a)** Show that the equation $3x + 2 \ln x - 5 = 0$ has just one root, in the interval [1, 2].
b) Use interval bisection to find the root correct to **i)** 1 d.p, **ii)** 2 d.p, **iii)** 3 d.p. noting the number of steps required in each case.
c) What is the least possible number of steps required to ensure accuracy to 3 d.p., using interval bisection on any equation, beginning with the interval $[a, b]$ where $|a - b| = 1$?

EXERCISES

19.1 HOMEWORK

For questions **1–4**, study the function $f(x)$ and then:
a) sketch the graph of $y = f(x)$,
b) find the interval(s) $[a, b]$ within which the root(s) of $f(x) = 0$ lie, where a and b are consecutive integers,
c) use the method of interval bisection to find the root(s) of $f(x) = 0$, correct to three significant figures.

1 $f(x) = 7 - 3x^2 - x^3$

2 $f(x) = 2^x - 5x - 1$

3 $f(x) = x^4 - x^3 - x^2 - x - 1$

4 $f(x) = 2x^2 + x - 2e^x$

5 The equation $2x^2 + x - 2e^x = 0$ has just one root (see question **4**), but the equation $2x^2 + 3x - 2e^x = 0$ has more roots.
a) Explain, with the aid of a sketch, why great care needs to be taken in finding the positive roots of the second equation.
b) Use the interval bisection method to find the two positive roots of $2x^2 + 3x - 2e^x = 0$, correct to three significant figures.

6 **a)** Sketch a graph of $y = x^2 + e^x$. **b)** Find $\frac{dy}{dx}$.
c) Use interval bisection to find the coordinates of the graph's stationary point.

7 Sketch graphs of $y = 1 - \tan x$ and $y = 2x$ $(-\pi \le x \le \pi)$.
a) Use interval bisection to solve the equation $2x + \tan x - 1 = 0$.
b) Deduce the coordinates of the point of intersection of $y = 1 - \tan x$ and $y = 2x$ $(-\pi \le x \le \pi)$ correct to three significant figures.

8 **a)** Use a graphics calculator to plot a graph of $y = \sin\frac{1}{x}$ $(-\pi \le x \le \pi)$.
b) Use interval bisection to find the highest root of the equation $\sin\left(\frac{1}{x}\right) = 0$
c) How many roots does the equation in **b)** have?

FIXED POINT ITERATION

CALCULATOR ACTIVITY

Exploration 19.4

Fixed point iteration

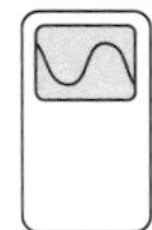

- Using the same scales on both axes plot the graphs of $y = x$ and $y = \frac{x^3 + 3}{7}$ for the domain $-5 \le x \le 5$.
- Use a combination of zoom and trace to find the coordinates of the three points of intersection, correct to three decimal places.
- What equation, of the form $f(x) = 0$, are the x-coordinates for the points of intersection the solution?

Conclusions

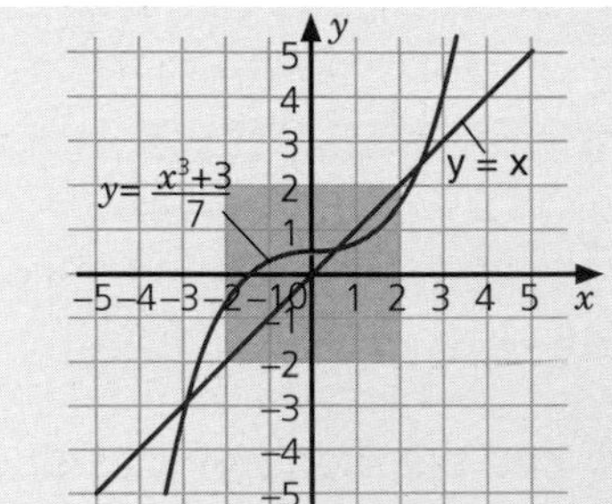

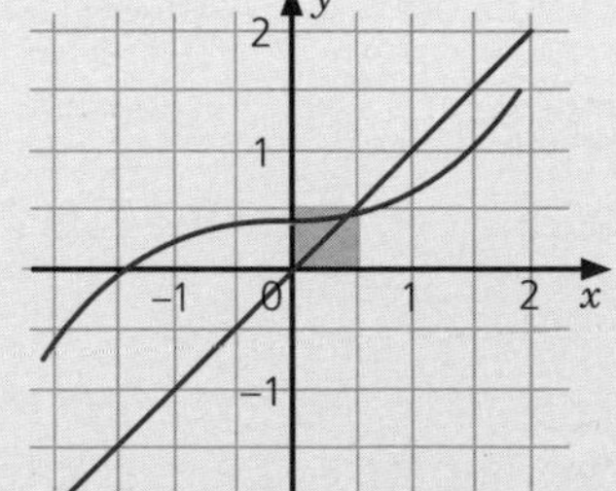

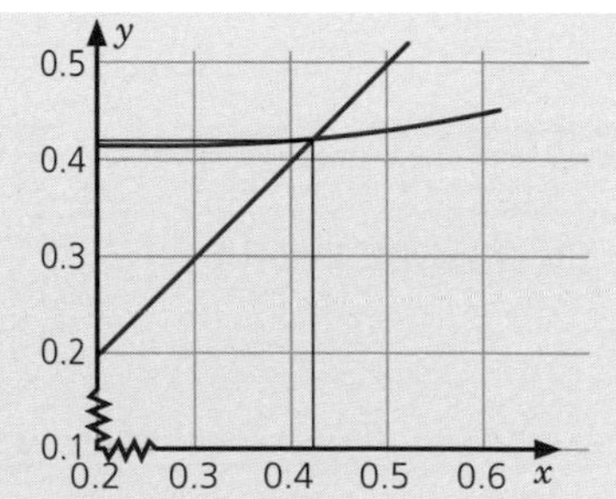

The superimposed graphs show three points of intersection.

Zooming in on the middle point of intersection reveals the coordinates as (0.441, 0.441), correct to three decimal places.

Zoom in similarly to find the lower and upper points of intersections, i.e. (−2.84, −2.84) and (2.40, 2.40).

By comparison with the results of Exploration 19.2 you will see that the x- (and y-) coordinates of the points of intersection are precisely the three roots of the equation $x^3 - 7x + 3 = 0$. This is not surprising since where our two graphs intersect, comparing right-hand sides:

$$x = \frac{x^3+3}{7} \Rightarrow 7x = x^3 + 3 \Rightarrow 0 = x^3 - 7x + 3$$

A fixed point iteration is based on rearranging an equation of the form f(x) = 0 into the form x = g(x) [in our example $g(x) = \frac{x^3+3}{7}$] and finding where the two graphs intersect.

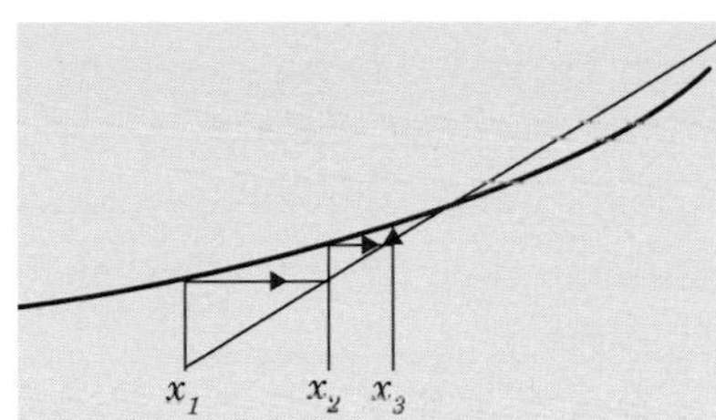

The iterative sequence for the middle root is generated as follows.

Let x_0 be a first approximation to a root of x = g(x). Then a second approximation x_1 is generated by: $x_1 = g(x_0) \quad \Rightarrow \quad x_1 = \frac{x_0^3+3}{7}$

Likewise: $x_2 = g(x_1) \quad \Rightarrow \quad x_2 = \frac{x_1^3+3}{7}$

and in general: $x_{n+1} = g(x_n) \quad \Rightarrow \quad x_{n+1} = \frac{x_n^3+3}{7}$

Let, say $x_0 = 0$, then $x_1 = \frac{0^3+3}{7} = 0.42857$ (5 d.p.)

$$\Rightarrow \quad x_2 = \frac{0.42857^3+3}{7} = 0.43982$$

$$\Rightarrow \quad x_3 = \frac{0.43982^3+3}{7} = 0.44073$$

$$\Rightarrow \quad x_4 = \frac{0.44073^3+3}{7} = 0.44080 \text{ etc.}$$

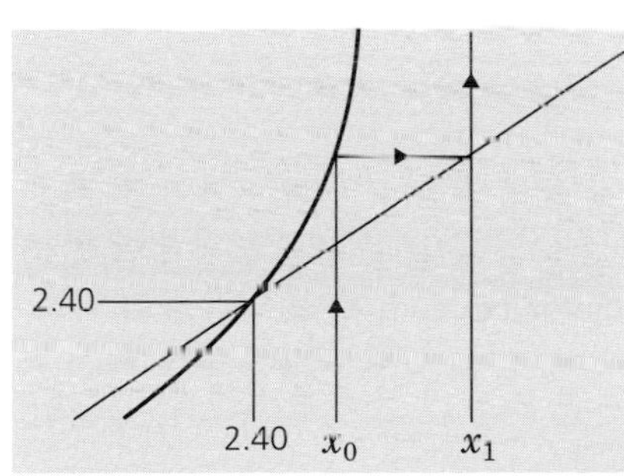

Notice that the sequence x_0, x_1, x_2, x_3, x_4 … converges towards the middle root which is 0.441 (correct to three decimal places).

Try other starting values (x_0) between say, –5 and 5.

Describe what happens to the sequence x_0, x_1, x_2, x_3, x_4 …

You should have found that any sequence x_0, x_1, x_2, x_3, x_4 … , such that x_0 lies between the lower and upper roots, converges towards the middle root. Any value for x_0 outside this range produces a divergent sequence, e.g. let $x_0 = 3$.

The convergence of the sequence x_0, x_1, x_2, x_3, x_4, … on the middle root for starting values between the lower and upper roots is based on the following idea.

A sequence of the form x_{n+1} = g (xn) will only converge on a root provided $|g'(\alpha)| < 1$, and, perhaps only for suitably chosen values for x_0.

In our example $g(x) = \frac{x^3+3}{7} \Rightarrow g'(x) = \frac{3x^2}{7}$ and for the middle root,

$\alpha \approx 0.441$, $g'(\alpha) = g'(0.441) = \frac{3 \times 0.441^2}{7} \approx 0.083$, which satisfies the condition $|g'(\alpha)| < 1$.

However, for the lower root:

$$\alpha = -2.84 \Rightarrow g'(\alpha) = g'(-2.84) = \frac{3\times(-2.84)^2}{7} \approx 3.46$$

and for the upper root:

$$\alpha = 2.40 \Rightarrow g'(\alpha) = g'(2.40) = \frac{3\times 2.40^2}{7} \approx 2.47$$

For both lower and upper roots we see that $|g'(\alpha)| > 1$, which means that the iterative sequence will not converge on either of them. Geometrically this is evident from the sequence diagram above.

To obtain the lower and upper roots of the equation, $f(x) = 0$, another rearrangement in the form $x = g(x)$ is required.

$$x^3 - 7x + 3 = 0 \quad \Rightarrow \quad x^3 = 7x - 3 \quad \Rightarrow \quad x = \sqrt[3]{7x-3}$$

which leads to the iteration:

$$x_{n+1} = \sqrt[3]{7x_n - 3}$$

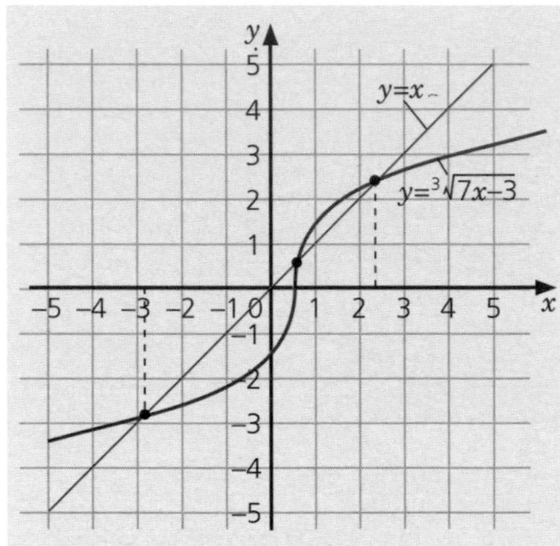

Now we can plot $y = x$ and $y = \sqrt[3]{7x-3}$ on a single graph.

Taking $x_0 = 2$ produces the iteration:

$$x_1 = \sqrt[3]{7\times 2 + 3} \qquad = 2.223\,98 \qquad \text{(5 d.p.)}$$

$$\Rightarrow \quad x_2 = \sqrt[3]{7\times 2.223\,98 + 3} = 2.324\,99$$

$$\Rightarrow \quad x_3 = \sqrt[3]{7\times 2.324\,99 + 3} = 2.367\,79$$

$$\Rightarrow \quad x_4 = \sqrt[3]{7\times 2.367\,79 + 3} = 2.385\,48$$

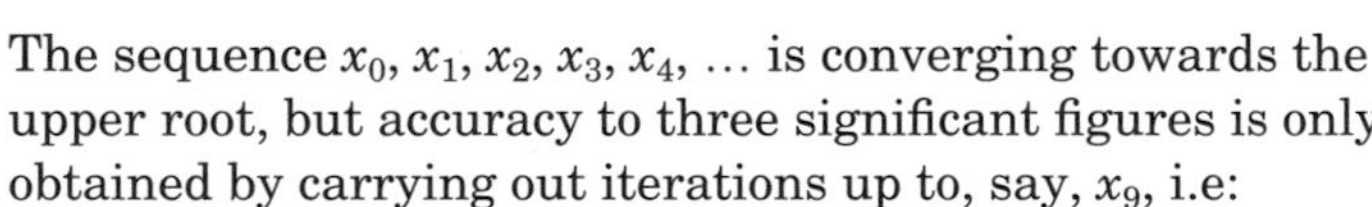

The sequence $x_0, x_1, x_2, x_3, x_4, \ldots$ is converging towards the upper root, but accuracy to three significant figures is only obtained by carrying out iterations up to, say, x_9, i.e:

$$x_8 = 2.397\,33 \qquad \text{and} \qquad x_9 = 2.397\,53$$

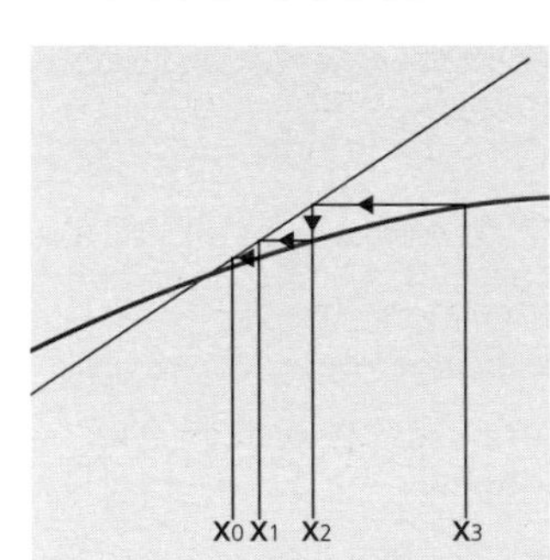

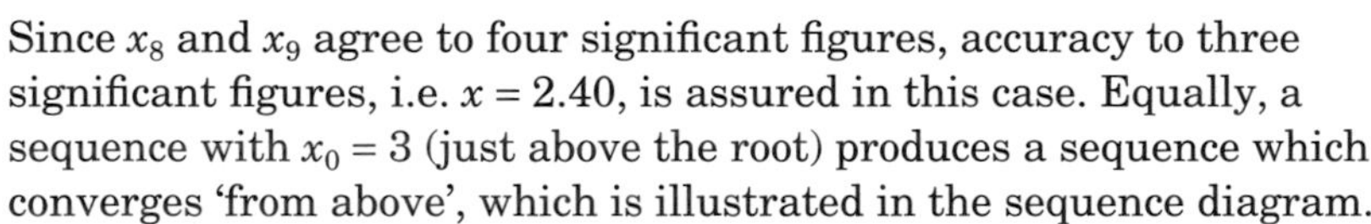

Since x_8 and x_9 agree to four significant figures, accuracy to three significant figures, i.e. $x = 2.40$, is assured in this case. Equally, a sequence with $x_0 = 3$ (just above the root) produces a sequence which converges 'from above', which is illustrated in the sequence diagram.

Using this iteration, all starting values for x_0 produce convergent sequences, either to the lower root or the upper root, depending on which side of the middle root you take for x_0.

We can see from the graphs of $y = x$ and $y = \sqrt[3]{7x-3}$ that for $\alpha = -2.84$ and $\alpha = 2.40$, $|g'(\alpha)| < 1$, since the gradient of the curve $g(x)$ is evidently less than 1 for these values of x, whereas for $\alpha = 0.441$, $|g'(\alpha)| > 1$.

Algebraically:

$$g(x) = \sqrt[3]{7x-3} = (7x-3)^{\frac{1}{3}} \quad \Rightarrow \quad g'(x) = \tfrac{1}{3}(7x-3)^{-\frac{2}{3}} \times 7 = \frac{7}{3\sqrt[3]{(7x-3)^2}}$$

$$g'(-2.84) = 0.2895 \quad g'(2.40) = 0.4056 \quad g'(0.441) = 11.88$$

Both iterative sequences we have met so far produce **staircase** sequence diagrams. A second type, the **cobweb** sequence diagram is illustrated in the following example.

Example 19.2

Find the only root of the equation $x^3 + 4x - 3 = 0$ using fixed point iteration $x_{n+1} = \dfrac{3 - x_n^3}{4}$.

Solution

The graphs of $y = x$ and $y = \dfrac{3 - x^3}{4}$ show that the root of $f(x) = 0$ lies between 0 and 1.

Taking $x_0 = 1$ as our starting value produces the iteration:

$$x_1 = \frac{3 - x_0^3}{4} = 0.5$$

$$x_2 = \frac{3 - 0.5^3}{4} = 0.718\,75$$

$$x_3 = \frac{3 - 0.718\,75^3}{4} = 0.657\,17 \text{ (5 d.p.)}$$

$$x_4 = \frac{3 - 0.657\,17^3}{4} = 0.679\,05 \text{ (5 d.p.)}$$

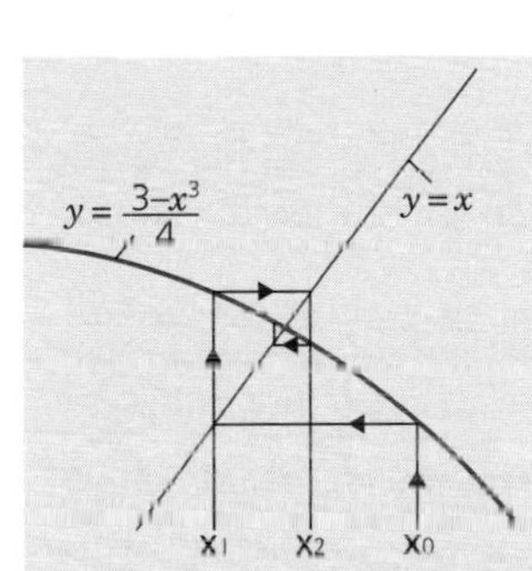

*The sequence $x_0, x_1, x_2, \ldots$ is **oscillating** and converging towards the only root if $x^3 + 4x - 3 = 0$, as illustrated in the sequence diagram.*

Check that the root is 0.674, correct to three decimal places. This is evident after ten iterations.

Taking $x_0 = 2$ also produces a convergent sequence, but taking $x_0 = 3$ produces an oscillating divergent sequence, even though $|g'(0.674)| < 1$:

$$g(x) = \frac{3 - x^3}{4} \rightarrow g'(x) = -\frac{3}{4}x^2 \rightarrow g'(0.674) = -\tfrac{3}{4} \times 0.674^2 = -0.341$$

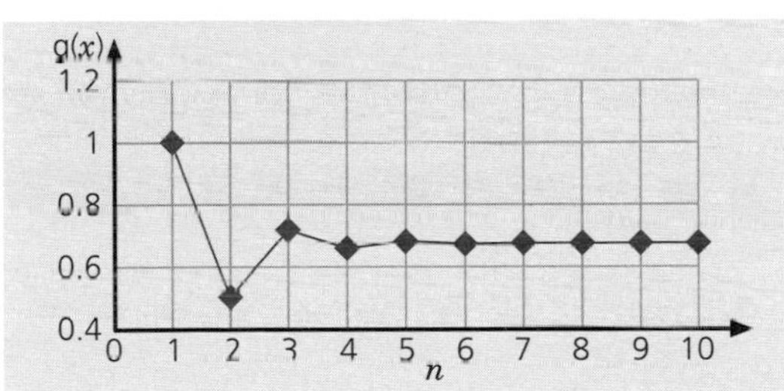

The diagram shows a spreadsheet output of the solution.

Use the flowchart to write a program for the fixed point iteration method and test it by working through the last example.

- Investigate the range of starting values x_0 for which the iteration converges.

- The interval of starting values for which the sequence converges is given by $-1.7014 \le x \le 2.1634$, working to five significant figures. Obtain the upper and lower bounds of this interval by decimal search or other simple systematic search. Can you adapt the method of interval bisection?

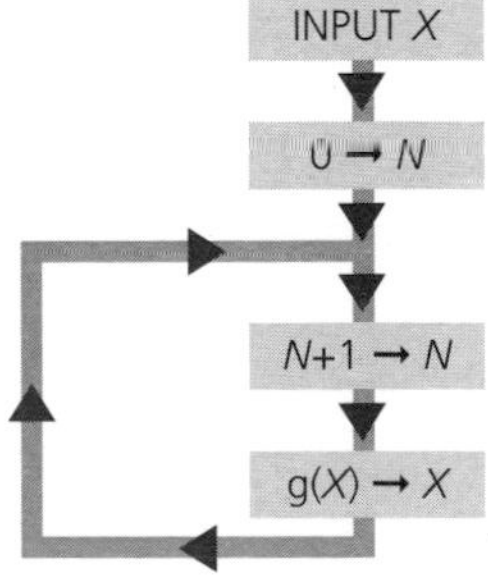

Exploration 19.5

Calculator chaos

The quadratic equation $2x^2 - x - 1 = 0$ has two rational roots: $2x^2 - x - 1 = 0 \Rightarrow (2x + 1)(x - 1) = 0 \Rightarrow x = -0.5$ or $x = 1$.

Rearranging the equation into the form $x = g(x)$ in one particular way gives $x = 2x^2 - 1$.

Now $g(x) = 2x^2 - 1 \Rightarrow g'(x) = 4x$. In particular:
$g'(-0.5) = -2$, and $g'(1) = 4$

so since $|g'(\alpha)| > 1$ for both roots, we would *not* expect a sequence converging towards either root from the iteration $x_{n+1} = 2x_n^2 - 1$.

- Use your program for fixed point iteration for various starting values x such that:

  a) $|x_0| > 1$, **b)** $|x_0| < 1$, **c)** $x_0 = \pm 0.5$ or ± 1.
- Describe the behaviour of the iteration in all three cases.

Conclusions

For values of x_0 such that $|x_0| > 1$ the sequence diverges, but for values of x_0 such that $|x_0| < 1$, apart from ± 0.5, the sequence is neither convergent nor divergent, in fact it is **chaotic**.

For $x_0 = 0.8$, the sequence continues (figures rounded to three significant figures): 0.28, –0.843, 0.422, –0.644, –0.171, –0.942, …
For $x_0 = 0.81$ the sequence continues:
0.312, –0.805, 0.296, –0.824, 0.360, –0.742, …

A slight variation in the starting value produces a completely different chaotic pattern.

- Use the iteration $x_{n+1} = axn^2 - 1$, for various values of a, to produce sequences. Examine their behaviour for various starting values, x_0, $|x_0| < 1$.
- Which range of values of a produce:
  i) divergent sequences, **ii)** convergent sequences,
  iii) chaotic sequences?

EXERCISES

19.2 CLASSWORK

1 **a)** Sketch the graph of $y = 4x^3 - x - 1$ and show that $4x^3 - x - 1 = 0$ has just one root, between 0 and 1.

b) Use the iteration: $x_{n+1} = \sqrt[3]{\dfrac{x_n + 1}{4}}$ to find the root, correct to three significant figures.

c) Illustrate your answer to **b)** using a staircase diagram.

KEY SKILLS
IT 3.2

2 **a)** Show that the equation $5x - 2e^{-x} = 0$ can be written in the form $x = 0.4e^{-x}$.

b) Use the fixed point iterative method to find, correct to three significant figures, the solution of the equation.

c) Illustrate your answer to **b)** using a cobweb diagram.

3 The equation $e^{2x} + x - 4 = 0$ has one root, between 0 and 1.

a) Show that the rearrangement $x = 4 - e^{2x}$ produces a sequence that oscillates between 4 and –2976.96, whatever value of x_0 you choose. Explain your answer graphically.

b) Show that the equation can be rearranged into the form $x = 0.5 \ln(4 - x)$ and use the iteration $xn_{+1} = 0.5 \ln(4 - x_n)$ to find the root, correct to three significant figures.

4 By choosing suitable forms for the function $g(x)$, use the fixed point iterative method to find three roots of the equation $x^3 - 3x + 1 = 0$, giving your answer correct to three significant figures.

EXERCISES

19.2 HOMEWORK

1 **a)** Sketch the graph of $y = 8 - 3x - 2x^3$.
b) Show, by differentiation, that the gradient function is always negative.
c) Use the iteration $x_{n+1} = \sqrt[3]{4 - 1.5x_n}$ to find the only root of the equation, correct to three significant figures.
d) Illustrate your answer to **c)** using a cobweb diagram.

2 **a)** Show that the equation $x^3 - 5x^2 + 7 = 0$ has a root between $x = 1$ and $x = 2$.
b) Use the iteration $x_{n+1} = \dfrac{-7}{x_n(x_n - 5)}$ to find the root, correct to three significant figures.
c) Show that the equation $x^3 - 5x^2 + 7 = 0$ has two other roots. Use suitable rearrangements in the form $x = g(x)$ to find them correct to three significant figures.

3 The function $f(x) = x^4 + x^2 - 3x + 7$ has one stationary point.
a) Using a fixed point iteration to solve a suitable cubic equation, find the coordinates of the stationary point.
b) Determine the nature of the stationary point and so sketch a graph of $y = f(x)$.

4 **a)** Show that the iteration given by:

$$x_{n+1} = \frac{1}{2}\left(x_n + \frac{a}{x_n}\right)$$

will converge towards the square root of a.
b) Use the iteration to find *both* values of $\sqrt{20}$, to three significant figures, illustrating your solutions diagramatically.

NEWTON–RAPHSON ITERATION

The two methods we have used so far produce sequences which converge to the roots of an equation $f(x) = 0$, but both involve quite a lot of repetitive work to achieve a given degree of accuracy. The Newton–Raphson iteration is based on the idea of drawing tangents to a curve in such a way that each new tangent drawn gives a closer approximation to the root.

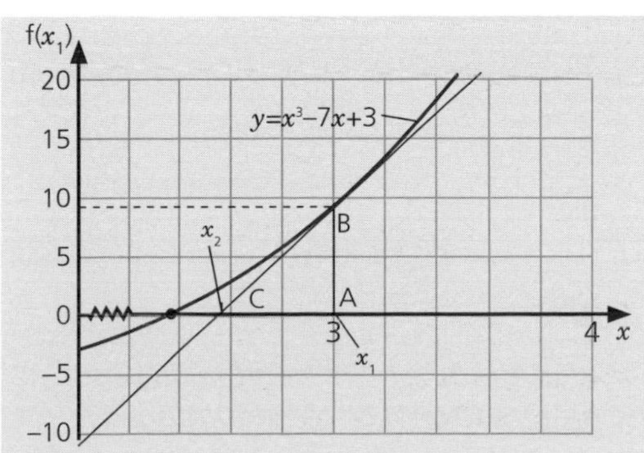

Returning to our example, let us try to find the upper root of the equation:

$f(x) = x^3 - 7x + 3 = 0$

Let $x_1 = 3$ be a first approximation to the root. Now:

$f'(x) = 3x^2 - 7 \quad \Rightarrow \quad f(3) = 3^3 - 7 \times 3 + 3 = 9$

and $\quad f'(3) = 3 \times 3^2 - 7 = 20$

Now we draw in a tangent to the graph of $y = f(x)$ at the point $(3, 9)$ with gradient 20.

The point where the tangent crosses the x-axis is the next approximation to the root, x_2. We can see that x_2 is considerably closer to the upper root than x_1. Now we repeat the process, this time drawing a tangent at $(x_2, \mathrm{f}(x_2))$ to generate x_3, and so on.

The algebraic connection between x_1 and x_2 is found by considering the gradient of the tangent in two different ways.

The gradient of the tangent through $(x_1, \mathrm{f}(x_1))$ is $\mathrm{f}'(x_1)$, but geometrically, part of the tangent BC is the hypotenuse of a right-angled triangle. We can see that the gradient of BC is given by:

$$\frac{\mathrm{AB}}{\mathrm{AC}} = \frac{\mathrm{f}(x_1)}{x_1 - x_2}$$

Equating the two expressions for the gradient of the tangent gives:

$$\mathrm{f}'(x_1) = \frac{\mathrm{f}(x_1)}{x_1 - x_2}$$

Now we can rearrange this formula to make x_2 the subject.

$$x_1 - x_2 = \frac{\mathrm{f}(x_1)}{\mathrm{f}'(x_1)} \Rightarrow x_2 = x_1 - \frac{\mathrm{f}(x_1)}{\mathrm{f}'(x_1)}$$

This leads to the general iteration formula:

$$x_{n+1} = x_n - \frac{\mathrm{f}(x_n)}{\mathrm{f}'(x_n)}, \quad n = 0, 1, 2, \ldots$$

KEY SKILLS IT 3.2

We can see how the iteration works by following through the successive approximations to the upper root of $x^3 - 7x + 3 = 0$, taking $x_o = 3$:

$$x_1 = x_0 - \frac{\mathrm{f}(x_0)}{\mathrm{f}'(x_0)} = 3 - \frac{\mathrm{f}(3)}{\mathrm{f}'(3)} = 3 - 0.45 = 2.55$$

$$x_2 = x_1 - \frac{\mathrm{f}(x_1)}{\mathrm{f}'(x_1)} = 2.55 - \frac{\mathrm{f}(2.55)}{\mathrm{f}'(2.55)} = 2.55 - 0.138\,43 = 2.411\,57$$

$$x_3 = x_2 - \frac{\mathrm{f}(x_2)}{\mathrm{f}'(x_2)} = 2.411\,57 - \frac{\mathrm{f}(2.411\,57)}{\mathrm{f}'(2.411\,57)} = 2.411\,57 - 0.013\,78 = 2.397\,80$$

$$x_4 = x_3 - \frac{\mathrm{f}(x_3)}{\mathrm{f}'(x_3)} = 2.397\,80 - \frac{\mathrm{f}(2.397\,80)}{\mathrm{f}'(2.397\,80)} = 2.397\,80 - 0.000\,13 = 2.397\,66$$

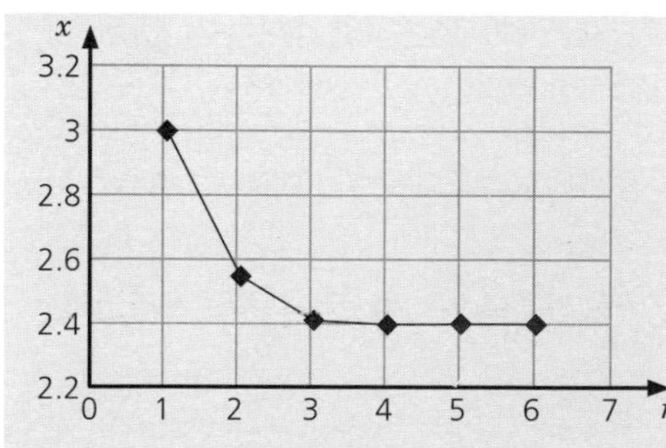

Note that the value of $\frac{\mathrm{f}(x_n)}{\mathrm{f}'(x_n)}$ is converging rapidly to 0 since f(xn) is converging rapidly to zero – which is what we want.

After just four iterations it is evident that the upper root is 2.398 correct to three decimal places.

The diagram shows a spreadsheet output of the solution.

CALCULATOR ACTIVITY

Exploration 19.6

Newton-Raphson Iteration

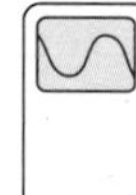

- *Use the flowchart to write a program for the Newton–Raphson iteration and use it to find all three roots of the equation* $x^3 - 7x + 3 = 0$.

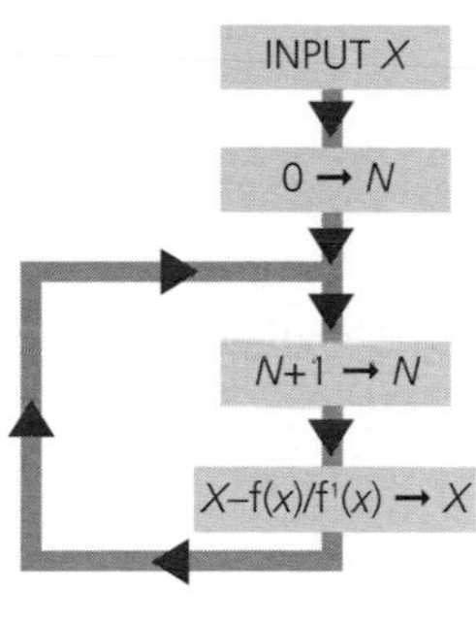

- *Does the iteration always produce a convergent sequence, whatever value of x_0 you might choose?*
- *What ranges should the initial approximation lie in so that it converges on:*
  a) *the lower root,*
  b) *the middle root,*
  c) *the upper root?*

Conclusions

The iteration will always converge for a continuous function $f(x)$, for any initial approximation x_0 (provided $f'(x_0) \neq 0$), but predicting which root will be found from a particular starting point can be difficult.

If x_0 is taken close to a root then the iteration should converge towards that root. If x_0 is taken further away then the sequence may converge towards any of the roots.

When an equation has, say, a single root but the curve $y = f(x)$ has turning points, problems can arise if an unsuitable value for x_0 is chosen. This is illustrated in the following example.

Example 19.3

A function is given by $f(x) = x^3 + 2x^2 + 3$.

a) *Sketch the graph of* $y = f(x)$ *and show that the equation* $f(x) = 0$ *has just one root in the interval* $[-3, -2]$.

b) *Use the Newton–Raphson iteration to find the root* $f(x) = 0$ *using the initial approximations:*
i) $x_0 = -3$ ***ii)*** $x_0 = -2$ ***iii)*** $x_0 = -1$.

c) *Comment on any differences you find.*

Solution

a)

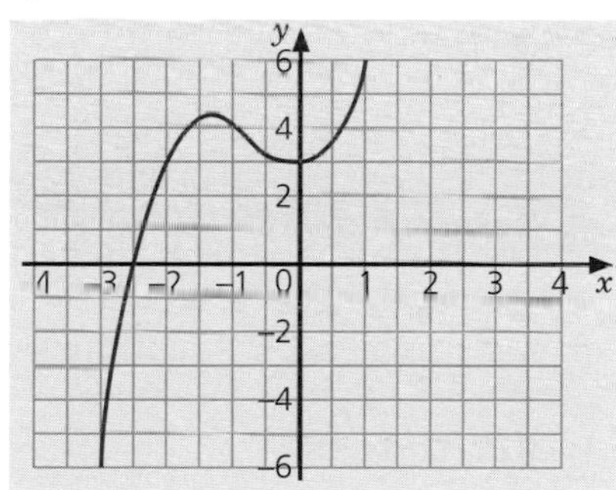

b) $f(x) = x^3 + 2x^2 + 3 \Rightarrow f'(x) = 3x^2 + 4x$

Hence the Newton–Raphson iteration is given by:

$$x_{x+1} = x_n - \frac{f(x_n)}{f'(x_n)} = x_n - \frac{x_n^3 + 2x_n^2 + 3}{3x_n^2 + 4x_n}$$

i) *Taking* $x_0 = -3$:
$x_1 = -2.6$
$x_2 = -2.493\ 117$
$x_3 = -2.485\ 620$
$x_4 = -2.485\ 584$

ii) *Taking* $x_0 = -2$
$x_1 = -2.75$
$x_2 = -2.521\ 390$
$x_3 = -2.486\ 373$
$x_4 = -2.485\ 584$

In both cases the iteration soon converges on the single root, $x = -2.49$ *(correct to three significant figures).*

iii) Taking $x_0 = -1$:

$x_1 = 3$
$x_2 = 1.769\ 231$
$x_3 = 0.870\ 588$
$x_4 = -0.028\ 574$
$x_5 = 26.808\ 238$
$x_6 = 17.659\ 140$

In this case the iteration does not seem to be converging.

c) *The critical feature here is that between the starting point* $x_0 = -1$ *and the root the curve has a turning point. The maximum point seems to act as a barrier to reaching the root. Although the behaviour of the sequence seems chaotic, it does in fact settle down eventually to converge on the root. Picking up the iteration after 47 steps gives:*

$x_{47} = 0.197\ 541$
$x_{48} = -3.203\ 746$
$x_{49} = -2.683\ 345$
$x_{50} = -2.506\ 645$
$x_{51} = -2.485\ 860$
$x_{52} = -2.485\ 584$

Provided a suitable starting point is chosen, the Newton–Raphson iteration is usually very efficient, in that convergence towards a root is quick compared with the general fixed point iteration. The following exploration reveals an interesting idea for the case of a cubic equation with three real roots.

Exploration 19.7

Newton–Raphson

- Show that cubic equation $x^3 - 2x^2 - x + 2 = 0$ has three roots, $x = -1$, 1 and 2. Apply the Newton–Raphson iteration with initial value

$$x_0 = \frac{1+2}{2} = 1.5$$

- Repeat for $x_0 = \frac{-1+2}{2} = 0.5$ and $x_0 = \frac{-1+1}{2} = 0$.
- What happens to the iteration in each case?
- Can you generalise the result?
- Does it apply to all cubic equations with three roots?

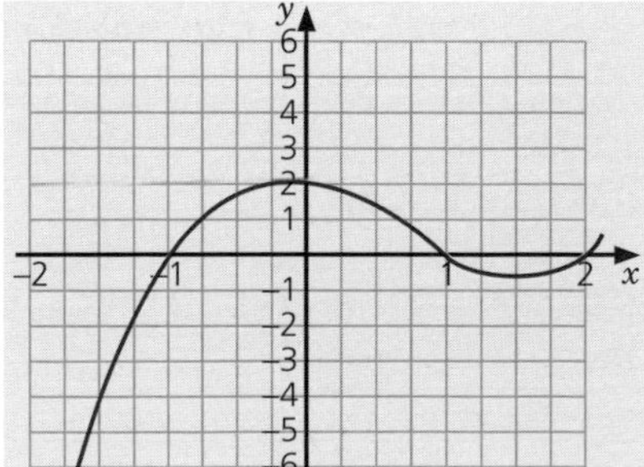

Conclusions

From the graph of $y = x^3 - 2x^2 - x + 2$ we can see that $y = 0$ when $x = -1$, 1 or 2.

Using the Newton–Raphson iteration with $x_0 = 1.5$:

$$x_1 = x_0 - \frac{\left(x_0^3 - 2x_0^2 - x_0 + 2\right)}{3x_0^2 - 4x_0 - 1} = 1.5 - \frac{(-0.625)}{-0.25} = -1$$

After one step of the iteration, $x_1 = -1$, which is the lower root. Using the iteration with $x_0 = 0.5$:

$$x_1 = x_0 - \frac{\left(x_0^3 - 2x_0^2 - x_0 + 2\right)}{3x_0^2 - 4x_0 - 1} = 0.5 - \frac{1.125}{-2.25} = 1$$

Using the iteration with $x_0 = 0$:

$$x_1 = x_0 - \frac{\left(x_0^3 - 2x_0^2 - x_0 + 2\right)}{3x_0^2 - 4x_0 - 1} = 0 - \frac{2}{-1} = 2$$

By starting the iteration at the mid-point of the middle and upper roots, we find the lower root in one step. Similarly, by taking x_1 as the mid-point of the lower and upper roots, we find the middle root in one step, etc.

To generalise, if a and b are any two of three roots, then taking $x_0 = \frac{a+b}{2}$ gives $x_1 = c$.

The method does seem to apply to any cubic equation with three distinct roots.

EXERCISES

19.3 CLASSWORK

For questions **1–5**, study the function $f(x)$ and then:

a) sketch the graph of $y = f(x)$,

b) using suitable initial approximation(s) find the root(s) of $f(x) = 0$, correct to three significant figures,

c) illustrate the method on your graph.

1 $f(x) = 4x^3 - 7x + 5$

2 $f(x) = 4x^3 - 7x + 1$

3 $f(x) = 5x^4 - 2x^3 - 9x^2 - 4x + 1$

4 $f(x) = 5 - x^2 - e^x$

5 $f(x) = \ln x - x^2 + 10$

6 **a)** Sketch the graph of $y = e^x - x - 4$.

b) Explain why the equation $e^x - x + 4$ has two roots.

c) Use the Newton–Raphson iteration to find the roots correct to three significant figures.

d) Why does the Newton–Raphson iteration break down if you take $x_0 = 0$?

7 By applying the Newton–Raphson iteration to the function $f(x) = 1 - \frac{a}{x^2}$ develop an iterative formula for calculating $\sqrt{a}$.
Confirm your iteration by finding $\sqrt{10}$ correct to three significant figures.

8 Use the Newton–Raphson iteration to find all stationary points on the graph of $y = x^4 + 2x^3 - 5x^2 - 3x$.
Illustrate your answer with a sketch.

9 Let $f(x) = xe^x - 1 - x$.

a) Sketch a graph of $y = f(x)$.

b) Find the positive root of the equation $f(x) = 0$, correct to three significant figures, taking initial approximation $x_0 = 1$:

i) using the fixed point iteration with $f(x) = \ln\left(1 + \frac{1}{x}\right)$,

ii) using the Newton–Raphson iteration.

c) Compare the efficiency of the two methods in **b)**.

EXERCISES

19.3 HOMEWORK

For questions **1–5**, study the function $f(x)$ and then:

a) sketch the graph of $y = f(x)$,

b) using suitable initial approximation(s) find the root(s) of $f(x) = 0$, correct to three significant figures,

c) illustrate the method on your graph.

1 $f(x) = 10 - 6x + 3x^2 - x^3$

2 $f(x) = 10 + 6x - 3x^2 - x^3$

3 $f(x) = 3x^4 + 3x^3 + 5x - 1$

4 $f(x) = x^5 + 4x^2 - 2$

5 $f(x) = 2^x - 3x - 4$

6 **a)** Sketch the graph of $y = x - 1 + \dfrac{4}{x^2}$.

b) Use the Newton–Raphson iteration to find the only root of the equation $x + \dfrac{4}{x^2} = 1$, with $x_0 = -1$.

c) What problems are encountered by taking:

i) $x_0 = 2$ **ii)** $x_0 > 0, x_0 \neq 2$?

7 By applying the Newton–Raphson iteration to the function $f(x) = 1 - \dfrac{a}{x^3}$, develop on iterative formula for calculating $\sqrt[3]{a}$.

Confirm your iteration by finding $\sqrt[3]{10}$ correct to three significant figures.

8 Use the Newton–Raphson iteration to find all stationary points on the graph of $y = e^x - x^3$.
Illustrate your answer with a sketch.

9 Let $f(x) = \dfrac{2x}{e^x} + 3$.

a) Sketch a graph of $y = f(x)$.

b) Find the negative root of the equation $f(x) = 0$, correct to three significant figures, taking initial approximation $x_0 = -1$:

i) using the fixed point iteration with $g(x) = -1.5e^x$,

ii) using the Newton–Raphson iteration.

c) Compare the efficiency of the two methods in **b)**.

THE TRAPEZIUM RULE

In chapters 8, 11 and 18 we have seen how to evaluate definite integrals analytically using known integrals

e.g. $\int_0^1 e^{2x}dx = \left[\frac{1}{2}e^{2x}\right]_0^1 = \int_0^1 \frac{1}{2}e^2 - \frac{1}{2}e^0 = \frac{1}{2}(e^2 - 1)$.

However, there are many definite integrals for which an analytic solution cannot be found. For example the definite integral $\int_a^b e^{-x^2}dx$ is important in statistics but we cannot find a known function for the indefinite integral $\int e^{-x^2}dx$.

In the first part of chapter 8, we found areas under straight line graphs by finding the area of a trapezium. Here we look at how trapezia may be used to estimate the area under a curve and hence to approximate the value of definite integrals.

Exploration 19.8 *Curves and trapezia*

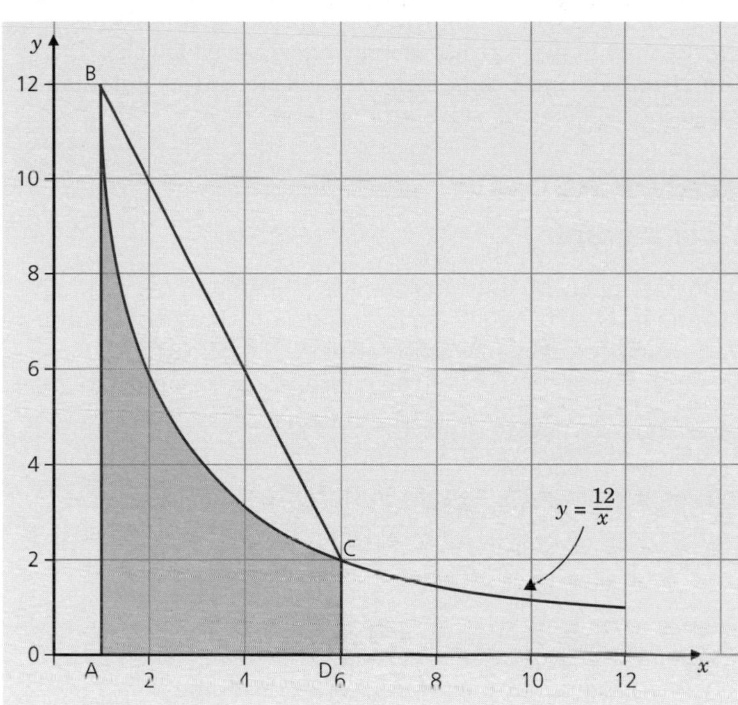

The diagram shows part of the graph of $y = \frac{12}{x}$.

- Estimate the area of the shaded region.
- Find the area of trapezium ABCD.
- Does this over- or under-estimate the shaded area?
- Instead of using one trapezium of width 5 units, use five trapezia of width 1 unit to estimate the area of the shaded region.
- Is this a better estimate? Is it good enough?
  How can you tell? How could you improve it further?

Fitting trapezia to the curve

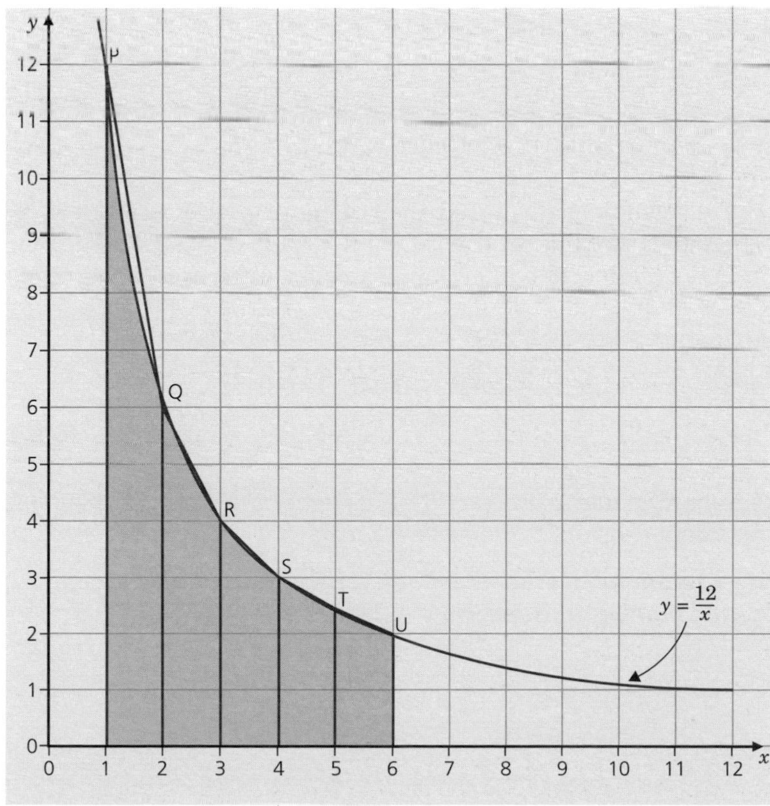

The area of trapezium ABCD = $\frac{1}{2}\times(12+2)\times 5 = 35$ units^2. This is an *over estimate* of the shaded area, with the unshaded area between the graph and the trapezium representing the error.

By using more but narrower trapezia the error may be reduced. Five trapezia, each of width 1 unit, are illustrated on the next diagram.
The chords PQ, QR, RS, ST, TU are a much closer fit to the curve than the chord BC.
Areas of the five trapezia are:

$\frac{1}{2}(12+6)\times 1$	=	9.0
$\frac{1}{2}(6+4)\times 1$	=	5.0
$\frac{1}{2}(4+3)\times 1$	=	3.5
$\frac{1}{2}(3+2.4)\times 1$	=	2.7
$\frac{1}{2}(2.4+2)\times 1$	=	2.2
Total	=	22.4

The value of 22.4 is still an over-estimate of the shaded area, but looks a much better approximation than 35 units^2. The error could be further reduced by considering even more, but even narrower, trapezia, e.g. ten trapezia, each of width 0.5 unit. The process of estimating the area under a graph using trapezia is called the **trapezium rule**. Like most numerical methods it may be automated, as illustrated in the following calculator activity.

KEY SKILLS
IT 3.2

CALCULATOR ACTIVITY

Exploration 19.9

Area under a graph

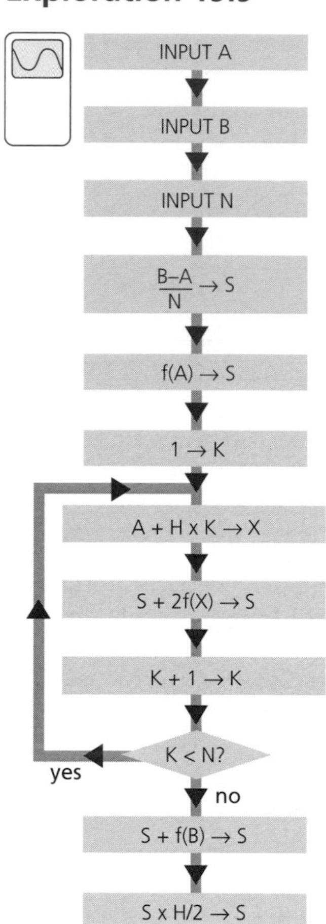

This program (left) may be used to estimate the area under a graph by splitting the interval $a \le x \le b$ into n trapezia. Values for a, b and n are entered from the keyboard using stores A, B and N. The calculator automatically works out the width of each trapezium, h as $\frac{b-a}{n}$, e.g. $a = 1, b = 6, n = 10$ gives $h = \frac{6-1}{10} = 0.5$.

Before you run the program, be sure to store the function $\frac{12}{x}$ as function f.

Confirm the result above by letting $A = 1, B = 6$ and $N = 5$.

- Run the program again with the same values for A and B, but $N = 10, 20, 50, 100$. Note the 'area' found for each value of N.
- Are you able to say what the area is, correct to three significant figures?

Checking the results

Results you should get are:

N	10	20	50	100
Area (6 s.f.)	21.7385	21.5615	21.5108	21.5035

This would seem to confirm that the true area = 21.5 correct to 3 s.f. The true area, correct to 6 s.f., is 21.5011. Check the following percentages errors in the approximations for different values of N.

N	10	20	50	100
% error	1.104	0.281	0.045	0.011

Example 19.4

Use the trapezium rule to estimate the area under the graph of $y = \frac{4}{1+x^2}$ *over the interval* $0 \le x \le 1$ *using five trapezia.*

Use the program to investigate what happens to the area as you increase the number of trapezia.

Solution

If $a = 0$, $b = 1$ *and* $n = 5$, *then* $h = \dfrac{b-a}{n} = 0.2$.

A table of function values gives:

x	0	0.2	0.4	0.6	0.8	1.0
y	4	3.8462	3.4483	2.9412	2.4390	2

Areas of the five trapezia are:

$$\begin{aligned}
&\tfrac{1}{2}(4+3.8462)\times 0.2 &&= 0.78462\\
&\tfrac{1}{2}(3.8462+3.4483)\times 0.2 &&= 0.72945\\
&\tfrac{1}{2}(3.4483+2.9412)\times 0.2 &&= 0.63895\\
&\tfrac{1}{2}(2.9412+2.4390)\times 0.2 &&= 0.53802\\
&\tfrac{1}{2}(2.4390+2)\times 0.2 &&= 0.44390\\
&\textit{Total} &&= 3.13494
\end{aligned}$$

The approximate area, using five trapezia, is 3.135 (3 d.p.)
Using the program with five trapezia will verify this result.
Increasing the number of trapezia gives, for example:

N	10	20	50	100
Area (6 s.f.)	3.13993	3.14118	3.14153	3.14158

The exact area is π *(3.141 59...), so you can see that with many, narrow trapezia a very good approximation is possible.*

Example 19.5

Use the trapexium method to estimate the value of $\int_0^1 e^{-x^2}dx$ *using five trapezia giving the answer to 2 d.p.*

Solution

The shaded region shows the area under the graph of $y = e^{-x^2}$ *that represent* $\int_0^1 e^{-x^2}dx$

To estimate the value of the definitie integral we estimate the area using trapezia. Consider five trapezia of width 0.2.

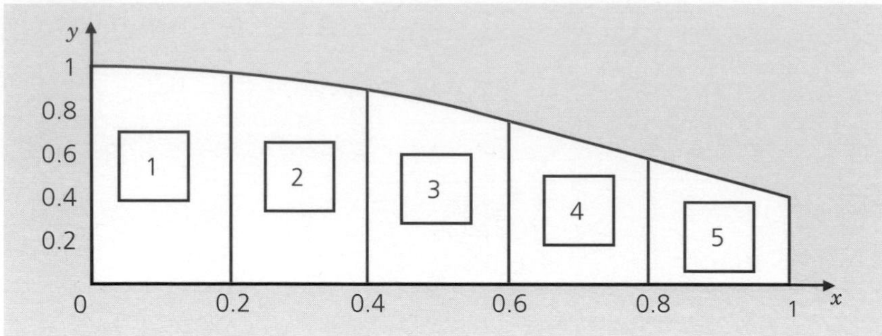

The areas of the five trapezia are:

1 $\frac{1}{2} \times 0.2 \times (e^{-0.2^2} + e^{0^2}) = 0.196$

2 $\frac{1}{2} \times 0.2 \times (e^{-0.4^2} + e^{-0.2^2}) = 0.181$

3 $\frac{1}{2} \times 0.2 \times (e^{-0.6^2} + e^{-0.4^2}) = 0.155$

4 $\frac{1}{2} \times 0.2 \times (e^{-0.8^2} + e^{-0.6^2}) = 0.122$

5 $\frac{1}{2} \times 0.2 \times (e^{-1^2} + e^{-0.8^2}) = 0.090$

Summing these gives 0.74 to 2 d.p. and an estimate to $\int_0^1 e^{-x^2}dx$ *using the trapezium method is 0.74.*

From the examples we can deduce a formula for estimating the values of $\int_a^b f(x)dx$ using the trapezium method with n trapezia of width h, where $h = \frac{(b-a)}{n}$.

$$\text{Estimate of} \int_a^b f(x)dx = \frac{1}{2} \times h \times [f(a) + 2f(a+h) + \dots + f(b)]$$

$$= \frac{1}{2} \times h \times [f(a) + f(b) + 2\sum_{i=1}^{i=n-1} f(a+ih)]$$

As the number of trapezia increases, with the width of each one decreasing, the sum of the areas will more closely approximate the required area.

Example 19.6

Use the trapezium method to estimate the value of $\int_{-0.5}^{1.5} \frac{1}{1+x^3}\,dx$ correct to 3 d.p.

Solution

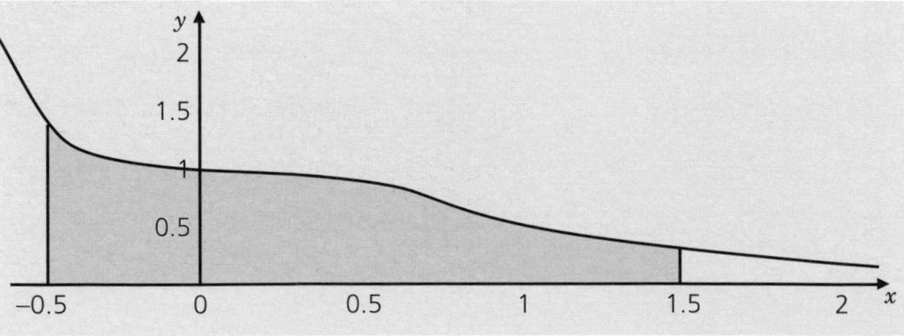

Suppose that we begin with five trapezia of width $h = 0.4$ then the estimate for the value of the definite integral is:

$\frac{1}{2} \times 0.4 \times [f(-0.5) + f(1.5) + 2(f(-0.1) + f(0.3) + f(0.7) + f(1.1))] = 1.53361$

with $f(x) = \frac{1}{1+x^3}$.

The following table shows the results as we increase the number of trapezia.

Number of trapezia	Width of trapezia	Estimate for integral
5	0.4	1.53361
10	0.2	1.52817
20	0.1	1.52666
40	0.05	1.52627
80	0.025	1.52617

We see that the last two estimates are correct to three decimal places and so we conclude that $\int_{-0.5}^{1.5} \frac{1}{1+x^3}dx = 1.526$ correct to 3 d.p.

EXERCISES

19.4 CLASSWORK

1 Use the trapezium rule, with the number of trapezia indicated in brackets, to estimate the following integrals. Illustrate each answer with a sketch.

a) $\int_0^3 x^2 dx$ (6) **b)** $\int_0^1 \frac{1}{1+x}dx$ (5)

c) $\int_{-1}^1 2^x dx$ (4) **d)** $\int_0^1 e^{x^2} dx$ (6)

2 A circle is drawn, radius 2 units, centre (0,0).
A point P is chosen at random on the circumference. It has coordinates (x, y).

a) Use Pythagoras' theroem to show that $x^2 + y^2 = 4$.
b) Rearrange the equation in **a)** in the form $y = \ldots$ and sketch its graph over the interval $-2 \le x \le 2$.
c) Use the trapezium rule, with four trapezia, to estimate the area under the curve in **b)** over the interval $0 \le x \le 2$.
d) Use the program to see what happens as you increase the number of trapezia (e.g. 10, 50, or even 100).
e) What is the significance of your result in **d)**?

3 A function $f(x)$ is given in tabular form as

x	1.8	2.0	2.2	2.4	2.6	2.8	3.0	3.2	3.4
$f(x)$	6.050	7.389	9.025	11.023	13.464	16.445	20.086	24.533	29.964

Use the trapezium rule to estimate the integral $\int_{1.8}^{3.4} f(x)dx$ with $h = 0.2$.

19.4 HOMEWORK

1 Use the trapezium rule, with the number of trapezia indicated in brackets, to estimate the following areas. Illustrate each answer with a sketch.

a) $\int_0^4 x^3 \mathrm{d}x$ (6) **b)** $\int_0^1 \frac{1}{x^2+1} \mathrm{d}x$ (5)

c) $\int_0^1 10^x \mathrm{d}x$ (4) **d)** $\int_{-3}^{3} (x-1)(x-2) \mathrm{d}x$ (6)

2 The velocity of a decelerating car is recorded each second in the following table.

t	0	1	2	3	4	5	6	7	8	9	10
v	20	12.13	7.36	4.46	2.71	1.64	1.00	0.60	0.37	0.22	0.13

Estimate the distance travelled in the 10 seconds, using the trapezium rule.

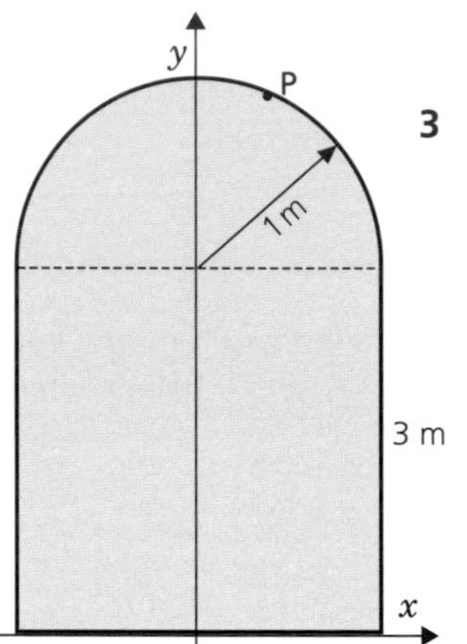

3 A Norman arched window is in the form of a semi-circle of radius 1 m, above a rectangle of height 3 m, as shown in the diagram.

a) Write down the exact area of the window.
b) Use your calculator to find this area correct to 3 s.f.
c) Taking the origin and axes as shown, use Pythagoras' theorem to show show that, for points such as P:
$y = 3 + \sqrt{1 - x^2}$
d) Use the trapezium rule with four trapezia to estimate the area of the window.
e) Use the computer program (page 410) to investigate how many trapezia would be necessary to give accuracy to 3 s.f.

MATHEMATICAL MODELLING ACTIVITY

Problem statement

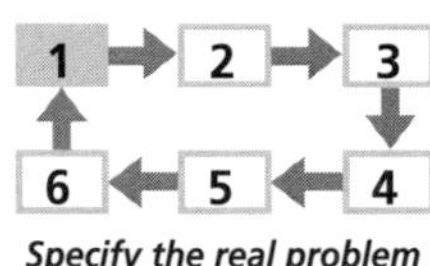

Specify the real problem

An investor is considering a manufacturing project which requires an investment of £10 000 now. She anticipates net returns of £5000 after years 1 and 2, £3000 after year 3 and £1000 after year 4. Should the investor go ahead with the project or not?

Set up a model

1 → 2 → 3 → 4 → 5 → 6

Set up a model

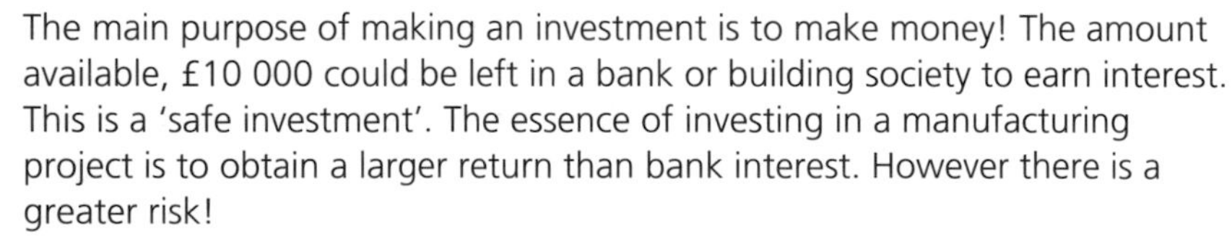

The main purpose of making an investment is to make money! The amount available, £10 000 could be left in a bank or building society to earn interest. This is a 'safe investment'. The essence of investing in a manufacturing project is to obtain a larger return than bank interest. However there is a greater risk!

The important variables are:
- the investment,
- the net returns,
- bank or building society interest rate.

In the problem we will investigate this risk by calculating the loss of the investment and interest and the gain from the anticipated net returns and interest over the five year period.

We make the following assumptions:

- the net returns are guaranteed,
- the net returns are invested in a bank,
- the interest rate over the five year period is constant.

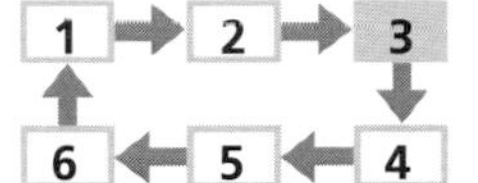

Formulate the mathematical problem

Mathematical problem

The capital available of £10 000 would be worth:

$$L = £10\,000\left(1+\frac{r}{100}\right)^4$$

if invested in a bank at a constant interest rate of r per cent. This is the total amount 'lost' if the investment goes ahead.
You should confirm that the total return plus interest is:

$$I = £5000\left(1+\frac{r}{100}\right)^3 + 5000\left(1+\frac{r}{100}\right)^2 + 3000\left(1+\frac{r}{100}\right) + 1000\,.$$

This is the total income if the investment goes ahead and the net returns are obtained.
The 'profit' on the investment is: $P = I - L$

and if $P > 0$ we would recommend that the person goes ahead with the investment.
The mathematical problem is to find the value of r for $P = 0$. This is the critical case, if r is less than this critical value then $P > 0$.

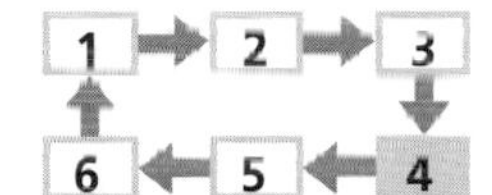

Solve the mathematical problem

Mathematical solution

If we let $1+\frac{r}{100} = x$ and $P = \text{f}(x)$ then:

$\text{f}(x) = 5000x^3 + 5000x^2 + 3000x + 1000 - 10\,000x^4$
and we must find x such that $\text{f}(x) = 0$.
Using the Newton–Raphson method:

$$x_{n+1} = x_n - \frac{\text{f}(x_n)}{\text{f}'(x_n)} = x_n - \frac{\left(5x_n^{\ 3} + 5x_n^{\ 2} + 3x_n + 1 - 10x_n^{\ 4}\right)}{\left(15x_n^{\ 2} + 10x_n + 3 - 40x_n^{\ 3}\right)}$$

choose $x_0 = 1$ (i.e. $r = 0$) for the starting value.

The first five iterations give:

$x_1 = 1.3333 \quad x_2 = 1.2202 \quad x_3 = 1.1923 \quad x_4 = 1.1907 \quad x_5 = 1.1907$

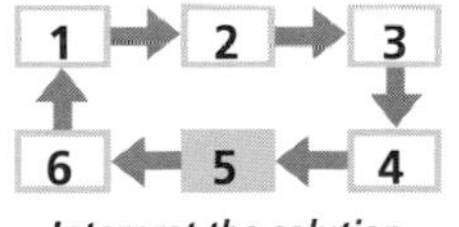

Interpret the solution

Interpretation

When $x = 1.1907$ the profit function is zero. Since $x = 1+\frac{r}{100}$ the critical interest rate is 19.07 per cent.
The graph of P against x shows that if $0 < r < 19.07$ the investment will make a profit. For example, for a constant interest rate of five per cent over the four year period the profit would be £3296.
Since bank interest rates to an investor are likely to be less than 19 per cent, the investment of £10 000 is recommended.

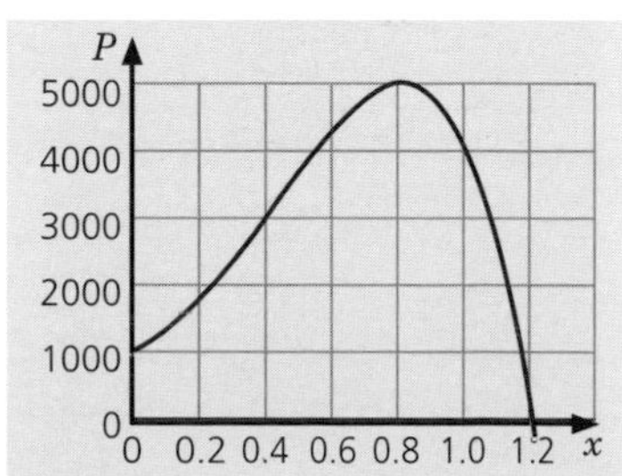

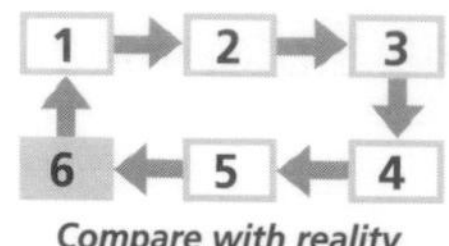

Refinement of the model

Give a brief criticism of the model. Investigate the effect of changing the assumptions and the amount of the net returns.

CONSOLIDATION EXERCISES FOR CHAPTER 19

1 By sketching the graphs of $y = 1 + \sin x$ and $y = x$, verify that the equation $x = 1 + \sin x$ has exactly one root.

Taking a suitable integer as first approximation, use an iterative method to find the value of this root correct to three decimal places. Explain how you can be confident that your result is accurate to three decimal places.

(Oxford Question 8, Specimen Paper P4, 1994)

2 Show that the equation $x^3 - x^2 - 2 = 0$ has a root α which lies between 1 and 2.

a) Using 1.5 as a first approximation for α, use the Newton–Raphson method once to obtain a second approximation for α, giving your answer to three decimal places.

b) Show that the equation $x^3 - x^2 - 2 = 0$ can be arranged in the form

$x = \sqrt[3]{f(x)}$ where $f(x)$ is a quadratic function.

Use an iteration of the form $x_{n+1} = g(x_n)$ based on this rearrangement and with $x_1 = 1.5$ to find x_2 and x_3, giving your answers to three decimal places.

(AEB Question 11, Specimen Paper 1, 1994)

3 The chord AB of a circle subtends an angle θ radians at the centre O of the circle, as shown in the diagram. Find an expression for the shaded area, in terms of r and θ. Given that this shaded area is $\frac{1}{6}$ of the area of the circle, show that θ is given by:

$$\sin\theta = \theta - \frac{\pi}{3}.$$

A B r θ O

By sketching the graphs of $y = \sin\theta$ and $y = \theta - \frac{\pi}{3}$ on the same diagram, verify that $\theta = 2$ is an approximate solution of the equation $\sin\theta = \theta - \frac{\pi}{3}$. Find a better approximation for θ using one application of Newton's approximation.

(NEAB Question 9, Specimen Paper 2, 1994)

4 On a single diagram, sketch the graphs of $y = \ln(10x)$ and $y = \frac{6}{x}$, and explain how you can deduce that the equation $\ln(10x) = \frac{6}{x}$ has exactly one real root.

Given that the root is close to 2, use the iteration:

$$x_{n+1} = \frac{6}{\ln(10x_n)}$$

to evaluate the root correct to three decimal places.

The same equation may be written in the form $x\ln(10x) - 6 = 0$. Taking $f(x)$ to be $x\ln(10x) - 6$, find $f'(x)$, and show that the Newton-Raphson iteration for the root of $f(x) = 0$ may be simplified to the form:

$$x_{n+1} = \frac{x_n + 6}{1 + \ln(10x_n)}.$$

Starting with initial approximation 2, it takes nine iterations using:

$$x_{n+1} = \frac{6}{\ln(10x_n)}$$

before successive iterates agree to six decimal places. Find how many iterations are needed to achieve this degree of accuracy using the Newton–Raphson method with the same initial value.

(UCLES Linear Question 15, Specimen Paper 1, 1994)

5 Use the Newton–Raphson method, with initial approximation 14, to find, correct to two decimal places, the positive root of the equation $x = 5\ln(x + 2)$.

(UCLES (Modular) Question 3, Specimen Paper 4, 1994)

6 Mavis wants to buy a computer originally advertised at £400, so she starts to do a paper round. She puts a fixed amount of her earnings each week into a savings account, which with interest produces **total** savings after t weeks of approximately £2500($e^{0.002t} - 1$).
Meanwhile the price of the computer drops by an average of £2 a week. Find whether she will have saved enough to buy the computer after 50 weeks.
Now take the formula for her savings to be exact, and assume that the price falls by exactly £2 a week. Find an equation for the number of weeks she will need to work before she has enough money to buy the computer. Show that this equation can be put into the form:
$t = a\ln(b - ct)$
where a, b, c are numbers. By carrying out five steps of the iteration:
$t_{n+1} = a\ln(b - ct_n)$
starting with the first approximation $t_0 = 50$, find the solution of this equation, rounding up your answer to the next highest integer.

(Oxford & Cambridge Question 3, Specimen Paper 2, 1994)

7 A sketch graph of $y = x^2 + px + q$ is shown. The vertex of the graph is at $(2, -3)$.

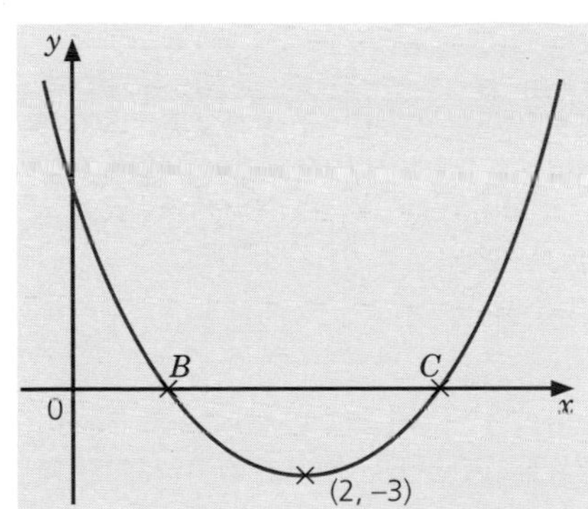

a) Find p and q. Hence calculate the x-coordinates of the points B and C.

b) Draw a sketch graph to show that the equation

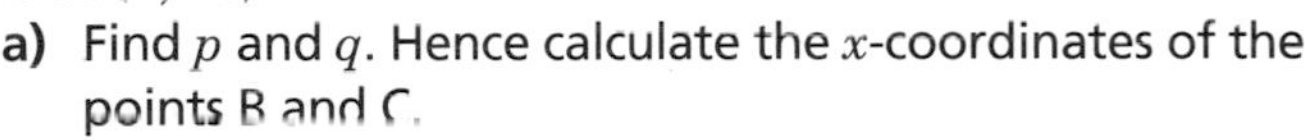

$x^2 + px + q = \sqrt{x}$ has two solutions.

c) Use the iterative formula: $x_{n+1} = \frac{1}{4}\left(x_n^2 - \sqrt{x_n} + 1\right)$

and a start value of 0.2 to find the smaller of the two roots correct to two decimal places, showing all intermediate values.

(SMP 16–19 (Pure with Applications) Question 10, June 1994)

8 An iterative sequence is defined by: $x_{n+1} = \frac{2x_n^3 + a}{3x_n^2}$ $(n = 0, 1, 2, \ldots)$

where $a > 0$.

a) Assuming that x_n tends to a limit L as $n \to \infty$, show that $L = \sqrt[3]{a}$.

b) **Use this result** to find $\sqrt[3]{3}$ correct to three decimal places, showing your working carefully.

(WJEC Question 4, Specimen Paper A1, 1994)

9 $f(x) = e^{0.8x} - \dfrac{1}{3-2x}, x \neq \dfrac{3}{2}$.

a) Show that the equation $f(x) = 0$ can be written as $x = 1.5 - 0.5e^{-0.8x}$.

b) Use the iteration formula $x_{n+1} = 1.5 - 0.5e^{-0.8x_n}$, with $x_0 = 1.3$, to obtain x_1, x_2 and x_3. Give the value of x_3, an approximation to a root of $f(x) = 0$, to 3 decimal places.

c) Show that the equation $f(x) = 0$ can be written in the form $x = p\ 1n(3 - 2x)$, stating the value of p.

d) Use the iteration formula $x_{n+1} = p\ 1n(3 - 2x_n)$ with $x_0 = -2.6$ and the value of p found in part **c)**, to obtain x_1, x_2 and x_3. Give the value of x_3, an approximation to the second root of $f(x) = 0$, to 3 decimal places.

(EDEXCEL, Question 7, Paper 2, January 2000)

10 **a)** Show that the equation $2^{1-x} = 4x + 1$ can be arranged in the form $x = \dfrac{1}{2}(2^{-x}) + q$, stating the value of the constant q.

b) Using the iteration formula $x_{n+1} = \dfrac{1}{2}(2^{-x_n}) + q$, $x_0 = 0.2$, with the value of q found in part **a)**, find x_1, x_2, x_3 and x_4. Give the value of x_4 to 4 decimal places.

(EDEXCEL, Question 2, Paper 2, June 1999)

11

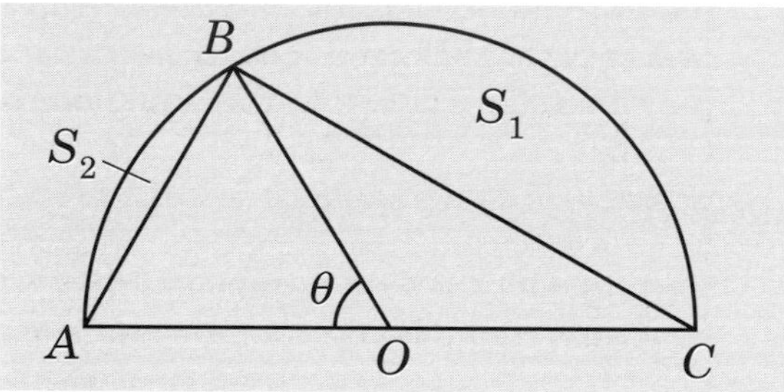

The diagram shows a semicircle ABC on AC as diameter. The midpoint of AC is O, and angle AOB = θ radians, where $0 < \theta < \frac{1}{2}\pi$. The area of the segment S_1, bounded by the chord BC is twice the area of the segment S_2, bounded by the chord AB. Show that $3\theta = \pi + \sin\theta$.

Use an iterative method, based on the rearrangement $\theta = \frac{1}{3}(\pi + \sin\theta)$, together with a suitable starting value, to find θ correct to 3 decimal places. You should show the value of each approximation that you calculate.

(OCR, Question 6, Specimen Paper 2, 2000)

Summary

■ **Interval bisection**

For a continuous function f and interval $[a, b] = a \leq x \leq b$, if $f(a)$ and $f(b)$ have opposite signs, then $f(x) = 0$ for some x in this interval.

Let $c = \dfrac{(a+b)}{2}$.

If $f(a)$ and $f(c)$ have opposite signs, let $c = b$ otherwise let $c = a$.
Repeat until the interval $[a, b]$ containing a root of the equation is narrow enough to give the desired accuracy.

■ **Fixed point iteration**

To solve $f(x) = 0$, rearrange into the form $x = g(x)$.

The iteration: $x_{n+1} = g(x_n)$ $n = 0, 1, 2, \ldots$

generates a convergent sequence towards a root α provided $|g'(\alpha)| < 1$ and initial approximation x_0 is close to α.

■ **Newton–Raphson iteration**

To solve $f(x) = 0$, find $f'(x)$ and use the iteration:

$$x_{n+1} = x_n - \frac{f(x_n)}{f'(x_n)} \qquad n = 0, 1, 2, \ldots$$

which generates a convergent sequence towards a root α provided the initial approximation x_0 is close to α.

Trapezium rule

■ Approximate a region under a graph representing an integral by a number of trapezia, each with equal width.

■ The sum of the areas of the trapezia is an approximation to the required integral.

■ As the number of trapezia increases, with the width of each one decreasing, the sum of the areas will more closely approximate the required area.

Mechanics and the real world

- *Mechanics is the study of structures and objects that remain at rest or move.*
- *Real situations are often very complex and simplifications need to be made to allow solutions to be found to them.*
- *Mathematical modelling is the process of using mathematics to solve real problems.*

WHAT IS MECHANICS?

The world around us is full of examples of the applications of mechanics. Whenever anything moves the laws of mechanics describe its motion and what is needed to cause and maintain that motion.

The study of mechanics in the context of objects that move is called **dynamics**. Some examples of problems in dynamics that you will be able to solve by the time you reach the end of this book are:

KEY SKILLS
C 3.1a

- How fast can a car go round a bend without spinning out of control?
- How long a piece of elastic should a bungee jumper use?
- How fast will a parachutist be moving when she hits the ground?
- How far will the chairs on a chairoplane ride swing out?
- How fast must the cars on a roller coaster travel to get through a corkscrew?

When someone sits on a chair it is important that the legs are strong enough to support them. When a structure such as a suspension bridge is built it is important that the towers and cables can support the deck and the traffic it carries. It is often necessary to make predictions about the strengths of structures that remain at rest. The study of mechanics in this context is known as **statics**.

Take a few moments to identify some examples of mechanics that you meet in your own life and classify them as examples of dynamics or statics.

Exploration 20.1

Mechanics in action

This diagram below shows a cut-away picture of a car.

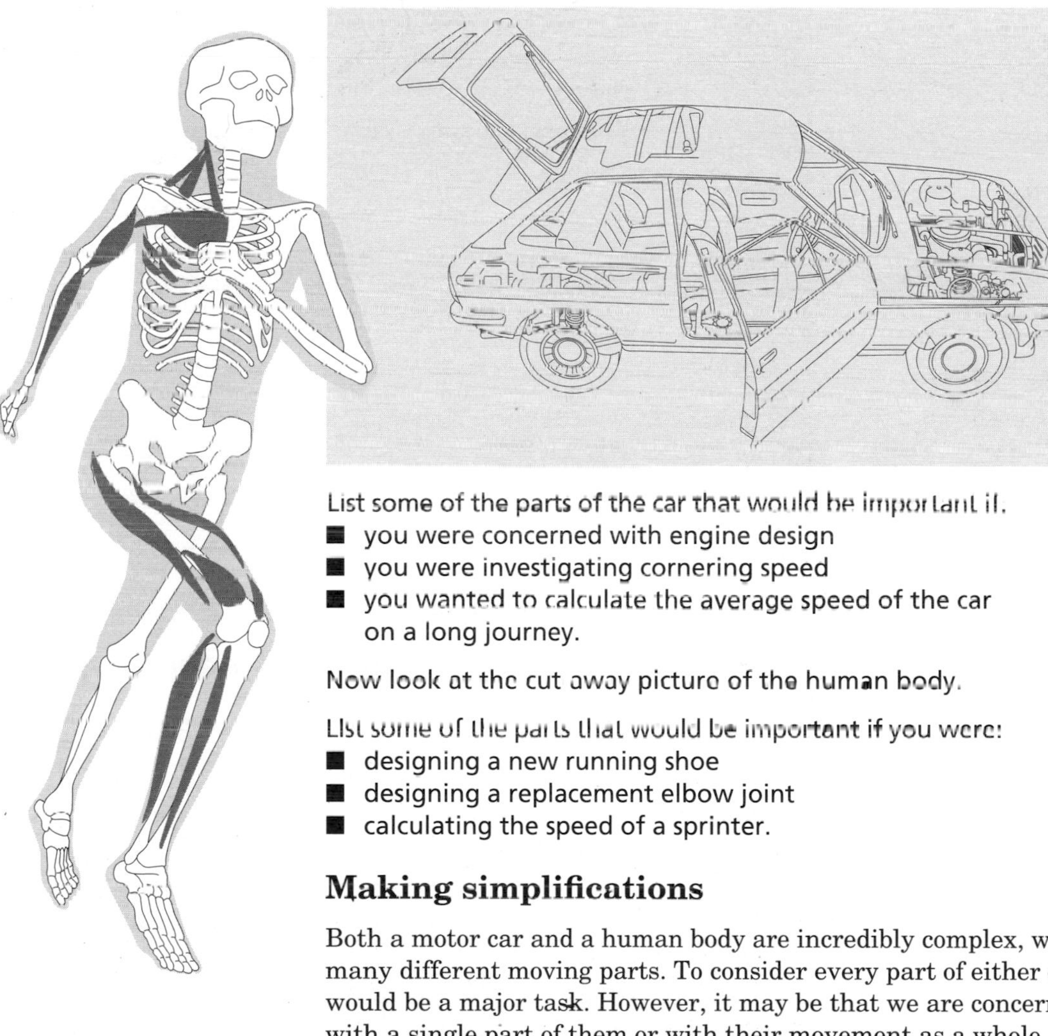

List some of the parts of the car that would be important if:

- you were concerned with engine design
- you were investigating cornering speed
- you wanted to calculate the average speed of the car on a long journey.

Now look at the cut away picture of the human body.

List some of the parts that would be important if you were:

- designing a new running shoe
- designing a replacement elbow joint
- calculating the speed of a sprinter.

Making simplifications

Both a motor car and a human body are incredibly complex, with many different moving parts. To consider every part of either of them would be a major task. However, it may be that we are concerned only with a single part of them or with their movement as a whole.

In mechanics it is often useful to make simplifications, so that solutions can be obtained to problems that otherwise would be too sophisticated to solve.

When describing the motion of a car we can consider it as a point moving along a line or curve, very much like an aircraft seen on a radar screen. We know how it is moving, but assume that it is at a single point or it is a particle, ignoring its size and the complex motions within it.

When describing the motion of a sprinter we may think of the sprinter as a point or particle that moves along a straight line, ignoring the motion of the arms, legs and internal structures.

In mechanics it is often very useful to assume that objects are points that have some of the same characteristics as the object, such as mass and speed, but ignore other characteristics such as rotation, size and the movement of internal parts. This process is an early stage of **mathematical modelling**, and is often described as using a **particle model**. When using a particle model it is important to be aware of the assumptions that have been made and whether or not there are other factors that should be taken into account.

Term	Meaning
Particle	A point mass or body that has mass, but no size.
Rigid body	A body that has shape and size, but that cannot change.
Rod	The most simple rigid body is a rod that has length but no thickness or depth.
Lamina	A sheet or surface that has zero or negligible thickness.
Uniform	This term is often used to describe a rod or lamina, that has exactly the same composition throughout, so that its density or other properties do not vary.
Light	Has no or negligible mass.
Inextensible	Cannot be stretched, usually used in the context of a string.
Smooth	No friction in this situation
Rough	Friction acts in this situation

MATHEMATICAL MODELLING

Mathematical modelling is the process by which real situations can be described mathematically and thereby problems can be solved. The process contains a number of phases or stages which are shown on the diagram.

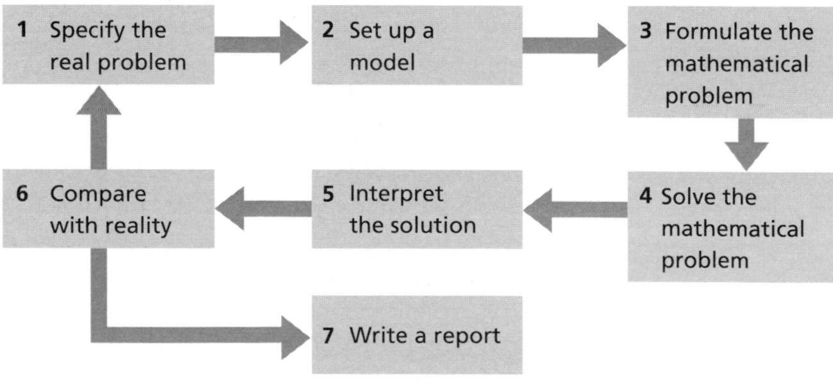

Each of these stages is now discussed briefly to give an overview of the whole process.

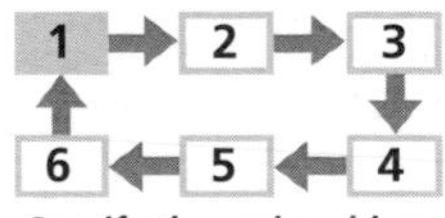

Specify the real problem

1 Problem statement

It is important to decide exactly what problem is to be solved. A clear ***problem statement*** can be an important first step if we are asked to tackle a vague problem that is not well defined.

Set up a model

2 Set up a model

This is a transfer from the problem statement to a model of that situation that can be analysed mathematically. Involved in this may be making a list of all the features that could or should be taken into account and then using this to specify a set of assumptions or simplifications to create a model of the situation. This model then provides a simplified situation from which to formulate and solve a mathematical problem.

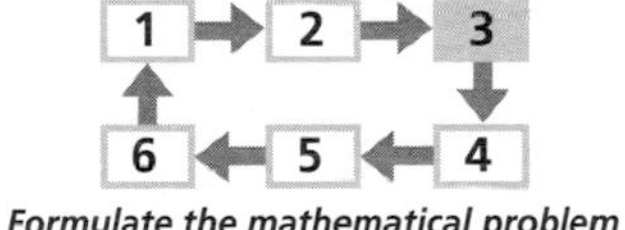

Formulate the mathematical problem

3 Formulate a mathematical problem

Once a simplified situation has been established it is necessary to define a mathematical problem to solve. This will consist of a highly specified mathematical problem, very much like the sort of problems that you will find in a student text book exercise.

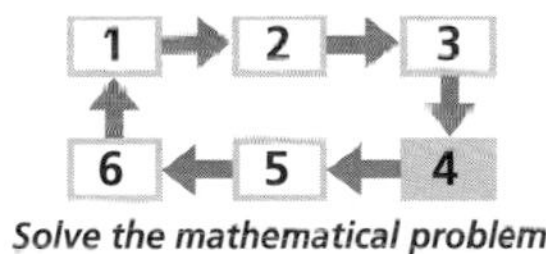

Solve the mathematical problem

4 Mathematical solution

At this stage mathematical techniques are used to solve the mathematical problem defined at the previous stage. In this book you will learn a number of techniques for solving problems that involve mechanics.

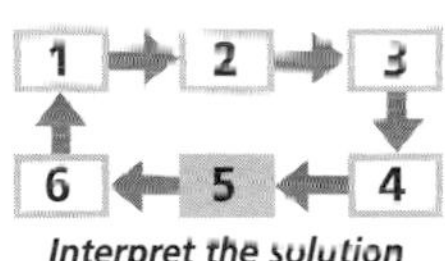

Interpret the solution

5 Interpretation

It is important to return to the original situation and interpret the solution in that context. It may well be that the original problem leads to a solution that is either impossible or unsafe, for example, or that the solution is quite reasonable.

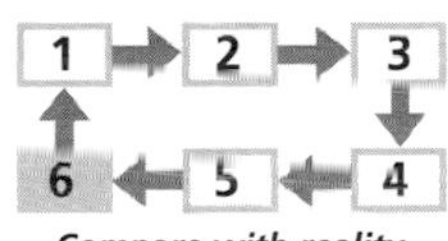

Compare with reality

6 Compare with reality

This stage develops naturally from the interpretation of the solution. Whenever predictions have been made it is important to try to validate them in some way. This can often be done by comparison with real situations Sometimes an experiment can be used to do this.

The comparison will either confirm that the solutions are reasonable or throw some doubt on their value. In the latter case, it is necessary to return to the original problem and modify the assumptions, so that a better outcome is produced. Repeating the modelling cycle in this way is called refining the model.

7 Report

Once a model that produces good solutions has been established, then the modelling process is completed with a report on the findings.

In this chapter you have begun to think about the first two stages of this process. As you study further you will learn how to solve different types of mathematical problems and to interpret the results. Almost all of the chapters contain a mathematical modelling activity that will help you to develop the sort of skills that you need if you are to apply the mechanics that you learn to real life problems. The following exercises help you to begin to think about making assumptions that form an essential part of the mathematical modelling process.

EXERCISES

20.1 CLASSWORK

1 A car can be modelled as a particle. State whether or not this is a reasonable assumption for each problem given below and if not state what other factors may need to be considered.
  a) Deciding how fast a car can go round a bend.
  b) Deciding how far apart to put sleeping policemen.
  c) Calculating the average speed for a long journey.
  d) Designing a car park.

2 Identify three sporting activities where it is:
  a) acceptable to model the athletes as particles,
  b) not acceptable to model the athletes as particles.

3 The Earth rotates about its axis. Is this factor important when considering:
  a) the orbit of the Earth round the sun,
  b) a child on a swing in the park,
  c) the launch of a space shuttle?

4 Select some objects that move and decide whether it is reasonable to model them as particles.
Give some different examples of situations where this model may not be reasonable.

5 Make a list of the features that you would consider when deciding whether or not to install a pedestrian crossing.

EXERCISES

20.1 HOMEWORK

1 A football could be modelled as a particle. Decide if this is an appropriate assumption for each situation described below.
  a) Predicting the speed at which it should be kicked to travel 20 m before bouncing.
  b) Deciding if the ball will go into the goal.
  c) Deciding how to kick it, so that it swerves past a line of defenders and into the goal.
  d) When describing its position on a football pitch.

2 When objects are modelled as particles, any rotation of the object as it moves is ignored. For example if a football is modelled as a particle, the rotation as it rolls is ignored.
  a) Give three examples where the rotation of an object can be ignored, because its effects are likely to be insignificant.
  b) Give three examples where the rotation of an object is important and should not be ignored.

3 The child on the swing shown here is to be modelled as a particle. Discuss what the position of the particle should be on the diagram.

4 A motorcycle could be modelled as a particle. Is this assumption appropriate when:

a) calculating the maximum speed at which to round a bend,
b) trying to predict the top speed on a straight road,
c) estimating the difference in top speeds for riders in upright or prone positions?

5 Make a list of the features that you think should be taken into account when trying to predict the maximum height that could be attained in a high jump contest.

Summary

After working through this chapter you should:

- be aware of the need to make simplifications
- be aware of some of the advantages and disadvantages of the particle model
- have had an introduction to mathematical modelling.

Force

- *A force can cause a change in the motion of an object.*
- *There are many different types of force. The most common examples are explored in this chapter.*

INTRODUCTION TO FORCE

Exploration 21.1

What do we understand by 'force'?

The word force is often used in an everyday sense, but has a more precise scientific meaning. What do you understand by the word force?

Consider the questions below, bearing in mind your answers to the question above.

- If you drop a ball, gravity exerts a downward force on the ball. What happens to the ball? What is the effect of this force?
- You apply the brakes on a bicycle that you are riding. The result of this action is a backward force. What is the effect of this force?
- A tennis ball is travelling towards you, and you hit it with a racquet. The racquet exerts a force on the ball. What is the effect of this force?
- You are travelling on a well-oiled skateboard on a level surface. What happens to your speed? Why? In a perfect environment how far would the skateboard move before stopping?

The effect of forces

The effect of a single force is to change the motion of an object. It can cause it to start moving, stop moving, change speed or change direction. If no force acts the motion of an object will not change, it will either stay still or move at a constant speed in a straight line for ever! Newton formally stated this in his **first law**:

> *Any body will remain at rest or move at constant speed in a straight line unless acted on by a force.*

Balanced or unbalanced forces

In reality there will be more than one force acting on any object and so we must consider the combined effect of these forces. In some cases the forces will balance each other out, so that the motion of the object will not change. In other cases the forces will not balance each other out, there will be an overall or resultant force, and so there will be a change in motion.

Example 21.1

A parachutist falls with an open parachute. Choose a suitable model and decide if the forces acting are in balance when:

a) *the parachute has just been opened,*
b) *terminal speed has been reached.*

Solution

The picture shows a parachutist and parachute. They can be modelled as a particle with two forces acting on it: gravity downwards and air resistance upwards.

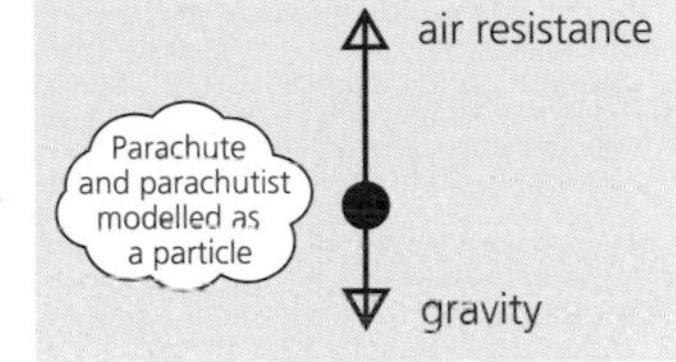

a) *When the parachute is first opened the parachutist starts to lose speed, and so the overall force must be upwards. This is illustrated in the diagram where the air resistance force is greater, so the resultant force is upwards.*

b) *At a later stage the parachute and parachutist are moving at a constant (terminal) speed, so the forces are in balance. This is shown in the diagram where both forces cancel each other out.*

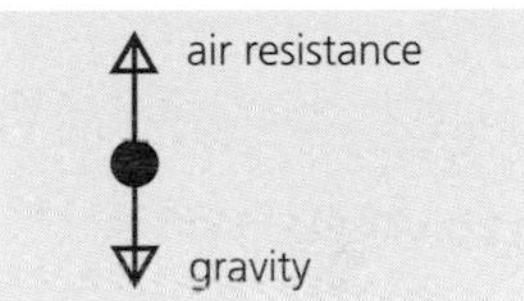

Example 21.2

A car travels along a straight horizontal road. Are the forces on the car balanced or unbalanced? What happens if it goes round a bend?

Car modelled as a particle

Solution

Consider now the forces acting on a car as it moves along a straight horizontal road. If we think of the car as a particle this is much easier. Whatever the motion, gravity will always pull down on the car and this will be balanced by upward forces on the wheels, so that the vertical forces are in balance.

upward force

gravity

Vertical forces in balance

If the car is moving forward there will also be resistance forces acting to try to slow down the car. If the car is gaining speed the forward force must be greater than the resistance forces, so the overall or resultant force is forwards.

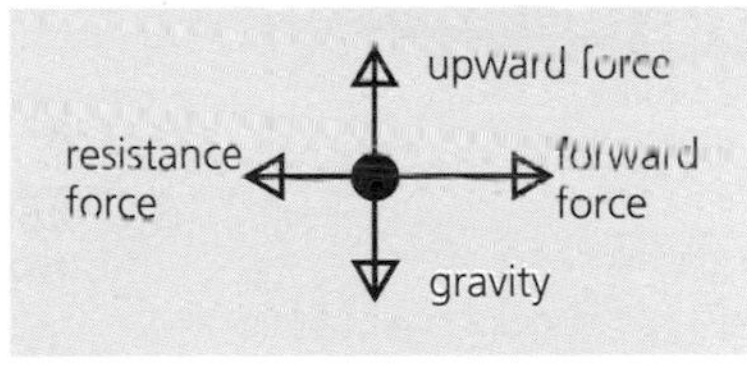

Car gaining speed

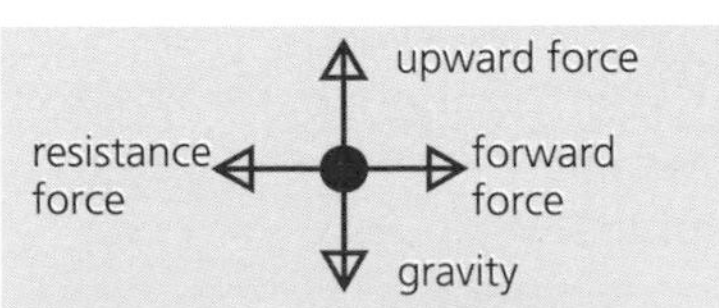

Car at constant speed

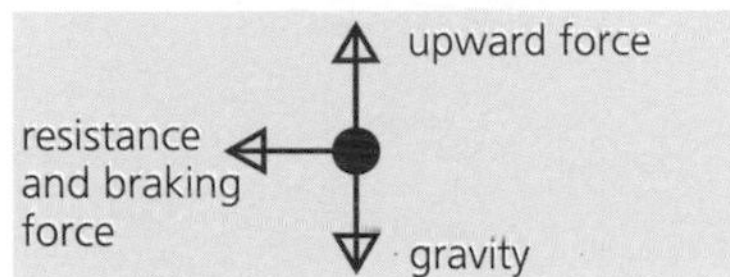

Car slowing down

If the car is moving at a constant speed such as when cruising at its top speed, then as the motion is constant, the forces on the car must be in balance.

If the car driver applies the brakes, then the forward force will be removed and a large backward force will act. Note that even though the force acts backwards the car continues to move forward until it stops.

If the car changes direction as it moves, for example as it goes round a bend, then there must also be a sideways force acting on the car to cause the change in motion.

EXERCISES

21.1 CLASSWORK

1 For each situation described below state whether or not the forces acting are in balance.
  a) A book resting on a table in a train that is travelling at constant speed along a straight set of tracks.
  b) A mass that is moving up and down on the end of a spring.
  c) A pendulum in a clock as it swings.
  d) A car going round a roundabout at a constant speed.
  e) A skateboard travelling down a slope at a constant speed.
  f) A stone falling through a fluid at its terminal speed.
  g) A bouncing ball while it is in contact with the ground.

2 Describe situations where each of the following are true.
  a) The forces acting on a moving object are in balance.
  b) The resultant force on an object acts in the direction in which it is moving.
  c) The resultant force on an object acts in the opposite direction to which it is moving.
  d) There is a force acting at an angle to the path of the object.

3 A cyclist free wheels down a hill.
  a) Describe what happens to his speed.
  b) Describe what happens to the resultant or overall force on him.

EXERCISES

21.1 HOMEWORK

1 For each situation described below, decide if the forces acting are in equilibrium.
  a) A sail boarder travelling at a constant speed in a straight line on a smooth lake.
  b) A water-skier describing an arc of a circle.
  c) A sledge travelling at a constant speed down a slope.
  d) The Earth as it orbits the sun.
  e) A bungee jumper, when she reaches her lowest position.
  f) A cup of coffee on a table in a train moving at a constant speed in a straight line up a hill.
  g) A car parked on a hill.

2 For each example below, describe when or under what conditions the forces acting could be in equilibrium.
  a) A crate on the back of a lorry.
  b) A bungee jumper.
  c) An ice puck that is sliding on ice.
  d) A diver ascending from the sea bottom.

3 A pebble is dropped into a deep pool of water.
  a) What happens to the speed of the pebble?
  b) What happens to the resultant force on the pebble?

4 Repeat question 3 for a car that freewheels to rest.

GRAVITY ON EARTH

Gravity is a force that the Earth exerts on all objects. On Earth the magnitude of this force is given by mg, where m is the mass in kilograms and g is a constant known as the **acceleration due to gravity**. On Earth g has the value of approximately $9.8\,\text{m s}^{-2}$. In fact the value of g does have slightly different values at different places, but in this book we shall take g as $9.8\,\text{m s}^{-2}$. The force of gravity always acts towards the centre of the Earth.

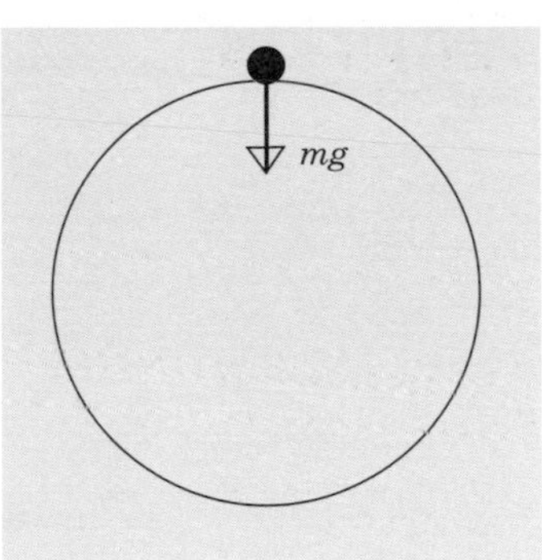

Example 21.3

Calculate the magnitude of the force of gravity on:

a) *a crate of mass 55 kg,* ***b)*** *a car of mass 1.2 tonnes.*
Illustrate these forces on a suitable diagram.

Solution

a) *Force of gravity given by* $mg = 55 \times 9.8 = 539$ *N*

b) *Note 1 tonne = 1000 kg.*
So $mg = 1200 \times 9.8 = 11\,760$ *N*

$mg = 539$ N

$mg = 11760$ N

The units of force are newtons, denoted by N. These forces are illustrated in the diagrams. Note that the force has been assumed to act at the centre of each object.

Note on weight

The force on a body exerted by gravity is often referred to as **weight**. In everyday language, weight and mass are often confused or interchanged. For example people may talk about the weight of a person being 66 kg, when they mean that their mass is 66 kg. Their weight is $66 \times 9.8 = 646.8$ N.

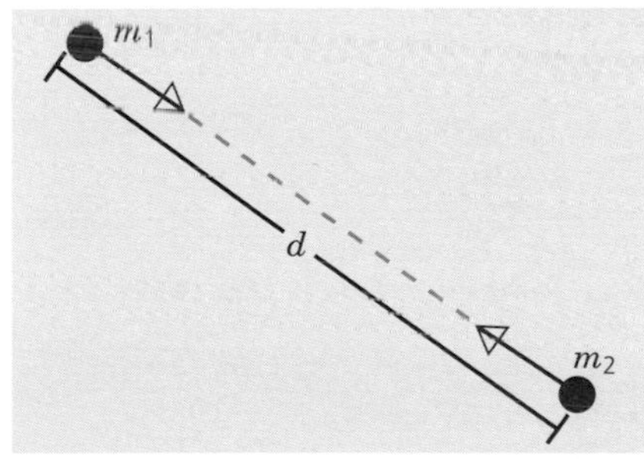

The universal law of gravitation

There is always a force of gravitational attraction between any two objects. For example there will be gravitational attraction between any two people, but fortunately the magnitude of this attraction is small enough to be insignificant. There are strong gravitational forces between the sun and other planets in the solar system. Without these forces the planets would not continue in their orbits.

Newton formulated a **law of universal gravitation**, based on his observations of the motion of the planets. This law states that the force of attraction between any two objects is: $\dfrac{Gm_1m_2}{d^2}$

where m_1 and m_2 are the masses of the objects, in kilograms, d is the distance between their centres, in metres, and G is a constant which has a value $6.67 \times 10^{-11}\,\text{kg}^{-1}\,\text{m}^3\,\text{s}^{-2}$.

Note that forces act on both objects as shown and both have the same magnitude.

Example 21.4

Use the data given below to calculate the force that the sun exerts on the Earth.

Mass of Earth $= 5.98 \times 10^{24}$ *kg*
Mass of sun $= 1.99 \times 10^{30}$ *kg*

Average distance between Earth and sun $= 1.47 \times 10^{10}$ *m*

Solution
The force is calculated using:

$$\frac{Gm_1m_2}{d^2} = \frac{6.67\times10^{-11}\times5.98\times10^{24}\times1.99\times10^{30}}{\left(1.47\times10^{10}\right)^2} = 3.67\times10^{24}\ N$$

Example 21.5

Use the universal law of gravitation and the data below to find the value of g on the moon.

Radius of moon $= 1.73 \times 10^{6}$ *m*
Mass of moon $= 7.38 \times 10^{22}$ *kg*

Solution
Consider a particle of mass M on the surface of the moon. Then the force acting on this mass is given by:

$$\frac{Gm_1m_2}{d^2} = \frac{6.67\times10^{-11}\times7.38\times10^{22}\times M}{\left(1.73\times10^{6}\right)^2} = 1.6M$$

As the particle has mass M, then the acceleration due to gravity is 1.6 m s^{-2} correct to 2 significant figures.

EXERCISES

21.2 CLASSWORK

Questions marked * involve the universal law of gravitation.
You will need to refer to the data in the worked examples for some questions.

1 Calculate the magnitude of the force of gravity on each object below and illustrate these forces on a diagram:
a) a box of mass 25 kg,
b) a table tennis ball of mass 3 grams,
c) a van of mass 1.8 tonnes.

2 The force exerted on a car by gravity is 8820 N. What is the mass of the car?

3 Estimate the size of the force that gravity exerts on:
a) a tennis ball, **b)** an elephant, **c)** a bicycle.

KEY SKILLS
N 3.2a
N 3.2d

4 Two objects of different masses are released together and allowed to fall. Does the mass of the objects affect the time that they take to fall? Try a simple experiment to confirm your answer.

5 On the moon the acceleration due to gravity is 1.6 m s^{-2}. Find the force of gravity exerted by the moon on an astronaut of mass 65 kg.

*6 Determine the magnitude of the gravitational attraction between a man of mass 70 kg and a woman of mass 60 kg if they are 1 m apart.

*7 The radius of the planet Venus is 4.59×10^6 m and it has a mass of 4.78×10^{24} kg. Find the value of g on the planet.

*8 Calculate the gravitational force that a person of mass 75 kg would experience when standing on the surface of the planet Mars. The mass of Mars is 6.55×10^{23} kg and the radius is 3.36×10^6 m.

*9 The distance between the centres of the Earth and the moon is 3.84×10^8 m. A spaceship wants to position itself so that the force of gravity of the moon exactly balances the force of gravity of the Earth. How far should the ship position itself from the centre of the Earth?

EXERCISES

21.2 HOMEWORK

Questions marked * involve the universal law of gravitation.
You will need to refer to the data in the worked examples for some questions.

1 Calculate the magnitude of the force of gravity acting on each object below and illustrate the forces on a diagram:
a) a student of mass 68 kg,
b) a letter of mass 50 grams,
c) a train of mass 200 tonnes.

2 As a ball falls, it experiences a force of 2.8 N, due to gravity. What is the mass of the ball?

3 Estimate the magnitude of the force that gravity exerts on:
a) a copy of this book, **b)** a horse, **c)** a tennis racquet.

4 Two similar objects of different masses are held at the same height and released together. What differences would you notice if this experiment were done on both Earth and the moon and the results were compared?

5 An astronaut of mass 74 kg steps onto a planet where $g = 5.2\ \mathrm{m\ s^{-2}}$. Find the force that gravity exerts on the astronaut.

6 A space probe of mass 200 kg lands on an unexplored planet. The probe's sensor detects that a force due to gravity of 3000 N is acting on the probe. Find the acceleration due to gravity on this planet.

*7 An astronaut of mass 68 kg is standing on a planet of radius 4×10^8 m. If the force of gravity on the astronaut is 500 N, find the mass of the planet.

*8 A satellite of mass 700 kg is placed into orbit at a height of 8×10^7 m above the surface of the Earth. The radius of the Earth is 6.37×10^6 m. Find the force that gravity exerts on the satellite.

*9 It is estimated that an unexplored planet has twice the mass of the Earth and that its radius is 1.8 times bigger. What would be the value of g on this planet?

CONTACT FORCES

Normal reaction

Think about a book resting on a shelf. Gravity exerts a **downward** force on the book, but the shelf exerts an **upward** force on it, to balance the force due to gravity.

The upward force is at right angles to the surface of the shelf and is called the **normal reaction** force, usually labelled R on diagrams.

The book also exerts a downward force on the shelf. This force has the same size or **magnitude** as the normal reaction, R, but acts in the opposite direction.

Example 21.6

Three boxes, each of mass 5 kg, are stacked one on top of another. Draw a diagram to show the forces acting on each box and find the magnitude of each force.

Solution

Start with the top box and work down. The forces on the top box are gravity and a normal reaction R_1. The force of gravity is 49 N and to balance this R_1 must be 49 N.

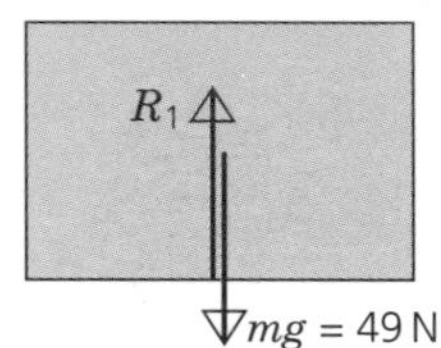

The middle box has a downward normal reaction force of magnitude R_1, the force of gravity and an upward normal reaction force, R_2. The normal reaction, R_2, must balance both R_1 and mg and so must have magnitude 98 N.

The bottom box again has two normal reactions and the force of gravity. The upward normal reaction force, R_3, must balance mg and R_2 and so has magnitude 147 N.

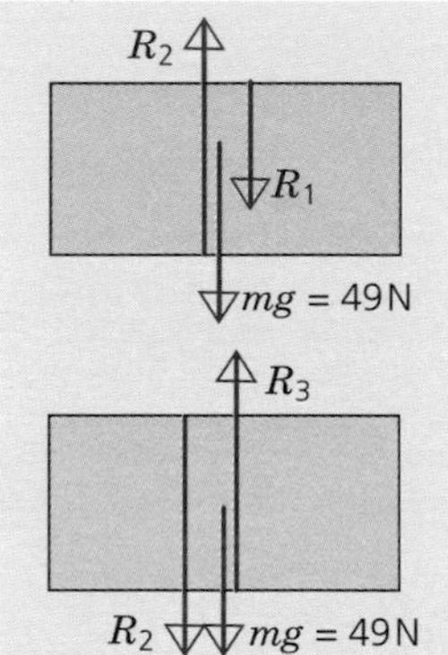

Example 21.7

At a fairground two dodgems are heading straight towards each other. Draw a diagram to show the forces on the dodgems when they collide.

Solution

Gravity acts on both cars and in both cases is balanced by a normal reaction, R_1.

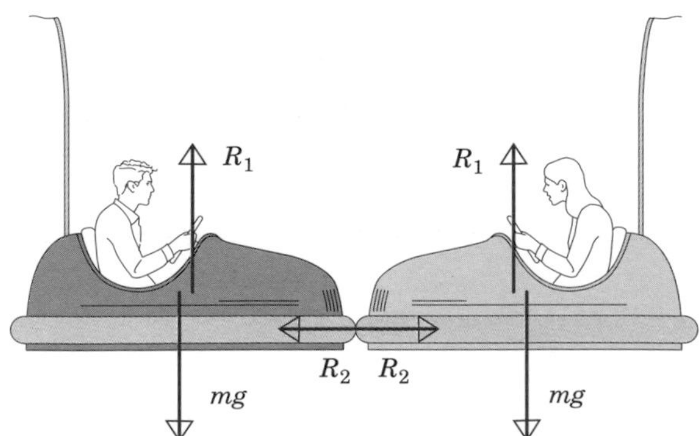

When the cars collide they exert normal reaction forces of equal size, R_2, but opposite directions at the point of contact.

Newton's third law

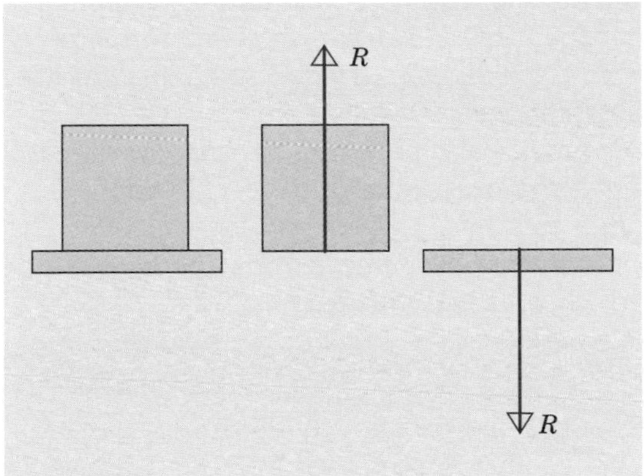

Whenever two surfaces are in contact, they exert forces on each other that are equal in magnitude, but acting in opposite directions.

Newton stated this formally in his **third law** of motion, as:

> *For every action there is an equal and opposite reaction.*

This law is easily seen to apply when considering normal reaction forces that act on surfaces in contact. However, it is important to remember that it is true when any force acts.

Friction

Imagine a man trying to push a heavy box, but it doesn't move. If he exerts a horizontal force on the box, then there must be another force acting on the box to balance the force he applies.

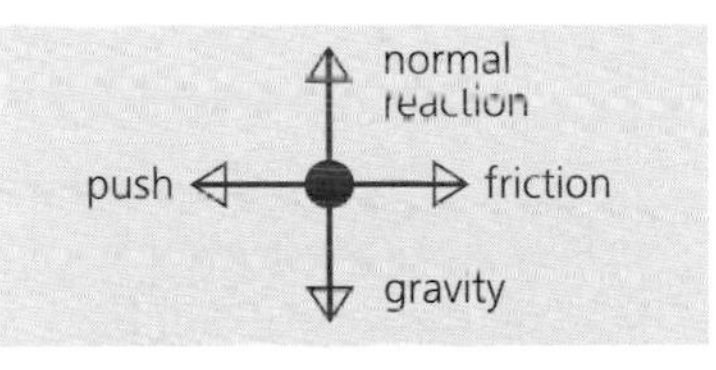

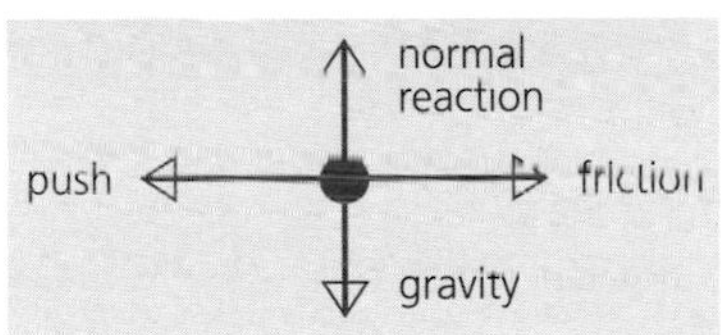

Modelling the box as a particle allows us to draw the force diagram (left).

The force that balances the push is friction, which acts because of the rough surfaces that are in contact. If the man pushes harder (bottom left) and the box stays still, the friction must have increased to match the greater force he exerts.

There is, however, a limit to the size or magnitude of the friction force and when the force applied exceeds this, then the box will begin to move, gaining speed.

Take a few moments to think about what factors affect the size or magnitude of the friction force.

The friction model

A model for the magnitude of a friction force is:

$$F \leq \mu R$$

where R is the magnitude of the normal reaction and μ is the **coefficient of friction**, a constant which depends on the surfaces in contact. When an object is at rest, F will be just sufficient to keep the forces in balance. When the object is about to move, or on the point of slipping, or actually moving, F takes its maximum value.

Exploration 21.2

Finding the value of μ

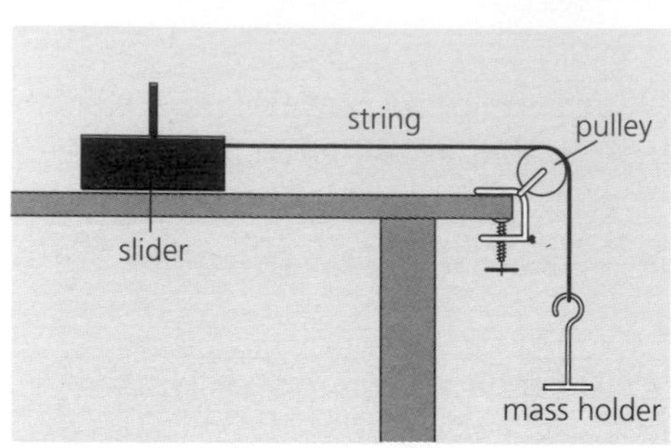

- *Set up the apparatus as shown in the diagram. Add 10 gram masses until the slider just begins to move. Assume that the force the string exerts on the slider is then equal to the maximum friction force. Record the mass needed to achieve this.*
- *Add a 100 gram mass to the slider and repeat the last step. Continue this procedure until you have six or seven results.*
- *Produce a table like this, which contains a sample set of results. (Use your own results.)*

Total mass of slider, M	$R = Mg$	Mass on string, m	Force exerted by string, mg
70 grams	0.686 N	30 grams	0.294 N
170 grams	1.666 N	70 grams	0.686 N

KEY SKILLS
N 3.1
N 3.2a
N 3.2d
N 3.3

- *Plot a graph of the friction force, F, which is assumed to be equal to the force exerted by the string, against R the normal reaction on the slider. The gradient of the line of best fit gives a value for μ.*
- *Comment on the accuracy of the friction model in the light of your experimental results.*

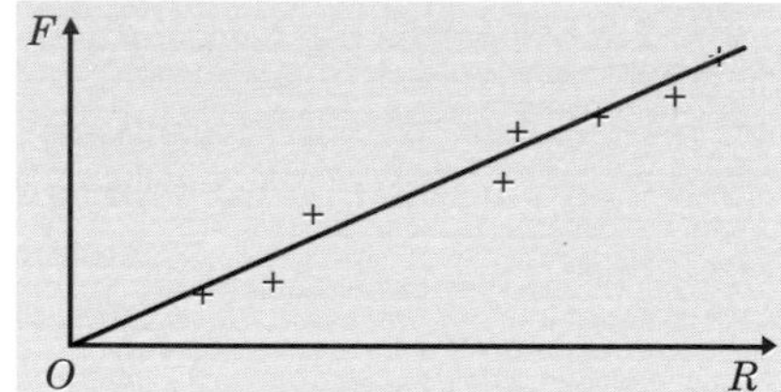

Example 21.8

A horse pulls a large sledge of mass 250 kg across a snow-covered horizontal surface at a constant speed. If the coefficient of friction between the snow and the sledge is 0.3, find the force exerted by the horse.

Solution

As the sledge moves at constant speed the forces acting must be in balance. Modelling the sledge as a particle gives the force diagram shown.

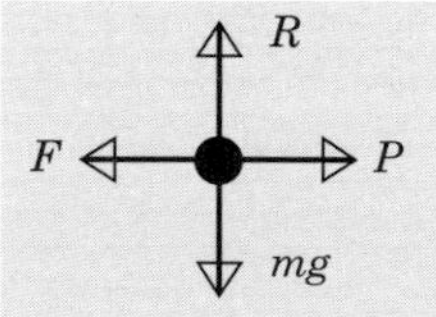

For the forces to be in balance:

$R = mg$

and

$P = F$

Since the sledge is sliding, the friction model gives:

$F = \mu R = \mu mg = 0.3 \times 250 \times 9.8 = 735\,N$

So to keep the forces in balance the horse exerts a force of 735 N.

Example 21.9

An accident investigator drags a car tyre along a road surface in an experiment to determine the value of μ for the tyre and the road. The mass of the tyre is 8 kg and he needs to exert a force of 60 N to move it at constant speed. Find the value of μ.

Solution
Modelling the tyre as a particle leads to the force diagram shown, where the forces are in balance.

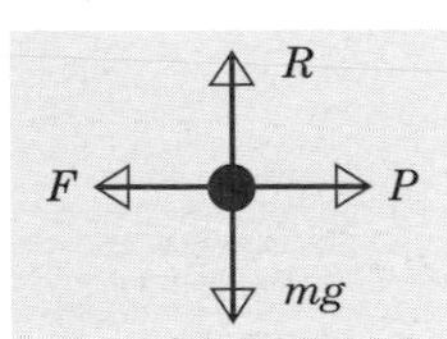

As the forces are in balance:
$R = mg = 8 \times 9.8 = 78.4$ *N*
and
$F = P = 60$ *N.*

Using the friction model, $F = \mu R$*, gives:*
$60 = \mu \times 78.4$

$$\mu = \frac{60}{78.4} = 0.765$$

Example 21.10

Draw a diagram to show the forces acting on a child sliding down a slide in a park.

Solution
Modelling the child as a particle allows us to represent her by a point.

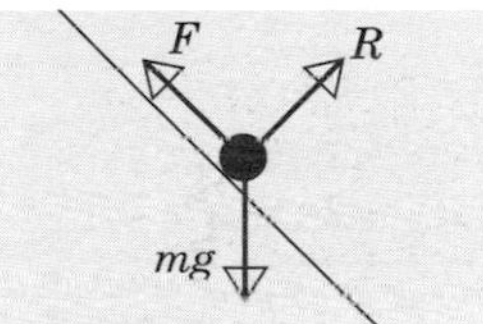

Gravity pulls down on her. There is a normal reaction, R*, at right angles to the slide. Friction acts parallel to the surface of the slide.*

EXERCISES

21.3 CLASSWORK

KEY SKILLS
N 3.2a
N 3.2b
N 3.2d
N 3.3

1 Calculate the magnitude of the normal reaction forces on:
a) a man of mass 75 kg standing on a horizontal surface,
b) a book of mass 0.6 kg resting on a table,
c) one leg of a three-legged stool of mass 2 kg,
d) one leg of a bed of mass 20 kg.

2 For each situation illustrated below draw a diagram to show the force of gravity, normal reactions and friction forces that are acting on the object that has been underlined.

a) A <u>box</u> on a table.

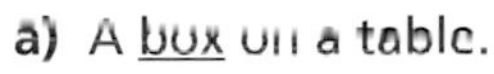
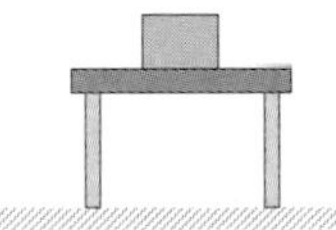

b) A <u>sledge</u> moving on a slope.

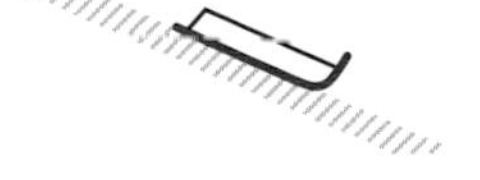

c) A <u>ball</u> as it hits the ground.

d) A <u>ladder</u> resting against a wall.

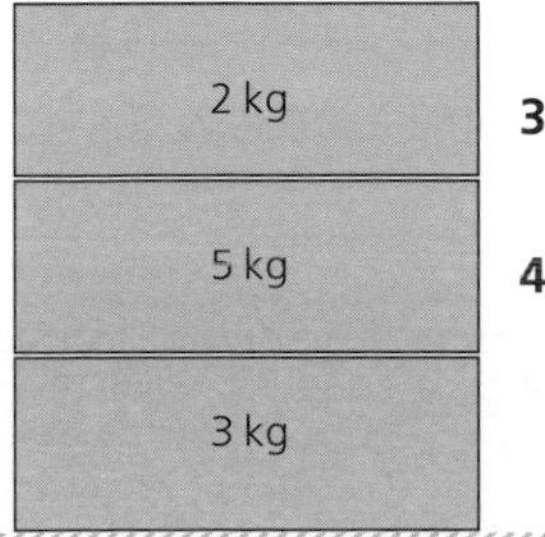

3 Three boxes are stacked as shown in the diagram. Draw diagrams to show the forces acting on each box and find their magnitudes.

4 Bottles of cooking oil are packed in boxes that have a mass of 12 kg when full. The tops of the boxes must not be subjected to a reaction force greater than 650 N or their contents will be damaged. How many boxes of cooking oil can be stacked in a single pile?

5 Each diagram shows a system that is at rest. In each case find the magnitude of the friction force acting and state the direction of the force.

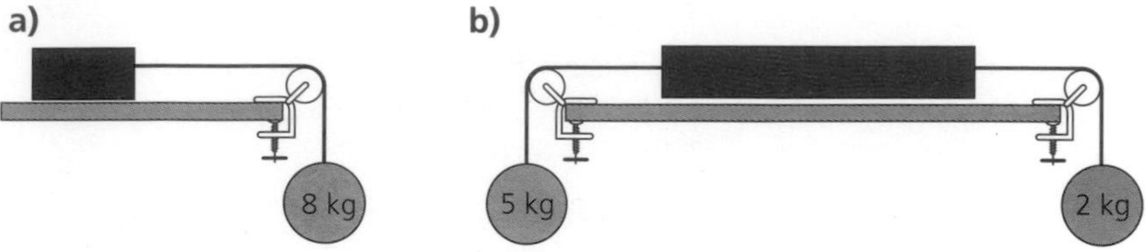

6 A crate of mass 50 kg rests on a horizontal surface and a horizontal force is applied to it. What is the magnitude of the friction force if the crate remains at rest and the applied force is:
a) 280 N, **b)** 200 N?

7 The coefficient of friction between a crate of mass 50 kg and the ground is 0.6. What is the greatest horizontal force that can be applied if the crate is to remain at rest on level ground?

8 A car locks its brakes on a horizontal road. What is the magnitude of the frictional force on the car if its mass is 1150 kg and the coefficient of friction between the tyres and the road is:
a) 0.9 on a dry road, **b)** 0.65 on a wet road?

9 A box of mass 10 kg is placed on a sledge of mass 11 kg, on horizontal (level) ground.
a) Draw diagrams to show the forces acting on the box and the sledge if a horizontal force is applied to the box.
b) Calculate the magnitude of all the normal reaction forces present.
c) The coefficient of friction between the sledge and the snow is 0.2 and between the box and the sledge it is 0.6. Does the sledge move if a horizontal force of 40 N is applied to the box?

10 An empty skip which has a mass of 500 kg is resting on a horizontal surface. The coefficient of friction between the skip and the ground is 0.68.
a) Calculate the magnitude of the normal reaction force on the skip.
b) Find the maximum value of the friction force, using the normal reaction found above.
c) Some boys try to move the skip. If each boy can exert a force of 400 N, how many are needed to move the skip?
d) In fact there are three boys unsuccessfully trying to move the skip. What is the magnitude of the friction force?

EXERCISES

21.3 HOMEWORK

1 Find the magnitude of the normal reaction forces on:
a) a woman of mass 50 kg standing on a horizontal surface,
b) a book of mass 500 grams on a shelf,
c) a crate of mass 2 tonnes, resting on the back of a lorry.

2 Find the magnitude of the normal reactions described below. In each case state clearly any assumptions that you make.
a) The reaction force on each leg of a table of mass 20 kg.
b) The reaction force on each wheel of a bus of mass 5 tonnes.

KEY SKILLS
N 3.3

3 For each situation illustrated below, draw a diagram to show the force of gravity, normal reactions and friction forces that are acting on the object that has been underlined.

a) A <u>plank</u> resting on 2 concrete blocks.

b) A <u>skier</u> travelling down a slope.

c) A <u>plank</u> leaning against a wall.

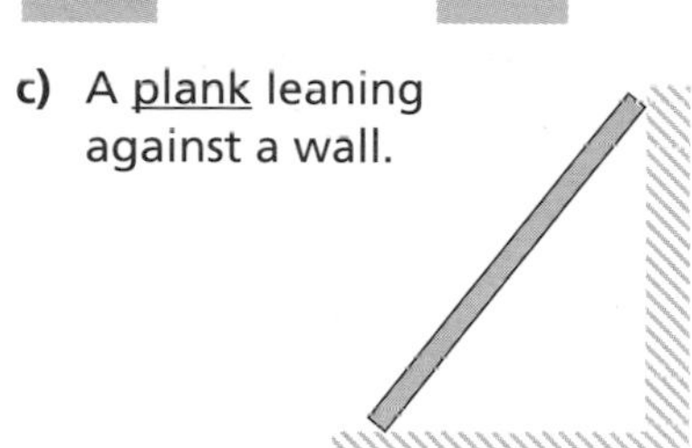

d) A <u>pole</u> stuck between two bars of a climbing frame.

150 kg
25 kg

4 A box of supplies of mass 150 kg is loaded onto a sledge of mass 25 kg. Draw a diagram to show the forces acting on the sledge when it is at rest on horizontal ground. Find the magnitude of each force.

5 Boxes that each have a mass of 30 kg are stacked in a pile eight boxes high. Find the reaction forces acting on the bottom box and illustrate them on a diagram.

6 If the forces shown in each diagram act, find the magnitude of the force that friction must exert if the object stays at rest in each case. Also state the direction of the friction force.

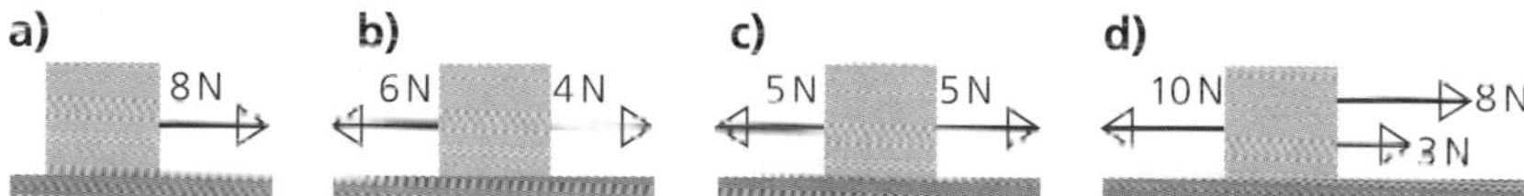

7 The coefficient of friction between a set of skis and the snow is 0.21. A skier stands on horizontal snow wearing these skis.

a) Find the normal reaction force on the skier with mass 71 kg.

b) What is the maximum forward force that can be applied to the skier if he is to remain at rest?

8 Tests carried out on a car of mass 1200 kg by police officers suggest that the friction force experienced when the car skids varies between 10 200 N and 6830 N, depending on the road conditions. What is the corresponding range of values for the coefficient of friction?

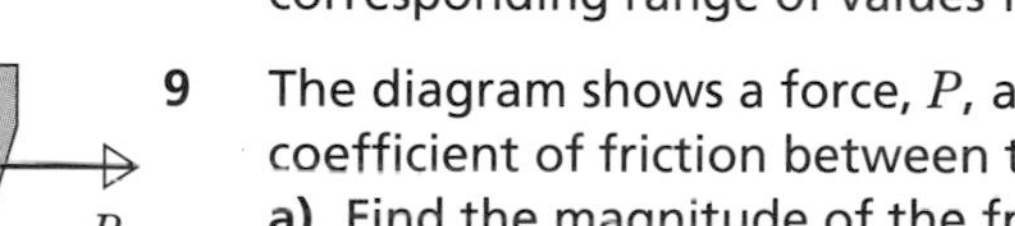

9 The diagram shows a force, P, acting on a skip of mass 500 kg. The coefficient of friction between the skip and the ground is 0.8.

a) Find the magnitude of the friction when the skip is moving.

b) Find the magnitude of the friction if the skip is at rest.

10 A car of mass 1000 kg is parked on a horizontal road with the hand brake on. (***Note:*** The hand brake only applies to the rear wheels.) The coefficient of friction between the tyres and the road is 0.8.

a) Assuming that the normal reaction forces on all the wheels are equal, calculate the magnitude of each force.

b) An attempt is made to move the car by applying a horizontal forward force. How big must this force be if the back wheels are to slide?

c) In fact the car will move with the back wheels sliding when a horizontal force of 800 N is applied. Calculate the reaction forces on the front and rear wheels of the car.

TENSION AND THRUST

Exploration 21.3

Stretching springs

- Think of some examples where a spring is stretched or compressed. What happens in these situations? What forces are exerted?
- What happens if you try to stretch a rod or a string? Are there similarities with the spring?

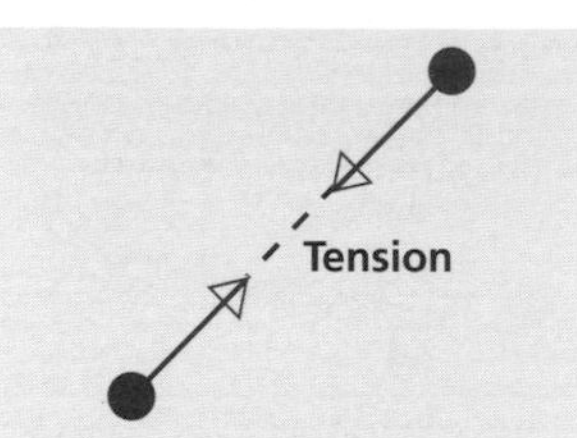

Compression

Stretching and compressing a spring

When a spring is **stretched** it exerts forces on the objects to which it is attached. The forces act along the spring towards its centre and have the same magnitude. These forces are known as **tensions**. When any other object is pulled, for example a normal string or a rod, there are also tension forces present in the same way.

When a spring is **compressed** it exerts forces that act away from its centre. These forces are known as **thrusts**. A rod can be in compression and exerts a thrust in the same way that a spring does. However, it is impossible for a string to exert a thrust. Why?

Example 21.11

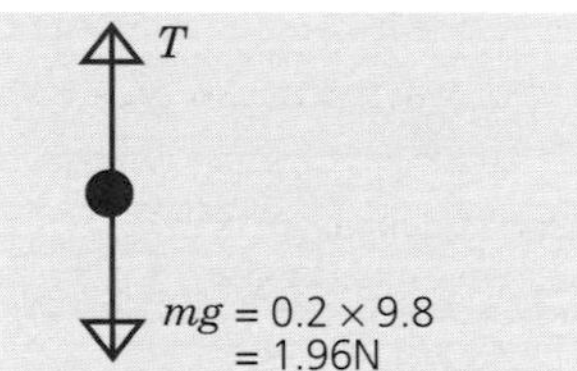

A spring stretches when it supports a mass of 200 grams. Find the tension in this spring.

Solution

The diagram shows the forces acting on the mass.
Gravity acts down and the tension, T, in the spring upwards.
The tension, T, balances the force of gravity so the tension in the spring must be 1.96 N.

Example 21.12

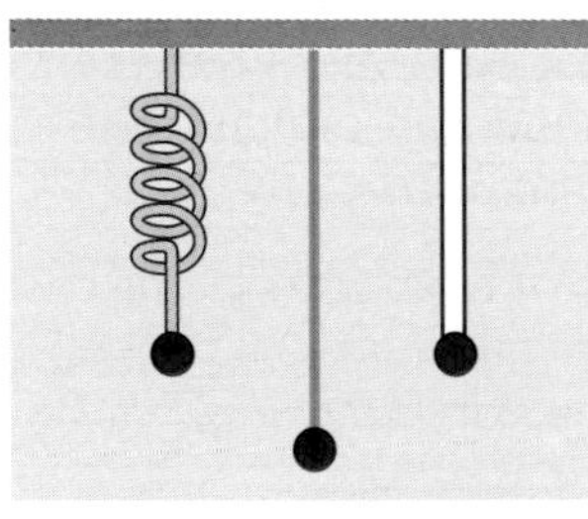

string tension = 2 N
2 N
rod tension = 2 N
2 N

Three identical objects are suspended using a spring, an inelastic string (which does not stretch) and a metal rod.

The spring stretches so that it exerts a force of 2 N.

a) *Find the mass of the objects.*
b) *What forces act in the other two cases?*

Solution

a) *The tension in the spring balances the force of gravity, so:*

$$T = mg \Rightarrow 2 = m \times 9.8 \Rightarrow m = \frac{2}{9.8} = 0.204 \text{ kg}$$

b) *In each case, the force of gravity on the objects is 2 N so the force of gravity, 2 N, must be balanced by an upward force of 2 N, as illustrated. In each of the other two cases the force of gravity, 2 N, must be balanced by an upward force of 2 N, as illustrated. Both the rod and the string also exert tension forces with the same magnitude and direction as the spring.*

Example 2.13

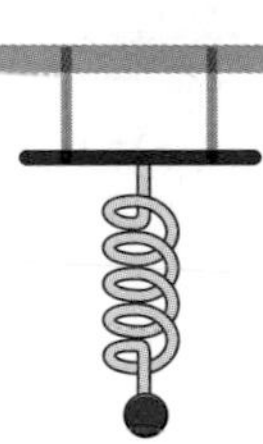

The diagram shows two inelastic strings supporting a bar of mass 100 grams, that in turn supports a spring and a further mass of 200 grams. Find the tension in the strings and the spring.

Solution

The diagram shows the forces acting on the 200 gram mass. The force T_1 acts upwards to balance the force of gravity and so has magnitude 1.96 N.

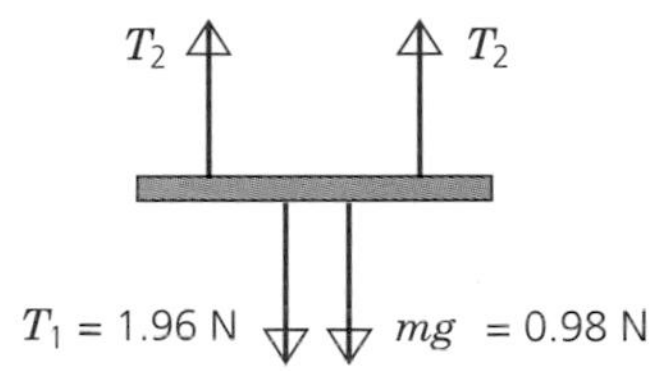

The diagram shows the forces acting on the bar. The downward forces exerted by gravity and the spring have a total magnitude of 2.94 N, which must be balanced by an upward force of 2.94 N. This is exerted by the two strings, so they must each have a tension of 1.47 N.

EXERCISES

21.4 CLASSWORK

KEY SKILLS
N 3.2d
N 3.3

1 A 1 kg mass is placed on a spring and causes it to be compressed. Find the thrust in this spring.

2 A cuckoo clock is controlled by a 50 gram mass that vibrates on the end of a spring.
   a) When the clock stops the mass remains at rest. Find the tension in the spring.
   b) The mass moves up and down from its central position. What happens to the tension in the spring as it moves up and down?

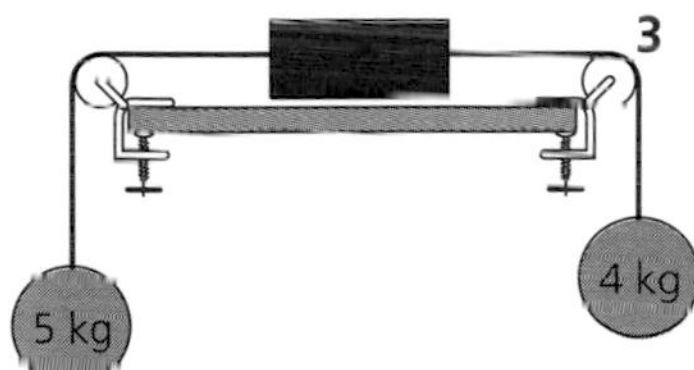

3 The diagram shows a system that is at rest.
   a) Find the tension in each string.
   b) Draw a diagram to show the forces acting on the block.
   c) What is the magnitude of the friction between the block and the plane?

4 The diagram shows a block of mass 500 grams which is attached to a spring on a horizontal surface. The coefficient of friction between the block and the plane is 0.7. The block is on the point of sliding.

   a) What is the magnitude of the normal reaction force on the block?
   b) What is the magnitude of the friction force?
   c) What is the tension in the spring?

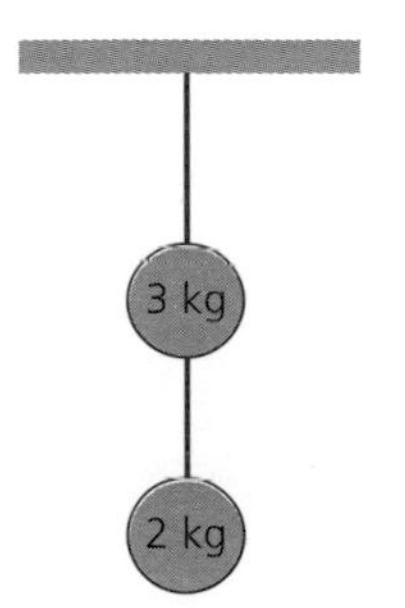

5 Consider the system of masses and strings, which is at rest.
   a) Draw a diagram to show the forces acting on the 3 kg mass.
   b) Find the tension in each string, assuming that the system is on Earth.
   c) What would be the tension in the strings if the system were on the moon? (Use $g = 1.6\,\mathrm{m\,s^{-2}}$)

6 A tower crane is lifting a load with a mass of 580 kg from rest on the ground. What can be deduced about the tension in the cable attached to the load if the load is:
a) at rest, **b)** rising at a constant 4 m s^{-1},
c) gaining speed as it rises?

7 Two people are using a rope and a pulley to lift the engine out of a car. If the mass of the engine is 250 kg, find the force that they must exert on the rope, to hold the engine in any one position.

8 For each system shown, calculate the tension in each rope if the system is at rest.

a)

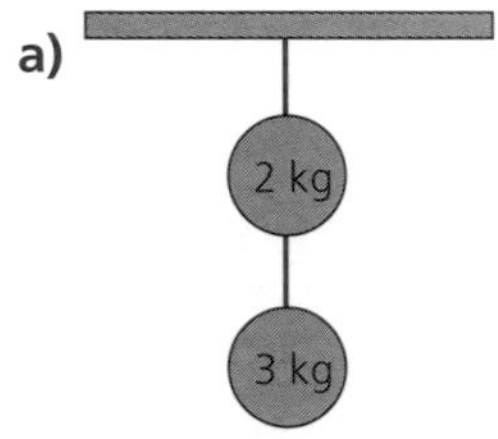

b)

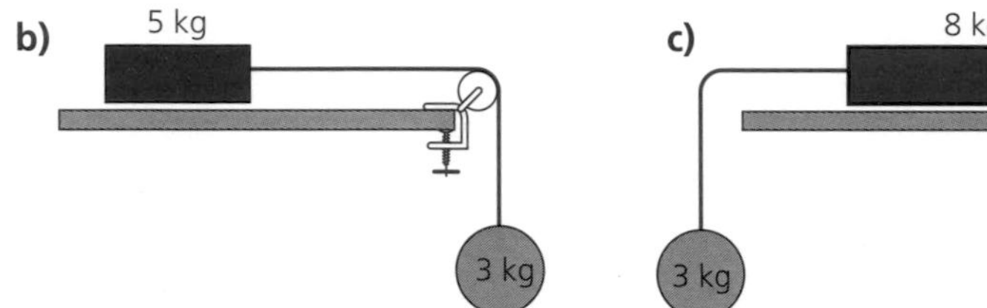

Find the coefficient of friction between the block and the surface in **b)** and **c)**, if the blocks are on the point of slipping.

EXERCISES

21.4 HOMEWORK

KEY SKILLS
N 3.2d
N 3.3

1 A spring stretches when supporting a load.
a) What is the tension for a load mass of 9 kg?
b) What is the mass of the load if the tension is 100 N?

2 The tension in a spring varies between 8 N and 12 N as the mass on the end moves up and down.
a) What would you expect the tension in the spring to be if the object were at rest?
b) Use you answer to **a)** to estimate the mass of the object.

3 The diagram shows a system that is at rest. The spring shown is stretched. Find the tension in the spring if:
a) there is no friction,
b) the coefficent of friction between the block and the plane is 0.4, and the block is on the point of sliding towards the pulley.

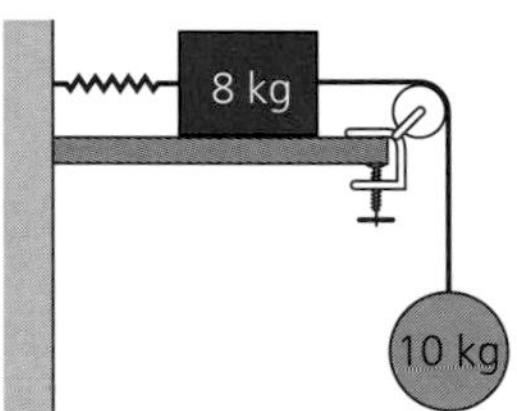

4 The diagram shows a system of masses and strings that is at rest.
a) Draw diagrams to show the forces acting on each mass.
b) Find the tension in each string.
c) If the strings were replaced by springs, what would be the tension in each spring?

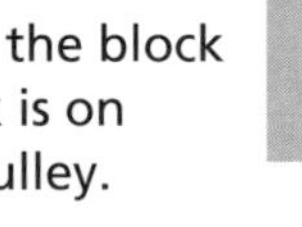

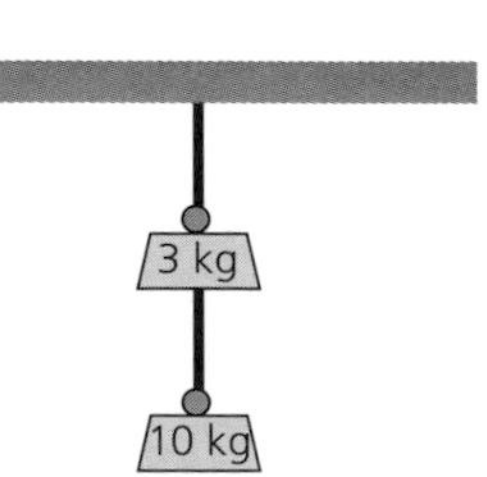

5 For each system shown, find the tension in the string if there is no movement. Find the coefficient of friction between the block and the plane if the block is on the point of sliding in each case.

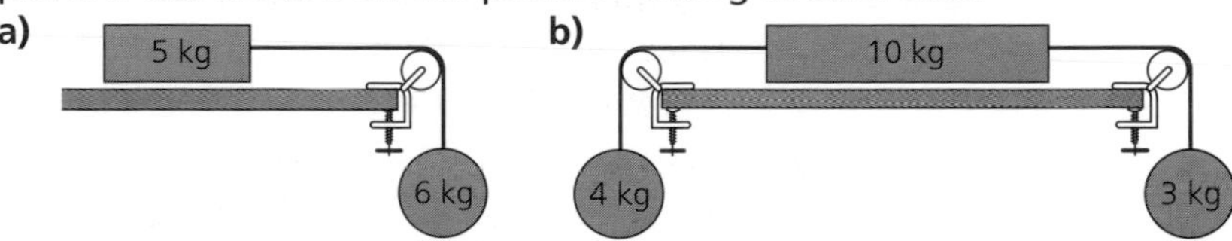

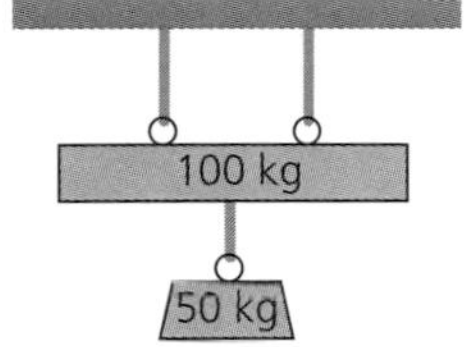

6 The diagram shows a steel beam of mass 100 kg that supports a load of mass 50 kg. Find the tensions in each cable, stating clearly any assumptions that you make.

7 The tension, T, in a spring is given by $T = 50e$, where e is the extension measured in metres. Three identical springs and three masses are arranged as shown.

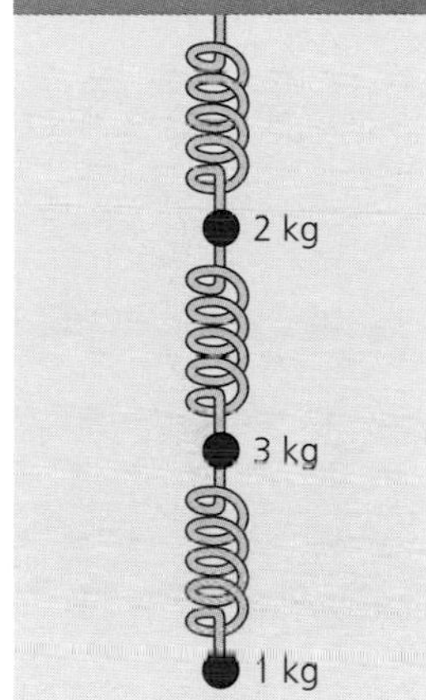

a) Find the tension in each spring.
b) Find the extension of each spring.

8 Draw diagrams to show the forces acting on each object that is underlined below.

a) A <u>pendulum bob</u> as it swings.

b) A <u>sign</u> supported by two cables.

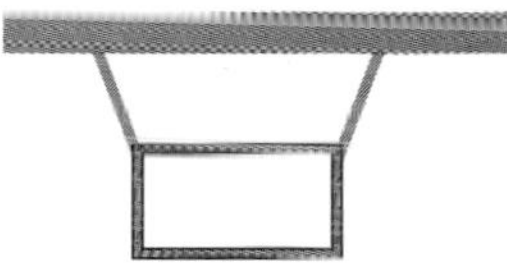

c) A <u>sledge</u> pulled as shown.

OTHER FORCES

In this chapter we have discussed the main types of force that we meet in this mechanics book. However there are a few others that we need to mention and these are described below.

Air resistance

This always acts in the opposite direction to any motion. It increases as the speed increases.

Upthrust or buoyancy

If an object is placed in a fluid then there will be an upward force due to the displacement of the fluid.

Electromagnetic forces

These are found in electric motors, for example. They are beyond the scope of this book.

Aerodynamic forces

An example of this type of force is the lift force on an aeroplane or a hydrofoil.

Note: The first and most crucial step in solving any mechanics problem is to identify the forces that are acting on the object under consideration.

Example 21.14

A ball is dropped into a pond. It falls to a lowest point and then rises up out of the water. Draw diagrams to show the forces acting on the ball at X where it is going down, Y at the lowest point and Z on the way back up.

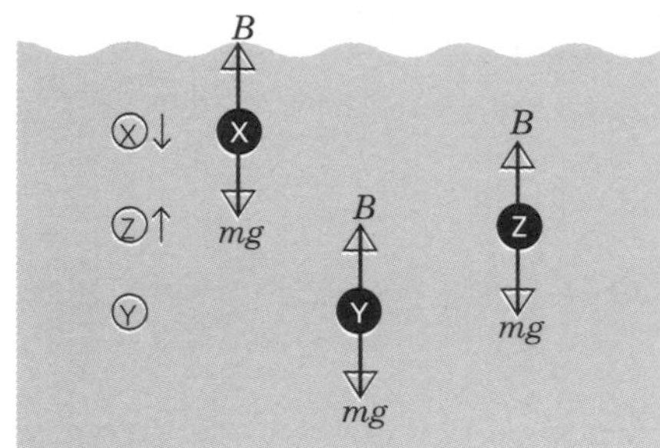

Solution

At X, there is gravity, but also an upward buoyancy force, B. As the ball must be losing speed, $B > mg$.

At the lowest point, Y, the same two forces act. As the motion is changing from downwards to upwards again $B > mg$.

At Z the same two forces act. As the ball is gaining speed as it rises, $B > mg$.

Example 21.15

Draw a diagram to show the forces acting on the aeroplane. What can be deduced about these forces if:

a) *the aeroplane is travelling at a constant speed,*

b) *the aeroplane is rising at a constant speed,*

c) *the aeroplane is gaining speed, in horizontal flight?*

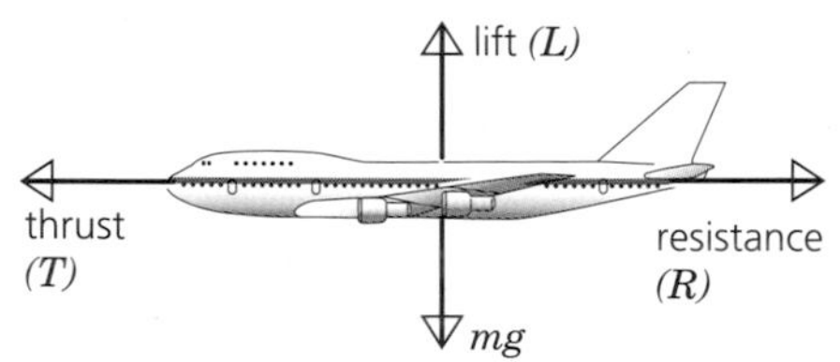

Solution

The diagram shows the forces present.

a) *The motion of the aeroplane does not change and so all the forces must be in balance giving $R = T$ and $L = mg$.*

b) *Here again the motion is not changing, so $R = T$ and $L = mg$.*

c) *As the aeroplane is gaining speed there must be an overall forward force, so $T > R$, but $L = mg$.*

CONSOLIDATION EXERCISES FOR CHAPTER 21

1 Draw a diagram to show the forces on a sailing dinghy.

2 A bottle is floating in a tank of water.

a) If the bottle is at rest show the forces acting on the bottle. What can be stated about the magnitude of each force?

b) The bottle is pushed down so that it bobs up and down in the water. Draw diagrams to show the forces on the bottle when it is at its highest and lowest positions.

c) Are the forces on the moving bottle ever in balance? If so when?

3 A marble is placed on a slope and once released it rolls down the slope.
a) Draw a diagram to show the forces acting on the marble.
b) What do you think the effect of the friction is on the motion of the marble?

4 A box is placed on a conveyor belt. Draw diagrams to show the forces acting if the box is:
a) at rest,
b) moving at constant speed,
c) gaining speed,
d) losing speed.

5 A conker on the end of a length of string is swinging in a circle. Show the forces that act on the conker. Is it possible for these forces to be in balance?

6 During a game of tennis the ball is hit by the racquet.
Draw a diagram to show the forces on the ball:
a) before it is hit,
b) while in contact with the racquet,
c) after it has been hit.

7 A golf ball is at rest on the ground when it is hit by a club.
Draw diagrams to show the forces acting on the ball when it is:
a) at rest on the ground,
b) in contact with the club on the ground,
c) in contact with the club off the ground,
d) moving but not in contact with the club or the ground.

POSSIBLE MODELLING TASKS

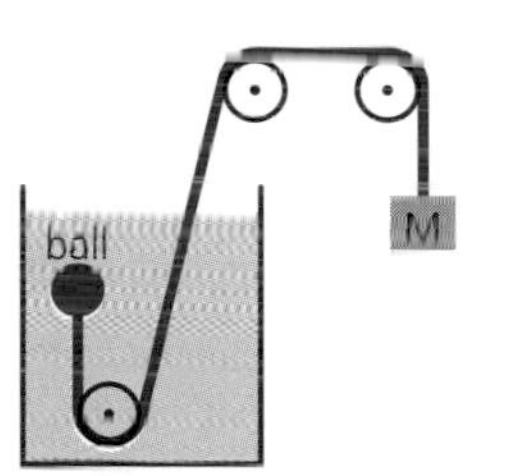

1 Devise and conduct an experiment to discover how the tension in a spring or string depends on its extension.

2 The diagram (left) shows an experiment that can be set up to explore how the buoyant force on an object varies with depth. Conduct your own experiment using this or another approach to find a relationship between the buoyant force and depth.

Summary

After working through this chapter you should:

- be able to identify different types of forces and draw force diagrams
- be able to calculate the force of gravity on an object on Earth
- be aware of the contact forces: friction and normal reactions
- be aware of the tension or compression that can be found in a spring or rod
- be able to determine whether or not forces are in balance by examining the motion of the object on which they act.

Vectors and forces

- *It is easy to see if horizontal or vertical forces are in balance, this idea can be extended to any forces.*
- *In many real problems, solutions can be obtained because all the forces are in equilibrium or balance.*

INTRODUCTION

Many of the quantities that we discuss in this book will be defined in terms of a size and a direction. A force has a size or magnitude, given in newtons, and a direction in which it acts. For example a force may have magnitude 80 N and act straight down. Quantities which have a magnitude and a direction are known as **vectors**.

Exploration 22.1

Recognising vectors

Think about each of the following quantities.

distance　　force　　speed　　mass　　velocity　　weight

- If they *are* vectors give a simple example of each one.
- If they *are not* vectors, explain why not.

Exploration 22.2

Force and vectors

Using pulleys and strings set up the system shown.

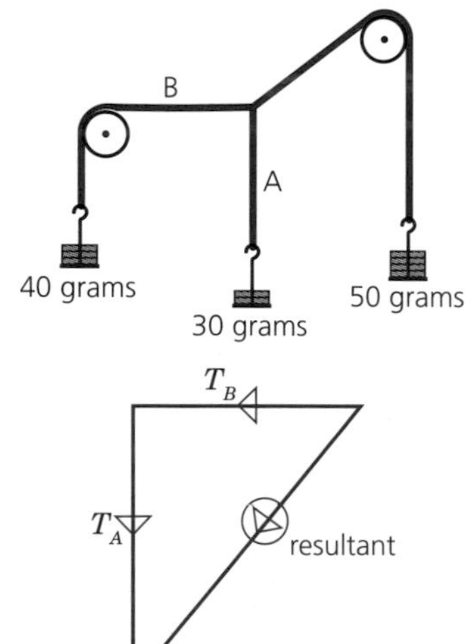

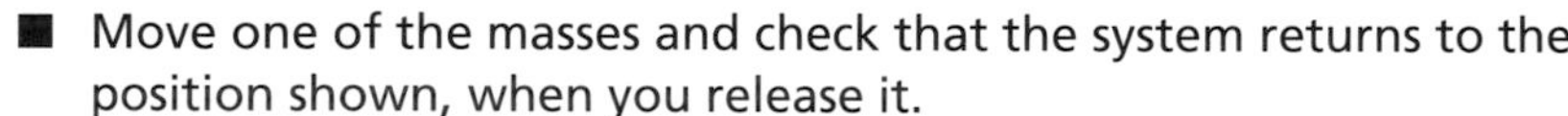

- Move one of the masses and check that the system returns to the position shown, when you release it.
- Verify that string A is vertical and string B is horizontal. Swap the 30 and 40 gram masses. What happens?
- Use three masses of 130 grams, 120 grams and 50 grams. Show that it is again possible to have one string vertical and one horizontal.
- Now use three different masses, suspending one at the end of each string. Decrease or increase the masses at the ends of the strings until one string is vertical and another horizontal.
  Find the tension in each string, by considering the forces acting where the masses are attached, and draw a diagram like the one shown. The horizontal and vertical force are equivalent to a single resultant. Find the size and direction of this resultant. How does it compare with the tension in the third string?
- Repeat the last step for another set of masses.

EXPRESSING FORCES AS VECTORS

Exploration 22.2 suggests that any force can be expressed as the resultant of a horizontal and vertical force.

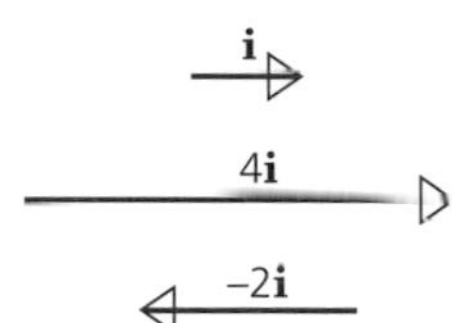

In Chapter 21, *Force*, we saw how easy it is to determine whether or not forces are in balance by looking at the horizontal and vertical forces separately. A more formal approach involves the use of **unit vectors i** and **j** that are perpendicular to each other, in the same two-dimensional plane. It is usual to take the vector **i** as horizontal, directed to the right. A force of 4**i** is a force of 4 N that acts horizontally to the right, and a force of –2**i** is a force of 2 N that acts horizontally to the left.

The vector **j** is usually assumed to act in a vertical direction, either up or down.

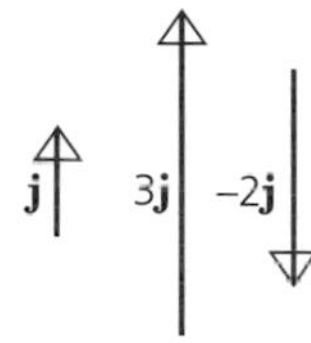

The diagram on the right shows the case when **j** is upwards. The vector 3**j** represents an upward force of 3 N, while –2**j** represents a downward force of 2 N.

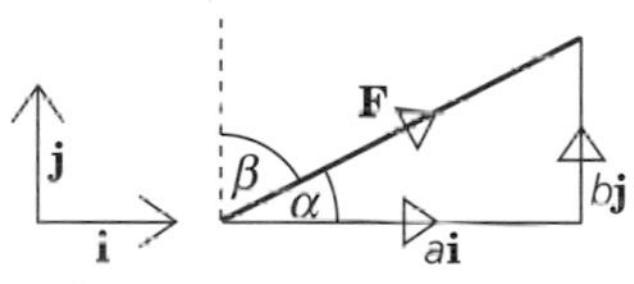

Forces that act in other directions can be expressed in the form $a\mathbf{i} + b\mathbf{j}$. The numbers a and b are known as the horizontal and vertical **components** of the force. If the force has magnitude F, then $a = F\cos\alpha$ and $b = F\cos\beta$ where α is the angle between the force and the **i** direction and β is the angle between the force and the **j** direction.

Example 22.1

*A force of magnitude 6 N acts at 30° to the horizontal as shown. Express this force in the form $a\mathbf{i} + b\mathbf{j}$, where **i** and **j** are horizontal and vertical unit vectors.*

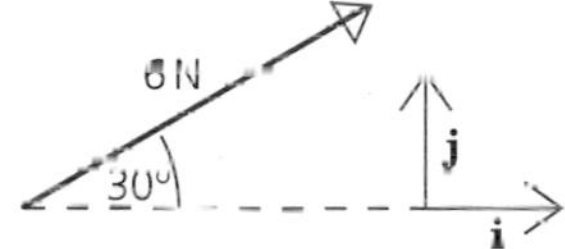

Solution

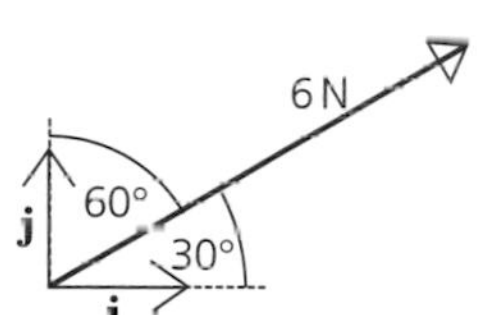

*Note that the angle between the force and the unit vector **i** is 30°, and the angle between the force and the unit vector **j** is 60°.*

So the horizontal component is $6\cos30°$ or 5.20 N and the vertical component is $6\cos60°$ or 3.00 N.

Now the force can be expressed as:
$6\cos30°\mathbf{i} + 6\cos60°\mathbf{j} = 5.20\mathbf{i} + 3.00\mathbf{j}$

The equivalence of these two forces to the original can be seen by considering the diagram on the right.

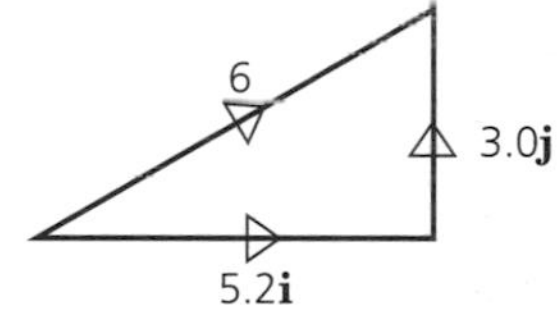

Example 22.2

*Three forces act at a point as shown in the diagram. Express each force in terms of the unit vectors **i** and **j**. Also find the resultant or combined effect of these forces.*

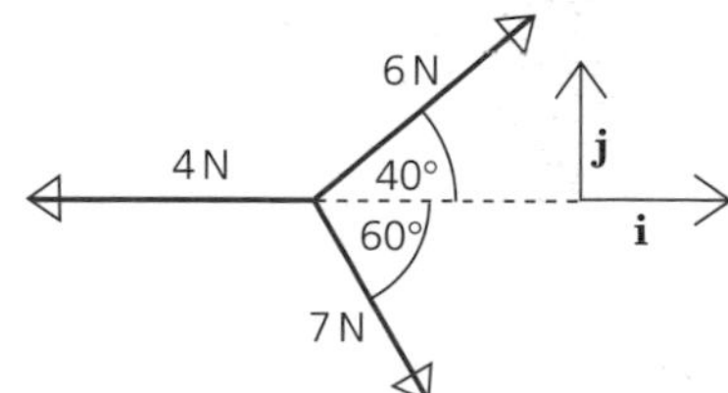

Solution

Considering each force in turn, gives the results in the table below.

Force	Vector form
4 N	$-4\mathbf{i}$
6 N	$6\cos40°\mathbf{i} + 6\cos50°\mathbf{j}$
7 N	$7\cos60°\mathbf{i} - 7\cos150°\mathbf{j}$ or $7\cos60°\mathbf{i} - 7\cos30°\mathbf{j}$

The resultant force, $\mathbf{F}$*, is the sum of all the individual forces.*

$$\mathbf{F} = (-4\mathbf{i}) + (6\cos 40°\mathbf{i} + 6\cos 50°\mathbf{j}) + (7\cos 60°\mathbf{i} - 7\cos 30°\mathbf{j})$$
$$= (6\cos 40° + 7\cos 60° - 4)\mathbf{i} + (6\cos 50° - 7\cos 30°)\mathbf{j}$$
$$= 4.10\mathbf{i} - 2.21\mathbf{j}$$

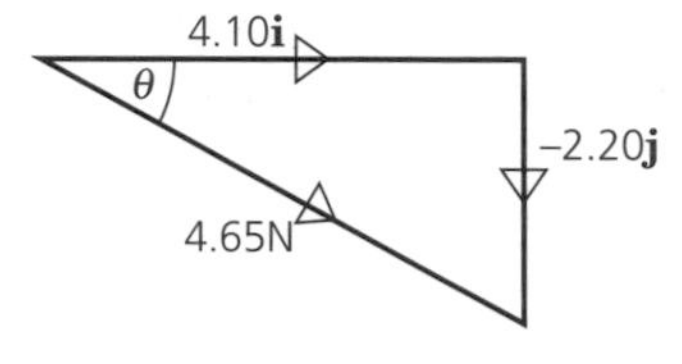

The force is illustrated in the diagram. The magnitude of $\mathbf{F}$ *is:*

$$F = \sqrt{4.10^2 + 2.21^2} = 4.7\text{ N (to two significant figures)}$$

The angle θ *to the* $\mathbf{i}$ *direction is:*

$$\theta = \tan^{-1}\left(\frac{2.21}{4.10}\right) = 28°\text{ (to the nearest degree)}$$

Example 22.3

The forces shown in the diagram act at a point. Find the magnitude and direction of the force $\mathbf{F}$*, if the resultant force is zero.*

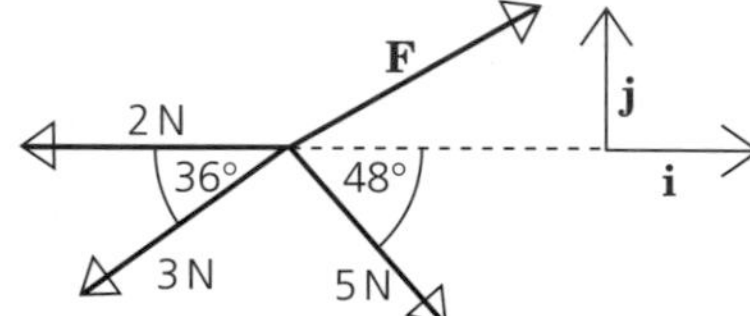

Solution

Assume that the force $\mathbf{F}$ *is* $a\mathbf{i} + b\mathbf{j}$*. Each force is expressed in terms of the unit vectors* $\mathbf{i}$ *and* $\mathbf{j}$ *in the following table.*

Force	Vector form
$\mathbf{F}$	$a\mathbf{i} + b\mathbf{j}$
2 N	$-2\mathbf{i}$
3 N	$-3\cos36°\mathbf{i} - 3\cos54°\mathbf{j}$
5 N	$5\cos48°\mathbf{i} - 5\cos42°\mathbf{j}$

The resultant force is:

$$(a\mathbf{i} + b\mathbf{j}) + (-2\mathbf{i}) + (-3\cos 36°\mathbf{i} - 3\cos 54°\mathbf{j}) + (5\cos 48°\mathbf{i} - 5\cos 42°\mathbf{j})$$
$$= (a - 2 - 3\cos 36° + 5\cos 48°)\,\mathbf{i} + (b - 3\cos 54° - 5\cos 42°)\mathbf{j}$$
$$= (a - 1.08)\mathbf{i} + (b - 5.48)\mathbf{j}$$

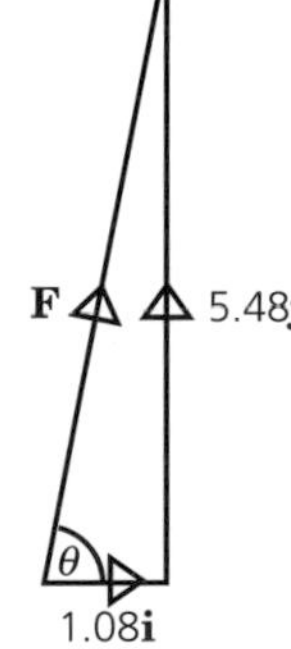

For the resultant to be zero, $a = 1.08$ *and* $b = 5.48$*, so the force* $\mathbf{F}$ *can be expressed as:*

$$\mathbf{F} = 1.08\mathbf{i} + 5.48\mathbf{j}$$

This is shown in the diagram on the left.

The magnitude can be found using Pythagoras' theorem.

$F = \sqrt{1.08^2 + 5.48^2} = 5.6$ N (to two significant figures)
The angle θ can be found using trigonometry.

$$\tan\theta = \frac{5.48}{1.08} \Rightarrow \theta = \tan^{-1}\frac{5.48}{1.08} = 79° \text{ (to the nearest degree)}$$

Thus the force **F** *has magnitude 5.6 N and acts at 79° above the unit vector* **i***.*

Vector form and algebraic notation

The force **F** shown in the diagram can be expressed in vector form:

$$\mathbf{F} = F\cos\alpha\mathbf{i} + F\cos(90° - \alpha)\mathbf{j}$$

As $\cos(90° - \alpha) = \sin\alpha$ this can be expressed as:

$$\mathbf{F} = F\cos\alpha\mathbf{i} + F\sin\alpha\mathbf{j}$$

Note that $F\cos\alpha$ is often referred to as the **horizontal component** and $F\cos(90° - \alpha)$ or $F\sin\alpha$ as the **vertical component** of the force.

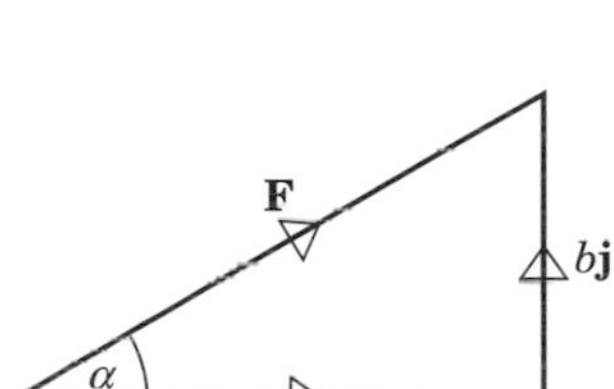

The force $\mathbf{F} = a\mathbf{i} + b\mathbf{j}$ has magnitude:

$$F = \sqrt{a^2 + b^2}$$

and direction:

$$\alpha = \tan^{-1}\frac{b}{a}$$

Column vectors are sometimes used as an alternative notation. The force $\mathbf{F} = a\mathbf{i} + b\mathbf{j}$ would be written as $\begin{pmatrix} a \\ b \end{pmatrix}$ in column vector form.

The force F shown would be expressed as $\mathbf{F} = \begin{pmatrix} F\cos\alpha \\ F\cos(90° - \alpha) \end{pmatrix}$.

EXERCISES

22.1 CLASSWORK

KEY SKILLS
N 3.2b
N 3.3

1 Express each force illustrated below in terms of the unit vectors **i** and **j**.

a)
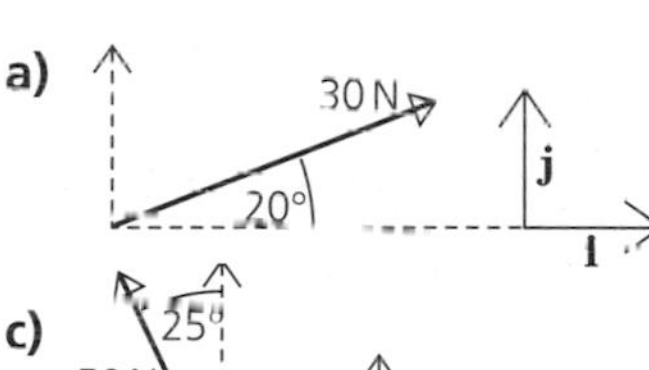

b)
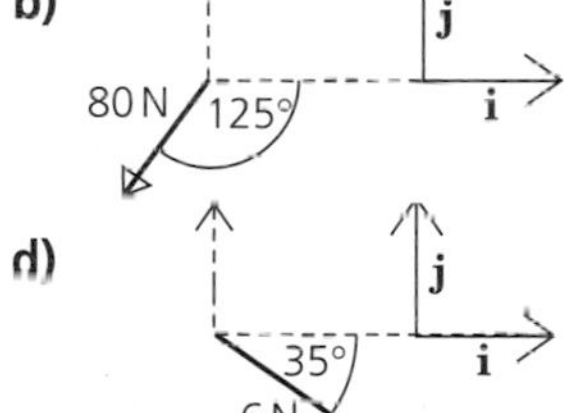

c) 50 N, 25°

d) 6 N, 35°

2 Express each force shown below as a column vector.

a)
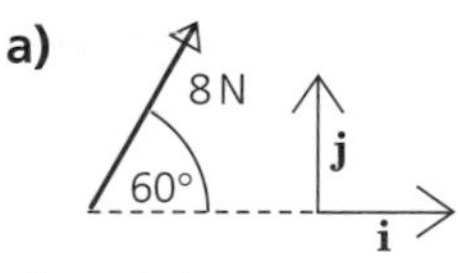

b)
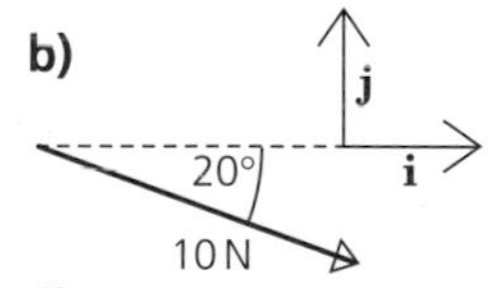

c)
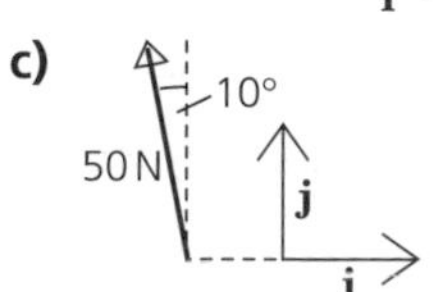

d)
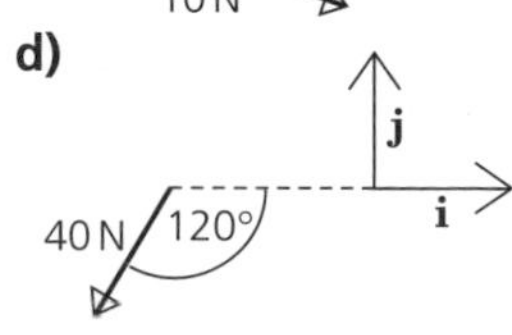

3 For each set of forces shown below, find in the resultant force in terms of the unit vectors $\mathbf{i}$ and $\mathbf{j}$. Find also the magnitude and direction of the resultant force.

a)

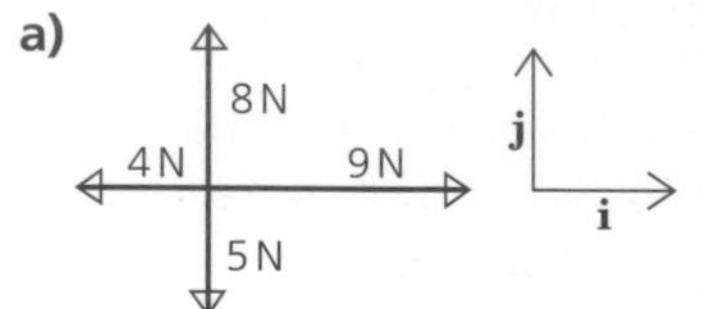

b)

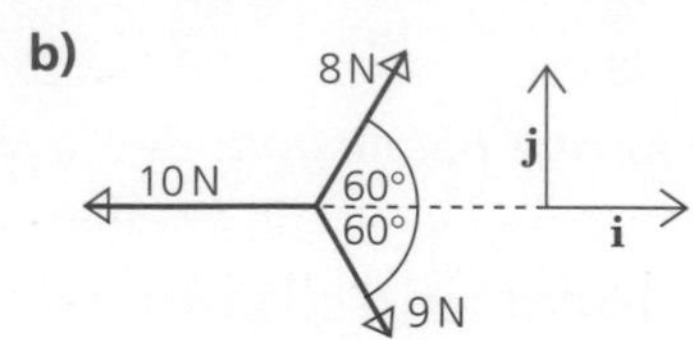

c)

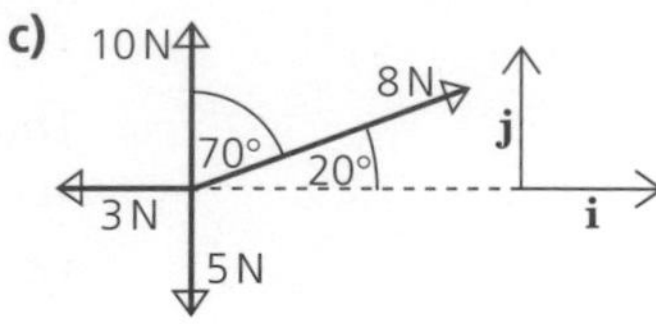

4 Find the magnitude of each force below and the angle it makes with the positive $\mathbf{i}$ direction.

a) $10\mathbf{i} + 12\mathbf{j}$ **b)** $16\mathbf{i} + 32\mathbf{j}$ **c)** $11\mathbf{i} + 8\mathbf{j}$
d) $22\mathbf{i} - 100\mathbf{j}$ **e)** $-16\mathbf{i} - 12\mathbf{j}$ **f)** $-3\mathbf{i} + 4\mathbf{j}$

5 Find the magnitude of each force below. Describe the direction in which the force acts.

a) $\begin{pmatrix} 3 \\ 2 \end{pmatrix}$ **b)** $\begin{pmatrix} -6 \\ 7 \end{pmatrix}$ **c)** $\begin{pmatrix} -4 \\ -2 \end{pmatrix}$ **d)** $\begin{pmatrix} -2 \\ 1 \end{pmatrix}$

6 Express each force illustrated in terms of perpendicular unit vectors $\mathbf{i}$ and $\mathbf{j}$.

a)

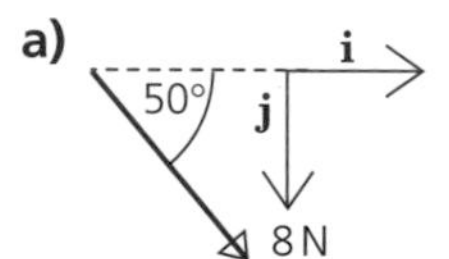

b)

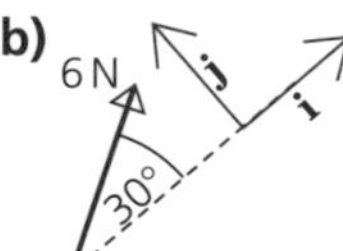

c)

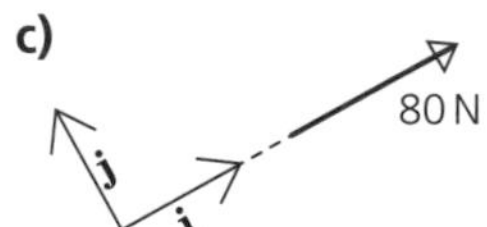

d

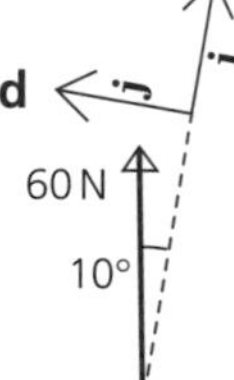

EXERCISES

22.1 HOMEWORK

1 For each force shown below, express it as a vector in terms of $\mathbf{i}$ and $\mathbf{j}$.

a)

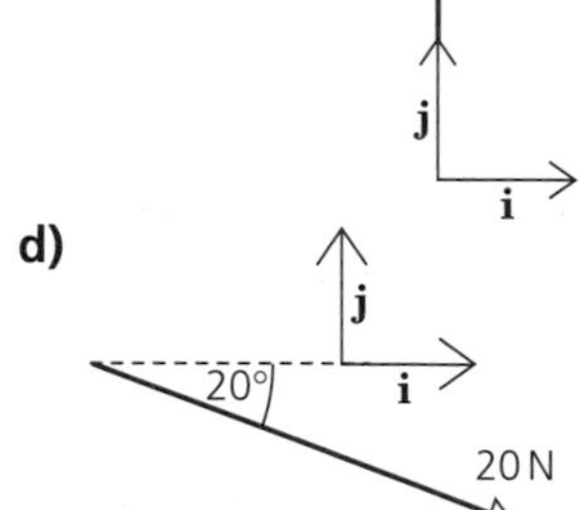

b)

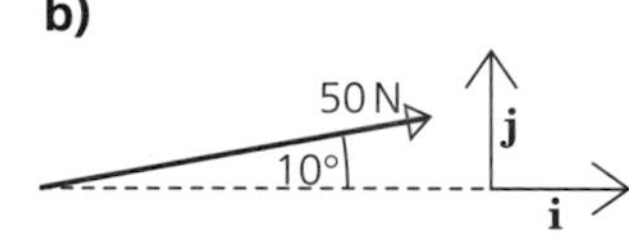

c)

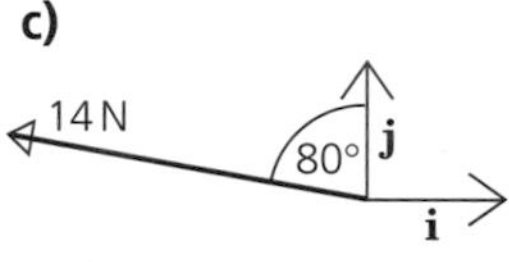

d)

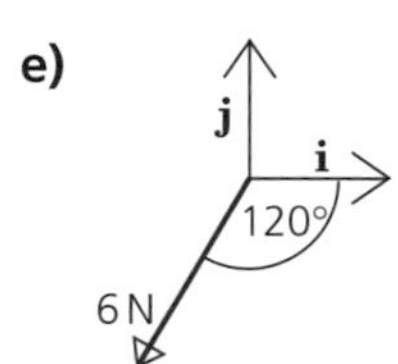

e)

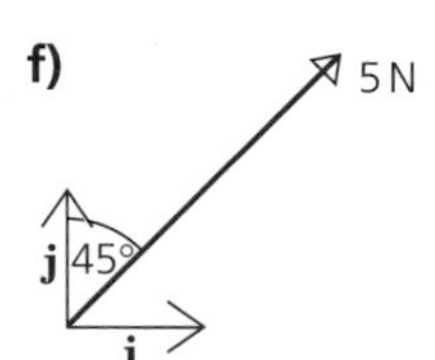

f)

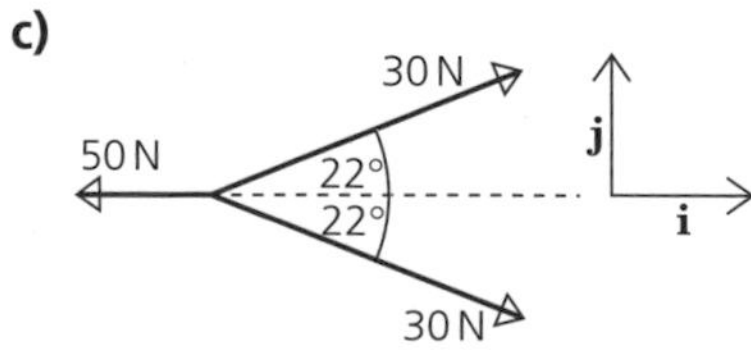

2 In each example below, find the resultant force in terms of the unit vectors $\mathbf{i}$ and $\mathbf{j}$.

a)

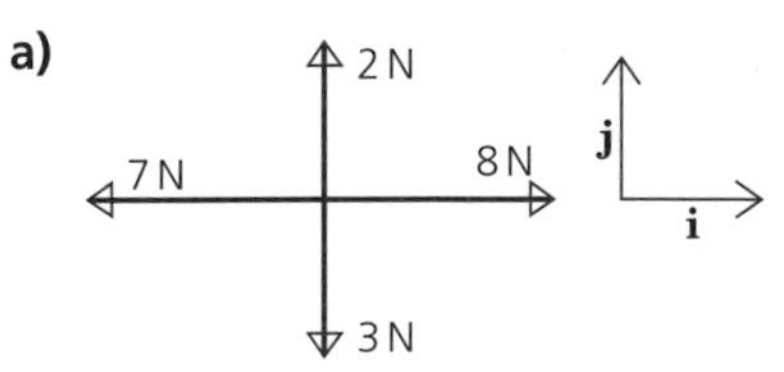

b)

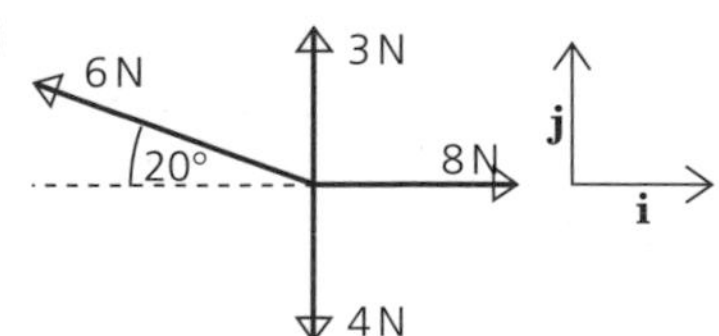

c)

3 Express each force below as a column vector.

a) 6N 70° j i

b) j 20° i 30N

c)

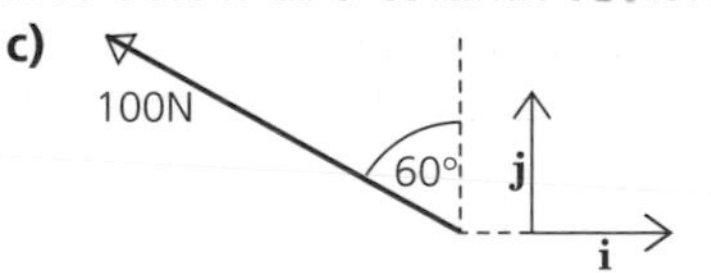

d) j 110° i 60N

4 Find the magnitude and direction of each force below. In each case draw a diagram, indicating the angle that you specify.

a) $3\mathbf{i} + 10\mathbf{j}$ b) $60\mathbf{i} - 110\mathbf{j}$ c) $-84\mathbf{i} - 30\mathbf{j}$
d) $-40\mathbf{i} + 20\mathbf{j}$ e) $6\mathbf{i} - 8\mathbf{j}$ f) $61\mathbf{i} + 12\mathbf{j}$

5 For each force below, find the magnitude and illustrate the direction clearly on a diagram, specifying one angle.

a) $\begin{pmatrix} 7 \\ 4 \end{pmatrix}$ b) $\begin{pmatrix} 6 \\ -2 \end{pmatrix}$ c) $\begin{pmatrix} 10 \\ 2 \end{pmatrix}$ d) $\begin{pmatrix} -6 \\ 8 \end{pmatrix}$

6 For each set of forces, find the resultant in terms of **i** and **j**. Give the magnitude of the resultant and the angle it makes with the **i** direction.

a)

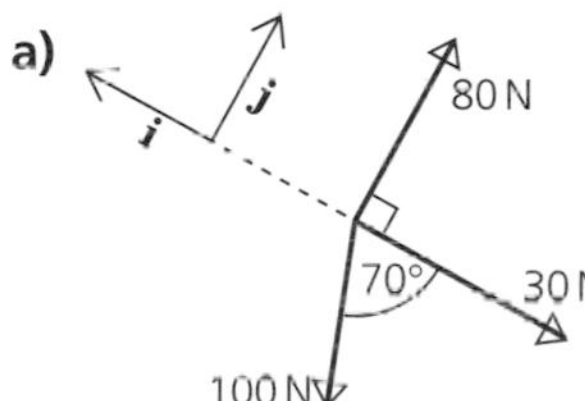

b)

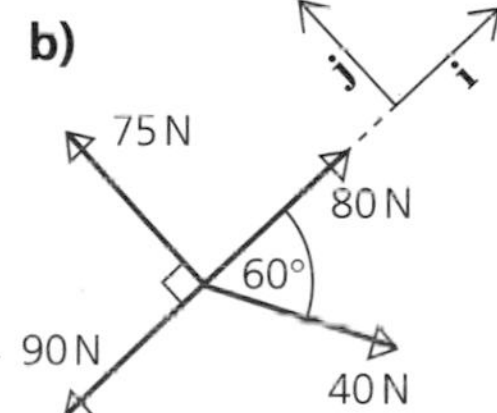

FORCES AND EQUILIBRIUM

From Newton's first law, if the resultant force on an object is zero, then the object will either remain at rest or move with a constant speed in a straight line. In our everyday life, we see many real situations where the resultant force is zero. We can now look more closely at problems involving this phenomenon, using the ideas of vectors.

Example 22.4

A car of mass 700 kg is travelling up a slope making an angle of 4° above the horizontal at a constant speed. Calculate the forward force that acts on the car, assuming that there are no resistance forces present. Comment on your result.

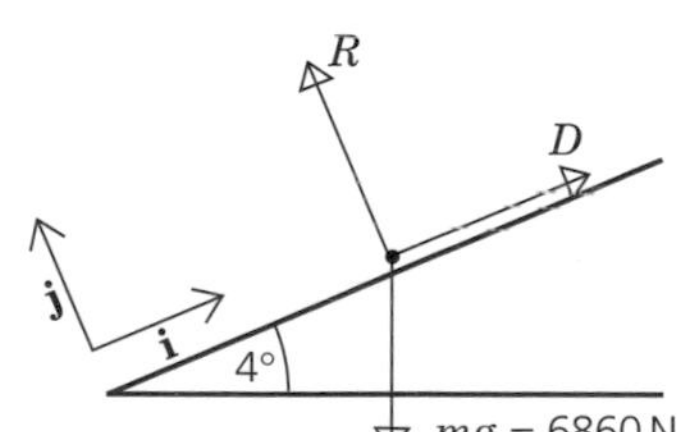

Solution

If the car is modelled as a particle which experiences no resistance, then there are three forces acting, namely gravity, the normal reaction, R, and a forward force, D.

*When considering objects on a slope it is often helpful to use unit vectors that are parallel and perpendicular to the slope. In this case **i** and **j** are taken as shown in the diagram. In problems like this, it is normal to talk about component of forces perpendicular and parallel to the slope rather than horizontal or vertical.*

Now each force can be expressed in vector form.

Force	Vector form
R	$R\mathbf{j}$
D	$D\mathbf{i}$
mg	$-6860\cos 86°\mathbf{i} - 6860\cos 4°\mathbf{j}$

The resultant force is:

$(D - 6860\cos 86°)\mathbf{i} + (R - 6860\cos 4°)\mathbf{j}$

As the car moves at a constant speed in a straight line the forces must be in equilibrium, so:

$D - 6860\cos 86° = 0$ *and* $R - 6860\cos 4° = 0$

This gives $R = 6840$ N and $D = 479$ N correct to three significant figures. So the car must exert a forward force of 479 N if it is to move up the slope. As in reality the car will experience a resistance force, the magnitude of D must actually be greater than 479 N.

Example 22.5

A hopper of cement is lifted by a crane and then pulled sideways until it is in the position shown. If the cables attached to the hopper are positioned as in the diagram and the mass of the hopper and its contents are 500 kg, find the tension in each cable.

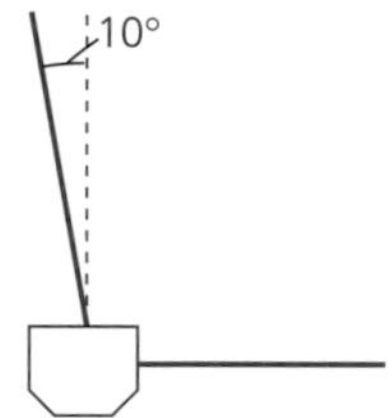

Solution

The forces acting on the hopper are the two tensions and the force of gravity, as shown in the diagram, where the hopper is modelled as a particle.

The resultant force on the hopper is:

$$\left(T_1 - T_2\cos 80°\right)\mathbf{i} + \left(T_2\cos 10° - 4900\right)\mathbf{j}$$

For equilibrium the resultant force is zero, so:

$$T_1 - T_2\cos 80° = 0 \qquad (1)$$

and

$$T_2\cos 10° - 4900 = 0 \qquad (2)$$

From equation (2):

$$T_2 = \frac{4900}{\cos 10°} = 4980 \text{ N to three significant figures.}$$

Substituting this value back into equation (1) gives:

$$T_1 = \frac{4900}{\cos 10°} \times \cos 80° = 864 \text{ N to three significant figures.}$$

Example 22.6

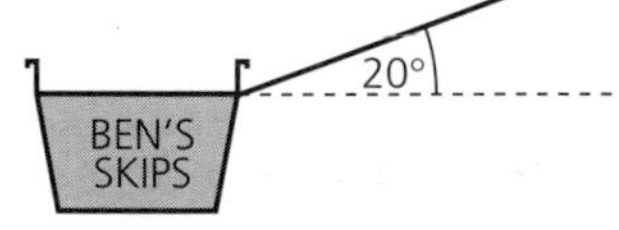

A break-down truck is being used to pull a skip of mass 2 tonnes over some rough ground. The coefficient of friction between the skip and the ground is 0.6. Find the tension in the rope, if the skip is on the point of sliding.

Solution

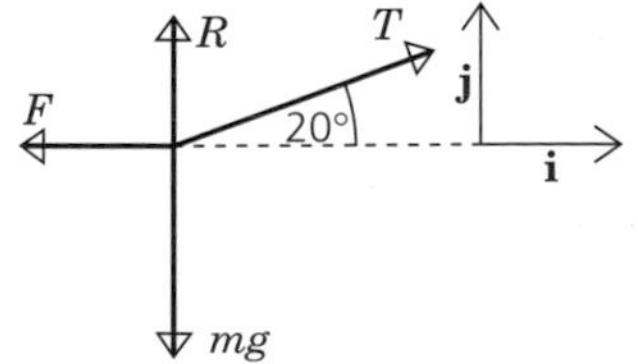

If the skip is modelled as a particle, then there are four forces acting, the force of gravity, mg, a normal reaction, R, friction, F, and the tension on the rope, T.

Each force can be expressed in vector form as below.

Force	Vector form
R	$R\mathbf{j}$
F	$-F\mathbf{i}$
T	$T\cos 20°\mathbf{i} + T\cos 70°\mathbf{j}$
mg	$-19\ 600\mathbf{j}$

The resultant force is:
$(T\cos20° - F)\mathbf{i} + (R + T\cos70° - 19\ 600)\mathbf{j}$

As the skip is on the point of sliding the forces acting must be in equilibrium, so both the horizontal and vertical components of the resultant force must be zero:

$T\cos 20° - F = 0$ *(1)*
and
$R + T\cos70° - 19\ 600 = 0$ *(2)*

Also because the skip is on the point of sliding, F takes its maximum value of μR or $0.6R$ in this case. So equation (1) becomes:

$T\cos 20° - 0.6R = 0$
or

$$R = \frac{T\cos 20°}{0.6}$$

Substituting this value of R in equation (2) to eliminate R gives:

$$\frac{T\cos 20°}{0.6} + T\cos 70° - 19\ 600 = 0$$

Now this can be solved for T.

$$T\left(\frac{\cos 20°}{0.6} + \cos 70°\right) = 19\ 600$$

$$T = \frac{19\ 600}{\frac{\cos 20°}{0.6} + \cos 70°} = 10\,300 \text{ N}$$ *to three significant figures (3 s.f.)*

Example 22.7

A block is placed on an inclined plane at an angle α to the horizontal. The coefficient of friction between the block and the plane is μ. Show that if the block is on the point of sliding:

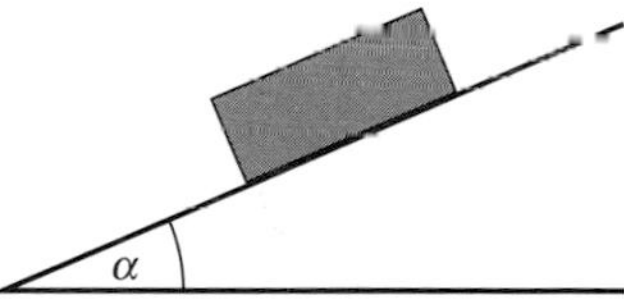

$\tan\alpha = \mu$

Solution

The diagram shows the forces acting on the block, which has been modelled as a particle.

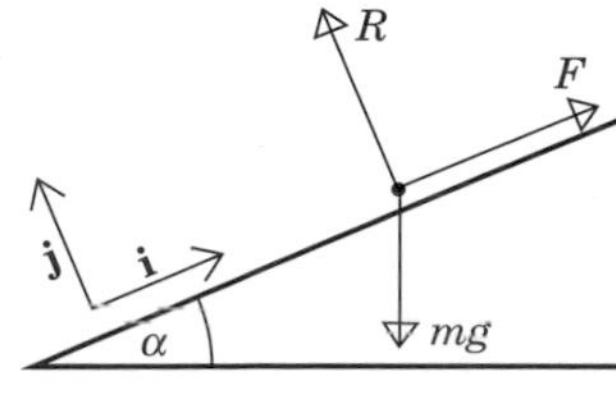

Using the unit vectors as shown, the resultant force is:
$(F - mg\sin\alpha)\mathbf{i} + (R - mg\cos\alpha)\mathbf{j}$

As the block is at rest the resultant must be zero, so:

$F - mg\sin\alpha = 0$ *(1)*
and
$R - mg\cos\alpha = 0$ *(2)*

As the block is on the point of sliding, $F = \mu R$, so equation (1) becomes:
$\mu R - mg\sin\alpha = 0$

Using equation (2) to eliminate R gives: $\mu mg\cos\alpha - mg\sin\alpha = 0$
so that:

$$\mu mg \cos\alpha = mg\sin\alpha$$

$$\mu = \frac{\sin\alpha}{\cos\alpha} = \tan\alpha$$

This angle α is known as the ***angle of friction.***

Example 22.8

The diagram shows two cables that support a sign of mass 3 kg.

a) *Draw a diagram to show the forces acting on the sign.*
b) *The resultant of these three forces is zero. Draw a diagram to illustrate this.*
c) *Use the sine rule to find the tension in each string.*

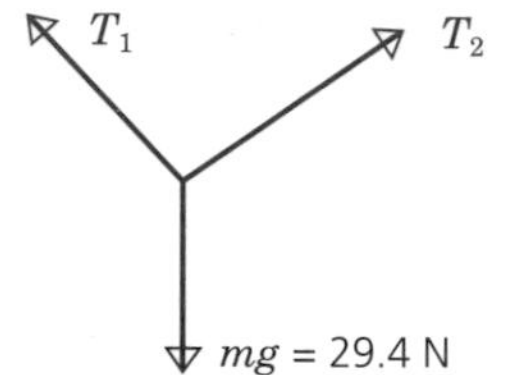

Solution

a) *The diagram shows the three forces acting, the force of gravity and the two tensions.*
b) *Because the resultant force is zero the three vectors representing the forces must combine to form a triangle. We begin by selecting one force, for example the force of gravity. This can be represented by a vector that points straight down. Then we add the tension T_2, beginning at the end of the gravity vector. Finally add T_1, beginning at the end of T_2, to complete the triangle.*

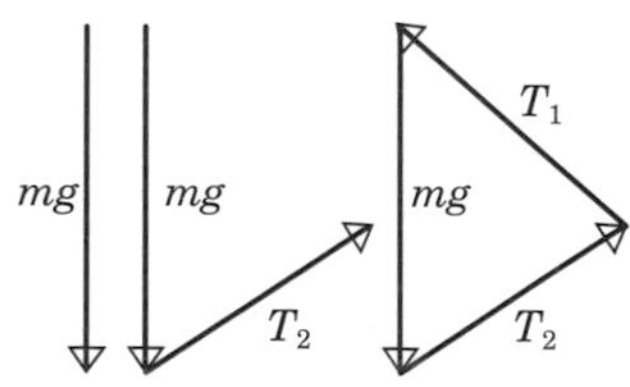

c) *Note that T_2 makes an angle of 30° with the horizontal and so is at 60° to the vertical. Also T_1 is at 40° to the horizontal and so is at 50° to the vertical. So the third angle in the triangle is 180° – (50° + 60°) = 70°.*

Applying the sine rule gives:

$$\frac{29.4}{\sin 70^\circ} = \frac{T_1}{\sin 60^\circ} = \frac{T_2}{\sin 50^\circ}$$

so

$$T_1 = \frac{29.4\sin 60^\circ}{\sin 70^\circ} = 27.1 \text{ N (to 3 s.f)}$$

and

$$T_2 = \frac{29.4\sin 50^\circ}{\sin 70^\circ} = 24.0 \text{ N (to 3 s.f)}$$

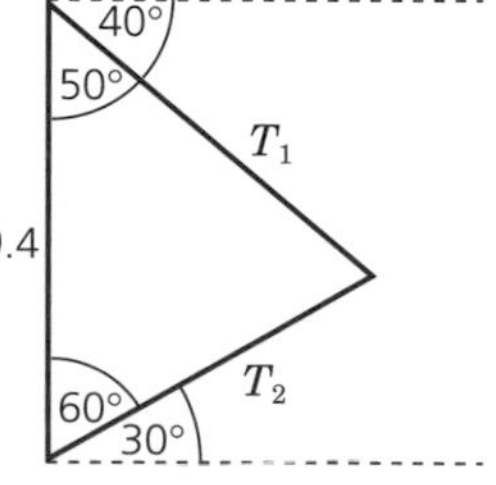

Three forces in equilibrium

When only three forces act on a body which is in equilibrium it can often be easier to use the approach of Example 3.8. This is because the forces will always form a triangle, and then the sine rule can be used.

If three forces act as shown, then this approach can be used to demonstrate that:

$$\frac{P}{\sin A} = \frac{Q}{\sin B} = \frac{R}{\sin C}$$

This result is known as **Lami's theorem**.

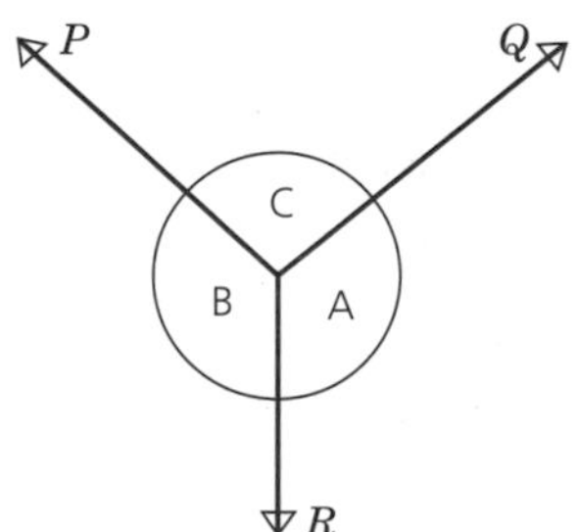

EXERCISES

22.2 CLASSWORK

KEY SKILLS
N 3.2
N 3.3

1 The diagram shows two cables and a light rod that support a mass of 50 kg. The rod and cables lie in a vertical plane.

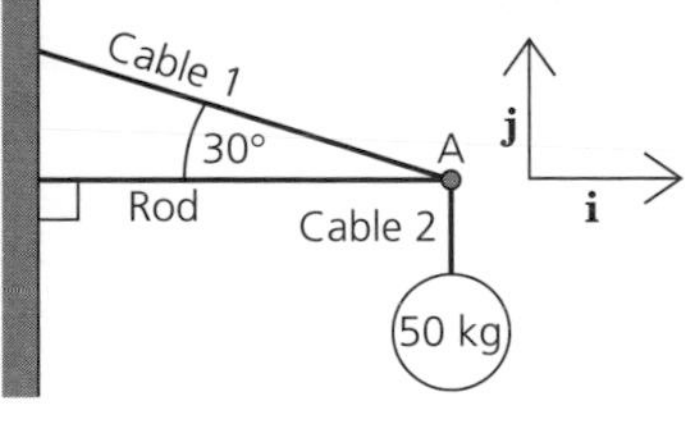

a) State the tension in cable 2.

b) Write each of the forces that act at the point A, in terms of the unit vectors $\mathbf{i}$ and $\mathbf{j}$.

c) Calculate the tension in cable 1 and the thrust in the rod.

d) A third cable is attached to the mass and pulled horizontally so that cable 2 makes an angle of 10° to the vertical as shown. Calculate the new tensions in cables 1 and 2. What happens to the force exerted by the rod?

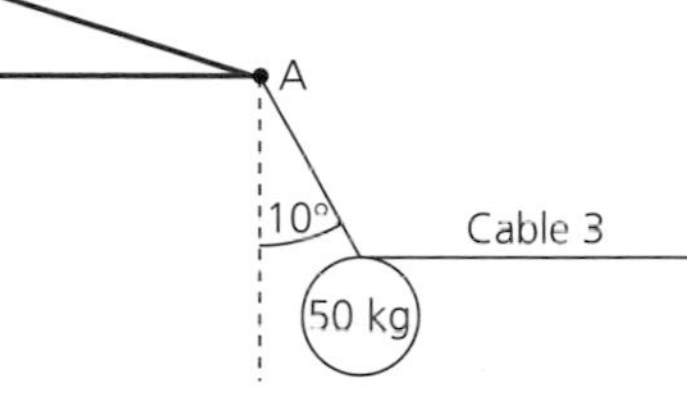

2 The diagram shows a heavy object suspended at rest by two strings.

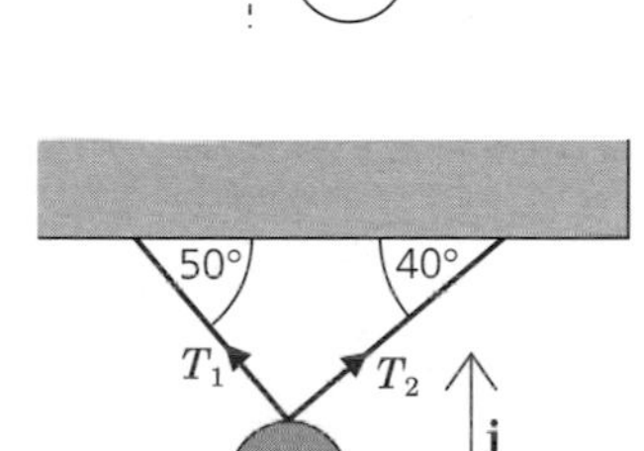

a) Draw a diagram to show the forces acting on the mass.

b) Express each force in terms of the unit vectors $\mathbf{i}$ and $\mathbf{j}$, which act horizontally and vertically respectively.

c) If the tension in the left hand string is 45 N, find the tension in the other string.

d) Find the mass of the object.

3 A child of mass 40 kg is trying to use a plastic tray as a sledge.

a) The child sits on the tray on a slope at 10° to the horizontal. Model the child and tray as a particle. Draw a diagram to show the forces acting on them.

b) Express each force in terms of unit vectors $\mathbf{i}$ and $\mathbf{j}$, which are parallel and perpendicular to the slope respectively. Then find the resultant force.

c) If the child remains at rest find the magnitude of each force.

d) The child tries a steeper slope at 30° to the horizontal, and finds that she gains speed as she slides. State what you can deduce about the magnitude of the friction force.

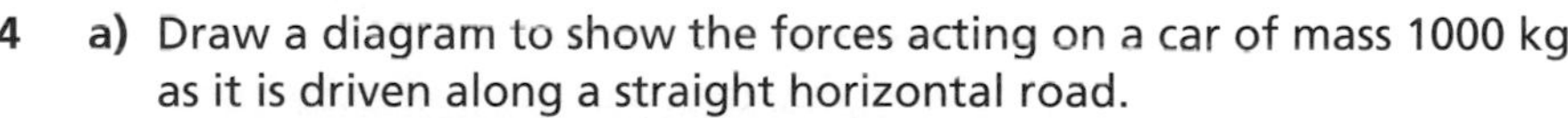

4 **a)** Draw a diagram to show the forces acting on a car of mass 1000 kg as it is driven along a straight horizontal road.

b) What is the relationship between the forward forces and the resistance forces when the car is travelling at top speed?

c) The maximum forward force that can be produced by the car is 2925 N. The resistance forces on the cars are given by $R = v^2 + 20v$, where v is the speed of the car in m s^{-1}. Find the top speed for the car.

d) Show that, when travelling down a slope inclined at 5° to the horizontal, the car experiences a forward force parallel to the slope of 854 N. What is the maximum speed of the car if it begins to freewheel from rest down the slope?

5 Three cables exert forces that act in a horizontal plane as shown, on the top of a telegraph pole.

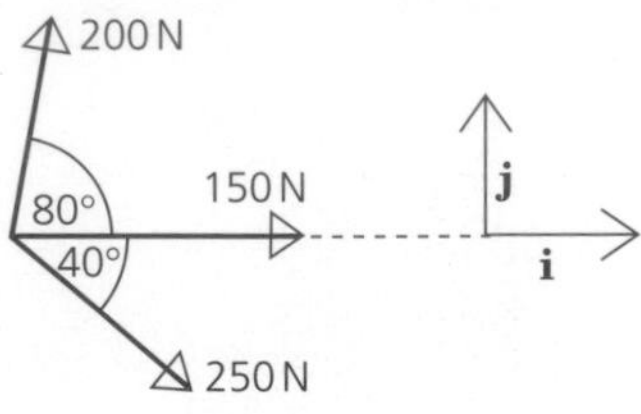

a) Find the resultant of these three forces, in terms of the unit vectors **i** and **j**.

b) A fourth force acts so that the forces on the pole are in equilibrium. Express this force in terms of **i** and **j**.

c) Find the magnitude of this force and draw a diagram to show the direction in which it acts.

d) The fourth cable does not lie in the same horizontal plane as the other cables and the tension in it is in fact 420 N. Find the angle between this cable and the horizontal.

e) Is it likely that the three original forces all act in the horizontal plane?

6 a) Find the tension in the rope shown in the diagram, if there is assumed to be no friction between the block and the slope.

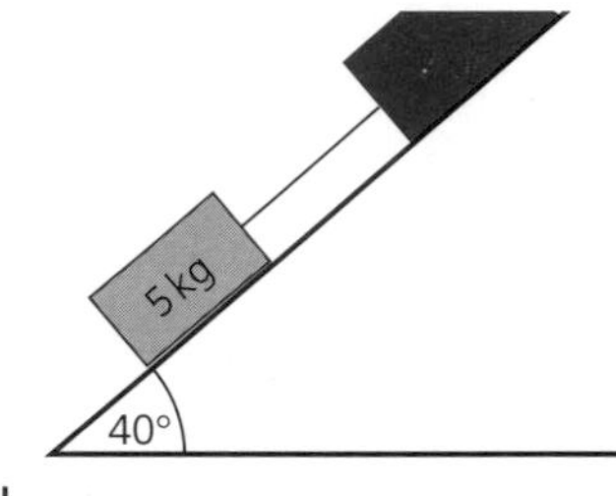

b) The coefficient of friction between the block and the plane is 0.4. Find the tension in the rope, if the block is on the point of sliding down the slope.

7 a) Two cables support an object of mass 50 kg as shown in part (a) of the diagram. Find the tension in each cable.

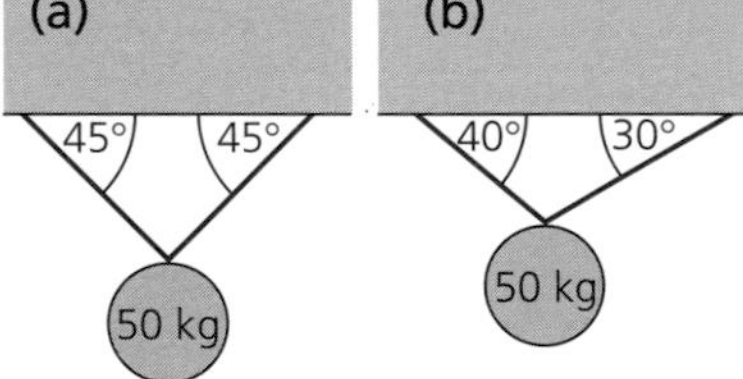

b) Repeat (a) for the second system, shown in part (b) of the diagram.

8 A car of mass 1.2 tonnes is parked on a slope that makes an angle of 8° to the horizontal.

a) Draw a diagram to show the forces acting on the car.

b) Using appropriate unit vectors, express each force in component form and find the resultant.

c) What is the magnitude of the friction forces acting on the car?

EXERCISES

22.2 HOMEWORK

KEY SKILLS
N 3.2
N 3.3

1 The forces shown in the diagram act on a ship that is being pulled by two tugs at a constant velocity.

a) Find the resultant of the 3000 N and 2000 N forces, in terms of the unit vectors **i** and **j**.

b) Find the other force marked, in terms of **i** and **j**, if all three are in equilibrium.

c) Find the magnitude of the third force and the size of the angle, α

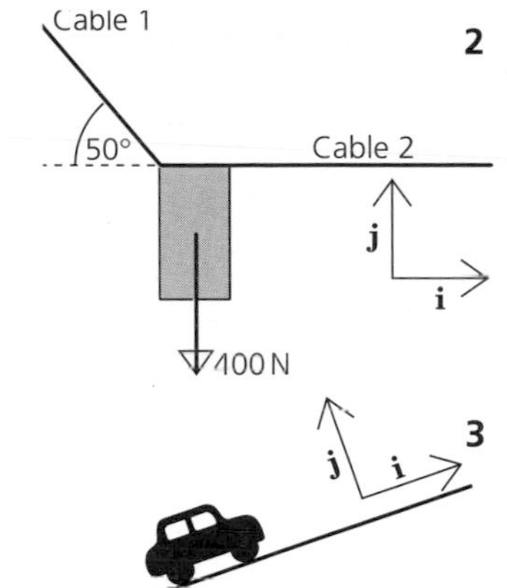

2 The diagram shows a crate that is being lowered into position with two cables. In the position shown the crate is at rest.

a) Let T_1 be the tension in cable 1 and T_2 be the tension in cable 2. Write down the resultant force in terms of T_1, T_2, $\mathbf{i}$ and $\mathbf{j}$.

b) Use the vertical component of the resultant to find the tension in cable 1.

c) Use the horizontal component of the resultant to find the tension in cable 2.

3 A car of mass 950 kg is parked on a hill as shown in the diagram.

a) Draw a diagram to show the forces acting on the car, if it is modelled as a particle.

b) Express the force of gravity, in terms of the unit vectors $\mathbf{i}$ and $\mathbf{j}$.

c) Find the magnitude of the friction and normal reaction forces.

4 A child hauls a sledge of mass 18 kg up a slope at 7° to the horizontal.

a) Assume that the rope is parallel to the slope and there is no friction between the sledge and the slope. Find the tension in the rope.

b) Explain which assumptions in (a) are unrealistic, and suggest any alternatives.

c) The rope in fact makes an angle of 10° to the slope. Find the tension in the rope and compare this to your solution for a horizontal rope.

5 A skier of mass 72 kg is travelling, at a constant speed, down a slope at 13° to the horizontal.

a) Find the friction force acting on the skier

b) What value of the coefficient friction does your answer to (a) suggest should be used when modelling the motion of the skier?

c) Criticise this model for friction and suggest how it could be modified.

6 Two removal men are carrying a bookcase up a flight of stairs. The mass of the bookcase is 30 kg. The higher man exerts a horizontal force P on the bookcase. The lower man exerts a force Q at 80° to the horizontal. Find the magnitude of the forces P and Q.

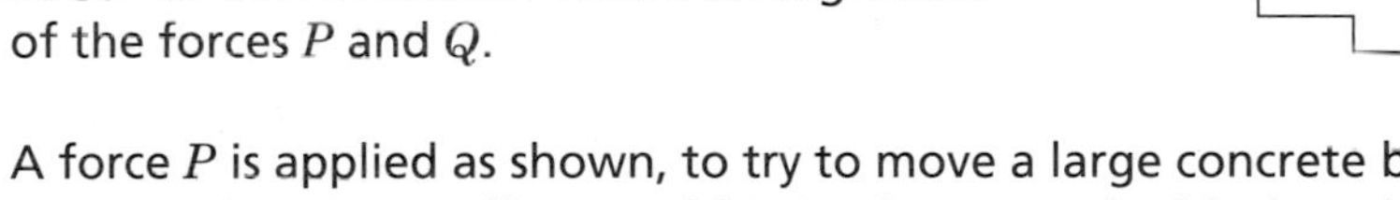

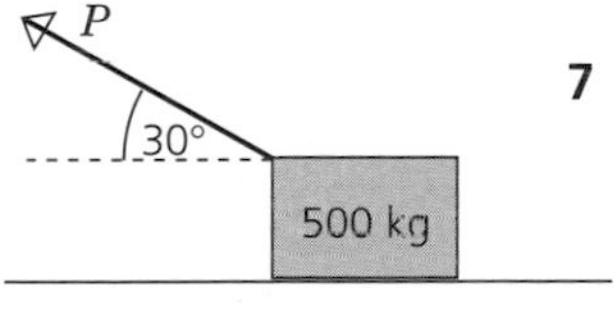

7 A force P is applied as shown, to try to move a large concrete block of mass 500 kg. The coefficient of friction between the block and the surface is 0.6. Find P when the block is on the point of sliding.

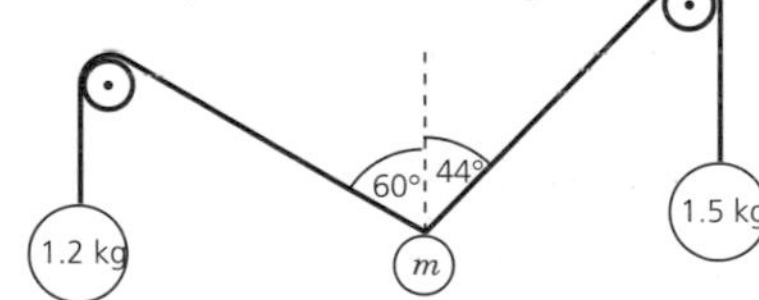

8 The system shown is in equilibrium.

a) Find the tension in each string.

b) Find the mass of the middle object.

CONSOLIDATION EXERCISES FOR CHAPTER 22

1 Two forces, of magnitudes 1 N and 3 N, act on a particle in the directions shown in the diagram. Calculate the magnitude of the resultant force on the particle and the angle between this resultant force and the force of magnitude 3 N.

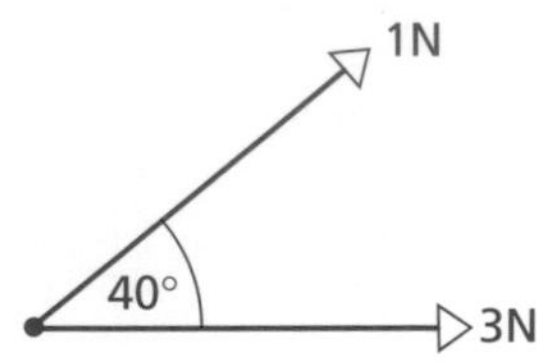

(OCR Question 1 Mechanics 1 Specimen Paper)

2 A particle P is attached to one end of a light inextensible string, the other end of the string being attached to a fixed point. A horizontal force of magnitude 50 N is applied to P, and P is in equilibrium under gravity with the string making an angle of 40° with the vertical, as shown in Fig 1.

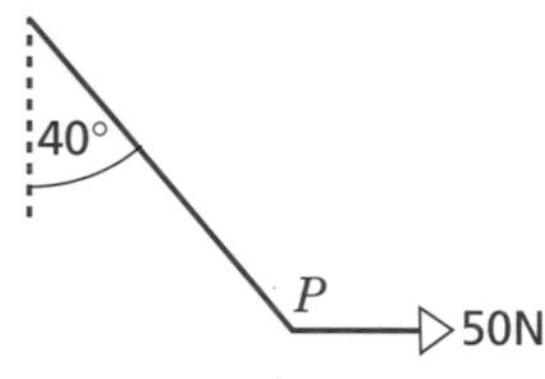

Find, to 3 significant figures,

a) the tension in the string,

b) the weight of P.

(EDEXCEL Question 1 Mechanics 1 Specimen Paper)

3 A smooth plane is inclined at an angle 10° to the horizontal. A particle P of mass 2kg is held in equilibrium on the plane by a force of magnitude F newtons, as shown in Fig 1.

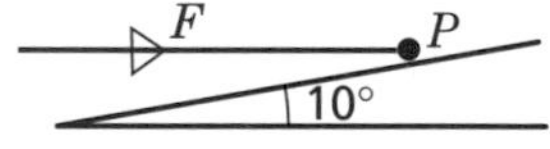

Find, to 3 significant figures,

a) the normal reaction exerted by the plane on P,

b) the value of F.

(EDEXCEL Question 2 Mechanics 1 Paper June 1998)

4 The diagram shows a box of weight 150 newtons which is being pulled along a rough horizontal surface at a constant speed. The tension in the rope pulling the box is 50 newtons, and the rope makes an angle of 30° with the horizontal.

The coefficient of friction between the box and the surface is μ.

a) Draw the diagram showing the forces acting on the box.

b) Calculate the value of

i) the normal reaction force R,

ii) the friction force F.

c) Calculate the value of μ.

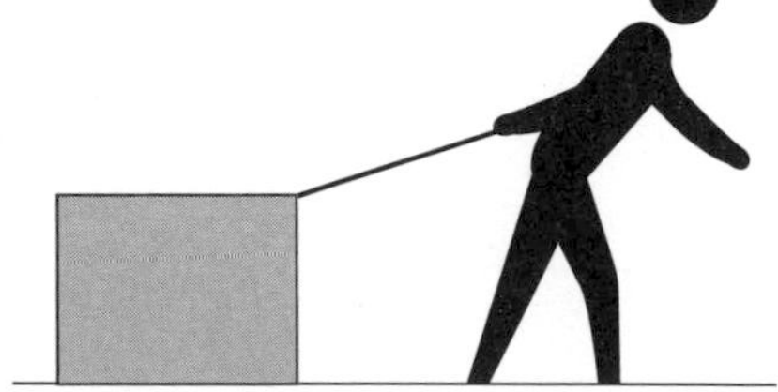

(AQA Spec A Question 4 Mechanics 1 Specimen Paper)

5 An object of mass 3kg is suspended by two horizontal light, inextensible strings. The strings make angles of 30° and 40° with the horizontal, as shown in the diagram.

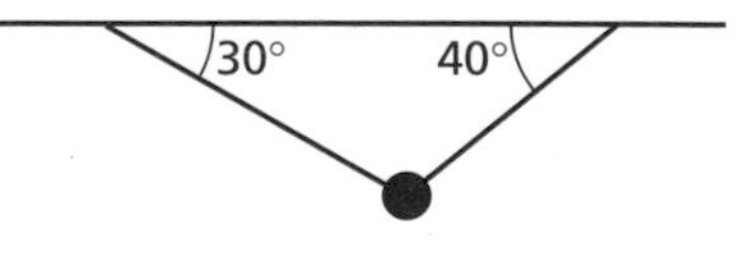

Find the magnitude of the tension in each string.

(AEB Question 15 AS Paper June 1999)

6 The two ends of a string are attached to two points A and B of a horizontal beam. A package of mass 2kg is attached to the string at the point C. When the package hangs in equilibrium $\angle BAC = 20°$ and $ABC = 40°$, as shown in Fig. 2.

By modelling the package as a particle and the string as light and inextensible, find, to 3 significant figures,

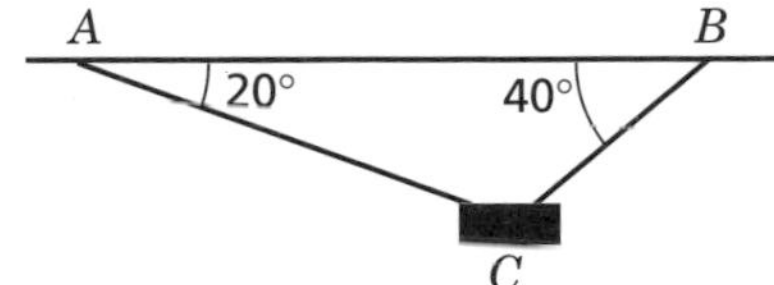

a) the tension in AC,

b) the tension in BC.

(EDEXCEL Question 4 Mechanics 1 Paper January 1997)

MATHEMATICAL MODELLING ACTIVITY

1 → 2 → 3 → 4 → 5 → 6

Specify the real problem

Problem statement

How steep should an artificial ski-slope be?

The first stage in solving a modelling problem is to identify the important features.

Make a list of the important features that you think should be considered in this problem.

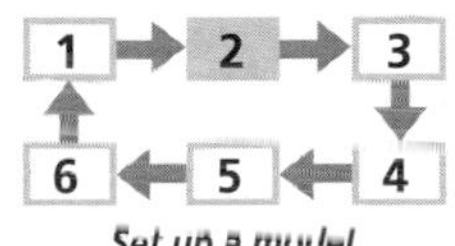

Set up a model

Set up a model

Having considered the features of a situation it is then necessary to draw up a set of assumptions that will allow a mathematical problem to be formulated. The assumptions set out below have been prepared as a possible way of starting the problem.

- The skier is modelled as a particle.
- The skier skis straight down the slope.
- The skier maintains a constant speed, unless pushing with the sticks.
- No air resistance acts on the skier.
- The coefficient of friction between the skier and the slope is 0.2.
- The mass of the skier is m kg
- The slope makes a constant angle α with the horizontal.

The assumptions allow a first simple model to be formulated.

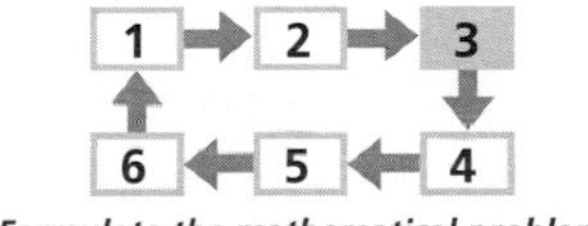

Formulate the mathematical problem

Formulate a mathematical problem

The skier skis down on a slope subject to a resistance force of $0.2R$. What angle should the slope make to the horizontal, if the skier is to travel with a constant speed?

1 → 2 → 3 → 4 → 5 → 6

Solve the mathematical problem

Mathematical solution

The diagram shows the forces acting.

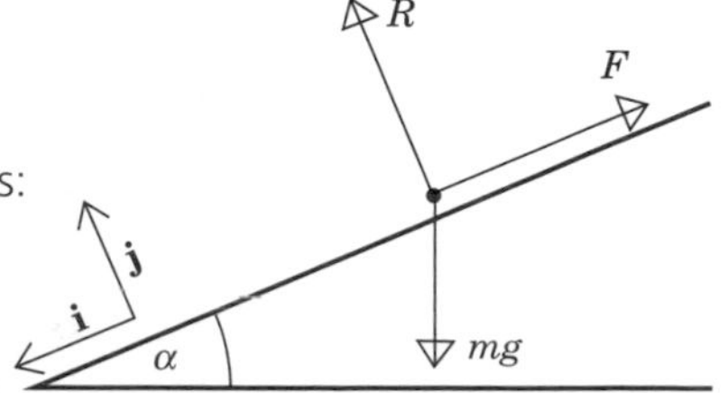

The resultant force can be expressed as:
$(mg\sin\alpha - F)\mathbf{i} + (R - mg\cos\alpha)\mathbf{j}$.

As the skier travels at a constant speed the resultant force is zero so,

$mg\sin\alpha - F = 0$ (1)

and

$R - mg\cos\alpha = 0$ (2)

But $F = 0.2R$ so equation (1) becomes:

$mg\ \sin\alpha - 0.2R = 0$ (3)

Eliminating R from equations (2) and (3) gives:

$mg\cos\alpha = 5mg\sin\alpha$

or

$\frac{\sin\alpha}{\cos\alpha} = \frac{1}{5} \Rightarrow \tan\alpha = \frac{1}{5}$

so $\alpha = 11.3°$.

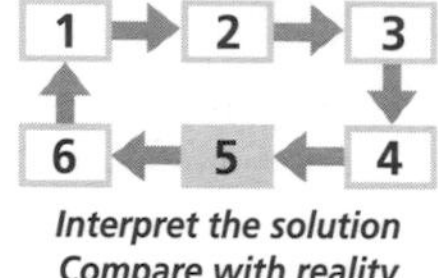

Interpret the solution
Compare with reality

Interpretation

If the slope makes an angle of 11.3°, skiers will be able to travel down it at a constant speed, but will need to push off to start moving.

Two problems that arise are that skiers may not travel straight down the slope and the air resistance on the skiers may be significant.

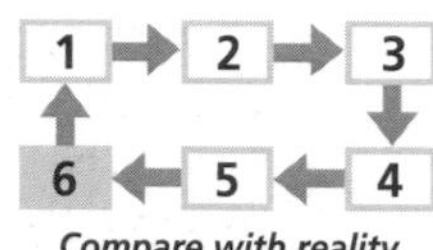

Compare with reality

Compare with reality

It may be possible for you to visit a local ski slope or obtain some data. Does the angle of 11.3° degrees seem about right? Is the model suggested for the friction reasonable?

Refining the model

Make an additional assumption about the path of the skier or the air resistance acting. Keep this refinement simple and use it to obtain a revised solution to the problem.

POSSIBLE MODELLING TASKS

1 What is the steepest hill that it would be possible to park a car on safely? (**Note**: The hand brake normally acts only on the back wheels.)

2 A 'button lift' is often used at artificial ski slopes to take skiers to the top of the slope. Investigate the forces that act on a skier who is using such a device.

3 A winch is to be installed at the top of a slipway to help sailors get their dinghies out of the water. How strong a rope would be needed for the winch?

Summary

After working through this chapter you should:

- be able to express forces in the form $a\mathbf{i} + b\mathbf{j}$
- be able to find the magnitude and direction of a force
- know that in equilibrium the resultant force is zero
- be able to find the magnitude of the forces that act on an object that is at rest or moving with constant velocity.

Kinematics in one dimension

- *There are many objects that move in only one dimension, for example, a car moving along a straight road or a ball that is dropped and allowed to fall.*
- *Simple formulae can be developed to deal with these cases.*

UNIFORM MOTION

Exploration 23.1

Motion of a dropped ball

Imagine that you drop a ball from the top of a tall building. You check the ball every second. Sketch a diagram to show the position of the ball at the end of every second while it is falling.

Example 23.1

A cyclist is travelling at a constant speed of 4 m s^{-1}. Sketch a graph of speed against time. What is the gradient of the line that you have drawn? What does it represent? Use the graph to find the distance travelled between:

a) *$t = 0$ and $t = 2$,*
b) *$t = 2$ and $t = 5$,*
c) *$t = 0$ and $t = T$.*

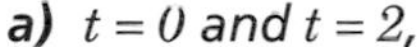

Sketch a graph of distance travelled against time. What is the relationship between the gradient of this graph and the speed?

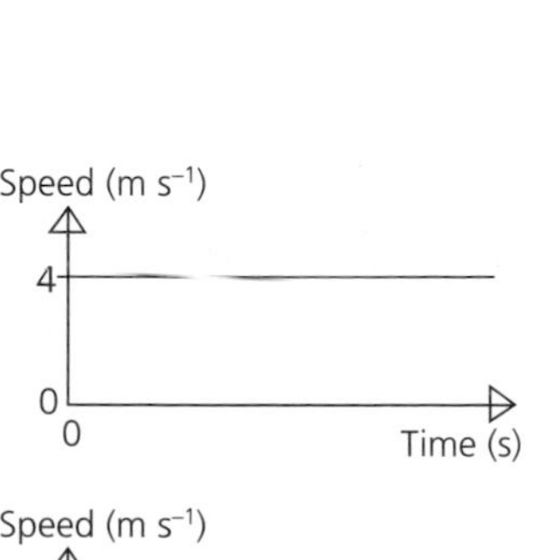

Solution

As the speed of the cyclist does not change this can be simply represented by a horizontal line, as shown. The gradient of the line is 0, which simply means that the speed is not changing.

The distance travelled is represented by the area under the line, between the required time points.

a) *For the distance between $t = 0$ and $t = 2$ we require the area of the shaded region shown. This gives distance $4 \times 2 = 8$ m.*

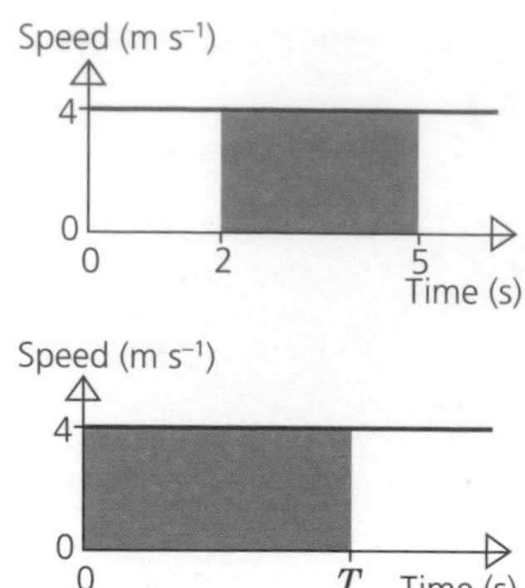

b) *For the distance between $t = 2$ and $t = 5$, we require the area of the shaded region shown.*
This gives distance $= 4 \times (5 - 2) = 12$ m.

c) *The distance between $t = 0$ and $t = T$ is illustrated by the area of the shaded region in the diagram.*
This gives distance $= 4 \times T = 4T$
The distance–time graph is simply a straight line because the distance travelled, s, is $s = 4t$. The gradient of the line is 4 which is the same as the speed of the cyclist.

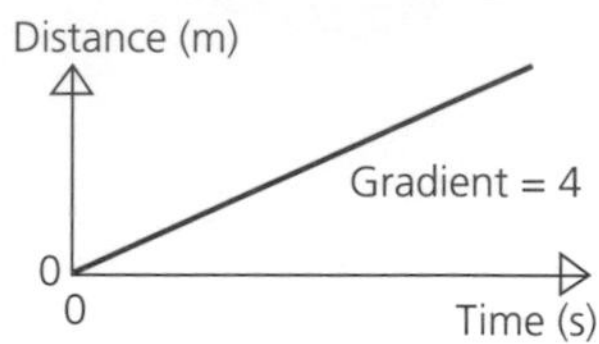

Example 23.2

The speed of a car increases at a constant rate from 0 to 15 m s^{-1} in a 10 second interval. Sketch a graph to show the speed of the car against the time. Find the gradient of the line and describe what information this gives about the motion of the car. Find the distance travelled by the car between:

a) *$t = 0$ and $t = 5$,*
b) *$t = 0$ and $t = T$.*

*Use the answer to **b)** to sketch a graph of distance against time. What is the relationship between the gradient of this graph and the speed?*

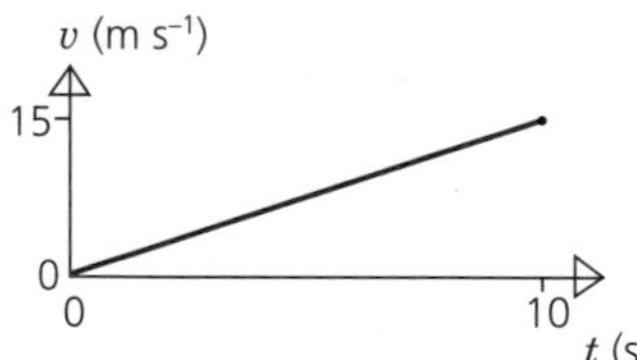

Solution

The sketch shows how the speed increases. The gradient of the line is given by $\frac{15}{10} = 1.5$. This value describes how the speed of the car increases, in this case by 1.5 m s^{-1} per second. This is known as the acceleration of the car. In this case it is 1.5 m s^{-2}. The speed of the car is then $v = 1.5t$.

a) *The distance travelled between $t = 0$ and $t = 5$ is represented by the area of the shaded region.*
So the distance is:
$\frac{1}{2} \times 5 \times (1.5 \times 5) = 18.75$ *m*

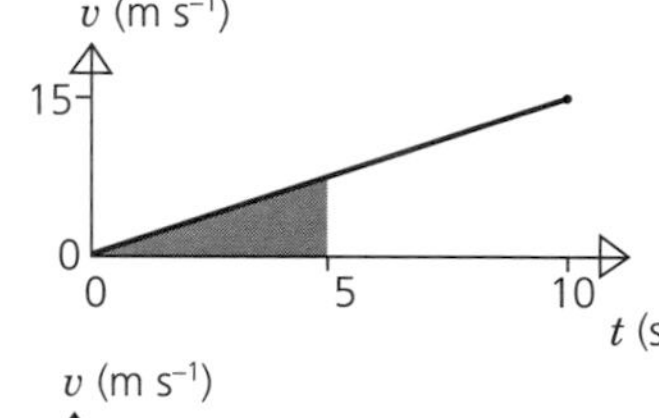

b) *The distance travelled between $t = 0$ and $t = T$ is represented by the area of the shaded region.*
This gives distance $= \frac{1}{2} \times T \times 1.5T = 0.75T^2$

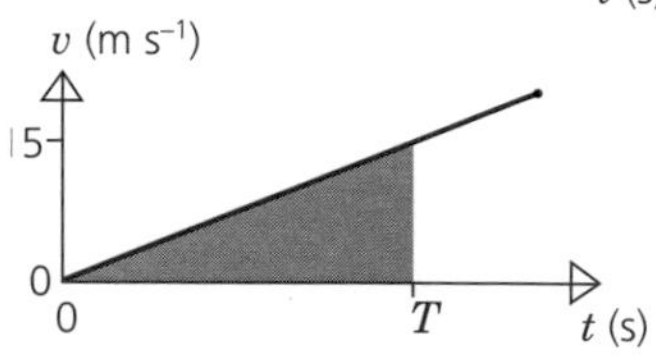

Using this result, we can draw a graph of distance against time as shown. Note that the gradient of this graph increases with time and that the speed also increases with time. In fact the gradient of the curve gives the speed at that time.

Gradient and area

The **gradient** of the distance–time graph shown gives the **speed**.

The **area under** the speed–time graph shown gives the **distance travelled**. The gradient of this speed–time graph gives the **acceleration**.

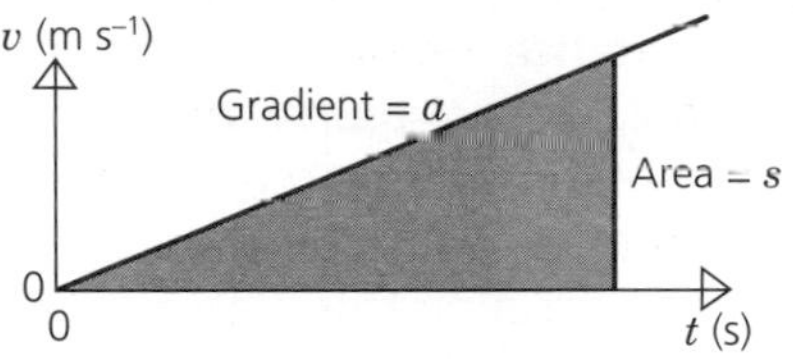

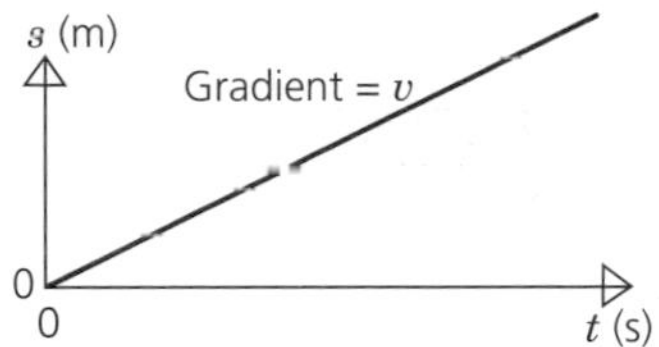

EXERCISES

23.1 CLASSWORK

1 An aeroplane is travelling along a straight line at a constant speed of 140 m s^{-1}. Sketch a graph of speed against time for this motion. Use this graph to find the distance travelled by the aeroplane in:
a) 5 seconds, **b)** T seconds.
What is the gradient of the line and what is the acceleration of the aircraft?

2 A hot air balloon rises vertically with a speed that is assumed to increase at a constant rate from 0 to 2 m s^{-1} over a 30-second period.
a) What is the acceleration of the balloon? Use this to find an expression for the speed of the balloon.
b) Assuming that the balloon's speed continues to increase at the same rate, find the distance that the balloon rises in:
i) 10 seconds, **ii)** 40 seconds, **iii)** T seconds.
c) Sketch a graph of the distance the balloon rises against the time.
d) Suggest a more realistic way for the speed of the balloon to increase.

3 A ball is dropped from a height of 18 m. As it falls, its speed at time t seconds is given by $v = 9.8t$ m s^{-1}.
a) Sketch a graph of speed against time for the ball, and find its acceleration.
b) Find a formula for the distance travelled by the ball in t seconds.
c) How long does it take for the ball to reach the ground?

4 A car is travelling at 10 m s^{-1} when it begins to increase its speed at a constant rate of 1.2 m s^{-2}. The car travels in a straight line.
a) Sketch a graph to show how the speed increases. Assume the speed starts to increase when $t = 0$.
b) Find the speed of the car when $t = T$.
c) Find the distance travelled by the car between:
i) $t = 0$ and $t = 5$, **ii)** $t = 0$ and $t = T$.
d) Sketch a graph of distance against time for the car.

EXERCISES

23.1 HOMEWORK

1 A car travels at a constant speed of 20 m s^{-1} along a straight line. Sketch a graph of speed against time for the car. Use the graph to find the distance travelled by the car in:
a) 10 seconds, **b)** t seconds.

2 A cyclist increases her speed from 0 to 5 m s^{-1} over a 15-second period. Assume that the speed increases at a constant rate and the cyclist travels along a straight line.

a) Sketch a graph of speed against time for the cyclist. Find the gradient of the line and state the acceleration of the cyclist.

b) Write down an expression for the speed of cyclist at time t.

c) Find the distance the cyclist travels in:

i) 5 seconds, **ii)** 15 seconds, **iii)** t seconds.

d) This question has assumed that the speed increases at a constant rate. Suggest an alternative model for the way the speed increases, illustrating this with a sketch graph. Would the total distance travelled in the 15 seconds be more or less than for the original model?

3 As a stone falls vertically from rest in a tank of water its speed at time t seconds is modelled by $v = 0.8t$ m s^{-1}.

a) Sketch a speed–time graph and find the acceleration of the stone.

b) Find an expression for the distance travelled by the stone.

c) How long does it take the stone to travel the 1.2 m to the bottom of the tank and what is its speed when it hits the bottom?

4 A train is travelling at 30 m s^{-1} when it begins to slow down at a rate of 2 m s^{-2}.

a) Sketch a graph of speed against time for the train.

b) How long does the train take to stop?

c) How far has it travelled before it stops?

d) What was the acceleration of the train?

EQUATIONS OF MOTION FOR CONSTANT ACCELERATION

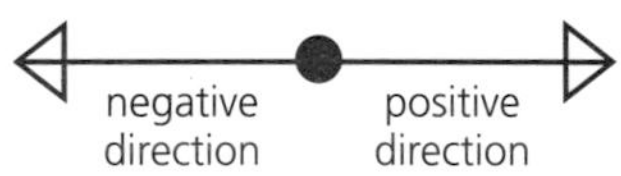

When motion is restricted to one dimension, the objects can move in one of two directions, one defined as **positive** and the other as **negative**. The **speed** of an object does not give any indication of its direction of motion. The **velocity** of an object describes the speed and direction of the motion. A velocity of +4 m s^{-1} describes motion with speed of 4 m s^{-1} in the positive direction, while a velocity of –4 m s^{-1} describe a motion with a speed of 4 m s^{-1} in the negative direction.

Accelerations can also be either positive or negative when motion is restricted to one dimension. Similarly an object can **move** in either a positive or negative direction. The distance an object moves simply tells us how far the object has travelled, so instead of working with distance we shall now use the vector term, **displacement**, which describes where an object is. The magnitude of the displacement describes how far the object is from the origin and the sign defines whether this is in the positive or negative direction.

Example 23.3

A car has a velocity u and experiences an acceleration a.

a) *Sketch a graph of velocity against time for the car.*

b) *Find an expression for the velocity of the car.*

c) *Find an expression for the distance travelled by the car.*

Solution

a) *The graph shows how the velocity changes with time.*

b) *The acceleration is a, so the gradient of the line will be a. This gives: $v = u + at$*

c) *The distance travelled is represented by the area shaded in the graph. The area of the rectangle is ut and the area of the triangle is $\frac{1}{2}at^2$, so the distance travelled is given by: $s = ut + \frac{1}{2}at^2$*

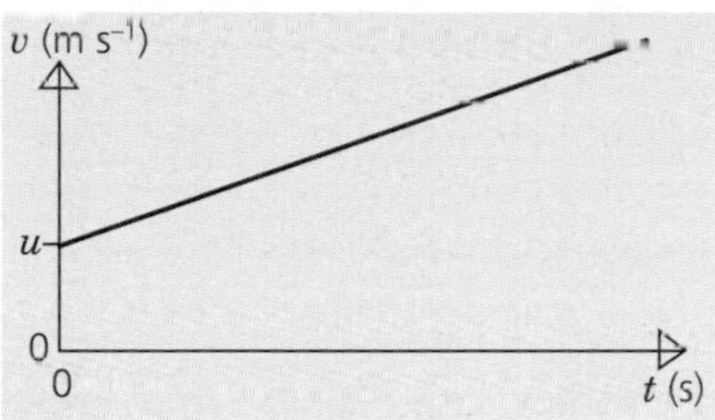

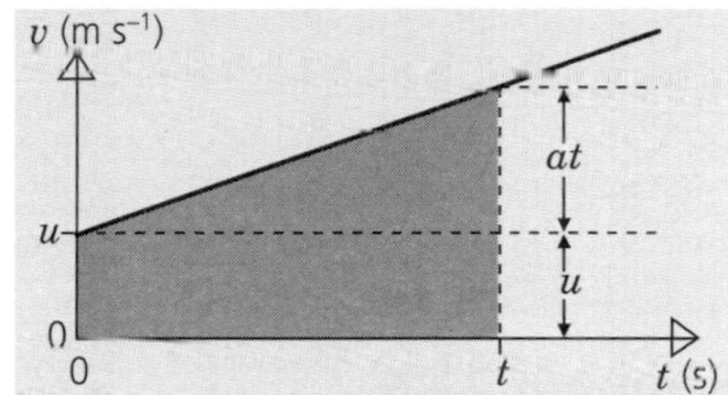

Note: *It is usual to denote the distance travelled by s.*

Example 23.4

Use the equations $v = u + at$ and $s = ut + \frac{1}{2}at^2$ to show that $v^2 = u^2 + 2as$.

Solution

Rearranging $v = u + at$ gives: $t = \dfrac{v - u}{a}$

Substituting this value for v into $s = ut + \frac{1}{2}at^2$ gives:

$$s = \frac{u(v-u)}{a} + \frac{a(v-u)^2}{2a^2}$$

$$\Rightarrow 2as = 2u(v-u) + (v-u)^2$$

$$\Rightarrow 2as = 2uv - 2u^2 + v^2 - 2uv + u^2$$

$$\Rightarrow 2as = v^2 - u^2$$

$$\Rightarrow v^2 = u^2 + 2as$$

Constant acceleration equations

The equations derived in the above examples are known as the **constant acceleration equations**. They can be used whenever an acceleration is constant. These equations are listed below, together with a fourth equation.

$$v = u + at$$

$$s = ut + \tfrac{1}{2}at^2$$

$$v^2 = u^2 + 2as$$

$$s = \tfrac{1}{2}(u + v)t$$

Note that s is displacement, v is final velocity, u is initial velocity, a is acceleration and t is time.

Example 23.5

A ball is dropped from a height of 5 m and falls from rest under the influence of gravity so that its acceleration is 9.8 m s⁻².

a) *When does the ball hit the ground?*

b) *How fast is it moving when it hits the ground?*

Solution

Assume 'down' is the positive direction in this problem.

a) *Using* $s = ut + \frac{1}{2}at^2$ *with* $a = 9.8$ *and* $u = 0$ *gives:*

$s = 0 \times t + \frac{1}{2} \times 9.8t^2$

When the ball hits the ground $s = 5$, *so* $5 = 4.9t^2$

so $t^2 = \sqrt{\frac{5}{4.9}} = 1.01$ *seconds*

b) *The velocity of the ball is given by:*

$v = u + at$

Using $u = 0$, $a = 9.8$ *and* $t = 1.01$ *gives:*

$v = 0 + 9.8 \times 1.01 = 9.90$ *m s*$^{-1}$

Example 23.6

A hot air balloon is rising at 0.5 m s^{-1} *at a height of 40 m, when it begins to experience a downward acceleration of 0.25 m s*$^{-2}$.

a) *Find the height that the balloon reaches before it stops rising.*
b) *How long does it take to move from its initial position, at a height of 40 m, to ground level?*
c) *At what speed is the balloon travelling when it reaches the ground?*

Solution

First note $a = -0.25$ *and* $u = 0.5$.

positive
direction

a) *Using* $v^2 = u^2 + 2as$ *we have:* $0^2 = 0.5^2 + 2 \times (-0.25)s$
because at the maximum height, $v = 0$, *which gives:*

$s = \frac{0.5^2}{2 \times 0.25} = 0.5$ *m*

so the balloon rises a further 0.5 m to 40.5 m.

b) *Relative to the original position, we require* $s = -40$.
Using $s = ut + \frac{1}{2}at^2$ *we obtain:*

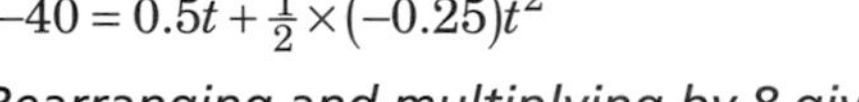

$-40 = 0.5t + \frac{1}{2} \times (-0.25)t^2$

Rearranging and multiplying by 8 gives:

$t^2 - 4t - 320 = 0$

and solving this quadratic equation gives $t = -16$ *or* $t = 20$.
We require the positive value, $t = 20$, *which means that it takes 20 seconds for the balloon to reach the ground.*

c) *Using* $v = u + at$, *with* $a = -0.25$, $u = 0.5$ *and* $t = 20$ *gives:*

$v = 0.5 + (-0.25) \times 20 = -4.5$ *m s*$^{-1}$

The balloon is travelling downwards at 4.5 m s^{-1}.

EXERCISES

23.2 CLASSWORK

1 A ball dropped from a height of 10 m has an acceleration of 9.8 m s^{-2}.
a) How long does it take to reach the ground?
b) How fast is it moving when it hits the ground?

2 Find the acceleration of each object below.
a) A skateboarder whose velocity increases from 0.5 m s^{-1} to 1.3 m s^{-1} in seven seconds.
b) A car that increases in velocity from 0 to 25 m s^{-1} in five seconds.
c) A skier whose velocity increases from 0.5 m s^{-1} to 7 m s^{-1} while travelling 20 m.
What assumptions have you had to make to answer this question?

3 A ball is thrown straight up into the air with an initial speed of 8 $m\,s^{-1}$ and has a downward acceleration of 9.8 $m\,s^{-2}$.
   a) Find the maximum height that the ball reaches if it is released 1.5 m above ground level.
   b) Find the speed of the ball when it hits the ground.

4 A cyclist was travelling at 6 $m\,s^{-1}$ when she slowed down and stopped in 5 m. Assume that the acceleration of the cyclist was constant.
   a) Find the acceleration of the cyclist.
   b) How long did it take the cyclist to stop?

5 A car travelling at 20 $m\,s^{-1}$ was 200 m from a set of traffic lights, which were red. The driver slowed down, until he was 50 m from the lights and travelling at 8 $m\,s^{-1}$, when the lights changed to green. He immediately began to accelerate, passing the lights at a speed of 15 $m\,s^{-1}$.
   a) What was the acceleration of the car while it was slowing down?
   b) If the driver had maintained the same acceleration would he have stopped before he reached the lights?
   c) How long was it before the lights changed to green?
   d) What was the acceleration of the car after the lights changed?
   e) How long did it take the driver to increase the speed of the car from 8 $m\,s^{-1}$ to 15 $m\,s^{-1}$?
   f) What was the total time taken to travel the 200 m?
   g) What was the average speed of the car?
   h) What assumptions have you had to make to solve this problem?

6 A car accelerated from rest at 3 $m\,s^{-2}$ for 10 seconds, travelled at a constant speed for 2 minutes and then took six seconds to stop. How far did the car travel in total?

7 A lift accelerated at 0.2 $m\,s^{-2}$ from rest for 10 seconds, then travelled at constant speed for 20 seconds, and then took 15 seconds to stop. Find the distance travelled by the lift if it was always moving upwards.

8 A ball is dropped from a height of 1 m and bounces, rebounding to a height of 70 cm.
   a) Find the speed of the ball when it hits the ground.
   b) Find the speed of the ball when it leaves the ground.
   c) If the ratio of the speeds before and after bouncing are in a constant ratio, find the height after the second bounce.

EXERCISES

23.2 HOMEWORK

1 Find the acceleration of each object described below.
   a) A train that increases its velocity from rest to 8 $m\,s^{-1}$ in 40 seconds.
   b) A ball whose velocity increases from 3 $m\,s^{-1}$ to 11 $m\,s^{-1}$ in four seconds.
   c) A car whose velocity decreases from 10 $m\,s^{-1}$ to 2 $m\,s^{-1}$ over 40 m.

2 A ball experiences an acceleration of $-9.8\,m\,s^{-2}$ after it has been thrown straight upwards with an initial speed of 2 $m\,s^{-1}$ from a height of 1 m.
   a) When is the velocity of the ball zero?
   b) What is the maximum height reached by the ball?
   c) Find the speed of the ball when it hits the ground.

3 A ball hits the ground travelling at $5\,\text{m}\,\text{s}^{-1}$ and rebounds in the opposite direction at $4\,\text{m}\,\text{s}^{-1}$. Find the acceleration of the ball if it is in contact with the ground for 0.5 seconds.

4 The *Highway Code* states that the braking distance for a car travelling at 30 mph ($13.4\,\text{m}\,\text{s}^{-1}$) is 45 m.
a) Find the acceleration of a car that stops in this way, and the time it takes for the car to stop.
b) What would be the stopping distance for a car travelling at 100 mph ($44.7\,\text{m}\,\text{s}^{-1}$)?
c) How long would the car take to stop?

5 A train accelerates at $0.4\,\text{m}\,\text{s}^{-2}$ from rest, until it reaches a velocity of $20\,\text{m}\,\text{s}^{-1}$. It then slows down, stopping in 100 m.
a) What is the total distance travelled by the train?
b) Find the time that the train is in motion.

6 A lift travels 5 m in 20 seconds. The graph shows how the velocity changes.
a) Express the maximum speed of the lift in terms of T and a, the acceleration of the lift during its first stage of motion.
b) Express the total distance travelled in terms of a and T.
c) If $T = 5$, find a and the maximum speed of the lift.

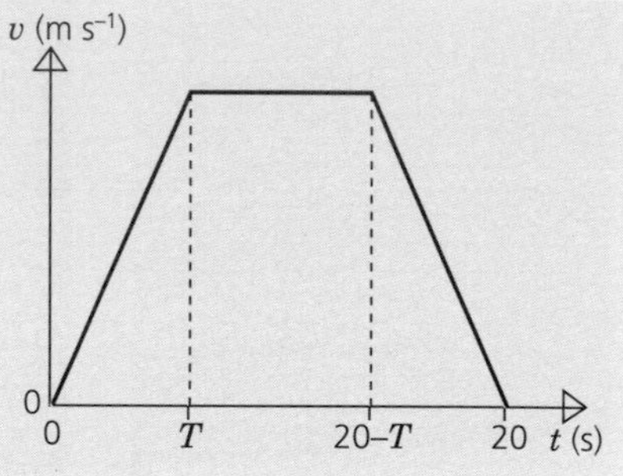

7 Two cars are level for an instant at a set of traffic lights, one is at rest and the other travelling at a constant $10\,\text{m}\,\text{s}^{-1}$. The car that was at rest catches up with the other car when they have both travelled 100 m.
a) Find the acceleration of the car that was at rest and the time that it took to travel the 100 m.
b) Find the speed of this car when it catches up with the other car.
c) Once the cars are level they both continue at a constant speed. How far apart are they after a further 20 seconds?

8 A cyclist travels 10 km in one hour. A possible model for the velocity of the cyclist is shown in the diagram.
a) Find the acceleration of the cyclist based on this model and the maximum speed reached.
b) Criticise this model and suggest a more suitable alternative.

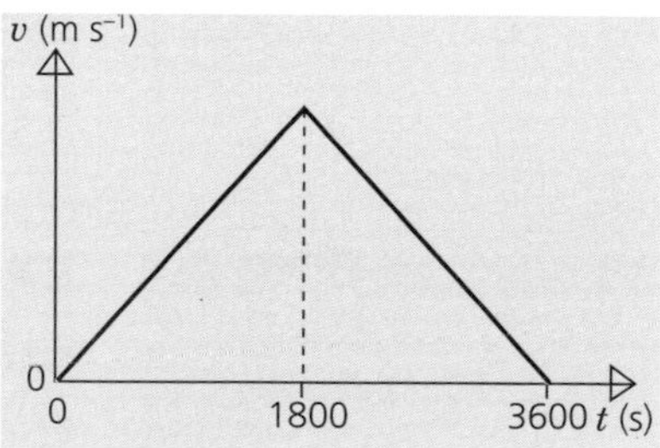

MATHEMATICAL MODELLING ACTIVITY

Problem statement

In many towns traffic calming schemes have now been introduced in residential areas. One of the most unpopular but effective methods is to use humps in the road called 'sleeping policemen'. How far apart should sleeping policemen be placed to ensure that vehicles do not exceed a speed of 30 mph ($13.4\,\text{m}\,\text{s}^{-1}$)?

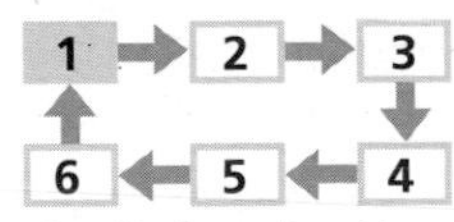
Specify the real problem

Set up a model

The first stage in setting up a model is to identify the important features. The list below includes the main features in this problem.

- The speed at which vehicles can cross the bumps.
- The acceleration of vehicles once they have crossed the bumps.
- The way in which vehicles slow down when approaching the bumps.

Are there any other features that you feel are important and should be included in the list?

Using this list of features it is now possible to draw up a set of assumptions, which is listed below.

- The cars cross the bumps at a speed of zero.
- The cars are treated as particles with no length.
- The cars stop according to the *Highway Code*, so that at 30 mph (13.4 m s^{-1}) it takes 14 m to stop.
- The acceleration of the cars once over the first bump is such that it can accelerate from 0 to 60 mph (26.8 m s^{-1}) in ten seconds.

Show that the acceleration of the car would be 2.7 m s^{-2} while gaining speed and –6.4 m s^{-2} while slowing down.

These assumptions allow a first model to be formulated.

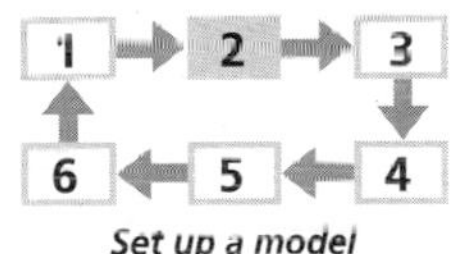
Set up a model

Formulate a mathematical problem

The diagram shows a sketch of a velocity time graph for the vehicle. Find the distance travelled by the car, as it is gaining speed and total distance covered.

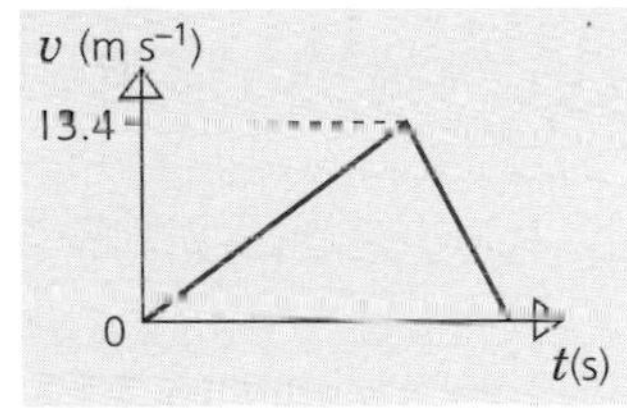

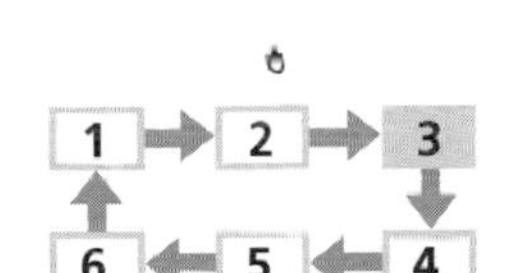
Formulate the mathematical problem

Mathematical solution

The distance travelled while the car accelerates can be found by first using the equation $v^2 = u^2 + 2as$ with $v = 13.4$ m s^{-1} (30 mph), $u = 0$ and $a = 2.7$ m s^{-2}. Show that $s = 33$ m.

The distance travelled by the car as it accelerates is 33 m, and it travels a further 14 m while braking. The total distance travelled by the car is 47 m.

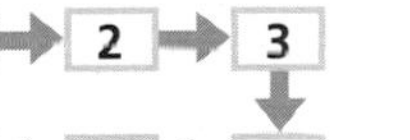
Interpret the solution

Interpretation

The speed bumps or sleeping policemen should be placed 47 m apart. What do you think will be the effects of the humps on the drivers?

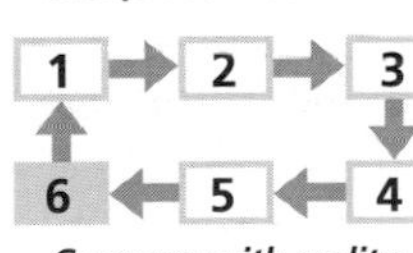
Compare with reality

Compare with reality

It is very likely that placing humps 47 m apart will cause a great deal of irritation for drivers and may result in other problems on the road.

As the distance between the humps is relatively small, it may be important to consider the length of the cars likely to travel on the stretch of road.

Very few drivers will actually accelerate from 0 to 60 mph in ten seconds under normal conditions. What other criticisms, if any, can be made of the results obtained? Can you find an existing traffic calming scheme to compare the results with?

Refining the model

In order to respond to the criticisms above define a new problem where the lengths of the vehicles are taken into account, and a more realistic figure is used for their acceleration. Find a solution to your revised problem.

POSSIBLE MODELLING TASKS

1 On Guernsey at many junctions a 'filter in turn' system operates. Vehicles take it in turn to leave from the roads joining the junction, one at a time from each road, taking each road in turn. Investigate how traffic would flow through a junction like this.

2 Consider a pedestrian crossing with traffic lights. Devise a timing schedule for the changing of the lights.

CONSOLIDATION EXERCISES FOR CHAPTER 23

1 A lift travels from rest from the ground floor and comes to rest again at a carpark 15 metres above the ground floor. The motion of the lift takes place in three stages. In the first stage the lift moves with a constant acceleration; it then moves with a constant velocity of 4m s^{-1}; and finally it moves with a constant retardation until it comes to rest. The times for the three stages of the motion are $1\frac{1}{2}$, t and 1 seconds, respectively.

a) Sketch a velocity–time graph to show the motion of the lift.

b) Hence, or otherwise, calculate the time for which the lift is in motion.

c) Calculate the average velocity of the lift during the motion.

(AQA Question 3 Specimen Paper A)

2 Two sprinters compete in a 100 m race, crossing the finishing line together after 12 seconds. The two models, A and B, as described below, are models for the motions of the two sprinters.

Model A The sprinter accelerates from rest at a constant rate for 4 seconds and then travels at a constant speed for the rest of the race.

Model B The sprinter accelerates from rest at a constant rate until reaching a speed of 9 m s^{-1} and then travels at this speed for the rest of the race.

a) for **model A**, find the maximum speed and the initial acceleration of the sprinter.

b) For **model B**, find the time taken to reach the maximum speed and the initial acceleration of the sprinter.

c) Sketch a distance time graph for each of the two sprinters on the same set of axes. Describe how the distance between the two sprinters varies through the race.

(AEB Question 2 Paper 3 June 1998)

3 A motor–cyclist drives at a steady speed of 30m s^{-1} along a straight road in a built–up area, thus breaking the speed limit. A policeman sits in a police car on the road and notes the motor–cycle's speed as it passes. The policeman takes 5s to get ready and then sets off in pursuit of the motor–cycle, which maintains its constant speed. The police car accelerates from rest with uniform acceleration 3 m s^{-2} until

it reaches a maximum speed of $45\,\text{m}\,\text{s}^{-1}$, after which it continues at this steady speed.

a) Draw on the same diagram speed–time graphs to illustrate the movements of the motor–cycle and police car.

T seconds after the motor–cycle passes the police car, the police car has reached its maximum speed, but has not yet overtaken the motor–cycle.

b) Find an expression for the distance travelled by the police car in terms of T.

c) Hence, or otherwise, find the time that elapses from the moment the motor–cycle passes the police car to the moment when the police car draws level with the motor–cycle.

(EDEXCEL Question 2 Mechanics 1 January 1998)

4 A straight stretch of a railway line passes over a viaduct which is 600m long. An express train on this stretch of line normally travels at a speed of $50\,\text{m}\,\text{s}^{-1}$. Some structural weakness in the viaduct is detected and engineers specify that all trains passing over the viaduct must do so at a constant speed of no more than $10\,\text{m}\,\text{s}^{-1}$. Approaching the viaduct, the train therefore reduces its speed from $50\,\text{m}\,\text{s}^{-1}$ with constant deceleration $0.5\,\text{m}\,\text{s}^{-2}$, reaching a speed of precisely $10\,\text{m}\,\text{s}^{-1}$ just as it reaches the viaduct. It then passes over the viaduct at a constant speed of $10\,\text{m}\,\text{s}^{-1}$. As soon a s it reaches the other end of the viaduct, it accelerates to its normal speed of $50\,\text{m}\,\text{s}^{-1}$ with constant acceleration $0.5\,\text{m}\,\text{s}^{-2}$.

a) Sketch a speed–time graph to show the motion of the train during the period from the time when it starts to reduce speed to the time when it is running at full speed again.

b) Find the total distance travelled by the train while its speed is less than $50\,\text{m}\,\text{s}^{-1}$.

c) Find the extra time taken by the train for the journey due to the speed restriction on the viaduct.

(EDEXCEL Question 5 Mechanics 1 June 1997)

5 The diagram shows an approximate (t, v) graph for the motion of a parachutist falling vertically; $v\,\text{m}\,\text{s}^{-1}$ is the parachutist's downwards velocity at time t seconds after he jumps out of the plane. Use the information in the diagram

i) to give a brief description of the parachutist's motion throughout the descent,

ii) to calculate the height from which the jump was made.

The mass of the parachutist is 90kg. Calculate the upwards force acting on the parachutist, due to the parachute, when $t = 7$.

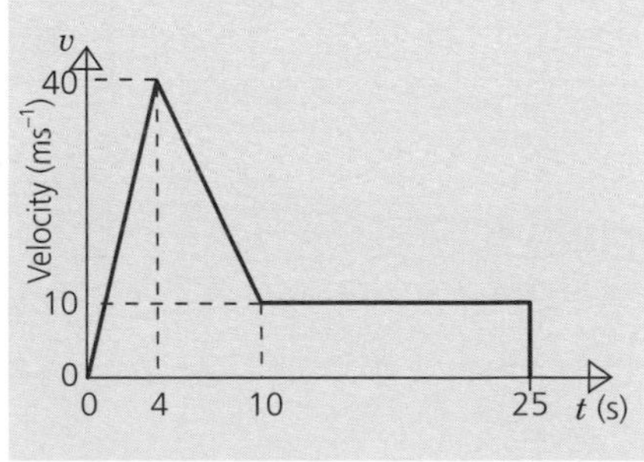

(OCR Question 6 Mechanics 1 Specimen Paper, 2000)

6 This question concerns a car and a cyclist that are modelled as particles, that travel in a straight line. The graph below shows a velocity–time graph for the car on a short journey, after which it remains at rest. The car travels 20 m at a constant speed.

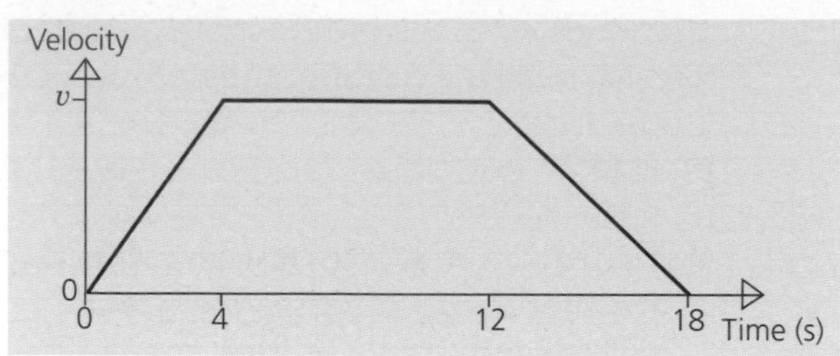

a) Find the acceleration of the car on each stage of the journey and sketch a graph to show how it varies.

b) Find the total distance travelled by the car.

A cyclist is next to the car at $t = 0$, when the car begins to move. The cyclist travels in the same direction as the car at a constant speed of $1.5\,\mathrm{m\,s^{-1}}$.

c) Does the car or the cyclist travel the greatest distance in the first 4 seconds? Find the time when they have travelled the same distance.

d) Would you encounter any difficulties if you do not model the car and cyclist as particles?

(AQA Specification B Question 6 Mechanics 1 Specimen Paper, 2000)

Summary

After working through this chapter you should:

- be able to use the constant acceleration equations:

$$s = ut + \tfrac{1}{2}at^2$$
$$v = u + at$$
$$v^2 = u^2 + 2as$$
$$s = \tfrac{1}{2}(u + v)t$$

- be aware of the conditions when these equations can be applied.

Motion and vectors

- *In real life motion is seldom restricted to one dimension.*
- *The ideas of motion developed in Chapter 23 can be extended into two dimensions.*

POSITION VECTORS

Exploration 24.1

Describing position and motion

Imagine a yacht sailing from a port at A to another port at B. You are at O, where you have a clear view of the yacht.

- How could you describe the **position** of the yacht?
- How could you describe the **motion** of the yacht?

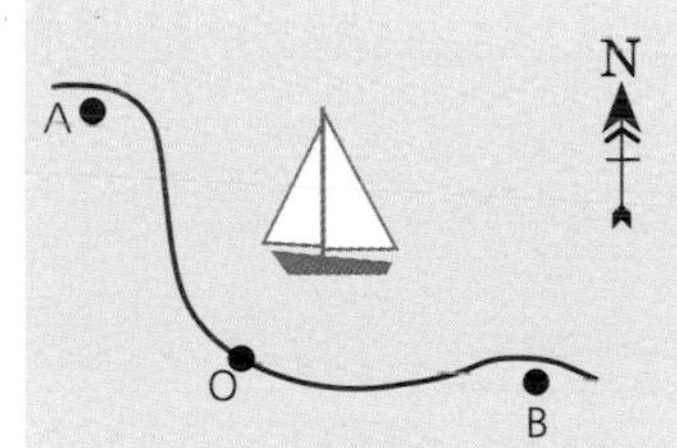

Relative position

In the exploration, O is a **fixed position** or **reference point**. The positions of the yacht as it moves can be described **relative to** that fixed point. In Mechanics, a **position vector** describes where an object is, relative to a **fixed origin** or reference point. It gives information about the distance of the object from the reference point, and its direction from that point.

This diagram again shows the yacht, but this time a position vector has been drawn in. The vector could be described as 'six kilometres on a bearing of 068°', or alternatively as $5.56\mathbf{i} + 2.25\mathbf{j}$, where $\mathbf{i}$ is a unit vector pointing east and $\mathbf{j}$ is a unit vector pointing north.

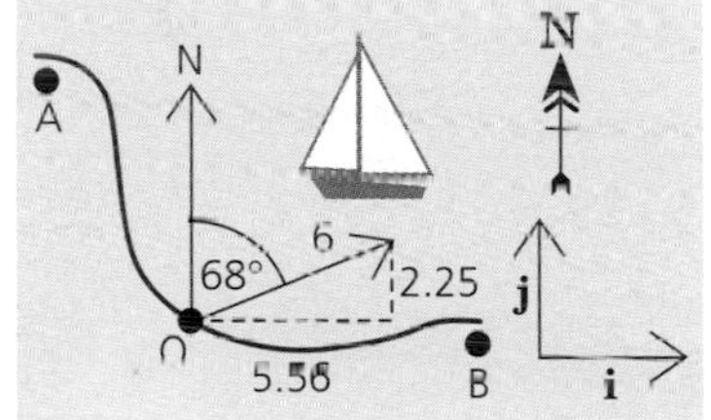

It is important to remember that every time the yacht, or any other object, moves, then its position vector changes. The diagram has now been revised to show the position vectors at four different times, and the path followed by the yacht. It is a common convention that $\mathbf{r}$ is used for the position vector of an object.

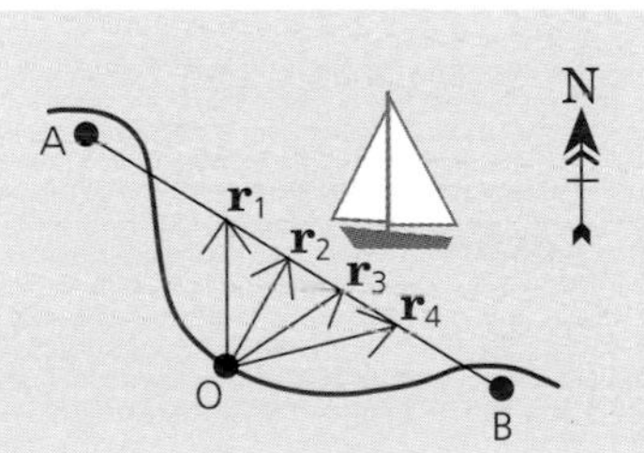

Example 24.1

The path of a rocket launched at a fireworks display is given by:

$$\mathbf{r} = 10t\,\mathbf{i} + \left[2(t-3)^3 + 54\right]\mathbf{j}$$

until the rocket explodes when $t = 3$. Find the position of the rocket when $t = 0, 1, 2$ and 3. Use this information to sketch the path of the rocket.

Solution

To find the position vectors, substitute the values $t = 0$, 1, 2 and 3 into

$\mathbf{r} = 10t\mathbf{i} + \left[2(t-3)^3 + 54\right]\mathbf{j}$

For $t = 0$:

$\mathbf{r} = 10 \times 0\mathbf{i} + \left[2(-3)^3 + 54\right]\mathbf{j} = 0\mathbf{i} + 0\mathbf{j}$

For $t = 1$:

$\mathbf{r} = 10 \times 1\mathbf{i} + \left[2(-2)^3 + 54\right]\mathbf{j} = 10\mathbf{i} + 38\mathbf{j}$

For $t = 2$:

$\mathbf{r} = 10 \times 2\mathbf{i} + \left[2(-1)^3 + 54\right]\mathbf{j} = 20\mathbf{i} + 52\mathbf{j}$

For $t = 3$:

$\mathbf{r} = 10 \times 3\mathbf{i} + \left[2(0)^3 + 54\right]\mathbf{j} = 30\mathbf{i} + 54\mathbf{j}$

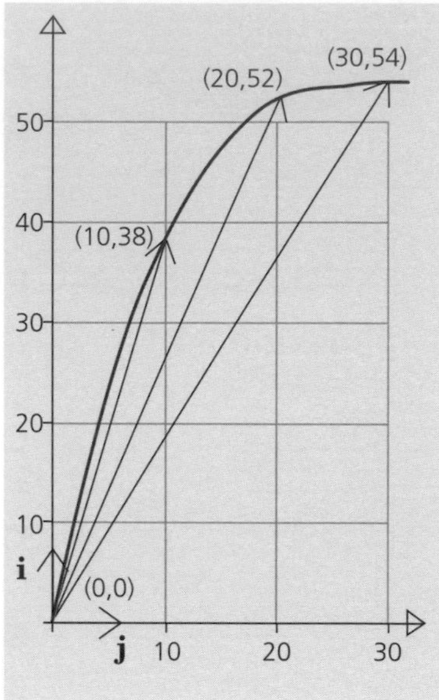

The diagram shows the position vectors that were calculated. The changing position of the rocket has been drawn as a smooth curve through the known positions.

GRAPHICS CALCULATOR ACTIVITY

Exploration 24.2

KEY SKILLS
IT 3.2

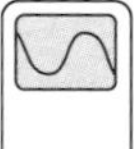

Plotting paths

For this activity your calculator must be set into parametric mode.

The position vector of an object that moves in two dimensions will be of the form: $\mathbf{r} = x\mathbf{i} + y\mathbf{j}$

where x and y are functions of time, t. In parametric mode it is possible to enter the expressions for x and y and plot the path of the object.

Consider:

$\mathbf{r} = 4t\mathbf{i} + \left(8 - 5t^2\right)\mathbf{j}$

where

$x = 4t$ and $y = 8t - 5t^2$

To enter these follow the instructions below.

Texas

Press Y=

Type 4T then ENTER

Type 8T-5T^2 then ENTER

Press WINDOW and enter the values below:

$X_{min} = 0$; $X_{max} = 9$ $X_{scl} = 1$
$Y_{min} = 0$; $Y_{max} = 6$; $Y_{scl} = 1$
$T_{min} = 0$; $T_{max} = 1.6$; $T_{step} = 0.1$

Then press GRAPH to see the path.

Casio

Press GRAPH

Type 4T, 8T-5T^2 and EXE

Press RANGE and enter the values below:

$X_{min} = 0$; $X_{max} = 9$; scl = 1
$Y_{min} = 0$; $Y_{max} = 6$; scl = 1

T, q min : 0 max : 1.6 ptch : 0.1

Then press EXE

1 T_{max} gives the maximum time value for the plotting process. Try changing this value from 1.6 to 1.0 and see what happens to the graph.

2 To produce a plot that gives the true shape of the path the value of X_{max} must be 1.5 times bigger than the value of Y_{max}. Try changing these values so that the plot fills the whole screen.

3 Try to describe situations where the motion of an object would follow the path you have plotted.

4 Now plot the path defined by:
$\mathbf{r} = 4t\mathbf{i} + (4t - 2.5t^2)\mathbf{j}$
How does it compare with the path you plotted above?

5 The path of the rocket in the worked example was defined by:
$\mathbf{r} = 10t\mathbf{i} + \left[2(t-3)^3 + 54\right]\mathbf{j}$ for $0 \le t \le 3$
Plot the path on your calculator. (Use $T_{max} = 3$, $X_{max} = 90$, and $Y_{max} = 60$)

6 Plot the path of objects that move with the position vectors given below: You will need to choose suitable values of X_{max}, Y_{max}, etc.

a) $\mathbf{r} = 4t\mathbf{i} + 3t\mathbf{j}$ for $0 \le t \le 5$

b) $\mathbf{r} = (3t - t^2)\mathbf{i} + 4t\mathbf{j}$ for $0 \le t \le 3$

c) $\mathbf{r} = \left(4 - \frac{1}{t}\right)\mathbf{i} + 3t\mathbf{j}$ for $1 \le t \le 10$

d) $\mathbf{r} = \left(t + \frac{1}{t}\right)\mathbf{i} + t\mathbf{j}$ for $1 \le t \le 5$

EXERCISES

24.1 CLASSWORK

1 A hockey ball is struck so that it begins to move on a pitch. Its position vector at time t seconds is given by $\mathbf{r} = (4t\mathbf{i} + 0.1t^2\mathbf{j})$m where $\mathbf{i}$ and $\mathbf{j}$ are unit vectors parallel and perpendicular to the side of the pitch.
a) Find the position vector when, $t = 0$, 1, 2, 4 and 6 seconds.
b) Sketch the path of the ball.

2 The yacht considered in the discussion at the start of this section moves with position vector relative to O:
$\mathbf{r} = 2t\mathbf{i} + (10 - 3t)\mathbf{j}$
where distances are in kilometres and time t is in hours.
a) The yacht leaves A when $t = 0$ and arrives at B when $t = 4$. Find the position vectors of A and B relative to O.
b) Find the position of the yacht when $t = 2$. Express this position relative to O using a distance and a bearing.
c) When is the ship at the position given by $3\mathbf{i} + 5.5\mathbf{j}$?

3 Two boats A and B move so that their position vectors in metres at time t seconds are:
$\mathbf{r}_A = (8 + 2t)\mathbf{i} + (4 - 3t)\mathbf{j}$ and $\mathbf{r}_B = 4t\mathbf{i} + 2t\mathbf{j}$
where $\mathbf{i}$ and $\mathbf{j}$ are unit vectors east and north respectively.
a) Find the positions of A and B, when $t = 0$, 2 and 3.
b) Sketch the path of each boat.
c) When does B reach the initial position of A? How far apart are the boats at this time?

4 The position vector of a javelin, in metres, at time t seconds, is modelled by:

$$\mathbf{r} = 15t\mathbf{i} + (2 + 10t - 5t^2)\mathbf{j}$$

where $\mathbf{i}$ and $\mathbf{j}$ are horizontal and vertical unit vectors respectively.

a) Find the position of the javelin when $t = 0$, 0.5, 1, 1.5 and 2.0.
b) Draw the path of the javelin.
c) Find the range of values of t for which the model is valid.
d) Find the length of the throw.
e) What problems may arise in modelling a javelin as a particle?

5 A snooker ball is struck by a cue and moves so that its position, relative to its starting point is:

$$\mathbf{r} = 0.5t\mathbf{i} + (0.4t + 0.08t^2)\mathbf{j}$$

where $\mathbf{i}$ and $\mathbf{j}$ are unit vectors parallel to the sides of the table.

a) Find $\mathbf{r}$ when $t = 0$, 1, 2 and 3.
b) Plot the path of the ball.
c) The table is not quite level. Draw an arrow on your diagram to show the direction of the slope.

6 A rocket was launched at a fireworks display. At time t seconds the position of the rocket, in metres, was:

$$\mathbf{r} = 20t\mathbf{i} + \left[(t-4)^3 + 64\right]\mathbf{j}$$

where $\mathbf{i}$ and $\mathbf{j}$ are horizontal and vertical unit vectors respectively. The rocket exploded when $t = 4$.

a) Find the position of the rocket when $t = 0$, 1, 3, 3.5 and 4.
b) Draw the path of the rocket.
c) In what direction was the rocket moving when it exploded?

7 A snooker table has the dimensions shown in the diagram. A ball has position vector $\mathbf{r} = (0.2\mathbf{i} + 0.3\mathbf{j})\,\text{m}$ when it is struck by the cue. It then moves so that it drops into the pocket marked X.

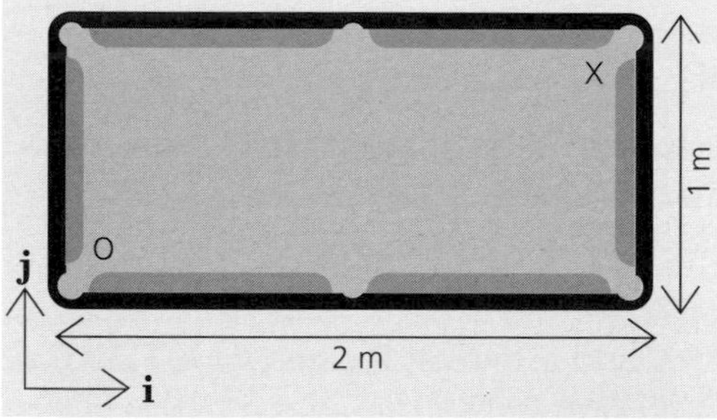

a) State the position vector of the ball at time t seconds when it drops into the pocket.
b) The position vector of the ball at time t seconds is given by: $\mathbf{r} = (a + bt)\mathbf{i} + (c + dt)\mathbf{j}$
Use the initial position of the ball to determine the values of the constants a and c.
c) The ball drops into the pocket two seconds after it was hit. Use this to find the value of the constants b and d.

EXERCISES

24.1 HOMEWORK

1 The motion of a car as it travels round a bend is described by the position vector:

$$\mathbf{r} = (0.5t^2 + 4t)\mathbf{i} + 3t\mathbf{j}$$

where $\mathbf{i}$ and $\mathbf{j}$ are perpendicular unit vectors, t is time in seconds and all distances are in metres.

a) Find the position of the car when $t = 0$, 1, 2 and 3.
b) Plot the path of the car.

2 A basket ball moves so that at time t seconds its position vector in metres is:

$$\mathbf{r} = 3t\mathbf{i} + (2 + 12t - 5t^2)\mathbf{j}$$

where $\mathbf{i}$ and $\mathbf{j}$ are horizontal and vertical unit vectors.

a) Find the positions of the basket ball when $t = 0$, 1 and 2.
b) Draw the path of the basket ball.
c) What is the maximum height of the ball?
d) Find the time for which the ball is in the air.
e) How far does the ball land from the point where it was thrown?

3 A football rolls on a sloping pitch so that its position vector, in metres, at time t seconds is:

$$\mathbf{r} = 3t\mathbf{i} + 0.1t^2\mathbf{j}$$

where $\mathbf{i}$ and $\mathbf{j}$ are perpendicular unit vectors.

a) Find the position of the football when $t = 0$, 1, 2, 3 and 4.
b) Plot the path of the ball.
c) On your plot draw an arrow to indicate the direction of the slope.

4 A cyclist is moving down a hill, so that her position vector, in metres, at time t seconds, is given by:

$$\mathbf{r} = 3t\mathbf{i} + (16 - 2t)\mathbf{j} \quad \text{for } 0 \le t \le 8$$

where $\mathbf{i}$ and $\mathbf{j}$ are horizontal and vertical unit vectors.

a) Plot the path and describe the slope of the hill.

Another cyclist moves down another hill with position vector:

$$\mathbf{r} = 2t\mathbf{i} + \left(16 - \frac{t^2}{9}\right)\mathbf{j}$$

b) Plot the path of this cyclist and describe the slope of the hill.
c) If the second cyclist descends the same vertical distance as the first cyclist, find the range of values of t for which the second model is valid

5 A ball moves so that its position vector, in metres, at time t seconds is:

$$\mathbf{r}_A = 4.7t\mathbf{i} + (1.7t - 5t^2)\mathbf{j}$$

and a second ball moves with position vector:

$$\mathbf{r}_B = 1.7t\mathbf{i} + (4.7t - 5t^2)\mathbf{j}$$

where $\mathbf{i}$ and $\mathbf{j}$ are horizontal and vertical unit vectors. The ball moves in the vertical plane that contains $\mathbf{i}$ and $\mathbf{j}$.

a) Show that both balls land in the same place. Describe the differences between the two paths.
b) Which ball is in the air for the longer time?

6 The diagram shows part of a blow football table. The ball moves so that its position vector, in cm, at time t seconds is:

$$\mathbf{r} = (50 - 20t)\mathbf{i} + 5t^2\mathbf{j}$$

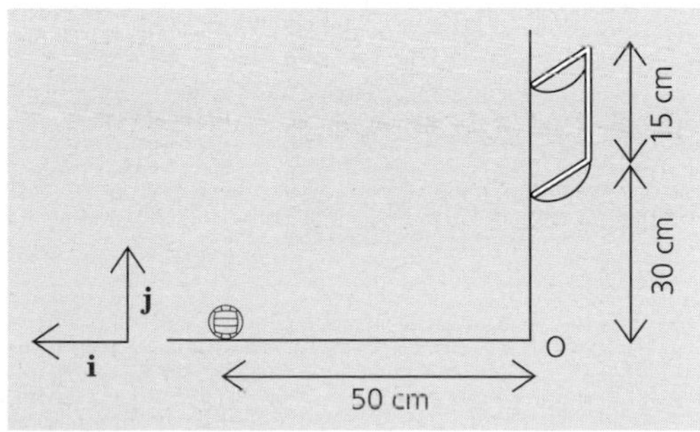

a) When does the ball hit the end of the pitch?
b) Is a goal scored? Sketch the path of the ball.

7 Two boats, A and B, move so that at time t seconds their position vectors, in metres, are:

$$\mathbf{r}_A = 3t\mathbf{i} + 2.5t\mathbf{j} \text{ and } \mathbf{r}_B = 2t\mathbf{i} + (t^2 - 4t + 8)\mathbf{j}$$

where $\mathbf{i}$ and $\mathbf{j}$ are perpendicular unit vectors.

a) Show that the paths of both boats have two points in common.
b) Find how far apart the boats are when boat B reaches the first of these points.

SPEED AND VELOCITY

Exploration 24.3

Motion of athletes as they run

Imagine a group of athletes on a running track competing in a middle distance race. What happens to the motion of the athletes as they run round the track?

The difference between speed and velocity

During a race, the **speed** of the athletes will almost certainly change from time to time, but overall, for the majority of the race, it will probably be reasonable to assume that the speed is constant. However, the **direction of motion** will change during the race. On the straight it will be constant, but on the bends it will change continually, always being **along the tangents** to the curves.

The speed of an object simply describes how fast an object moves.

The **average velocity** of an object is defined as the change in position or displacement divided by the time taken.

$$\text{Average velocity} = \frac{\text{displacement}}{\text{time taken}}$$

The velocity of an object describes both how fast it moves and in which direction. The velocity is in fact the **rate of change of position**.

Example 24.2

A jet-ski moves from position A to position B in 30 seconds. The position vector of A is $\mathbf{r}_A = 50\mathbf{i} + 100\mathbf{j}$ and the position vector of B is $\mathbf{r}_B = 200\mathbf{i} - 20\mathbf{j}$.

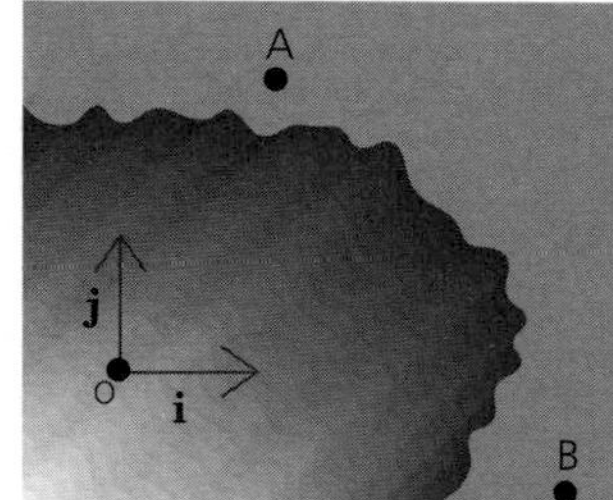

a) *Find the average velocity of the jet-ski, in terms of $\mathbf{i}$ and $\mathbf{j}$.*
b) *Find the magnitude of the average velocity.*
c) *Explain why the average speed of the jet-ski is greater than the answer to **b)**.*

Solution

a) *The displacement of the jet-ski will be:*

$$\mathbf{r}_B - \mathbf{r}_A = (200\mathbf{i} - 20\mathbf{j}) - (50\mathbf{i} + 100\mathbf{j}) = 150\mathbf{i} - 120\mathbf{j}$$

$$\text{Average velocity} = \frac{\text{displacement}}{\text{time taken}} = \frac{150\mathbf{i} - 120\mathbf{j}}{30} = 5\mathbf{i} - 4\mathbf{j}$$

b) *The magnitude of the average velocity is $\sqrt{5^2 + 4^2} = 6.4$ m s^{-1}.*
c) *If the jet-ski travelled from A to B directly at a constant speed, its average speed would be 6.4 m s^{-1}. However, it cannot do this as there is some land in the way, so its speed must be greater than 6.4 m s^{-1}.*

Example 24.3

A cyclist rides over the small hill shown in the diagram. Draw arrows to represent the velocity of the cyclist at each position shown.

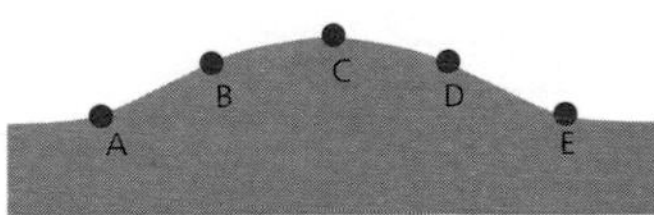

Solution

The direction of motion will always be at a tangent to the curve of the hill. The cyclist will probably lose speed between A and C and gain speed between C and E, so shorter arrows indicate a lower speed near to the top of the hill.

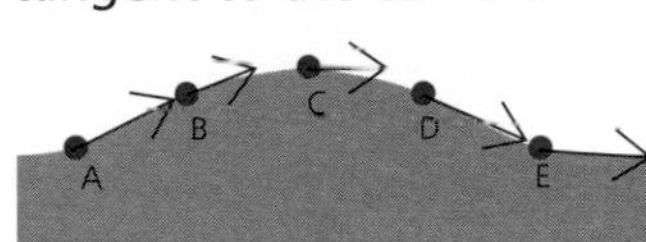

Example 24.4

A motor boat is travelling at a speed of 3 m s^{-1} on a bearing of 230°. Express the velocity of the boat in terms of unit vectors **i** *and* **j** *that are directed east and north respectively.*

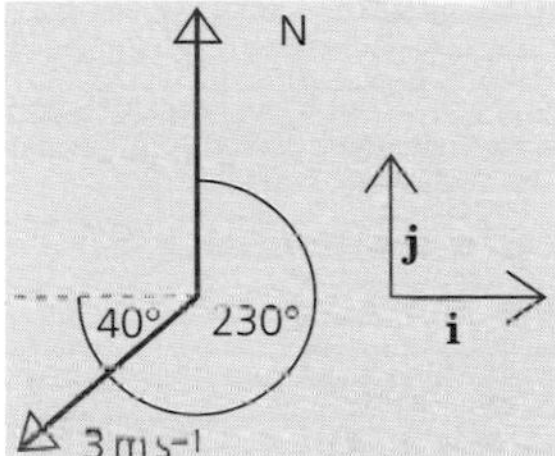

Solution

The velocity vector can be treated in exactly the same way as force vectors were in the previous chapter.

$\mathbf{v} = -3\cos 40°\,\mathbf{i} - 3\cos 50°\,\mathbf{j} = -2.30\mathbf{i} - 1.93\mathbf{j}$

EXERCISES

24.2 CLASSWORK

1 Express each velocity given below in terms of the unit vectors **i** and **j** which are east and north respectively.

a) A jet-ski moving at 5 m s^{-1} on a bearing of 050°.

b) An aeroplane flying at 85 m s^{-1} on a bearing of 302°.

c) A competitor in an orienteering competition running at 3 m s^{-1} on a bearing of 188°.

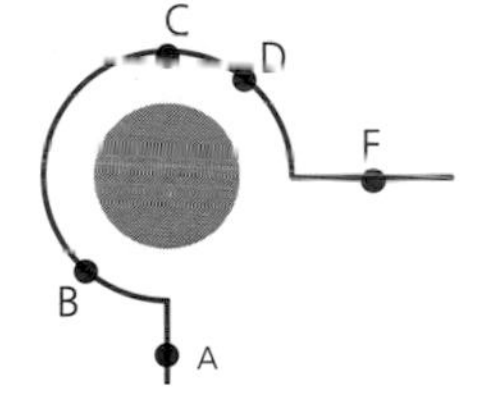

2 A car maintains a constant speed while negotiating a roundabout. Draw arrows to show the velocity of the car at each point shown on the diagram.

3 Describe situations in which the motion of an object is likely to have:

a) constant velocity,

b) velocity with constant direction only,

c) constant speed, but variable velocity.

4 The positions of three boats are recorded, in metres, when $t = 0$ and when $t = 20$ seconds, and are listed in the table below.

	$\mathbf{r}(0)$	$\mathbf{r}(20)$
A	$4\mathbf{i} + 10\mathbf{j}$	$4\mathbf{i} + 110\mathbf{j}$
B	$100\mathbf{i} + 100\mathbf{j}$	$80\mathbf{i} + 20\mathbf{j}$
C	$-38\mathbf{i} + 110\mathbf{j}$	$46\mathbf{i} + 10\mathbf{j}$

a) Find the average velocity of each boat, in terms of **i** and **j**, and then find the magnitude of each average velocity.

b) Sketch the path of each boat.

c) If all the boats move with constant speed what can be deduced about the speed of A, B and C?

5 Three aeroplanes, A, B and C, are approaching an airport. The velocities of the planes are given as:

$$\mathbf{v}_A = (100\mathbf{i} + 20\mathbf{j})\ \text{m s}^{-1} \quad \mathbf{v}_B = (60\mathbf{i} - 150\mathbf{j})\ \text{m s}^{-1} \quad \mathbf{v}_C = (-40\mathbf{i} - 160\mathbf{j})\ \text{m s}^{-1}$$

where $\mathbf{i}$ and $\mathbf{j}$ are unit vectors east and north respectively.

Find the speed of each aeroplane and the bearing on which they are flying.

6 A train travelling up a steady incline has a velocity of $(40\mathbf{i} + 2\mathbf{j})$ m s^{-1} where $\mathbf{i}$ and $\mathbf{j}$ are horizontal and vertical unit vectors respectively. Find the speed of the train and the slope of the incline.

7 A child sits on a roundabout that rotates anti-clockwise. The child has speed 2 m s^{-1} and describes a circle of radius 1.8 m.

a) Express the velocity of the child at positions A and B in terms of the unit vectors $\mathbf{i}$ and $\mathbf{j}$.

b) Find the time it takes for the child to get from A to B.

c) Find the average velocity of the child between A and B.

d) When the child returns to position A, what is her average velocity?

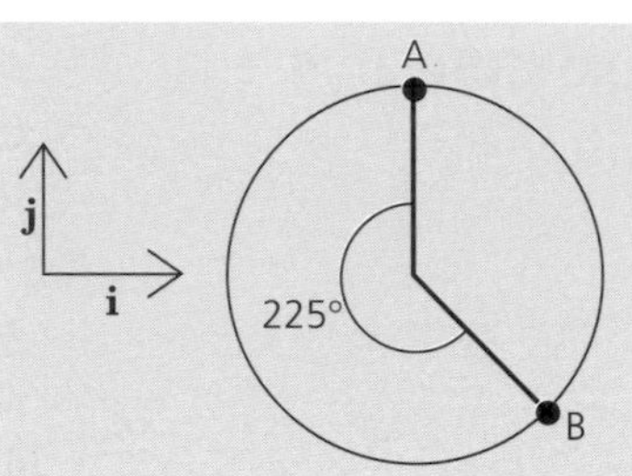

8 A bird flies between two trees. The position vector of the second tree is $(40\mathbf{i} + 80\mathbf{j})$ m s^{-1} relative to the first tree, where $\mathbf{i}$ and $\mathbf{j}$ are unit vectors east and north respectively. It takes the bird 10 seconds to complete the flight.

a) Show that it is possible to model the velocity of the bird as $\mathbf{v} = (4\mathbf{i} + 8\mathbf{j})$ m s^{-1}.
Explain the assumptions on which this model is based.

b) What criticisms can be made of this model?

c) A revised model for the velocity at time t seconds is:

$$\mathbf{v} = \frac{6}{25}t(10 - t)\mathbf{i} + \frac{12}{25}t(10 - t)\mathbf{j} \quad \text{for } 0 \le t \le 10$$

Show that the bird travels directly from A to B.

d) Find an expression for the speed of the bird, at time t seconds.

e) Find the initial and final speeds of the bird and the maximum speed reached.

f) What advantages or disadvantages does the revised model have compared to the original model?

EXERCISES

24.2 HOMEWORK

1 Express each velocity given below in terms of the unit vectors $\mathbf{i}$ and $\mathbf{j}$, east and north respectively.

a) A hill walker moving at 1 m s^{-1} on a bearing of 074°.

b) A ship sailing on a bearing of 250° at 6 m s^{-1}.

c) A hovercraft travelling at 30 m s^{-1} on a bearing of 125°.

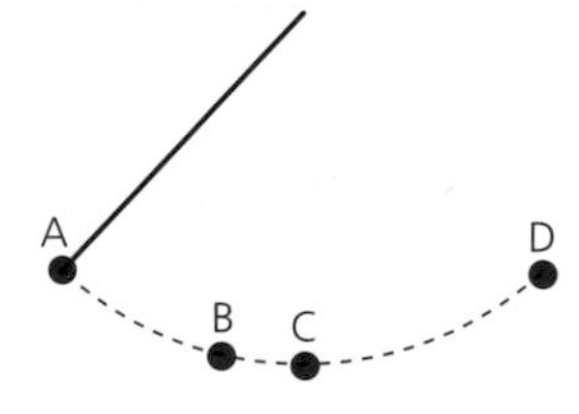

2 The diagram shows the path of a pendulum that swings between A and D. Draw vectors to represent the velocity of the bob on the end of the pendulum at each point as:

a) it swings from A to D, **b)** it swings from D to A.

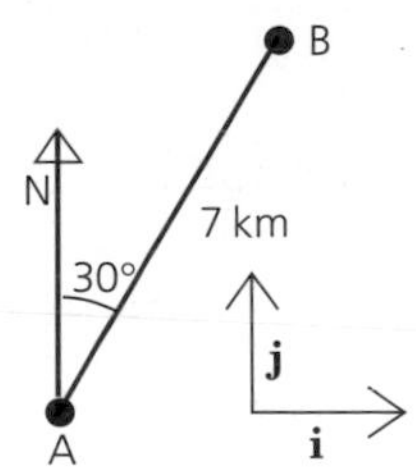

3 The bearing of town B from town A is 030° and they are 7 km apart. A car travels from A to B in eight minutes.
a) Find the position vector of B relative to A, using units of metres.
b) Find the average velocity of the car and its magnitude, in $m\,s^{-1}$.
c) What can you deduce about the average speed of the car?

4 The velocity of a ship, in $m\,s^{-1}$, at three positions, A, B and C is expressed in terms of unit vectors **i** and **j**, which are east and north respectively.

$$\mathbf{v}_A = 8\mathbf{i} + 6\mathbf{j} \quad \mathbf{v}_B = 3\mathbf{i} - 4\mathbf{j} \quad \mathbf{v}_C = -2\mathbf{i} - 6\mathbf{j}$$

a) Express each velocity as a bearing and a speed.
b) If the ship travels for 120 seconds with each velocity, find its final position, relative to its starting point.
c) Sketch the path of the ship and criticise your answer to **b)**.

5 The radar screen shows the position of a helicopter at two-second intervals. It is initially at A, it then moves to B and then to C.
a) Find the average velocity of the helicopter between A and B.
b) Find the average velocity of the helicopter between B and C.
c) Find the speed and bearing of the helicopter, assuming it moves with the average velocity between B and C.

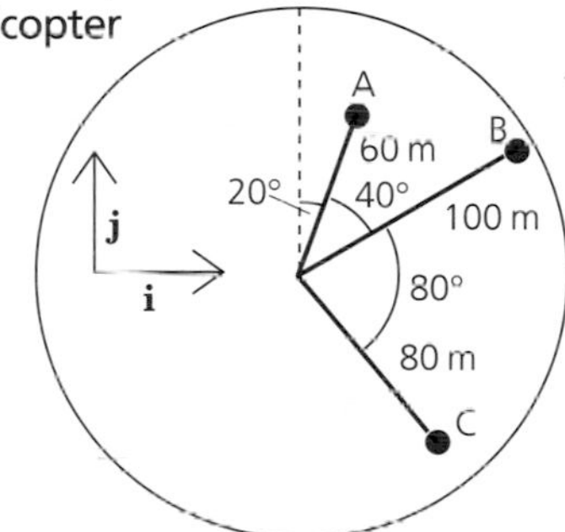

6 A bicycle is moving up a hill with velocity $(2\mathbf{i} + 0.2\mathbf{j})\ m\,s^{-1}$, where **i** and **j** are horizontal and vertical unit vectors respectively.
a) Find the speed of the cyclist.
b) What angle does the hill make with the horizontal?
c) If the cyclist travels at the same speed up a slope at 2° to the horizontal, find her velocity.

7 Two children, Anil and Ben, amuse themselves on a long train journey by playing with a ball. The train is moving at $40\ m\,s^{-1}$ and the children remain seated.

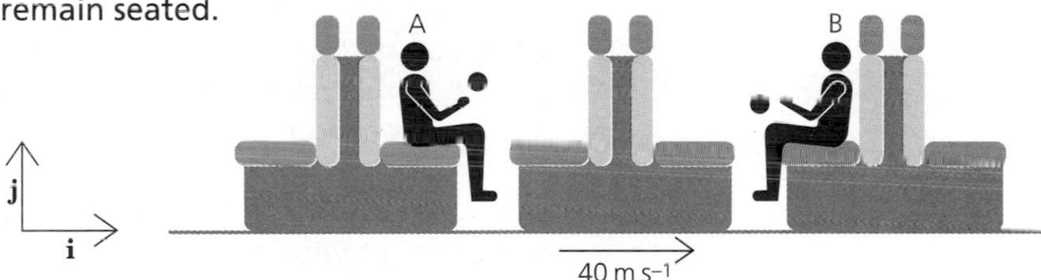

Find the velocity of the ball, in terms of the perpendicular unit vectors **i** and **j**, if:
a) Anil is holding the ball,
b) the ball is travelling horizontally away from Ben at $5\ m\,s^{-1}$,
c) Anil throws it towards Ben at $10\ m\,s^{-1}$, at an angle of 10° above the horizontal.

8 The velocity in $m\,s^{-1}$ of a ball that is thrown into the air is modelled as:

$$\mathbf{v} = 10\mathbf{i} + (8 - 10t)\mathbf{j}\ m\,s^{-1}$$

at time t seconds, where **i** and **j** are horizontal and vertical unit vectors respectively.

a) Find the initial speed and direction of motion of the ball.
b) When the ball reaches its highest position it is travelling horizontally. Find the time when this takes place and the horizontal distance travelled at this time.
c) In practice the ball is travelling at 8 m s^{-1} horizontally when it reaches its highest point. Devise a revised model for the horizontal component of velocity, which does not alter the initial speed, but gives a speed of 8 m s^{-1}, when the ball is moving horizontally.
d) Criticise your revised model.

ACCELERATION

Exploration 24.4

What is acceleration?

Which of the objects described below are accelerating?

- A car slowing down to stop at a pedestrian crossing.
- A parachutist who has reached terminal speed.
- A teenager on a fairground ride that rotates at a constant rate.
- A cyclist travelling along a country lane at a constant speed.
- A planet orbiting the sun.

What we mean by acceleration

The term **acceleration** is used to describe how the velocity of an object is changing. If the velocity is constant, then the acceleration is zero. If the velocity changes in any way, then the object is accelerating. The acceleration is defined as the **rate of change of velocity**.

In this section only objects that have constant acceleration will be considered.

The constant acceleration formulae developed in Chapter 22, *Vectors and forces* can also be expressed in vector form.

$$\mathbf{v} = \mathbf{u} + \mathbf{a}t$$

$$\mathbf{r} = \mathbf{u}t + \tfrac{1}{2}\mathbf{a}t^2 + \mathbf{r}_0$$

Note that $\mathbf{r}_0$ is the initial position.

Example 24.5

A bullet leaves the barrel of a gun 1.5 m above ground level, travelling horizontally at 70 m s^{-1}. It experiences a downward acceleration of 10 m s^{-2}. When does the bullet hit the ground and how far has it travelled horizontally?

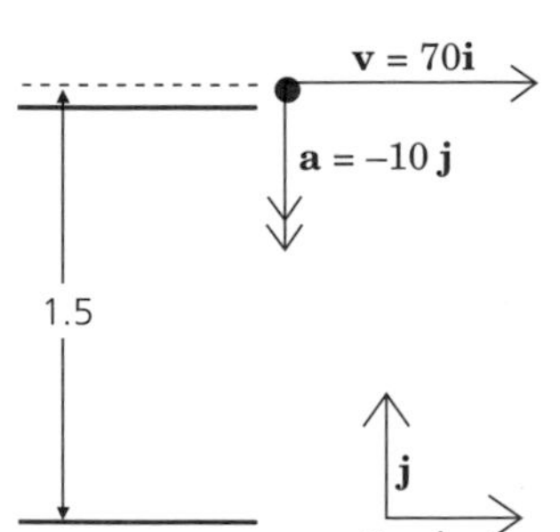

Solution

The diagram shows the bullet modelled as a particle at its initial position, with vectors to show its initial velocity and acceleration. The initial velocity is $\mathbf{u} = 70\mathbf{i}$, the acceleration is $\mathbf{a} = -10\mathbf{j}$ and the initial position $\mathbf{r}_0 = 1.5\mathbf{j}$.

Using the constant acceleration equation:

$$\mathbf{r} = \mathbf{u}t + \tfrac{1}{2}\mathbf{a}t^2 + \mathbf{r}_0$$

gives:

$$\mathbf{r} = 70\mathbf{i}t + \tfrac{1}{2}\times -10\mathbf{j}t^2 + 1.5\mathbf{j} = 70t\mathbf{i} + \left(1.5 - 5t^2\right)\mathbf{j}$$

The bullet will hit the ground when the $\mathbf{j}$ component of $\mathbf{r}$ is zero.

This occurs when:

$1.5 - 5t^2 = 0$

$\Rightarrow \quad t^2 = \dfrac{1.5}{5} = 0.3$

$\Rightarrow t = 0.548 \text{ s}$

When $t = 0.548$ s *the position vector is:*

$\mathbf{r} = 70 \times 0.548\,\mathbf{i} + 0\,\mathbf{j} = 38\mathbf{i}$ *(to two significant figures)*

So the horizontal distance travelled by the bullet is 38 m, to the nearest metre.

Example 24.6

A boat leaves a marker buoy where it was at rest. It experiences an acceleration of 1.2 m s^{-2} on a bearing of 070° for ten seconds and then travels with a constant velocity for a further 20 seconds.

Find the position and velocity of the boat after:
a) *10 seconds,* ***b)*** *30 seconds.*

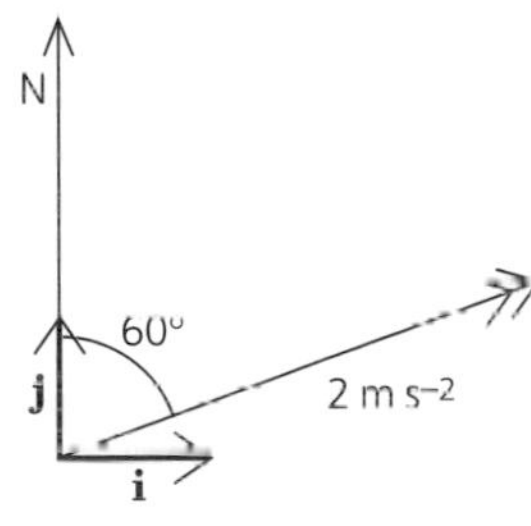

Solution

The diagram shows the acceleration of the boat at its initial position. The unit vectors **i** *and* **j** *are east and north respectively.*
The acceleration can be expressed as:

$$\mathbf{a} = 2\cos 30°\mathbf{i} + 2\cos 60°\mathbf{j} = \sqrt{3}\mathbf{i} + 1\mathbf{j}$$

a) *In this case both* $\mathbf{u} = 0\mathbf{i} + 0\mathbf{j}$ *and* $\mathbf{r}_0 = 0\mathbf{i} + 0\mathbf{j}$ *so using:*

$$\mathbf{r} = \mathbf{u}t + \tfrac{1}{2}\mathbf{a}t^2 + \mathbf{r}_0$$

gives:

$$\mathbf{r} = \frac{1}{2}\mathbf{a}t^2 = \frac{\sqrt{3}}{2}t^2\mathbf{i} + \frac{1}{2}t^2\mathbf{j}$$

and using:

$$\mathbf{v} = \mathbf{u} + \mathbf{a}t$$

gives:

$$\mathbf{v} = \mathbf{a}t = \sqrt{3}t\mathbf{i} + t\,\mathbf{j}$$

So when $t = 10$:

$$\mathbf{r} = 50\sqrt{3}\mathbf{i} + 50\mathbf{j}$$

and:

$$\mathbf{v} = 10\sqrt{3}\mathbf{i} + 10\mathbf{j}$$

b) *The boat now moves with a constant velocity of* $10\sqrt{3}\mathbf{i} + 10\mathbf{j}$*, so in the next 20 seconds its position changes by:*

$$20\left(10\sqrt{3}\mathbf{i} + 10\mathbf{j}\right) = 200\sqrt{3}\mathbf{i} + 200\mathbf{j}$$

So its final position, in metres, is given by:

$$\mathbf{r} = \left(50\sqrt{3}\mathbf{i} + 50\mathbf{j}\right) + \left(200\sqrt{3}\mathbf{i} + 200\mathbf{j}\right) = 433\mathbf{i} + 250\mathbf{j}$$

The final velocity, in m s^{-1}*, is:*

$$\mathbf{v} = 10\sqrt{3}\mathbf{i} + 10\mathbf{j}$$
$$= 17.3\,\mathbf{i} + 10\mathbf{j}$$

EXERCISES

24.3 CLASSWORK

1 A boat is initially moving at $2\,\text{m}\,\text{s}^{-1}$ on a bearing of 045°.
   a) Express this initial speed in terms of the unit vectors $\mathbf{i}$ and $\mathbf{j}$, which are east and north respectively.
   b) The boat then experiences an acceleration of $(0.1\mathbf{i} + 0.3\mathbf{j})\,\text{m}\,\text{s}^{-2}$. Find the velocity of the boat when it has been accelerating for ten seconds.
   c) Find the position of the boat at the end of the ten-second period, taking its starting point as the origin.

2 A bullet is fired with an initial velocity of $180\mathbf{i}\,\text{m}$ from a point with position vector $1.5\mathbf{j}\,\text{m}\,\text{s}^{-1}$. The bullet experiences an acceleration of $-10\mathbf{j}\,\text{m}\,\text{s}^{-2}$. The unit vectors $\mathbf{i}$ and $\mathbf{j}$ are horizontal and vertical respectively.
   a) Find expressions for the velocity and position of the bullet, t seconds after it is fired.
   b) Find the time taken for the bullet to reach the ground and the horizontal distance travelled.
   c) What is the speed of the bullet when it hits the ground?

3 An aeroplane is initially at rest at the origin. For the first five seconds of its motion down a runway, the aeroplane experiences an acceleration of $16\,\text{m}\,\text{s}^{-2}$. Use unit vectors $\mathbf{i}$ and $\mathbf{j}$ parallel and perpendicular to the runway respectively.
   a) Find the position and velocity of the aeroplane after the first five seconds.

   The acceleration then changes to $(4\mathbf{i} + 6\mathbf{j})\,\text{m}\,\text{s}^{-2}$ and remains constant for a further 20 seconds.
   b) Find the position and velocity of the plane at the end of this 20-second period.

4 A child on a slide experiences an acceleration of $(2\mathbf{i} - 1.5\mathbf{j})\,\text{m}\,\text{s}^{-2}$. Assume that the child begins from rest, and is at the origin.
   a) If the child starts at rest find an expression for the position of the child, at time t seconds.
   b) Sketch the path of the child for $0 \le t \le 3$.
   c) If the child takes three seconds to reach the bottom of the slide, find the length of the slide.
   d) What is the speed of the child at the bottom of the slide?

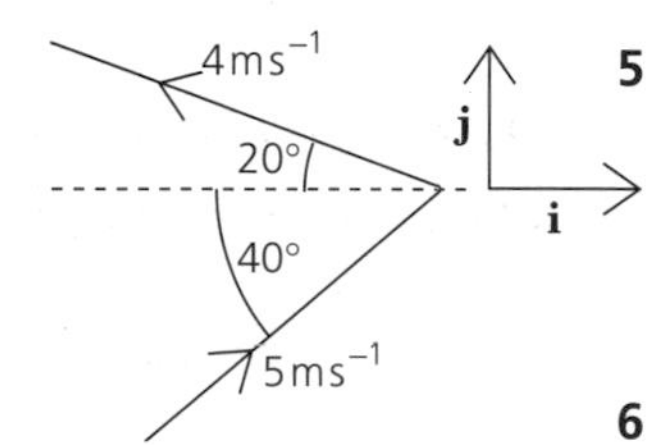

5 A ball that was moving at $5\,\text{m}\,\text{s}^{-1}$ is hit and then moves at $4\,\text{m}\,\text{s}^{-1}$. The diagram shows the change in direction.
   a) Express both velocities in terms of the unit vectors $\mathbf{i}$ and $\mathbf{j}$.
   b) Find the average acceleration of the ball while in contact with the bat, if this contact is maintained for 0.1 seconds.

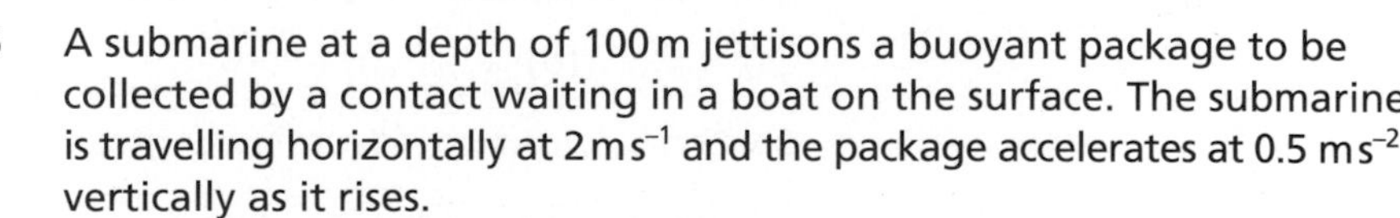

6 A submarine at a depth of 100 m jettisons a buoyant package to be collected by a contact waiting in a boat on the surface. The submarine is travelling horizontally at $2\,\text{m}\,\text{s}^{-1}$ and the package accelerates at $0.5\,\text{m}\,\text{s}^{-2}$ vertically as it rises.
   a) Find an expression for the velocity and position of the package relative to its point of release.
   b) Sketch the path of the package.
   c) Find the speed of the package when it reaches the surface, and its distance from the boat, if the boat was above the submarine when the package was jettisoned.
   d) Why is the acceleration given likely to be unrealistic?

7 A football is kicked so that it leaves the ground with a speed of $30\,\mathrm{m\,s^{-1}}$, travelling at 40° above the horizontal. The unit vectors $\mathbf{i}$ and $\mathbf{j}$ are horizontal and vertical respectively.

a) Express the initial velocity of the ball in terms of $\mathbf{i}$ and $\mathbf{j}$.

b) What assumptions have been made if the acceleration of the ball in modelled as $-10\mathbf{j}$?

c) Find expressions for the velocity and position of the ball if it leaves the ground at the origin.

d) When does the ball hit the ground again? Find the horizontal distance that it has travelled, correct to the nearest metre.

e) Comment on your answer to **d)** in the light of your answer to **b)**.

8 When an aeroplane leaves a runway its velocity is $(100\mathbf{i} + 50\mathbf{j})\,\mathrm{m\,s^{-1}}$, where $\mathbf{i}$ and $\mathbf{j}$ are horizontal and vertical unit vectors respectively. Ten seconds after take-off, its position, relative to where it leaves the runway, is $(1200\mathbf{i} + 600\mathbf{j})\,\mathrm{m}$.

a) Find the acceleration of the aeroplane, stating any assumptions that you make.

b) Find the speed of the aeroplane after 10 seconds.

EXERCISES

24.3 HOMEWORK

1 The cue ball on a snooker table is struck so that it moves at $1.2\,\mathrm{m\,s^{-1}}$ parallel to the long side of the table.

a) Find the initial velocity of the ball in terms of $\mathbf{i}$ and $\mathbf{j}$.

b) As the table slopes slightly it experiences an acceleration $0.1\mathbf{j}$. Find an expression for the velocity of the ball.

c) After 1.5 seconds the ball has travelled the distance required by the player. Find its velocity and position relative to its starting point.

d) Do you think the cue ball hits the ball it was aimed at?

2 A shot put is launched so that it initially moves at $10\,\mathrm{m\,s^{-1}}$ at an angle of 40° above the horizontal. It experiences an acceleration of $-10\mathbf{j}\,\mathrm{m\,s^{-2}}$ and initially has position vector $2\mathbf{j}\,\mathrm{m}$.

a) Express the initial velocity of the shot put in terms of $\mathbf{i}$ and $\mathbf{j}$.

b) Find an expression for the position of the shot after t seconds.

c) When does the shot hit the ground? For what range of values of t is your answer to **b)** valid?

d) Find the length of the throw.

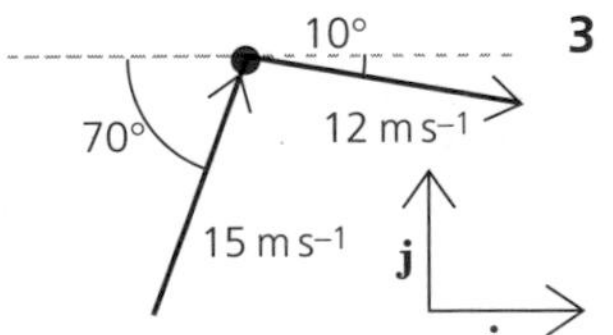

3 The diagram shows the velocity of a football, before and after it is kicked.

a) Express both velocities in terms of the perpendicular unit vectors $\mathbf{i}$ and $\mathbf{j}$.

b) Find the acceleration of the ball if it is in contact with the player's boot for 0.5 seconds.

c) State any assumptions that you made to obtain your answer to **b)**. Suggest a possible revised assumption that may be more realistic.

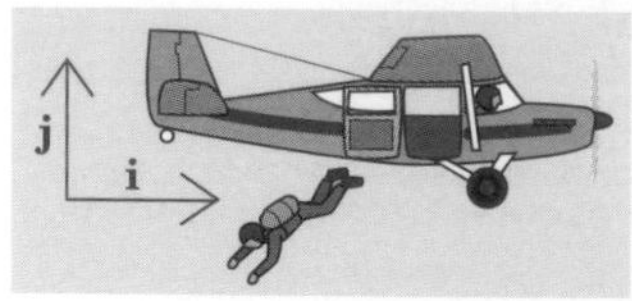

4 A sky diver jumps out of a moving aeroplane, that is travelling horizontally at $50\,\text{m s}^{-1}$. Assume that $\mathbf{i}$ and $\mathbf{j}$ are unit vectors, horizontal and vertical respectively. The sky diver's acceleration is $-10\mathbf{j}\,\text{m s}^{-2}$.

a) Explain why the initial velocity of the sky diver is $50\mathbf{i}\,\text{m s}^{-1}$.

b) Find the velocity of the sky diver after 20 seconds freefall.

c) Calculate the speed of the sky diver and comment on your result.

d) If the terminal speed of a sky diver is $80\,\text{m s}^{-1}$, suggest the range of values for which your model is valid.

5 A hockey ball is moving at $3.4\,\text{m s}^{-1}$. It experiences an acceleration of $25\,\text{m s}^{-2}$ at right angles to its path, while it is in contact with a hockey stick. Assume that the acceleration acts for 0.6 seconds.

a) If the velocity of the ball is initially $3.4\mathbf{i}\,\text{m s}^{-1}$, express the acceleration in terms of the perpendicular unit vectors $\mathbf{i}$ and $\mathbf{j}$.

b) Find the velocity of the ball after it has been hit.

c) Find the angle through which the motion of the ball has been deflected.

6 As a skateboarder travels down a slope, he experiences an acceleration $(\mathbf{i} - 0.05\mathbf{j})\,\text{m s}^{-2}$. Assume that the skateboarder starts at rest at the top of the slope. The unit vectors $\mathbf{i}$ and $\mathbf{j}$ are horizontal and vertical respectively.

a) Find an expression for the position vector of the skateboarder at time t seconds.

b) Find an expression for the distance travelled.

c) How long does it take the skateboarder to travel 20 m down the slope? What are the velocity and speed at this time?

7 A hot air balloon rises from rest at a point on the ground. After 10 seconds its position vector, relative to its starting point, is $(5\mathbf{i} + 20\mathbf{j})$ m, where $\mathbf{i}$ and $\mathbf{j}$ are horizontal and vertical unit vectors respectively.

a) Find expressions for the acceleration and velocity of the balloon, at time t seconds.

b) The horizontal movement of the balloon is due to the wind. After the first ten seconds the horizontal component of the velocity remains constant. Find the position of the balloon ten seconds later.

8 A firework starts at rest and experiences an acceleration of $4.8\,\text{m s}^{-2}$ at an angle of 80° to the horizontal for 4 seconds before it explodes. Find the height of the rocket when it explodes, and the distance it has travelled.

9 A jet-ski is initially moving at $10\,\text{m s}^{-1}$. It experiences an acceleration of $1.8\,\text{m s}^{-2}$ at right angles to its direction of motion. Find the speed of the jet-ski after 5 seconds and its change in position in this time.

MATHEMATICAL MODELLING ACTIVITY

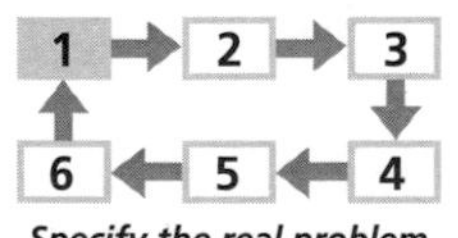

Specify the real problem

Problem statement

Will an umbrella keep you dry when it is raining?

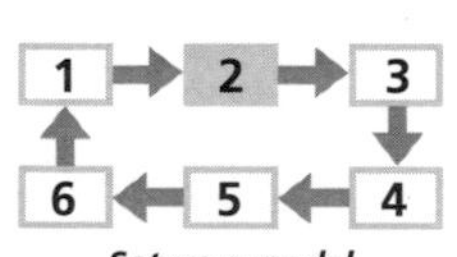

Set up a model

Set up a model

The first stage in setting up a model is to identify the important features. The list below includes the main features.

- The size and position of the umbrella.

- The speed at which the person holding the umbrella is walking.
- The speed of the falling rain and the angle at which it falls.

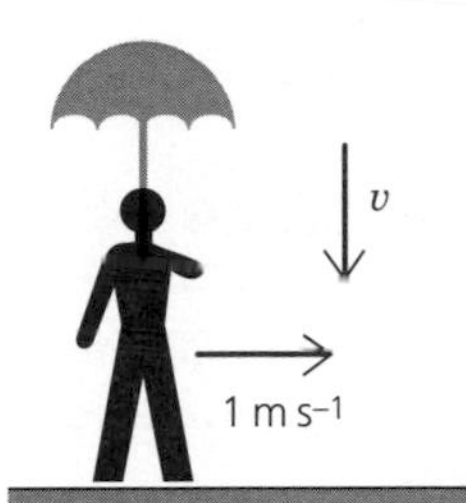

Are there other important factors that you feel should be included? Having considered these features a set of assumptions can now be set up.

- The rain falls vertically at a constant v m s^{-1}.
- The person walks at 1 m s^{-1}.
- The umbrella is at a height of 2 m and has a radius of 50 cm.
- The person is modelled as a vertical rod and the umbrella handle is also vertical and an extension of the person.

These assumptions allow a simple first model to be formulated.

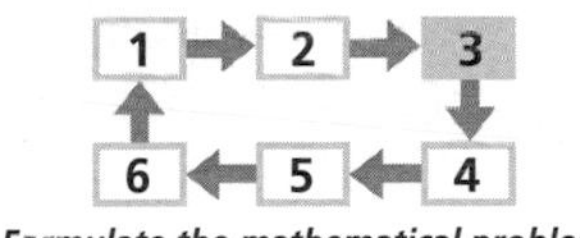

Formulate the mathematical problem

Formulate a mathematical problem

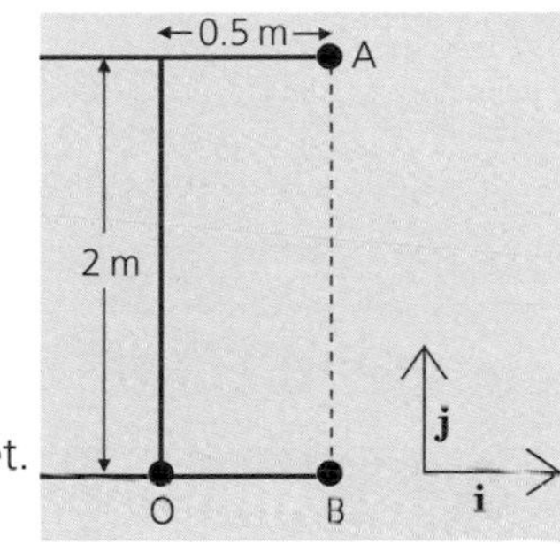

Consider a drop of rain at A. It has a velocity $-v\mathbf{j}$ and its initial position is $0.5\mathbf{i} + 2\mathbf{j}$.

The velocity of the person is $1\mathbf{i}$.

Find v if the rain drop lands at the person's feet.

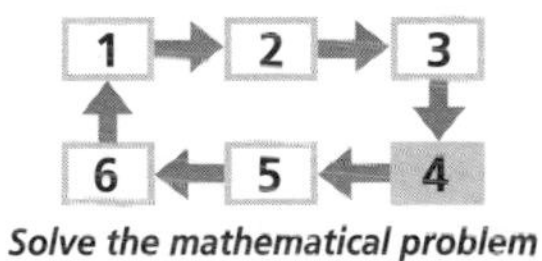

Solve the mathematical problem

Mathematical solution

The position of the rain drop is:

$$\mathbf{r} = 0.5\mathbf{i} + (2 - vt)\mathbf{j}$$

When the raindrop hits the ground at B the time taken to fall from A is:

$$t = \frac{2}{v}$$

The time taken for the person's feet to get to B is 0.5 seconds, so their feet will be dry if $t < 0.5$ or:

$$\frac{2}{v} < t \quad \Rightarrow v > 4 \text{ m s}^{-1}$$

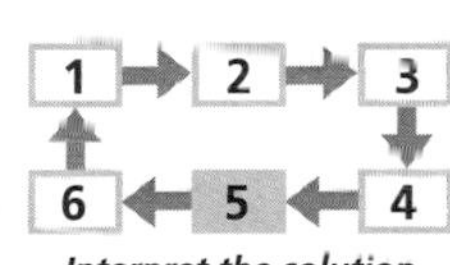

Interpret the solution

Interpretation

The person will not get wet unless the rain falls at a speed of less than 4 m s^{-1}. Is it reasonable to assume that the rain falls a speed greater than 4 m s^{-1}?

If your answer is yes, then your umbrella will keep you dry.

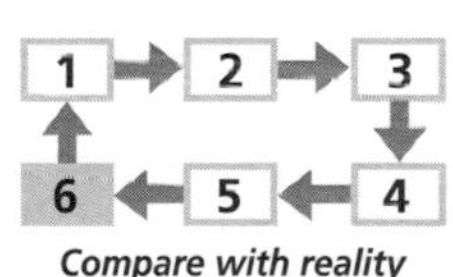

Compare with reality

Compare with reality

The rain does not always fall straight down and often descends at an angle.

There are very few people who are seen walking with their umbrellas vertical. They will often position them at an angle to provide greater protection.

The two reasons outlined above illustrate some of the inadequacies of the original model. Can you find other criticisms of the original model?

Refining the model

Select one or both of the two criticisms outlined above, define a revised set of assumptions and solve the revised problem.

POSSIBLE MODELLING TASKS

Hockey players are often taught to stop a ball before hitting it. Explain why this is a good technique and develop a strategy for hitting moving balls.

CONSOLIDATION EXERCISES FOR CHAPTER 24

1 A model assumes that an aeroplane has an initial velocity of $200\mathbf{i}$ m s^{-1} and experiences an acceleration of $(-0.5\mathbf{i} - 0.05\mathbf{j})$ m s^{-2} in preparation for landing. The initial position of the aeroplane was $(-50\,000\mathbf{i} + 4000\mathbf{j})$ m with respect to an origin 0. The unit vectors $\mathbf{i}$ and $\mathbf{j}$ are horizontal and vertical respectively. After accelerating for 200 seconds the velocity of the aeroplane is assumed to remain constant until it lands. The aeroplane lands when the vertical component of its position vector is zero.

a) Find:
   i) The time it takes for the aeroplane to move from its initial position to the point where it first touches the ground
   ii) The position of the aeroplane when it first touches the ground.
   iii) The speed of the aeroplane when it first touches the ground.

b) Comment on the assumption that the velocity of the aeroplane is constant during the final stage of its flight.

(AQA Specification B Question 3 Mechanics 1 Specimen Paper 2000)

2 Two cars A and B are moving on straight horizontal roads with constant velocities. The velocity of A is 20 m s^{-1} due east, and the velocity of B is $(10\mathbf{i} + 10\mathbf{j})$ m s^{-1}, where $\mathbf{i}$ and $\mathbf{j}$ are unit vectors directed due east and due north respectively. Initially A is at the fixed origin O, and the position vector of B is $300\mathbf{i}$ m relative to O. At the time t seconds, the position vectors of A and B are $\mathbf{r}$ metres and $\mathbf{s}$ metres respectively.

a) Find expressions for $\mathbf{r}$ and $\mathbf{s}$ in terms of t.
b) Hence write down an expression for $\overrightarrow{AB}$ in terms of t.
c) Find the time when the bearing of B from A is 045°.
d) Find the time when the cars are again 300 m apart.

(EDEXCEL Question 7 Mechanics 1 Specimen Paper 2000)

Summary

After working through this chapter you should:

- be able to use vectors to describe positions, velocities and accelerations in two dimensions
- use the constant acceleration equations
  $\mathbf{v} = \mathbf{u} + \mathbf{a}t$
  and
  $\mathbf{r} = \mathbf{u}t + \frac{1}{2}\mathbf{a}t^2 + \mathbf{r}_0$
  in two dimensional situations.

Newton's first and second laws

- *An applied force will cause a change in the motion of a particle.*
- *The change in motion depends on the mass, initial velocity and force applied.*

Exploration 25.1

Motion

- Think about an ice hockey puck that is hit and moves across the ice. What happens to the motion of the puck? What difference would it make if the two surfaces in contact were perfectly smooth?
- Consider a parachutist falling through the air. What happens to the motion as the parachutist falls?

NEWTON'S FIRST LAW

During his study of mechanics, Newton formulated his first law of motion which states:

> *All bodies will continue to remain at rest, or move in a straight line at constant speed, unless acted on by an external force.*
>
> *In fact there are very rarely, if ever, any situations where no external forces act on a body. However if all the forces acting on an object are in* ***equilibrium*** *or balance, the object can be treated as if there were no external force acting.*

An alternative way of stating Newton's first law is:

All bodies will continue to remain at rest, or move in a straight line with constant speed, if the forces acting are in equilibrium.

Example 25.1

A parachutist of mass 71 kg is falling at a constant speed. Find the upward force acting on the parachutist.

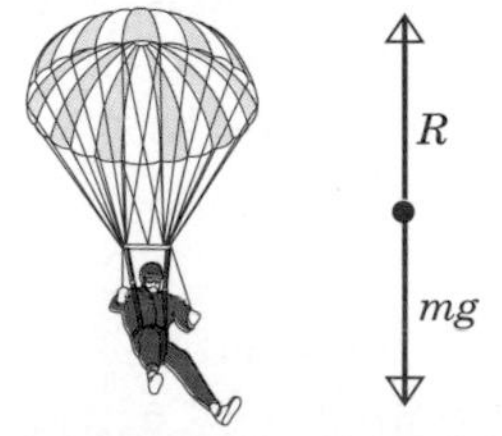

Solution

Consider the parachute and parachutist together as a particle. There are two forces acting, air resistance, R, which acts up, and gravity, mg, which acts down. As the speed of the parachutist is constant, these forces must be in balance, so that their resultant is zero. So:

$R = mg = 71 \times 9.8 = 695.8$ N

Example 25.2

A lorry of mass 20 tonnes is travelling up a hill inclined at 4° to the horizontal. If there are assumed to be no resistance forces on the lorry, and it travels at a constant speed, find the forward force on the lorry.

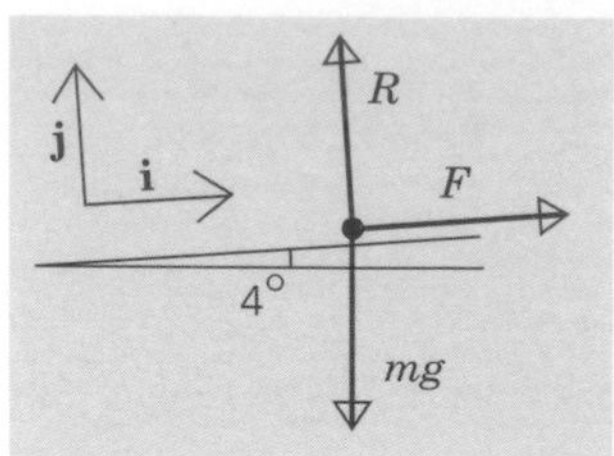

Solution

The diagram show the forces acting on the lorry, when it is modelled as a particle. Gravity acts downward, F is the forward force on the lorry and R the normal reaction.

Using the unit vectors as shown in the diagram gives the resultant force as:

$(F - mg\cos 86°)\mathbf{i} + (R - mg\cos 4°)\mathbf{j}$

As the lorry is moving at a constant speed the resultant force must be zero, so,

$F - mg\cos 86° = 0$

and

$R - mg\cos 4° = 0$

The forward force F is then 13 700 N (to three significant figures).

EXERCISES

25.1 CLASSWORK

1 A parachutist of mass 80 kg is falling at a constant speed. Find the upward force acting on him.

2 A motorboat is travelling at a constant speed of 8 m s^{-1}. If a forward force of 780 N acts on the boat, find the magnitude of the resistance forces. What assumptions have you made to reach your answer?

3 The resistance forces on a car are assumed to be proportional to the speed of the car. When the car is travelling at 40 m s^{-1} the resistance force is 1800 N.
a) Find the constant of proportionality.
b) Find the forward force needed to keep the car moving at 30 m s^{-1}.
c) Further investigation suggests that at 10 m s^{-1} the resistance forces are 600 N. Suggest an alternative linear model for the resistance force and use this to find the forward force required to maintain a constant speed of 30 m s^{-1}.

4 A puck, attached to a length of string fixed at O, describes a circle on a smooth horizontal table top, as shown in the diagram. Sketch the path of the puck if the string breaks at A. What happens to the speed of the puck?

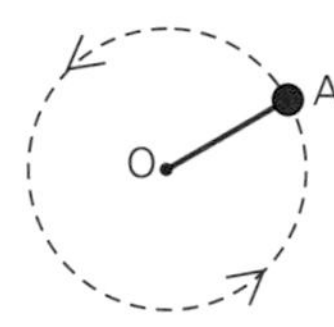

5 A car of mass 900 kg is travelling up a slope inclined at 3° to the horizontal. Find the forward force exerted by the car if it is travelling at a constant speed, and there is no resistance to motion.

6 A cyclist of mass 73 kg is free-wheeling down a slope inclined at 5° to the horizontal. If there are assumed to be no resistance forces, and the cyclist travels at a constant speed, find the force exerted by the brakes if the speed of the cyclist is:
a) 10 m s^{-1}, **b)** 5 m s^{-1}.

7 The resistance force exerted by a parachute can be modelled as $R = 196v$, where v is the velocity. Find the terminal speeds for a parachutist of mass:
a) 68 kg, **b)** 78 kg.

8 A slide in a park is at 40° to the horizontal. Children reach a maximum speed partway down the slide. The coefficient of friction between the slide and a child is 0.2. Find the magnitude of the resistance forces acting on a child of mass 45 kg.

EXERCISES

25.1 HOMEWORK

1 A diver of mass 69 kg is rising from the sea bed at a constant speed. Find the upward force acting on the diver.

2 An aeroplane is travelling at a constant velocity. If a forward force of 2080 N is acting on the plane, find the magnitude of the resistance forces on the plane.

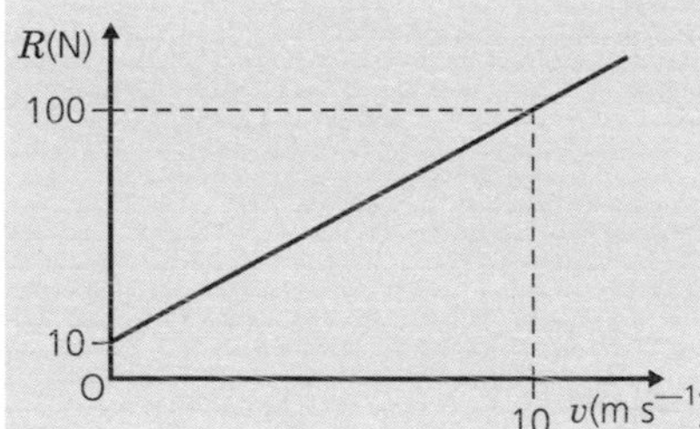

3 The graph shows how the resistance forces on a skateboard vary with speed.

a) Find an algebraic model for the resistance force.

b) What forward force must be acting on the skateboard if it is to move at a constant velocity of $5\,\text{m}\,\text{s}^{-1}$?

c) Criticise the model for the resistance forces and sketch a graph of an alternative.

4 The diagram shows a car travelling round a bend. A child drops a coin out of the window in the position shown. Sketch the path of the coin.

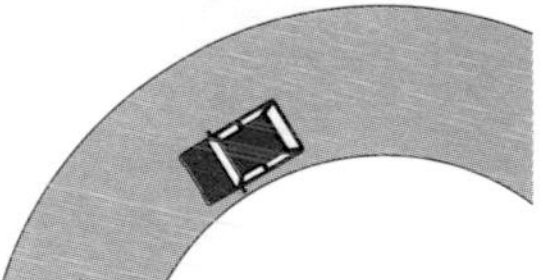

5 A child of mass 40 kg is travelling down a slope on a sledge of mass 10 kg at a constant speed. If there is a friction force of 471 N acting on the sledge, find the angle between the slope and the horizontal.

6 A lorry is ascending a hill inclined at 6° to the horizontal at a constant speed. The mass of the lorry is 13 000 kg. Find the magnitude of the forward force on the lorry, if no resistance forces are present.

7 The resistance force, R, on a car is related to the speed, v, of the car by $R = 20v$. The mass of the car is 980 kg.

a) Find the forward force acting on a car that is moving at a constant speed of $32\,\text{m}\,\text{s}^{-1}$.

b) Find the forward force acting on a car that is travelling up a hill, inclined at 3° to the horizontal. The speed of the car is a constant $20\,\text{m}\,\text{s}^{-1}$.

8 The terminal speed of a parachutist of mass 60 kg is $6\,\text{m}\,\text{s}^{-1}$.

a) Assume that the air resistance force, R, on the parachutist is proportional to her speed. Find a model of the air resistance.

b) Which would be the terminal speed for a parachutist of mass 80 kg?

NEWTON'S SECOND LAW

Newton's first law states that if no force acts on an object it will remain at rest or move with a constant velocity. Newton's second law describes how the motion of an object changes when a force acts. The law states:

When a resultant force acts on a body it produces an acceleration that is proportional to the applied force.

In this chapter the use of the law will be restricted to bodies with constant masses. In this case Newton's second law can be stated as:

$$\mathbf{F} = m\mathbf{a}$$

The equation $\mathbf{F} = m\mathbf{a}$ is a vector equation, but if we are concerned with motion in a straight line, or wish simply to consider the magnitudes of $\mathbf{F}$ and $\mathbf{a}$, then it can be used in the form $F = ma$.

Exploration 25.2

When is $F = ma$ not appropriate?

Try to identify some situations where it would not be appropriate to use Newton's second law in the form $F = ma$.

Example 25.3

Find the force required to make a car of mass 1050 kg accelerate at 2 m s^{-2}.

Solution

Using $F = ma$ with $m = 1050$ and $a = 2$ m s^{-2} gives:

$F = ma = 1050 \times 2 = 2100$ *N*

Example 25.4

As a crane lifts a crate of mass 700 kg off the ground, the crate experiences an acceleration of 0.6 m s^{-2}. Find the tension in the cable.

Solution

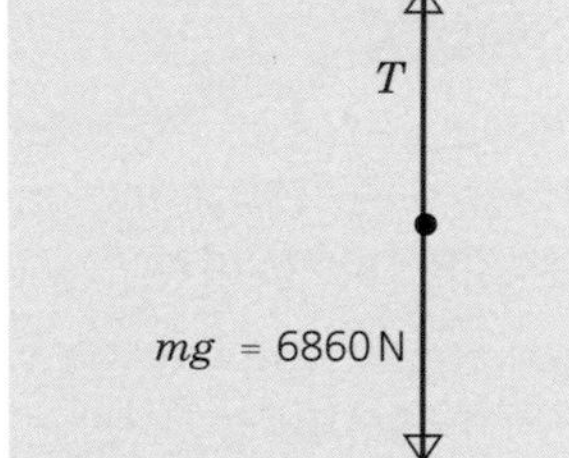

Modelling the crate as a particle, and assuming that the tension and gravity are the only forces acting on the crate, gives the force diagram shown.

As the acceleration is upward we shall take upwards as the positive sense in this case. So the resultant force is $T - 6860$. Using $F = ma$ gives:

$T - 6860 = 700 \times 0.6 = 420 \Rightarrow T = 7280$ *N*

So the tension in the cable is 7280 N.

Example 25.5

A skier of mass 65 kg is on a ski slope that is inclined at 20° to the horizontal. If the skier experiences a friction force of 120 N, find the acceleration of the skier. What factor may be important in reality, but has not been included in your solution?

Solution

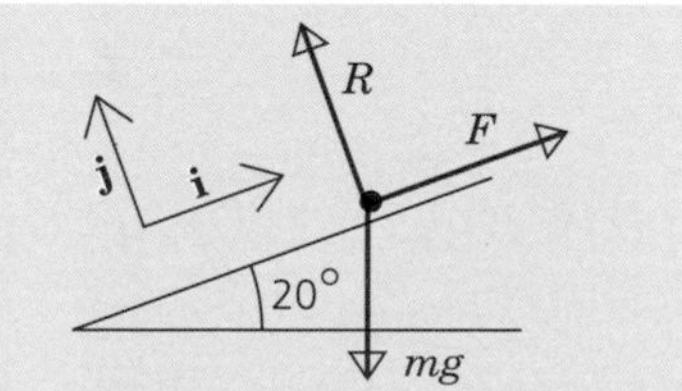

Assuming that there is no air resistance, and modelling the skier as a particle gives the force diagram shown. If unit vectors are introduced parallel and perpendicular to the slope, then the resultant force is:

$(F - mg\cos 70°)\mathbf{i} + (R - mg\cos 20°)\mathbf{j}$

As there is no change in the component of motion perpendicular to the slope:

$R - mg\cos 20° = 0$

and so the resultant force is:

$(F - mg\cos 70°)\mathbf{i} = (120 - 637\cos 70°)\mathbf{i}$

To find the acceleration, this force must be divided by the mass to give:

$$\mathbf{a} = \frac{(120 - 637\cos 70°)\mathbf{i}}{65} = -1.51\mathbf{i}$$

So the skier experiences an acceleration of 1.51 m s^{-2} down the slope. The factor that has been ignored in this solution is air resistance which would reduce the acceleration of the skier.

Example 25.6

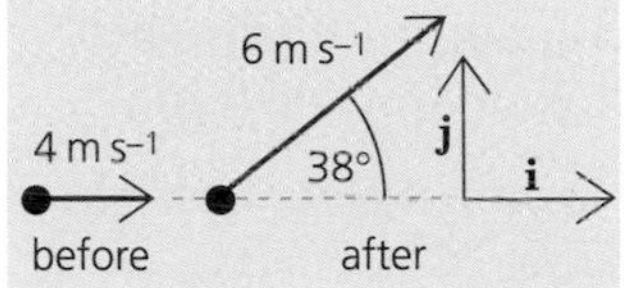

The diagram shows the path of a hockey ball of mass 0.25 kg, before and after it has been hit by a stick.

a) Find the change in velocity of the ball.
b) If the ball is in contact with the stick for 0.2 seconds, calculate the magnitude of the average force on the ball.
c) What aspect of the ball's motion has not been considered?

Solution

a) The initial velocity of the ball is:

$$\mathbf{u} = 4\mathbf{i}$$

while the final velocity is:

$$\mathbf{v} = 6\cos 38°\,\mathbf{i} + 6\cos 52°\,\mathbf{j}$$

So the change in velocity is:

$$\mathbf{v} - \mathbf{u} = (6\cos 38° - 4)\mathbf{i} + 6\cos 52°\mathbf{j} = 0.728\mathbf{i} + 3.694\mathbf{j}$$

b) The average acceleration is:

$$\frac{\mathbf{v} - \mathbf{u}}{t} = \frac{0.728\mathbf{i} + 3.694\mathbf{j}}{0.2} = 3.64\mathbf{i} + 18.47\mathbf{j}$$

The average force can now be found using $\mathbf{F} = m\mathbf{a}$, as:

$$\mathbf{F} = 0.25(3.64\mathbf{i} + 18.47\mathbf{j}) = 0.910\mathbf{i} + 4.62\mathbf{j}$$

The magnitude of this force is:

$$F = \sqrt{0.901^2 + 4.62^2} = 4.7 \text{ N} \quad \textit{(to two significant figures)}$$

c) The rotation of the ball as it rolls is one factor that has been ignored in the solution of this problem.

EXERCISES

25.2 CLASSWORK

1 Calculate the magnitude of the force required to make each object experience the acceleration stated.
a) A lorry of mass 30 tonnes accelerating at 0.5 m s^{-2}.
b) A ball of mass 200 grams accelerating at 9.8 m s^{-2} while it falls.

2 Calculate the acceleration that each object would experience when acted on by the force stated.
a) A force of 300 N acting on a child of mass 45 kg on a slide.
b) A force of 80 N acting on a table-tennis ball of mass 3 grams.

3 A lift has mass 400 kg and holds three people of masses 60 kg, 70 kg and 52 kg. Find the tension in the lift cable if it is moving upwards and:
a) accelerating at 0.02 m s^{-2},
b) travelling at constant speed,
c) has an acceleration of –0.15 m s^{-2}.

4 A car of total mass 1200 kg is travelling at 30 m s^{-1} when the brakes are applied. It is assumed that the brakes cause a constant force of 9000 N to act.
   a) What is the acceleration of the car?
   b) How far does the car travel before it stops?
   c) How long does it take the car to stop?

5 A motorcycle skids 24 m before stopping on a horizontal surface.
   a) By assuming that the coefficient of friction between the tyre and the road is 0.8, find the acceleration of the motorcycle.
   b) Find the speed of the motorcycle when it began to skid.
   c) What forces, that you have not considered above, could also act on the motorcycle? How would they effect your answer to **b)**?

6 A ball of mass 200 grams is moving at 2.5 m s^{-1} when it is hit by a bat. It then moves at 3 m s^{-1} and has been deflected by 30° from its original path.
   a) Find the change in velocity of the ball in terms of the unit vectors **i** and **j** that are parallel and perpendicular to the original direction of motion.
   b) Find the magnitude of the average force exerted on the ball by the bat, if they are in contact for 0.5 seconds.

7 The forces shown act on a 5 kg mass.
   a) Find the resultant force on the mass in terms of the unit vectors **i** and **j**.
   b) Find the acceleration of the mass.
   c) What are the magnitude and direction of the acceleration?

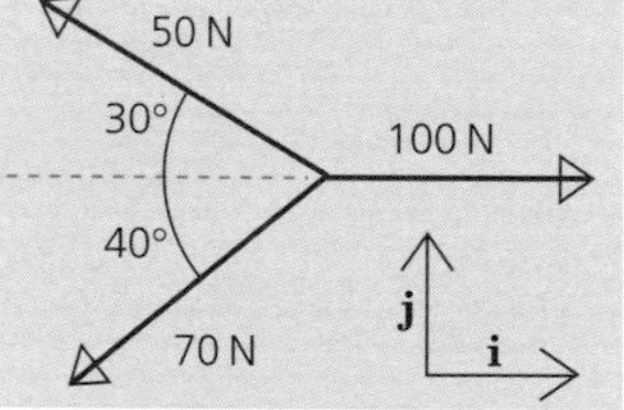

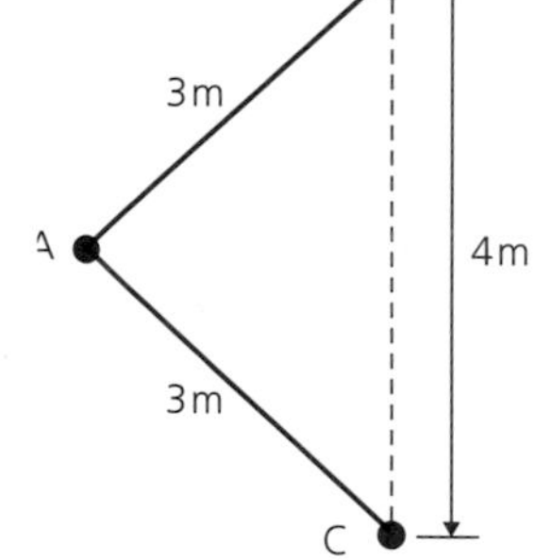

8 An archaeologist discovers the remains of an ancient catapult that would have been used to launch rocks. Elastic ropes were used to join A to B and C.
   a) Find the force needed to give a rock of mass 20 kg an initial acceleration of 20 m s^{-2}.
   b) Find the angle between the two ropes and hence find the tension in each rope.
   c) Before release the catapult was held in position by soldiers. The soldiers would have had an average mass of 75 kg and the coefficient of friction between their feet and the ground was 0.4. How many soldiers were needed to hold the catapult in position?

9 A car of mass 900 kg is at rest on a slope that makes an angle of 5° to the horizontal. Assume that there are no resistance forces present.
   a) Find the resultant force on the car.
   b) Find the speed that the car reaches if it is allowed to free wheel for five seconds.
   c) If there are resistance forces present, and their effect is to reduce the resultant force by 20%, revise your answer to part **b)**.

EXERCISES

25.2 HOMEWORK

1 Calculate the magnitude of the force required to make each object accelerate as described.
   a) A table tennis ball of mass 3 grams accelerating at 9.8 m s^{-2} as it falls.
   b) An aeroplane of mass 3000 kg accelerating at 5 m s^{-2}.

2 Find the magnitude of the acceleration that would be produced in each example below, assuming that any other forces are in balance.
a) A force of 3000 N acting on a car of mass 800 kg.
b) A force of 500 N acting on a bullet of mass 50 grams.

3 A crane is lifting, vertically, a load of mass 700 kg. Find the tension in the lifting cable if the load:
a) is accelerating upwards at 0.01 m s^{-2},
b) is accelerating downwards at –0.2 m s^{-2},
c) is travelling at constant speed.

4 A bicycle and rider of mass 74 kg are travelling at 10 m s^{-1}, when the brakes are applied and a retarding force of 200 N acts on the bicycle.
a) Find the acceleration of the bicycle.
b) How far does the bicycle travel before it stops?
c) How long does it take for the bicycle to stop?

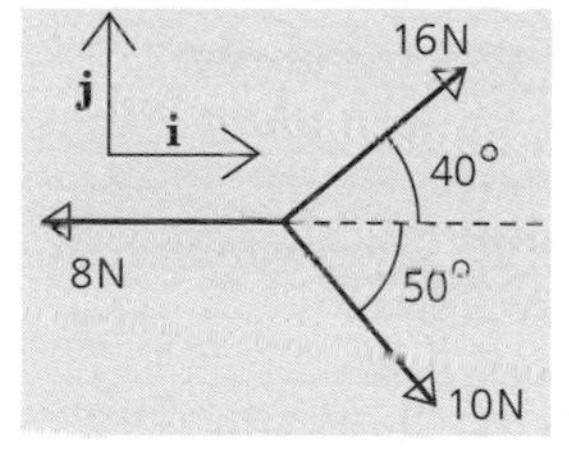

5 The three forces shown act on a 2 kg mass.
a) Find the resultant force on the mass in terms of $\mathbf{i}$ and $\mathbf{j}$.
b) Find the acceleration of the mass in terms of $\mathbf{i}$ and $\mathbf{j}$.
c) What are the magnitude and direction of the acceleration?

6 A skier is on a slope inclined at 15° to the horizontal. Assume that there is no friction between the skis and the slope. The mass of the skier and her skis is 75 kg.
a) Find the resultant force on the skier in terms of the unit vectors $\mathbf{i}$ and $\mathbf{j}$, and the normal reaction R.

b) Explain why the acceleration of the skier is $-a\mathbf{i}$.
c) Find the acceleration of the skier.
d) If the acceleration of the skier is in fact $-1.54\mathbf{i}$ m s^{-2}, find the friction force acting on the skier.

7 A cyclist of mass 74 kg free-wheels down a hill inclined at 8° to the horizontal.
a) Find the component of the force of gravity parallel to the slope.
b) What is the acceleration of the cyclist if no resistance forces act?
c) What is her speed at the bottom of the hill, 50 m from where she started to move?

8 A car of mass 1000 kg is accelerating up a slope at 2° to the horizontal. If the acceleration of the car is 0.8 m s^{-2} and there are no resistance forces, find the forward force acting on the car.

9 A spaceship of mass 8000 kg is drifting sideways in space at 0.5 m s^{-1}. At O it fires its engines which exert a constant forward force of 1000 N.
a) Draw a diagram to show how you would expect the ship to move.
b) Express the acceleration of the spaceship in terms of the unit vectors $\mathbf{i}$ and $\mathbf{j}$ shown.
c) Find expressions for the velocity and position of the ship relative to O.
d) The engines fire for ten seconds. Sketch the path of the spaceship.
e) Find the velocity of the spaceship after the engines are turned off and its position relative to O after a further 20 seconds.

CONNECTED PARTICLES

Exploration 25.3

Investigating pulleys

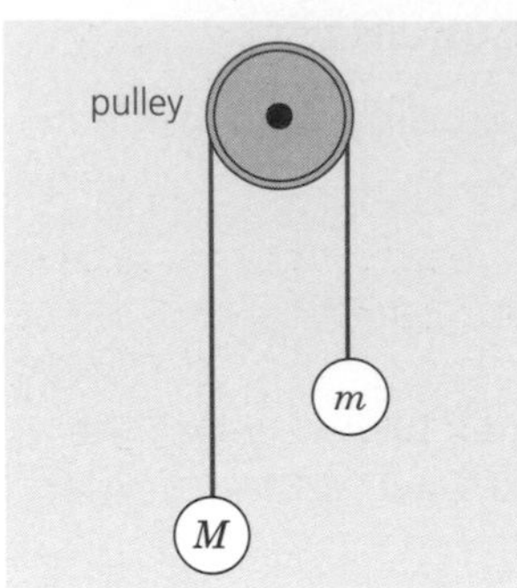

Consider the situation shown in the diagram, where two objects are connected by a string that passes over a pulley. They are held in the position shown and released.

- What happens if:
  a) $M > m$,
  b) $M < m$,
  c) $M = m$?
- Consider the forces acting on each mass. How do the two tension forces compare?
- How do the velocity and acceleration of each mass compare?

Forces in strings

When objects are connected by a string, provided that the string remains taut:

a) the tension forces acting on each object have the same magnitude.

b) the velocity and acceleration of both objects have the same magnitudes.

Example 25.7

A 5 kg mass is joined to a 7 kg mass by a string as shown in the diagram. Find the acceleration of each mass.

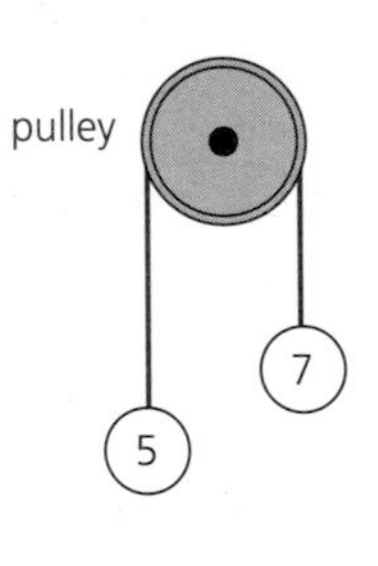

Solution

Both masses will have accelerations with the same magnitudes, a, but opposite directions. The diagrams show the forces on each mass and the direction of the acceleration.

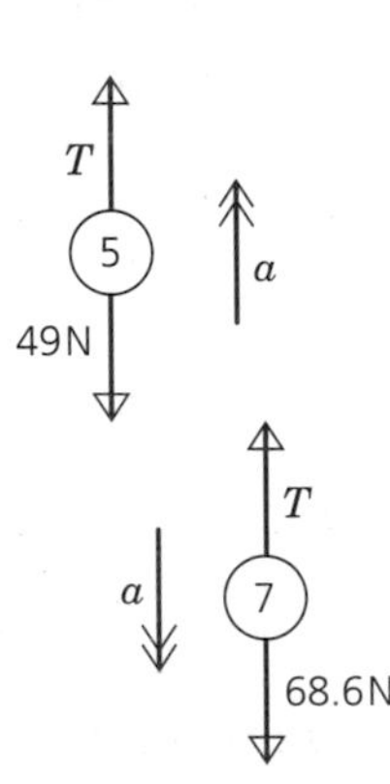

For the 5 kg mass the acceleration is upward, as is the resultant force which has magnitude $T - 49$, so:

$F = ma$

$T - 49 = 5a$ (1)

Similarly for the 7 kg mass, but noting that the resultant force and acceleration are downward give:

$F = ma$

$68.6 - T = 7a$ (2)

From equation (1):

$T = 49 + 5a$

and substituting into equation (2) gives

$7a = 68.6 - (49 + 5a)$

$7a = 19.6 - 5a$

$12a = 19.6$

$$a = \frac{19.6}{12} = 1.63 \text{ m s}^{-2}$$

Example 25.8

The diagram shows a block of mass 5 kg resting on a horizontal surface and attached by a string to a 2 kg mass. The coefficient of friction between the block and the surface is 0.15. Find the acceleration of the block.

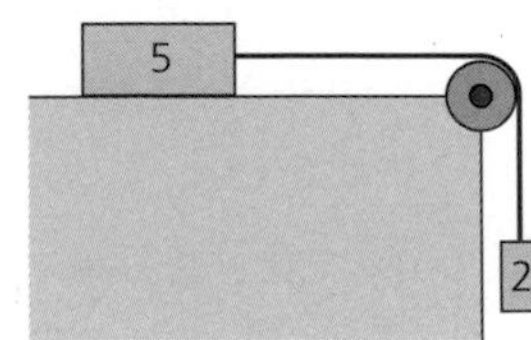

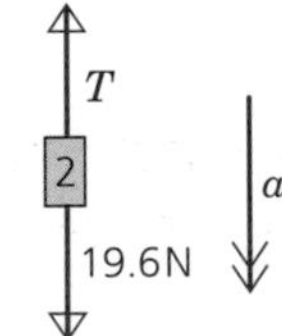

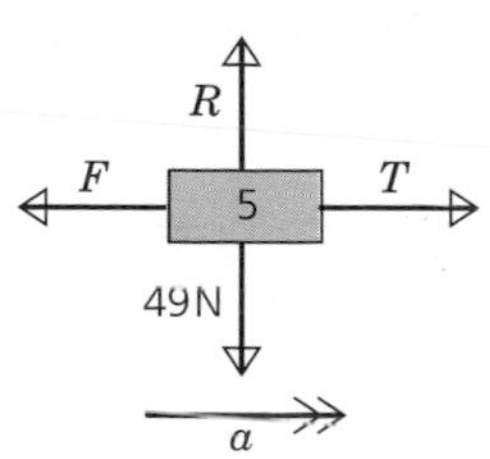

Solution

Note that the acceleration of both the block and the mass will have the same magnitude, a.

Consider first the mass. The acceleration is downward and so is the resultant force which has magnitude 19.6 – T. Using $F = ma$ gives:

$19.6 - T = 2a$

$\Rightarrow T = 19.6 - 2a$ (1)

Now consider the block. The reaction force will balance the force of gravity, so $R = 49$. The friction can then be found using:

$F = \mu R = 0.15 \times 49 = 7.35$

The resultant force on the block will act to the right so:

$T - F = 5a$

$\Rightarrow T - 7.35 = 5a$ (2)

Substituting for T in equation (2) from equation (1) gives:

$19.6 - 2a - 7.35 = 5a$

$7a = 12.25$

$a = 1.75$ m s^{-2}

Exploration 25.4

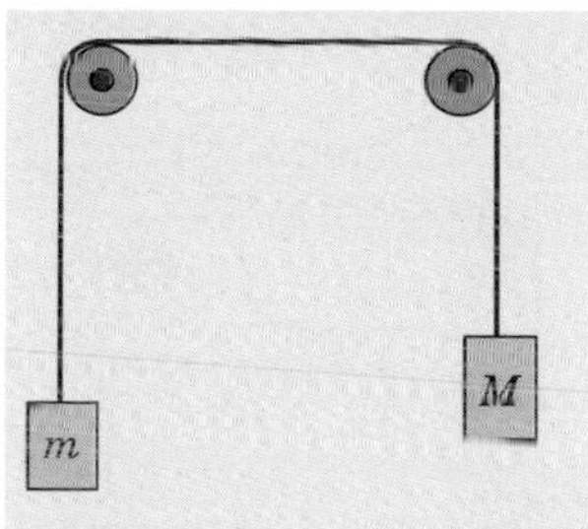

Practical activity

- Set up the apparatus shown, where two masses M and m are connected by a string passing over two pulleys. Arrange the pulleys as high as possible and choose the length of the string so that when one mass is on the floor the other is just below the pulley.
- Select masses so that there is a small difference between m and M, for example 150 grams and 170 grams. Observe the motion that takes place, when the system is released with the lighter mass at floor level. Record the distance travelled by each mass and the time taken. Using your results calculate the acceleration of each mass. (Hint: $s = ut + \frac{1}{2}at^2$)
- Use the approach of Example 25.7 to predict the acceleration of the masses.
- Compare your observed and predicted acceleration. What factors have been ignored in your prediction? Would they explain any difference that you have observed?
- Repeat the last three steps for some different pairs of masses.

Example 25.9

A van of mass 1100 kg is towing a car of mass 750 kg. Normally the van has a maximum acceleration of 1.9 m s^{-2}. Find the maximum acceleration of the van when towing and the tension in the tow rope under these conditions, if there is a resistance force of 300 N on the car.

Solution

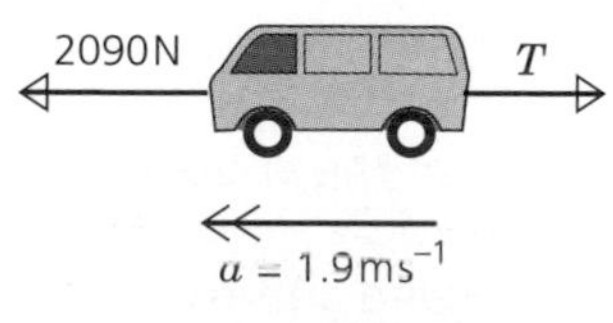

To produce an acceleration of 1.9 m s^{-2} requires a resultant force of magnitude:

$F = ma = 1100 \times 1.9 = 2090$ *N*

Assuming that there is a forward force of 2090 N on the van, the resultant force is 2090 – T which produces an acceleration a. So using Newton's second law, $F = ma$, gives:

$2090 - T = 1100a$ (1)

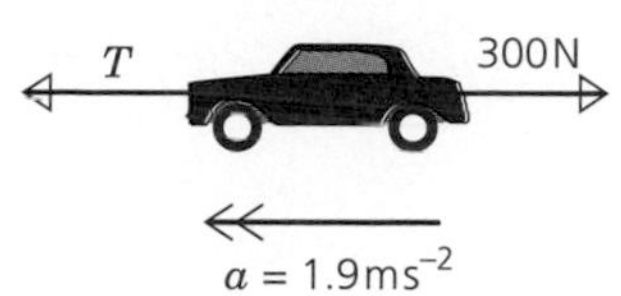

Considering the towed car, there will be a resultant force of T – 300 which gives an acceleration a. So using Newton's second law, $F = ma$, gives:

$T - 300 = 750a$ (2)

From equation (1):
$T = 2090 - 1100a$
This can be substituted into equation (2) to give:
$(2090 - 1100a) - 300 = 750a$
$1790 = 1850a$
$a = \frac{1790}{1850} = 0.9676\ m\ s^{-2}$
This value can now be substituted into:
$T = 2090 - 1100a$
to give:
$T = 2090 - 1100 \times 0.9676 = 1026\ N$

EXERCISES

25.3 CLASSWORK

1 A car of mass 1000 kg tows a caravan of 700 kg. Both experience resistance forces of 250 N, and the car exerts a forward force of 2000 N.
a) If T is the magnitude of the force that the car exerts on the caravan, find the resultant force on the car and the resultant force on the caravan in terms of T.
b) Use Newton's second law to write down two equations, if both car and caravan have acceleration a.
c) Solve the two equations to find the values of T and a.
d) How long does it take the car and caravan to reach a speed of $10\,m\,s^{-1}$?

2 **a)** Find the acceleration of the masses shown in the diagram if:
i) $m = 5$ kg and $M = 3$ kg,
ii) $m = 400$ grams and $M = 500$ grams,
iii) $m = 1$ kg and $M = 1$ kg.
b) Express the acceleration of the system in terms of m, M and g.

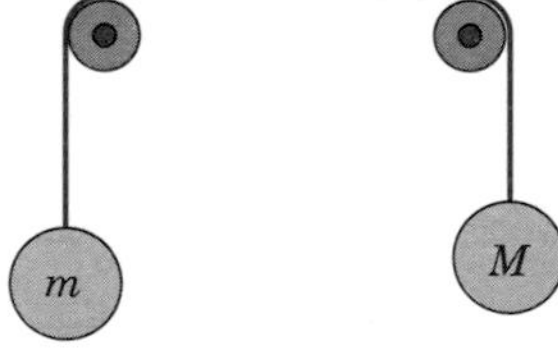

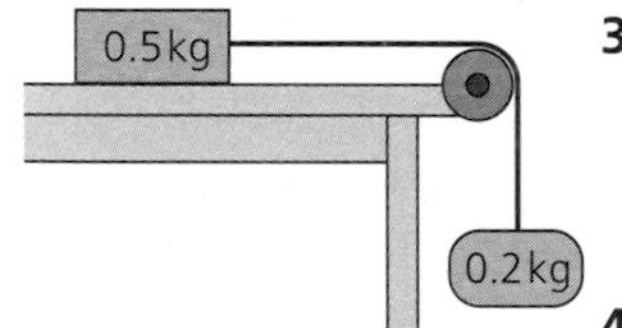

3 The diagram shows a block resting on a horizontal surface and attached to a mass by a string. Find the acceleration of each mass if:
a) there is no friction between the block and the surface,
b) the coefficient of friction between the block and the surface is 0.3.

4 The diagram shows a train that pulls two carriages. The engine is able to exert a forward force of 10 000 N. Each carriage is subjected to resistance force of 4000 N. The engine has a mass of 5 tonnes and each carriage has a mass of 2 tonnes.

a) By modelling the whole train as a single particle, find the acceleration of the train.
b) By considering the last carriage, find the tension in the coupling between the two carriages.
c) Find the tension in the coupling between the engine and the first carriage.

5 Two blocks of masses 3 kg and 5 kg are connected by a string as shown in the diagram.

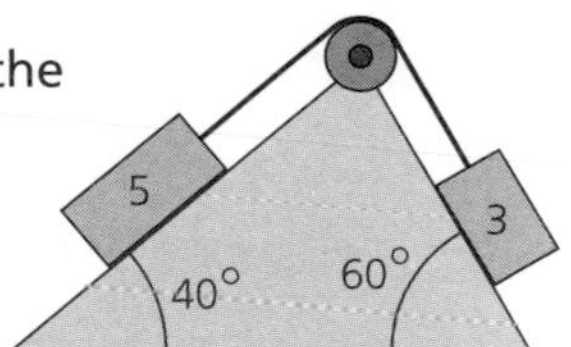

a) If there is no friction between the blocks and the surfaces, find the acceleration of each block.
b) If the coefficient of friction between either mass and the slopes is 0.1, find the tension in the string and the acceleration of each mass.

6 The masses shown are connected by a string.

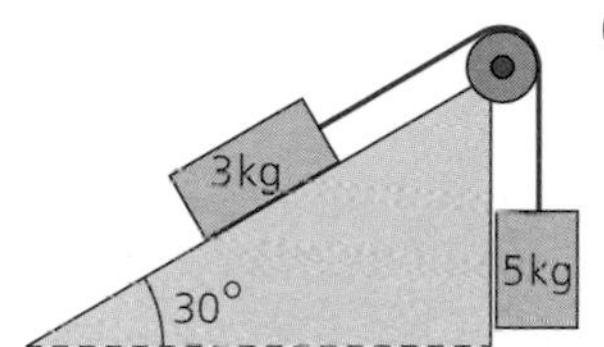

a) If there is no friction between the slope and the mass, find the acceleration of both masses.
b) If the coefficient of friction between the mass and the slope is 0.7, find the tension in the string and the acceleration of each mass.

EXERCISES

25.3 HOMEWORK

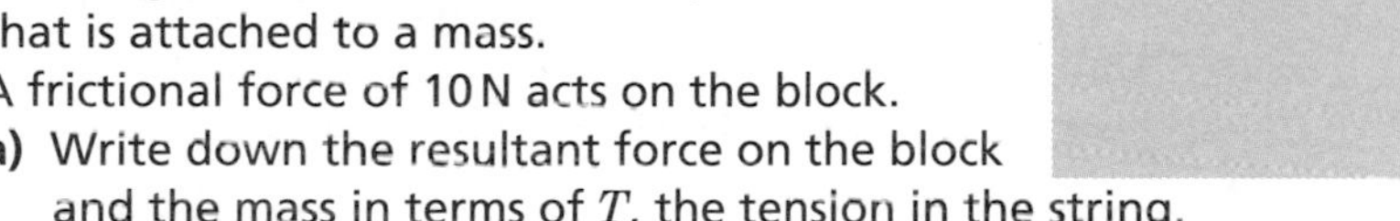

1 The diagram shows a block on a plane that is attached to a mass.
A frictional force of 10 N acts on the block.
a) Write down the resultant force on the block and the mass in terms of T, the tension in the string.
b) Find expressions for the acceleration of the block and the mass.
c) Find the tension in the string and the acceleration of each mass.

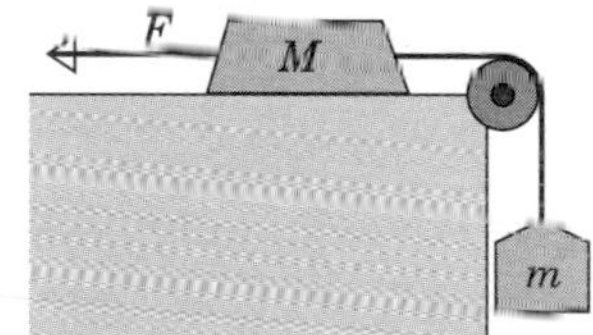

2 Find the acceleration of each mass and the tension in the string if:
a) $F = 20$ N, $M = 10$ kg and $m = 4$ kg,
b) $F = 0$, $M = 1$ kg and $m = 0.5$ kg,
c) $F = 10$ N, $M = 6$ kg and $m = 2$ kg.

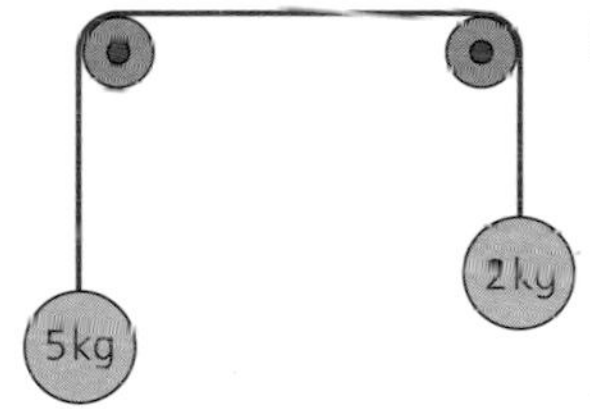

3 The diagram shows two masses connected by a string passing over two pulleys
a) Express the resultant force on each mass in terms of T, the tension in the string.
b) Find expressions for the acceleration of each mass.
c) Find the tension in the string and then the acceleration of each mass.
d) Which assumptions have you made in order to solve this problem?

4 A car towing a caravan exerts a force of 5400 N. The mass of the car is 1100 kg and the mass of the caravan is 700 kg.
a) The acceleration of the car and caravan is 2.5 m s^{-2}. Find the total resistance on the car and caravan.
b) If this total resistance is divided equally between the car and caravan, find the force that the car exerts on the caravan.

5 A car tows an unbraked trailer down a hill that is inclined at 4° to the horizontal. The mass of the car is 1000 kg and the mass of the trailer is 200 kg.
a) If the cars brakes exert a force of 200 N find the acceleration of the car and trailer.
b) Find the force that the car exerts on the trailer.

6 The diagram shows two blocks connected by a string passing over a smooth pulley. Find the acceleration of each mass and the tension in the string if there is no friction present.

MATHEMATICAL MODELLING ACTIVITY

Specify the real problem

Problem statement

When is a hill too steep to drive up?

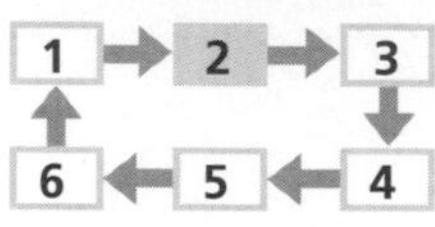

Set up a model

Set up a model

The list below gives the main features of the problem.

- the forward force that can be exerted by the car
- the slope of the hill

Are there any other factors which you feel are important in this problem? The assumptions listed below will allow the model to be formulated.

- The car can be modelled as a particle of mass m kg.
- The hill is at a constant angle of α to the horizontal.
- The car can exert a maximum forward force of $2.5m$ N.

Justify using a value of $2.5m$ N for the maximum forward force.

Formulate the mathematical problem

Formulate a mathematical problem

Find the angle, α, between the slope and the horizontal when the forces on the car are in equilibrium.

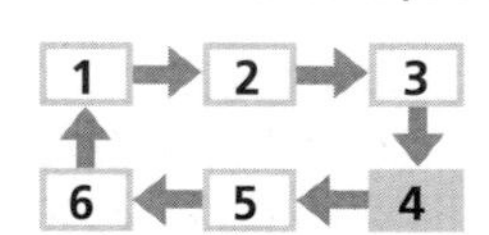

Solve the mathematical problem

Mathematical solution

The diagram shows the forces acting. The resultant force can be expressed in terms of the unit vectors $\mathbf{i}$ and $\mathbf{j}$ as:

$$(2.5m - mg\sin\alpha)\mathbf{i} + (R - mg\cos\alpha)\mathbf{j}$$

When in equilibrium, both components of the resultant force will be zero, so:

$$2.5m - mg\sin\alpha = 0$$

Rearranging gives:

$$\sin\alpha = \frac{2.5}{g} \Rightarrow \alpha = \sin^{-1}\left(\frac{2.5}{9.8}\right) = 15°$$

Interpret the solution

Interpretation

A car can continue to travel up a slope at 15° to the vertical if driven flat out, if it is moving at the bottom of the hill. The car would only be able to maintain speed, and not accelerate.

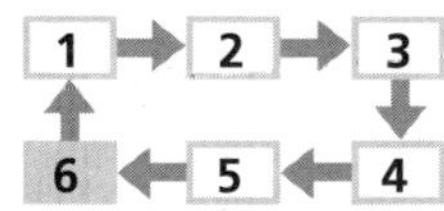

Compare with reality

Compare with reality

Find the angle that a hill with 1:5 gradient makes with the horizontal. Comment on the solution in the light of this.

One criticism that could be made of this model is that the wheels of the car may spin on a steep slope.

What other criticisms can you make of this model?

Refining the model

A typical car will have two driving wheels that provide the forward force on the car, using friction between them and the road.

From the mathematical solution the total reaction force on the car is $mg\cos\alpha$ which is equal to $9.5m$ N for the 15° slope. Assume that the reaction on each wheel is a quarter of this figure, that is $2.4m$ N.

The friction for each driving wheel is $1.25m$ N.

So using $F \le \mu R$ gives:

$$1.25m \le \mu \times 2.4m \Rightarrow \mu \ge \frac{1.25}{2.4} = 0.52$$

if the wheels do not slip.
Do you think it is likely that the wheels will slip?

POSSIBLE MODELLING TASKS

1 Use a rope passed over a peg or bar with masses attached as shown to investigate the friction between the rope and the bar.

2 Drop a ball and record how high it bounces each time and the total time for a number of bounces. Use your results to estimate the value of g.

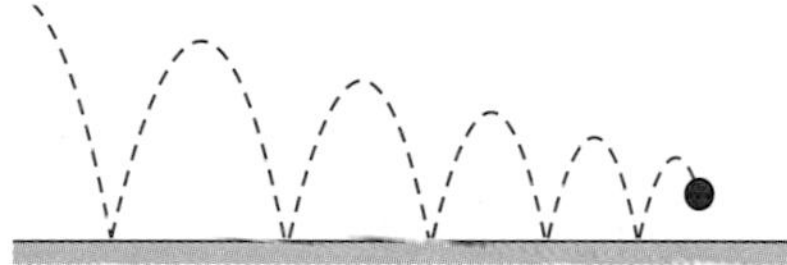

KEY SKILLS
C 3.1a
C 3.1b

3 Drop a ball from a high building. Record the time taken to fall. Use this to estimate g and investigate the effects of air resistance on the ball.

4 The *Highway Code* contains a table of stopping distances. Some assumptions are given in the table. What other assumptions do you think have been made? Investigate the effects of hills and towing unbraked trailers or caravans on the stopping distances given.

5 Find a gentle constant slope. Allow a cyclist or skateboarder to free-wheel down the slope. Record the time taken to travel a range of distances. Find the acceleration of the skateboarder or cyclist at different times and try to find a model for the resistance forces acting on him.

6 A solicitor writes to you asking for assistance. His client was stationary in a car when it was hit by a motorcycle. The motorcycle left a 78 ft (24 m) skid on the road as it skidded down the hill into the car. The solicitor would like you to prepare a report on the speed that the motorcycle was travelling when it hit the car.

CONSOLIDATION EXERCISES FOR CHAPTER 25

1 **A child is sliding at a constant speed of $4\,\text{m s}^{-1}$ down a long slide. The child has a mass of 45 kg. The slide is inclined at an angle of 40° to the horizontal. Assume that a constant friction force, of magnitude 89 N, acts on the child.**

a) **Use the data given to explain why air resistance must be taken into account when modelling the motion of the child. Find the magnitude of the air resistance acting on the child, when he is travelling at a constant speed of $4\,\text{m s}^{-1}$.**

b) **Assume that the magnitude of the air resistance is proportional to the speed of the child. The next time that he uses the slide he starts from rest and accelerates. Find his acceleration, when he is moving at $1\,\text{m s}^{-1}$.**

(AEB Question 2 Paper 3 June 1999)

2 A particle P has mass 3 kg and moves in a horizontal plane under the action of a constant horizontal force. The velocity of P is initially $(2\mathbf{i} + 9\mathbf{j})\,\text{m s}^{-1}$, and 2s later is $(5\mathbf{i} + 3\mathbf{j})\,\text{m s}^{-1}$, where $\mathbf{i}$ and $\mathbf{j}$ are perpendicular horizontal vectors.

Find

a) the magnitude of the horizontal force acting on P, giving your answer in N to one decimal place,

b) the angle this force makes with the vector $\mathbf{j}$, giving your answer in degrees to one decimal place.

(EDEXCEL Question 1 Mechanics 1 January 1998)

3 A skier, of mass 72 kg, slides down a slope, inclined at an angle 20° to the horizontal. The maximum speed of the skier is $7\,\text{m s}^{-1}$. Model the skier as a particle that moves in a straight line. The coefficient of friction between the skis and the snow is 0.2.

a) Find the magnitude of the air resistance acting on the skier, when she is travelling at her maximum speed.

b) A simple model assumes that the air resistance on the skier has a constant magnitude. Describe the main difficulty that this presents when modelling the motion of the skier that starts at rest.

c) A refined assumption is that the air resistance on the skier is proportional to her speed. Find a model for the resistance force based on this assumption and use it to find the acceleration of the skier, when she is moving at $2\,\text{m s}^{-1}$.

d) Explain what happens to:

i) the magnitude of the friction force and

ii) the magnitude of the air resistance,

if the skier carries a small, but heavy, rucksack, that increases her mass, but does not cause her shape to change in any way. Give reasons for your answers.

(AQA Specification B Question 5 Mechanics 1 Specimen Paper 2000)

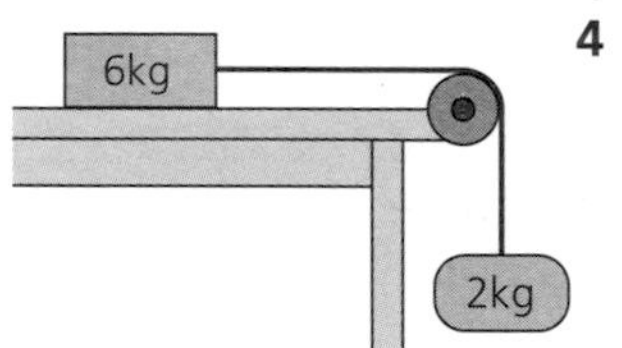

4 A block, of mass 6 kg, rests on a rough, horizontal surface. The coefficient of friction between the block and the surface is 0.2. A light, inextensible, string attached to the block passes over a smooth pulley. A weight, of mass 2 kg, hangs from the other end of the string, as shown in the diagram.

Find the tension in the string and the acceleration of the block.

(AQA Specification BQuestion 8 Mechanics 1 Specimen Paper 2000)

5 A particle of mass m rests on a rough plane inclined at an angle α to the horizontal, where $\tan \alpha = \frac{3}{4}$. The particle is attached to one end of a light inextensible string which lies in a line of greatest slope of the plane and passes over a small light smooth pulley P fixed at the top of the plane. The other end of the string is attached to a particle B of mass 3m, and B hangs freely below P, as shown in Fig. 4. The particles are released from rest with the string taut The particle B moves down with acceleration of magnitude $\frac{1}{2}$ g. Find

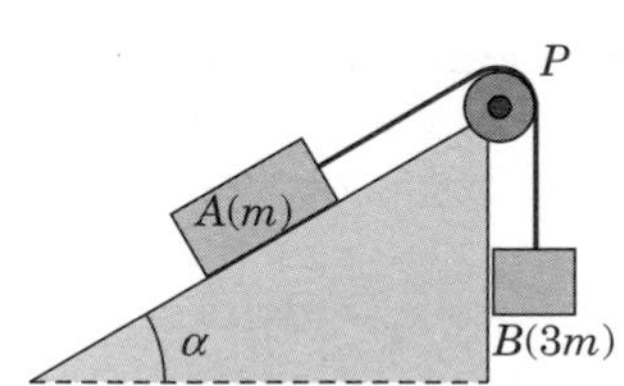

a) the tension in the string

b) the coefficient of friction between A and the plane.

(EDEXCEL Question 6 Mechanics 1 Specimen Paper)

6 Two light scale pans A and B, are connected by a light cord which hangs over a smooth peg. Two particles of mass pm and qm are placed on A and B, respectively, and the system is released from the rest. In the resulting motion, A moves downwards with acceleration $\frac{1}{2}g$.

a) i) Find, in terms of p, m and g, the tension in the string.
ii) Show that $p = 3q$.

b) The particles of mass pm and qm are then both placed on the scale pan A and a particle of mass $4m$ is placed on B. The system is again released from rest and A again accelerates downwards at a rate of $\frac{1}{2}g$.
i) By using the result in part **a) ii)**, or otherwise, find another equation in p and q.
ii) Hence find the values of p and q.

(AQA Specification A Question 7 Mechanics 1 Specimen Paper 2000)

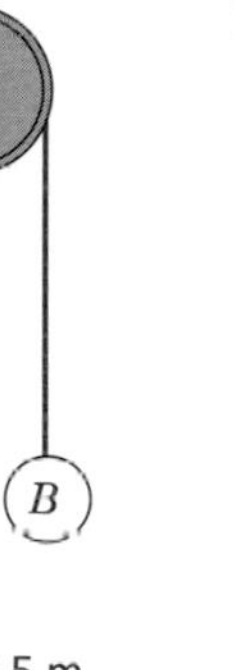

7 i) Particles A, of mass 0.4 kg, and B, of mass 0.3 kg, are attached to the ends of a light inextensible string. The string passes over a fixed peg, and the system is released from rest with both parts of the string taut and vertical, and each particle 0.5 m above a fixed horizontal plane (see diagram). Neglecting all resistances to motion, find

a) the acceleration of A and the tension in the string,
b) the time after release at which A hits the plane.

ii) The results in part **i)** are based on a mathematical model in which resistances to motion are neglected. Describe briefly one resisting force, other than air resistance, which would be present in a real system in which objects of unequal mass, hanging from a string passing over a fixed support, are in motion.

When this force is taken into account, state with reasons whether each of the following would be smaller or larger than the value calculated in part **i)**:

a) the acceleration of A;
b) the tension in the string acting on A.
c) the tension in the string acting on B.

What can you conclude about the tension in the string in this case?

(OCR Question 7 Mechanics 1 Specimen Paper)

8 Figure 5 shows a particle A, of mass $3m$, on a plane inclined at an angle α to the horizontal, and a particle B, of mass $2m$, on a plane inclined at an angle $90° - \alpha$ to the horizontal, where $\tan \alpha = \frac{4}{3}$. The plane on which A moves is rough, the coefficient of friction between A and the plane being $\frac{1}{3}$. The plane on which B moves is smooth. A and B are connected by a string passing over a small smooth pulley fixed at C, the highest point of the two planes. The string is assumed to be light and inextensible. The particles are released from rest with the string taut and the sections AC and BC of the string parallel to lines of greatest slope in the respective planes, and A moves down the plane. Given that neither particle has reached the top or the bottom of its respective plane,

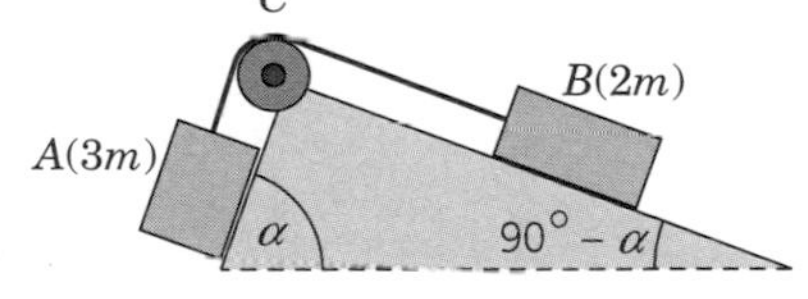

a) show that the frictional force acting on A has magnitude $\frac{3}{5}mg$,
b) find
  i) the magnitude of the acceleration of the particles in terms of g,
  ii) the magnitude of the tension in the string in terms of m and g.
c) State where you have used the assumption that
  i) the string is inextensible,
  ii) the pulley is smooth.

(EDEXCEL Question 8 Mechanics 1 June 1998)

Summary

After working through this chapter you should:

- be able to apply Newton's first law
- be able to make predictions about motion by using Newton's second law
- solve problems involving connected particles.

Momentum and collisions

- *The mass of an object and its velocity are important factors in a collision.*
- *Momentum is the product of the mass of an object and its velocity.*
- *Momentum is a fundamental quantity of motion.*

MOMENTUM

When we want to change or cancel the motion of an object, we need to exert a force to do so. Two factors that will influence the size of the force needed are the **velocity** of the object concerned, and its **mass**. Objects with greater masses and velocities will require greater forces, or forces that act for longer, than will smaller, slower objects. In this chapter we explore what happens when there are changes in motion, and in particular in the case of collisions.

Which of the objects below, would it be possible for a human being, of average strength and fitness, to stop?

- A football travelling at 70 mph.
- A small car moving at 2 mph.
- A 70 kg rugby player moving at 10 m s^{-1}.

You may find it helpful to express all the velocities in the same unit. Remember,

$$1\,\text{mph} \approx \frac{1600}{3600} = \frac{4}{9}\ \text{m s}^{-1}$$

In all these situations, both the mass and speed of the objects are important factors. If the motion of an object is to be changed, the force required to produce the change will depend on the **mass** of the object and the **acceleration**, or **change in velocity**. Newton realised that both mass and velocity were important and defined a fundamental quantity of motion, now known as **momentum**.

The momentum of an object is defined as:

$$m\mathbf{v}$$

where m is its mass and $\mathbf{v}$ its velocity.

As velocity is a vector, then momentum must also be a vector quantity. However in the same way that it is often useful to talk about the speed of an object, it is useful to talk about the magnitude of the momentum.

Example 26.1

Calculate the magnitude of the momentum of:
a) *a sprinter of mass 65 kg travelling as 8 m s^{-1},*
b) *a lorry of mass 30 tonnes travelling at 20 m s^{-1}.*

Solution

The magnitude of the momentum is given by mv, where m is the mass and v the speed.

a) *Here $m = 65$ kg and $v = 8\,\text{m s}^{-1}$ so:*

$mv = 65 \times 8 = 520\,\text{kg m s}^{-1}$

b) *Here $m = 30\,000$ kg and $v = 20\,\text{m s}^{-1}$ so:*

$mv = 30\,000 \times 20 = 600\,000\,\text{kg m s}^{-1}$

Example 26.2

Two train trucks are set into motion so that they have the same momentum. One truck moves at $3\,\text{m s}^{-1}$ and has mass 240 grams. The second truck moves at $1.8\,\text{m s}^{-1}$. Find the mass of the second truck.

Solution

Momentum of first truck $= 3 \times 0.24$

$= 0.72\,\text{kg m s}^{-1}$

Momentum of second truck $= 1.8m$

The momentum is equal so:

$$1.8m = 0.72$$

$$m = \frac{0.72}{1.8} = 0.4 \text{ kg or } 400 \text{ grams}$$

EXERCISES

26.1 CLASSWORK

1 Calculate the magnitude of the momentum of each object described below.

a) A ball of mass 0.2 kg travelling at $20\,\text{m s}^{-1}$.

b) A ferry of mass 800 tonnes travelling at $5\,\text{m s}^{-1}$.

c) A bullet of mass 10 grams travelling at $950\,\text{m s}^{-1}$.

2 Two pucks of masses 8 grams and 16 grams are fired along straight tracks at constant speeds. The diagram shows their positions after a period of time. How does the momentum of each puck compare?

3 A skater follows a curved path, moving at a constant speed. What happens to the skater's momentum?

4 Two particles have the same momentum. One has mass 0.7 kg and the other 0.9 kg. The lighter particle moves at $13.5\,\text{m s}^{-1}$. Find the speed of the other particle.

5 A ball of mass 350 grams falls from rest and hits the ground when it has fallen 2 m. Find the momentum of the ball when it hits the ground.

EXERCISES

26.1 HOMEWORK

1 Calculate the magnitude of the momentum of each object that moves as described below.

a) A sprinter of mass 68 kg travelling at $7\,\text{m s}^{-1}$.

b) A lorry of mass 10 tonnes travelling at $20\,\text{m s}^{-1}$.

c) A table tennis ball of mass 3 grams moving at $4\,\text{m s}^{-1}$.

2 An athlete claims that her momentum remains constant as she runs round a track. Is this claim justified?

3 When a rocket takes off its mass decreases as fuel is used up. What happens to the momentum of the rocket if the speed increases at the same rate that the mass is decreasing?

4 A car, of mass 1100 kg, accelerates at 0.5 m s^{-2} from an initial speed of 5 m s^{-1}. Find the momentum of the car after it has travelled 50 m.

5 A ball, of mass 400 grams, is thrown vertically upwards at a speed of 4 m s^{-1}. The initial height of the ball is 1.5 m. Find the momentum of the ball when it hits the ground.

IMPULSE AND CHANGE OF MOMENTUM

When the motion of any object changes, it is because there is a force acting. The force could act for any length of time. In this section we explore the relationship between the force, the time for which it acts and the resulting change in momentum. This can be useful in many situations. For example in a car crash it may be easy to estimate the change of momentum and the time taken for a vehicle to come to rest. The forces that acted during the collision can then be estimated.

Exploration 26.1

When a ball bounces on the ground, the force acts on the ball for a very short period of time. It would be very difficult to measure either the time of contact or the force acting on the ball. However, it is relatively easy to describe the change in momentum.

- Try to describe other situations where it would be hard to measure forces and contact times, but where the change in momentum is easier to observe.

Impulse

When a force acts for a short time, we often refer to its effects as an **impulse**. For a constant force, Newton's second law states that

$F = ma$ but as $a = \dfrac{(v-u)}{t}$ this can be expressed as:

$Ft = mv - mu.$

Impulse, I is defined as the change in momentum, so:

$I = mv - mu$ and also $I = Ft$

While the idea of impulse is very useful for forces that act for a very short time, the results above are valid for any situation, such as one in which the time for which the force acts can be measured.

The units of I are N s, or newton seconds. **Note:** The units N s and kg m s^{-1} are the same.

It is also interesting to note that Newton's second law can be expressed in terms of momentum. Consider a force F. Then by Newton's second law:

$F = ma$ or $F = m\dfrac{dv}{dt}$

If m is a constant, then $F = \dfrac{d(mv)}{dt}$

This shows that the resultant force is equal to the rate of change of momentum. It was in this form that Newton originally stated his second law.

Example 26.3

A car involved in a collision has a mass of 900 kg and is brought to rest from a speed of 10 m s^{-1}.

a) *Find the impulse on the car.*
b) *If the car is brought to rest in a period of 1.5 seconds, find the average force acting on the car.*

Solution

a) *Here the initial speed of the car is 10 m s^{-1} so, $u = 10$, the final speed is 0, so $v = 0$, and $m = 900$.*
Using $I = mv - mu$ gives:
$I = 900 \times 0 - 900 \times 10 = -9000$ *N s*
Note that I is negative because the force involved acts to oppose the motion of the car.

b) *Using $I = Ft$ with $t = 1.5$ gives:*
$-9000 = F \times 1.5$
$$F = \frac{-9000}{1.5} = -6000 \text{ N}$$

Example 26.4

When a ball, of mass 100 grams, bounces on a horizontal surface. It hits the ground travelling at 5 m s^{-1} and rebounds at 3 m s^{-1}. The ball is in contact with the ground for 0.02 seconds.
Find:

a) *the impulse on the ball,*
b) *the average force acting on the ball,*
c) *the average reaction force exerted by the ground on the ball.*

Solution

a) *In this case $m = 0.1$, $v = -3$ and $u = 5$.*
$I = mv - mu$
$= 0.1 \times (-3) - 0.1 \times 5$
$= -0.8$ Ns
The negative sign indicates that the impulse is upwards.

b) *Using $Ft = I$ gives:*
$F \times 0.02 = -0.8$
$F = -40$N
The average force is 40 N upwards.

c) *Two forces act on the ball, the reaction upwards and the force of gravity downwards, so:*
$R - 0.1 \times 9.8 = 40$
$R = 40 + 0.98 = 40.98$ N

EXERCISES

26.2 CLASSWORK

1 When a superball of mass 75 grams bounces on the floor, a downward velocity of 3 m s^{-1} is converted to an upward velocity of 2.5 m s^{-1}.

a) Find the magnitude of the impulse on the ball.
b) If a lighter superball of mass 50 grams experiences the same change in velocity, find the magnitude of the impulse on this ball.

2 At a fairground a dodgem with a mass of 300 kg including passengers hits the side of the driving area at a speed of 2 m s^{-1} and bounces back at 0.5 m s^{-1}.

a) Find the magnitude of the impulse on the car.
b) If the car is in contact with the side of the area for 1.2 seconds, find the average force on the car.

3 In a road traffic accident a car of mass 1500 kg, travelling at 5 m s^{-1}, hits a stationary vehicle and is brought to rest in two seconds.
a) Find the magnitude of the impulse on the car.
b) Find the average force on the car.

4 A diver of mass 55 kg dives from a board at a height of 5 m into a pool.
a) Show that, if air resistance is ignored, the diver is travelling at 9.9 m s^{-1} when she hits the water.
b) When she hits the water she moves for a further 1.2 seconds before stopping. Find the magnitude of the impulse on the diver.
c) What is the average force exerted on her?

5 Two roller skaters collide head on at a skating rink. They have initial velocities of 3 m s^{-1} and −4 m s^{-1}. Their masses are 45 kg and 50 kg respectively. After the collision the lighter skater has velocity −1 m s^{-1}.
a) Find the impulse on this skater.
b) The other skater experiences an impulse of the same magnitude, but opposite direction. Find the velocity of this skater after the collision.

6 A ball, of mass 250 grams, falls from a height of 3 m and rebounds to a height of 2 m. The ball is in contact with the ground for 0.1 seconds.
a) Find the impulse on the ball, while it is in contact with the ground.
b) Find the average reaction force exerted by the ground on the ball.

7 In a collision a force of 9000 N acts on a car, of mass 1200 kg, for 3 seconds bringing the car to rest.
a) Find the speed of the car before the collision.
b) The same impulse is exerted on another car, of mass 900 kg, which is also brought to rest. Find the speed of this car before the collision.

8 A ball, of mass m, is dropped from a height H onto a horizontal surface and rebounds to a height h. Find the magnitude of the impulse that the ball experiences while in contact with the ground.

EXERCISES

26.2 HOMEWORK

1 A croquet ball of mass 300 grams is hit by a mallet and moves at 0.8 m s^{-1}.
a) Find the magnitude of the impulse that the ball received when it was hit.
b) If the same impulse were given to a ball of mass 500 grams, what would its speed be?

2 A ball of mass 60 grams hits the ground travelling at 4 m s^{-1} and rebounds at 2 m s^{-1}.
a) Find the momentum of the ball when it hits the ground and when it rebounds.
b) Find the impulse on the ball.
c) If the ball was in contact with the ground for 0.5 seconds, find the average force on the ball.

3 A ball of mass 500 grams is travelling at 6 m s^{-1}. It is caught and brought to rest in 0.6 seconds.
a) Find the magnitude of the impulse on the ball as it is brought to rest.

b) Find the force on the ball, if this is assumed to be constant.
c) Describe how the force on the ball may change as it is caught.

4 A parachutist of mass 75 kg is travelling vertically at $5\,\mathrm{m\,s^{-1}}$ when he lands on horizontal ground and comes to rest.
a) What is the impulse of the ground on the man?
b) Explain why he should bend his legs upon landing.
c) He bends his legs and becomes stationary after 1.8 seconds. Calculate the average force the ground exerts on the man.
d) If he doesn't bend his legs, and the impulse lasts for only 0.3 seconds, calculate the average force the ground exerts on the man.

5 Experiments suggest that a car of mass 1000 kg moving at $13\,\mathrm{m\,s^{-1}}$ can be brought to rest in 1.2 s, when in collision with a solid wall. The use of crumple zones can extend this time to 1.9 s. Find the average force on a car with and a car without crumple zones.

6 The speed of a lorry, of mass 30 tonnes, is reduced from $20\,\mathrm{m\,s^{-1}}$ to $14\,\mathrm{m\,s^{-1}}$ over a period of 8 seconds.
a) Find the impulse on the lorry.
b) Find the average force acting on the lorry.

7 A ball, of mass m, hits a wall at a speed U and rebounds at a speed of $\frac{3U}{4}$. The ball is in contact with the wall for T seconds.
a) Find the impulse on the ball.
b) Find the average force on the ball.

8 A ball, of mass m, is thrown upwards from a height h, with speed U. When it bounces on the ground it rebounds to a length of $\frac{3h}{4}$.

Find the impulse exerted on the ball by the ground.

COLLISIONS AND CONSERVATION OF MOMENTUM

During a collision it is very hard to monitor the forces acting, or even the direction in which they act. This is true whether we are considering a collision between two balls on a snooker table, or two cars in an accident. However, we can still find out a lot about a collision by comparing the momentum before and after impact. In this section we examine the change in momentum during a collision.

Exploration 26.2

Collision of two vehicles

What happens when two vehicles collide? Consider the situations below, commenting on which objects gain speed and which lose speed as a result of the collision.

- A lorry colliding with a stationary car.
- A car colliding with a stationary lorry.
- An Intercity 125 train colliding with a fly.

Exploration 26.3

Collisions

This activity can be carried out using equipment that is available in most mathematics or science departments, such as the 'Unilab Collisions Kit' or an air track. It is very simple to set up. The instructions here refer to the 'Collisions Kit'.

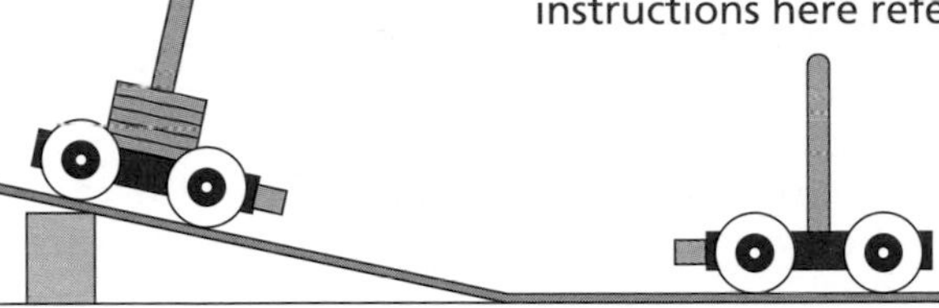

- Set up the apparatus as shown in the diagram. Let one buggy roll down the slope so that it collides with the stationary buggy. What happens?
- Attach Velcro to the buggies, so that they stick together after collision. What happens?
- In each situation, describe what happens to the momentum of each buggy.
- Vary the masses of the buggies so that heavy buggies collide with light buggies, and vice versa. What happens to the momentum of the buggies in each case?

Momentum in collisions

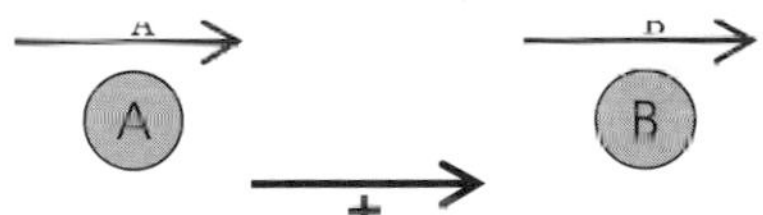

Consider the simple case of two masses A and B, where A has mass m_A and velocity u_A and B has mass m_B and velocity u_B.

Assume that A is travelling faster than B so that they collide, and that they travel along a straight path.

Their velocities will be changed by the collision so the diagram can be completed by letting v_A and v_B represent their respective velocities after the collision.

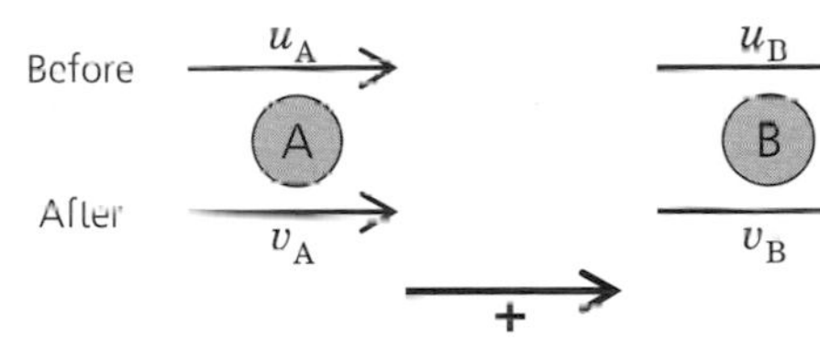

During the impact both masses experience an impulse (i.e. Ft where F is the force exerted and t is the time for which the force is acting).

Impulse $I = mv - mu$

so the impulse on each mass is:

$$I_A = m_A v_A - m_A u_A$$

$$I_B = m_B v_B - m_B u_B$$

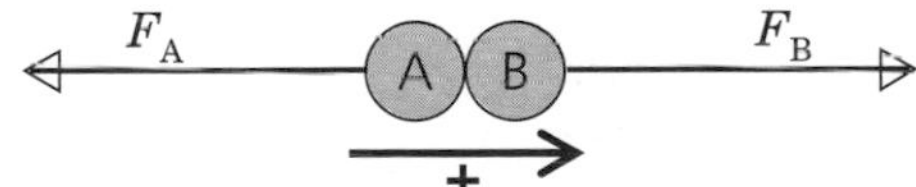

Since the *size* of the force is the same for both masses, we can see that the forces F_A and F_B have the relationship:

$$F_A = -F_B$$

Since they both act for the same time:

$$F_A t = -F_B t$$

or:

$$I_A = -I_B$$

Using $I = mv - mu$ gives:

$$m_A v_A - m_A u_A = -(m_B v_B - m_B u_B)$$

and rearranging gives:

$$m_A v_A + m_B v_B = m_A u_A + m_B u_B$$

This is an extremely important equation. It can also be expressed as follows:

total momentum after the impact = total momentum before the impact

This important result is known as **conservation of momentum**.

Example 26.5

On the track of a model railway, a truck with a mass of 0.2 kg is moving at 2 m s⁻¹ towards a stationary truck of mass 0.3 kg. The trucks collide and join together during the collision. Find how fast they are moving after the collision.

Solution

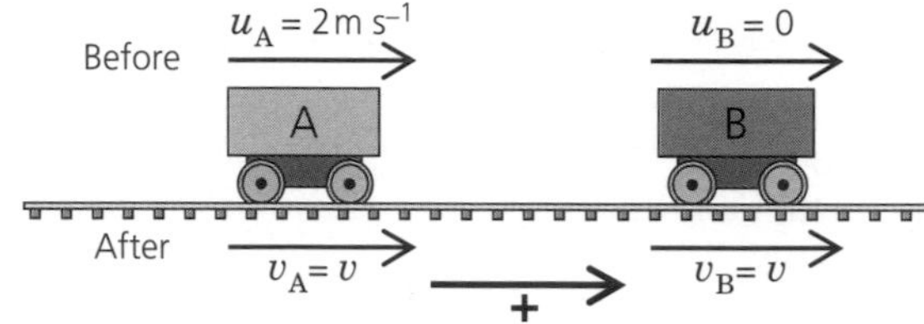

The diagram summarises the collision. Note that $v_A = v_B$ because the trucks join together during the collision so both v_A and v_B can simply be referred to as v.

Using conservation of momentum:

$m_A v_A + m_B v_B = m_A u_A + m_B u_B$

gives:

$0.2v + 0.3v = 0.2 \times 2 + 0.3 \times 0 \quad \Rightarrow 0.5v = 0.4$

$v = 0.8\,m\,s^{-1}$

So the trucks collide and move together after the collision with speed 0.8 m s⁻¹.

Example 26.6

Two balls are moving directly towards each other. Ball A has mass 3 kg and is moving with speed 5 m s⁻¹ and ball B has mass 2 kg and is moving with speed 2 m s⁻¹. After the collision ball A continues to move in its original direction but at the reduced speed of 1 m s⁻¹. Find how ball B is moving after the collision.

Solution

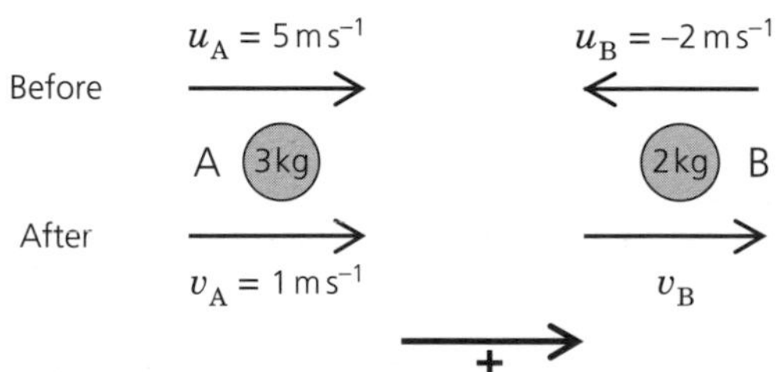

Defining the positive direction to the right as shown in the diagrams gives

$u_A = 5$, $u_B = -2$ *and* $v_A = 1$.

Using conservation of momentum:

$m_A v_A + m_B v_B = m_A u_A + m_B u_B$

gives:

$3 \times 1 + 2v_B = 3 \times 5 + 2 \times -2 \quad \Rightarrow 2v_B = 8$

$v_B = 4\,m\,s^{-1}$

The value for v_B tells us that B moves away from the collision at 4 m s⁻¹. Since it is also positive it moves to the right.

Exploration 26.4

Assumption about collisions

In the above example we have ignored several features of the motion of the balls. What are these features?

Rotation and impact

In the examples we have considered so far, the balls are moving directly towards each other with constant speed. This means they must be moving on a horizontal surface or guide of some sort. If they are moving on a smooth horizontal wire then the assumptions used in the example are probably quite good. However, if they are moving on a horizontal surface, the balls will almost certainly rotate as they move. The effects of this on the collision could well be very significant. Snooker players make a great deal of use of the rotation of the balls to enable them to gain advantages in the position of the balls on the table, and to achieve those impossible shots!

The rotation of the balls may well affect the collision but the model of two particles considered above gives a good prediction, if the effects of the rotation are not significant.

Example 26.7

A boy of mass 50 kg stands on a skateboard of mass 4 kg. He is not moving when he decides to jump off the skateboard. If he jumps forward with speed 1 m s⁻¹, find the velocity of the skateboard.

Solution

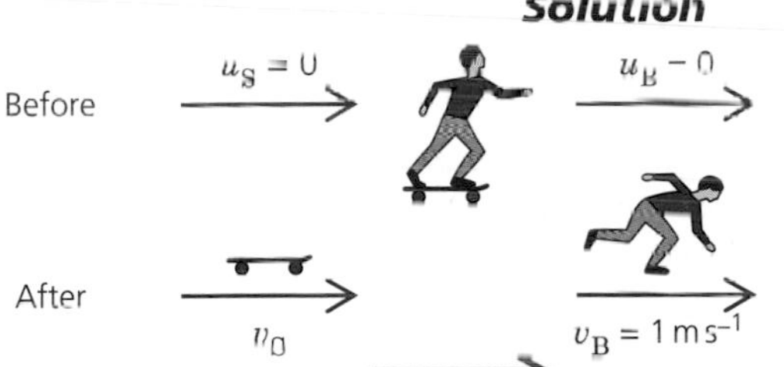

Defining the positive direction to be to the right allows the known velocities to be specified. The initial velocity of the boy is $u_B = 0$ and his final velocity $v_B = 1$. The initial velocity of the skateboard is $u_S = 0$ and its final velocity is v_S.

Using conservation of momentum:

$m_A v_A + m_B v_B = m_A u_A + m_B u_B$

gives:

$4v_S + 50 \times 1 = 4 \times 0 + 50 \times 0 \Rightarrow 4v_S = -50$

$v_S = -12.5\,m\,s^{-1}$

It can now be seen that the skateboard moves at 12.5 m s⁻¹. The negative sign indicates that the velocity of the skateboard is in the direction to the left on the diagram.

It is helpful to draw any unknown vectors on diagrams pointing in the positive direction. Then if we obtain a negative value for any of them, we know it represents a quantity in the negative direction.

EXERCISES

26.3 CLASSWORK

1 Two balls of mass 100 grams from a Velcro catching game collide. Before the collision they are both travelling in the same direction with speeds of 5 m s^{-1} and 2 m s^{-1}. During the collision they stick together and then move with the same velocity.

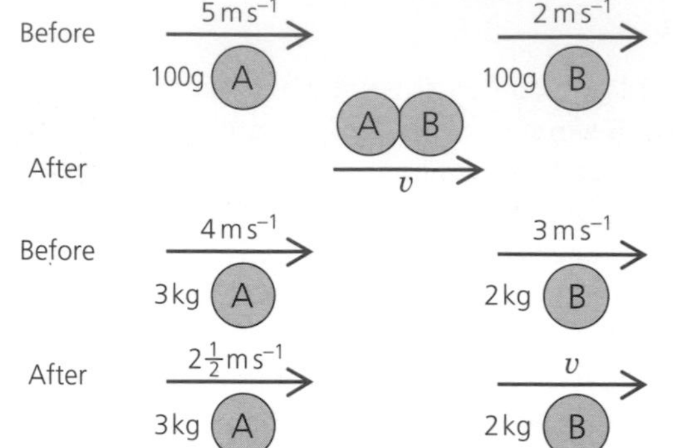

a) What is the total momentum of both balls before the collision?
b) What is the total momentum after the collision?
c) Find the speed of the balls after the collision.

2 The two particles shown in the diagram collide on a smooth horizontal surface. After the collision, the lighter particle moves with speed v.
a) What is the total momentum of the particles before the collision?
b) Find the value of v.

3 Two bodies, with masses of 250 grams and 450 grams, approach each other from opposite directions, on a smooth horizontal surface with speeds of 8 m s^{-1} and 2 m s^{-1} respectively. The heavier body has its direction of motion reversed by the collision and moves away at 1 m s^{-1}. Find the speed, v, of the lighter body after the collision.

4 A lorry of mass 8 tonnes is travelling at 10 m s^{-1} when it hits a stationary car of mass 1020 kg. If the two vehicles move together after the collision, what is their initial combined speed?

5 Particle A, with mass 3 kg and speed 5 m s^{-1}, collides with a particle B, which is a 2 kg mass initially at rest. If particle A continues to travel in the same direction but with a speed of 1 m s^{-1}, find the speed with which B is moving after the collision.

6 If, in question **5**, the two masses join together, find the speed with which they move after the collision.

7 A firework display includes a rocket which sends a 0.3 kg mass into the air. When travelling horizontally at the top of its trajectory it explodes into two pieces of masses 0.1 kg and 0.2 kg. If the speed of the 0.3 kg mass is 10 m s^{-1} before the explosion and the 0.2 kg mass is propelled at a speed of 12 m s^{-1} in the same direction after the explosion, find the speed of the 0.1 kg mass.

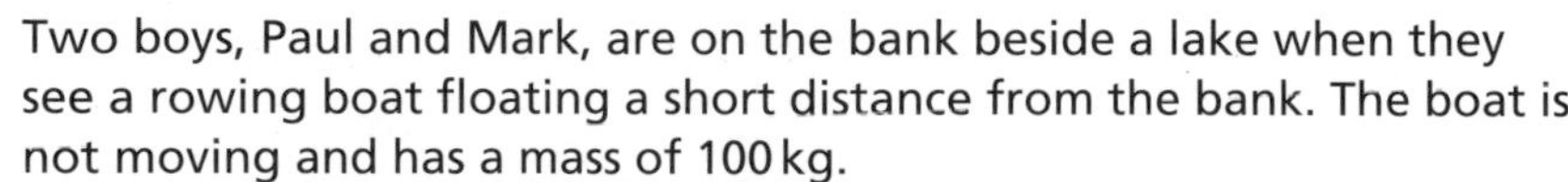

8 Two boys, Paul and Mark, are on the bank beside a lake when they see a rowing boat floating a short distance from the bank. The boat is not moving and has a mass of 100 kg.

Paul, who has a mass of 50 kg, decides to jump from the bank into the boat and to do this he first runs at right angles to the bank towards the water. On the edge of the lake he jumps and lands in the boat. If he has a horizontal speed of 5 m s^{-1} just before landing in the boat, calculate the speed with which he and the boat move immediately after he lands in the boat.

EXERCISES

26.3 HOMEWORK

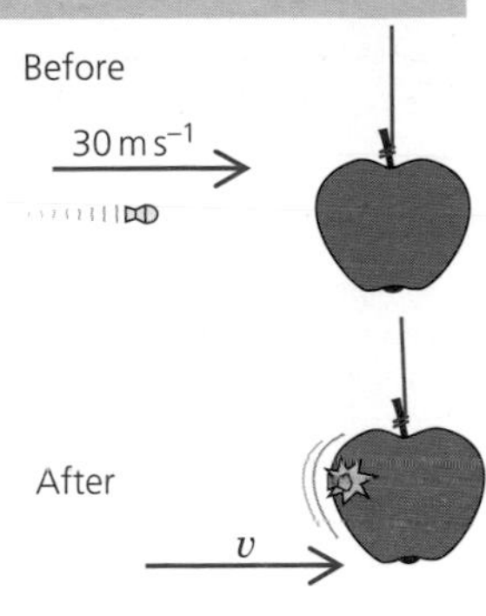

1 An air gun pellet of mass 1 gram travelling at 30 m s^{-1} hits the centre of an apple of mass 120 grams. The apple is suspended by a string and is at rest before the pellet hits it and becomes embedded in it.

a) What is the total momentum of the two objects before the collision?

b) What is the total momentum after the collision?

c) Find the speed of the apple after the pellet has become embedded within it.

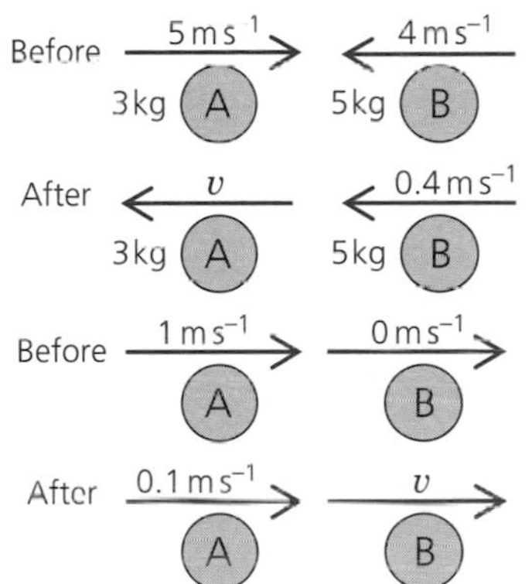

2 The two bodies shown collide on a smooth horizontal surface.

a) What is the total momentum of the two bodies before the collision?

b) What is the total momentum after the collision?

c) Find the value of v, the speed of the 3 kg mass after the collision.

3 A snooker ball collides directly with an identical ball which is initially at rest. The first ball has its speed reduced from 1 m s^{-1} to 0.1 m s^{-1} but continues to move in the same direction. Find the speed with which the second ball moves after the collision.

4 Particle A of mass m travels on a smooth horizontal surface at 6 m s^{-1}. It collides with particle B which has a mass of 3 kg and travels at 4 m s^{-1} directly towards A. Both particles have their direction of motion reversed by the collision. A now has a speed of 2 m s^{-1} and B has a speed of $1\frac{1}{3}$ m s^{-1} Find the mass of particle A.

5 A bullet of mass m is fired from a gun of mass 2.4 kg. After the bullet is fired at a speed of 400 m s^{-1} the gun recoils at 3 m s^{-1}.

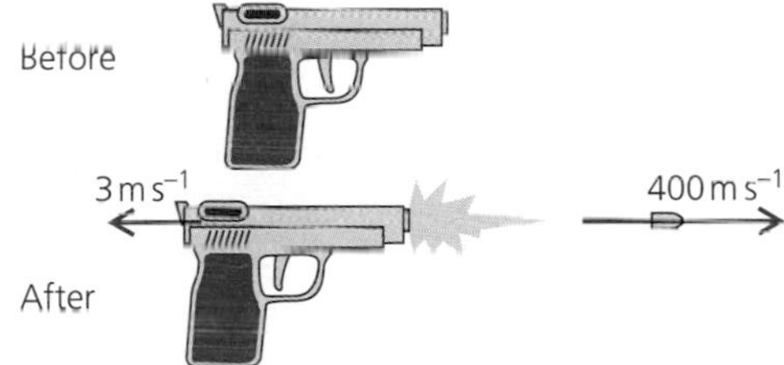

Find the value of m, the mass of the bullet in grams.

6 A model railway truck of mass 120 grams travels on a smooth, horizontal track at speed v. It strikes a stationary truck of mass 180 grams and the trucks become coupled together. The trucks move with speed 12 cm s^{-1} after the collision. Find the value of v (to the nearest cm s^{-1}).

7 A bullet of mass 6 grams is fired at a wooden block of mass 36 grams which is initially at rest on a smooth horizontal surface. The bullet approaches the block with a horizontal speed v and becomes embedded in the block. Find the value of v to the nearest m s^{-1}, if the block moves at a speed of 7 m s^{-1} after the bullet has hit it.

8 A ping pong ball has a mass of 10 grams and collides directly with a football which has a mass of 1 kilogram. Just before they collide the balls are travelling towards each other, the ping pong ball with a speed of 6 m s^{-1} and the football with a speed of 1 m s^{-1}. After the collision, the ping pong ball has its direction of motion reversed and a speed of 4 m s^{-1}. How is the motion of the football affected?

MATHEMATICAL MODELLING ACTIVITY

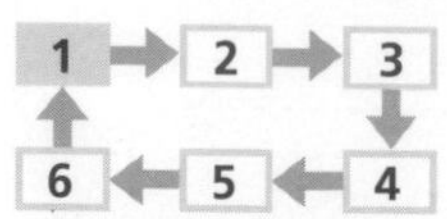

Specify the real problem

Problem statement

Many safety conscious groups have called for the introduction of seat belts in coaches. Develop a mathematical argument to support this call.

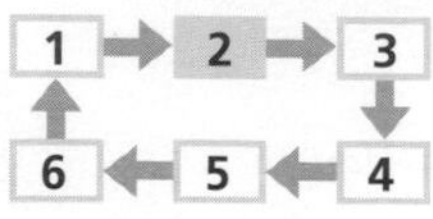

Set up a model

KEY SKILLS
C 3.1a

Set up a model

Discuss the important features that should be considered in solving this problem. The problem will be developed by considering head on collisions between two vehicles. The assumptions below have been made:

- The maximum speed of impact will be 70 mph (31 m s^{-1}).
- The mass of a loaded lorry will not exceed 38 tonnes.
- The mass of a loaded coach will not exceed 10 tonnes.
- The mass of a car will not exceed 1.5 tonnes.
- Momentum is conserved in all collisions.
- Vehicles move together after collisions.

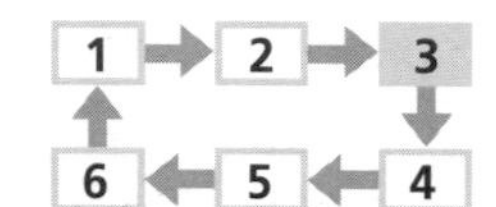

Formulate the mathematical problem

Formulate a mathematical problem

Find an expression for the combined speed, V, of the vehicles after a collision, if they are initially moving towards each other at speed u and have masses m and M.

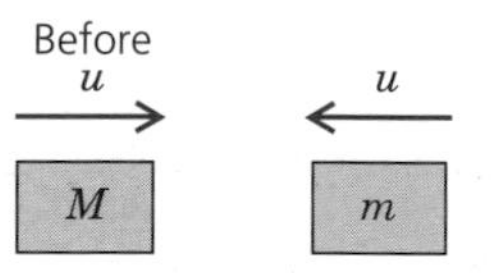

After

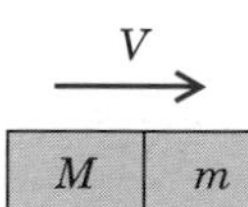

Estimate the acceleration experienced by the passengers in the vehicles if the collision lasts three seconds.

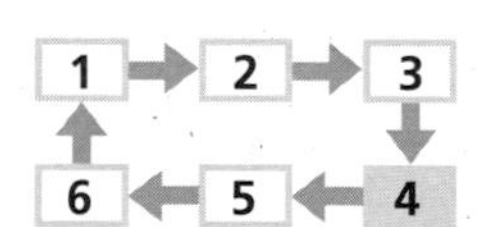

Solve the mathematical problem

Solve the mathematical problem

Using conservation of momentum gives: $Mu - mu = V(M + m)$
so that:

$$V = u\left(\frac{M-m}{M+m}\right)$$

Show that the reduction in the velocity of a passenger in the vehicle of mass M is:

$$\frac{2mu}{m+M}$$

and for a passenger in the vehicle of mass m is:

$$\frac{2Mu}{m+M}$$

If the two vehicles are brought to rest in a time of T seconds then the magnitudes of the average accelerations in the experiment will be:

$$\frac{2mu}{T(m+M)} \text{ and } \frac{2Mu}{T(m+M)}$$

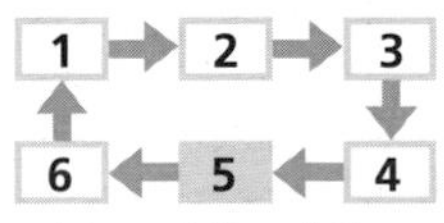

Interpret the solution

Interpretation

Consider a head-on collision between a car and a coach at 70 mph, when the collision lasts three seconds.

Here $u = 31$ m s^{-1}, $M = 10\ 000$ and $m = 1500$; so the acceleration experienced by the passengers in the car is:

$$\frac{2 \times 10\ 000.31}{3(10\ 000 + 1500)} = 18.0 \text{ m s}^{-2}$$

The acceleration experienced by the passengers in the coach is:

$$\frac{2 \times 1500}{3(10\,000 + 1500)} = 2.7 \text{ m s}^{-2}$$

There is clearly a major difference between the magnitudes of these accelerations. If the time of the collision was reduced, then both these figures would increase, but the ratio would be the same.
Consider head on collisions between two coaches and a coach and a lorry. Finally give your conclusions.

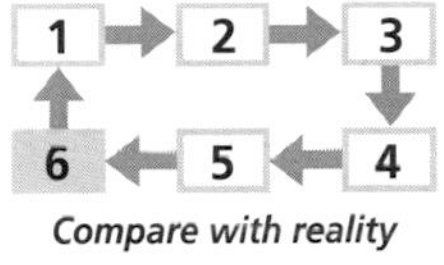

Compare with reality

Compare with reality

The *Highway Code* stopping distances are based on an acceleration of -6.6 m s^{-2}. Comment on the experiences of the passengers in the collisions you have considered.

Suggest any weaknesses of the model considered above.

POSSIBLE MODELLING TASKS

1 Investigate the change in momentum when a golf ball is hit by a club.

2 A car of mass 1000 kg drives into the back of a stationary car of a similar mass. They skid a distance of 15 m. Estimate the initial speed of the moving car.

CONSOLIDATION EXERCISES FOR CHAPTER 26

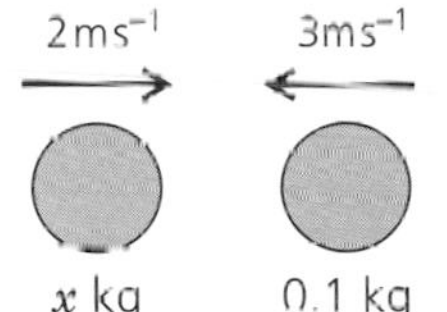

1 Two particles, of masses x kg and 0.1 kg, are moving towards each other in the same straight line and collide directly. Immediately before the impact, the speeds of the particles are 2 m s^{-1} and 3 m s^{-1} respectively (see diagram)

i) Given that both particles are brought to rest by the impact, find x.

ii) Given instead that the particles move with equal speeds of 1 m s^{-1} after the impact, find the three possible values of x.

(OCR Question 3 Mechanics 1 Specimen Paper)

2 A particle A of mass m is moving with speed $2u$ in a straight line on a smooth horizontal table. It collides with another particle B of mass km which is moving in the same straight line on the table with speed u and in the opposite direction to A. In the collision, the particles form a single particle which then moves with speed $\frac{2}{3}u$ in the original direction of A's motion.

Find the value of k.

(EDEXCEL Question 1 Mechanics 1 June 1997)

3 A particle A of mass 3m is moving in a straight line on a horizontal table. It collides with another particle B of mass m moving in the same straight line on the table. Immediately before the collision the speed of A is $3u$, the speed of B is $4u$ and the particles are moving directly towards each other. In the collision, the two particles join to form one single particle C. Find

a) the speed of C immediately after the collision;

b) the magnitude of the impulse exerted by B on A in the collision.

Distance from pivot (m)	Force required (N)

Using your data, deduce a relationship between the force and distance.

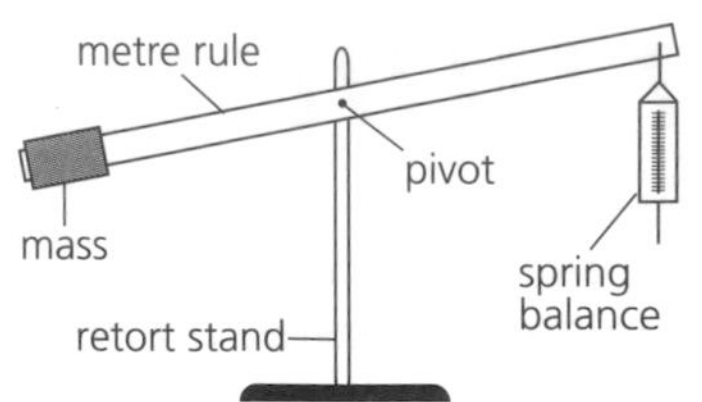

If you can't find a suitable barrier, you can improvise one from a metre rule pivoted on a rod, by drilling a hole in it and attaching a mass to one end.

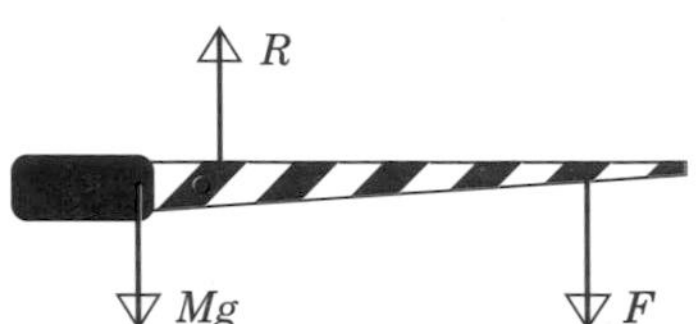

Forces acting

The diagram shows the forces acting on the barrier considered in the explorations. The three forces are Mg, the force of gravity which can be assumed to act at a point to the left of the pivot, R, the reaction force exerted by the pivot and F, the force exerted by the string.

The two forces Mg and F each have a turning effect on the barrier, but in opposite directions, so their turning effects are balanced when they both act. If one force were removed, the barrier would begin to turn. For example if F were removed, the barrier would start to rise. The force, R, at the pivot does not have a turning effect. No matter how large a force is applied at the pivot, the barrier will not begin to turn.

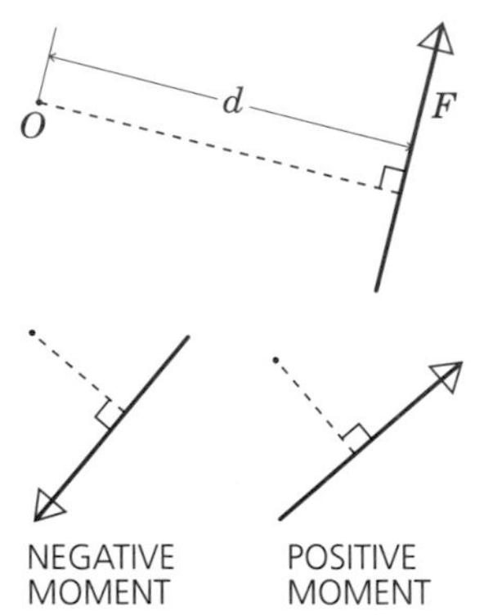

The turning effect of a force is the **moment** of the force. The moment depends on the force and where it is applied.

The moment of the force F about the point O is Fd, where d is the perpendicular distance from O to the force.

Moments can cause either clockwise or anti-clockwise rotation. It is conventional to define clockwise moments as negative and anti-clockwise moments as positive. The units for moments are newton-metres (Nm).

Example 27.1

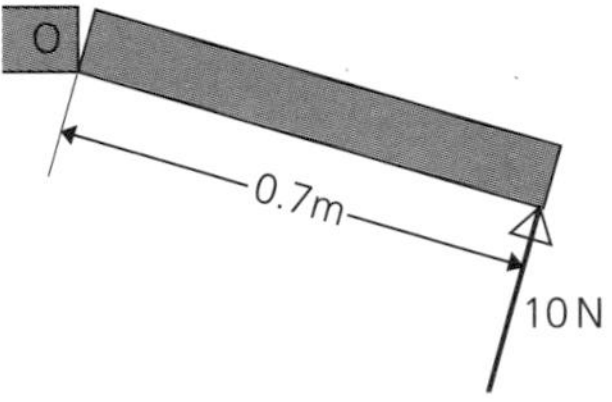

The diagram shows a door, hinged at O. A force of 10 N acts at right angles to the door, at a distance of 0.7 m from O. Find the moment of the force about O.

Solution

The moment will be anti-clockwise and so positive. Here $F = 10\,\text{N}$ *and* $d = 0.7\,\text{m}$*, so:*

moment $Fd = 10 \times 0.7 = 7\,\text{Nm}$

Example 27.2

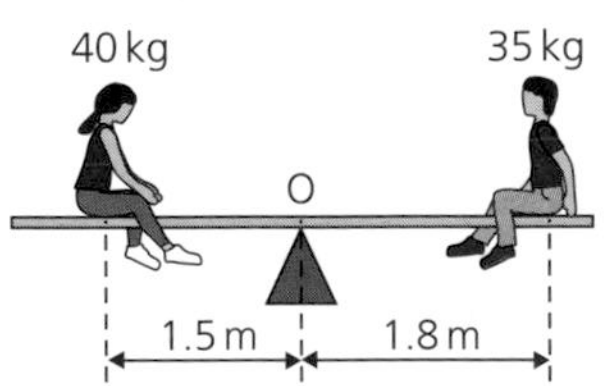

A simple seesaw consists of a plank pivoted at its centre, as shown in the diagram. Two children sit on it in the positions shown, and then the plank is allowed to move.

a) *Draw a diagram to show the forces acting on the plank.*

b) *Find the moment of each force about the pivot.*

c) *Find the total moment about O and state what happens when the plank is allowed to move.*

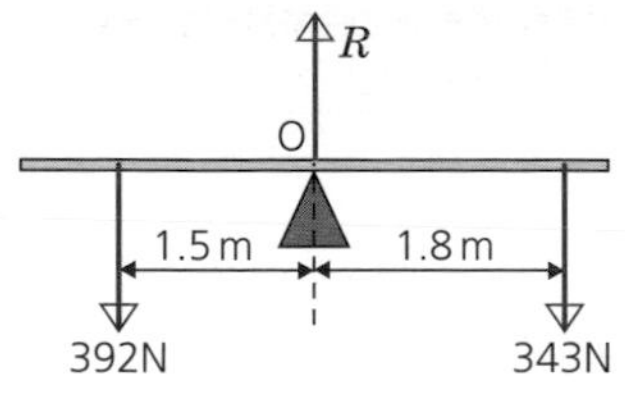

Solution

a) The diagram shows the force acting on the plank.

b) Moment of $R = 0$ (as it acts through O)
Moment of the 343 N force $= -343 \times 1.8 = -617$ Nm (negative as it is clockwise)
Moment of the 392 N force $= 392 \times 1.5 = 588$ Nm

c) The total moment is simply found by adding the individual moments.
Total moment $= 0 - 617 + 588 = -29$ Nm
As this is negative the plank would begin to rotate clockwise.

EXERCISES

27.1 CLASSWORK

1 Find the moment of each force about the point O.

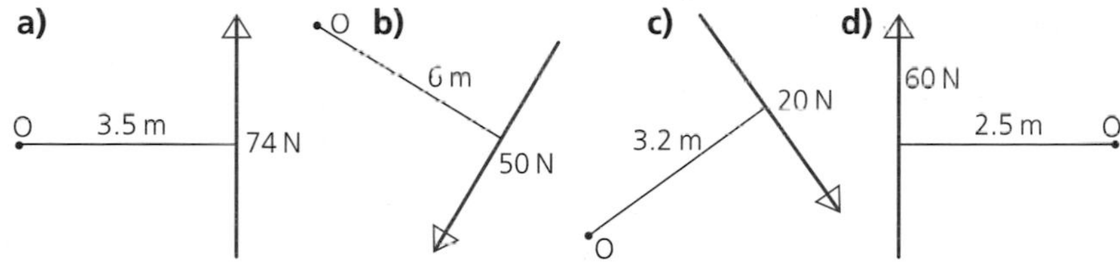

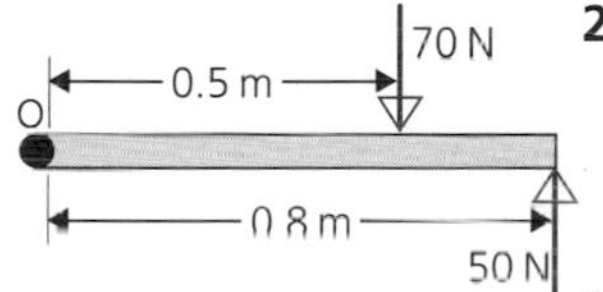

2 Two people are trying to open a door by pushing on opposite sides. They exert forces as shown.

a) Find the moment of both forces about O.

b) What is the total moment? What happens to the door?

3 Find the total moment about O for each object shown.

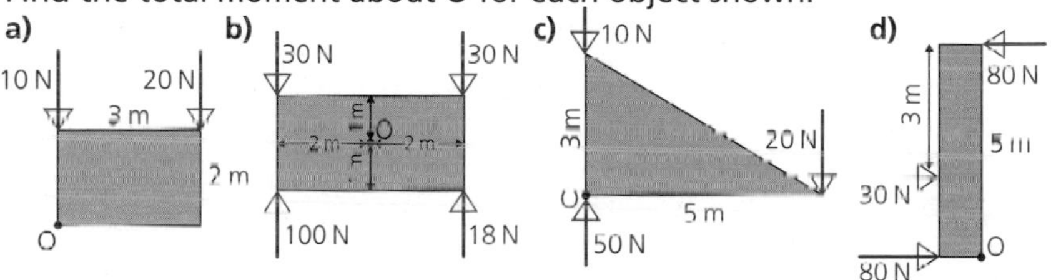

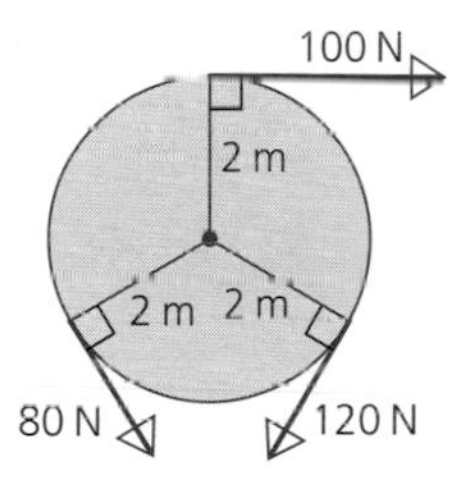

4 Three children exert forces, as shown, on a playground roundabout. Find the total moment on the roundabout.

5 Find the distance OA if the magnitude of the moment of each force illustrated below is 30 Nm.

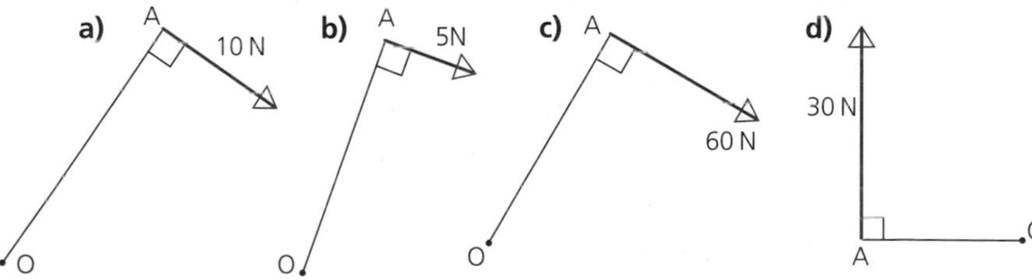

6 The diagram shows a spanner of length 30 cm being used to undo a nut.

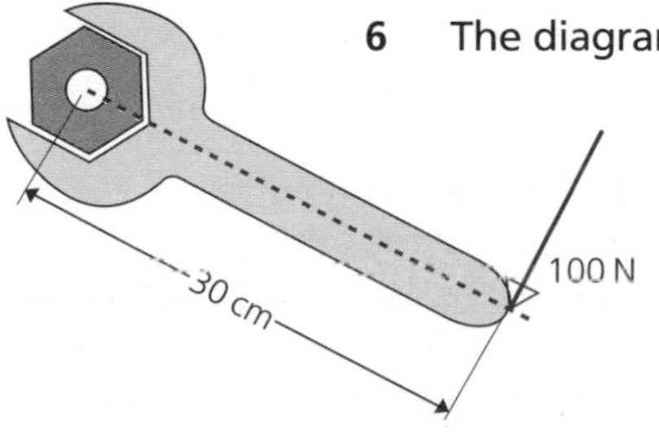

A constant force of 100 N acts as shown. Find the moment of this force.

EXERCISES

27.1 HOMEWORK

1 Find the moment of each force about the point O, stating if your answer is a clockwise or anticlockwise moment.

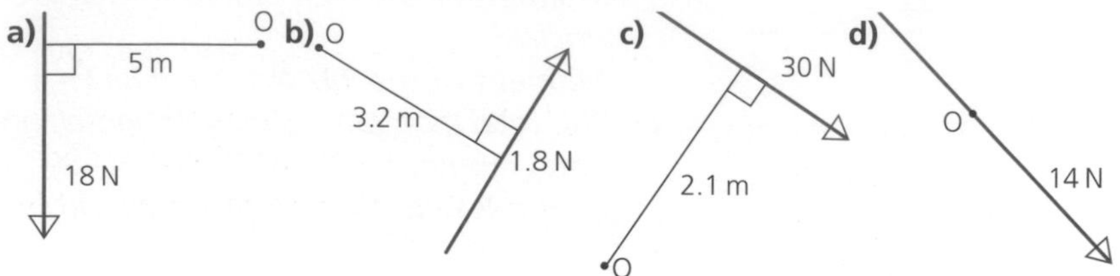

2 Ann and Bob have masses of 20 kg and 25 kg respectively. They sit on a seesaw with Ann 1.5 m from the centre.

Ann Bob

a) How far from the centre is Bob, if the total moment about its centre is zero?

b) Both children move 40 cm further away from the centre. Find the total moment on the seesaw. What happens to the seesaw now?

3 Find the resultant moment about O for each object shown.

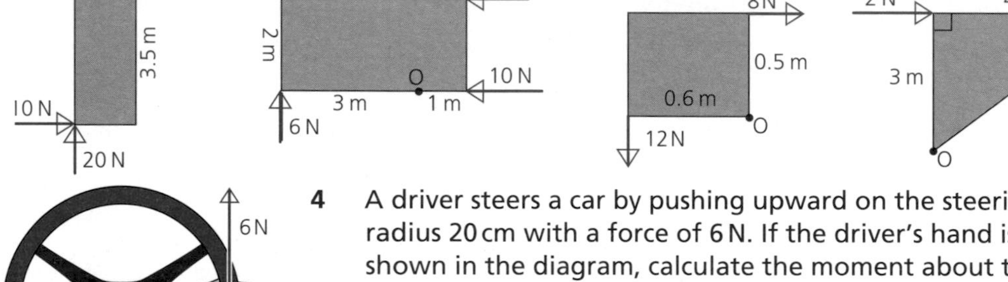

6 N

4 A driver steers a car by pushing upward on the steering wheel of radius 20 cm with a force of 6 N. If the driver's hand is in the position shown in the diagram, calculate the moment about the centre of the wheel. As the wheel turns does the moment remain constant? Give reasons for your answer.

A D O B 10 N C

5 In the diagram, O is at the centre of a square ABCD. If the moment produced by a force of 10 N acting along the line BC is 4 Nm, calculate the length of a side of the square.

6 Find the distance OA if the moment about O which is produced by the given force is 24 Nm in each case.

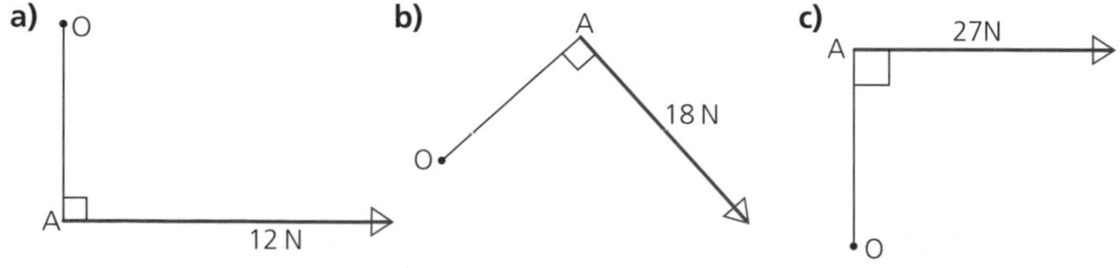

MOMENTS AND EQUILIBRIUM

When forces act on a particle, if the **resultant** force is zero, its motion will not change. However for a larger body the forces may be applied in such a way that although the resultant is zero, there is a rotation due to the turning effects of the forces. For example think about a Catherine wheel firework. The forces acting on it will have a resultant of zero, because it remains in the same place, but the forces will have a turning effect which causes it to start to spin. The ideas of equilibrium are extended in this section to take account of the turning effects of the forces acting.

Take a few minutes to think about the following questions.

1 Two strings are attached to a sheet of material as shown in the diagram. What happens if the strings are pulled?
2 Is it possible to position the strings so that there is no rotation?
3 In Chapter 3, we found that if the resultant force on an object is zero it will not accelerate. What additional requirement is necessary for there to be no movement at all?

Requirements for equilibrium

For equilibrium there are two requirements that must both be satisfied.

a) The resultant force must be zero.
b) The total moment must be zero.

Example 27.3

A book of mass 2 kg stands on a bookshelf in the position shown in the diagram. If the mass of the shelf is negligible, find the reaction forces exerted at each end of the shelf.

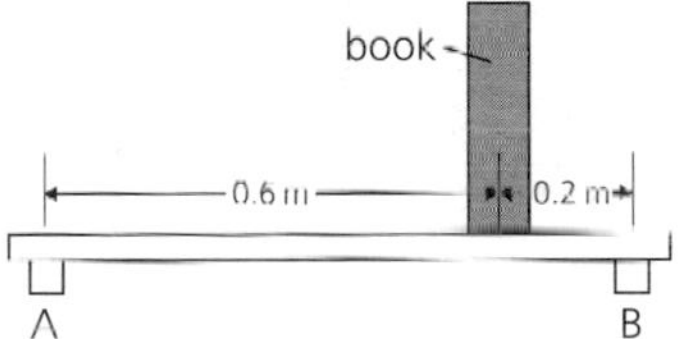

Solution

The diagram shows the forces acting on the shelf, which are the reactions R and S at the ends plus a 19.6 N force where the book rests.

As the upward forces must balance the downward forces:
$R + S = 19.6$
Taking moments about A gives:
moment of $R = 0$
moment of force of 19.6 N $= -0.6 \times 19.6 = -11.76$
moment of $S = 0.8S$
Total moment $= 0.8S - 11.76$
As the total moment must be zero:
$0.8S - 11.76 = 0$

$$S = \frac{11.76}{0.8} = 14.7\ N$$

Now using $R + S = 19.6$ *with* $S = 14.7$ *gives:*
$R + 14.7 = 19.6 \Rightarrow R = 19.6 - 14.7 = 4.9\ N$

Example 27.4

A metal rod of mass 2 kg is supported as shown in the diagram.

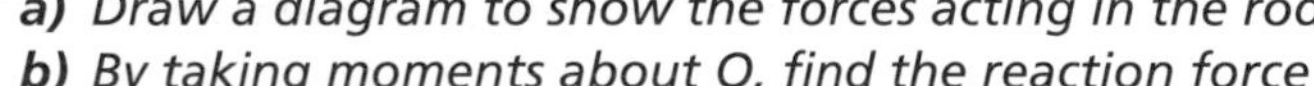

a) *Draw a diagram to show the forces acting in the rod.*
b) *By taking moments about O, find the reaction force exerted by the other support.*
c) *By considering the resultant force, find the reaction force exerted on the rod at O.*

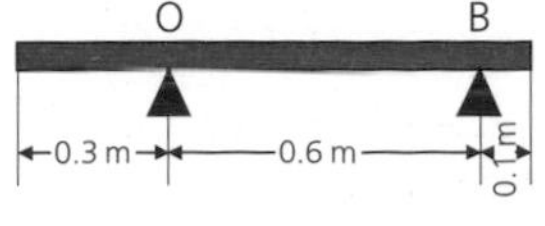

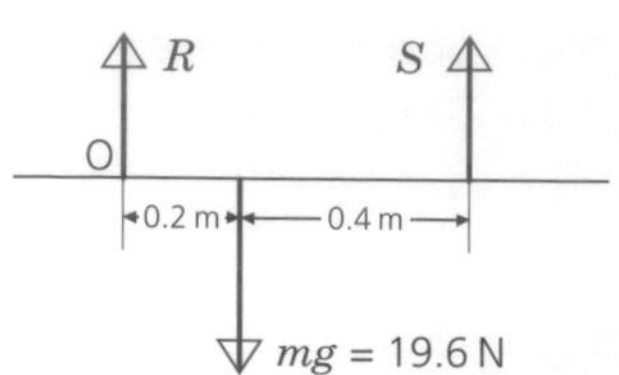

Solution

a) *The diagram shows the forces acting, reaction forces R and S at the two supports and the force of gravity, 19.6 N acting down. Assume that the force of gravity acts at the centre of the rod.*

b) *Taking moments about O for each force:*

moment of $R = 0$

moment of $S = 0.6S$

moment of $mg = -0.2 \times 19.6 = -3.92$

As the rod is at rest the total moment must be zero, so:

$0.6S - 3.92 = 0$

$\Rightarrow S = \dfrac{3.92}{0.6} = 6.53$ *N (correct to three significant figures)*

c) *The resultant force on the rod must be zero and so:*

$R + S = 19.6$

As $S = 6.53$ *this becomes:*

$R + 6.53 = 19.6 \Rightarrow R = 13.07$ *N*

Hence $R = 13.1$ *N (correct to three significant figures)*

EXERCISES

27.2 CLASSWORK

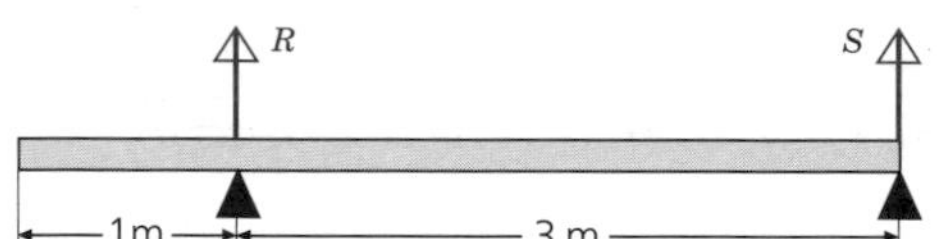

1 The diagram shows a metal bar of mass 20 kg resting on two supports and the reaction forces that they exert.

a) Draw a diagram to show where the force of gravity acting on the bar acts.

b) By taking moments show that $S = 65\frac{1}{3}$ N.

c) Find R.

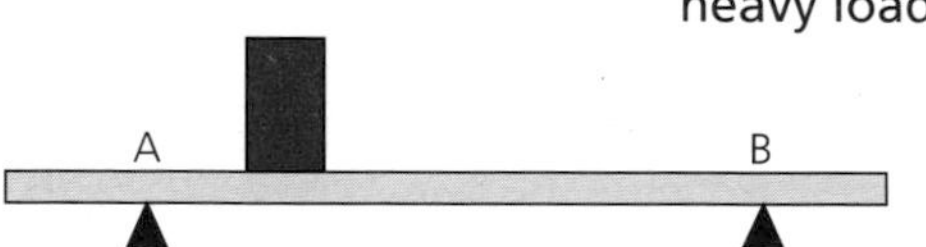

2 The diagram shows a beam that rests on two supports and carries a heavy load as shown. Which of the following statements is true?

a) The reaction force on the plank at A is equal to the reaction force at B.

b) The reaction force on the plank is greater at A than B.

c) The reaction force on the plank is greater at B than A.

d) The total of the reaction forces on the plank at A and B is zero.

e) There are only two reaction forces acting on the plank.

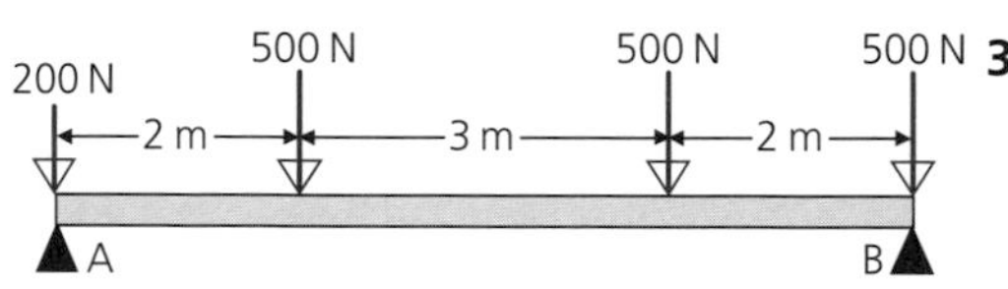

3 A beam supports the loads shown. Find the reaction forces acting on the beam if:

a) its mass is negligible,

b) its mass is 100 kg.

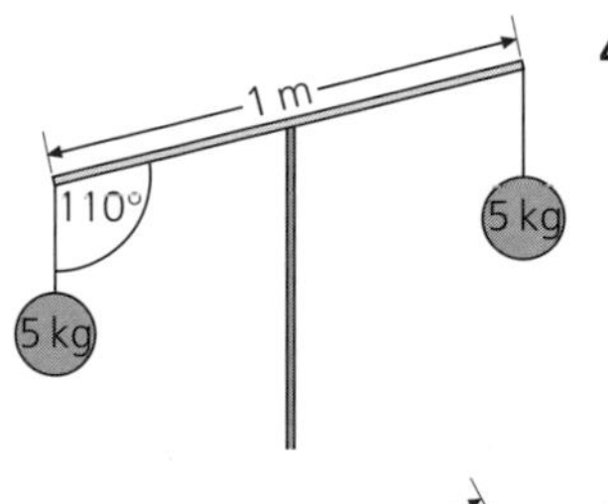

4 The diagram shows a ruler smoothly pivoted at its centre with equal masses suspended from it at each end. It is held in the position shown and then released.

a) What do you think will happen when the ruler is released?

b) Find the moment, about the centre of the ruler, of each force acting on the ruler and then the total moment. Does this confirm the prediction you made in part **a)**?

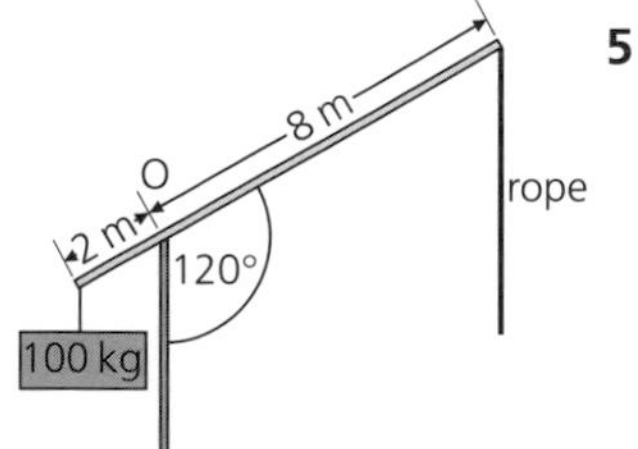

5 The diagram shows a light beam and a rope.

a) If the beam makes the angle shown with the vertical, find the tension in the rope when the system is at rest, by taking moments about O.

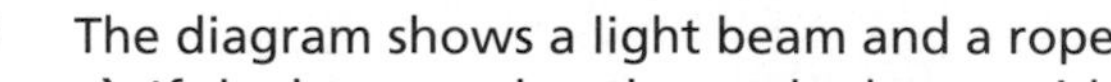

b) If the beam is horizontal and the rope is still vertical, what happens to the tension in the rope?

6 A plank of mass 20 kg and length 5 m rests on two supports as shown in the diagram.

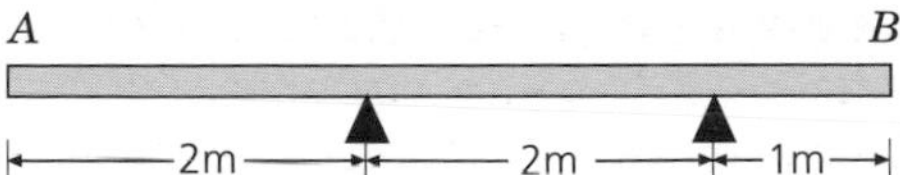

A child of mass 35 kg walks on the plank. How close can the child walk to the ends A and B of the plank?

EXERCISES

27.2 HOMEWORK

1 A metal bar of mass 100 kg rests on two supports. Find the magnitude of M and N as shown on the diagram.

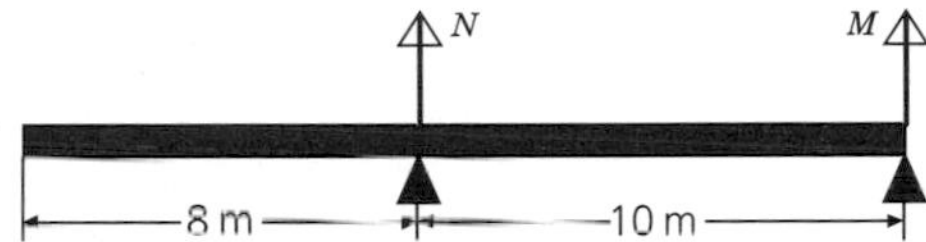

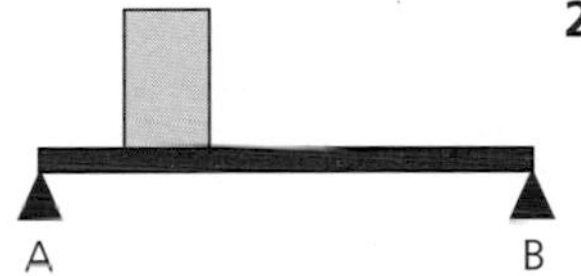

2 The diagram shows a beam that rests on two supports and carries a heavy load as shown.
a) How many reaction forces act on the plank?
b) How does the reaction at A compare with the reaction at B?

3 The beam in the diagram supports the loads shown. Find the reaction forces acting on the beam if:
a) its mass is negligible,
b) its mass is 50 kg.

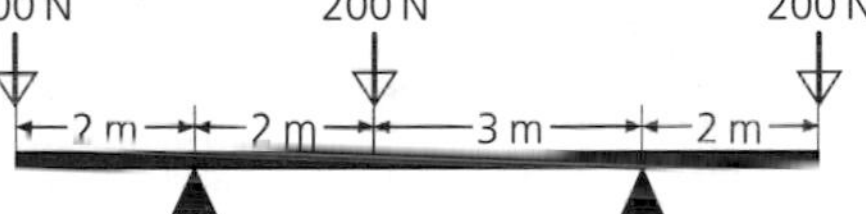

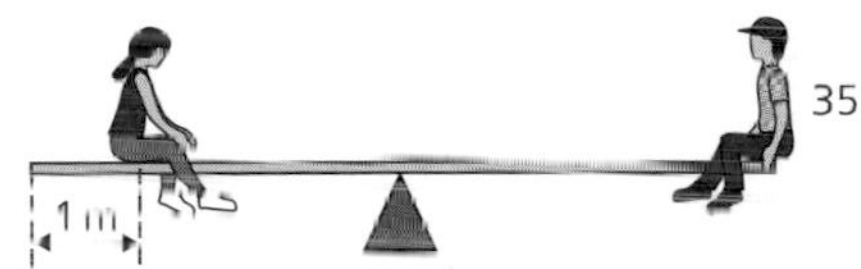

4 A boy of mass 35 kg sits on the end of a light 6 m plank which pivots at its centre. When a girl sits 1 m from the other end the plank balances. Find the mass of the girl.

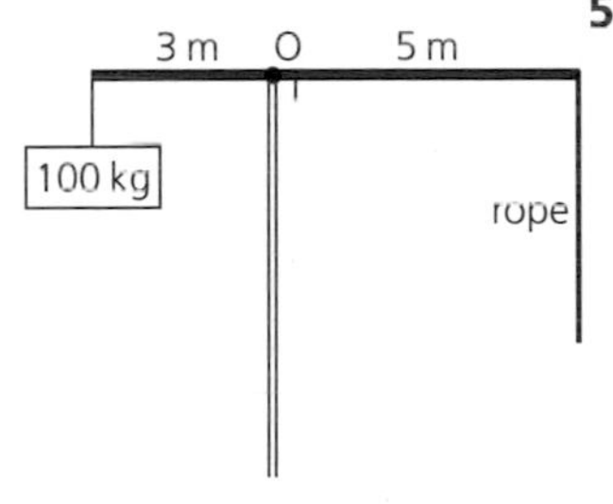

5 The diagram shows a beam of mass 20 kg with a mass of 100 kg attached to one end and a rope attached to the other end.
a) By taking moments, find the tension on the rope.
b) Find the reaction at O.
The same beam is then allowed to tilt at 30° to the horizontal, and the rope is held so that it forms a right angle with the beam.
c) By taking moments about O find the tension in the rope.

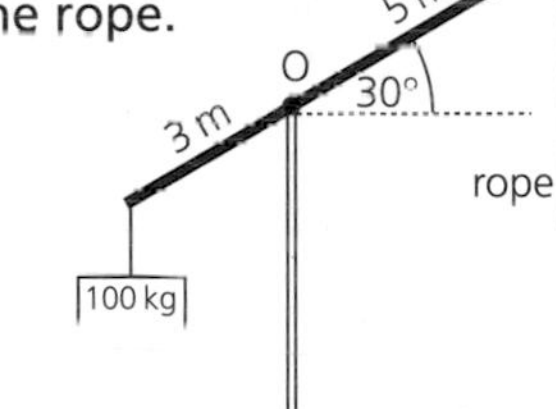

6 A uniform plank of mass 20 kg and length 5 m is inserted between two bars at A and B. A girl of mass 50 kg initially stands at C.

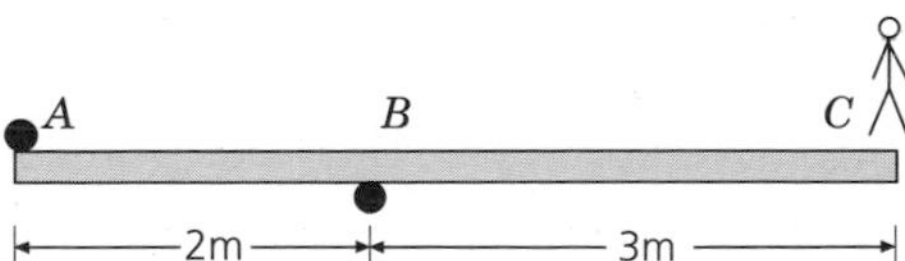

a) Find the reaction forces at A and B when the girl is at C.
b) How far past B can the girl walk?

MATHEMATICAL MODELLING ACTIVITY

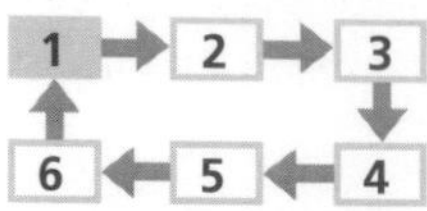

Problem statement

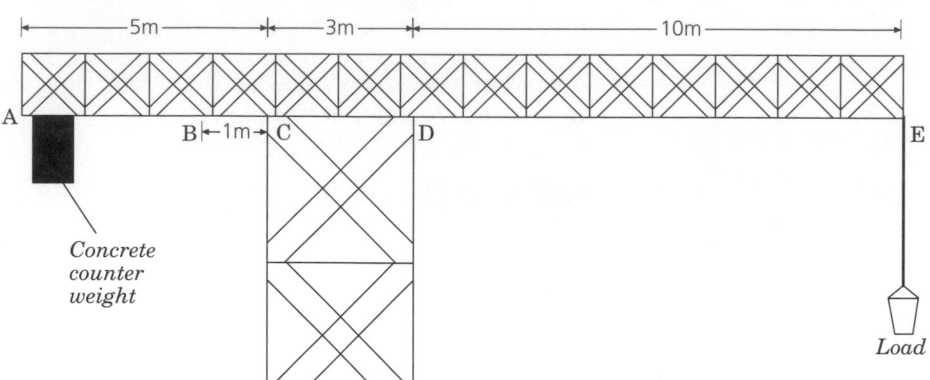

The diagram shows a tower crane. When the crane is lifting a load a concrete counter weight is moved to ensure that the top of the crane remains in equilibrium. Find the greatest load that can be lifted by the crane.

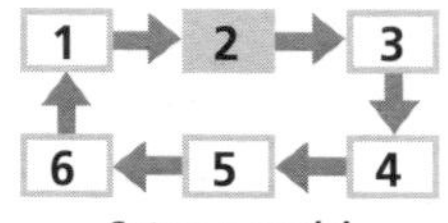

Set up a model

The following assumptions allow us to set up a simple model.

- The top part of the crane is modelled as a uniform rod that rests on the top of the vertical part of the crane.
- The loads are always suspended from point E.
- The loads always rise at a constant speed.
- The concrete counter weight can move between the points A and B.
- The mass of the top part of the crane is m.
- The mass of the counter weight is M.

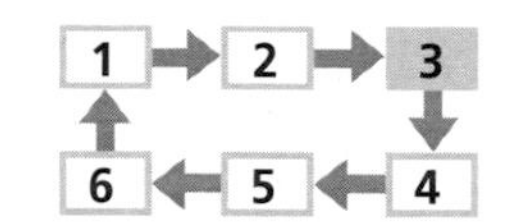

Formulate a mathematical problem

a) Find the mass of the concrete counter weight if it is positioned at B, when there is no load.

b) Find the maximum load that can be lifted if the concrete counter weight is at A.

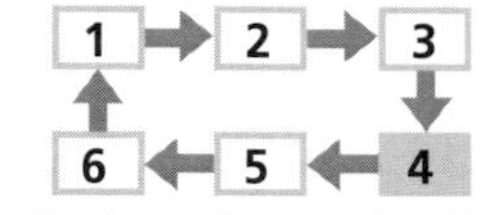

Mathematical solution

a) The diagram shows the forces acting. Taking moment about C gives

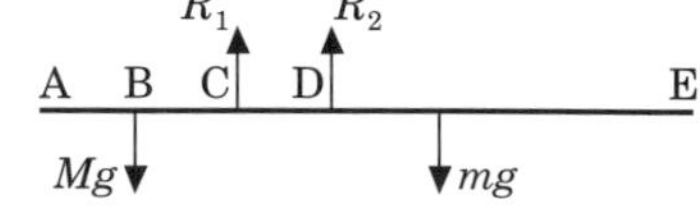

$Mg + 3R_2 = 4mg$

Explain why M will have its maximum value if $R_2 = 0$.

In this case $M = 4\,\mathrm{m}$

b) The diagram shows the forces acting, where T is the tension in the cable lifting the load.
Taking moments about D gives:
$32\ mg = 3R_1 + mg + 10T$

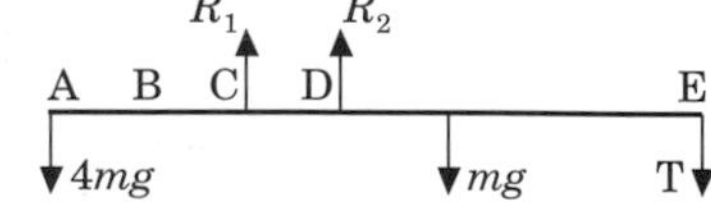

Explain why T will have its maximum value when $R_1 = 0$.

In this case $T = 3.1mg$

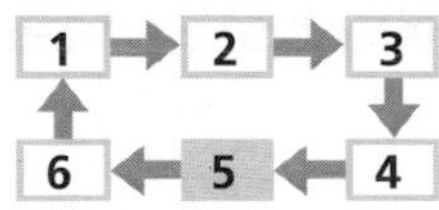

Interpret the solution

Interpretation

For this crane the mass of the counter weight can be up to 4 times the mass of the top section of the mass and the load can be up to 3.1 times the mass of the top section.

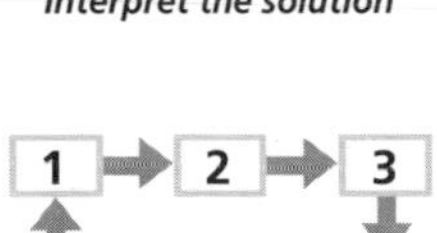

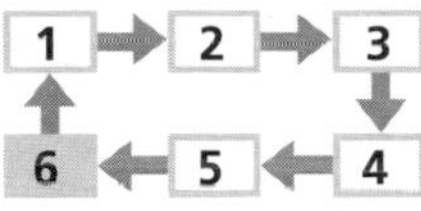

Compare with reality

Compare with reality

In reality the top section will not just rest on the tower and the loads will accelerate as they first begin to move.

Refinement of the model

If the load experiences a maximum acceleration of a ms^{-2}, show that the maximum mass of the load is given by $\dfrac{31mg}{10(a+g)}$

POSSIBLE MODELLING TASKS

1 Is it possible to design a road barrier that stays up when it is up and down when it is down? Investigate designs that might have this property.

CONSOLIDATION EXERCISES FOR CHAPTER 27

1 A uniform rod AB has length 8 m and mass 12 kg. A particle of mass 8 kg is attached to the rod at B. The rod is supported at a point C and is in equilibrium in a horizontal position, as shown in the diagram.
Find the length of AC.

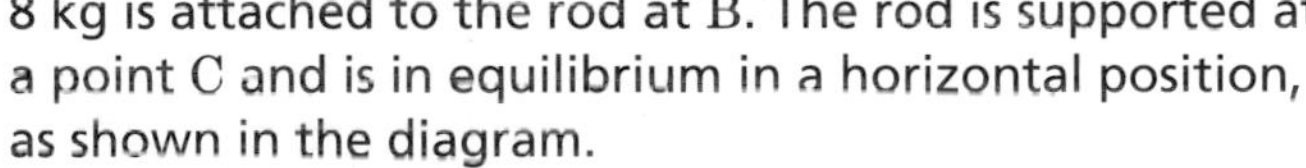

(EDEXCEL Question 2 M1 January 97)

2 A gymnast of mass 36 kg hangs by one hand from the point of P on a bar AB of length 3 m and mass 12 kg. The bar is suspended by two vertical cables which are attached to the ends A and B, and it is hanging in equilibrium in a horizontal position, as shown in Fig. 2. The tension in the cable at A is twice the tension in the cable at B. By modelling the bar as a uniform rod, and the gymnast as a particle,

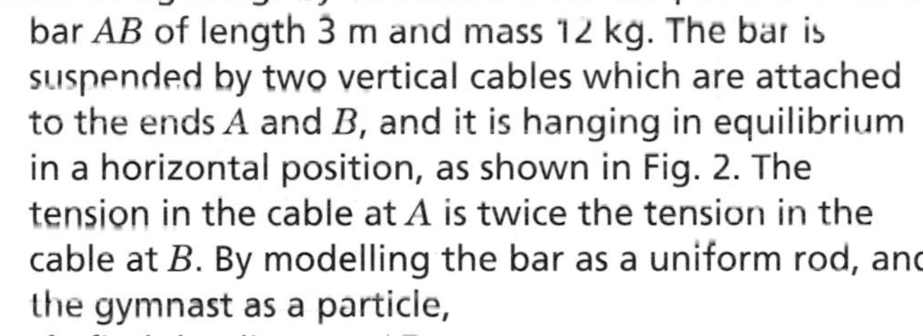

a) find the distance AP.
b) State two ways in which, in your calculation, you have used the model of the bar as a 'uniform rod'.

(EDEXCEL Question 3 M1 June 97)

3 A uniform plank of wood AB, of mass 15 kg and length 2 m, is supported by a smooth pivot at the point C, where BC = 0.6 m. Andrea, whose mass is 30 kg, sits at one end of the plank at A, and Andrea's father Ben sits at the other end of the plank at B, as shown in the diagram. The plank remains horizontal in equilibrium.

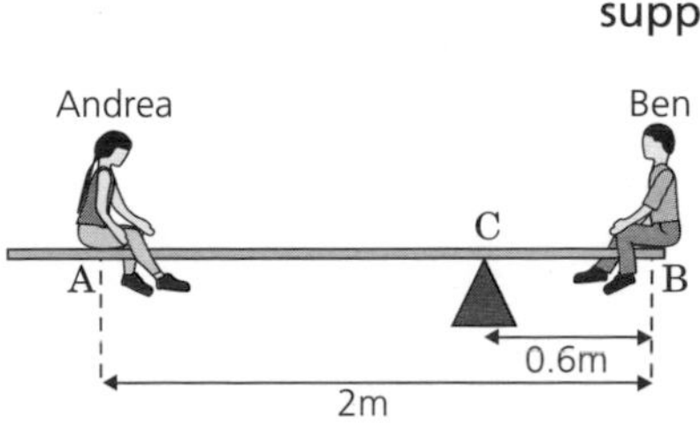

a) Suggest suitable models for the plank and for Andrea and Ben in order to determine the mass of Ben.
b) Find the mass of Ben.

(EDEXCEL Question 2 M1 June 1995)

4 A large uniform plank of wood of length 8 m and mass 30 kg is held in equilibrium by two small steel rollers A and B, ready to be pushed into a saw-mill. The centres of the rollers are 50 cm apart. One end of the plank presses against roller A from underneath, and the plank rests on top of roller B, as shown in the diagram. The rollers are adjusted so that the plank remains horizontal and the force exerted on the plank by each roller is vertical.

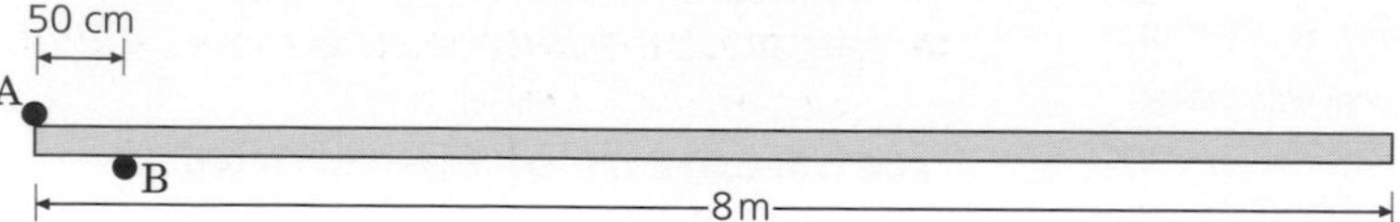

a) Suggest a suitable model for the plank to determine the forces exerted by the rollers.

b) Find the magnitude of the force exerted on the plank by the roller at B.

c) Find the magnitude of the force exerted on the plank by the roller at A.

(EDEXCEL Question 2 M1 January 1996)

Summary

After working through this chapter you should:

- be able to calculate the magnitude of the moment of a force using the magnitude force multiplied by the perpendicular distance, Fd
- know that a positive moment indicates an anticlockwise turning effect and a negative moment a clockwise turning effect
- know that for equilibrium both the resultant force and the total moment must be zero

Data

Statistics is about gathering, communicating, analysing and interpreting data. In this chapter we begin the story by:

- *introducing various types of data*
- *presenting data in the form of stem-and-leaf displays, and histograms.*

INFORMATION AND DATA

Statistics is all about gathering, communicating, analysing and interpreting **information**. The information is obtained from various sources, and in its basic form it is called **data**. There are two distinct types of data, which are **qualitative** and **quantitative**.

Qualitative data

Qualitative information, as the term suggests, is descriptive information. It may be expressed as a property, or in terms of categories, or as a quality for example: colour, gender, nationality, style, ...

Quantitative data

Information that has a natural hierarchy, such as data in numerical form, is described as quantitative. Such numerical information may be separated into **continuous data** and **discrete data**.

When measurements are made, the data gathered are generally continuous since all values within a particular span are possible. An example of this is the length of a person's stride, which might be any length between, say, 0.3 m and 1.3 m.

Discrete data are usually obtained by counting. For example, the number of letters delivered daily to a house might be 0, 1, 2, 3, 4, 5, ... or any other **integer** but it cannot be any other sort of number. Discrete data may also arise when there is an order in the information, such as the sizes available in some clothes – large, medium or small.

Many brands of T-shirts are available in five sizes: XL, L, M, S, and XS; these sizes are discrete data.

Exploration 28.1

Types of data

Categorise the following information

- height of students
- area of noticeboards
- type of footwear
- age of teachers
- colour of flowers
- make of car
- number of open windows in a room
- number of items of jewellery worn

Limits

Age

When asked her age, a student said, 'I am 17 years old.' Does she mean that she is precisely 17? Or, is she 17 to the nearest whole year? Or, does she mean something else?

The way in which ages are recorded means that, if this student's age is x, then $17 \le x < 18$.

The student will have given her age as 17 from the day of her 17th birthday (i.e. the day precisely 17 complete years since she was born) up to the day before her 18th birthday.

Nearest

Measurements are frequently recorded 'to the nearest cm', or 'to the nearest kg' or 'to the nearest minute'. The length of a pencil that is actually 12.6 cm long would be recorded as 13 cm to the nearest cm, and one of actual length 12.49 cm would be recorded as 12 cm to the nearest cm. Pencils for which the lengths are recorded as 12 cm could have a length, p cm, where $11.5 \le p < 12.5$.

Frequency

When collecting information, for instance the colour of cars in a car park, there will be repeated examples of particular colours. There may be four yellow cars, 13 red cars, eight blue cars and 20 cars of other colours. The information is qualitative. The number of cars of each colour is the **frequency of observation** of that item of information. Inevitably in gathering any information there will be a collection of frequencies associated with the items of data. The frequencies are not the data, they tell us something about the **distribution** of the data.

Presentation of data

Qualitative data may be presented in a **frequency table** such as the one below.

Colour of car	Number of cars observed
Yellow	4
Red	13
Blue	8
Others	20

A **pie chart** is another effective way of displaying data of this nature.

A circle is divided into sectors, the angles of which are proportional to the frequency of the quality represented. In this case the angles are as shown.

other colour: $\frac{20}{45} \times 360° = 160°$

red: $\frac{13}{45} \times 360° = 104°$

blue: $64°$

yellow: $32°$

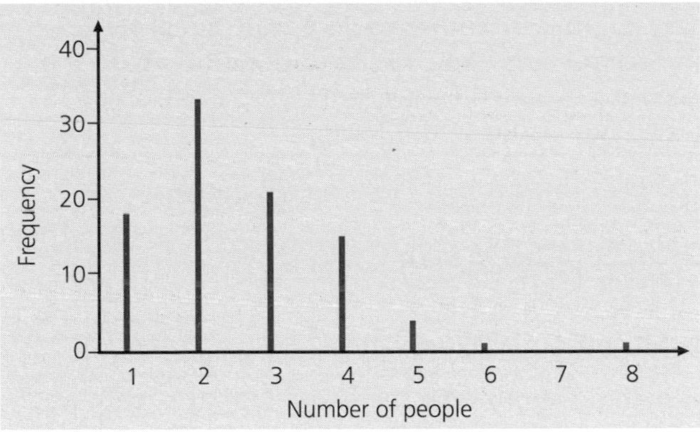

Note that someone looking at the pie chart is likely to think that the **area** of the sector represents the frequency of observation of the quality concerned, rather than the angle. Is this a fair representation? Why?

Discrete data may also be displayed in a **frequency line graph** as in the diagram.

Is this an appropriate display for discrete data? Why?

EXERCISES

28.1 CLASSWORK

KEY SKILLS
N 3.1
N 3.3

1 Collect data on a range of topics, such as number of subjects, age of students, weight of students, colour of hair, make of calculator and number of desks. Categorise the data into:

a) qualitative data, **b)** discrete numerical data,
c) continuous numerical data.

2 For each data set in question 1, construct a table, bar chart, line diagram or pie chart, choosing whichever of these is most appropriate.

Justify your choice of presentation.

3 A census of the households in a village results in the following family sizes being recorded.

3 4 5 3 4 2 2 4 3 4 3 6 5 3 4 4 5 2 1 3 2 1 4 4 3 1 2 1 3 2 4 1
3 5 4 3 4 5 6 2 1 5 6 3 4 2 5 1 2 1 3 1 4 4 5 3 4 2 1 3 4 3 1 4
4 5 4 3 2 2 3 4 2 4 2 2 1 3 4 3 5 6 1 4 2 3 2 3 2 1 1 2 3 5 2

Construct an appropriate tabulation of these data and describe what they reveal.

Ilustrate the data in an appropriate diagram.

EXERCISES

28.1 HOMEWORK

1 State whether the following data are discrete or continuous.

a) the daily rainfall at a particular location
b) the monthly numbers of telephone calls
c) the numbers of defective fuses produced
d) the duration of long-distance telephone calls
e) the ages of students in a class

2 Classify the following as qualitative or quantitative, and discrete or continuous.

a) gender (M/F)
b) height (cm)
c) GCSE grades in Statistics (A to G)
d) examination mark in Statistics (%)
e) blouse size (8 to 18)
f) car owner (0 = No, 1 = Yes)
g) weekly self-study time (% of 30 hour norm)

3 Mandy was asked by her maths teacher to do a statistics project. She represented her school at hockey, so she decided to record the number of goals scored per match by her team over a season of 35 matches. She recorded her results in this table.

Number of goals	0	1	2	3	4
Number of matches	12	13	7	2	1

Display the data in an appropriate diagram.

Does this tell you anything about how successful Mandy's team was?

STEM-AND-LEAF DISPLAYS

A method of presenting data, using the items of data themselves, which provides a swift and convenient way of collecting, storing and displaying numerical data is known as a **stem-and-leaf display**. Suppose the items of data are:

274, 286, 345, 402, 193, 237, 318.

Each item has a **most significant part** and a **next most significant part**. For instance, the most significant part of 274 may be the 2 since it represents 200; then the next most significant part is the 7. The **stem** of the stem-and-leaf display is constructed from these significant parts. The stem acts as a vertical scale, so for the above data, the stem would be as shown on the left.

1
2
3
4

The **next most significant** part of the item of data becomes a **leaf** along an appropriate branch of the display.

1		
2	7	leaf from the item 274
3		
4		

The collection of seven items of data could be represented by the stem-and-leaf display.

1	9		
2	7	8	3
3	4	1	
4	0		

Only the most significant and next-most-significant parts of the data are stored in the display. No attempt is made to round the data, the presentation is done by **truncating** the items, the 4 of 274 is lost. Thus, the 2-branch would contain any item in the range 200 to 299. Truncation is a feature of this method of presenting data.

Unit

At this stage, there is no indication of the magnitude of the displayed data. To remedy this it is necessary to indicate the unit of the display.

Unit is 10

1	9		
2	7	8	3
3	4	1	
4	0		

In this case the unit is 10 because a **factor of 10** is needed to scale a displayed item such as 27 to its true magnitude.

Grouped frequency tables

A stem-and-leaf display can be used to build up a **frequency table**. The number of leaves on any branch represents the frequency of occurrence of the items of data.

The following grouped frequency table can be constructed from the display above.

Class	Frequency
$100 \le x < 200$	1
$200 \le x < 300$	3
$300 \le x < 400$	2
$400 \le x < 500$	1

Exploration 28.2

KEY SKILLS
N 3.1
N 3.3

Stem and leaf displays

Display the following collections of data in appropriate stem-and-leaf displays indicating the unit in each case.

a) 4818, 1212, 3425, 4478, 5891, 3257, 2176, 4665, 2217, 4119

b) 0.320, 0.044, 0.278, 0.413, 0.456, 0.163, 0.389, 0.418, 0.058

c) 8.2, 3.2, 3.0, 2.8, 1.5, 6.6, 5.3, 1.5, 8.9, 7.7, 4.0, 2.8, 5.6, 6.3, 5.7, 7.4

d) 894, 947, 904, 933, 906, 920, 916, 941, 899, 925, 935, 924, 947, 937, 916, 909

e) 0.013, 0.026, 0.014, 0.019, 0.023, 0.008, 0.013, 0.018, 0.007, 0.028, 0.034, 0.038, 0.006, 0.041, 0.028

Draw up frequency tables corresponding to the stem-and-leaf displays you have constructed.

Developing the stem-and-leaf display

The data in (d) of the above exploration may be displayed using a unit of 10, like this.

Unit is 10

8	9	9												
9	4	0	3	0	2	1	4	2	3	2	4	3	1	0

However, it is also possible to consider the most significant part of the data item 894 to be 89, then the leaf part would be 4.

Doing this to all the data leads to the following display (overleaf).

Unit is 1

89	4	9	
90	4	6	9
91	6	6	
92	0	5	4
93	3	5	7
94	7	1	7

This creates a somewhat different impression of the distribution of the data. Which is the more appropriate?

Exploration 28.3

KEY SKILLS
N 3.3

Appropriate stems

Choose appropriate stems, display each of the following collections of data and record the unit.

a) 0.98, 1.13, 1.31, 0.95, 1.13, 1.21, 0.96, 1.11, 0.88, 1.04, 1.17, 1.09, 1.16
b) 895, 1080, 888, 1152, 1035, 1041, 1162, 1082, 948, 920, 987
c) 10.02, 10.01, 10.00, 10.01, 10.02, 9.98, 10.03, 9.99, 9.98
d) 348, 342, 354, 340, 385, 327, 385, 358, 351, 330, 346, 358, 344, 351, 340, 353, 382

Two-part and five-part stems

Two-part stem

The sort of technique explored above is not always the most appropriate. Consider the data shown in the following stem-and-leaf display.

Unit is 1

0	4	3	7	0	6	7	3	1	0	8	2	3	7	3	3	1
1	1	5	1	8	3											
2	2															

The data span the range 0 to 22 and choosing a different 'most significant part' is not realistic. However, it is possible to split each stem into two equal parts – **lower** and **upper** – denoted by '–' and '+' respectively. Then the two-part stem display of the data looks like this.

0–	4	3	0	3	1	0	2	3	3	3	1
0+	7	6	7	8	7						
1–	1	1	3								
1+	5	8									
2–	2										

Note that the lower part potentially contains the 0, 1, 2, 3, 4 leaves and the upper part the 5, 6, 7, 8, 9 leaves.

The same decay is still seen in the distribution of the data.

Using a two-part stem is rather like taking a magnifying glass to the data.

Five-part stem

On occasions we may want to tighten up the width of values of the data as shown by a simple stem-and-leaf display. Consider the following data.

0.9, 1.7, 2.7, 3.1, 3.4, 4.2, 4.8, 5.7, 5.6, 6.3, 6.2, 6.9, 7.4, 7.3, 8.4, 8.7, 9.8, 10.9, 11.5, 13.2, 15.4

Here is one possible stem-and-leaf display.

Unit is 0.1

0	9
1	7
2	7
3	1 4
4	2 8
5	7 6
6	3 2 9
7	4 3
8	4 7
9	8
10	9
11	5
12	
13	2
14	
15	4

It is rather sparse, perhaps hinting at a degree of symmetry in the data or perhaps suggesting that the data are evenly distributed. Telescoping the display may help in gaining an appropriate view of the data. This is achieved by combining pairs of stems thus halving the number of 'branches'. For instance, the data: 2.7, 3.1, 3.4; are displayed on a **T**-stem (T being common to **Two** and **Three**). This would appear as:

T	2 3 3

Note that the data has had to be further truncated. Similarly, 4.2, 4.8, 5.7, 5.6 are displayed as:

F	4 4 5 5

(F being common to **F**our and **F**ive). The full five-part stem display is:

Unit is 1

O	0 1
T	2 3 3
F	4 4 5 5
S	6 6 6 7 7
E	8 8 9
1O	0 1
1T	3
1F	5

(O representing Zer**o** and **O**ne; **S** representing **S**ix and **S**even, **E** representing **E**ight and Nin**e**). Then the underlying symmetry of the data becomes apparent.

Exploration 28.4

Two and five part stem-and-leaf diagrams

- Use a five-part stem to display these sets of data.

a) 4.9, 0.1, 1.2, 5.0, 0.2, 3.2, 0.3, 4.7, 1.9, 1.3, 1.5, 2.9, 2.6, 0.9, 7.2, 6.9, 9.9, 1.8, 1.8, 4.0, 14.1, 0.9, 5.7, 3.9, 3.3, 6.1, 1.7, 8.2, 7.5, 4.1, 2.6, 3.5, 2.9, 1.1, 3.0, 1.2, 3.8, 0.6, 1.7, 2.3, 5.1, 2.6, 9.2

b) 14, 13, 12, 12, 10, 22, 19, 11, 13, 11, 10, 10, 25, 11, 11, 16, 15, 20, 10, 14, 12, 14, 21, 13, 11, 10, 21, 23, 20, 23, 11, 15, 15, 10, 10, 12

- Use a two-part stem to display these sets of data.

c) 26, 39, 42, 19, 29, 10, 5, 58, 25, 37, 53, 18, 14, 58, 26, 14, 36, 21, 22, 22, 8, 24, 19, 5, 25, 24, 44, 39, 1, 21, 33, 53, 41, 1, 3, 10, 9, 43, 40, 23, 15, 8, 27

d) 2.4, 4.4, 3.9, 0.1, 2.1, 3.3, 5.3, 4.1, 6.7, 0.1, 0.3, 1.0, 0.9, 4.3, 4.0, 2.3, 1.5, 0.8, 2.7, 2.6, 0.8, 2.2, 2.2, 5.0, 2.0, 3.1, 0.1, 2.7, 3.9, 3.0, 0.1, 3.4, 2.8, 0.6, 3.1, 1.7, 4.0

Histograms

The data shown in the display records the hand-spans, in centimetres, of a group of 55 children.

Unit is 0.1

Stem	Leaf
12	0
13	
14	5
15	2 6
16	0 1 2 3 4 7
17	0 2 5 9
18	1 2 4 5 6 6 7 8
19	0 2 2 4 5 5 6 8 8 8 9
20	0 2 4 5 6 7 8 9
21	2 3 6 6 7
22	0 1 2 8
23	
24	2
25	
26	2 5 9

It is clear from this display that there was no child whose hand-span fell between 13 cm and 14 cm, but there is no reason to believe that such children do not exist. The distribution of these data appears reasonably symmetric with a peak in the 16 cm to 22 cm range.

A **histogram** is a means of displaying continuous data graphically, conveying the general characteristics of the data.

Consider the following representation of the data.

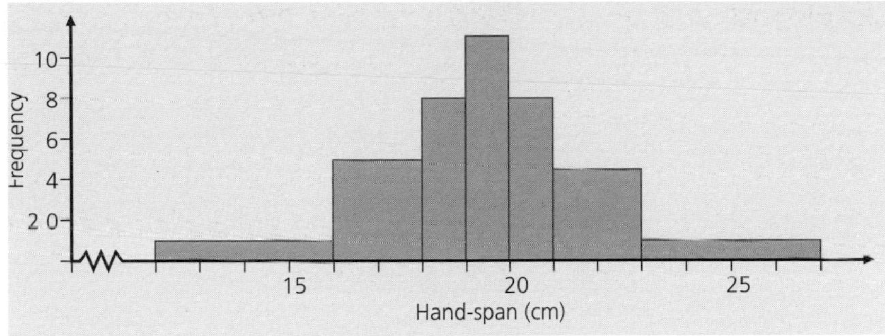

Along the 12 cm, 13 cm, 14 cm, 15 cm branches there are four items of data altogether. When these branches are combined and treated as one, the result will be one unit high and 4 cm wide. If the 16 cm and 17 cm branches are combined, the result is five units high and 2 cm wide containing ten items of data.

How many units high is the newly-created 21 cm and 22 cm branch? In a histogram, the **frequency** associated with any class of measures is represented by the **area** of the block in the display.

$$\begin{aligned}\text{Frequency} &\propto \text{area}\\ &= \text{width of interval} \times \text{height of block}\\ &= \text{class width} \times \text{frequency density}\end{aligned}$$

The terms **class width** and **frequency density** are commonly used when working with histograms.

A more formalised approach to constructing a histogram is illustrated in the following example.

Example 28.1

Construct a histogram to display these data using the classes given.

Class	Frequency
$0 \le x < 0.5$	12
$0.5 \le x < 1.5$	32
$1.5 \le x < 2.5$	20
$2.5 \le x < 4.5$	20
$4.5 \le x < 6.5$	6
$6.5 \le x < 10.5$	2

Solution

The first step is to calculate the widths of each of the classes. The first class is of width 0.5, the next is of width 1.0 and so on.

The next step involves the definition of frequency density inherent in the following relation.

Frequency $\propto$ class width $\times$ frequency density

The results of these two steps are recorded in the expanded table below.

Class	Frequency	Class width	Frequency density
$0 \le x < 0.5$	12	0.5	$12 \div 0.5 = 24$
$0.5 \le x < 1.5$	32	1.0	32
$1.5 \le x < 2.5$	20	1.0	20
$2.5 \le x < 4.5$	20	2.0	10
$4.5 \le x < 6.5$	6	2.0	3
$6.5 \le x < 10.5$	2	4.0	0.5

Finally, the histogram can be drawn using a linear scale on the x-axis.

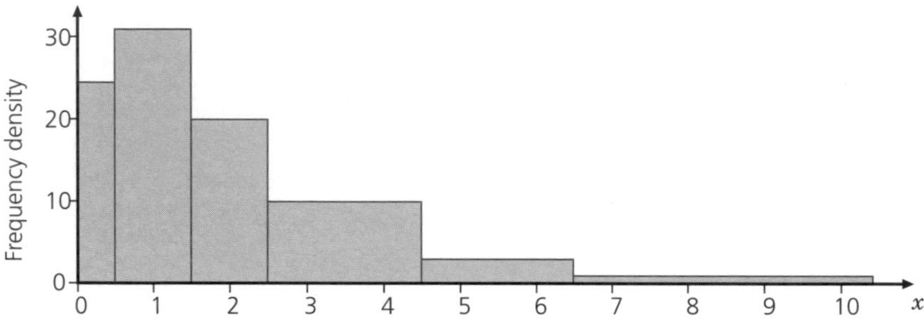

Example 28.2

The mass of each of 125 pizzas made for a frozen food company was recorded in grams, to the nearest 10 g. The results were tabulated as given in the table below.

Mass of pizza (g)	Number of pizzas
200–220	15
230–240	32
250	34
260	19
270–280	14
290–300	7
310–340	4

a) *What is the range of masses in the 200–220 class?*
b) *Identify the true class limits for each of the classes in the table.*
c) *Calculate the class widths for each class.*
d) *Construct a histogram of the data.*

Solution

a) *The mass, M, of a pizza is recorded to the nearest 10 g. Hence, if $195 \le M < 205$, the recorded mass would be 200. This means the class 200–220 would contain all pizzas in the range $195 \le$ mass < 225.*

b)* and *c)

Class	True class limits	Class width
200–220	$195 \le M < 225$	30
230–240	$225 \le M < 245$	20
250	$245 \le M < 255$	10
260	$255 \le M < 265$	10
270–280	$265 \le M < 285$	20
290–300	$285 \le M < 305$	20
310–340	$305 \le M < 345$	40

d) *To construct a histogram where the class widths vary, we need to calculate appropriate frequency densities. Since every class width is a multiple of 10, the following frequency densities are quite acceptable.*

Frequency	15	32	34	19	14	7	4
Frequency density	5	16	34	19	7	3.5	1

The classes have in effect, been treated as having widths of 3, 2, 1, 1, 2, 2 and 4.

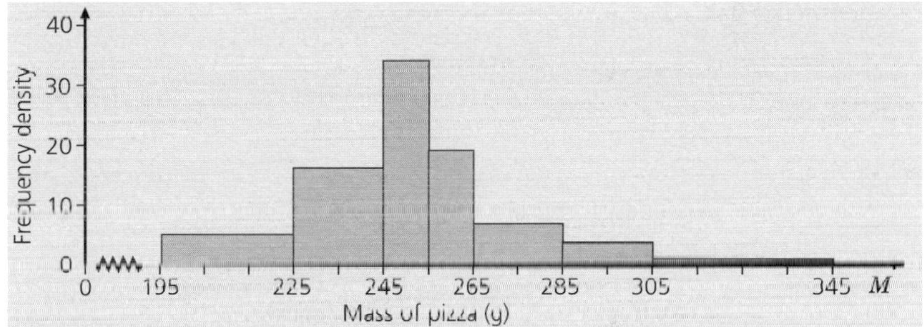

Relative frequency density

In the previous section, the idea of frequency density was introduced to cater for varying class widths in grouped frequency tables. This does have a drawback in that frequency densities are not unique; the class widths used in the solution to Example 28.2 were 3, 2, 1, …, rather than 30, 20, 10, … which produced frequency densities 5, 16, 34, … as opposed to 0.5, 1.6, 3.4, … . Would the histogram have been essentially different using class widths of 30, 20, 10?

One approach to unifying this is to express the frequencies as proportions of the total frequency, giving rise to relative frequencies. For the data in Example 28.2, the results are as follows.

Frequency	15	32	34	19	14	7	4
Relative frequency	$\frac{15}{125}$	$\frac{32}{125}$	$\frac{34}{125}$	$\frac{19}{125}$	$\frac{14}{125}$	$\frac{7}{125}$	$\frac{4}{125}$
or	0.12	0.256	0.272	0.152	0.112	0.056	0.032

What is the sum of the relative frequencies? Will this always be the case?

If these relative frequencies are now used in conjunction with true class widths to produce **relative frequency densities**, and a histogram is then drawn, the total area of the blocks in the histogram will always be one square unit.

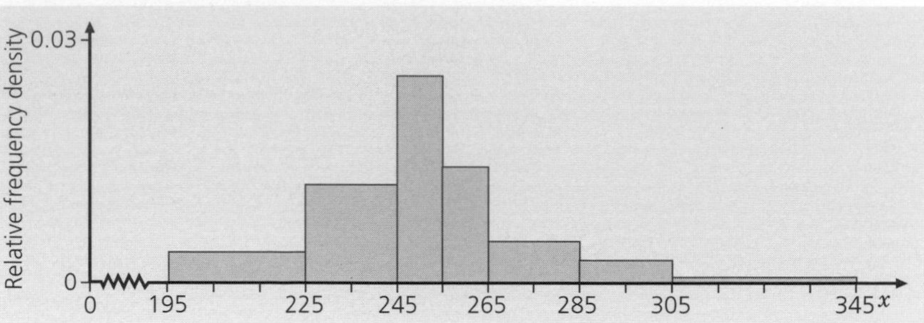

Example 28.3

The life-times of a collection of 80 calculator batteries are recorded in the table. Calculate the frequency relative densities.

Lifetime (months)	0–2	2–4	4–10	10–20	20–40
Number of batteries	32	17	18	9	4

Solution

Frequency densities require the class widths, so this ought to be included.

Life	0–2	2–4	4–10	10–20	20–40
Frequency	32	17	18	9	4
Class width	2	2	6	10	20
Frequency density	16	8.5	3	0.9	0.2
Relative f.d.	.2	.10625	.0375	.01125	.0025

EXERCISES

28.2 CLASSWORK

KEY SKILLS
N 3.3

1 Construct a frequency table with appropriate classes for each of the following stem-and-leaf displays.

a) *Unit is 10*

3	5
4	7 7 8
5	0 3 3 3 5 6 8 8 9 9
6	1 3 4 8
7	0 1

b) *Unit is 0.01*

6	7 7
7	2 3 5 5 9
8	5
9	0 1

2 Display the following data sets on appropriate stem-and-leaf displays.

a) 15, 19, 17, 17, 18, 18, 16, 16, 20, 21, 22, 19, 17, 16
b) 2100, 2350, 1800, 1850, 2500, 2000, 1900
c) 0.003, 0.008, 0.009, 0.010, 0.008, 0.011, 0.011, 0.008
Suggest, in each case, what the data might represent.

3 Recover the original data from the following two-part stem display.

Unit is 1

2–	3	0	4	0	3	2	2	1	0	1		
2+	9	5	5	7	6	8	7	8	9	8	7	8
3–	0	2	1	1	1	3	2					
3+	5	8	7	8	5							
4–	3	1										
4+	7	9	6									
5–	0											

Comment on the distribution of the data. Construct a frequency table.

4 Use a five-part stem to display these data.

5, 0, 12, 11, 1, 0, 2, 0, 0, 12, 3, 0, 10, 10, 1, 0, 1, 10, 1, 2, 12, 12, 9, 12, 1, 2, 1, 4, 8

5 The teachers in a school were asked what age they were when they started teaching. The results are given in this table.

Age (years)	22–24	25–29	30–34	35–44	45–54
Number of teachers	60	20	12	5	1

a) What are the upper class limits for each of the age classes?
b) Write down the widths of each of the classes and calculate the corresponding frequency densities.
c) Draw a histogram of these data and comment on the distribution of ages at which these teachers commenced teaching.

6 Forty students each measured the distance they travelled from home to their college to the nearest mile. The results were collated and they were then asked to produce a histogram.

Distance from home to college (miles)	2–4	5–7	8–10	11–13	14–16
Frequency	5	8	13	10	4
Centre	3	6	9	12	15

a) Amend this table to produce a relative frequency histogram.
b) Use your relative frequency histogram to estimate the proportion of students who live **i)** between two and five and **ii)** between seven and 14 miles from home.

EXERCISES

28.2 HOMEWORK

1 Rewrite the data in their original form from the stem-and-leaf diagrams below.

a) *Unit is 10*

0	1	1	2	7	
1	4	5	9	9	9
2	0	2	3		
3	1	4			
4	9				

b) *Unit is 0.01*

O	0	1				
T	2	2	2	3		
F	4	4	4	4	5	5
S	6	6	7			
E	8	8	8	8	9	
1O	0	1	1	1		
1T	2	2	3			
1F	4					

KEY SKILLS
N 3.1

2 Twenty nine-year-old children are each timed to tie their shoe laces with the following results, in seconds.

64, 75, 37, 48, 59, 50, 68, 65, 43, 52, 60, 79, 76, 83, 56, 88, 72, 65, 63, 79

Represent these data by a stem-and-leaf display.

3 Some data given in a stem-and-leaf diagram looked like this.

Unit is 1

78	4	9		
79	1	3	6	
80	2	2	4	7
81	1	4	9	9
82	3	3		
83	0	2	3	
84	1	4	5	

Rewrite this as a two-part stem-and-leaf diagram with unit 10.

4 The data below are the results of an experiment in which each of a group of children had to complete independently a particular puzzle. The values quoted are the completion times, in minutes.

2.4 2.0 1.6 1.4 1.8 1.1 1.6 1.7 1.6 2.1 2.0 1.4 2.2 2.3 2.5 2.3 1.7 1.7 1.8 1.9 1.4 1.4 1.9 1.8 1.6 1.7 2.1 1.8 1.7 1.9

Represent these data by a stem-and-leaf display using five-part stems.

5 The following were results of a test of the numerical aptitude of a group of schoolchildren.

Score	10–29	30–39	40–49	50–59	60–69	70–79	80–100
Number of schoolchildren	80	140	20	10	5	0	45

a) Identify the true class limits and widths of these classes.

b) Draw a histogram for these data and comment on the distribution of scores.

6 The table below shows the weekly take-home pay of a group of 1000 people.

Pay x (£)	Frequency
$0 \le x < 160$	41
$160 \le x < 185$	43
$185 \le x < 190$	51
$190 \le x < 200$	142
$200 \le x < 210$	231
$210 \le x < 220$	212
$220 \le x < 240$	175
$240 \le x < 260$	105

a) Illustrate these data on a relative frequency density histogram where the total area of the histogram is one square unit.
b) Use this diagram to give an estimate of the proportion of workers with take-home pay between £155 and £213.

CONSOLIDATION EXERCISES FOR CHAPTER 28

1 State whether the following data are discrete or continuous.

a) waiting times for arrival of a bus
b) occupancy rate of hotel rooms
c) fish caught by an angler in a competition by weight
d) fish caught by an angler in a competition by number
e) FT share index
f) shop's daily takings

2 State whether each of the following variables are qualitative or quantitative, and discrete or continuous.

a) hair colour
b) journey time to college from home
c) postal code
d) attendance at cinema
e) house type
f) house size

3 An usherette at a cinema recorded at the end of the showing of a film the number of each type of coin she had in her tray. The results are show below.

Coin	1p	2p	5p	10p	20p	50p	£1
Frequency	17	36	12	28	10	9	25

Display this data in a suitable diagram.

4 At the end of the day, the owner of a small corner shop cashed up. He made a record of how many of each type of coins and notes he had in the till. The results were as follows.

Type of note/coin	1p	2p	5p	10p	20p	50p	£1	£5	£10	£20	£50
No. of that type	86	112	84	50	70	43	28	12	4	5	2

Display this data in an appropriate diagram. Are there any difficulties with this?

5 The accompanying data represent the daily numbers of customers visiting a shop over an 84-day period.

28 42 52 50 29 71 15 34 45 48 38 28 83 13 49 32 37 41 43 66 19 34 49
35 54 29 75 22 35 43 56 45 38 77 25 35 54 38 66 56 89 25 45 53 36 51
55 79 24 43 55 44 67 58 91 21 36 48 56 42 67 92 23 43 56 76 59 61 98
26 45 51 62 54 73 126 34 56 67 78 75 82 153 31

a) Present these data using a stem-and-leaf display.
b) Construct a grouped frequency distribution, not using constant class widths, from your stem-and-leaf display.

6 The maximum height that 42 plants of the same species grew to was recorded. The results were recorded to the nearest cm and they are reproduced below.

Height (cm)	10–14	15–19	20–24	25–29	30–34
Frequency	6	12	11	8	5

a) What are the **i)** maximum **ii)** minimum heights in the class 20–24?
b) Draw a histogram of the given data.

7 Twenty-five competitors in a shot-putt competition had the lengths of three putts each measured to the nearest metre. This gave 75 results in all. The results are tabulated below.

Length (m)	0–9	10–12	13–15	16–18	19–22
Frequency	30	18	15	7	5

a) What are the **i)** maximum **ii)** minimum lengths in the class 13–15?
b) Calculate the width of each class.
c) Calculate appropriate frequency densities and present the data in a histogram.

8 The following data represents the distance from the centre of the board at which each of 12 darts lands (to the nearest cm).
14 cm, 12 cm, 14 cm, 17 cm, 5 cm, 26 cm, 16 cm, 8 cm, 17 cm, 22 cm, 19 cm, 31 cm, 20 cm

Show this in a two-part stem-and-leaf display indicating the unit.

9 The table below shows the hourly numbers of prescriptions dispensed by a large pharmacy over a period of time.

Number dispensed per hour	Number of hours
0–9	7
10–19	22
20–29	33
30–39	45
40–49	29
50–75	17
over 75	6
total	160

a) i) What type of data are these, discrete or continuous?
ii) Why does this cause a problem in constructing a histogram to represent the information?
b) i) What other problem has also to be overcome before the histogram can be constructed?
ii) Draw a histogram to represent these data.

Summary

- In this chapter we have distinguished between information which is qualitative or quantitative in nature and identified **discrete** data and **continuous** data.
- Diagrammatic presentations of data include **line graphs**, **bar diagrams** and **pie charts**.
- The data may be used to present themselves in **stem-and-leaf displays**.

One-part

Unit is 1

4	2 5 3
5	8 1 0 4 6
6	2 1 5 4
7	4 3 6

Two-part

Unit is 1

4–	2 3
4+	5 7 6
5–	0 4 3 2
5+	6 9 8
6–	3 1

Five-part

Unit is 10

F	4 5 5
S	7 7 6 7 6
E	9 8 8 8
1O	0 0 1
1T	2 3
1F	4

frequency = class width × frequency density

Summary statistics 1

In this chapter:

- *we introduce, as measures of location or average for a collection of data, the median, the mean and the weighted mean*
- *we extend the methods of presenting data to include cumulative frequency polygons*
- *we analyse symmetry in data and define skewness.*

Exploration 29.1

What do we need to know?

Consider the data presented in the stem-and-leaf diagram below.

Unit is 1

Stem	Leaves								
0	9	9	9	9					
1	3	7	3	7	2	5	8		
2	5	8	4	7	3	5	1	5	9
3	7	4	3	2	0	8			
4	5	6	2	5	3				
5	8	6	9						
6	4	1	8						
7	7	4							
8	3								
9									
10	4	7							
11	8								

This is a display of the time, in seconds, taken by 43 cars to pass through a continental motorway toll section. Answer the question, 'How long does it take for a car to pass through the toll section?'

There are two measures representative of data which may be useful in answering this – one representing the 'typical value' and another which indicates the 'sort of range of values' likely to be found. In statistical terms, these are measures of **location** or **average** and **dispersion** or **spread**.

There are many types of average and several kinds of spread. In this chapter we shall concentrate on averages.

MEASURES OF LOCATION

Mode

The **mode** is the most commonly occurring value or item of data, or, in other words, the one that appears most frequently. In the context of the data under consideration, the most commonly occurring value is 9 seconds. Is it reasonable, though, to consider 9 seconds as being typical of the time taken to pass through this continental motorway toll? Almost certainly not!

It may be more appropriate to consider the **modal class**. Referring back to the diagram, the 2-branch has the greatest frequency. Hence, it would be reasonable to say that the mode is a time between 20 and 30 seconds. This is the **longest branch in the stem-and-leaf** diagram.

The modal class may be the class with the highest frequency when the data are presented in a frequency table; but it may not!

Time t (s)	Frequency
$0 \le t < 10$	4
$10 \le t < 20$	7
$20 \le t < 30$	9
$30 \le t < 40$	6
$40 \le t < 50$	5
$50 \le t < 60$	3
$60 \le t < 120$	9

We need to proceed with great caution if the classes into which the data are grouped vary in width. Under these circumstances frequency density is a more accurate indicator of the modal class, as a histogram readily shows.

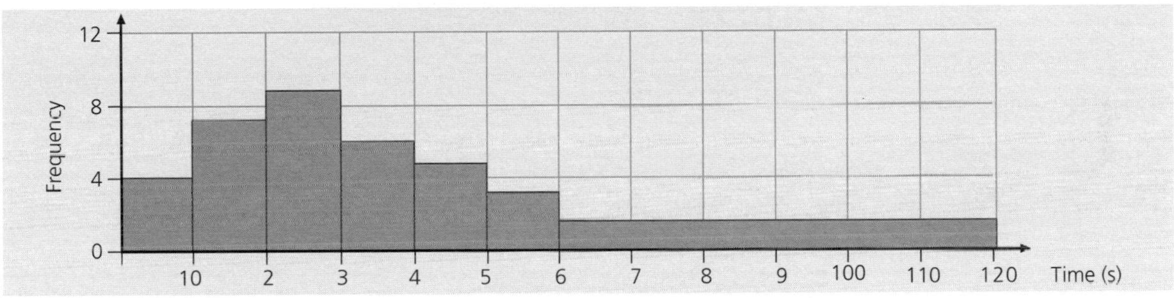

The prominence of the 20–30 seconds class is apparent. The 60–120 seconds class, which has the same frequency, is now seen more clearly!

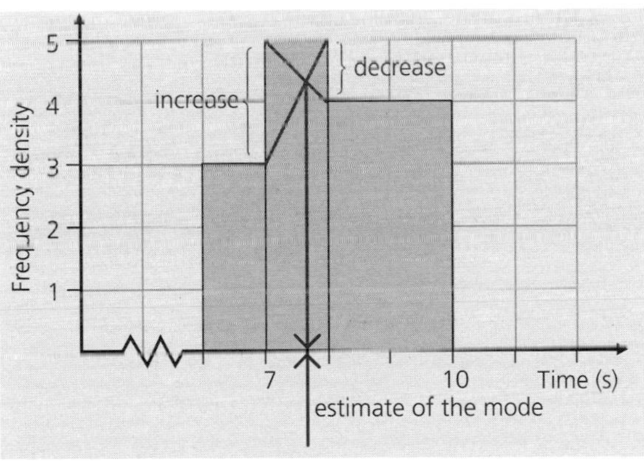

Having used the histogram to identify the modal class, it is possible to find an estimate of the mode. The diagram offers a simple graphical method of finding this estimate.

The method assumes that the mode divides the modal class in the **same ratio** as the *increase* in frequency density to the *decrease* in frequency density. In the diagram, this ratio is $(5 - 3) : (5 - 4)$ which is equivalent to $2 : 1$. Hence the mode divides the modal class in the ratio $2 : 1$, and an estimate of the mode is $7\frac{2}{3}$.

Example 29.1

Refer back to the motorway toll times frequency table above. Determine an estimate of the modal time.

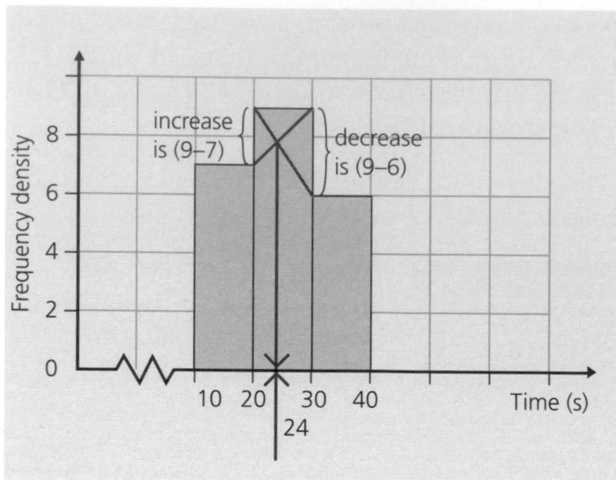

Solution

Here, the mode divides the modal class in the ratio 2 : 3. Hence an estimate of the mode is 24.

Is it possible to derive a formula for this estimate of the mode? Suppose the increase in frequency density is I, and the decrease is D. Then the estimate of the mode is given by:

$$\text{estimate} = x + \frac{I}{I+D} \times W$$

where W is the width of the modal class, and x is its lower bound.

In Example 29.1 $I = 2$, $D = 3$, $W = 10$ cm and $x = 20$ seconds.

Hence estimate of the mode = $20 + \frac{2}{5} \times 10 = 24$ seconds.

MEDIAN

Step-by-step

The centre or middle item of the data is known as the **median**. One approach to identifying the median is to:

- place the data in order
- locate the middle item
- hence, identify the median.

Suppose we need to identify the median of the following collection of data.

8, 15, 7, 10, 4, 3, 8, 6, 5, 7, 8

Placing the data in order yields:

3, 4, 5, 6, 7, 7, 8, 8, 8, 10, 15

The middle item is the one which is equidistant from the extreme values. Since there are eleven items of data, the middle is the sixth from either end.

sixth
↓
3 4 5 6 7 7 8 8 8 10 15
↑
median

Hence, the median of this collection of data is 7.

Even total

For the collection above, the total number of items is odd, which led to the median being one of the actual recorded items of data. In the following case, the total is an even number, which means the centre value of the data is midway between two of the recorded items.

4, 5, 0, 3, 9, 4, 8, 9, 9, 1

Ordering the data gives:

0, 1, 3, 4, 4, 5, 8, 9, 9

and locating the middle value yields:

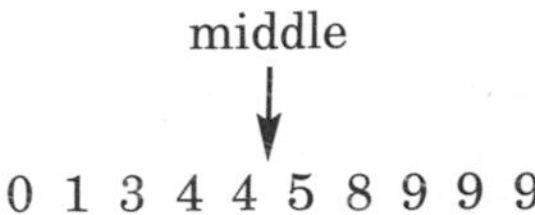

Hence, the median, which is midway between 4 and 5, is 4.5.
Now try identifying the median of the motorway toll times.
You probably found that the median is 32 seconds, but you are likely to agree that the process is rather tedious when there are many items of data. Several techniques have been developed, which depend on the format in which the data are available.

Stem-and-leaf

When the data are presented in a stem-and-leaf display, the first step towards identifying the median is to **order** the leaves. This involves placing the leaves on every branch in order of magnitude. The **ordered stem-and-leaf display** for the motorway toll times (page 544) looks like this.

Stem	Leaves								
0	9	9	9	9					
1	2	3	3	5	7	7	8		
2	1	3	4	5	5	5	7	8	9
3	0	2	3	4	7	8			
4	2	3	5	5	6				
5	6	8	9						
6	1	4	8						
7	4	7							
8	3								
9									
10	4	7							
11	8								

The next step is to locate the middle of the data – the item which is the same distance from either end of the data. In this instance, there are 43 items of data, hence the middle item is the 22nd item since it has 21 items on either side of it.

← 21 items   22nd   21 items →
←——— 43 items ———→

In the most basic terms, what we need to do is to count from each extreme until the count reaches 21; the median is then the next item.

One method of recording this counting process is to keep a running total as we count along each branch, until the branch containing the median is encountered. (Why is it not realistic to record the count for this branch?)

Depth										
4	0	9	9	9	9					
11	1	2	3	3	5	7	7	8		
20	2	1	3	4	5	5	5	7	8	9
(6)	3	0	2	3	4	7	8			
17	4	2	3	5	5	6				
12	5	6	8	9						
9	6	1	4	8						
6	7	4	7							
4	8	3								
3	9									
3	10	4	7							
1	11	8								

This count of the position of the median *relative to the nearer extreme* is known as the **depth**. In this case the median has a unique depth of 22. Note that the branch containing the median does not have a depth recorded, instead it has (in brackets) the number of leaves on the branch.

Note that where the total number of items of data is even, the median lies midway between the middle two items of data.

If there are n items of data then the depth of the median is $\frac{n+1}{2}$.

Exploration 29.2

Using depths

Order the following stem-and-leaf display.

Unit is 10

0	7	8	8							
1	8	1	3	8	7					
2	9	8	8	4	8	8	4	5	4	0
3	3	3	3	3	3	3	5			
4	0	3	0	7	2	8	9	5	8	
5	8	3	8	3						
6	6	4								
7	4	4	9	0						
8	3	3	0							
9	1									

Use depths to identify the median of the data collection.

Grouped frequency table

If the data are presented in a frequency table, then it is only possible to obtain an **estimate** of the median. This is done either graphically or arithmetically.

Cumulative frequency

One graphical approach uses a process similar to calculating the depths of a stem-and-leaf display, except that only the depth from the lower extreme is calculated. This is known as the **cumulative frequency**. Then the cumulative frequency of the upper extreme is equal to the total number of items of data.

The cumulative frequencies for the earlier frequency table of the motorway toll times are given below.

Time t (s)	Frequency	Cumulative frequency
$0 \le t < 10$	4	4
$10 \le t < 20$	7	11
$20 \le t < 30$	9	20
$30 \le t < 40$	6	26
$40 \le t < 50$	5	31
$50 \le t < 60$	3	34
$60 \le t < 120$	9	43

What information can be gained from the cumulative frequency?

Consider the cumulative frequency of 20. This tells us that there are 20 items of data with values less than 30 seconds. Similarly, the cumulative frequency of 34 indicates that there are 34 times which are less than 60 seconds. There is a natural link between any given cumulative frequency and the upper bound of the corresponding class. Hence, when it comes to constructing a cumulative frequency graph, the points to be plotted come from the following series of data.

Upper class value (s)	Cumulative frequency
10	4
20	11
30	20
40	26
50	31
60	34
120	43

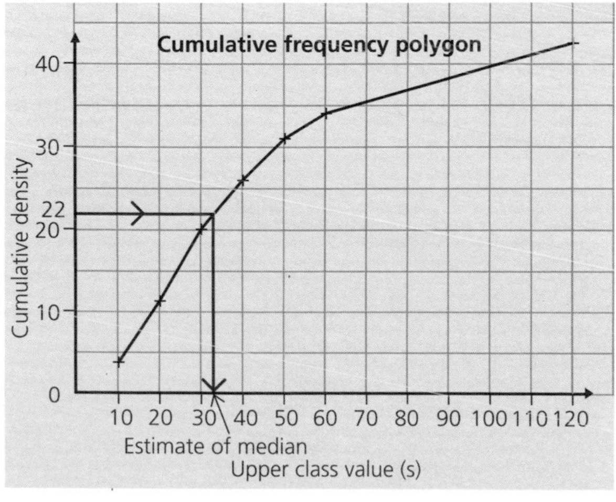

The resulting graph looks like this. It can be used to find the median.

Note that this does not necessarily produce the same value for the median as is found using the stem-and-leaf display.

The cumulative frequency of the median is $\frac{n+1}{2}$, where n is the total of the frequencies of the classes. Again, the median is the 22nd value which is about 33 seconds.

Sigma notation

There are many instances in studying Statistics which involve a process of 'adding up'. Because it occurs in so many cases, there is a standard notation which we use. This symbol Σ, called **sigma**, is a letter from the Greek alphabet. It is the equivalent of capital S. We use it to represent 'the sum of ...'.

An example of its use is in identifying the cumulative frequency of the median of a grouped frequency distribution. The total of the frequencies is found by adding up the frequencies of all the classes. We write this as:

$\sum f_i$

This may be written in any of the following ways.

$\sum_{\text{all data}} f_i$ or $\sum_i f_i$ or $\sum f$

where f_i represents the frequency of the ith class.

Example 29.2

Study these data.

Time (s)	100	110	120	130	150–200
Frequency	3	8	5	4	3

a) *Identify the frequencies for each of the five classes.*
b) *Find the cumulative frequency of the median.*
c) *Construct a cumulative frequency graph.*
d) *Estimate the median.*

Solution

a) *The frequencies are:* $f_1 = 3, f_2 = 8, f_3 = 5, f_4 = 4, f_5 = 3$.

b) *To find the cumulative frequency of the median, we need to find the total, n, of the frequencies.*

$$n = \sum_{i=1}^{5} f_i \text{ (i.e. add up the five frequencies)}$$

$$= (3 + 8 + 5 + 4 + 3) = 23$$

Hence the cumulative frequency of the median is $\frac{23+1}{2}$ *which is 12.*

c) *Recall that cumulative frequency refers to upper class values, so the data for the cumulative frequency graph are as shown in this table. Hence, the graph looks like this.*

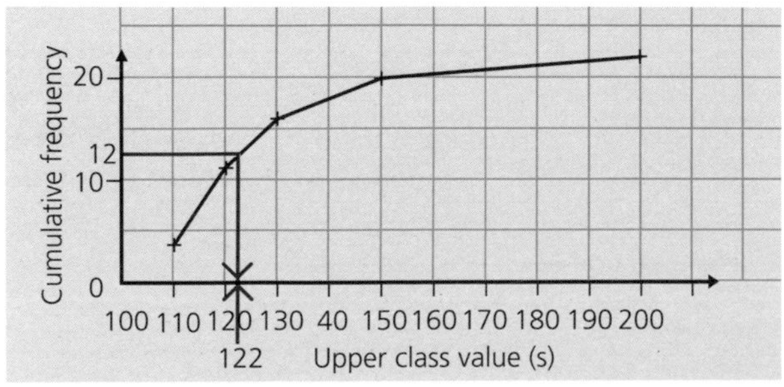

d) *The estimate for the median is found by locating its cumulative frequency on the graph and reading from the horizontal scale. This produces an estimate of 122 s.*

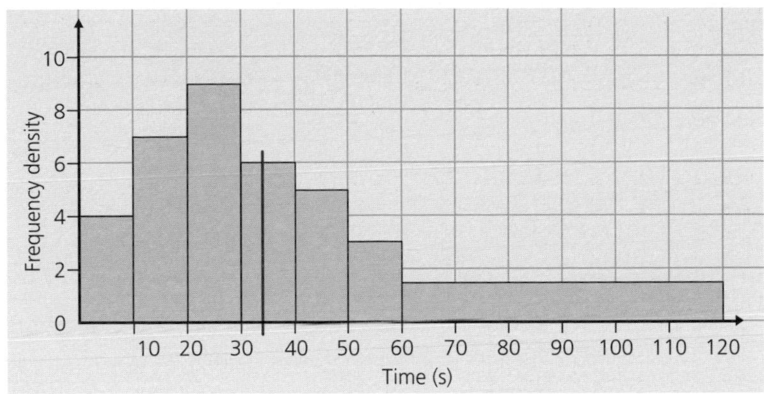

Histogram

A less common graphical approach makes use of a histogram and its property that area represents frequency. We need to locate the class containing the median, using perhaps a cumulative frequency table.

By definition, the median is in the middle of the data, so what we need to do is to find where a vertical line drawn in the histogram divides it so that the area of the blocks are the same on either side (see the diagram). The area of the first three blocks can be calculated.

$$(4 \times 10 + 7 \times 10 + 9 \times 10) = 200$$

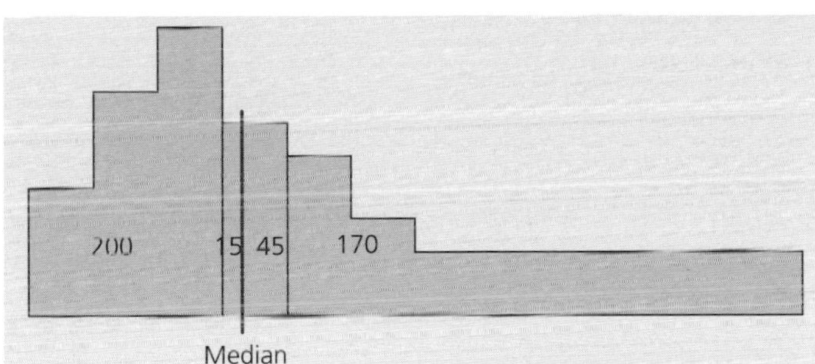

The area of the block containing the median is 60 and the remaining area is 170. Thus the total area can be considered to be 430.

The median must divide its class in the ratio 15 : 45 and so, this method of estimating the median from grouped data produces the estimate:

$$30 + \frac{15}{60} \times 10 = 32.5$$

Linear interpolation

The arithmetic approach starts from the cumulative frequency table and involves linear interpolation. Consider the section of the cumulative frequency graph where the median is located.

The cumulative frequency of the median is 22. Since 22 divides the cumulative frequencies in the ratio 2 : 4, the median will divide the class units 30 to 40 in the same ratio. Hence, this method of estimating the median produces this estimate.

$$30 + \tfrac{2}{6} \times (40 - 30) = 33\tfrac{1}{3}$$

This estimate should agree with the one given by the cumulative frequency graphical approach. Why?

Example 29.3

The data represent the distances, in centimetres, that a group of 40 children were able to achieve in 'standing' jumps. Use an ordered stem-and-leaf display to find the median standing jump.

Unit is 1

Stem	Leaves
4	7
5	4 2
6	3 1 8 7
7	9 7 4 1 4
8	8 7 0 6 5 4 1
9	6 5 5 4 2 8
10	8 7 3 1 5
11	4 5 3 7
12	8 1 2
13	4 1
14	2

Solution

The ordered stem-and-leaf display and the associated depths are:

Depth
Unit is 1

Depth	Stem	Leaves
1	4	7
3	5	2 4
7	6	1 3 7 8
12	7	1 4 4 7 9
19	8	0 1 4 5 6 7 8
(6)	9	2 4 5 5 6 8
15	10	1 3 5 7 8
10	11	3 4 5 7
6	12	1 2 8
3	13	1 4
1	14	2

Since there are 40 items of data, the median has a depth of $20\frac{1}{2}$. This means that the median lies halfway between two items of data. The 9-branch contains the median – as indicated by the absence of a depth for that branch. The leaf 2 on that branch has a depth of 20, as does the leaf 4 from the other extreme. The median lies halfway between these, and thus corresponds to a leaf value 3. This represents a standing jump of 93 cm.

Example 29.4

The 'standing jump' data are presented below in a grouped frequency table. Use this to construct a histogram and calculate an estimate of the median from this.

Jump (cm)	**Frequency**	**Class width**	**Frequency density**
40–60	3	2	1.5
–80	9	2	4.5
–90	7	1	7
–100	6	1	6
–110	5	1	5
–130	7	2	3.5
–150	3	2	1.5

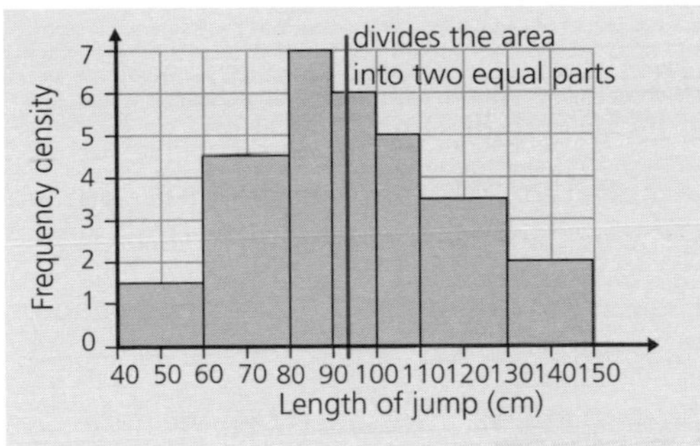

Solution

The histogram would be based on the frequency densities shown above.

The totals of the areas of the 'blocks' before and after the 'median block' can be considered to be 190 and 150; the median block would then be represented by an area of 60. The median is required to divide the area evenly into two sections of 200 units. Hence, the median divides its class in the ratio 10 : 50. Thus the estimate of the median based on the histogram is 91.7 cm.

Discrete data

The very nature of quantitative discrete data will often mean that the median of a collection of such data is one of the items of data. Two examples below illustrate ways of:

a) identifying the median in the case of an ungrouped frequency table of data,

b) estimating it where the data are presented in grouped frequency form.

Thirty-nine people were asked to state how many pairs of shoes they possessed.

Number of pairs of shoes	Frequency	Cumulative frequency
6	2	2
7	4	6
8	7	13
9	12	25
10	8	33
11	4	37
12	2	39

In the third column, the cumulative frequencies have been added to the frequency table. Because the data are discrete, the cumulative frequencies relate directly to the data values. In other words, the cumulative frequency 13 is associated with eight pairs of shoes; the cumulative frequency graph would include the point with coordinates (8, 13).

What might be an appropriate way of linking the points?

One approach is to link the points in a series of steps as shown below.

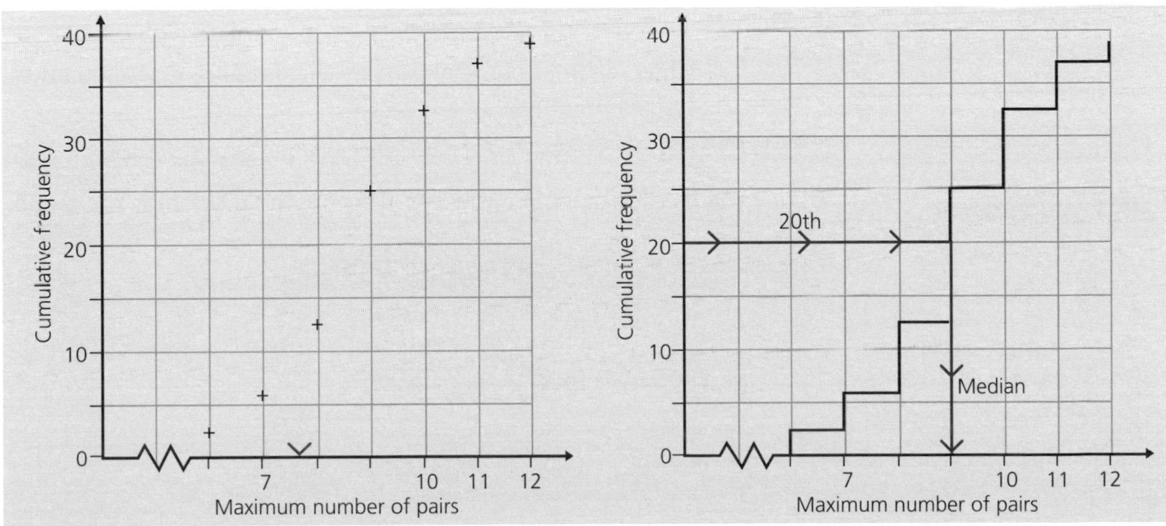

Why is this appropriate?

Since there are 39 items of data, the median item is the 20th which, from the graph, can be seen to be 9 pairs of shoes.

Alternatively, examining the table, the 13th item is 8, the 14th, 15th, up to the 25th are each 9, hence the median number of pairs of shoes is 9.

b) Sixty-seven children were asked how many novels they had read in the previous twelve months.

Number of books read	Frequency	Cumulative frequency
0–9	27	27
10–19	18	45
20–29	11	56
30–39	5	61
40–59	3	64
60–79	2	66
80–99	1	67

In this table, the data have been grouped. Because the data are discrete, the true class limits for a class such as 20–29 are 20 and 29 (not 29.5, 29.9, ... etc.) hence the cumulative frequency of 56 relates to the upper class value 29.

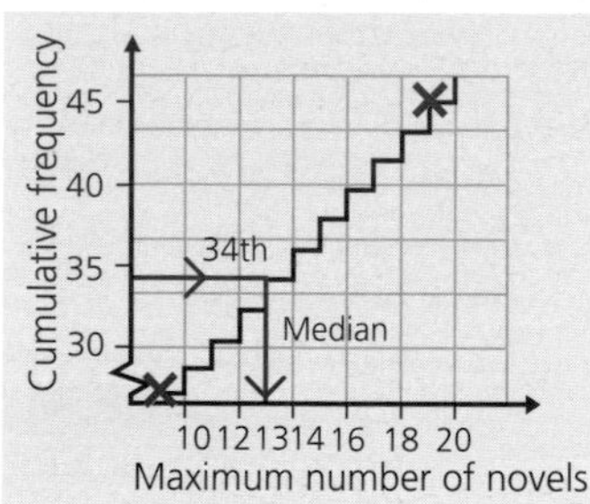

It could be argued that making the assumption that the number of novels read in any class is evenly distributed across the class would lead to linking consecutive points with a series of steps, as here.

The median is the 34th item of data. Hence, using the step graph, it is estimated to be 13 novels.

Clearly, this process would be extremely tedious and, since it is recognised that only an estimate of the median is to be obtained, the line segment approach can be adopted as in the continuous data case.

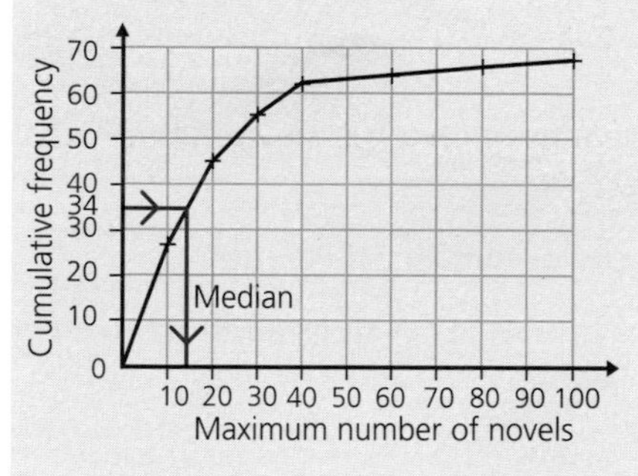

Care needs to be exercised in the construction of the graph, and in reading from it.

Alternatively, linear interpolation may be used. An estimate of the median is provided by:

$$9 + \frac{34 - 27}{18} \times 10$$

upper limit of lower class (9) — class has a span of 10 (10)

which amounts to 12.9. But as the data are discrete hence the median must be 13 novels.

EXERCISES

29.1 CLASSWORK

1 What is the median number of people in a household? Identify the mode.

Number in family	Number of families
1	15
2	20
3	22
4	23
5	11
6	4

KEY SKILLS
N 3.2c
N 3.3

2 The number of flowerheads on the foxgloves found in a small woodland were counted. The results are presented below. Estimate the modal number of flowerheads.

Number of flowerheads	Number of foxgloves
0–19	6
20–29	22
30–39	33
40–49	45
50–69	29
70–99	24

Obtain an estimate of the median number of flowerheads:

a) using a cumulative frequency graph,
b) using linear interpolation.

3 The populations in some Norfolk villages are given below.

933 410 956 1285 351 499 1414 2095 161 1488 1085 597
749 2444 1043 1303 3563 1124 4427 288 1099 1773 714 1314
623 893 234 532 2099 1243 709 521 472 655 308 613
483 442 189 198 541 351 940 705 439 399 732 101
341 452 324 3587

a) Choose appropriate class intervals and present these data in a grouped frequency table.
b) Obtain an estimate of the median population using a cumulative frequency graph.
c) Compare the estimate in **b)** with the actual median of the data.

4 Obtain an estimate of the median for each of the stem-and-leaf displays of **a)** and **b)** of Exploration 28.4.

5 The table records the time, in seconds, taken by each member of a group of 165 girls, to complete a simple crossword.

Time (s)	Number of girls
480–539	22
540–569	29
570–599	54
600–629	33
630–659	17
660–719	10

a) Draw a histogram of these data.
b) Use your histogram to estimate the median time and the modal time.
c) Compare your median in **b)** to the estimate obtained using linear interpolation.

EXERCISES

29.1 HOMEWORK

1 A lecturer has to pass through twelve sets of traffic lights on her route into university. She records the number of sets which she has to stop on each journey for 100 journeys.

Number of times stopped	Number of journeys
≤ 1	0
2	1
3	3
4	8
5	15
6	21
7	22
8	17
9	9
10	3
11	1
12	0

These records are shown in this table. Write down the mode.

a) Construct a cumulative frequency table for these data.

b) Draw a cumulative frequency step graph.

c) Locate and write down the median number of occasions the lecturer is stopped at traffic lights on a journey.

2 The number of components produced each day by a production line is recorded in this table. Write down the modal class.

Number of components	Number of days
500–509	16
510–519	44
520–529	47
530–539	31
540–549	18

Obtain an estimate of the median number of components:

a) using a cumulative frequency graph,

b) using linear interpolation.

KEY SKILLS
N 3.2c

3 A student records his journey times, in minutes, each morning for a period of six weeks. These times are as shown here.

15.2	16.7	20.5	17.8	21.2	14.7	16.8	17.3	15.6	15.3
16.8	18.7	19.3	19.6	18.2	15.6	18.8	17.4	16.7	18.2
15.6	16.9	17.3	18.7	20.2	20.4	18.4	16.7	17.9	18.4

a) Present these data in an ordered stem-and-leaf display.

b) Use your stem-and-leaf display to obtain an estimate of the median time.

4 Lecturers are asked to limit their lectures to 50 minutes. A Statistics student records the durations, in minutes, of the lectures she attends and presents them in the following display.

Unit is 0.1

```
45 | 2 3 5
46 | 7 6 2 1 3
47 | 5 8 7 1 2 1
48 | 9 6 5 0 1 3 6
49 | 2 7 6 5 3 2 8
50 | 1 2 3 8 6 7 5 9 0 0 5
51 | 3 7 4 6 7 2 0 1 5
52 | 2 7 0 3
53 | 5 6 2
```

a) Present the data in an ordered stem-and-leaf display, adding the depths of each branch.

b) Use your ordered display to identify the median time.
c) Construct a histogram of these data and use this to obtain an estimate of the median.
d) Explain any difference in the two values you have found for the median of these data.

5 Obtain estimates of the medians for the data in **c)** and **d)** of Exploration 28.4.

MEAN

The **mean** is the measure of location which is generally associated with the term 'average'. In simple terms, it is obtained by adding up the items of data and dividing by the number of items. Adding up all the motorway toll times of Exploration 29.1 produces a total of 1722 seconds and there are 43 such times, hence the mean time is:

$$\text{mean } = \frac{\sum t}{n} = \frac{1722}{43} = 40.05 \text{ seconds}$$

Grouped frequency

Consider again the grouped frequency version of the motorway times from Exploration 29.1.

Class (s)	Frequency
$0 \le x < 10$	4
$10 \le x < 20$	7
$20 \le x < 30$	9
$30 \le x < 40$	6
$40 \le x < 50$	5
$50 \le x < 60$	3
$60 \le x < 120$	9

When the data are presented in this way, we need to take several decisions, in order to calculate an estimate of the mean of the data. Note the use of the word 'estimate'. Why is it used?

Firstly, how do we interpret, say, the frequency 6 and the associated class '30–40'? There are six items of data in the range 30–40 s. The best that can be done without any further information is to interpret this as six items with an average value 35 s. In other words, applying this principle to the grouped frequency table yields the following table.

Representative time (s)	Frequency
5	4
15	7
25	9
35	6
45	5
55	3
90	9

(Why is the representative value of the last class 90?)

In effect, the grouped frequency data have been replaced by:
four occurrences of 5 seconds,
seven occurrences of 15 seconds,
nine occurrences of 25 seconds,

and so on. Perhaps the easiest way of totalling the time represented in these data is to use a combination of simple multiplication followed by addition. The table below summarises this process.

Time	Frequency	Time × frequency
5	4	20
15	7	105
25	9	225
35	6	210
45	5	225
55	3	165
90	9	810
Total	43	1770

Hence, the estimate of the mean obtained by this method is found as follows.

$$\text{Estimate of mean} = \frac{\sum xf}{\sum f} = \frac{1770}{43} = 412 \text{ seconds}$$

where x is the representative value for a class, and f is the corresponding frequency.

Note: The mean of this distribution of data is often written as $\bar{x}$, which is x with a line above it. This symbol is often referred to as 'x-bar'.

$$\bar{x} = \frac{\sum xf}{\sum f}$$

Why is this not the same as the mean found earlier? Which is likely to be the more accurate?

CALCULATOR ACTIVITY

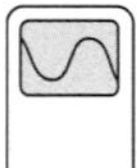

Inputting frequency data

Statistical calculators usually allow frequency data to be input.

You may find that you can store the items of data in one list and their corresponding frequencies in another list.

Try to input the following frequency distribution.

x (cm)	6	8	9	10	12
f	2	5	12	7	4

Check that your calculator produces these values.

$n = 30$
$\Sigma x = 278\,\text{cm}$
$\bar{x} = 9.2667\,\text{cm}$

Try inputting the following discrete data distribution and check that the calculator produces the correct median value of 19.5 (lying between the 11th and 12th item).

x	16	18	19	20	22
f	2	5	4	7	4

Exploration 29.3

Coding

Consider the following data which are the air pressure recordings in mb for one week.

1012, 1008, 1002, 996, 990, 1002, 1004

What is their mean?

Now consider the same values with 1000 mb subtracted.

12, 8, 2, –4, –10, 2, 4

Their total is readily obtained as 14, hence their mean is 2. To find the mean of the original recordings, you need only add 1000.

This is an example of transforming or **coding** data to simplify manual calculations of the mean. In this case, the transformation was a translation where:
coded value = air pressure – 1000

Hence mean (coded) values = mean (air pressure – 1000)
= mean (air pressure) – 1000

Inverting this leads to:
mean (air pressure) = mean (coded values) + 1000

Other transformations are also possible; among these are:

a) $\frac{\text{air pressure} - 1000}{2}$ **b)** $\frac{\text{air pressure}}{100}$

c) $\frac{\text{air pressure}}{2} - 500$ **d)** $\frac{\text{air pressure} - 990}{2}$

Applying **a)** to the data yields:
coded data: 6, 4, 1, -2, -5, 1, 2

and so the mean (coded data) = $\frac{7}{7}$ = 1. The inversion of the transformation mean (air pressure) = 2 × mean (coded data) + 1000
= 2 × 1 + 1000

producing the same result as before.

Have a go at applying the other transformations.

Example 29.5

The heights of 32 children in a class are recorded, to the nearest centimetre, in this table.

Height (cm)	140–149	150–159	160–169	170–179	180–189
Number of children	4	10	7	9	2

Calculate an estimate of the mean using the midpoint of the class 160–169 to translate the data and a scale factor of $\frac{1}{10}$.

Solution

Since these data are grouped, representative values are needed for each group. The data are recorded to the nearest centimetre, which indicates, for instance, that a height in the range 148.5–149.5 would be recorded as 149. So the true class limits are as shown overleaf.

Height (cm)	Frequency	Representative value	Coded value, x
$139.5 \le h < 149.5$	4	144.5	–2
$149.5 \le h < 159.5$	10	154.5	–1
$159.5 \le h < 169.5$	7	164.5	0
$169.5 \le h < 179.5$	9	174.5	1
$179.5 \le h < 189.5$	2	184.5	2

The mean of the coded values is:

$$\frac{\sum xf}{\sum f} = -\frac{5}{32}$$

Hence an estimate of the mean height is:

$$10 \times \left(-\frac{5}{32}\right) + 164.5 = 162.9 \text{ cm}$$

EXERCISES

29.2 CLASSWORK

1 The values below show the contents, x, of each of 15 match-boxes.

40, 41, 42, 42, 40, 39, 40, 40, 42, 41, 40, 41, 40, 40, 42

a) Calculate the mean content.
b) Use the coding; $y = x - 40$, to find y, and hence $\bar{x}$.

KEY SKILLS
N 3.2c
N 3.2d

2 The table below records the number of students absent from 80 tutorials during a year.

Number absent	Number of tutorials
0	5
1	21
2	27
3	12
4	8
5	5
6	2

a) Calculate the mean number of absences.
b) Use your calculator to obtain the mean number of absences.
c) If your calculator has the facility, use it to estimate the median number of absences.

3 The masses, x grams, of the fruit contents in 200 examples of canned fruit are recorded in the table.

Mass of fruit (g)	300	325	350	375	400	425	450
Number of cans	10	24	59	51	31	18	7

a) Use the coding $y = (x - 350)/25$, to calculate $\bar{y}$, hence obtain an estimate of the mean mass of fruit per tin.
b) Use your calculator to obtain an estimate of the mean mass of contents directly from the table.

4 Forty-five students were asked how long it took them to travel to school. The results are shown below.

Time take to travel to school (minutes)	**Frequency**
0–9	22
10–19	0
20–29	0
30–39	7
40–49	9
50–59	7

a) Estimate the mean time taken to travel to school.
b) Comment on the 0–9 (minutes) class.

EXERCISES

29.2 HOMEWORK

1 Recorded below are the marks obtained by 20 students in a Statistics examination.

56, 62, 40, 26, 46, 41, 67, 52, 70, 56,
48, 79, 50, 78, 46, 81, 47, 0, 54, 59

a) Calculate the mean mark.
You are now told that the 'zero' was due to absence rather than lack of knowledge.
b) What is a more appropriate mean mark?

KEY SKILLS
N 3.2c
N 3.2d

2 One Saturday there were 90 hockey matches played in the Midlands. The number of goals scored in each game was recorded.

Number of goals	**Number of matches**
0	17
1	25
2	18
3	14
4	10
5	3
6	1
7	2

a) Calculate an estimate of the mean number of goals per game.
b) Use your calculator to obtain an estimate of the mean.
c) If your calculator has the facility, use it to obtain an estimate of the median number of goals.

3 The heights, x, in centimetres, were measured of the intake of male Science students at a university. The results are given in the table.

Height (cm)	135	145	155	165	175	185	195
Number of students	14	56	342	401	143	77	23

a) Use the coding $y = (x - 155)/10$, to calculate $\bar{y}$, hence, obtain an estimate of the mean height.

b) Use your calculator to obtain an estimate of the mean height directly from the table.

4 Estimate the mean number of runs scored by the cricketer below.

Number of runs	Frequency
0–5	1
6–10	0
11–20	0
21–30	0
31–40	7
41–60	4
61–80	2
81–100	1
101–150	5

Comment on the distribution of these data.

SYMMETRY IN DATA

Exploration 29.4

Comparing averages

So far in this chapter we have concentrated on finding a measure of location, an average, for the motorway toll times. From the grouped frequency presentation of the data estimates were found to be:

mode 24 seconds
median 33.3 seconds
mean 41.2 seconds

Choose the average you feel to be most representative of the data and justify your choice.

Symmetry

These diagrams illustrate data which are perfectly symmetrically distributed.

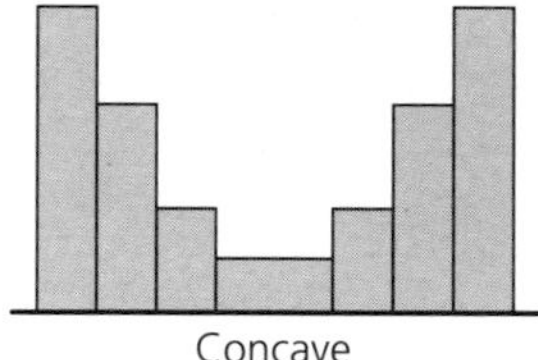
Concave

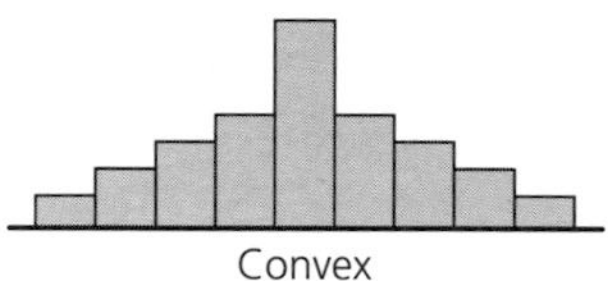
Convex

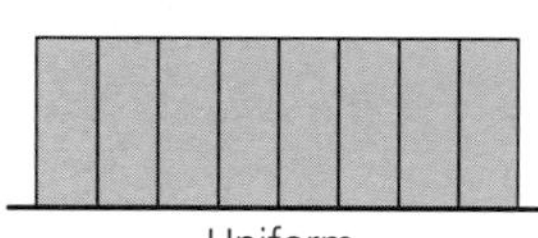
Uniform

Whilst the natures of the distributions are different, they have one feature in common which is that there is no difference between their mean and median.

This difference '**mean** – **median**' is a simple measure of **symmetry**, or lack of it. If data are perfectly symmetric then the difference is zero. Data which are reasonably symmetrically distributed will have a difference close to zero. The **sign** of the difference provides an indication of the nature of the **lack of symmetry** or **skewness**.

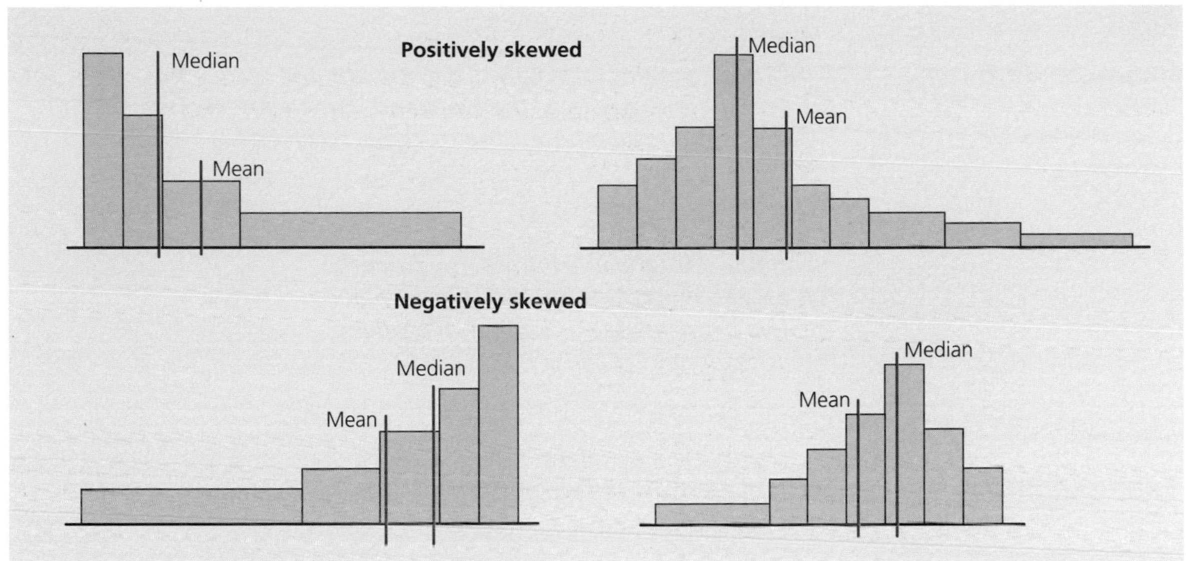

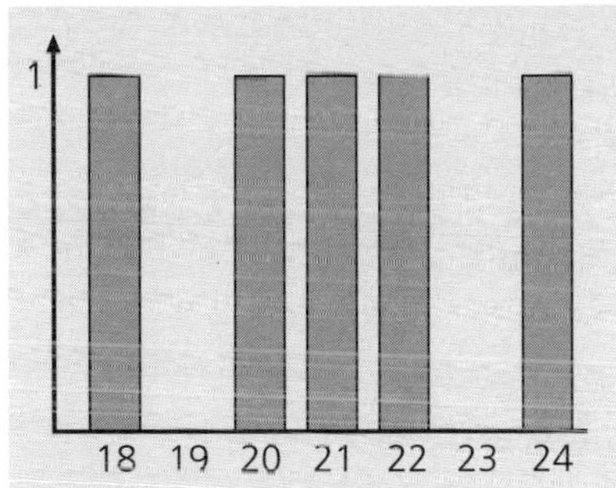

Why is the mean larger than the median for positively skewed data? Which measure of location is better? Consider the following data.

{18, 20, 21, 22, 24}

These could be displayed quite simply as shown here.

The mean is 21 and the median is also 21. The data are symmetrically distributed.

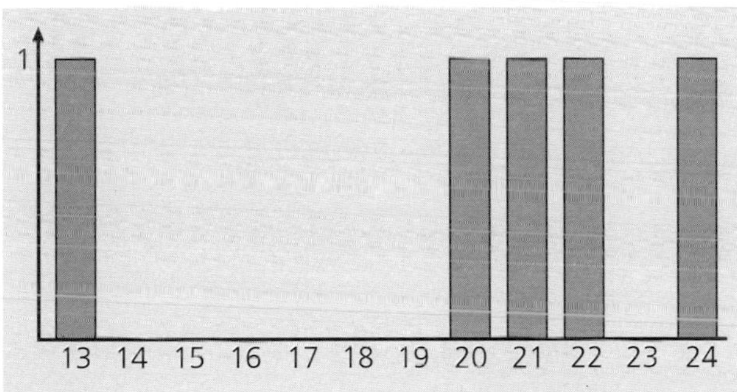

Now suppose that the 18 should have been 13, then this display would look like this.

Clearly the data are negatively skewed. What has happened to the two measures of location?

The median is still 21, but the mean has been reduced to 20. Thus the effect of skewing the data in this way has been to reduce their mean but it has had no effect on the median.

This property of the **median**, of not being affected by skew in data, leads to it being classified as a **robust** measure of location. But this does not make the median a better measure. The median's robustness is because it fails to take into account anything but the middle of the distribution. The mean, on the other hand, does take into account all the data. As a result of this it is affected by unusually large or unusually small values or by inaccurately recorded values.

One useful feature of the mean is that we can calculate the total of all the data from our known value of the mean and of the number of items of data.

total of data = number of items × mean

Example 29.6

A group of twelve students were discussing the wages they were paid for working one day over the weekend. The mean pay was £25.50. What was the total amount the students received?

Solution

Since:

mean pay = total pay ÷ number of students

it is easy to invert this relationship to yield:

total pay = mean pay × number of students

Hence total pay = £25.50 × 12

= £306.00

Example 29.7

The table records the weights, in kilograms, of the baggage of 79 passengers on a train.

Class (kg)	0–	1–	2–	5–	8–12
Frequency	11	21	33	6	8

a) *Using linear interpolation, calculate an estimate of median baggage weight.*

b) *Calculate an estimate of the mean weight.*

c) *Describe the symmetry of the distribution.*

Solution

a) *The cumulative frequency table is helpful in calculating the estimate for the median.*

Upper class value (kg)	1	2	5	8	12
Cumulative frequency	11	32	65	71	79

Cumulative frequency of the median is $\frac{79+1}{2}$ *= 40*

Thus the median lies in the 2–5 kg class

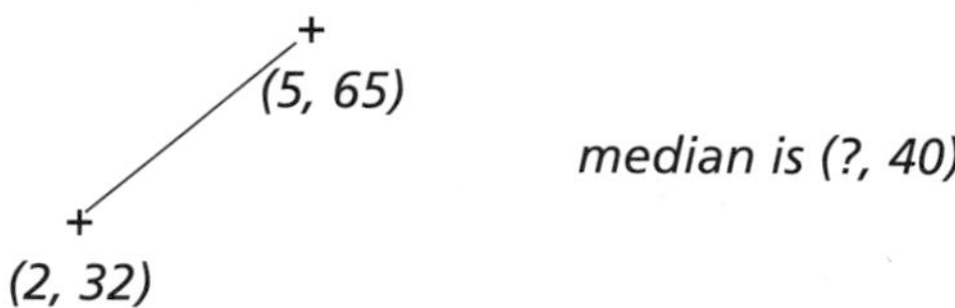

and it divides the class in the ratio 8 : 25.

Thus the estimate is:

$$2 + \frac{8}{33} \times 3 = 2.7 \text{ kg}$$

b) *The appropriate representative values for the classes, when calculating an estimate for the mean, are the mid-class values.*

Mid-class values x	0.5	1.5	3.5	6.5	10	
Frequency f	11	21	33	6	8	$\sum f = 79$
$x \times f$	5.5	31.5	115.5	39	80	$\sum xf = 271.5$

Hence

$$\bar{x} = \frac{271.5}{79}$$

$$= 3.4 \text{ kg}$$

c) Since the estimate for the mean is greater than that for the median, i.e.

mean – median > 0

the data are positively skewed.

WEIGHTED MEANS

Exploration 29.5

Index numbers

Index numbers are frequently in the news. They are the subject of comment in newspapers, and on the radio, in television reports. The Retail Price Index is commonly quoted. Find out about the RPI. Find out about other index numbers.

Weighted means

Imagine you are running a café and that you offer your customers, when they order coffee, a choice from:

a) High Mountain, **b)** Kenyan,
c) Mocha, **d)** Columbian.

You charge the same amount irrespective of the coffee chosen.

Your task is to ascertain how much it is likely to cost you to provide this service to your customers. Once you know this you will be able to decide how much you should charge a customer for coffee.

Your coffee suppliers volunteer the information that the four coffees sell in the ratio 6 : 10 : 3 : 1 and cost 58p, 49p, 66p, 40p per 100 g respectively.

This is sufficient information to establish the likely average cost of a cup of coffee (i.e. the cost to *you* of the coffee). The data values are the prices per 100 g that you have to pay, the ratios can be considered to be 'relative' frequencies or, in this context, 'weights'. Hence, to estimate the average cost to you of a cup of coffee, you need to calculate the mean of the following distribution.

Cost per 100 g x (p)	**Weight** w
58	6
49	10
66	3
40	1

The weighted mean is thus:

$$\frac{\sum xw}{\sum w} = \frac{58 \times 6 + 49 \times 10 + 66 \times 3 + 40 \times 1}{6 + 10 + 3 + 1} = \frac{1076}{20} = 53.8$$

The interpretation of this result is that it is going to cost you, on average, 53.8 p to purchase 100 g of the customer's choice of coffee.

Note: The 'weights' used in this example could have been expressed in a variety of ways, all of which would lead to the same weighted mean.

For instance, they could have been expressed:
as percentages: 30% : 50% : 15% : 5%

or as common fractions: $\frac{3}{10} : \frac{1}{2} : \frac{3}{20} : \frac{1}{20}$

Using the definition:

$$\text{weighted mean} = \frac{\sum x_i w_i}{\sum w_i}$$

leads to 53.8 in all cases.

Why? What advantage may there be in expressing weights in this way?

Example 29.8

The cost of salad vegetables in consecutive years is given in the table.

Vegetable	Cost in year 1 (p)	Weight	Cost in year 2 (p)
Tomato	45	0.4	54
Lettuce	27	0.3	28
Spring onion	15	0.1	20
Peppers	89	0.1	160
Sweetcorn	25	0.1	20

Calculate the weighted means of salad vegetables in each of years 1 and 2.

Solution

The weighted mean costs in years 1 and 2 are:
Year 1: $45 \times 0.4 + 27 \times 0.3 + 15 \times 0.1 + 89 \times 0.1 + 25 \times 0.1 = 39\text{p}$
Year 2: 50p

Mean of combined groups of data

Two students independently collect leaves from a privet hedge and measure their lengths. One student, Christine, reports that she measured 80 leaves and her leaves had a mean length of 15.8 mm. David measured 50 leaves and his mean was 17.5 mm.

What is the mean length of a leaf?

In our first approach to this, we can use the mean to recover the total of the data. Christine's leaves totalled:

$$(15.8 \times 80) = 1264\,\text{mm}$$

and David's totalled:

$$(17.2 \times 50) = 860\,\text{mm}$$

Thus, the total length of all 130 leaves is 2124 mm. Hence, the mean leaf length is:

$$2124 \div 130 = 16.3\,\text{mm}$$

Another approach is to use a weighted mean.

Christine's data had a mean of 15.8 and represented 80 out of 130 lengths. David's data had a mean of 172 and represented 50 out of 130 lengths. Hence, the overall mean length is the weighted mean:

$$\frac{80}{130} \times 15.8 + \frac{50}{130} \times 17.2 = 16.3$$

Why are these approaches equivalent?

EXERCISES

29.3 CLASSWORK

1 *Unit is 1*

Stem	Leaves
0	6
1	2 7 9 3 8 6
2	5 6 9 4 6 8 8 1 6
3	9 7 0 4 1 5 6
4	0 3 7 8 1 0 3 9 9 6 5
5	1 4 7 0 3 6 0 2 5 9
6	8 5 4 1 0 0 8 5 2 1 0
7	1 5 7 2 2 6 6
8	9 3 2 4 7 2
9	9 7
10	6 5 9 4
11	4 8 2 3
12	7

a) Use an ordered stem-and-leaf display to find the median of the data given above.

b) Write down the frequencies of the classes for the following collection of classes.

KEY SKILLS
N 3.2c
N 3.2d

Collection of classes	Frequencies of classes
0–	
20–	
40–	
60–	
80–	
100–130	

and use these to calculate an estimate of the mean.

c) Comment on the distribution of these data.

2 The table below records the weight loss, in kilograms, of each of 150 people attending a dietary clinic.

Weight loss x (kg)	Number of people
$-2 \leq x < -1$	3
$-1 \leq x < 0$	7
$0 \leq x < 1$	12
$1 \leq x < 2$	19
$2 \leq x < 3$	38
$3 \leq x < 5$	46
$5 \leq x < 10$	25

a) What do you think the negative values indicate?

b) Obtain estimates of the values of:
i) the mean, **ii)** the median.

c) Present the data in a histogram.

d) Comment on the symmetry of these data.

3 A type of concrete is made by mixing gravel, sharp sand and cement in the ratio 3 : 2 : 1. If the gravel costs £4 per tonne, sharp-sand £7 per tonne and cement £49 per tonne, calculate the cost of half a tonne of concrete.

4 Four groups of students sit the same Statistics examination, with the following results.

Group	Mean mark	Number of students
A	56	22
B	62	26
C	47	23
D	51	29

Calculate the mean mark for the 100 students.

5 The costs, in pence, of certain food items in two consecutive years are recorded in the table. The relative importance of the items is indicated by the weights.

Item	Potatoes	Eggs	Cheese	Meat
Cost in Year 1	21	69	189	285
Cost in Year 2	24	89	209	315
Weight	2	5	4	9

a) Calculate weighted means for each year.
b) Calculate the percentage change in expenditure over the two years.

EXERCISES

29.3 HOMEWORK

1 The reaction times, in seconds, of 38 drivers were measured with the results as shown in the table.

Reaction time (s)	< 0.3	0.3–	0.4–	0.5–	0.6–	0.8–1.0
Number of drivers	4	9	6	6	9	4

a) Present these data in a histogram and obtain an estimate of the mean reaction time.
b) Construct a cumulative frequency graph for these data and obtain an estimate of the median reaction time.
c) Comment on the symmetry of the data.

KEY SKILLS
N 3.2c
N 3.2d
N 3.3

2 Study these data.

Height of plant (nearest cm)	Number of plants
0–5	19
6–10	14
11–20	16
21–30	5
31–50	4

a) Draw a histogram of these data.
b) Obtain estimates of:
i) the mean, **ii)** the median,
height of plant.
c) Comment on the distribution of heights.

3 Two children baked biscuits. Jane's 22 biscuits had a mean mass of 12 g. Colin's 28 biscuits had a mean mass of 14.5 g. Calculate the mean mass of all the 50 biscuits produced.

4 Sample A has a mean of 10 whereas sample B has a mean of 30. The samples are combined. Calculate the resulting mean in each of these cases. Explain your answers.

a) $n_A = n_B = 50$ **b)** $n_A = 90$ $n_B = 10$ **c)** $n_A = 20$ $n_B = 80$

5 The fat content of the four options for school lunch was as follows; the meals were chosen in the proportion 30% : 35% : 25% : 10%.

Meal	Fat (g)	Weight
A	63	6
B	24	7
C	45	5
D	32	2

a) Explain how the weights were obtained.
b) Calculate a weighted mean and explain your result.

CONSOLIDATION EXERCISES FOR CHAPTER 29

1 The following are the numbers of persons on a sightseeing coach tour on each of 100 days in the holiday season.

Class (number of persons)	Frequency
under 10	17
10–14	5
15–19	3
20–29	7
30–34	11
35–39	37
40–44	20

a) Identify the modal class.
b) Calculate an estimate of the mode using a histogram of the data.

2 Calculate estimates of:

a) the mean,
b) the median,

for the following data which shows the distribution of lengths of fish sampled from a trout farm.

Length (cm)	Frequency
0–4	12
–6	25
–8	17
–10	38
–12	12
–14	9
–16	5
–18	4
–20	3
–22	18
–24	26
–26	9
–28	2

3 The following are the ages of 25 people living in an old people's home.

65 72 73 81 60 69 75 78 86 82 87 64 73
72 66 80 69 80 76 74 81 93 65 72 72

a) Use a suitable stem-and-leaf diagram to find the median of these data.
b) Construct a suitable frequency table for these data and use it to calculate an estimate of the mean age.
c) Comment on the distribution of these data.

4 Find the mean and the median for each of these two data sets and construct a simple illustration for each.

a) 2 5 7 9 12
b) 1 2 6 7 10 11 12

Construct a data set of five values:

c) with mean 7 and median 4,
d) with mean 4 and median 7,
and illustrate each.
e) Comment on the symmetry or the lack of symmetry in each of the four data sets.

5 A weekly newspaper offers a free book to new subscribers. The five books on offer cost £7.50, £12, £6.99, £4.99 and £13.25 respectively and are chosen in the proportion:

18% : 15% : 31% : 28% : 8%.

Calculate the weighted mean cost to the newspaper of offering this incentive.

6 A company uses four raw materials in its production process. The cost per kg of each is given in this table:

Material	Cost per kg (£) in year 1	Weight	Cost per kg (£) in year 2
A	7.30	6	7.50
B	8.40	3	8.60
C	2.15	9	2.70
D	10.45	2	9.95

Calculate an index for the cost of production in Year 2 based on production costs in Year 1. Interpret the index.

7 There are three possible routes from Philip's home to his college. Over a term, he drove by route A 20 times with a mean journey time of 23.4 minutes. He also travelled by route B 20 times with a mean journey time of 25.7 minutes and by route C 15 times with a mean journey time of 26.0 minutes. Calculate his overall mean journey time.

8 A packaging process is supposed to fill small boxes with approximately 50 raisins, so that each box will weigh the same. A count of the contents of each of a selection of 120 boxes resulted in the data below.

57	51	53	52	50	59	51	51	52	52	44	53
45	57	49	53	58	47	51	48	49	49	44	54
46	52	55	54	47	53	49	52	49	54	57	52
52	53	49	47	51	48	55	43	55	47	53	43
48	46	54	46	51	48	53	56	48	47	49	57
55	53	50	47	57	49	43	58	52	44	46	59
57	47	42	59	49	53	41	48	59	53	45	45
56	40	46	49	50	57	47	52	48	50	45	56
47	42	48	46	44	53	47	55	48	51	52	54
49	51	53	48	50	45	55	49	48	53	56	52

a) Use a two-part stem-and-leaf diagram to display these data.
b) Calculate the median number of raisins in the box.
c) Estimate the mean number of raisins per box.

9 The numbers of people per household in a road were recorded as shown in this table.

Number of people	1	2	3	4	5	6	7	8
Number of households	4	8	12	20	13	5	2	1

a) Use a step cumulative frequency diagram to find the median number of people per household.
b) Calculate the mean number of people.
c) Identify the modal number of people.
d) Which is the most appropriate measure of location for these data?

10 The following table summarises the birth weights of a random sample of 100 babies born with breathing problems.

Birth weight (kg)	Number of babies
1.0 –	12
1.4 –	17
1.6 –	23
1.8 –	14
2.0 –	10
2.2 –	9
2.4 –	8
2.8 –	4
3.2 – 3.8	3

a) Write down the upper class boundary of the first class.
b) Represent these data by a histogram.
c) Estimate the number of babies whose birth weight was between 2.1 kg and 2.5 kg.
d) Calculate estimates of the mean and the standard deviation of this sample of birth weights.
e) Calculate estimates of the median and the quartiles of these birth weights.
f) Comment on the skewness of the data.
g) State, giving a reason, which of **d)** or **e)** you would recommend using to summarise the data in the table.

(EDEXCEL Question 8, Paper T1, June 99)

Summary

■ Measures of location

Mode: the item with greatest frequency

Median: the middle of the data; its cumulative frequency is $\frac{n+1}{2}$

Mean: $\bar{x} = \frac{\sum xf}{n}$

Weighted mean: $\frac{\sum xw}{\sum w}$

■ Symmetry

Perfectly symmetric: mean – median = 0
Positively skewed: mean – median > 0
Negatively skewed: mean – median < 0

Summary statistics 2

In this chapter:

- *we introduce various measures to describe the spread or dispersion of a range of data, including the range, quartile spread and standard deviation*
- *we use box and whisker diagrams as visual displays of symmetry and spread of data.*

In Chapter 29, *Summary statistics 1*, we discussed how to identify typical times. In this chapter we shall consider the 'spread' of times.

MEASURES OF DISPERSION

Range

Perhaps the most simple measure of spread is the difference between the largest and smallest items of data i.e. the difference between the extremes. This is the **range**. In the case of the motorway toll times (page 544) the longest time recorded was 118 seconds and the shortest time was 9 seconds, hence the range of these data is given by:

range = 118 – 9 = 109 seconds

This measure of spread does not take into account anything about the distribution of the data other than the extremes.

Quartile spread

A more trustworthy measure is the range of the **middle half** of the data. To identify this range we need to find the items of data which are positioned halfway between the extremes and the median. Take the case of the data collection on page 546.

3 4 5 6 7 7 8 8 8 10 15

(arrows under 5, under the second 7 — median — and under the third 8)

By writing them in order, we can identify the middle 'half' of the data. We find that it lies between the values of 5 and 8.

It is now possible to identify the values between which the middle half of the motorway toll times lie. Take a moment to find them.

You should have found that the middle half of these times lies between 18 seconds and 58 seconds.

In general, the items of data lying midway between the median and the extremes are known as the **quartiles**. It is more usual to refer to them as the first or **lower** quartile and the third or **upper** quartile. The difference between them is called the **interquartile range** (IQR) or **quartile spread** (QS).

In this case of the motorway toll times, the quartile spread is 40 seconds.

Stem-and-leaf

As for the median, there are corresponding techniques for finding the quartiles. With the 43 motorway toll times, the depth of the median is 22, hence the depth of the quartiles is 11 (recall depth is a count of distance from the nearer extreme).

	Depth	Stem	Leaves	
	4	0	9 9 9 9	
depth of quartile	11	1	2 3 3 5 6 6 8	*11th item from extreme*
	20	2	1 3 4 5 5 5 7 8 9	
	(6)	3	0 2 3 4 7 8	
	17	4	2 3 5 5 6	
depth of quartile in here	12	5	6 8 9	*11th item from extreme*
	9	6	1 4 8	
	6	7	4 7	
	4	8	3	
	3	9		
	3	10	4 7	
	1	11	8	

If there are n items of data, the quartiles have a depth of $\frac{n+1}{4}$.

Five-number summary

The values of the extremes, quartiles, and median of a collection of data provide a simple summary of the distribution.

	Lower	Upper
M	32	
Q	18	58
E	9	118

A graphical version of this five-number summary table, known as a **box-and-whisker diagram**, provides a visual presentation enabling us to focus on each of the four quarters of the data.

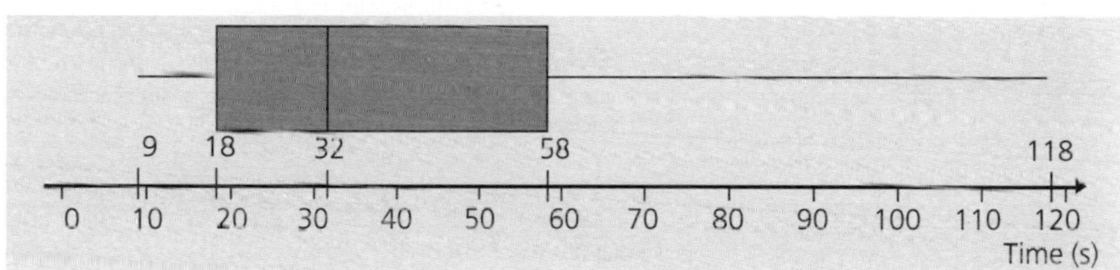

Vertical lines mark the quartiles and the median. These are joined to make a box containing the middle half of the data. From the quartiles, horizontal lines are drawn to the extremes – the lines are the 'whiskers'. What features of the distribution are apparent from a box-and-whisker diagram?

Grouped frequency table

The quartiles may also be found using cumulative frequencies. Unlike using depths, the cumulative frequencies of the first and third quartiles differ and are at $\frac{1}{4}(n + 1)$ and $\frac{3}{4}(n + 1)$ when there are n items of data.

The cumulative frequency table is reproduced overleaf.

	Upper class value(s)	Cumulative frequency
	10	4
First quartile →	20	11
	30	20
	40	26
	50	31
Third quartile →		←
	60	34
	120	43

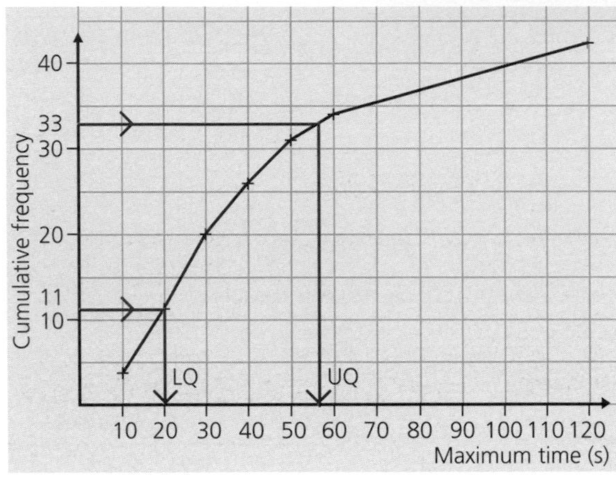

Graphical approach

For the motorway times, the quartiles are the 11th and 33rd items. The cumulative frequency graph can be used as illustrated where the values are:

lower quartile: 20 seconds
upper quartile: 56.7 seconds

Hence the quartile spread is:
56.7 – 20 = 36.7 seconds

Note: These values differ from those obtained using the stem-and-leaf display.

Linear interpolation

Again, as was the case for the median, linear interpolation may be used. In this instance, there is little to be done to calculate the lower quartile. The calculation of the upper quartile is:

+ (60, 34)

upper quartile (?, 33)

+ (50, 31)

Upper quartile: $50+\frac{2}{3}\times 10 = 56\frac{2}{3}$

Lower quartile: 20

Hence, linear interpolation yields the same result. Can you explain why?

Discrete data

If the data are discrete then their quartiles may be found as in the following illustrations.

Pairs of shoes (see page 553)	6	7	8	9	10	11	12
Frequency	2	4	7	12	8	4	2
CF	2	6	13	25	33	37	39

Since n = 39, the cumulative frequencies of the quartiles are: cumulative frequency

Q1: $\frac{39+1}{4}=10$ Q3: $\frac{3}{4}(39+1)=30$

Interpreting the cumulative frequency table: there are six people with seven or fewer pairs of shoes and 13 people with eight or fewer. Hence the tenth item of data is eight pairs of shoes. Similarly, the 30th item of data is ten pairs of shoes.

$\Rightarrow$ Q1 = 8 and Q3 = 10 and the quartile spread is 2.

Number of novels read (see page 554)	0–9	10–19	20–29	30–49	50–69	70–79	80–99
Frequency	27	18	11	5	3	2	1
CF	27	45	56	61	64	66	67

	Cumulative frequency	Quartile
Q1	$\frac{1}{4}(67+1) = 17$	$0 + \frac{17}{27} \times 10 = 6.30$
Q3	$\frac{3}{4}(67+1) = 51$	$19 + \frac{6}{11} \times 10 = 24.45$

Recall that the data are discrete, hence the estimates of the quartiles are:

Q1 = 7 Q3 = 25

and the quartile spread is 18 novels.

CALCULATOR ACTIVITY

Exploration 30.1

Calculating quartiles

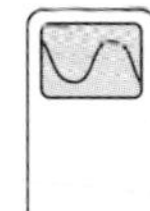

Some graphical calculators will present estimates of the quartiles, but check the definition used.

You may find that your calculator will display data in a box-and-whisker diagram. However, since this presentation often uses the same quartiles, its relevance may be limited.

Example 30.1

The heights of 49 earthenware jars found on an archaeological site are given in the table.

a) *Use linear interpolation to calculate estimates of the quartiles.*
b) *Provide an estimate of the interquartile range.*
c) *Draw a box-and-whisker diagram of the data.*

Class (cm)	Frequency
16–	6
18–	9
20–	8
22.5–	6
25–	7
27.5–	9
30–32	4

Solution

a) *The first step is to calculate the cumulative frequency distribution.*

Upper class value (cm)	18	20	22.5	25	27.5	30	32
Cumulative frequency	6	15	23	29	36	45	49

There are 49 items of data.

Hence the cumulative frequencies of the quartiles are:

Lower quartile CF: $\frac{1}{4}(49+1)=12.5$

Upper quartile CF: $\frac{3}{4}(49+1)=37.5$

Lower quartile: this lies in the 18–20 class

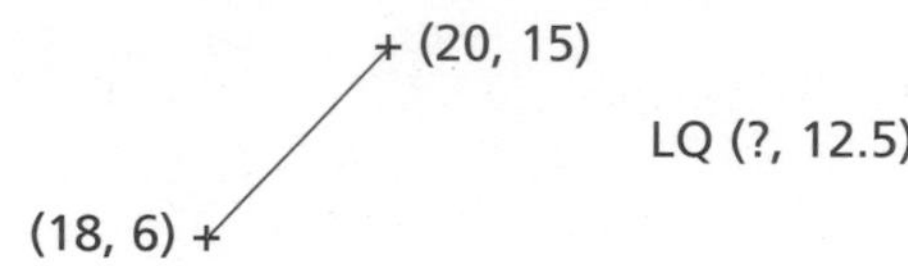

$\text{LQ} = 18+\frac{6.5}{9}\times 2=19.4 \text{ cm}$

Upper quartile: is in the 27.5–30 class

+ (30, 45)

UQ (?, 37.5)

(27.5, 36) +

$\text{UQ} = 27.5+\frac{1.5}{9}\times 2.5=27.9 \text{ cm}$

b) *An estimate of the IQR is 27.9 – 19.4 i.e. 8.5 cm.*

c) *The median is needed for a box-and-whisker display of the data and is:*

$22.5+\frac{2}{6}\times 2.5=23.3 \text{ cm}$

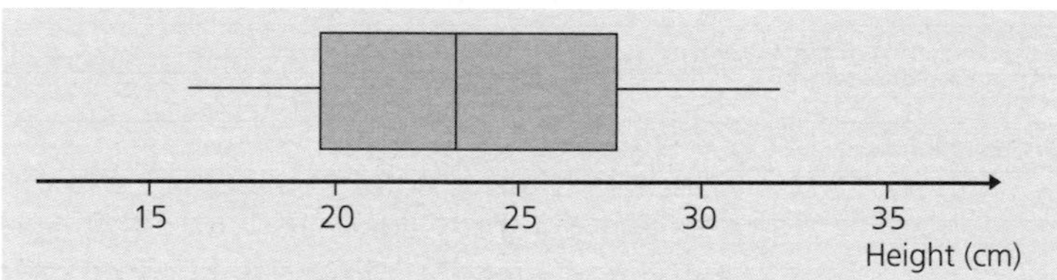

Note: With grouped frequency, the lower and upper extremes are estimates of the lower and upper limits of the first and last classes.

Exploration 30.2 *Comparing distributions*

Three package holiday companies were asked to provide prices for 220 different 14-day all-inclusive holidays. The data returned by the companies are given in this table.

Company A		Company B		Company C	
Cost (£)	**Number of holidays**	**Cost (£)**	**Number of holidays**	**Cost (£)**	**Number of holidays**
100–	62	0–	5	150–	10
200–	20	100–	30	250–	45
250–	30	200–	40	300–	65
300–	73	300–	50	350–	50
500–	30	400–	45	400–	30
550–600	5	500–	35	450–550	20
		600–700	15		

Estimates for the median and quartiles of the costs for the holidays offered by company A are:

median $250 + \frac{28.5}{30} \times 50 = £297.50$

lower quartile $100 + \frac{55.25}{62} \times 100 = £189.11$

upper quartile $300 + \frac{53.75}{73} \times 100 = £373.63$

Hence, a five-number summary for these data is:

	Lower		Upper
Median		297.50	
Quartiles	189.11		373.63
Extremes	100		600

Verify that a five-number summary for the costs of the holidays offered by Company B is:

	Lower		Upper
Median		371.00	
Quartiles	250.63		490.56
Extremes	0		700

Obtain a five-number summary for the data provided by Company C.

Exploration 30.3

Value for money

A convenient visual method of comparing the three collections of data is to present a 'box-and-whisker' of each on one schematic diagram with a single scale.

Schematic diagram

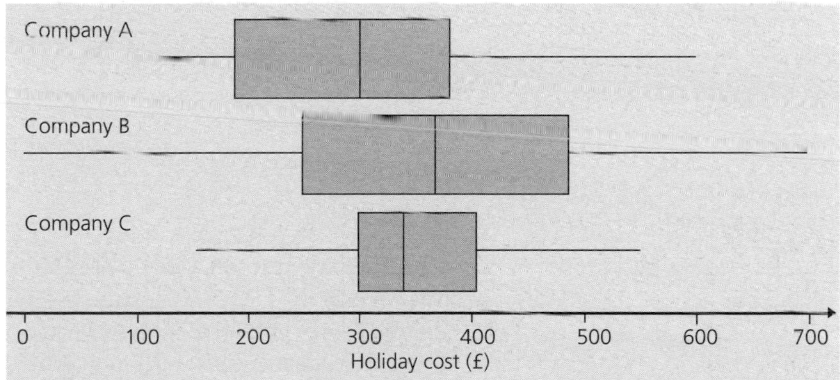

Which company would you choose for your fortnight's holiday? Discuss your answer.

BOX-PLOTS AND OUTLIERS

Using a modification of the box-and-whisker diagram, the same features of symmetry, location and spread can be demonstrated at a glance and unusually large or small items of data can be highlighted.

> ***Note:***
> QS quartile spread
> LQ lower quartile
> UQ upper quartile

Fences are values defined in relation to the quartiles of the distribution.

Inner fences: the lower quartile is calculated as LQ – 1QS
the upper quartile is calculated as UQ + 1QS

Outer fences: these are calculated as LQ – 2QS
UQ + 2QS

In many distributions, approximately 95–96 per cent of the items will be between the inner fences. So it would be an unusual item of data which would lie further away from the median than an inner fence. Such items of data are referred to as **outliers**.

In many distributions, less than 0.1 per cent of data lie outside the outer fences. These items are sometimes referred to as **extreme outliers** or they may be described as **far out**!

Note that in some instances inner and outer fences are not distinguished. Under these circumstances fences are calculated as: LQ – 1.5QS, UQ + 1.5QS.

For the motorway toll times (page 544), the quartiles are 18 s and 58 s, and the quartile spread is 40. Hence the fences have the following values.

	Lower	**Upper**
Inner fences:	18 – 40 = –22	58 + 40 = 98
Outer fences:	18 – 80 = –62	58 + 80 = 138

Note that, in this case, the lower fences are negative and so there are no items of data outside these. Note also that the upper outer fence is larger than any of the items of data. However, there are items of data, 104, 107, 118 with values larger than the upper inner fence. It would be appropriate to describe these items as outliers.

The modified box-plot of these data looks like this.

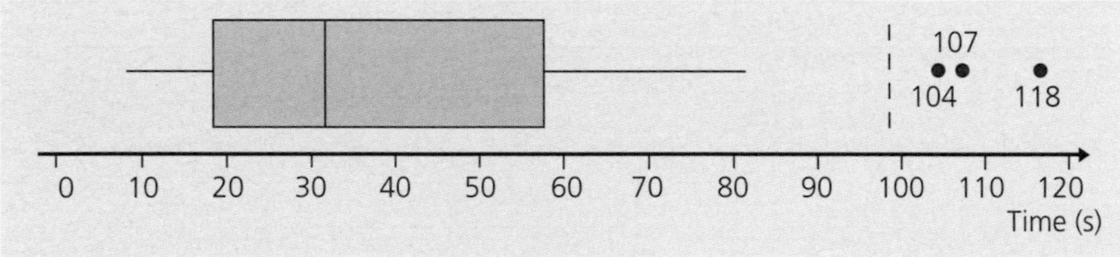

Notice that:

a) the 'whiskers' now only go out to the item of data just inside the inner fence(s),
b) the fences are shown as dotted vertical lines but may be omitted,
c) the outliers are individually marked.

EXERCISES

30.1 CLASSWORK

> **KEY SKILLS**
> N 3.2b
> N 3.2c
> N 3.3

1 Calculate the range and quartile spreads for each of the following data collections.

a) 6, 6, 8, 9, 9, 10, 11
b) 0.1, 0.2, 0.2, 0.3, 0.4, 0.4, 0.4, 0.5, 0.5, 0.6, 0.7
c) 312, 313, 315, 316, 320, 328, 330, 333, 358
d) 4.1, 4.2, 4.3, 4.5, 4.5, 4.6, 4.6, 4.6, 4.6, 4.7, 4.8, 4.9

2 Calculate the median for each data collection in question 1 and draw box-and-whisker diagrams for each collection.

3 **a)** Calculate the interquartile range for the following data.
b) Identify the outliers in the data.
c) Draw a box-plot of the data and comment on their distribution.

5.41 2.89 4.78 7.12 3.37 6.50 6.23 8.62 4.99 13.7 7.26 1.37 5.62
8.11 4.68 15.8 6.82 9.85 6.63 9.35 5.43 4.79 6.55 1.88 0.04

4 **a)** Order these data and identify their median and quartiles.
b) Calculate inner fences and draw a box-plot of the data.
c) Identify outliers in the data.

4.53	2.18	7.93	1.98	15.80	3.73	3.59	0.04	0.94	3.04
1.18	3.52	9.94	6.27	8.81	1.27	4.96	3.7	3.01	0.13
5.91	5.27	6.28	8.60	5.56	4.28	8.59	5.14	8.86	0.18
3.36	0.77	3.46	6.17	7.94	8.92	8.26	8.39	1.88	3.36
3.76	1.66	5.06	4.87	4.35	4.15	8.03			

5 In a survey, 27 guest houses and hotels were randomly selected and the price of one night's bed-and-breakfast was collected for four different times of the year.

	Frequency			
Cost of B&B (£x)	Spring	Winter	Autumn	Summer
$0 \le x < 10$	1	0	0	0
$10 \le x < 20$	3	3	7	2
$20 \le x < 25$	4	0	2	0
$25 \le x < 30$	2	4	4	3
$30 \le x < 35$	3	3	6	3
$35 \le x < 40$	6	3	3	2
$40 \le x < 50$	1	10	3	10
$50 \le x < 60$	6	2	1	3
$60 \le x < 70$	1	2	1	3
$70 \le x < 80$	0	0	0	0
$80 \le x < 100$	0	0	0	1

a) For each period of the year, calculate estimates of the median and quartile costs, and produce a five-number summary of the data.
b) Draw box-and-whisker diagrams for the data of each period in a single schematic diagram.
c) Discuss the similarities and differences in the distributions of prices.

EXERCISES

30.1 HOMEWORK

1 Calculate the range and interquartile range for each of the following sets of data.
a) 2, 3, 4, 5, 5, 6, 7, 9, 11, 12, 12
b) 45, 46, 52, 55, 59, 62, 68, 73, 75, 84
c) 101.3 101.4 101.6 101.7 101.7 101.8 102.0 102.3 102.3 102.4 102.6
d) 506 503 507 504 510 511 526 513 517 508 515 513 508 509 516

2 Calculate the median for each data set in question 1 and hence draw the associated box-and-whisker diagrams.

3 Calculate, using a cumulative frequency graph, estimates of the median and quartiles for the following data.

Time (s)	1–10	11–20	21–30	31–40	41–50	51–100
Frequency	2	12	28	21	11	6

KEY SKILLS
N 3.3

4 The heights of a random sample of 23 daffodil leaves were measured with the following ordered results, in centimetres.

20.0 26.5 26.5 27.0 27.5 28.0 28.0 28.0 28.5 28.5 29.0 30.1
30.5 30.5 31.5 32.0 32.0 33.5 34.0 34.0 34.5 38.0 44.5

a) Identify the median and the upper and lower quartiles.
b) Hence determine the inner and outer fences.
c) Construct a box-plot of the data.
d) Identify any outliers, noting which if any are far out.

5 The weights of 99 cod landed in each of two ports are recorded in the table.

Weight (lbs)	0–	10–	12–	14–	16–	18–	20–40
Number of fish Port A	33	22	21	10	7	3	3
Number of fish Port B	12	15	32	21	10	4	5

a) Estimate the median and quartile weights of fish landed in each port.
b) Provide a five-number summary for the data in each port.
c) Display the distribution of weights of these cod in a schematic diagram.

Comment on the distributions of fish weights in the two parts.

STANDARD DEVIATION

The interquartile range measures the spread of the middle 'half' of the data and is closely linked to the median. We can define a measure of dispersion, taking into account all the data, which is linked instead to the mean: the average squared deviation from the mean.

Consider the following collections of data.
I 18, 20, 21, 22, 24
II 15, 19, 21, 23, 27
III 3, 5, 6, 7, 9
IV 13, 20, 21, 22, 24

Squared deviation from the mean

The mean of collection I is 21, hence the deviations from the mean are:

–3, –1, 0, 1, 3

and the average (or mean) of these deviations is zero.

Squaring the deviations from the mean gives these squared deviations:

9, 1, 0, 1, 9

and the mean squared deviation is $\frac{20}{5}$ i.e. 4.

Verify for yourself that the **mean squared deviations** for the other three collections of data are:

II 16
III 4
IV 14

These results seem reasonably sound, since collections I and III produce the same value, which is less than the value for II. However, is it reasonable that the spread of collection II is four times that of collection I?

Some reflections on this situation may lead to the conclusion that this squared deviation is more a measure of the square of the spread. So, it may be appropriate to find the square root of this, to use as the measure of spread.

The square roots of the mean squared deviations are:

I 2
II 4
III 2
IV 3.742

These measures seem to reflect intuitive impressions of the dispersion of the data in each of the collections.

The term **standard deviation** is applied to this square root of the mean squared deviation about the mean.

Standard deviation = $s = \sqrt{\frac{1}{n}\sum\left(x - \bar{x}\right)^2}$

The **mean squared deviation** from the mean from which the standard deviation is obtained is known as the **variance.**

Variance $s^2 = \frac{1}{n}\sum\left(x - \bar{x}\right)^2$

Exploration 30.4

Mean, variance and standard deviation

Find the mean, the variance, and the standard deviation for each of the following collections of data.

- 4, 6, 8, 10, 12
- 2, 3, 3, 4, 4, 4, 5, 5, 6
- 12, 13, 13, 14, 14, 14, 15, 15, 16, 20

Alternative method of calculation

Consider the following data collection

3, 4, 6, 9, 8, 7, 2, 3, 7, 8, 8, 5, 6

The mean is $\frac{76}{13} = 5\frac{11}{13} = 5.846\,15...$ and variance is $4\frac{126}{169} = 4.745\,56...$.

Evaluating $\left(x - \bar{x}\right)$ for each item of data involves rather a lot of tedious arithmetic; squaring these deviations makes matters worse. There is a method which arrives at the same value for the variance but only involves the mean of the data once rather than n times.

This method involves finding the mean of the squares of the data and subtracting from this the square of the mean of the data.

In this case the mean of the squares = $\frac{\sum x^2}{n} = \frac{506}{13} = 38\frac{12}{13} = 38.923\,08...$

and the square of the mean = $(\bar{x})^2 = \left(\frac{76}{13}\right)^2 = 34\frac{30}{169} = 34.177\,51$

Hence, the variance $= \frac{\sum x^2}{n} - (\bar{x})^2 = 38.923\,076\,9 - 34.177\,514\,8 = 4.745\,562\,1$ which agrees with the previous value.

So it seems that it may be considerably easier to evaluate the variance of a collection of data using:

variance = mean of squares minus square of mean

Example 30.2

Calculate the standard deviation of the following collection of data.

4, 4, 5, 5, 5, 5, 6, 6, 6, 6, 6, 6, 6, 8, 9, 10, 11

Solution

The sum is 108 and the sum of the squares is 750. Hence, the variance is

mean of squares – square of means = $\frac{750}{17} - \left(\frac{108}{17}\right)^2 = 3.757\,87...$

The standard deviation is $\sqrt{3.7578} = 1.94$ *correct to two decimal places.*

Exploration 30.5

Calculating variance

Use the alternative method described above to calculate the variance for each of the following data collections.

- 2, 3, 4, 4, 5, 6, 8
- 0, 0, 0, 1, 1, 1, 2, 2, 3, 4, 6
- 13, 15, 18, 19, 19, 20, 20, 20, 20, 21, 21, 22, 24

Frequency distribution

In the same way that the mean can be evaluated from data presented as a frequency distribution, so can the variance. Consider the following data.

Length x (cm)	0.2	0.3	0.4	0.5	0.6	0.7
f	2	4	7	9	5	2

The mean of this distribution is found as $\frac{\sum xf}{\sum f}$.

The mean of the squares will similarly be found from $\frac{\sum x^2 f}{\sum f}$.

A convenient way of laying this out in a table is as follows.

x (cm)	0.2	0.3	0.4	0.5	0.6	0.7	Σ
f	2	4	7	9	5	2	29
xf	0.4	1.2	2.8	4.5	3.0	1.4	13.3
x^2f	0.08	0.36	1.12	2.25	1.8	0.98	6.59

The mean of the data is $\frac{13.3}{29}$ and the mean of the squares is $\frac{6.59}{29}$.
Hence the variance is

$$\frac{6.59}{29} - \left(\frac{13.3}{29}\right)^2 = 0.0169...$$

Now consider these data.

Mass m (g)	Frequency
0–	4
10–	9
20–	3
30–	3
40–60	1

A representative value is needed for each class, and this is the midpoint of the class. Hence the grouped frequency distribution is represented in this table.

Mass m (g)	5	15	25	35	50
f	5	9	3	3	1

Then the calculation can proceed as in the previous problem yielding:

$$\text{mean mass} = \frac{\sum xf}{\sum f} = \frac{390}{21}$$

$$\text{mean of squares} = \frac{\sum x^2 f}{\sum f} = \frac{10\,200}{21}$$

Hence, the variance is $\frac{10\,200}{21} - \left(\frac{390}{21}\right)^2 = 140.8163$ and the estimate of the standard deviation is $\sqrt{140.8163...} = 11.83$.

Exploration 30.6 *Coding*

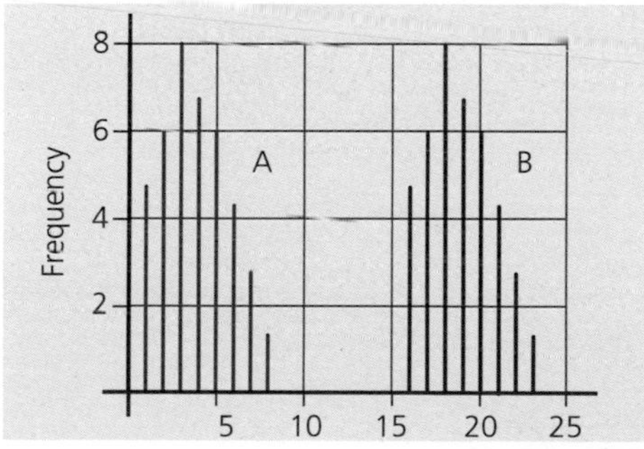

In Chapter 29, *Summary statistics 1*, we saw the effect that coding, by translating or by scaling, had on the mean of a data distribution. Consider the two distributions illustrated here.

Are there any differences between collections A and B?

They are in different places on the number line – hence their locations are different. But they are spread out in the same way, and so their dispersions (or standard deviations) should be the same.

Check that they are the same, given that their frequency distributions are as in the table.

A	1	2	3	4	5	6	7	8
B	16	17	18	19	20	21	22	23
Frequency	5	6	8	7	6	4	3	1

(For distribution A, s is 1.8735.)

Now consider the two distributions below.

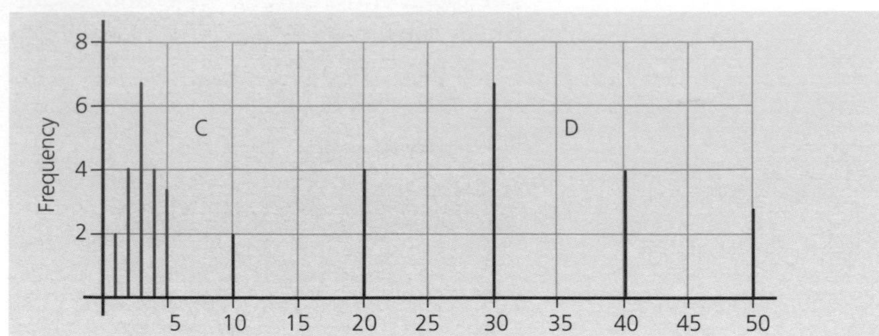

They are differently located, and differently dispersed. Collection C ranges from 1 to 5 and collection D ranges from 10 to 50 in a similar manner. Show that the standard deviation of D is ten times that of C where:

C	1	2	3	4	5
D	10	20	30	40	50
Frequency	2	4	7	4	3

In this exploration, you have seen that coding data using a translation has no effect on their spread i.e. does not change their variance or standard deviation. But, using scaling in coding alters the standard deviation by the same scale factor. What effect does it have on the variance?

A combination of translating and scaling:

$$y = \frac{(x \pm \alpha)}{\beta} = \frac{x}{\beta} \pm \delta$$

will result in the standard deviation of the y-data being the factor, $\frac{1}{\beta}$, times the standard deviation of the x-data.

Example 30.3

Use the coding:

$$y = \frac{x - 0.55}{0.1}$$

to facilitate the calculation of:

a) *the mean,*

b) *the variance,*

c) *the standard deviation,*

of the distribution of lengths of off-cuts of timber recorded in the table.

Length (x m)	**Frequency**
$0.2 \le x < 0.3$	6
$0.3 \le x < 0.4$	5
$0.4 \le x < 0.5$	8
$0.5 \le x < 0.6$	10
$0.6 \le x < 0.7$	8
$0.7 \le x < 0.8$	5
$0.8 \le x < 0.9$	8

Solution

Coded midpoint y	Frequency f	yf	y^2f
–3	6	–18	54
–2	5	–10	20
–1	8	–8	8
0	10	0	0
1	8	8	8
2	5	10	20
3	8	24	72
Σ	50	6	182

The distribution of the coded data is shown in the table above, along with the calculations needed to find the variance of y.

Variance of $y = s_y{}^2 = \frac{182}{50} - \left(\frac{6}{50}\right)^2 = 3.6256$

and hence the standard deviation of y *is 1.904 10.*

Since the translation has no effect on spread, the standard deviation of x *is*

$s_x = 0.1 \times s_y - 0.190$ correct to two decimal places

Thus the answers are:

a) *Mean of* x: $0.1 \times \quad + 0.55 = 0.562$

b) *Variance of* x: $(0.1)^2 \times 3.6256 = 0.036\,256 = 0.0363$

c) *Standard deviation of* x: $0.190\,41 = 0.19$

EXERCISES

30.2 CLASSWORK

1 Calculate the mean of the following collection of data. Hence, calculate the variance using:

a) the squared deviations from the mean,

b) the mean of the squares of the data.

1, 2, 2, 3, 3, 3, 3, 4, 4, 4, 5, 5, 6, 7, 8

2 Calculate the standard deviation of the following distribution of shoe sizes.

Size	4	5	6	7	8	9	10	11	12
f	5	8	12	10	10	15	10	8	2

a) Use the squared deviation about the mean.

b) Use the mean of the squares of the data.

KEY SKILLS
N 3.2c
N 3.2d

3 Use the coding: $y = \frac{x-5}{10}$

to estimate the mean, variance and standard deviation of the following distribution of weights.

Weights (g)	0–	10–	20–	30–	40–50
Representative value, x	5	15	25	35	45
Frequency	8	22	45	15	10

4 The speeds of cars travelling on a dual carriageway are recorded in the table.

Speed (mph)	20–30	–40	–50	–60	–70	70–100
Number of cars	2	12	18	32	28	28

Calculate an estimate of the standard deviation of the speeds.

EXERCISES

30.2 HOMEWORK

1 The following data collection gives the age last birthday of a group of ten sixth-formers.
17 17 16 19 16 18 17 18 18 17

Calculate the mean of the data. Hence calculate the variance using:
a) the squared deviations from the mean,
b) the mean of the squares of the data.
c) Comment on the accuracy of the mean.

2 Calculate the standard deviation of the following distribution using:

a) the squared deviations from the mean,
b) the mean of the squares of the data.

Number of pets owned	0	1	2	3	4	5 or more
Number of families	6	7	5	1	1	0

KEY SKILLS
N 3.2c
N 3.2d

3 Study these data.

Length x (cm)	0–	1–	2–	3–	4–	5–	6–7
Frequency	5	12	31	18	14	6	4

a) Use the coding $y = x - 2.5$ to calculate estimates of the mean, variance and standard deviation of y.
b) Hence, write down estimates of these measures for the length, x.

4 A record of the amount spent at the buffet car by passengers on a particular train journey is summarised below.

Amount spent x (£)	Number of passengers
0.50– 0.99	46
1.00–1.99	85
2.00–2.99	93
3.00–4.99	52
5.00–7.49	15
7.50–9.99	10

Calculate estimates of the mean and standard deviation of the amount spent per passenger.

Exploration 30.7

Combining collections of data

In Chapter 29, *Summary statistics 1*, we saw that it is possible to calculate the mean of a combined collection of data, if we know the individual means of the individual collections. Knowing the mean and variance of individual collections also enables us to calculate the variance of the combined collection.

Suppose a collection of six items of data has a mean of $\frac{22}{6}$ and a variance of $\frac{35}{9}$.

The total of their squares, Σx^2, can be obtained using the 'mean of squares etc.' definition of the variance.

Variance = $\dfrac{\sum x^2}{n} - \bar{x}^2$

therefore:

$$\frac{35}{9} = \frac{\sum x^2}{6} - \left(\frac{22}{6}\right)^2$$

and so,

$$\sum x^2 = 6\left(\frac{35}{9} + \frac{484}{36}\right)$$

This results in

$$\sum x^2 = 104$$

Suppose another collection of data, this time ten items, has a mean of 4 and variance of 1.4. What is the total, Σy^2, of the squares of this collection of data?

The same process as before yields.

$$\sum y^2 = 10(1.4 + 16) = 174$$

Imagine, now, that the two collections of data are combined to form one collection. What are the mean and variance of the combined collection?

In Chapter 29, *Summary statistics 1*, we discovered how to calculate the mean of the combined collection.

$$\text{Mean of combined} = \frac{\text{total value of data}}{\text{number of items of data}} = \frac{\sum x + \sum y}{6 + 10} = \frac{22 + 40}{16} = 3.875$$

Similarly, the variance can be found, using the mean of squares minus squares of mean approach.

$$\text{Variance of combined} = \frac{\text{total of squares}}{16} - 3.875^2$$

$$= \frac{\sum x^2 + \sum y^2}{16} - 3.875^2 = \frac{104 + 174}{16} - 3.875^2$$

$$= 2.359\,375 = 2.359 \text{ correct to three decimal places}$$

Example 30.4

Two collections of data are summarised in the table below.

Collection	Number of items	Mean	Variance
x	32	3	$2\frac{3}{16}$
y	28	6	$3\frac{1}{14}$

The data are combined into a single collection. Calculate:
a) *the mean,*
b) *the variance,*
c) *the standard deviation,*
of the collection.

Solution

a) *The total of the individual collections are:*

$\Sigma x = 32 \times 3 = 96$

$\Sigma y = 28 \times 6 = 168$

Hence, the mean of the combined data $= \dfrac{96+168}{32+28} = 4.4$

b) *The totals of the squares are:*

$\sum x^2 = 32(2.1875 + 3^2) = 358$

$\sum y^2 = 28(3\frac{1}{14} + 6^2) = 1094$

Then the variance of the combined collection $= \dfrac{358+1094}{60} - 4.4^2 = 4.84$

c) *The standard deviation is merely the square root of the variance i.e. 2.2.*

Outliers and standard deviation

Earlier in this chapter (see page 578), the concept of an outlier was introduced. The definition used there is **robust**; it is not affected by the presence or otherwise of outliers in the data collection.

Another definition is sometimes used: items of data which are **more than two standard deviations** away from the mean are described as outliers.

The mean and standard deviation for the motorway toll times are:

$\bar{x} = 40.0 \quad s = 27.5$ to one decimal place.

Using the two standard deviations definition for outliers leads to items of data greater than or less than 40.00 ± 2 × 27.5 being described as outliers. Hence, items of data which are:

less than –15
or more than 95

would be described as outliers.

Which motorway toll times (page 544) are outliers using the two standard deviations definition?

Exploration 30.8

Outliers

Suppose the longest recorded time in the motorway toll example (page 544) had been 5 minutes (i.e. 300 seconds) instead of 118 seconds.

What would the mean and standard deviation of the times be? Which times would now be described as outliers using the two standard deviation definition?

Which items does the definition based on quartiles identify as outliers in this case?

Discuss the validity of the two definitions. Use the $\bar{x} \pm 2s$ definition to identify outliers in the data collections of:

- Question 1 Exercise 30.1 Classwork
- Question 1 Exercise 30.1 Homework

Standardised values

There are occasions when we need to compare items from different data collections. A student studying Engineering gained a mark of 52 in her Soil Mechanics examination and a mark of 57 in the examination on Mathematical Modelling. Superficially, it appears that she did better in Modelling than in Mechanics. However, if the mean marks in the two examinations were:

Examination	Mean mark
Soil Mechanics	44
Modelling	60

then, her score of 52 which is above the exam average is relatively better than the mark of 57 which is below the exam average.

Suppose this student also sat examinations in Structures and in Dynamics with the following results.

Examination	Mark	Mean mark
Structures	58	50
Dynamics	63	57

It is now more difficult to determine in which exam she performed better, since her mark in each is higher than the mean. It could be argued that she did better in Structures, where her mark is 8 above the mean, than in Dynamics, where she was only 6 marks above the mean. However, suppose that the spread of marks in the two examinations is as follows.

Examination	Standard deviation
Structures	6.8
Dynamics	2.6

Now her mark in Dynamics can be seen to be particularly noteworthy, since it is more than two standard deviations above the mean, whereas the mark in Structures is not.

Relating items of data to the mean and expressing the difference from the mean in terms of the standard deviation of the data is a convenient way of **standardising data**. In the case of this Engineering student, her standardised examination scores are obtained.

Examination	Mark	Mean	Standard deviation	Standardised mark
Structures	58	50	6.8	$\frac{58-50}{6.8} = 1.23$
Dynamics	63	57	2.6	$\frac{63-57}{2.6} = 2.31$
Soil Mechanics	52	44	3.1	
Modelling	57	60	5.0	

What are her standardised scores in the other two examinations? In which exam did she do best?

Re-expression

Standardised scores such as 1.23, 2.31, etc. from the above do not seem like marks. For the sake of convenience, these may be re-expressed to give the appearance of marks, whilst retaining the comparability that standardisation offers.

Suppose all the examination marks are to be presented as if each examination produced marks with a mean of 55 and a standard deviation of 15. Then the standardised score is multiplied by the new standard deviation (15) and to this is added the assumed mean (55). The student's score in Structures would be presented as:

$$1.23 \times 15 + 55 = 73.45$$

Show that the re-expressed scores in the other exams are: 89.65, 93.71, 46.

Exploration 30.9

Re-expression

In one school, Russian is offered as an option to Year 12 students. The marks that the students studying Russian obtained were:

28, 33, 43, 46, 54, 57, 64, 70, 83, 95

- Calculate the mean and standard deviation of these marks.
- Find the standardised score for each of the marks, giving it correct to two decimal places.
- Re-express the scores to have a mean 50 and standard deviation 12.
- The student who obtained 46 in the Russian examination also studies Latin. He scored 57 in his Latin examination where the mean mark was 66 and the standard deviation 10.3. In which exam did he do better?

CONSOLIDATION EXERCISES FOR CHAPTER 30

KEY SKILLS
N 3.2b
N 3.2c
N 3.2d
N 3.3

1 a) Explain how the median and quartiles of a distribution can be used when describing the shape of the distribution.
Summarised below is the distribution of masses of new potatoes, in grams to the nearest gram.

Mass (g)	Frequency
19 or less	2
20 – 29	14
30 – 39	21
40 – 49	34
50 – 59	39
60 – 69	42
70 – 79	13
80 – 89	4
90 or more	2

b) Use linear interpolation to estimate the median and quartiles of this distribution. Hence describe its skewness.

c) Draw a box-and-whisker plot to illustrate these data.

(ULEAC, Question 7, Specimen paper T1, 1994)

2 Tubs of margarine are claimed on the label to contain 250 grams. The actual weights of margarine in a random sample of 15 tubs were as follows. The weights are given correct to the nearest gram.

261	252	242	240	254
257	252	250	265	249
253	248	259	246	252

a) Construct a stem-and-leaf diagram to represent these data, using a two-part stem.

b) Comment on the shape of the distribution of weights, with particular reference to the claim that tubs contain 250 grams.

c) Use your calculator to find the mean and standard deviation of the weights of margarine in this sample.

d) Explain briefly how one would ensure that a greater proportion of tubs contained 250 grams or more or margarine by adjusting:

i) the mean, **ii)** the standard deviation.

(MEI, Question 1, Paper S1, June 1992 (modified))

3 A small business has 12 employees. Their weekly wages, £x, are summarised by: $\sum x = 2501$ $\sum x^2 = 525\,266.8$

a) Calculate the mean and standard deviation of the employees' weekly wages.

A second business has 17 employees. Their weekly wage, £y, has a mean of £273.20 and a standard deviation of £23.16.

b) Find $\sum y$ and show that $\sum y^2 = 1\,277\,969$.

c) Now consider all 29 employees as a single group. Find the mean and standard deviation of their weekly wages.

(MEI, Question 1, Paper S1, January 1993)

4 A frequency diagram for a set of data is shown here.

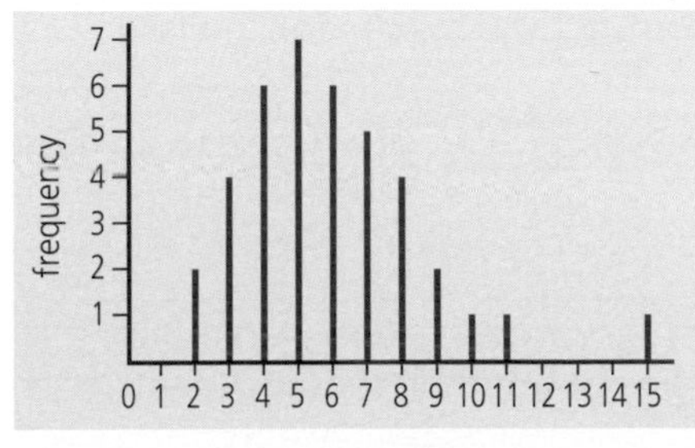

a) Find the median and the mode of the data.

b) Given that the mean is 5.95 and the standard deviation is 2.58, explain why the value 15 may be regarded as an outlier.

c) Explain how you would treat the outlier if the diagram represents:

i) the ages (in completed years) of children at a party,

ii) the sums of the scores obtained when throwing a pair of dice.

d) Find the median and the mode of the data after the outlier is removed.
e) Without doing any calculations state what effect, if any, removing the outlier would have on the mean and on the standard deviation.
f) Does the diagram exhibit positive skewness, negative skewness or no skewness? How is the skewness affected by removing the outlier?

(MEI, Question 1, Paper S1, June 1993)

5 The table gives an analysis of a random sample of 200 sales of unleaded petrol at a petrol station.

Volume of petrol (litres)	Number of sales
5 or less	6
10 or less	20
15 or less	85
20 or less	148
25 or less	172
30 or less	184
35 or less	194
40 or less	200

a) Use linear interpolation to estimate:
i) the median volume of unleaded petrol sales,
ii) the upper and lower quartiles.
Hence write down the interquartile range.
b) Construct, on graph paper, a box-plot of the distribution of sales of unleaded petrol.

(Oxford, Question 8, Specimen paper 3, 1996)

6 An angler made a record of the weights (in lb) of the 200 fish he caught during one year. These are summarised in the table.

Weight of fish (mid-class value) (lb)	0.5	1.25	1.75	2.25	2.75	3.5	4.5	5.5	7.0	10.5
Number of fish in the class	21	32	33	24	18	21	16	12	11	12
Class width	1	0.5	0.5	0.5	0.5	1	1	1	2	5

Using the information supplied in the table:
a) calculate suitable frequency densities and, on graph paper, construct a histogram of the data,
b) calculate estimates of the mean and standard deviation of the weights of the fish.

How are the estimates of the mean and standard deviation likely to differ from the true values? Give brief reasons for your answers.

(Oxford, Question 6, Specimen paper 3, 1996)

7 The children in classes A and B were each given a set of arithmetic problems to solve. Their times, to the nearest minute, were recorded and they are summarised in the table below.

	Class A	Class B
Smallest value	5	10
Largest value	27	26
Q1	9	13
Q2	15	15
Q3	18	22

a) On graph paper and using the same scale for both, draw box plots to represent these data.
b) Compare and contrast the results for the two classes.

(EDEXCEL Paper T1, Question 3, Jan 1997)

8 Students are entered for an accountancy examination. A random sample is to be taken from the marks obtained by these students.

Mark	(5 | 3 means 53)	Totals
5	0 1 3 3 4 4	(6)
5	5 6 7 9	(4)
6	1 1 3 3 4 4 4	(7)
6	5 7 8 8 9	(5)
7	3 3 4 4 4 4	(6)
7	5 5 6 6 7 7 7 7 8 8 8 9 9	(13)
8	0 0 1 1	(4)

The mark x obtained by each of 45 students randomly selected from those students who sat the accountancy examination was recorded. The stem and leaf diagram below summarises the marks.

a) Using graph paper and showing your scale clearly, construct a box plot to represent this data.

b) Comment on the skewness of this distribution.

For the above sample, $\Sigma x = 3085$ and $\Sigma x^2 = 215\,569$.

c) Find the mean and the standard deviation of this sample of marks.

The mean and the standard deviation of the marks of all the students who sat the examination were 65 and 16.5 respectively. The examiners decided that the mark of each student should be scaled by having 10 marks subtracted and then reduced by a further 10%.

d) Find the mean and the standard deviation of the scaled marks.

(EDEXCEL Paper T1, Question 8, January 2000)

9 Whig and Penn, solicitors, monitored the time spent on consultations with a random sample of 120 of their clients. The times, to the nearest minute, are summarised in the following table.

Time	Number of clients
10 – 14	2
15 – 19	5
20 – 24	17
25 – 29	33
30 – 34	27
35 – 44	25
45 – 59	7
60 – 89	3
90 – 119	1
Total	120

a) By calculation, obtain estimates of the median and quartiles of this distribution.

b) Comment on the skewness of the distribution.

c) Explain briefly why these data are consistent with the distribution of times you might expect in this situation.

(EDEXCEL Paper T1, Question 9, January 1999)

Summary

- **Range:** the difference between the largest and smallest values in a collection of data
- **Quartile spread:** the 'middle half' of the data between the lower and upper quartiles
- **Variance:** $s^2 = \frac{1}{n}\sum\left(x-\bar{x}\right)^2 = \frac{1}{n}\sum x - \bar{x}^2$

  $s^2 = \dfrac{\sum x^2 f}{\sum f} - \left(\dfrac{\sum xf}{\sum f}\right)^2$ for grouped data.
- **Standard deviation:** $s = \sqrt{\text{variance}}$

  variance = mean of squares – square of the mean
- The measure of location and spread can be displayed in a box-and-whisker diagram of the data.

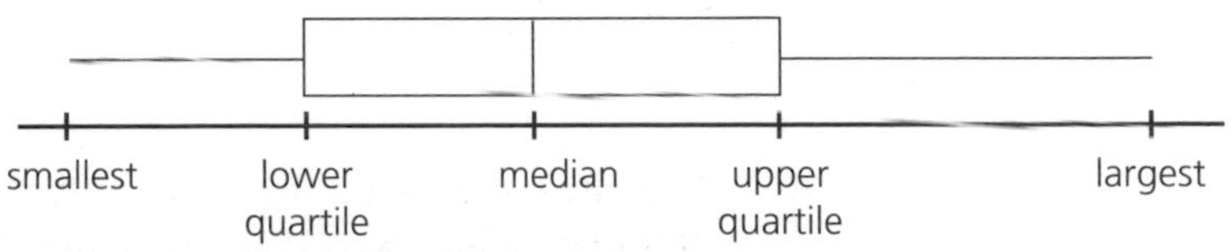

Probability

In this chapter we look at the mathematical structure of likelihood, chance and probability, processes which underpin all data analysis. After working through it you should be able to:

- *set up models to study data*
- *draw inferences from data*
- *make sensible judgements based on your conclusions*
- *use the techniques to generate conclusions and predictions, drawn from various data sources.*

THE LANGUAGE OF CHANCE

In everyday speech we use the words 'possible' and 'probable' to indicate degrees of likelihood. A typical weather forecast may sound like this: '*... there is a possibility of showers in the east, but, in the west, rain is probable before dawn.*' What do you think the forecaster means?

In the language of mathematics and statistics, both 'rain in the west' and 'showers in the east' are **possibilities**, or **events**, or **situations that could occur**. The forecaster was trying to indicate that there was a chance that either would happen but, that in her opinion, there was a greater likelihood of 'rain in the west'.

The forecaster had in mind a 'likelihood scale' such as:

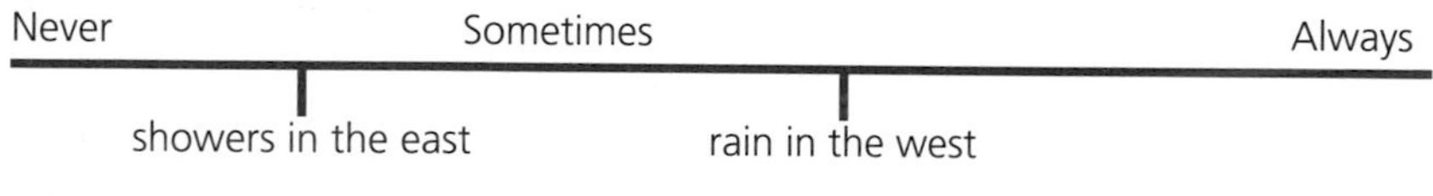

where she had mentally located the two events mentioned in the forecast.

The probability scale

Where do you think the following events should be placed on the scale?

A The United Kingdom will win more gold medals than any other country at the next Olympics.
B The next baby born in Scotland will be a girl.
C It will rain tomorrow.
D The 4:15 train will leave on time.
E There will be change of government at the next general election.
F A coin will land 'heads'.

One possible result would be:

Never	Unlikely	Sometimes Evens	Highly likely	Always
↑	↑	↑	↑	↑
A	*C*	*B, F*	*E*	*D*

where the 'sometimes' has been expanded. Events such as the landing of a coin where arguably there are two equally plausible and equally likely outcomes may have the label 'evens', or 'fifty-fifty', or '50%' attached. In this context, 50 per cent indicates the **proportion** of occasions that coins land heads.

What proportions do you think could be attached to events A, B, C, D and E?

Probable results

There seems to be little likelihood of event A occurring, and so five per cent or less would be reasonable. It could be argued that a girl is just as likely as a boy and so 50 per cent would be appropriate for event B. As far as event C is concerned, there are many factors which could have an influence on this. However if the diagram above is a guide, then 30 per cent to 40 per cent is plausible. Those who run the railways may argue that 85 per cent of trains leave on time. General elections do not happen very often and arguments over politics consume much of the intervening time. The diagram indicates that a response of about 75 per cent is anticipated.

Proportions, or percentages, such as 50%, 75%, 30% could be written as $\frac{1}{2}$, $\frac{3}{4}$, 0.3 or in any appropriate form. These numbers are the **probabilities** associated with the various events.

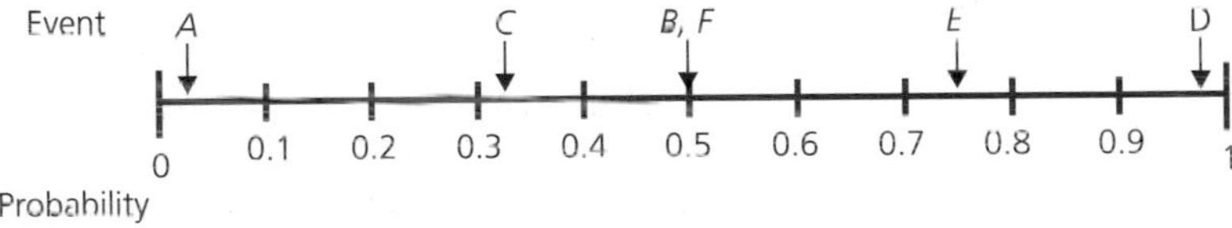

Probability is a number, lying between zero and one, which measures the likelihood of occurrence of the event to which it refers.

Notation

A common notation for the probability of an event is P(event).

Thus, for the events described: $P(B) = \frac{1}{2}$
Write down the probability of the events A, C, D, E and F using this notation.

Exploration 31.1

Events and liklihoods

Define ten events and discuss the likelihood of each happening. Display the events on a likelihood scale and assign probabilities to each one.

Symmetry and equal likelihood

The probability that a coin lands 'heads' is $\frac{1}{2}$. Why? Two assumptions have been made:

- there are only two possible ways in which a coin can land,
- these ways are equally likely.

An ordinary cubical die has six faces which show the numbers 1, 2, 3, 4, 5 and 6, respectively. What is the probability that the die will land, having been rolled, so that the face with 5 on it is uppermost?

If we assume that the die is a cube and is perfectly symmetrical, then the likelihood of any face landing uppermost is the same. There is only one way for a 5 to appear uppermost, but there are six *possible* outcomes. Thus the probability of a 5 appearing is $\frac{1}{6}$.

Consider a ten-faced die where each face is equally likely to appear uppermost. The die has the numbers 0, 1, 2, .., 8, 9 on its faces. What is the probability of a multiple of 3 appearing?

There are ten possibilities. Of these, the multiples of three are 3, 6, 9. Thus the probability is $\frac{3}{10}$. This leads to the definition:

$$\text{probability of an outcome} = \frac{\text{number of events in the outcome}}{\text{total number of possible events}}$$

where it is assumed that the events are equally likely, and that the outcome consists of a number of equally likely events. The previous example had 'die resulting in a multiple of three' as the outcome. The equally likely events which contributed to this outcome are the 3, 6 or 9. There were ten possible events. Hence, the probability must be $\frac{3}{10}$.

The term 'outcome space' is sometimes used in place of outcome, and 'possibility space' or 'sample space' may be used instead of 'all possibilities'. So, you may come across the following definition.

$$\text{P(outcome)} = \frac{\text{number of events in the outcome space}}{\text{number of events in the possibility space}}$$

Exploration 31.2

Determining probability

Determine the probability of each of the following outcomes.

- a prime number on a cubical die
- a prime number on a ten-faced die
- at least one head when two coins are flipped
- an ordinary pack of cards being cut at a heart

In each case make sure you identify the equally likely events in the sample space and the ones in the outcome space.

Relative frequency and empirical probability

Is it always raining where you live? It almost certainly isn't, but what is the chance that it will rain tomorrow? One possible way of finding out is to consult meteorological records and use relative frequencies. Suppose the records show that, over a period of seven days, there were three rainy days. In these circumstances a reasonable estimate for the chance of a rainy day is $\frac{3}{7}$. The table represents an extract from the records.

Week	Number of rainy days
1	3
2	1
3	3
4	0
5	1
.	.
.	.
.	.

During the second week recorded there was only one rainy day. The relative frequency, or proportion, of wet days during that particular week was $\frac{1}{7}$. However, over the first two weeks, the proportion of wet days was $\frac{4}{14}$. Which of these two proportions do you think is the better to use as an estimate for the probability of a rainy day?

Perhaps you preferred the individual weekly relative frequencies. For the five weeks shown, these are:

$\frac{3}{7}, \frac{1}{7}, \frac{3}{7}, \frac{0}{7}, \frac{1}{7}$

Written as decimals, to two places, they are:

0.43, 0.14, 0.43, 0.00, 0.14

There is a good deal of variation in these, which is not surprising. However, it is difficult to decide which, if any, of these should be used to tackle the question about rain tomorrow.

The cumulative relative frequencies for this period are:

$\frac{3}{7}, \frac{4}{14}, \frac{7}{21}, \frac{7}{28}, \frac{8}{35}$ or, as decimals:

0.43, 0.29, 0.33, 0.25, 0.23.

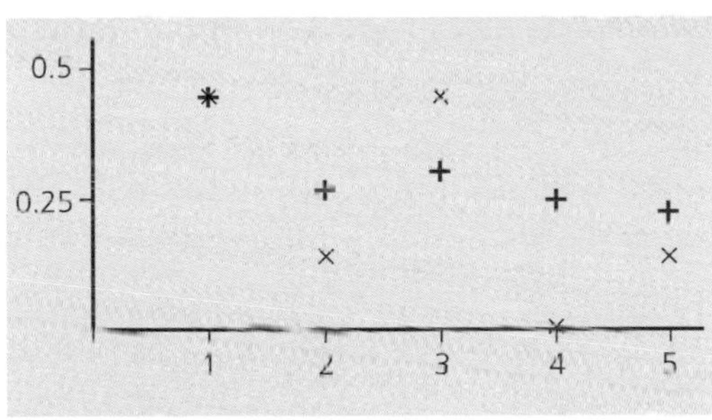

These cumulative relative frequencies still vary, although much less than the individual weekly proportions. Accumulating the information in this way using **cumulative relative frequencies** provides an estimate of the longterm **experimental** or **empirical probability**.

We can present this analysis graphically, as in this diagram, where × and + represent individual and cumulative frequencies respectively.

Exploration 31.3 *Deciding whether the weather will be wet*

■ An extract from the meteorological records over a period of six months for a different region yields the following data.

Week	1	2	3	4	5	6	7	8	9	10	11	12	13	14	15	16	17	18	19	20	21	22	23	24	25	26
Number of wet days	3	0	1	0	4	1	5	6	2	5	2	1	1	0	1	2	1	3	0	1	0	1	0	5	3	7

Calculate:

a) individual weekly relative frequencies,

b) successive cumulative relative frequencies,

for the proportion of wet days, and plot a graph of the results. Discuss the outcome of your work.

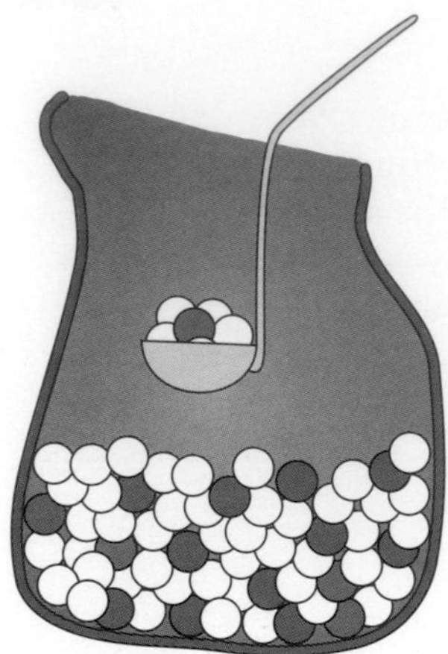

KEY SKILLS
N 3.1
N 3.2b
N 3.2c
N 3.2d
N 3.3
IT 3.2

- Conduct an experiment to see how appropriate longterm relative frequency is to measure a known proportion. You need a large collection (say 50, 100, 200) of identically-shaped objects (tiddly winks, beads or marbles). A known proportion ($\frac{1}{5}$, $\frac{1}{4}$, $\frac{1}{3}$) of the objects need to be distinguishable from the others in appearance (for example a different colour, say red).
  Place the beads in a container (bag, box).
  - Randomly distribute them within the container (shake the bag). Obtain, randomly, a sample of beads (a spoon is a useful device, or the lid of a small box). Record the number of beads in the sample and the number of red beads included in it. Return the sample to the bag. Now repeat the process.
  - When you have conducted enough repeats, you are in a position to examine the effectiveness of cumulative relative frequency as a measure of proportion (or probability). Calculate individual sample relative frequencies and the cumulative relative frequencies. Plot a graph of the results. Interpret the results of your experiment and compare with the known proportion red beads.
  - The diagram below shows the results of an experiment recorded using a spreadsheet. What proportion of the beads are red?

Sample	No. of Red	No. in Spoon	Cumul. Reds	Cumul. total	Relative Freq.	Cumul. RF	Sample	No. of Red	No. in Spoon	Cumul. Reds	Cumul. total	Relative Freq.	Cumul. RF
1	2	7	2	7	2/7	2/7	11	2	9	30	130	2/9	0.231
2	0	8	2	15	0	2/15	12	5	15	35	145	1/3	0.241
3	3	16	5	31	3/16	5/31	13	5	17	40	162	5/17	0.247
4	3	11	8	42	3/11	0.190	14	2	13	42	175	2/13	0.240
5	4	13	12	55	4/13	0.218	15	1	12	43	187	1/12	0.230
6	4	13	16	68	4/13	0.235	16	6	15	49	202	2/5	0.243
7	2	13	18	81	2/13	0.222	17	3	12	52	214	1/4	0.243
8	0	10	18	91	0	0.198	18	3	15	55	229	1/5	0.240
9	5	15	23	106	1/3	0.217	19	3	13	58	242	3/13	0.240
10	5	15	28	121	1/3	0.213	20	2	12	60	254	1/6	0.236

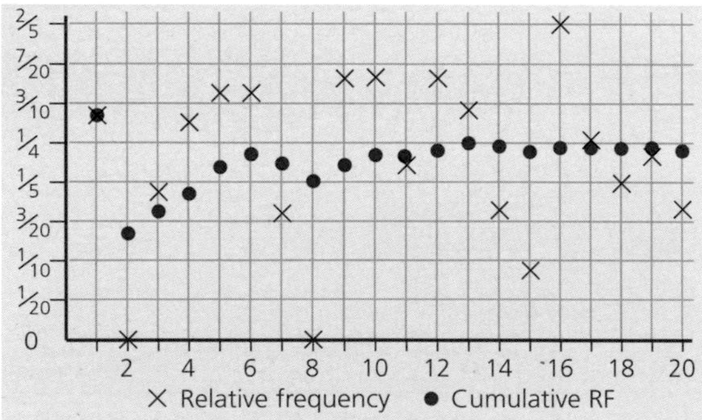

Some classical results

There are several important results concerning probability which always hold true. We have already encountered the first of them: the probability of an event is never more than 1, nor is it less than zero.

Complementary events

The second result is very simple but extremely valuable, as we shall see as the chapter progresses: the probability of an event and its complement add up to 1.

In the previous section we considered rainy days. The complement of a rainy day is a dry day, or alternatively, a day that is not rainy. What this result indicates is that, if the probability of a rainy day is $\frac{3}{7}$, then, the probability of a dry day is $1-\frac{3}{7}$ or $\frac{4}{7}$.

Notation

If E represents an event, then a common notation for the complement of E is $\bar{E}$. Sometimes the alternative notation of E' is used. In this textbook, the former notation will be used. Hence:

$$P(E) + P(\bar{E}) = 1 \quad \text{or:} \quad P(E) = 1 - P(\bar{E})$$

The third and fourth results concern combinations of events. Consider the following weather records for twelve randomly chosen days.

Day	Weather		
a	dry	hot	still
b	wet	hot	windy
c	wet	cold	still
d	wet	hot	still
e	dry	cold	still
f	dry	hot	windy
g	wet	hot	windy
h	dry	hot	still
i	wet	cold	windy
j	wet	cold	still
k	dry	hot	windy
l	dry	hot	still

What is the probability that one of the randomly chosen days was hot?

Altogether, there are twelve days, and eight of these are described as hot, hence:

$$P(\text{hot}) = \frac{8}{12}$$

What is the probability that one of the days is both hot and wet?

There are three days that are both hot and wet.

$$P(\text{hot} \cap \text{wet}) = \frac{3}{12}$$

Now let's focus our attention solely on those days described as hot. These are the days **a**, **b**, **d**, **f**, **g**, **h**, **k** and **l**. What is the probability that the weather is wet given that it was hot?

There are eight hot days; of these, three are described as wet. Hence: P(wet given that the day was hot) = $\frac{3}{8}$

This is known as the **conditional probability** of a day being wet knowing that it is hot.

Notation

A common notation for this is:

$$P(\text{wet} \mid \text{hot}) = \frac{3}{8}$$

The vertical line indicates that the event of interest is a day being wet given that it is hot. What is P(hot | wet)?

To find out, we need to focus only on those days that were wet. There are six wet days. Of these, three are hot (we know this already – how?). Hence, the probability of a hot day given that it is wet is $\frac{3}{6}$. This is not the same as P(wet | hot).

Note that: P(wet∩hot) = P(hot) × P(wet | hot) = P(wet) × P(hot | wet)

Exploration 31.4

Examining conditional probability

- Return to the twelve randomly chosen days, above. Define your own two events, say events *A*, *B*.
  - **a)** Explore the relationship between the three probabilities: P(*A*∩*B*), P(*B*), P(*A* | *B*)
  - **b)** Explore the relationship between: P(*A*∩*B*), P(*A*), P(*B* | *A*)
- Now repeat the first part for another pair of events.

The multiplication law

The third result which concerns conditional probabilities is:

$$P(A \cap B) = P(A) \times P(B \mid A)$$

or:

$$P(A \cap B) = P(B) \times P(A \mid B)$$

This result is always true, for any events *A*, *B*. The special case is where the conditional probability of event *A* occurring is the same as the unconditional probability. In other words, when:

$$P(A \mid B) = P(A)$$

Under these circumstances A and B are said to be **independent events**. A direct consequence of this is:

$$P(A \cap B) = P(A) \times P(B)$$

when *A* and *B* are independent. This result, known as the **multiplication law** for independent events, is very important. It can be extended for any number of events which are independent.

$$P(A \cap B \cap C) = P(A) \times P(B) \times P(C) \text{ etc.}$$

Exploration 31.5

New York

Cape Town

Independent events

- Define an event. Now define another event which you feel is independent of your first event. (For example: if the first event is 'It will rain in Cape town, South Africa, tomorrow', the second event could be 'It will be windy in New York, USA, tomorrow'.)
- Define five other pairs of independent events.

Inclusive events

Returning to the weather data on page 599, what is the probability that a day is *either* wet *or* hot? There are eleven of these days (every day apart from day **e)**), so the probability is $\frac{11}{12}$.

The common notation for this event is: P(wet$\cup$hot) = $\frac{11}{12}$

Note that in saying 'wet or hot', we include all those events where the day was both wet *and* hot. Previously, we found that:

P(wet) = $\frac{6}{12}$ P(hot) = $\frac{8}{12}$ P(wet$\cap$hot) = $\frac{3}{12}$

Can we find a relationship between the probabilities of the four events:

wet hot wet *and* hot wet *or* hot?

We find that: P(wet$\cup$hot) + P(wet$\cap$hot) = P(wet) + P(hot)

Exploration 31.6

Inclusive events

- Return to the twelve days and define your own two inclusive events, say A and B. Explore the relationship between the probabilities of the events:
  A, B, $A \cup B$, $A \cap B$
- Repeat this for another pair of events.

The addition law

The fourth result concerning the probability of inclusive events is:

$P(A \cap B) + P(A \cup B) = P(A) + P(B)$

This result is always true regardless of the definition of events A and B.

The special case applies when the events in question do not occur together. Under these circumstances the events are called **mutually exclusive**. Since mutually exclusive events do not occur together:

$P(A \cap B) = 0$

which, in turn, implies that:

$P(A \cup B) = P(A) + P(B)$

This is a result know as the **addition law** for exclusive events.

Example 31.1

Three ordinary coins are flipped. What is the probability that at least one head appears?

Probability of outcome = $\dfrac{\textit{number of events in outcome space}}{\textit{number of events in sample space}}$

Solution

One approach to solving this is to identify all the ways where at least one head occurs. These are:

{HTT, THT, TTH, HHT, HTH, THH, HHH}

This set of outcomes is the outcome space. We now need to identify the sample space i.e. all possible ways that three coins could fall, which is:

{TTT, HTT, THT, TTH, HHT, HTH, THH, HHH}

We are now in a position to use the definition:

P(outcome) = $\dfrac{\text{number of events in the outcome space}}{\text{number of events in the possibility space}}$

Thus, P(at least one head) = $\frac{7}{8}$

Alternative solution

It is equally valid and, perhaps, quicker to use some of the probability results. The question concerns the outcome 'at least one head'. It is often worth considering the complementary outcome; the complement to 'at least one' is 'less than one'. In this case, 'less than one head' is 'no head'. Then: P(at least one head) + P(no head) = 1
Hence, the very useful result: P(at least one head) = 1 – P(no head)
The outcome corresponding to 'no head' is quite simply 'three tails'. The probability of three coins landing tails can be found using the result for independent events: $P(A \cap B \cap C) = P(A) \times P(B) \times P(C)$
In this case, we require:
P(tail and tail and tail) = P(tail) × P(tail) × P(tail) = $\frac{1}{2} \times \frac{1}{2} \times \frac{1}{2} = \frac{1}{8}$
hence: P(at least one head) = 1 – P(no head) = 1 – $(\frac{1}{8}) = \frac{7}{8}$

Example 31.2

A cubical die with faces numbered 1, 2, ... 6, is rolled. Two coins are independently flipped. What is the probability that the coins land showing at least one head or the die shows a multiple of three?

Solution

This is a question about inclusive combined events. Its solution could be obtained by using: $P(A \text{ or } B) + P(A \text{ and } B) = P(A) + P(B)$
In this case, event A might be 'a multiple of three' and event B might be 'at least one head'. For the die, two of the six equally likely outcomes are multiples of three, hence: $P(A) = P(\text{multiple of three}) = \frac{2}{6}$
For the two coins:
$P(B) = P(\text{at least one head}) = 1 - P(\text{no head}) = 1 - (\frac{1}{2})^2 = \frac{3}{4}$
It is reasonable to assume that the outcomes of rolling the die and flipping the coins are independent, hence:
$P(A \text{ and } B) = P(A) \times P(B) = \frac{2}{6} \times \frac{3}{4} = \frac{1}{4}$
We are now in a position to answer the question.
$P(A \text{ or } B) = P(A) + P(B) - P(A \text{ and } B) = \frac{1}{3} + \frac{3}{4} - \frac{1}{4} = \frac{5}{6}$

Alternative solution

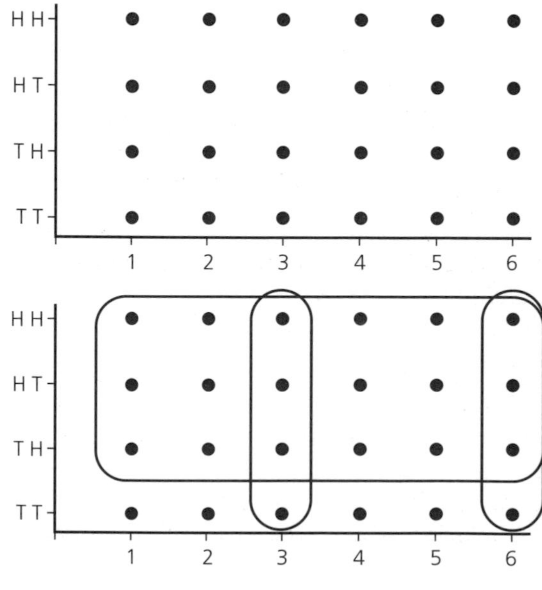

Again there is another way to approach the problem. The method of identifying equally likely elements in sample and outcome spaces can be used. Whilst it might be considered to be rather lengthy, the approach outlined here introduces a graphical way of identifying sample spaces.

The method requires us to identify the sample spaces for the die and the coins separately. These are:
Die: {1, 2, 3, 4, 5, 6}
Coins: {HH, HT, TH, TT}
Now we display the possible contributions as points on a grid.

Each of the 24 points represents an equally likely event in the sample space. The elements of the outcome space can be identified and counted.

There are 20. Hence:
$P(\text{at least one head or a multiple of three}) = \frac{20}{24} = \frac{5}{6}$

Example 31.3

A market gardener grows some vegetables organically and others conventionally, using fertilisers. She uses fertilisers for $\frac{4}{5}$ of her produce. Carrots make up 15 per cent of her conventional produce and 30 per cent of her organic produce.

a) *What proportion of the gardener's produce are carrots?*
b) *A thief breaks into the market garden and is caught stealing carrots. What is the probability that they were organically grown?*

Solution

There is quite a lot of information to take in. It may help to display this information diagrammatically, in a ***tree diagram****. The first bit of information is about organic or conventional methods of growing. The second, about vegetable type, is dependent on the growing method.*

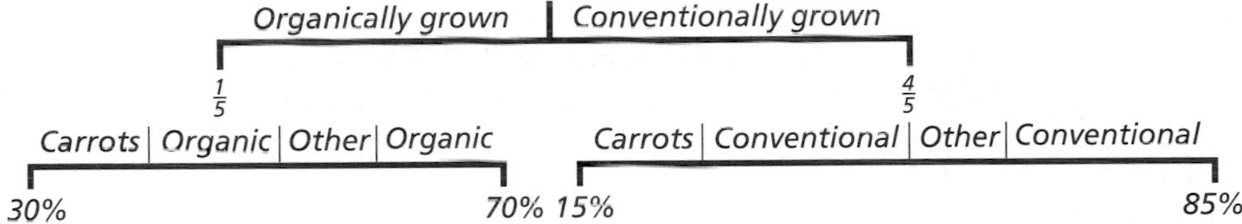

Notice the conditional events.

a) *30 per cent of organically grown vegetables are carrots and $\frac{1}{5}$ of the vegetables are grown organically. Hence:*
P(organically grown and a carrot) = $\frac{1}{5} \times 30\% = 6\%$

Similarly: P(conventionally grown and a carrot) = $\frac{4}{5} \times 15\% = 12\%$
Hence:
P(carrot) = P(C and organic) + P(C and conventional) = $6\% + 12\% = 18\%$

b) *The question seeks the probability :* P(organic | carrot).
Since we know that: P(carrot and organic) = P(C) × P(organic | C)
This can be rearranged to yield:
P(organic | C) = P(C and organic) ÷ P(C) = $6\% \div 18\% = \frac{1}{3}$

EXERCISES

31.1 CLASSWORK

1 From an ordinary pack of 52 cards, one card is selected.
a) What is the probability that the card is:
i) a club, **ii)** the king of clubs, **iii)** a black king?
b) Consider the outcomes of selecting a club, a king, a red king. Which of the three possible pairs of outcomes are:
i) independent, **ii)** mutually exclusive, **iii)** neither?

2 A jar contains twelve red gobstoppers and eight white gobstoppers. Two gobstoppers are taken out randomly (without replacement). Using a tree diagram, find the probability that:
a) both are red, **b)** they are of different colours.

3 Box X contains two white discs, box Y contains one white and one black disc. Two coins are flipped, if the outcome is two tails then a disc is selected at random from box X. Otherwise, a disc is randomly selected from box Y.
a) What is the probability that a white disc is selected?
b) Given that a white disc is selected what is the probability it came from box Y?

EXERCISES

31.1 HOMEWORK

1 Two octahedral dice with faces numbered 1, 2, 3, 4, 5, 6, 7, 8 are rolled. What is the probability of at least one 6 appearing? What is the probability that the outcome on one die is at least 6 and the outcome on the other is less than 6?

2 **a)** For two events A, B, explain why $P(A) = P(A \text{ and } B) + P(A \text{ and } \bar{B})$
b) John swims about once a week. Gill swims on three-quarters of the days that John does, but only a third of the days that John does not. What is the probability that Gill has a swim?

3 Two cards are selected randomly and without replacement from an ordinary pack of 52 cards. The ace in each suit is assumed to be numbered 1. The court cards (jacks, queens, kings) are assumed to have the values 11, 12, 13 respectively.
a) A is the outcome that the first card is prime, B is the outcome that the second card is even. Calculate:
i) $P(A)$ **ii)** $P(B)$
iii) $P(A|B)$ **iv)** $P(B|A)$.
b) X is the outcome that the first card is less than 11, Y is the outcome that the second card is 10 or more. Calculate:
i) $P(X)$ **ii)** $P(Y)$
iii) $P(X|Y)$ **iv)** $P(Y|X)$.

4 A box contains three red and three blue cubes. Another box contains four red and three blue cubes. A cube is removed randomly from the first box and placed in the second box. A cube is now randomly selected from the second box. Use a tree diagram to calculate the probability that:
a) the cube finally selected is red,
b) if the selected cube is red then the cube removed from the first box was also red.

SOME WAYS OF COUNTING ELEMENTS IN A SAMPLE SPACE

Factorial notation

Have you ever overheard this sort of thing?

'It's been a dreadful week. On Monday it was foggy all day, Tuesday it blew a gale, and Wednesday it didn't stop raining ... '

Sometimes weather conditions like these do occur, even if not always in that particular order. A summary of the order of events might be:

	Monday	Tuesday	Wednesday
	fog	gale	rain
or, more briefly:	F	G	R

Suppose that these events *did* occur on three consecutive days, in what other sequences might they occur? There are six distinct sequences. FGR FRG GFR GRF RFG RGF

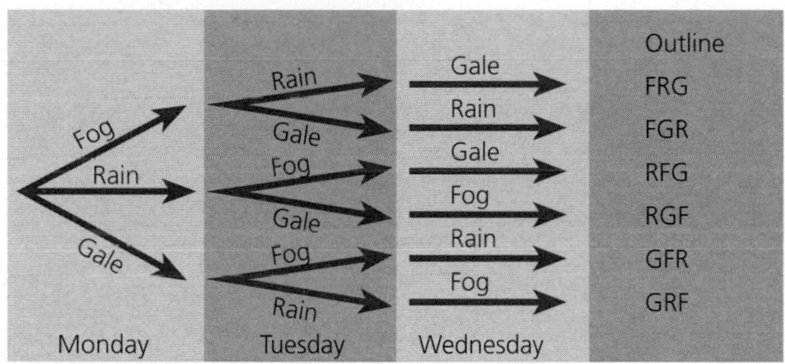

This approach is not necessary if all we want to do is to determine the number of different arrangements. Notice that for Monday, there are three possible outcomes (F, G, R). Then, there are only two possible outcomes for Tuesday. This leaves one for Wednesday. Hence the total number of possible arrangements of F, G, R is: $3 \times 2 \times 1 = 6$.

Suppose it is known that on four consecutive days the weather was fog, rain, gale, and cold. How many different arrangements of these events are possible?

There are 24, since there is a choice of four weather types for the first day, then a choice of three for the next (hence a total of 4×3 possibilities so far), and a choice of two for the third. Finally, only one possibility is left for the final day. Hence the number of possible arrangements of these four weather types is: $4 \times 3 \times 2 \times 1 = 24$.

This sort of number pattern: $3 \times 2 \times 1 \quad 4 \times 3 \times 2 \times 1$
occurs frequently in the study of Statistics. Consequently, it is given its own notation: $3 \times 2 \times 1$ is written as $3!$ and this is called **three factorial** or, equally correctly, **factorial three**.

CALCULATOR ACTIVITY

Exploration 31.7

Evaluating factorials

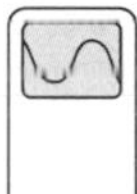

Your calculator will probably evaluate factorials directly. If it does, check that 3! is 6 and that 4! is 24.

Evaluate: **a)** 5! **b)** 6! **c)** 10! **d)** 1!

Factorial zero

Notice that:
4! is 4 times 3! and
5! is 5 times 4! and
6! is 6 times 5!.
Why is this?

Using the number patterns, we can see that:
$3! = 3 \times 2 \times 1$ and
$4! = 4 \times 3 \times 2 \times 1 = 4 \times 3!$
and similarly for the other results.

A generalisation of this is:

$n! = n \times (n - 1)!$

A consequence of this generalisation would seem to be that:

$1! = 1 \times (1 - 1)! = 1 \times 0!$

But: $1! = 1$

What does this imply about the value of 0!?

It suggests that:

$0! = 1$

Check this on your calculator.

Example 31.4

Statistically speaking, what do these two situations have in common?

a) *Five children: John, Andrew, Philippa, Kate, and Colette, are drawing lots to be last to have an injection. What is the probability that they will be drawn in alphabetical order?*

b) *A restaurant offers its customers a meal consisting of three courses. For the first course there is a choice of one of the following dishes:*
pâté, melon, prawn cocktail, avocado.
For the main course, the diners have a choice of:
venison, turbot, steak, stir-fry vegetables, pulse pie.
For the final course, there is:
ice cream, cheese.
How many different meals are possible?

Solution

a) *Clearly, there is only one arrangement which results in the children being in alphabetical order. This is:*
Andrew Colette John Kate Philippa
The total number of possible orders is 5! since there is a choice of five for the first in line to receive the injection, the second can then be anyone of four, and so on. This leads to the number of distinct orders being $5 \times 4 \times 3 \times 2 \times 1$ or 5!.
Hence, the probability that they will be in alphabetical order is $\frac{1}{120}$.

b) *In this problem we can readily arrive at the following response:*

	First course	*Main course*	*Final course*
Choice of	*4*	*5*	*2*

Hence, there is a total of $4 \times 5 \times 2 = 40$ possible meals.

Distinct sequences

Let's return to the conversation about the weather that we overheard on page 604.

'Then the gales returned on Thursday and Friday ... '

So the weather pattern for these five weekdays was FGRGG.

How many distinct sequences of these five are there?

If all five days had different weather, then there would be 5! distinct sequences. But that is not the case here. Consider one possible sequence: FRGGG.

If the GGG had all been different they could have been arranged in 3! distinct ways. Instead, there is *only one* arrangement. Consider another, possible sequence: GFGGR.

Again, there is only one distinct arrangement of the three Gs in place of the 6 (i.e. 3!) possible ways were they all different. Thus there is only $\frac{1}{6}$ of the number of sequences possible if all days were different. Hence, the number of distinct **arrangements of five** events where **three are identical** is $5! \div 3!$

Suppose that the week in question culminated in: '... As for the weekend, well that was a total washout. It rained the whole time ... '

So, what we've now got is the following sequence: FGRGGRR

How many distinct sequences of these seven events are possible?

The same sort of arrangement which led to $\frac{5!}{3!}$ for five events, three of which were identical can be applied here. In this case, there are seven events, three alike of one sort, and three alike of another sort. Hence, the total possible arrangements are $\frac{7!}{3!3!}$, or 140.

This result can be generalised.

The number of distinct arrangements of n objects where p are allied of one type, q alike of another, r alike of a third type, etc. is $\frac{n!}{p!q!r!}$

Example 31.5

a) How many distinct arrangements of the five letters of the following words are there?
i) RADAR ii) ERROR iii) HELEN

b) If the letters of RADAR are randomly arranged, what is the probability that the resulting sequence will be symmetric?

Solution

a) i) In RADAR, two letters are As and two are Rs, hence the number of distinct arrangements is $\frac{5!}{2!2!}$. This comes to 30.
ii) In ERROR, there are three Rs. Hence, the number of distinct arrangements is $\frac{5!}{3!} = 20$.
iii) In HELEN, there are two Es. Hence the number of distinct arrangements is $\frac{5!}{2!} = 60$.

b) The symmetric arrangements of the letters of RADAR are: RADAR and ARDRA. Hence, the probability required is $\frac{2}{30}$ or $\frac{1}{15}$.

Two types of object

There is a particular case of the previous result which will recur in the study of statistics. This is where there are n objects but only two different types. For example, the seven days we have heard about in this section might have been described as:

wet dry wet dry dry wet wet

where only two different descriptions are used. The total number of different sequences of these description is $\frac{7!}{4!3!} = 35$

Where there are n objects of which r are of one type and the rest, $(n - r)$, are of another type, the number of distinct arrangements is $\frac{n!}{r!(n-r)!}$

Example 31.6

a) How many distinct ways are there of arranging the letters ABBA? List all of them.

b) A bicycle rack has spaces for ten cycles. Three identical bicycles are to be placed in the rack. In how many ways may this be done?

c) In how many ways can a group of eight people be divided into a group of three and a group of five?

Solution

a) In ABBA there are four letters consisting of two As and two Bs. Hence, the number of distinct arrangements is: $\frac{4!}{2!2!} = 6$.
The six arrangements are AABB, ABAB, ABBA, BABA, BAAB, BBAA.

b) This problem can be modelled by the sort of arrangements considered above. The way to do this is to consider the rack as consisting of 'occupied spaces' and 'not-occupied spaces'. An occupied space could be written as O, and not-occupied as N. Thus, this becomes a problem about having ten letters in a line, of which three are Os and seven Ns. There are $\frac{10!}{7!3!}$ *distinct ways of arranging these letters. Hence there are 120 different ways of placing the three cycles in the rack.*

c) This can be treated in the same way as in part ***b)****. The people chosen for the smaller group could be labelled S, and those chosen for the larger group L. Then this problem is equivalent to finding how many ways eight letters consisting of three Ss and five Ls can be arranged. The answer is* $\frac{8!}{3!5!} = 56$.

EXERCISES

31.2 CLASSWORK

1 The lunch-time menu of a seaside café offers the following.
First course: soup or fruit juice
Second course: plaice and chips or ham salad or cheesy baked potato
Third course: ice cream or apple pie with cream

a) How many different three-course lunches are possible?
b) What is the probability of a customer having a meal which includes ham salad?
c) State the assumptions you have made in answering **b)**.

2 In the staffroom of a sixth-form college there are 50 pigeon-holes for staff mail. The principal of the college has been given six free tickets to the theatre. She decides to place them randomly in the 50 pigeon-holes. In how many ways may this be done?

3 A squad of 17 players is named for a football team to play in a final of a competition. How many different teams of eleven players can be chosen from the squad if:

a) all players can play in all positions,
b) the players are specialists and:
two only play in goal (one is needed in the team)
five play only in defence (three are needed in the team)
six play only in mid-field (four are needed in the team)
four play only in attack (three are needed in the team)?

EXERCISES

31.2 HOMEWORK

1 A man has two jackets, eight pairs of shorts, three ties and five pairs of trousers. How many distinct outfits are possible?

2 **a)** How many distinct arrangements of the work PLYMOUTH are possible using all the letters?
b) How many of the arrangements in **a)** begin with two vowels?

3 Six disco tickets are given randomly to 32 children in a class.
a) How many different ways are there of doing this?
b) There are 20 girls and twelve boys in the class. In how many ways will:
i) three tickets go to boys and three go to girls,
ii) all six go to girls,
iii) four go to girls and two to boys?

PERMUTATIONS AND COMBINATIONS

The following is a list of descriptions that could be applied to the weather on a day: misty, cold, dry, freezing, windy, raining, sunny, hot.

Each of a group of people was asked to list, in reverse order of preference, the three types of day they least like. How many different ways of doing this are there?

The least favourite could be any one of the eight types, then the next least favourite could be chosen from seven, the final selection is from the remaining six. This gives: $8 \times 7 \times 6$ different selections where the order of selection matters. This may be called a **permutation**.

A permutation is an **ordered arrangement of *r* objects from *n* objects**.

In this particular case, the group of people were asked to list a permutation of three descriptions from eight. The total number of permutations of three objects from eight unlike objects is:

$$8 \times 7 \times 6$$

and this can be written in factorial form as:

$$\frac{8 \times 7 \times 6 \times 5 \times 4 \times 3 \times 2 \times 1}{5 \times 4 \times 3 \times 2 \times 1} = \frac{8!}{5!} = \frac{8!}{(8-3)!}$$

The notation, ${}_8P_3$ or ${}^8P_3$, is used for this.

In general: ${}_nP_r = \dfrac{n!}{(n-r)!}$

Suppose the group of people had instead, been asked to list their three least favourite types of day, but not necessarily to indicate the order of preference? How does this affect the number of arrangements?

Consider one permutation, say 'freezing, windy, misty'.

As a permutation, this indicates that 'freezing' is the least desirable, 'windy' the next least followed by 'misty'. Again as a permutation this is different from 'windy, freezing, misty'.

There are 3! permutations of windy, freezing and misty in total. Hence, the number of selections of three descriptions from the eight is:

$$8 \times 7 \times 6 \div 3! \text{ or } \frac{8!}{(5!3!)}$$

The term **combination** is often used for the process of **selecting r objects from n objects** when the **order** of selection **does not matter**. The notation used is:

$${}_nC_r = \frac{n!}{(n-r)!r!} \quad \text{or sometimes, } {}^nC_r\text{, or even } \binom{n}{r}$$

Take care! There is potential for confusion with other areas of mathematics with this last notation.

Example 31.7

a) Evaluate the following.

i) ${}_5P_2$ *ii)* ${}_5C_2$ *iii)* ${}_9P_4$ *iv)* ${}_{10}C_7$

b) i) How many different hands of five cards is it possible to deal from an ordinary pack of 52 cards?

ii) How many five card hands will have no high cards? (A high card is a king, queen, jack or ace.)

iii) What is the probability that a five-card hand has no high card?

Solution

a) i) $${}_5P_2 = \frac{5!}{(5-2)!} = \frac{5!}{3!} = \frac{5\times4\times3\times2\times1}{3\times2\times1} = 5\times4 = 20$$

ii) $${}_5C_2 = \frac{5!}{3!2!} = \frac{5!}{3!} = \frac{5\times4}{2\times1} = 10$$

iii) $${}_9P_4 = \frac{9!}{(9-4)!} = \frac{9!}{5!} = 9\times8\times7\times6 = 3024$$

iv) $${}_{10}C_7 = \frac{10!}{3!7!} = \frac{10\times9\times8}{3\times2\times1} = 120$$

b) i) Dealing five cards from a pack of 52 is equivalent to selecting the five when the order does not matter. Hence, the number of possible five-card hands is:

$${}_{52}C_5 = \frac{52!}{5!47!} = \frac{52\times51\times50\times49\times48}{5\times4\times3\times2\times1} = 2\,598\,960$$

(i.e. nearly 2.6 million).

ii) The number of five-card hands with no high cards can be found by considering the selection to be a pack of 36 'low cards'. Hence the number is:

$${}_{36}C_5 = \frac{36!}{31!5!} = \frac{36\times35\times34\times33\times32}{5\times4\times3\times2\times1} = 376\,992$$

(i.e. nearly 380 thousand).

iii) The probability required is:

$$\frac{376\,992}{2\,598\,960} = 0.145\,05$$

Exploration 31.8

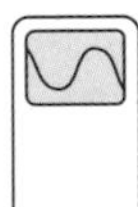

CALCULATOR ACTIVITY

Permutations and combinations

Many calculators have nPr and nCr programmed into the available functions. Explore your calculator for either or both of these facilities and try to evaluate the permutations and combinations in Example 31.7.

CONSOLIDATION EXERCISES FOR CHAPTER 31

1 Two cubical dice are rolled. The sum of the outcomes is noted. Use an appropriate diagram to identify the possibility space. Use the possibility space to find:
a) $P(A)$, where A is the set of all events in which the sum is even,
b) $P(B)$, where B is the event that the sum is a multiple of 4,
c) $P(C)$, where C is the event that the sum is prime.

2 A tetrahedral die with faces numbered 1, 2, 3, 4 is rolled three times. Use a tree diagram to find the probability of the following events:
a) there are at least two even outcomes,
b) there are at least two consecutive even outcomes,
c) the outcomes are EOE or OEO, where E represents even outcome, O represents an odd outcome.

3 A coin is flipped five times. What is the probability that:
a) the sequence of outcomes is HTHTH or THTHT,
b) the first flip results in H and the fifth results in T,
c) the first and last flips result in the same outcome?

4 A bag contains four milk chocolates and two plain chocolates. Two chocolates are randomly removed and eaten. What is the probability that they are both the same type?

5 A cubical die with faces numbered 1, 2, 3, 4, 5, 6 and an octahedral die with faces numbered 0, 0, 1, 1, 2, 2, 3, 3 are rolled.
a) Display the sample space in a suitable diagram.
b) Calculate the probability that:
  i) exactly one die shows a score of 1,
  ii) the total of the outcomes on the two dice is 5,
  iii) the product of the outcomes on the two dice is 0,
  iv) the outcome on the octahedral die is 2 less than the outcome on the cubical die.

6 A standard pack of 52 cards is shuffled. The top card is examined. The card is returned and the pack is shuffled again. The top card is again examined. Calculate the probability that:
a) both cards are black,
b) the two cards are of different colours,
c) both cards are court cards (J, Q, K or ace),
d) at least one card is a court card,
e) the first card is a king and the second is red.

7 A bag contains s sweets and t toffees. Two are removed and eaten. Calculate the probability, in terms of s and t, that:
a) both are toffees, **b)** neither is a toffee,
c) there is one sweet and one toffee.

8 A woman has two pairs of shoes, four skirts and three blouses. How many different outfits consisting of a blouse, a pair of shoes and a skirt can be made out of these?

9 **a)** How many six-digit numbers can be formed using all the digits 3, 4, 5, 6, 7, 8?
b) How many of these are odd?
c) How many are greater than 600 000?
d) How many are odd numbers greater than 600 000?

10 Fifteen teachers, six men and nine women, volunteer to sit on the curriculum committee. The head teacher decides that the committee is to have only six members.

a) How many different ways can the six members of the committee be chosen from the 15 volunteers?

b) How many of these ways consist of:

i) exactly four men and two women,

ii) at least one man?

11 Each of eight people has a coin. They each flip their coin.

a) In how many different ways can exactly five heads and three tails result?

b) Calculate the probability that, when eight coins are flipped, exactly five heads occur.

12 Six black marbles, four red marbles and two white marbles are placed in a straight line.

a) In how many distinct ways can this be done?

b) In how many ways will there be a white marble at each end?

c) In how many ways will there be the same colour marble at each end?

13 A pack of 52 cards is shuffled. A hand of five cards is dealt.

a) How many distinct hands are possible?

b) How many hands consist of five diamonds?

c) What is the probability that a hand of five cards consists of five cards of the same suit?

14 A tetrahedral die has its faces numbered 1, 1, 1, 4.

a) Calculate the probability of not getting a 4 when:

i) the die is rolled once,

ii) the die is rolled twice,

iii) the die is rolled five times,

iv) the die is rolled N times?

b) What is the smallest value of N, if the probability in **a) iv)** is less than 0.0001?

15 My car is rather unreliable. The battery functions properly on only 90 per cent of the occasions I try to use it. When the battery does function properly, the engine starts with probability $\frac{2}{3}$. What is the probability that the engine starts?

16 Two cubical die – one red and one blue – are rolled together.

a) Illustrate the possible outcomes in a suitable diagram.

b) If it is known that the sum of the outcomes on the two dice is 6:

i) what is the probability that the outcome on the blue die is 2 more than the outcome on the red die,

ii) what is the probability that the difference between the outcomes on the two dice is 2,

iii) what is the probability that the difference between the outcomes on the two dice is 3?

c) If it is known that the difference between the outcomes on the two dice is 4, what is the probability that the sum of the outcomes is 8?

17 In the town square, there are two large flowerbeds. One has 40 flowers of which 15 are *salvia*. The other flowerbed has 30 flowers of which twelve are *salvia*. A flowerbed is selected and a flower is chosen at random from that bed. The bed with the larger number of flowers is twice as likely to be selected.

a) Write down the probability that the bed of 40 flowers is chosen.
b) Draw a labelled tree diagram to model the scenario described.
c) Calculate the probability that a *salvia* is chosen from the larger bed.
d) Calculate the probability that a *salvia* is chosen.
e) Given that a *salvia* is chosen, calculate the probability that it came from the first bed.

18 In a certain town, 20 per cent of the adult population had at some time been innoculated against 'flu. It is known that there is a chance of 1 in 10 of an adult catching 'flu when innoculated. The chance of catching flu rises to 75 per cent when not innoculated.

a) Calculate the probability of an adult catching 'flu.
b) Given that an adult has caught 'flu, what is the probability the person had been innoculated?

19 There are two different routes A, B into town from college. The chance of encountering a delay on the two routes is:

A: $\frac{2}{5}$ B: $\frac{3}{5}$

Three lecturers X, Y, Z, independently choose route A with probabilities:

X: $\frac{4}{7}$ Y: $\frac{3}{5}$ Z: $\frac{8}{35}$

Find the probability that:

a) X **b)** Y **c)** Z

is delayed on their way to town.

20 At a large community college, the probability that a blue-eyed student is left-handed is 0.15. The probability that a left-handed student is blue-eyed is 0.3. The probability that a student is either blue-eyed or left-handed is 0.2.

Let l, b, x represent the probability that a student is left-handed, blue-eyed, left handed *and* blue-eyed respectively.

a) Demonstrate that $b = 2l$.
b) Express the probability that a student is either blue-eyed or left-handed in terms of l, b, x, hence, in terms of l.
c) Calculate the probability that a student is left-handed and blue-eyed.

21 A lottery consists of selecting five different letters of the 26 letters in the alphabet.

a) How many ways may this be done assuming that the order of selection does not matter?
b) The first prize goes to contestants who select the same five letters as those chosen randomly by a computer. What is the probability of winning the first prize?
c) Only those selections which include at least three of the computer's selected numbers win prizes in the lottery. What is the probability that a selection fails to win a prize?

22 A national lottery requires contestants to select six different numbers from the numbers 1, 2, 3, ..., 48, 49.

a) How many different ways may this be done (the order of selection does not matter)?
b) What is the probability that a contestant's selection matches the

selection made by the lottery computer?

c) Any selection which includes at least three of the lottery computer's selection wins a prize. Calculate the probability that a contestant's selection:
   i) contains no number also selected by the computer,
   ii) contains exactly one number also selected by the computer,
   iii) contains exactly two numbers also selected by the computer,
   iv) wins a prize.

23 In a group of six students, four are female and two are male. Determine how many committees of three members can be formed containing one male and two females.

(ULEAC Question 1, Paper S1, January 1993)

24 An urn contains three red, four white and five blue discs. Three discs are selected at random from the urn. Find the probability that:

a) all three discs are the same colour, if the selection is with replacement,

b) all three discs are of different colours, if the selection is without replacement.

(ULEAC Question 6, Paper S1, June 1993)

25 Doctors estimate that three people in every thousand of the population are infected by a particular virus. A test has been devised which is not perfect, but gives a positive result for 95 per cent of those who have the virus. It also gives a positive result for two per cent of those who do not have the virus.

Suppose that someone selected at random takes the test and that it gives a positive result. Calculate the probability that this person really has the virus.

(Nuffield Question 5, Specimen paper 2, 1996)

26 An insurance company offering comprehensive policies to car drivers classifies each applicant as being high-risk, average-risk or low-risk. The probability that a high-risk driver will submit a claim in any year is 0.4, the corresponding probabilities for an average-risk driver and a low-risk driver are 0.2 and 0.1 respectively. The proportions of the policy holders who have been classified as high-risk, average-risk and low-risk are 0.3, 0.6 and 0.1, respectively.

a) Calculate the probability that a randomly-chosen policy holder will submit a claim in a year.

b) Given that a randomly-chosen policy holder did make a claim in one year, calculate the conditional probability that the policy holder was a high-risk driver.

c) Two brothers have comprehensive policies with the company, one is classified as average-risk and the other as low-risk. Calculate the probability that exactly one of the two brothers will submit a claim in a year.

(WJEC Question 7, Specimen paper A3, 1994)

27 In Britain, one per cent of pregnancies results in twins. The probability that twins are identical is $\frac{1}{3}$, and in that case the twins will be of the same sex. Twins which are non-identical are, independently of one another, equally likely to be of either sex.

a) Calculate the probability of each of the following events.
(A) A pregnancy results in identical twins.
(B) A pair of non-identical twins are of the same sex.
(C) A pair of twins are of the same sex.

b) At a maternity hospital, two sets of twins are due on the same day. What is the probability that all four babies are of the same sex?

c) Find the probability that a pair of twins are identical given that they are of the same sex.

(MEI Question 2, Paper S1, January 1993)

28 When one card is selected at random from a pack of playing cards,
A is the event 'the card is an ace',
B is the event 'the card is black',
C is the event 'the card is a club',
D is the event 'the card is a diamond'.
For each of the following pairs of events state whether the events are mutually exclusive, independent, neither or both.
a) A and B, **b)** B and C, **c)** C and D.

(NEAB Question 1, Specimen paper 8, 1994)

29 A child has a bag containing twelve sweets of which three are yellow, five are green and four are red. When the child wants to eat one of the sweets, a random selection is made from the bag and the chosen sweet is then eaten before the next random selection is made.

a) Find the probability that the child does not select a yellow sweet in the first two selections.

b) Find the probability that there is at least one yellow sweet in the first two selections.

c) Find the probability that the fourth sweet selected is yellow given that the first two sweets selected were red ones.

(ULEAC Question 6, Specimen paper T1, 1994)

30 The events A and B are mutually exclusive. Given that
$P(A) = 0.4$ and $P(B)$ 0.5 find
a) $P(A \cap B)$, **b)** $P(A \cup B)$, **c)** $P(A' \cap B)$.

(EDEXCEL Paper T1, Question 1, January 2000)

31 The probability that for any married couple the husband has a degree is $\frac{6}{10}$ and the probability that the wife has a degree is $\frac{1}{2}$. The probability that the husband has a degree, given that the wife has a degree, is $\frac{11}{12}$.
A married couple is chosen at random.
Find the probability that
a) both of them have degrees, **b)** only one of them has a degree,
c) neither of them has a degree.
Two married couples are chosen at random.

d) Find the probability that only one of the two husbands and only one of the two wives have a degree.

(EDEXCEL Paper T1, Question 8, January 1999)

32 The three events E_1, E_2 and E_3 are defined in the same sample space. The events E_1 and E_3 are mutally exclusive. The events E_1 and E_2 are independent.
Given that $P(E_1) = 2/5$, $P(E_3) = 1/3$ and $P(E_1 \cup E_2) = 5/8$, find
a) $P(E_1 \cup E_3)$, **b)** $P(E_2)$.

(EDEXCEL Paper T1, Question 2, June 1998)

33 The letters of the word MATHEMATICS are written, one on each of 11 separate cards. The cards are laid out in a line.

a) Calculate the number of different arrangements of these letters.

b) Determine the probability that the vowels are all placed together.

(EDEXCEL Paper T1, Question 3, June 1998)

Summary

- **Probability:**
  probability of an outcome = $\dfrac{\text{number of events in the outcome}}{\text{total number of possible events}}$
- **Notation:**
  probability of event $E \equiv \mathrm{P}(E)$
  probability of complementary event $\equiv \mathrm{P}(\bar{E}) = 1 - \mathrm{P}(E)$
  conditional probability of A given that B has occurred $\equiv \mathrm{P}(A \mid B)$
  probability of events A and $B \equiv \mathrm{P}(A \cap B)$
  probability of events A or $B \equiv \mathrm{P}(A \cup B)$
- The **multiplication law**: $\mathrm{P}(A \cap B) = \mathrm{P}(A) \times \mathrm{P}(B \mid A) = \mathrm{P}(B) \times \mathrm{P}(A \mid B)$
- The **addition law**: $\mathrm{P}(A \cup B) = \mathrm{P}(A) + \mathrm{P}(B) - \mathrm{P}(A \cap B)$
- **Independent events**: $\mathrm{P}(A \mid B) = \mathrm{P}(A) \Rightarrow \mathrm{P}(A \cap B) = \mathrm{P}(A) \times \mathrm{P}(B)$
- **Mutually exclusive events**: $\mathrm{P}(A \cap B) = 0 \Rightarrow \mathrm{P}(A \cup B) = \mathrm{P}(A) + \mathrm{P}(B)$
- A **permutation** is an ordered arrangement of r objects from n objects.
  $${}_n\mathrm{P}_r = \frac{n!}{(n-r)!}$$
- A **combination** is the process of selecting r objects from n objects when order does not matter.
  $${}_n\mathrm{C}_r = \frac{n!}{r!(n-r)!}$$

Expectation

- *When trying to predict the possible financial outcome of an event, it is useful to consider the expected gain.*
- *In this chapter we shall explore the relationship between expected gain, fair games, mean and variance.*

FAIR GAMES

Exploration 32.1

Some you win ...

A sign at a Summer Scout Fete said: 'Win £1 for just a 10p stake!'

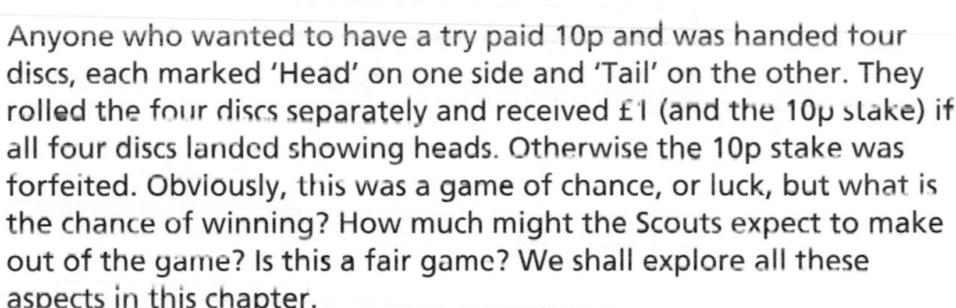

Anyone who wanted to have a try paid 10p and was handed four discs, each marked 'Head' on one side and 'Tail' on the other. They rolled the four discs separately and received £1 (and the 10p stake) if all four discs landed showing heads. Otherwise the 10p stake was forfeited. Obviously, this was a game of chance, or luck, but what is the chance of winning? How much might the Scouts expect to make out of the game? Is this a fair game? We shall explore all these aspects in this chapter.

To explore what might happen when this game is played, we could try:

- calculating theoretical probabilities,
- rolling four coins and recording the outcome repeatedly,
- simulating the game using a calculator, spreadsheet, or other means.

The theoretical approach will be discussed later in the chapter. You might like to explore coin rolling yourself. In this section we shall consider how we can simulate the game using random numbers.

Simulation

The outcome of rolling a disc can be one of two possibilities (head or tail). If we assume that these are equally likely, we can use a simple correspondence between a random digit and the outcome of the roll: an even digit means a head and an odd digit means a tail.

Then any group of four random digits represents one 'go' of the game, worth 10p each time.

Try a simulation of the game using random digits. Does your exploration provide any answers to the questions above?

1	3	2	9
T	T	H	T
2	7	3	2
H	T	T	H
4	1	5	8
H	T	T	H

Example 32.1

The output from a calculator producing three-digit random decimals is given below. Convert these decimals into groups of four digits and code them as heads and tails.

0.745	0.560	0.772	0.885	0.559	0.900
0.597	0.122	0.536	0.006	0.174	0.692
0.291	0.886	0.866	0.902	0.136	0.084
0.924	0.133	0.608	0.006	0.306	0.696
0.219	0.079	0.175	0.200	0.080	

Solution

We start by rewriting the decimal fractions from the table above, omitting the first zero and the decimal point in each one. Then we replace odd digits with 'T' and even digits (or zero) with 'H'.

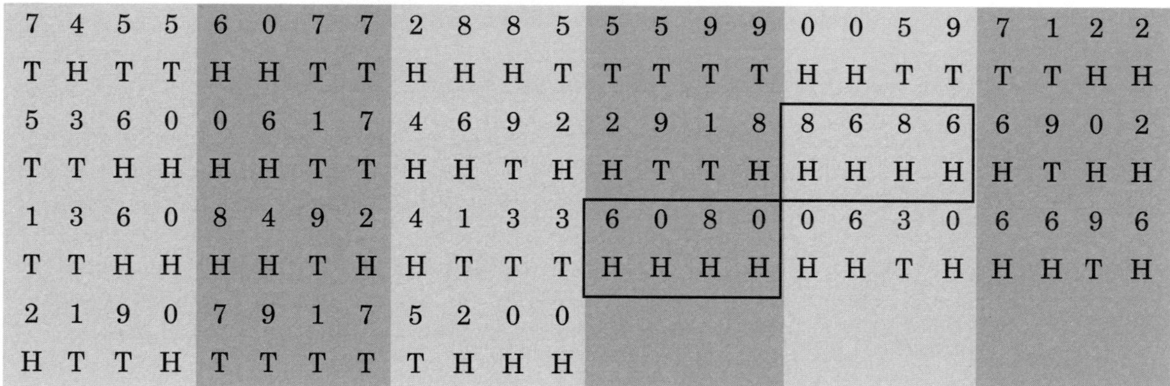

7	4	5	5	6	0	7	7	2	8	8	5	5	5	9	9	0	0	5	9	7	1	2	2
T	H	T	T	H	H	T	T	H	H	H	T	T	T	T	T	H	H	T	T	T	T	H	H
5	3	6	0	0	6	1	7	4	6	9	2	2	9	1	8	8	6	8	6	6	9	0	2
T	T	H	H	H	H	T	T	H	H	T	H	H	T	T	H	H	H	H	H	H	T	H	H
1	3	6	0	8	4	9	2	4	1	3	3	6	0	8	0	0	6	3	0	6	6	9	6
T	T	H	H	H	H	T	H	H	T	T	T	H	H	H	H	H	H	T	H	H	H	T	H
2	1	9	0	7	9	1	7	5	2	0	0												
H	T	T	H	T	T	T	T	T	H	H	H												

This now represents 21 goes at the game. In these, 19 result in the Scouts gaining the contestant's 10p stake money, and two (boxed in the table above) result in the contestant winning £1 and regaining the stake.

Expected gain

The simulation shows that:

- the chance of winning £1 is only $\frac{2}{21}$,
- the Scouts make a loss of 10p having paid out $2 \times$ £1 and taken $19 \times$ 10p,
- the game appears to be reasonably fair, since neither the contestants nor the Scouts seem, on average, to have much of an advantage.

The actual net income to the Scouts is:

$$10\text{p} \times 19 + (-100\text{p}) \times 2$$

This was for 21 attempts at winning. It is very unlikely that the Scouts would know in advance exactly how many people were going to play their game. It might be more reasonable to consider the net income per game:

$$\frac{10\text{p} \times 19 + (-100\text{p}) \times 2}{21} = -\frac{10}{21}\text{p per game.}$$

This can be written as:

$$10\text{p} \times \frac{19}{21} + (-100\text{p}) \times \frac{2}{21}$$

This gives the net income per game as:

the sum of (net gain × experimental probability of winning)

This simulation is just an example of what might happen when someone plays the game. Other simulations will produce different results. The Scouts might be more interested in the likely outcome in the long term. They want to know if, on average, they can expect to make a profit out of this game.

Looking at the theoretical probabilities helps to gain a longterm view. Assuming that the probability of a head is $\frac{1}{2}$, the chance that four discs independently show heads is:

$$\left(\frac{1}{2}\right)^4 \quad or \quad \frac{1}{16}$$

On average, once in every 16 games the Scouts can expect to pay out £1

i.e. they expect to pay $\frac{1}{16} \times 100\text{p}$ *per go.*

On 15 out of 16 occasions, they can expect to gain 10p

i.e. they expect to gain $\frac{15}{16} \times 10\text{p}$ *per go.*

The **expected net gain** to the Scouts is:

$$\frac{15}{16} \times 10\text{p} - \frac{1}{16} \times 100\text{p} = 3\frac{1}{8}\text{ p } per\ go.$$

There are two very important ideas in the work we have done so far.

Expected gain is the expected net gain per go to the Scouts, and can be thought of as:

$$\text{Expected gain} = \frac{15}{16} \times 10\text{p} \quad + \quad \frac{1}{16} \times -100\text{p}$$

$$= \sum \text{gain} \times \text{probability}$$

A **fair game** is one where the expected gain is the same for both contestant and organiser.

This means that the **expected gain is zero**.

The theoretical probabilities show that, in the long term, the organisers of the game should gain $3\frac{1}{8}$p for every 10p staked. Perhaps it is not a fair game in providing both organiser and contestant the same expected gain but it was all for charity!

Example 32.2

In a game, a coin is flipped until the first head appears. To take part in the game, each player pays the banker 20p. The banker pays the player an amount according to the number of times the coin has to be flipped to get a head.

No. of flips	Amount banker pays
1	20p
2	10p
3	5p
4	2p
5	1p
6 or more	zero

No player is allowed more than five flips.

Calculate the expected gain to the player. Is the game fair?

Solution

*At the end of a game, the gain to the player is the amount the banker has paid the player, less the 20p the player has paid to take part in the game. So the expected gain to the player is the expected amount the banker pays **minus** 20p.*

*We need to find the probabilities associated with each number of flips, to find this expected amount paid. To calculate these probabilities, we also need to make assumptions about **independence**, i.e. the result of flipping one coin does not depend on the result of flipping another. For instance, the probability that the first head appears on the third flip requires the flips to be:*
tail (T) then tail (T) then head (H).
And so we require:

$$\begin{aligned} P(TTH) &= P(T) \times P(T) \times P(H) \\ &= \frac{1}{2} \times \frac{1}{2} \times \frac{1}{2} \end{aligned}$$

assuming that individual flips of the coins are independent.

Amount banker pays	Probability
20	$\frac{1}{2}$
10	$\frac{1}{4}$
5	$\frac{1}{8}$
2	$\frac{1}{16}$
1	$\frac{1}{32}$
0	$\frac{1}{32}$ (= 1 – sum of other probabilities)

Expected bank pay out $= 20 \times \frac{1}{2} + 10 \times \frac{1}{4} + \ldots + 0 \times \frac{1}{32}$
$\approx 13.3\text{p}$

So the expected gain to the player is 20p less than this, which gives –6.7p. Since this is not zero, the game is not fair.

EXERCISES

32.1 CLASSWORK

1 At the School Fete, Year 7 decide to offer a prize of £10 to anyone who scores five heads when rolling five coins. Anyone who tries but fails has to pay 10p.

Using random digits, simulate 25 goes at this game. Answer the following questions:

i) based on your simulation, and
ii) based on theoretical probabilities.
a) What is the probability of winning the prize?
b) What can Year 7 expect to gain in offering this game?
c) Is the game fair?

2 A simple fruit machine has three windows.

The windows show apples, bananas or cherries. The probability of this varies according to the window and the fruit as shown in this table.

Prizes are given when the three windows all display the same fruit.

	Apple	Banana	Cherry
First window	0.3	0.2	0.5
Second window	0.3	0.1	0.6
Third window	0.2	0.1	0.7

Three bananas win £10, three apples win £2 and three cherries win 50p.

Work out a way of simulating 30 attempts at winning a prize using this fruit machine.

What does your simulation suggest the probability of winning the top prize is?

If it cost 20p a go, calculate the theoretical probability of:
a) three bananas,
b) winning a prize,
and evaluate the expected net gain to the owner of the fruit machine.

3 A businessman has £250 000 to invest. He is considering investing in a business enterprise where he estimates the chance of differing financial returns, in two years' time are as shown in this table.

Return	£400 000	£300 000	£150 000	£50 000
Probability	0.25	0.5	0.2	0.05

a) What is the expected return of this investment?
b) Is he likely to have a larger return by placing his money on deposit where there is a guaranteed annual interest rate of five per cent?

4 An insurance company estimates the probability of a disaster such as a fire or flood completely demolishing a house in any year is $\frac{1}{750}$. The company insures 50 000 houses against such a disaster and the average insured value is £80 000.

a) The company charges an annual premium of £100 to each householder. Is this likely to be sufficient to cover the expected payout?
b) How much should the premium be if the company wants to make a total annual profit of 1 million pounds from the premiums?

5 The faces of three tetrahedral dice give scores of 1, 2, 3 and 4. The dice are rolled, and the player's counter is moved a number of squares on the game board, according to the outcome of the roll of dice.

Outcome	Action
4,4,4	3 squares clockwise
one or two 4s	1 square clockwise
no 4	1 square anticlockwise

a) Calculate the probability of each of the outcomes.
b) Calculate the expected move.

EXERCISES

32.1 HOMEWORK

1 A stallholder in a fairground offers £5 for a 25p stake to anyone who can roll three ordinary dice and get a multiple of three on each die. Use random numbers to simulate 30 attempts at winning this prize. Does your simulation indicate that this is a fair game? Calculate the theoretical expected gain to the stallholder. (Winners received their 25p stake money back.)

2 A child's roulette wheel consists of a disc with twelve equal sectors marked 1 to 12, which are coloured green, red or black. The instruction booklet suggests the following method of play.

One child acts as banker, whilst others play as gamblers. The gamblers place a stake of their choice on a colour and then they receive a prize as follows, if their colour appears on the wheel.

Number	Colour	Prize
1, 6, 7, 12	green	zero
2, 3, 4, 9, 10, 11	red	double the stake
5, 8	black	four times the stake

In all cases the stake is forfeited.

a) Devise a method of simulating the game and work out the outcome for 36 spins of the wheel.
b) Is the game fair?
c) Calculate the theoretical expected gain for a gambler who always places a stake of 50p on the black.

3 A motor car insurance company estimates that the risk of its having to pay a claim for any motorist depends on the details as shown in the table. The overall average claim costs the company £1000.

Category	Young	Single and inexperienced	Married and experienced	Advanced
Risk	0.25	0.10	0.05	0.01

a) Assume the company has the same number of policy holders in each category.
   i) How much is it likely to have to charge as a premium in order to break even?
   ii) How much should the premium be to make a profit of £250 000, assuming it has 50 000 policy holders?
b) i) It is argued that it is fairer to motorists to make the premium reflect the risk. The company decides to charge a premium to each category in the ratio 5 : 2 : 2 : 1.
   If the company is to break even, how much should it charge motorists in each category?
   ii) What should the premiums be to make a profit of £250 000, if the numbers of motorists in each category are 2000 : 13 000 : 30 000 : 5000?

4 Five ordinary dice are rolled in a game. If they all give a score of 6, a prize of £50 is given for a 50p stake. Any other outcome resulting in at least one 6 yields a prize of £1.

a) Calculate the probability of:
   i) winning the £50 prize,
   ii) winning the £1 prize.
b) What is the expected gain to the player of the game?
c) What stake would make this a fair game?

MEAN AND VARIANCE

Mean

In the last section we thought of expected gain as longterm average gain. Why is the expected gain the same as the average – or **mean** – gain? Once again, the Scout's game can be used to illustrate the reason for this.

Imagine that the game is played 16 times and that the contestant wins exactly once. The results of these 16 plays are as shown in this table.

Gain to Scouts	Number of times this gain occurs
10p	15
−100p	1

The mean gain is $\dfrac{10\text{p}\times 15+(-100\text{p})\times 1}{16}$

which is the same as the expression for the expected gain per game.

So mean gain = expected gain
= sum of products of gain × probability of outcome resulting in the gain

$$\text{E(gain)} = \sum_{\text{all outcomes}} \text{gain} \times \text{probability of related outcome.}$$

More formally, if X is a random variable, the link between the mean and the expected value is defined as:

$$\begin{aligned}\text{mean value} &= \mathrm{E}(X)\\ &= \sum_{\text{all } x} x \times \mathrm{P}(X = x)\end{aligned}$$

Example 32.3

The random variable, X, represents the sum of the outcomes on two tetrahedral dice with possible scores 1 to 4. X can take the values 2, 3, 4, 5, 6, 7 or 8 with probability $\frac{1}{16}, \frac{2}{16}, \frac{3}{16}, \frac{4}{16}, \frac{3}{16}, \frac{2}{16}, \frac{1}{16}$.

What is the expected value of X?

Solution

The expected value of X is:

KEY SKILLS
N 3.2d

$$\begin{aligned}\mathrm{E}(X) &= \sum_{x=2}^{8} x \times \mathrm{P}(X = x)\\ &= 2\times\frac{1}{16}+3\times\frac{2}{16}+4\times\frac{3}{16}+5\times\frac{4}{16}+6\times\frac{3}{16}+7\times\frac{2}{16}+8\times\frac{1}{16}\\ &= \frac{80}{16}\end{aligned}$$

Hence, the mean of X is 5.

Variance

The mean of squares was introduced with the work on variance. For a random variable this can be defined as the expected value of the square of the random variable:

$$\mathrm{E}(X^2) = \sum x^2 \times \mathrm{P}(X = x)$$

Then, the variance of X can be written as:

$$\text{variance of } X = \mathrm{E}(X^2) - \{\mathrm{E}(X)\}^2$$

using the 'mean of squares minus square of mean' definition.

Example 32.4

The mean of the squares for the tetrahedral dice in Example 5.3 can be found as:

$$\begin{aligned}E(X^2) &= \sum_{x=2}^{8} x^2 \times P(X = x)\\ &= 2^2 \times \frac{1}{16} + 3^2 \times \frac{2}{16} + \cdots + 8^2 \times \frac{1}{16}\\ &= \frac{440}{16}\end{aligned}$$

Find the variance.

Solution

Using the equation above, the variance is: $\mathrm{Var}(X) = E(X^2) - \{E(X)\}^2$

$$= 27.5 - 5^2 = 2.5$$

Example 32.5

A bag contains four orange discs and four green discs which are identical in all other aspects. Two players play a game in which they take turns to select a disc randomly from the bag. The disc is not returned after selection. The game ends when the first green disc is drawn. Calculate the mean and variance of the number of selections.

Solution

First, we need to determine the possible number of selections and the associated probability for each number. The outcomes are not independent, since the discs are not returned to the bag.
The possible number of selections is 1, 2, ..., 5. The associated probabilities may be established from a tree diagram.

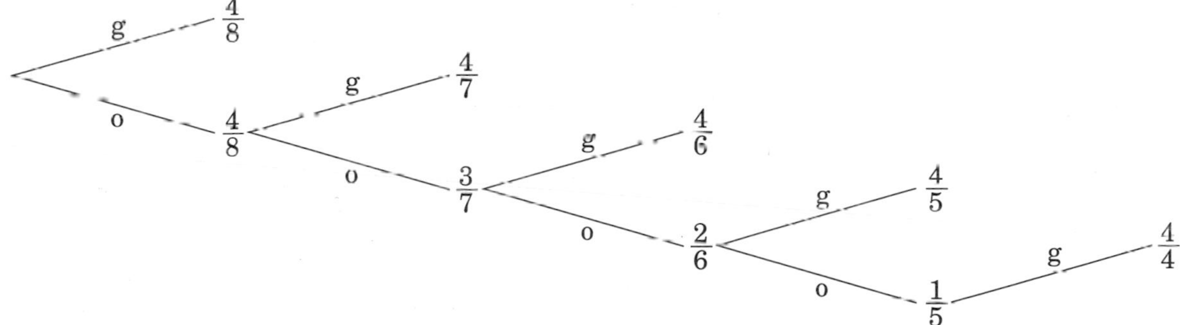

Multiplying along the branches produces the following probabilities.

No. of selections	Probability
1	$\frac{4}{8} = \frac{1}{2}$
2	$\frac{4}{8} \times \frac{4}{7} = \frac{2}{7}$
3	$\frac{4}{8} \times \frac{3}{7} \times \frac{4}{6} = \frac{1}{7}$
4	$\frac{4}{8} \times \frac{3}{7} \times \frac{2}{6} \times \frac{4}{5} = \frac{2}{35}$
5	$\frac{4}{8} \times \frac{3}{7} \times \frac{2}{6} \times \frac{1}{5} \times \frac{4}{4} = \frac{1}{70}$

Hence the expected number of selections is:

$$1\times\tfrac{1}{2}+2\times\tfrac{2}{7}+3\times\tfrac{1}{7}+4\times\tfrac{2}{35}+5\times\tfrac{1}{70}$$

which is equal to 1.8.

The variance may be established using

$$\mathrm{E}(X^2)-\text{mean}^2$$

giving

$$\left(1^2\times\tfrac{1}{2}+2^2\times\tfrac{2}{7}+3^2\times\tfrac{1}{7}+4^2\times\tfrac{2}{35}+5^2\times\tfrac{1}{70}\right)-1.8^2$$

which gives 0.96.

EXERCISES

32.2 CLASSWORK

KEY SKILLS
N 3.2d

1 Use expectation to calculate the mean and variance of the outcome on a cubical die with faces numbered 1 to 6.

2 The distribution of the weekly number of breakdowns, X, of a machine which produces sticks of lead for pencils has the following probability function.

x	0	1	2	3	4
$P(X=x)$	0.10	0.15	0.45	0.25	0.05

Calculate the mean and variance of X.

3 Two dice are rolled, and the score is taken as the value of the larger number. If the value is the same on both dice, the score is taken as the value on either die. List the possible pairs of results from the throws of the dice, then give all the possible scores, and their probabilities. Calculate the mean and variance of the scores.

4 A motorist passes through two sets of traffic lights. The probability that the first set is at green is $\frac{1}{2}$; the probability that the second set is at green is $\frac{1}{3}$.

a) Draw a tree diagram and find the probabilities that the motorist has to wait: **i)** at neither set, **ii)** at just one set, **iii)** at both sets.

b) Find the expected number of waits and the variance of the number of waits.

5 Two cubical dice – one red and the other blue – are rolled. The outcome on the blue is subtracted from that on the red. What are the possible differences? What are the associated probabilities? Use expectation to calculate the mean difference and the variance of the difference.

EXERCISES

32.2 HOMEWORK

1 A game is played in which an ordinary pack of 52 cards is shuffled and then the top card is turned over. The player scores the value of this card where:

- an ace counts as 1,
- picture cards count as 10,
- all other cards are face value.

a) Calculate the expected value of the score.
b) Calculate the variance of the score.

2 The number of emergencies requiring the assistance of one particular fire-station in a day have probabilities as shown in this table.

x	0	1	2	3	4	5
$P(X=x)$	0.05	0.25	0.35	0.15	0.15	0.05

Calculate the mean and variance of X.

3 **a)** A multiple choice test consists of five questions, each with two options. A student guesses all the answers. Find the mean and the variance of the number of correct answers.
b) Repeat part **a)** for a test with three options for each answer.

4 A disc with faces labelled H and T and a cubical die with faces numbered 1 to 6 are thrown together. If the disc shows H, the score recorded is that shown on the die. If the disc shows T, the score recorded is twice that shown on the die.

Find the mean and variance of the score recorded.

5 Let X represent the outcome on a tetrahedral die with faces numbered 1 to 4. Let Y represent the outcome on a cubical die with faces numbered 1 to 6. What are the mean and variance of X and of Y?

A random variable, Z, is found by doubling the outcome on the tetrahedral die and adding it to the outcome on the cubical die, i.e.

$$Z = 2X + Y$$

Write down the possible values of Z and the associated probabilities. Find the expected value of Z and its variance.

CALCULATING VARIANCE: THE GENERAL CASE

The way in which variance has been calculated above included an example of finding the expected value of a function of a random variable. The function involved was the square of the random variable:

$$\mathrm{Var}(X) = \mathrm{E}(X^2) - \text{mean}^2$$

expected value of the square of X

Calculating $\mathrm{E}(X^2)$ involved summing products of x^2 and $P(X = x)$.

Note: It is $P(X = x)$ i.e. the probability of the random variable having the value x rather than x^2.

This is an example of a more general extension to other functions of random variables where the expected value of $f(X)$ is defined as:

$$E(f(X)) = \sum_{all\ x} f(x)P(X = x)$$

We can apply this general principle, in the following example and exercises.

Example 32.6

Louise works for an estate agency. She receives a fixed monthly income, and commission based on the number of houses she sells per month. Her total income, in pounds, is $200X + 400$ where X is the number of houses she sells in the month. The probability of her selling various numbers of houses is shown in this table.

x	1	2	3	4	5	6	7	≥ 8
$P(X = x)$	0.05	0.1	0.25	0.3	0.15	0.1	0.05	0

What is her mean monthly income?

Solution

Louise's income, T, is a function of the random variable X. We need to find the expected value of this function:

$$\begin{aligned} E(T) &= E(200X + 400) \\ &= \sum_{x=1}^{7}(200x + 400)P(X = x) \\ &= 600 \times 0.05 + 800 \times 0.1 + 1000 \times 0.25 + 1200 \times 0.3 + 1400 \times 0.15 \\ &\quad + 1600 \times 0.1 + 1800 \times 0.05 \\ &= 1180 \end{aligned}$$

So, her mean monthly income is £1180.

EXERCISES

32.3 CLASSWORK

1 The random variable, X, has probability function $P(X = x)$ for $x = 1, 2, 3, 4$ as shown in this table.

x	1	2	3	4
$P(X = x)$	0.1	0.2	0.3	0.4

Calculate each of the following.

a) $E(X)$ **b)** $E(2X)$ **c)** $E(2X + 3)$ **d)** $E(5X - 3)$

e) $E(X^2)$ **f)** $E(2X^2)$ **g)** $2E(X) + 3$ **h)** $5E(X) - 3$

Comment on your answers to **c)**, **d)**, **g)** and **h)**.

2 A double-glazing salesman receives a commission for each sale he makes, together with a fixed daily income. The number of sales, X, he makes in a day lies between 0 and 5 with probability as shown in the table.

x	0	1	2	3	4	5
$P(X = x)$	0.4	0.2	0.3	0.05	0.03	0.02

His daily income, Y, is given by:

$$Y = 30X + 20$$

Calculate his expected weekly income assuming he works on five days per week. What is his mean weekly income if he works six days per week?

3 A number, X, can take values 0, 1, 2, 3, 4, 5 and 6 with probabilities as in the table.

x	0	1	2	3	4	5	6
$P(X = x)$	0.005	0.11	0.22	0.33	0.22	0.11	0.005

Calculate:

a) the mean of Y where $Y = 3X - 2$,

b) the variance of Y,

c) the variance of X.

What is the relationship between the variances of X and Y?

4 The number of days that it will take a contractor to complete a particular construction may be represented by a random variable X with the following probability distribution.

x	8	9	10	11	12
$P(X = x)$	0.2	0.4	0.2	0.1	0.1

Calculate the expected value of X.

If the contractor's profit is $Y = £1000(11 - X)$, calculate his expected profit from the construction. Find the probability that the contractor makes a profit of more than £1000 on this construction.

5 The number of students, N, in a German conversation class varies from 1 to 4, with probability as shown in this table.

x	1	2	3	4
$P(N = x)$	0.2	0.25	0.25	0.3

The price, £P per hour, that a student has to pay is given by the following relation.

$$P = 16 - \tfrac{1}{2}N^2$$

a) Find the expected cost per hour for a student willing to join a class of any size, and the variance of the cost.

b) Find the expected income per hour of the teacher, and its variance.

EXERCISES

32.3 HOMEWORK

1 The probability function, $P(X = x)$, for the random variable X is set out in this table.

x	1	2	3
$P(X = x)$	0.2	0.5	0.3

Calculate each of the following.

a) $E(X)$ **b)** $E(1 - 2X)$ **c)** $E(2X)$
d) $1 - 2E(X)$ **e)** $E(X^2)$ **f)** $E(X^2 + X)$

Comment on the relation you see:
i) between the results in **a)**, **b)**, **c)** and **d)**,
ii) between the results in **a)**, **e)** and **f)**.

2 The number, X, of insurance policies sold weekly by a saleswoman and the associated probabilities are given in this table.

x	0	1	2	3	4	5	6	≥ 7
$P(X = x)$	0.3	0.2	0.15	0.1	0.1	0.1	0.05	0

The saleswoman receives a fixed income of £50 per week plus £100 for every insurance policy she sells. Calculate her mean weekly income and its variance.

3 A number, X, can take values 1, 2, 3 and 4 with probabilities given in this table.

x	1	2	3	4
$P(X = x)$	0.2	0.3	0.4	0.1

Calculate:
a) the mean of Y where $Y = 2X - 1$, **b)** the variance of Y,
c) the variance of X.

What is the relationship between the variances of X and Y?

4 The cost of van hire is £24 per day plus a fixed charge of £10. A man estimates the number of days he will need to hire a van and the associated probabilities as shown in this table.

x	2	3	4
$P(X = x)$	0.4	0.35	0.25

a) Express the cost of van hire, C, as a function of the number of days, X.
b) Find his expected cost and the variance.

5 Experience has shown that vehicles emerging from a tunnel have speeds V with the following distributions.

Speed v (mph)	30	40	50	60	70
$P(V = v)$	0.1	0.2	0.3	0.3	0.1

The braking distance at speed v is $v+\frac{v2}{20}$ feet.

What is the mean braking distance for a vehicle coming out of the tunnel? What is the probability that a vehicle coming out will exceed the mean braking distance?

CALCULATOR ACTIVITY

Exploration 32.2

Does your calculator accept probabilities?

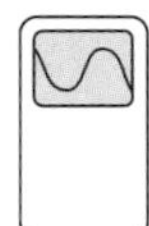

Some statistical calculators will accept data with associated probabilities (as compared to frequencies). You could find out whether yours will, by trying to input the following data in the same way that you would input frequencies.

x	1	2	3	4
$P(X=x)$	0.1	0.3	0.4	0.2

You should find that: $n=1$

$$\sum x = 2.7$$

$$\sum x^2 = 8.$$

if your calculator accepts probabilities.

Σx is really the expected value, $\Sigma x P(X=x)$ and Σx^2 is the expected value of the square of X, $\Sigma x^2 P(X=x)$.

Use your calculator to find the variance of X. It should come out at 0.81.

How might you find the expected value of a function, using your calculator?

Suppose $Y=15-\frac{12}{x}$, then the values of Y and corresponding probabilities are as in this table.

y	3	9	11	12
$P(Y=y)$	0.1	0.3	0.4	0.2

Putting this distribution into the calculator produces:
mean of $Y = 9.8$ variance of $Y = 6.36$.

The outcomes on a single die may be represented as $U(1, n)$. This signifies that they are uniformly distributed with the minimum and maximum possible values as 1 and n respectively. Identify the value of n for a cubical die and for a tretrahedral die.

Mean of uniform distributions

What was the mean of the outcomes on a cubical die? In what way does this mean relate to the distribution U(1, 6)? Do you agree that the mean is 3.5, which can be determined from $\frac{6+1}{2}$?

Now consider U(1, 4) and write down what you think the mean will be. Check with a tetrahedral die.

In general terms, the mean for a random variable which is distributed as U(1, n) is: mean $=\frac{n+1}{2}$

Verify this for an octahedral die with faces numbered 1, 2, … , 8.

Consider the random variable distributed as U(a, b) where a and b are integers and $b = a + n - 1$, so that there are n consecutive numbers in the general discrete uniform variate. What do you think its mean is?

Recall the results on coding from Chapter 29, *Summary statistics 1*. The values of the random variable U(a, b) can readily be obtained from $x \sim$ U(1, n) by a simple translation. This is, in effect, a coding: $Y = X + a - 1$

Hence the mean of Y can be obtained from the mean of X. Show that:

mean of U(a, b) = $\frac{a+b}{2}$.

Variants of uniform distribution

Look back at the outcomes on a cubical die. What was the variance? In what way is the variance related to the minimum and maximum possible values of U(1, 6)?

The value of the variance is conveniently written as $\frac{35}{12}$ or $\frac{6^2-1}{12}$.

Now look back at the outcome on a tetrahedral die and compare the variance in this case. Note that its value 1.25 may be written as $\frac{4^2-1}{12}$.

Thus the variance for a random variable X, distributed as U(1, n) is:

variance = $\frac{n^2-1}{12}$

Verify this for the outcomes on an octahedral die with faces numbered 1, 2. … , 8.

Note: The results on coding found in Chapter 30, *Summary statistics 2* indicate that the variance for the random variable $Y \sim$ U(a, b) is exactly the same as for $X \sim$ U(1, n). This is because the transformation involved in $Y = X + a - 1$ is a translation. Translating has no effect on the spread. Thus for U(a, b):

variance = $\frac{n^2-1}{12} = \frac{1}{12}(b-a)(b-a+2)$

Example 32.7

A disc is marked with 1 on one side and 2 on the other. Let X be the random variable which models the number on the visible face of the disc when it is flipped and lands. Calculate the mean and variance of X.

Solution

An appropriate model for X is:

x	1	2
P($X = x$)	$\frac{1}{2}$	$\frac{1}{2}$

Hence: $\mu_X = 1\frac{1}{2}$ *and* $\sigma_X{}^2 = \frac{1}{4}$

Example 32.8

A tetrahedral die has the numbers 3, 4, 5, 6 on its faces. Consider the distribution of the possible outcomes when the die is randomly rolled.

a) *Describe an appropriate model.*
b) *Write down the value of the mean outcome.*
c) *Verify that the variance of the outcomes is 1.25.*

Solution

a) *An appropriate model is the discrete uniform distribution* $X \sim \mathrm{U}(3, 6)$ *where* $\mathrm{P}(X = x) = \frac{1}{4}$.

b) *The mean is 4.5.*

c) *To verify the variance, establish its value from first principles. Using variance = (mean of squares) – (square of mean) gives:*

$$\text{variance} = \tfrac{1}{4}(3^2 + 4^2 + 5^2 + 6^2) - (4.5)^2$$
$$= 21.5 - 20.25 = 1.25$$

as required.

Example 32.9

A cubical die has the numbers 4, 5, 6, 7, 8, 9 on its faces. The die is rolled randomly and the number on the uppermost face is recorded. Let X *be the random variable which models this outcome. The random variable* Y *is defined by the relationship:* $Y - 3X - 5$.

a) *Write down the mean and the variance of X.*

b) *Determine the mean and variance of Y.*

Solution

a) $X \sim \mathrm{U}(4, 9)$*, hence mean of* $X = \dfrac{4+9}{2} = 6.5$.

There are six consecutive integers in $\mathrm{U}(4, 9)$ *hence the variance of* X *is* $\dfrac{6^2+1}{12} = 2\frac{11}{12}$.

The relationship between Y *and* X *can be treated as coding, hence:*

mean of $Y = 3 \times (\text{mean of } X) - 5 \quad = 14.5$

b) *Variance of* $Y = 3^2 \times (\text{variance of } X) \quad = 9 \times \frac{35}{12} = 25.8$

EXERCISES

32.4 CLASSWORK

1 A regular icosohedron has 20 faces.

a) What is the probability, if it is thrown in the air, that it will land on any given face?

The faces are numbered 1, 2, 3, ... , 20, to make a die. The random variable X represents the number on the face on which the icosohedron lands.

b) Verify that the mean and variance of X are 10.5 and 33.25 respectively.

2 The discrete random variable X has the probability distribution shown.

x	-1	0	1
$\mathrm{P}(X = x)$	$\frac{1}{3}$	$\frac{1}{3}$	$\frac{1}{3}$

Verify that the distribution is uniform and that the mean and variance are given by $\dfrac{n+1}{2}$ and $\dfrac{n^2-1}{12}$ respectively.

3 A contestant in a quiz game scores a mark for a correct response and loses a mark if the response is not correct.

a) Describe as fully as possible an appropriate model for the distribution of marks received for a question.
b) Write down the mean mark and the standard deviation of the mark for a question.
c) Calculate the probability that a contestant's mark for a single response is within two standard deviations of the mean mark for a question.

4 A random variable X has the following distribution:

X	-2	-1	0	1	2
$P(X=x)$	$\frac{1}{5}$	$\frac{1}{5}$	$\frac{1}{5}$	$\frac{1}{5}$	$\frac{1}{5}$

a) State an appropriate model for X.
b) Write down the mean of X.
c) Determine the variance of X.
d) Hence find:
i) $\text{Var}(X+4)$ ii) $\text{Var}(2X)$ iii) $\text{Var}(2X+4)$.

EXERCISE

32.4 HOMEWORK

1 A regular dodecahedron is a solid with 12 faces. A die is made by numbering the faces 1, 2, 3, … , 12. The random variable X represents the number on the face on which the dodecahedron lands.
a) State an appropriate model for X.
b) Verify by direct calculation that the mean and the variance are 6.5 and $11\frac{11}{12}$ respectively.

A second dodecahedral die has the numbers 6, 7, 8, … , 17 on its faces. The random variable Y represents the number on the face on which this die lands.

c) State which of the mean and variance of Y will vary from the parameters for X. Justify your response.

2 The discrete random variable X has the probability distribution $U(-6, -1)$.

a) Write down the mean of X.
b) Determine the standard deviation of X.

3 A computer program generates a random integer R in the range 0–4 inclusive. It independently generates a random integer S in the range 5–9 inclusive. The program is run many thousands of times.

a) State appropriate models for R and S.
b) Write down the means of the distributions of R and S.
c) Explain why the variances of the distributions of R and S are the same, and state this value.

4 X is a discrete uniform variate modelled as $U(2, 5)$. Y is a discrete uniform variate modelled as $U(-6, -3)$. Calculate the mean and variance of:

a) X b) Y c) $X-8$ d) $2Y+12$ e) $5-2X$
f) $2X+5$ g) $6-Y$ h) $-5Y$

CONSOLIDATION EXERCISES FOR CHAPTER 32

1 A fairground stallholder invites contestants to shuffle a pack of cards and turn over the top card. The contestant wins a prize (and receives the stake money back) according to the poster. If the stake money is 10p, calculate the expected gain to the stallholder.

Turn the Ace of Spades into
£5

2 Two bags each contain five identical discs. Each set of discs has the numbers 1 to 5 painted on them. A gambler randomly selects one disc from each bag and adds the two numbers. The gambler then receives a prize or pays a forfeit according to the sum obtained.

Determine the expected gain to the gambler.

Sum	Prize	Forfeit
2	£1.00	
3	20p	
4		10p
5		10p
6		40p
7		10p
8		10p
9	20p	
10	£1.00	

3 A boy and a girl play a game where they take turns to select (at random) one ball from a bag containing four blue and four red balls. They keep the ball selected on each occasion. The winner is the first one to select a red ball. Calculate the probability that the game ends with the first, second, third, fourth, fifth ball drawn. What is the mean number of balls drawn?

4 In the competition 'Brain of Britain', contestants are asked a series of questions until they fail to provide a correct answer or they provide five correct answers consecutively. They receive a point for every correct answer and a bonus point for five correct answers. What is the expected number of points a contestant is awarded if her chance of correctly answering a question is $\frac{1}{2}$?

5 Two ordinary dice are thrown. If the sum of the outcomes is 12 the player receives £1.00. The player receives 50p if the sum is 10 or 11. For any other sum, the player pays 10p. What is the expected win for the player?

6 By choosing a suitable example, or otherwise, establish that:

$$E(X^2)-\{E(X)\}^2 \neq 0$$

What is this difference known as? Under what circumstance is this difference zero?

7 A discrete variable X has probability distribution specified in this table.

x	-1	0	1	2
$P(X=x)$	0.25	0.10	0.45	0.20

a) Find $P(-1 \leq x < 1)$.
b) Find $E(2X+2)$.

(ULSEB Question 2, S1/S10, June 1993)

8 A box contains eight discs of which five are red and the remainder green. Three discs are withdrawn at random without replacement.

Calculate:

a) the probability that all three are green,

b) the probability that none of the three is green,

c) the expected number of green discs withdrawn.

9 A quiz team of three is to be selected from a group of four women and five men. If the members of the team are selected at random, calculate the expected number of women and the variance of the number of women.

10 A company uses computers in its business. The company replaces a certain number of computers each year, depending on the reliability of individual machines in the previous year. If the number of computers purchased is represented by the random variable X, the probabilities associated with the possible values of X are shown in this table.

x	0	1	2	3	≥4
$P(X=x)$	0.1	0.3	0.4	0.2	0

The cost of a new computer is £1200. A reduction of $£50x^2$ is offered by a supplier. What amount does the company expect to spend on new computers at the end of the year?

11 A wealthy businessman has his own private aeroplane. He wants to insure it for £250 000. An insurance company estimates that the likelihood of:

- a total loss is 0.0025,
- a 50 per cent loss is 0.01,
- a ten per cent loss is 0.1.

The company wants to make an expected annual profit of £2000 in providing this insurance.

What premium should it charge?

12 A simplified game of *Pontoon* is played as follows.

A player has two packs of cards in front of him and he picks one card at random from each pack. The score for each card is the numerical face value, except that jacks, queens and kings are worth 10 and an ace is worth 11. The overall score for a game is the sum of the scores on the two cards. By considering all possible pairs, write down the distribution of the total score on the two cards and find its mean and variance. If the rules said a player had to beat 14 to win a game, would he be happy?

13 The discrete random variable X has the probability function shown below.

x	1	2	3	4	5
$P(X=x)$	0.2	a	a	0.2	b

For this distribution $E(X) = 3$.

a) Find the values of a and b.

b) Write down the name of the distribution of X.

c) Find $\text{Var}(X)$.

(EDEXCEL Paper T1, Question 3, January 2000)

14 When a certain type of cell is subjected to radiation, the cell may die, survive as a single cell or divide into two cells with probabilities $\frac{1}{2}$, $\frac{1}{3}$, $\frac{1}{6}$ respectively.

Two cells are independently subjected to radiation. The random variable X represents the total number of cells in existence after this experiment.

a) Show that $P(X = 2) = \frac{5}{18}$.
b) Find the probability distribution for X.
c) Evaluate $E(X)$.
d) Show that $\mathrm{Var}(X) = \frac{10}{9}$.

(EDEXCEL Paper T1, Question 6, January 1999)

15 The discrete random variable X has the probability function shown in the table below.

x	1	2	3	4	5
$P(X = x)$	0.2	0.3	0.3	0.1	0.1

Find

a) $P(2 < X \leq 4)$,
b) $E(3.7)$,
c) $E(X)$,
d) $\mathrm{Var}(X)$,
e) $E(X^2 + 4X - 3)$.

(EDEXCEL Paper T1, Question 5, June 1998)

Summary

- The expectation of a function is the same as the mean.
- The expected value of a function is the mean value of the function.
- In games of chance: expected gain = E(gain) = $\sum$gain × probability
- For a fair game, E(gain) = 0.
- For probability distributions:
  expected value $= E(X) = \sum_{\text{all } x} x \times P(X = x)$ = mean
  variance $= E(X^2) - (\text{mean})^2$
- Expected value of a function $= E(g(X)) = \sum_{\text{all } x} g(x) \times P(X = x)$
- For the uniform discrete distribution: mean is $\frac{n+1}{2}$
  variance is $\frac{n^2 - 1}{12}$

Bivariate data

In this chapter we investigate:

- *how to present linked pairs of data and how to explore the nature of the link between the two variables,*
- *one way of modelling a linear relationship,*

SCATTERGRAPHS AND COVARIANCE

All the random variables we have studied so far have been single variables or **univariates**. We shall now study **two-variable** or **bivariate data**. An example of bivariate data is given here.

Time (minutes)		
Conditions:	Dry	Wet
Runner	X	Y
A	35.5	37.4
B	40.4	40.5
C	38.8	39.6
D	39.9	39.8
E	38.0	37.1
F	37.2	36.1
G	34.7	36.7
H	37.9	36.8

The data are the times taken by eight young runners in two 10 km races. The races were run on the all-weather track at their school under different weather conditions. What are the mean times in the dry and in the wet for these runners? $\bar{x} = 37.8$ and $\bar{y} = 38.0$

This seems to indicate that the runners take about $\frac{2}{10}$ of a minute more in the wet than in the dry. Is there any other comment you could make about the times?

It is clearly possible to identify the way the times are spread out. The standard deviations of the times are: $s_x \approx 1.853$ and $s_y \approx 1.580$

This suggests that there is more of a spread of times in the dry.

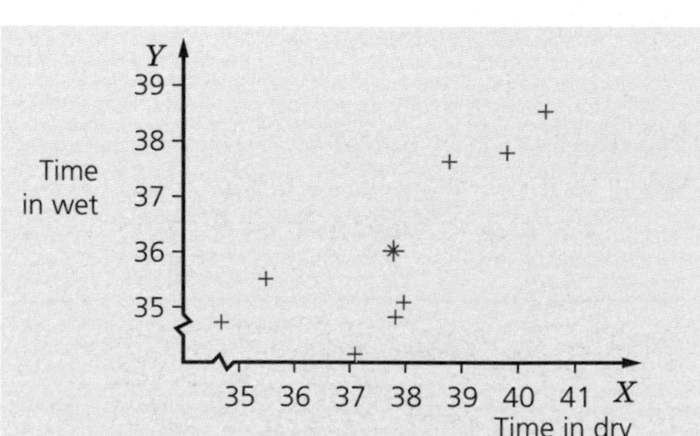

In this elementary analysis we have treated the data as two collections of single variables. However, there are two times given for each runner. This allows us to make a valid pairing of the times and so treat the data as bivariate. Then we can display the data graphically in a scattergraph or scatter diagram.

What does this display suggest about the time a runner takes in the dry and the time taken in the wet?

The display suggests a link or **positive correlation** between the times. This means that longer dry times are associated with longer wet times and shorter dry times are associated with shorter wet times.

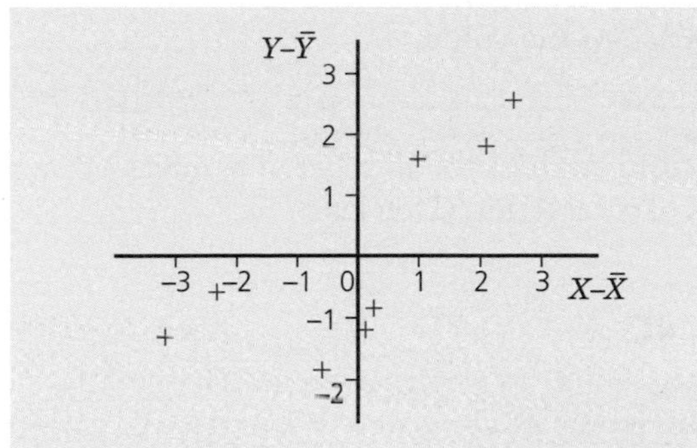

The point (37.8, 38.0), marked differently on the scattergraph is the **mean point**, i.e. the point with the two means as its coordinates. Notice that virtually all the points representing the actual data are either *above and to the right* or *below and to the left* of the mean point. This is a feature of bivariate data which are positively correlated. This graph shows the data related to the respective means. It was produced from the data in the table below in which the respective means were subtracted from the individual times.

Times relative to means		
Runner	$X-\bar{X}$	$Y-\bar{Y}$
G	−3.1	−1.3
A	−2.3	−0.6
F	−0.6	−1.9
H	+0.1	−1.2
E	+0.2	−0.9
C	+1.0	+1.6
D	+2.1	+1.8
B	+2.6	+2.5

The runners at the points which are above and to the right of the mean are C, D and B. What do the relative times of these three runners have in common? The pair of relative times for each of C, D and B are positive. Now consider the runners whose points are below and to the left of the mean point. What do their relative times have in common? These are G, A and F and in each case the pairs of relative times are negative.

The times for each of these six runners show a positive correlation. The 'same sign' nature,

(+, +) or (− , −)

of their times **relative to the mean** is an indicator of positive correlation. The remaining two runners, H and E, have times which are not positively correlated. How do their relative times indicate this? We can see that these have opposite signs:

(+, −)

If the product of a runner's relative times is formed then that product has the same sign as the nature of the correlation shown in the runner's times. The products of the relative times for each runner is shown below.

Runner	G	A	F	H	E	C	D	B	Total
Product $(X-\bar{X})\times(Y-\bar{Y})$	+4.03	+1.38	+1.14	−0.12	−0.18	+1.6	+3.78	+6.5	+18.13

The total, 18.13, of these products provides one measure of the correlation. This total, +18.13 is positive. What would happen to the total if more runners' times were included? Suppose the new times, generally, also showed positive correlation, it seems quite reasonable that there would be an increase in the value:

$$\sum_{\text{all runners}} \left\{ \left(x - \bar{x} \right) \left(y - \bar{y} \right) \right\}$$

It would be sensible to take into account the number of runners by finding the average amount of correlation. This leads to:

$$\frac{\Sigma\left\{ \left(x - \bar{x} \right) \left(y - \bar{y} \right) \right\}}{n}$$

where n is the number of runners, or in general, the number of data pairs. This measure is known as the **covariance** of X and Y.

There are two common notations in use:

$$\begin{aligned} \text{cov}(x, y) &= s_{xy} \\ &= \frac{1}{n} \sum_{\text{all }(x,y)} \left\{ \left(x - \bar{x} \right) \left(y - \bar{y} \right) \right\} \end{aligned}$$

So the covariance of the times for the two 10 km races is:

$$\begin{aligned} s_{xy} &= \frac{18.13}{8} \\ &\approx 2.266 \end{aligned}$$

Exploration 33.1

KEY SKILLS
N 3.2
N 3.3
IT 3.2
IT 3.3

Covariance

a) **i)** Calculate the mean times, $\bar{u}$, $\bar{v}$ for the following collection of data.

U (s)	2082	2120	2232	2274	2280	2328	2394	2424
V (s)	2202	2244	2166	2208	2226	2376	2388	2430

ii) Calculate the times relative to their respective means.

iii) Plot a scattergraph of these data and compare with the previous scattergraph.

iv) Demonstrate that the covariance of U and V is 8158.5 and comment on its value.

b) The same eight runners, A to H take part in a 10 km race on grass. The weather conditions were dry. These are their results.

Runner	A	B	C	D	E	F	G	H
Time, z, (minutes)	37.5	39.1	38.5	38.8	38.0	37.6	36.7	37.8

i) Calculate the mean, $\bar{z}$ of these race times.

ii) Calculate, the covariance of the all-weather 'dry' time and the grass track 'dry' time. Comment on the value.

iii) Draw a scattergraph showing the dry weather times for each of the eight runners on the two types of surface. Comment on the link between the times.

Product moment correlation coefficient

Let us look back to the data in Exploration 33.1 part **a)**. This is the same as the original data for the runners' times, the only changes that have been made are in the units used i.e. seconds as opposed to minutes, and in the order of the runners: G, A, F, H, E, C, D, B. This means that these data should show exactly the same correlation, but the two covariances are very different.

$\text{cov}(x, y) \approx 2.266 \ldots$
$\text{cov}(u, v) \approx 8158.5$

This is decidedly unsatisfactory. The measure of correlation should be independent of the units of measurement used but changing units from minutes to seconds seems to change the spread of the data. The standard deviations found above were:

s_x 1.853 $\qquad$ s_y 1.580
and for the times in seconds
s_u 111.2 $\qquad$ s_v 94.77

Try dividing the covariance by each of the relevant standard deviations.

You should find:

$$\frac{s_{xy}}{(s_x s_y)} = \frac{2.266}{(1.853 \times 1.580)} \approx 0.774$$

$$\frac{s_{uv}}{(s_u s_v)} = \frac{8158.5}{(111.2 \times 94.77)} \approx 0.774$$

so these measures agree with each other. Clearly, this is a far more satisfactory measure of correlation. It is known as **Pearson's product moment correlation coefficient** (PMCC). It is usually represented by r.

Definition: $r = \dfrac{s_{xy}}{(s_x s_y)}$

Exploration 33.2

Calculating r

Calculate the product moment correlation coefficient for the dry weather 10 km race times, i.e. calculate:

$$r = \frac{s_{xz}}{(s_x s_z)}$$

Comment on the result.

(You should find $r \approx 0.967$ which suggests a more positive correlation between the 'dry' times than between the times for the all-weather track. Is this the conclusion you reached in Exploration 33.1b?)

An alternative approach

The way in which the covariance is calculated: $\frac{1}{n}\Sigma\{(x-\bar{x})(y-\bar{y})\}$ is fraught with potential for 'rounding' errors and subsequent errors in the value of the product moment correlation coefficient. You may recall the way in which variance was introduced in Chapter 30, *Summary statistics 2*.

$$s_x^2 = \tfrac{1}{n}\Sigma(x-\bar{x})^2$$

which was shown to be exactly the same as: $s_x^2 = \frac{1}{n}\Sigma x^2 - \bar{x}^2$

i.e. the mean of the squares minus the square of the mean. The covariance can be calculated in an exactly similar way: $s_{xy} = \frac{1}{n}\Sigma xy - \bar{x}\,\bar{y}$

i.e. **the mean of the products minus the product of the means.**

The advantage of this is that the original data are used rather than the relative data and that the means we need only enter the calculation at the end.

In the case of the all weather track data:

$$\begin{aligned}\Sigma xy &= 35.5 \times 37.4 + 40.4 \times 40.5 + \ldots + 37.9 \times 36.8 \\ &= 11\,509.33\end{aligned}$$

Hence the covariance is:

$$\begin{aligned}s_{xy} &= \frac{11509.33}{8} - 37.8 \times 38.0 \\ &\approx 2.266\end{aligned}$$

Exploration 33.3

Mean of products minus product of means

a) Calculate the covariance, s_{xz}, using this alternative method. (1.305)

b) **i)** Calculate the covariance, s_{yz}.

ii) Show that the correlation coefficient between the all-weather 'wet' times and the 'dry' grass times is 0.867.

Exploration 33.4

CALCULATOR ACTIVITY

Bivariate data

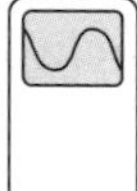

Will your calculator accept bivariate data? Will it enable you to evaluate:

a) covariance, **b)** the product moment correlation coefficient, r? Find out.

Interpretation of *r*

Pearson's product moment correlation coefficient, r is a sound measure of correlation. It will always lie between –1 and +1. The closer it is to these values, the greater the degree of correlation, or more strictly, **linear correlation** in the data. If r is close to zero, it is unlikely that there is any linear correlation in the data. The sign of the coefficient is an indication of the positive or negative nature of the correlation.

Example 33.1

The eight runners who have featured in this chapter also recorded times for a 10 km race carried out on grass in wet weather. Their times are shown below.

Runner	A	B	C	D	E	F	G	H
Wet grass time, W (minutes)	38.5	40.6	40.3	40.4	39.9	42.3	39.6	43.2
Wet all weather time, Y (minutes)	37.4	40.5	39.6	39.8	37.1	36.1	36.7	36.8

(The wet all-weather track times are also reproduced for convenience.)

a) *Plot a scattergraph for these data, comment on the correlation exhibited in them.*

b) *Calculate the product moment correlation coefficient for these data and interpret its value.*

Solution

a)

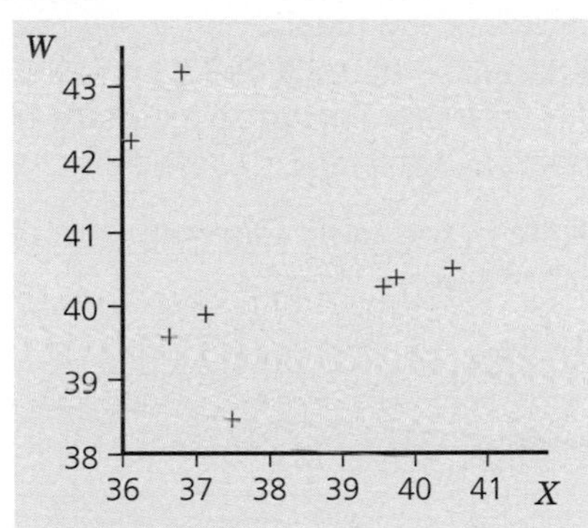

The runners who are fast in the wet on the all-weather track seem to be slow in the wet on grass. But the slower all-weather track runners do not seem to be noticeably fast or slow on grass in similar conditions.

b) $\Sigma yw = 12\,338.4$, *hence the covariance is:*

$s_{yw} = -0.5$

and the correlation coefficient is

$$r \approx \frac{-0.5}{(1.5796 \times 1.4)} \approx -0.266$$

The sign indicates a negative correlation in the data. However, the value, –0.226, is not close to 1, so it is unlikely that there is any linear correlation.

EXERCISES

33.1 CLASSWORK

KEY SKILLS
N 3.2
N 3.3

1 Explain what Pearson's product moment correlation coefficient measures. Why is this a better measure of correlation than covariance?

x, km	69	65	62	61	59	70	71	75
y, $	0.52	0.25	0.55	0.20	0.62	0.47	0.25	0.37

a) Calculate the covariance of the data in the table. What inference are you able to draw from the value you have calculated?

b) Calculate the product moment correlation coefficient for these data and comment on its value.

c) The variables u, v are defined as:
$u = x - 65$, $v = 100(y - 0.40)$.
Determine the value of $\text{cov}(u, v)$ and compare this with the covariance you found in **a)**.

d) What is the product moment correlation coefficient of the transformed data? Comment.

e) Plot a scattergraph of the data and comment on the relationship between unit cost, $\$y$, and length, x km.

2 **a)** Plot a scattergraph of the data in the table below.

Date: x	10	11	12	13	14	15	16	17	18	19
Milk yield: y	1183	1159	1288	1254	1269	1274	1316	1318	1399	1322

b) Do the data exhibit correlation?
c) Calculate the mean:
i) date, **ii)** milk yield, **iii)** product.
d) Use your calculation to estimate the value of Pearson's product moment correlation coefficient for these data. Comment.

3 The data in the table represent the total live births recorded for a period of twelve months.

Month: x	1	2	3	4	5	6	7	8	9	10	11	12
Live births: y (1000s)	63.5	73.0	67.4	69.7	65.9	67.2	62.9	63.6	63.1	59.2	59.9	61.7

a) Plot a scattergraph for these data. Identify the data pair which may be termed an outlier. Comment on the correlation of the data.
b) Calculate the product moment correlation coefficient for these data:
i) excluding the outlier, **ii)** including the outlier.
c) Comment on the results of your calculations.

4 The data represent the recorded crime rate (per thousand households) over a period of a year. The crime rate is calculated on the last day of each month. Use a code to represent the month and calculate the product moment correlation coefficient for the data. What interpretation do you put on its value?

Month	Jan	Feb	Mar	Apr	May	June	July	Aug	Sep	Oct	Nov	Dec
Crime rate	45.5	43.5	43.9	47.0	54.7	64.3	71.9	76.0	77.0	76.9	76.4	75.4

5 Explain why each of the following statements may be incorrect.
a) When the product moment correlation coefficient is close to zero the two variables are not associated.
b) If the product moment correlation coefficient is 0.975 then an increase in one variable causes an increase in the other.
c) Flowers in a garden are watered and the correlation coefficient between the petal size and the amount of water given is 0.073, so it follows that there is no relation between petal size and quantity of water given to the flower.

EXERCISES

33.1 HOMEWORK

KEY SKILLS
N 3.2
N 3.3

1 The yield per hectare of a crop is supposed to depend on the amount of rainfall in the month preceding its harvest. Nine areas are monitored and the values of yield (y) and the corresponding rainfall (x) are recorded. The results are given in the table below.

x	14.7	10.3	18.6	13.4	14.7	13.6	16.7	11.7	12.1
y	8.3	10.2	15.3	6.4	11.8	12.0	13.4	11.9	9.9

a) Plot a scatter diagram of the data and comment on whether the diagram supports the theory that there is a linear association between y and x.
b) Calculate the covariance of x and y.
c) You are given that the standard deviations of x and y are $s_x = 2.4160$ and $s_y = 2.5165$. Use these together with part **b)** to calculate the product moment correlation coefficient.
d) Does your answer to **c)** support your answer to **a)**? Give reasons.

2

Student	A	B	C	D	E	F	G	H	I	J
French mark (x)	56	50	72	67	31	50	65	40	80	61
German mark (y)	60	50	67	75	64	56	73	48	76	62

a) Plot a scattergraph for the above data and identify the outlier. Suggest reasons to account for it.
b) Calculate the product moment correlation coefficient for these data:
i) including the outlier, **ii)** excluding the outlier.
Comment.

3 State in each case whether you would expect a positive correlation, a negative correlation or no correlation.

a) total weight of passengers on a bus and its fuel consumption in miles per gallon
b) number of hours piano practice and number of wrong notes
c) shoe size and mean number of hours sleep
d) ice-cream sales and sales of sunglasses

4 A student calculated the product moment correlation coefficient between height above sea level and mean July temperature for a number of towns.

Heights were given in feet and temperatures in degrees Fahrenheit. She wanted to find the product moment correlation coefficient between heights in metres and temperatures in degrees Celsius. If there are 3.28 feet per metre, and if temperature °C = $\frac{5}{9}$(°F – 32), how should she correct her calculations?

5 Use diagrams to help to provide an explanation of the terms:

a) perfect correlation, **b)** zero correlation.

LEAST SQUARES REGRESSION MODEL

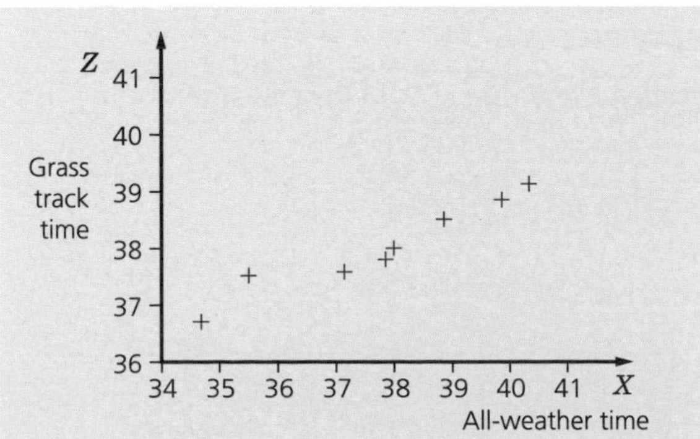

In Exploration 33.2 you probably found that the correlation coefficient between the 'dry' times is 0.967. This is sufficient evidence to support the view that there is positive linear correlation between the times to race 10 km on an all-weather track and on a grass track when the weather conditions are dry. Linear correlation suggests that a straight line is a reasonable model for the relationship between the two variates, Z and X.

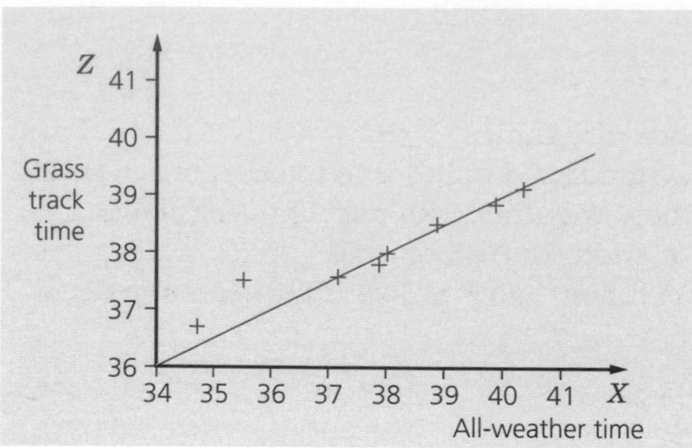

There are several ways of arriving at a linear model for bivariate data. The one we shall study is known as a **least squares regression line** or, simply, a **regression line**. However, before formally considering the derivation of this line, let us look at this diagram.

A line has been drawn representing a model for the relationship. This line passes through the points with coordinates:

(36.0, 37.0) and (40.0, 39.0)

It therefore, has gradient, m, where:

$$m = \frac{39 - 37}{40 - 36} = 0.5$$

Since, it passes through (36, 37) and has a gradient of 0.5, its equation is:

$$\hat{Z} - 37 = 0.5(X - 36)$$

(the hat symbol, $\hat{Z}$, is used to distinguish model from data). This can be rearranged into:

$$\hat{Z} = 0.5X + 19$$

The 'squares' referred to in the 'least squares regression' are the squares of the residuals of the difference between the data and the model i.e. $(Z - \hat{Z})^2$. More precisely, it is the total of all these squared residuals for each of the eight points. For the model:

$$\hat{Z} = 0.5X + 19$$

The calculation of this sum of squared residuals is shown in this table.

Data		Model	Squared difference
X	Z	$\hat{Z} = 0.5X + 19$	$(Z - \hat{Z})^2$
35.5	37.5	36.75	0.5625
40.4	39.1	39.2	0.01
38.8	38.5	38.4	0.01
39.9	38.8	38.95	0.0225
38.0	38.0	38.0	0.0
37.2	37.6	37.6	0.0
34.7	36.7	36.35	0.1225
37.9	37.8	37.95	0.0225
		$\sum\left\{(Z - \hat{Z})^2\right\} =$	0.75

This particular model produces a value of 0.75 for the sum of the squared differences.

Exploration 33.5 *Sum of squared residuals*

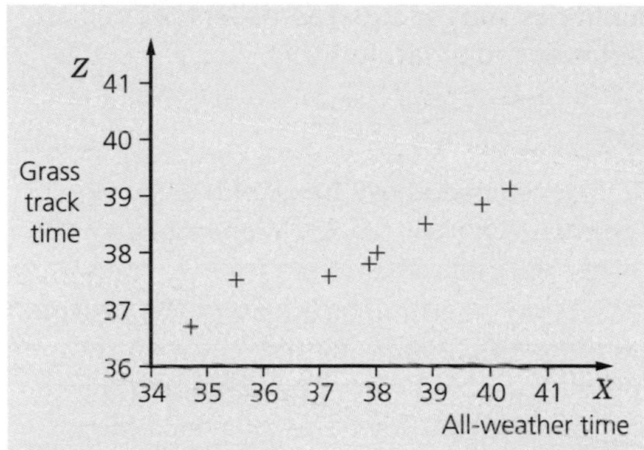

Make a copy on graph paper of this diagram, from the data on pages 636 and 638. On your copy draw what you think is an appropriate straight line to model the relationship. Now *calculate* the equation of the line you have drawn. Use the same process of identifying two points on the line, as above.

Continue with the process and obtain the value of:

$$\sum\left\{\left(Z-\hat{Z}\right)^2\right\}$$

for your linear model. Compare the value you obtain with the one on this page.

KEY SKILLS
N 3.2
N 3.3
IT 3.2
IT 3.3

Gradient of the least squares regression line

The 'least squares regression' line is the linear model which produces the smallest possible value for the sum of the squared differences between data and model. The least squares line always passes through the **mean point** which implies that its equation is of the form:

$$\hat{Z}-\overline{Z} = \text{gradient} \times (X-\overline{X})$$

The gradient of the least squares line is the ratio of the covariance of x and z to the variance of x. In other words:

$$\text{gradient} = \frac{s_{xz}}{s_x^{\,2}}$$

which leads to the equation for the least squares regression line:

$$z-\overline{z} = \frac{s_{xz}}{s_x^{\,2}}(x-\overline{x})$$

For these data, $s_{xz} = 1.305$ and $s_x^{\,2} = 3.435$, which leads to the least squares model.

$$\hat{z}-38.0 = \frac{1.305}{3.435}(x-37.8)$$

Simplifying this:

$$\hat{z} \approx 23.6393\ldots + 0.379913x$$

The value of the sum of squared differences:

$$\sum\left\{\left(Z-\hat{Z}\right)^2\right\} = 0.2737\ldots$$

which is smaller than the total for the model on page 643/4.

Exploration 33.6 *Calculating the regression equation*

In Exploration 33.3 you showed that the correlation coefficient between all-weather wet condition times and grass track dry condition times was 0.867. This indicates that there is a positive linear relation between the times. Calculate the regression equation:

$$\hat{z}-\overline{z} = m(y-\overline{y})$$

and show that it can be rearranged into:

$$\hat{z} \approx 22.8076 + 0.3998\, y$$

Hence show that the minimum sum of squared differences between data and model is approximately 1.050.

Factor and response

Each of the regression models developed above has treated the dry grass race time as being *dependent upon* or being a *response to* another variable. In each case, the other variable was a race time on the all-weather track. The all-weather time is given the status of the **factor** producing the response. It is important to distinguish between the factor variable and the response variable before embarking on the calculation of the equation of a regression line. The 'response-factor' issue may be reflected in the description given to a regression. For instance, the regression model:

$$\hat{z} = 23.64 + 0.3799x$$

developed earlier can be described as the equation of the line of regression of z on x to indicate that the response, z, depends on the factor, x.

It may be relevant to calculate the equation of the line of regression of x on z. In which case, the equation would be:

$$\hat{x} - \bar{x} = \frac{s_{xz}}{s_z^{\,2}}\left(z - \bar{z}\right)$$

The model would be trying to fit all-weather track times for each given dry grass time. This is different from the process which leads to the $\hat{z}$ model. The $\hat{x}$ model turns out to be:

$$\hat{x} - 37.8 = \frac{1.305}{0.53}(z - 38.0)$$

This x on z model is derived by minimising $\sum\left\{(x - \hat{x})^2\right\}$ not $\sum\left\{(z - \hat{z})^2\right\}$. The equation simplifies to give:

$$\hat{x} = 2.462\,264\,\hat{z} - 55.766$$

Is it obvious that the two models are not the same? When this $\hat{x}$ model is rearranged as:

$$z = 22.65 + 0.4061\hat{x}$$

it can be compared directly to the $\hat{z}$ model:

$$\hat{z} = 23.64 + 0.3799x$$

We can now see that the two equations do not represent the same straight line.

Example 33.2

A young sprinter was looking back over the best times she had recorded in 100 m races each year. The times are shown in the table.

Ages, a (years)	12	13	14	15	16	17	18	19
Time, T (seconds)	19.1	15.5	15.1	14.6	12.2	12.1	11.3	10.8

a) *Calculate the product moment correlation coefficient for these data. Comment on the value you obtain.*

b) *Calculate the equation of an appropriate least squares regression line model for these data.*

c) *Provide an interpretation for the gradient of the line.*

d) *Use the equation you have calculated to predict the best time the sprinter will take for 100 m when she is aged:*
i) 20 ii) 30.
Comment on the predictions.

Solution

a) *The correlation coefficient is:*

$$r = \frac{s_{at}}{s_a s_t} = \frac{5.65625}{\sqrt{5.25}\sqrt{6.749\,84}} \approx -0.9502$$

This indicates that there is negative correlation between the sprinter's age and her best time for 100 m. The value obtained is a strong indicator of a linear model.

b) *You need to decide which of the variables is the response and which is the factor. The sprinter's best 100 m time is dependent on her age. Hence the regression equation needed is the 'time on age':*

$$\hat{t} - \bar{t} = \frac{s_{at}}{s_a^{\,2}}(a - \bar{a})$$

i.e.

$$\hat{t} - 13.8375 = \frac{-5.656\,25}{5.25}(a - 15.5)$$

which simplifies to:

$$\hat{t} = 30.5369 - 1.0774a$$

c) *The gradient, – 1.0774, indicates that the sprinter's best time reduces by 1.0774 seconds each year.*

d) *This requires us to use the equation to find the values of* $\hat{t}$ *for* $a = 20$ *and* $a = 30$.

i) $\hat{t}(20) = 30.5369 - 1.0774 \times 20 = 8.99$

ii) $\hat{t}(30) = 30.5369 - 1.0774 \times 30 = -1.78$

Note

The first of the values suggests that this sprinter is likely to be a world record holder by the time she is 20. The second value is utterly ridiculous! The first is unlikely, the second is impossible.

The final part of Example 33.2 raises an important issue regarding the use of regression lines. A regression line provides a linear model which is valid only in the range of the factor variable. Using the model outside the range of the factor is not justified and can, clearly, lead to silly results.

A further issue is that of cause and effect. Clearly the sprinter's times improved as she got older. But was her age the cause of the improvement? It may be a contributory factor but other factors such as training are going to play a role. Try to avoid confusing correlation with causation.

CALCULATOR ACTIVITY

Exploration 33.7

Regression calculations

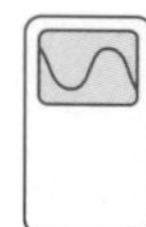

Calculators which allow bivariate data to be input often offer regression calculations. The model they often use is the equation of the line of regression of y on x and they present this in the simplified form:

$\hat{y} = a + bx$

Use the data from Example 33.2 to discover how to extract the regression coefficients, a and b, and model predictions, $\hat{y}$, from your statistical calculator.

EXERCISES

33.2 CLASSWORK

1 A survey of children in a primary school revealed the following data.

Age of child, a	4	5	6	7	8	9	10	11	12
Pocket money, p	25	80	100	130	140	140	200	180	250

a) Plot the data on a scattergraph. Mark the mean point.
b) Draw a line, through the mean point, which you feel is an appropriate model for the relationship between age and pocket money.
c) Calculate the equation of the line you have drawn and use this to determine the residuals. Determine the sum of the squared residuals.
d) Determine the product moment correlation coefficient for the data. What interpretation is it reasonable to put on its value?
e) Calculate the equation of the line of regression of pocket money on age.
f) Use this equation to determine the sum of squared residuals and compare this with the result you obtained in **c)**.

2 **a)** Determine the equation of the line of regression of y on x for the data.

x	3	5	7	9	11	13	15	17	19	21
y	8	13	15	18	20	24	26	30	31	34

b) Use your equation to provide an estimate of y when $x = 10$.
c) Explain briefly why it is inappropriate to use the equation in **a)** to determine what value of x gives rise to $y = 25$.
d) Why is it inappropriate to use the equation in **a)** to provide an estimate of y when $x = 30$?

3 There is a belief that the risk of heart disease is negatively related to the red wine intake.

Wine intake	3	3.5	4	5	6	8	10	25	35	75	80
Heart disease risk	72	65	108	61	53	58	47	43	31	21	18

a) Determine the correlation coefficient for the data in the table. Does this support the belief?

b) Use an appropriate least squares regression line to estimate the risk when the wine intake is 52.

c) Calculate the equation of the least squares regression line which is appropriate to estimate the wine intake for a given heart disease risk. Comment on this process.

4 Drinking water goes through a variety of purification processes before it enters the domestic supply. A new filtration process is tested for its effectiveness in removing suspended matter from flowing water.

Flow of water, x	1	2	3	6	10	20
Measure of removal, y	0.36	0.30	0.27	0.10	0.051	0.022

A) a) Determine the product moment correlation coefficient for these data.

b) Calculate the equation of the line of regression of removal (y) on flow (x).

c) How do you interpret the gradient of this equation?

d) Estimate the removal of suspended matter when the flow is:
i) 5 **ii)** 15 **iii)** 25.

e) Comment on the likely reliability of each of the estimates.

B) An alternative model of the relationship between the flow (x) and the removal (y) is:

$$\frac{1}{y} = a + bx$$

a) Calculate the product moment correlation coefficient between x and $\frac{1}{y}$. Compare this with the value in **A) a)**.

b) Using an appropriate least squares method, determine values of a and b.

c) Use your new equation to estimate the removal when the flow is 15.

5 An Investigation in the development of the ear of a cocker spaniel produced the following data.

Age (weeks)	2	4	8	9	10	12	15
Area	6	18	45	57	68	112	245

a) Calculate the product moment correlation coefficient of age and area.

b) A model of the development of a dog in its puppy stage is proposed where the relationship between age and ear area is quadratic. Calculate the product moment correlation coefficient of $(\text{age})^2$ and area.

c) Determine an appropriate model of the relationship between age and ear area, based on these data.

EXERCISES

33.2 HOMEWORK

1 The value of two variables, x and y, are recorded on eight separate occasions during the course of an experiment. The values are given in the table below.

x	2	4	6	8	10	12	14	16
y	11.9	11.0	10.3	9.5	9.1	8	7.3	6.6

a) It is suspected that there might be a linear relationship between x and y.
Calculate the product moment correlation coefficient r and state with reasons whether you believe that such a relationship exists.
b) Show that the regression line of y on x is $y = 12.6 - 0.374x$.
c) Calculate the equation of the regression line of x on y.
d) By looking at the table explain why it may not be very useful to obtain the regression line of x on y.

2 Two variables x and y are supposed to be related by a law of the form $y = a + bx$.

An experiment yields the following parts of values for x and y.

x	1	2	3	4	5	6	7
y	1.0	2.5	1.7	2.0	3.0	5.0	4.5

a) Calculate the regression line of y on x.
b) Calculate the product moment correlation coefficient, r.
c) Determine the sum of the squared residuals in this case and verify that it is equal to $n(1 - r^2)s_y^{\,2}$.

3 The amount of a chemical, y (in grams), is related to the time, t (in seconds), for which a particular chemical reaction has been taking place. The table below gives the observations taken during the conduct of an experiment involving this reaction.

Time, t (s)	300	430	600	790	900	1200
Quantity, y (g)	7	9	15	22	23	29

a) Calculate the product moment correlation coefficient, r, for the data and state, with reasons, whether you think that the relationship between y and t is a linear one.
b) Which variable is the factor and which is the response?
c) Calculate the equation of the appropriate regression line, bearing in mind your answer to **b)**.
d) Predict the average amount of chemical produced after:
i) 800 seconds,
ii) 2000 seconds.
Comment on the reliability of each prediction.

4 A medical researcher recorded the level of absorption (y) corresponding to given doses (x) of a specific drug.

x	1	2	3	4	5
y	0.95	0.72	0.62	0.57	0.49

a) Plot a scatter diagram of y against x and calculate the equation of the regression line of y on x in the form $y = a + bx$.
b) The researcher believes that x and y may be related by an equation of the form $\frac{1}{x} + \frac{1}{y} = \frac{1}{k}$, where k is a constant. Plot a scatter diagram of $\frac{1}{y}$ against $\frac{1}{x}$ and calculate the equation of the regression of $\frac{1}{y}$ on $\frac{1}{x}$ in the form $\frac{1}{y} = a + \frac{b}{x}$. Compare the gradient, b with that predicted by the researcher's equation.
c) Compare the two models for the data.

CONSOLIDATION EXERCISES FOR CHAPTER 33

1

x	4.3	4.9	9.0	10.2	11.8	17.0	21.2	23.0
y	5.2	5.3	6.8	12.6	15.0	16.5	21.6	27.2

a) Plot a scattergraph of the data.
b) Calculate the value of the product moment correlation coefficient.
c) Explain whether you feel that the variables are linearly related.

2 An experiment is set up which involves suspending various masses from a coiled metal spring. The total length of the spring is measured for each mass. The results are shown in the table.

Mass (x)	5	10	15	20	25	30	40	50
Length (y)	143	150	158	160	163	170	180	193

a) Determine the equation of the line of regression of length on mass in the form: $y = a + bx$
b) Use your equation to estimate the length of the spring when the mass is 45.
c) What meaning may be attached to the gradient, b?

3

Age	4:5	5:6	6:8	8:7	9:7	10:1	11:1	12:5
Hours	14	14.2	14.4	15.5	15.5	15.8	15.9	18.0

The ages of eight randomly-selected children are recorded (years:months) together with an estimate of the time (in hours) they spent awake the previous day.

a) Calculate the product moment correlation coefficient for these data.
b) Interpret the value you obtain.
c) Plot a graph of the data and review your interpretation.

4

Preservative	0.25	0.35	0.40	0.60	0.65	0.80	0.95	1.00
pH	7.5	7.4	7.3	7.3	7.4	7.6	7.7	7.9

a) Calculate the product moment correlation coefficient for these data and interpret its value.
b) Plot a scattergraph of the data and review your interpretation.
c) Investigate whether (preservative)^2 is a better independent variable.

5 A chemist measured the speed, y, of an enzymatic reaction at twelve different concentrations, x, of the substrate and the results are given below.

x	$\frac{1}{2}$	$\frac{1}{3}$	$\frac{1}{4}$	$\frac{1}{6}$	$\frac{1}{7}$	$\frac{1}{8}$	$\frac{1}{9}$	$\frac{1}{10}$	$\frac{1}{11}$	$\frac{1}{12}$	$\frac{1}{13}$
y	0.204	0.218	0.189	0.172	0.142	0.149	0.111	0.125	0.123	0.112	0.096

The chemist thought that the model relating y and x could be of the form

$$y = a + \frac{b}{x}$$

a) Plot a scatter diagram of y against $\frac{1}{x}$.

b) Find the equation of the regression line in the above form, giving coefficients to three significant figures.

Use $\sum\left(\frac{1}{x}\right)^2 = 793$ and $\sum\left(\frac{y}{x}\right) = 11.23$.

c) Find, to two significant figures, the sum of squares of residuals for your equation.

Originally the data included an observation $\left(\frac{1}{5}, 0.269\right)$.

d) Plot this point on your scatter diagram and explain why you think this value has been omitted.

The sum of squares of the residuals of the equation which included the observation $\left(\frac{1}{5}, 0.269\right)$ is 0.0086.

e) Compare this residual sum of squares with the value calculated in **c)** and comment whether the difference is consistent with your answer to **d)**.

(ULEAC Question 8, Specimen paper T2, 1994)

6 A company monitored the number of days (x) of business trips taken by executives of the company and the corresponding claims (£y) they submitted to cover the total expenditure of these trips.

A random sample of ten trips gave the following results.

x (days)	10	3	8	17	5	9	14	16	21	13
y (£)	116	39	85	159	61	94	143	178	225	134

a) Plot these data on a scatter diagram.
Give a reason to support the calculation of a regression line through these points.

b) Find and equation of the regression line of y on x, in the form $y = a + bx$.

Use $\sum x^2 = 1630$ and $\sum xy = 17\,128$.

c) Interpret the slope b and intercept a of your line.

d) Find the expected expenditure of a trip lasting eleven days.

e) State, giving a reason, whether or not you would use the line to find the expected expenditure of a trip lasting two months.

(ULEAC Question 9, Paper S2, January 1993)

7 The yield of a batch process in the chemical industry is known to be approximately linearly related to the temperature, at least over a limited range of temperatures. Two measurements of the yield are made at each of eight temperatures within this range, with the following results.

Temperature, x (°C)	180	190	200	210	220	230	240	250
Yield, y (tonnes)	136.2 136.9	147.5 145.1	153.0 155.9	161.7 167.8	176.6 164.4	194.2 183.0	194.3 175.2	196.5 219.3

Use $\sum x = 1720$ and $\sum x^2 = 374\,000$.

a) Plot all the data on a scatter diagram.

b) For each temperature, calculate the mean of the two yields. Calculate the equation of the regression line of these mean yields on temperature. Draw this regression line on your scatter diagram.

c) Predict, using your regression line, the yield of a batch at each of the following temperatures.

i) 185°C **ii)** 245°C **iii)** 300°C

Discuss the amount of uncertainty in each of your three predictions.

d) In order to improve predictions of the mean yield at various temperatures in the range 180°C to 250°C, it is decided to take a further eight measurements of yield. Recommend, giving a reason, the temperatures at which these eight measurements should be carried out.

(AEB Question 8, Specimen paper 2, 1994)

8 A random sample of students who are shortly to sit an examination are asked to keep a record of how long they spend revising, in order to investigate whether more revision time is associated with a higher mark. The data are given below, with x hours being the revision time (correct to the nearest $\frac{1}{2}$ hour) and y% being the mark scored in the examination.

x	0	3	4.5	3.5	7	5.5	5	6.5	6	10.5	2
y	36	52	52	57	60	61	63	63	64	70	89

$n = 11$ $\sum x = 53.5$ $\sum y = 667$ $\sum x^2 = 338.25$

$\sum y^2 = 42129$ $\sum xy = 3366.5$

a) Obtain the value of the product moment correlation coefficient for the data.

b) Specify appropriate null and alternative hypotheses, and carry out a suitable test at the five per cent level of significance.

c) Without further calculation, state the effect of the data $x = 2$, $y = 89$ on the value of the product moment correlation coefficient. Explain whether or not this point should be excluded when carrying out the hypothesis test.

(MEI Question 1, Paper S2, January 1994)

9 The following data relate to trials carried out in a laboratory to examine the relationship between the amount of a certain chemical used in a process and the concentration of the final product.

Amount of chemical, x (g)	22	24	30	32	34	36	40	42	44	46
Concentration, y		1.1	1.6	0.9	1.9	1.5	1.1	1.8	2.4	1.2

$\sum x = 350$ $\sum y = 15.2$ $\sum x^2 = 12\,852$ $\sum xy = 544.8$

a) **i)** Draw a scatter diagram of the data. Your x-axis should run from 0 to 120 and your y-axis from 0 to 8.

ii) Calculate the equation of the regression line of y on x and draw this line on your scatter diagram.

iii) Use the regression equation to estimate the concentration if 80 g of chemical is used.

iv) Give two reasons why the estimate made in **a) iii)** is likely to be unreliable.

A further trial is carried out using 120 g of chemical. The resulting concentration is 7.5.

b) **i)** Add the further information to your scatter diagram.

The regression equation for all eleven points is $y = -0.783 + 0.0666x$.

ii) Draw this line on your scatter diagram.

An estimate is required of the concentration when 80 g of chemical is used.

c) Explain how you would make such an estimate and how confident you would feel about your estimate in each of the following circumstances.

i) There is no time for further trials but it is believed that the relationship over the observed amounts of chemical is approximately linear and the last point was reliable.

ii) There may have been an error in the last observation. There is time to carry out three more trials.

(AEB Question 8E, Paper 9, Winter 1994)

10 A technician monitoring water purity believes that there is a relationship between the hardness of the water and its alkalinity. Over a period of ten days, she recorded the data in this table.

Alkalinity (mg/l)	33.8	29.1	22.8	26.2	31.8	31.9	29.4	26.1	28.0	27.2
Hardness (mg/l)	51.0	45.0	41.3	46.0	48.0	50.0	46.3	45.0	45.3	43.0

a) Plot the data on graph paper with 'Alkalinity' on the horizontal axis. Mark the mean point.

b) The technician decides to calculate the equation for the least squares regression line of hardness on alkalinity. Show that this line has gradient 0.821 and find its equation.

(OUDLE Question 4, Specimen S1, 1994)

Summary

- The covariance of x and y:

  $$\text{cov}(x,y) = s_{xy} = \frac{1}{n}\sum xy - \bar{x}\bar{y}$$

- Pearson's product moment correlation coefficient:

  $$r = \frac{Cov(x,y)}{\{sd(x)sd(y)\}} = \frac{s_{xy}}{s_x s_y}$$

- The equation of the line of regression of y on x:

  $$\hat{y} - \bar{y} = \frac{s_{xy}}{s_x^{\ 2}}(x - \bar{x})$$

- The equation of the line of regression of x on y:

  $$\hat{x} - \bar{x} = \frac{s_{xy}}{s_y^{\ 2}}(y - \bar{y})$$

- The minimum sum of squared residuals is:

  $n(1 - r^2)\, s_y^{\ 2}$

The normal probability model

In this chapter:

- *we introduce a widely-discussed probability model – the classical bell-shaped normal distribution,*
- *we discover how all normally-distributed variables are characterised by their mean and variance,*
- *we shall use standardisation and the distribution function for the standardised normal variate,*

THE NORMAL PROBABILITY DENSITY FUNCTION

On a field work week, a group of students explored coastal footpaths.

Unit = 0.10 cm

1	1E	8
1	2O	
1	2T	
2	2F	5
6	2S	6 7 7 7
12	2E	8 8 8 8 9 9
22	3O	0 0 0 0 0 0 0 1 1 1
32	3T	2 2 2 2 2 2 2 2 3 3
46	3F	4 4 4 4 4 4 4 5 5 5 5 5 5 5
58	3S	6 6 6 6 6 6 6 6 7 7 7 7
80	3E	8 8 8 8 8 8 8 8 8 8 8 8 9 9 9 9 9 9 9 9 9 9
105	4O	0 0 0 0 0 0 0 0 0 0 0 0 0 0 1 1 1 1 1 1 1 1 1 1 1
133	4T	2 2 2 2 2 2 2 2 2 2 2 2 2 2 2 2 2 2 2 2 3 3 3 3 3 3 3 3
(30)	4F	4 4 4 4 4 4 4 4 4 4 4 4 4 4 4 5 5 5 5 5 5 5 5 5 5 5 5 5 5 5
137	4S	6 6 6 6 6 6 6 6 6 6 6 6 6 6 6 6 7 7 7 7 7 7 7 7 7 7 7 7 7 7 7
107	4E	8 8 8 8 8 8 8 8 8 8 8 8 8 8 8 9 9 9 9 9 9 9 9 9 9 9
81	5O	0 0 0 0 0 0 0 0 0 0 0 1 1 1 1 1 1 1 1 1
61	5T	2 2 2 2 2 2 2 2 2 2 2 2 3 3 3 3 3 3 3
42	5F	4 4 4 4 4 4 4 5 5 5 5 5 5
29	5S	6 6 6 6 7 7 7 7 7
20	5E	8 8 8 9 9 9 9 9
12	6O	0 0 0 1 1
7	6T	3 3 3 3
3	6F	4
2	6S	6
1	6E	8

One activity involved them in measuring random samples of leaves on natural hedgerows. The site had been chosen for the diversity of natural flora. In this diversity were examples of honeysuckle hedging. The group measured a total of 300 honeysuckle leaves. Their results are shown in the ordered five-part stem-and-leaf display here.

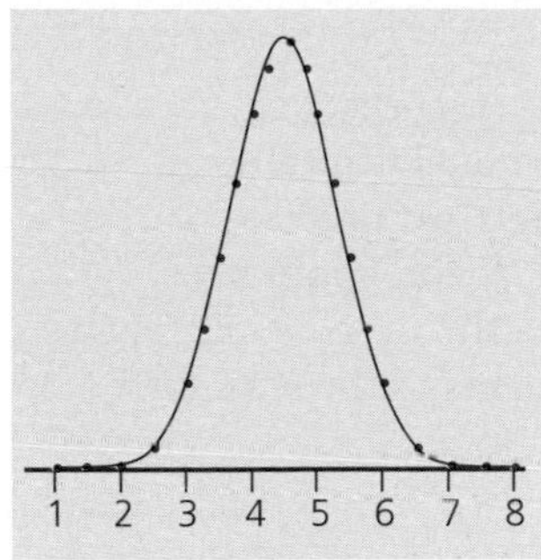

The distribution of lengths is symmetric with a peak in the middle and with tails at both ends. The **normal distribution curve** is a model with these characteristics. The **curve** for the normal model, with the same mean (4.50) and standard deviation (0.84) as the collection of honeysuckle leaf lengths, is shown in this diagram.

We can compare the data and the model by putting them into similar form. The **relative frequency histogram** from Chapter 28, *Data*, is appropriate. The table below provides the information needed to construct the histogram shown next to it. Remind yourself how relative frequency densities are calculated.

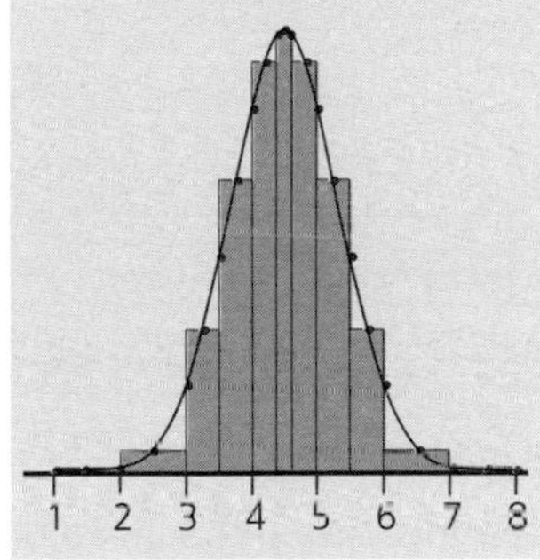

Length, l cm	Class width	Frequency	Relative frequency	Relative frequency density
$1 \le l < 2$	1	1	1/300	0.0033
$2 \le l < 3$	1	11	11/300	0.0367
$3 \le l < 3.5$	0.5	27	27/300	0.18
$3.5 \le l < 4$	0.5	41	41/300	0.2733
$4 \le l < 4.4$	0.4	53	53/300	0.4417
$4.4 \le l < 4.6$	0.2	30	30/300	0.5
$4.6 \le l < 5$	0.4	56	56/300	0.4667
$5 \le l < 5.5$	0.5	46	46/300	0.3067
$5.5 \le l < 6$	0.5	23	23/300	0.1533
$6 \le l < 7$	1	12	12/300	0.04

Is the curve a reasonable model for the distribution of lengths of honeysuckle leaves? Clearly the curve is not in any way an exact fit for the histogram. However, the curve does seem to follow the pattern of the histogram. Try the following Calculator activity, to find out something about the **normal curve**.

CALCULATOR ACTIVITY

Exploration 34.1

The normal curve

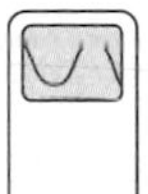

The normal curve is symmetric. It peaks on its axis of symmetry and it tails off to zero. The curve is asymptotic to the x-axis in both directions. An example of a function which possesses these properties is:

$$f(x) = e^{-x^2}$$

a) Try drawing the graph $y = e^{-x^2}$. Describe what you find. You should find that the curve has the desired properties, but its axis of symmetry is $x = 0$.

b) You need to translate the graph so that its axis of symmetry is $x = 4.5$. Try replacing x by $(x - 4.5)$ and drawing a graph of the resulting function. You should now have a curve which begins to resemble the one above, but its maximum value is too great.

c) Try drawing the graph of $y = 0.5e^{-(x-4.5)^2}$. This is much closer to the desired curve.

d) You might like to explore the curve still more before reading further.

Interpreting the results

Both the mean and the standard deviation are important in determining the appropriate normal curve to model the relative frequency density. Remember the **standardisation** process introduced in Chapter 30, *Summary statistics 2*, and again in Chapter 33, *Bivariate data*. Standardisation is the process of relating the data to the mean and expressing this in terms of the standard deviation. The **standardised value** of x is:

$$\left(\frac{x - 4.5}{0.84}\right)$$

The normal curve **density function** appropriate for the data has the form:

$$f(x) = \frac{1}{0.84\sqrt{2\pi}} e^{-0.5\left(\frac{x-4.5}{0.84}\right)^2}$$

Return to your calculator to see what difference this makes to the appearance of the curve.

Comparing data and model

Once the mean and standard deviation have been identified, the normal model is uniquely defined. This model has a number of properties related to these parameters. For instance, approximately five per cent of the normal model's variates are more than two standard deviations away from the mean i.e. approximately five per cent are either more than $(4.50 + 2 \times 0.84) \approx 6.18$ or less than $(4.50 - 2 \times 0.84) \approx 2.82$. What proportion of the actual honeysuckle leaf lengths lies in these regions?

Data	Proportion
more than 6.18	$0.04 \times (7 - 6.18) \approx 0.03$
less than 2.82	$0.0033 + 0.0367\,(2.82 - 2) \approx 0.03$

It is possible to obtain an estimate of this proportion from the relative frequency histogram using the technique we met in Chapter 28, *Data*. The proportion of the data in that histogram is shown in the table.

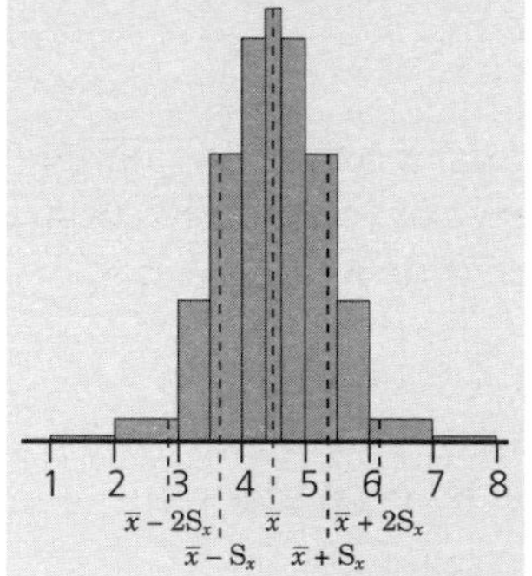

This suggests that about six per cent of the leaf lengths are more than two standard deviations away from the mean. The normal model is quite close to this. The proportion is shown in this relative frequency histogram.

Another property is that about 68 per cent of the normal model's variate is within one standard deviation of the mean. This implies that the proportion of the model's variates lying between 3.66 and 5.34 is about 68 per cent. From the histogram the proportion of the data between these limits is as shown in the table.

Data	Proportion
3.66 to 4.0	$0.2733(4 - 3.66)$
4.0 to 4.4	$0.4417(4.4 - 4)$
4.4 to 4.6	$0.5(4.6 - 4.4)$
4.6 to 5.0	$0.4667(5 - 4.6)$
5.0 to 5.34	$0.3067(5.34 - 5)$
	total 66%

So, again the model is reasonably close to this estimate of the proportion of the data.

Exploration 34.2 *Measuring pebbles*

Another activity during the fieldwork week involved taking samples at various parts of the beach at the coastal location. One of the samples had 168 pebbles and the length of each pebble was measured. They recorded their result in the table shown below.

Length l mm Number of pebbles, f	$l < 4$ 0	$4 \le l < 4.5$ 3	$4.5 \le l < 5.5$ 5	$5.5 \le l < 6$ 14	$6 \le l < 6.5$ 18
l mm f	$6.5 \le l < 7$ 12	$7 \le l < 7.5$ 17	$7.5 \le l < 8$ 19	$8 \le l < 8.5$ 18	
l mm f	$8.5 \le l < 9$ 17	$9 \le l < 10$ 21	$10 \le l < 11$ 12	$11 \le l < 12$ 7	$12 \le l < 13$ 4
l mm f	$13 \le l < 14$ 1	$l \ge 14$ 0			

The mean length of pebble was 8.02 mm and the standard deviation was 1.82 mm.

- Draw a relative frequency density histogram for these data.
- Use the histogram to estimate the proportion of the pebbles with lengths more than two standard deviations from the mean.
- Estimate the proportion with lengths within one standard deviation of the mean.

The appropriate normal probability model has the density function:

$$f(x) = \frac{1}{1.82\sqrt{2\pi}} e^{0.5\left(\frac{x-8.02}{1.82}\right)^2}$$

Draw this density function on your histogram and compare the model's proportions with the data's.

Normal probability paper

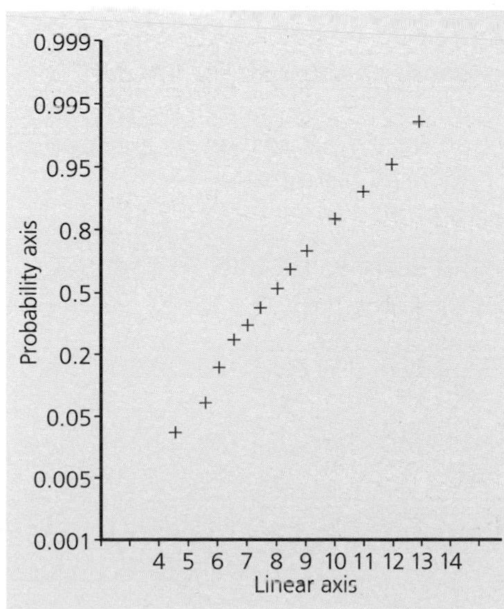

It is possible to judge how well the normal model fits the data by using specially-prepared graph paper known as **normal probability paper**. The x-axis of the paper has a perfectly standard linear scale. The y-axis is anything but linear. It is designed so that a **cumulative proportion** plot of a normal variate produces a straight line graph. This is a plot of the pebble data, using normal probability paper.

We need to take care reading the y-scale because of its non-linear nature. Note that it is not possible to plot the final point. The way to interpret this plot is simple. If the plot seems to be a straight line then there is reason to believe that the normal distribution is a reasonable fit.

Try plotting the honeysuckle data on normal probability graph paper and interpret the outcome.

EXERCISES

34.1 CLASSWORK

KEY SKILLS
N 3.2
N 3.3

1 The data records the speeds, in miles per hour, of 1018 cars entering a speed check area on a main road.

Speed, v mph Number of cars, f	$30 < v \le 40$ 16	$40 < v \le 50$ 106	$50 < v \le 60$ 232
v f	$60 < v \le 65$ 138	$65 < v \le 70$ 152	$70 < v \le 75$ 132
v f	$75 < v \le 80$ 104	$80 < v \le 90$ 98	$90 < v \le 110$ 30

a) Illustrate these data in a histogram.
b) Calculate an estimate of:
  i) the mean speed **ii)** the standard deviation of the speed.
c) Mark on your histogram the values corresponding to:
  i) the mean, **ii)** the mean standard deviation,
  iii) the mean two standard deviations.
d) From your histogram estimate the proportion of speeds which:
  i) are more than two standard deviations away from the mean,
  ii) lie within one standard deviation of the mean,
  iii) lie between one and two standard deviations from the mean.
e) Compare the proportions in **d)** with those of a normal distribution.
f) Write down the density functions for a normal model with the same mean and standard deviation as yours.

2 **a)** Using the data in question **1**, construct a cumulative proportion table.
b) Plot the results in **a)** on normal probability paper.
c) Does your plot support the view that the data may be modelled using a normal distribution?
d) Use your plot to estimate:
  i) the mean, **ii)** the standard deviation of the speeds.
e) Use your plot to estimate the proportion of cars with speed greater more than 77 mph.
f) Use your plot to estimate the speed exceeded by 75 per cent of the cars.

3 **a)** Construct a relative frequency density histogram for the data in question **1**.
b) Superimpose the density function from your answer to question **1 f)** onto the relative frequency density histogram.
c) Compare the curve and the histogram.

4 The data represent the monthly sales income, in £000s, of a random selection of 150 estate agents.

Sales, x Number, f	$80 \le x < 100$ 6	$100 \le x < 110$ 17	$110 \le x < 120$ 21	$120 \le x < 125$ 12
x f	$125 \le x < 130$ 12	$130 \le x < 140$ 20	$140 \le x < 150$ 20	$150 \le x < 160$ 15
x f	$160 \le x < 180$ 15	$180 \le x < 220$ 12		

a) Represent these data in a histogram.
b) Calculate estimates of the mean and variance of x.
c) Determine the proportion of sales:
   i) more than two standard deviations from the mean,
   ii) within one standard deviation of the mean,
   iii) between one and two standard deviations from the mean.
d) Compare the proportions in c) with those of an appropriate normal model.
e) Superimpose on your histogram the frequency density function for the normal model with mean equal to 137.5 and standard deviation equal to 27.5. Compare your model and the data.

EXERCISES

34.1 HOMEWORK

KEY SKILLS
N 3.2b
N 3.3c
N 3.2d
N 3.3

1 The heights (to the nearest cm) to which a particular species of plant grow are recorded for a sample of 200 such plants. The results are given in the table below.

Height (cm)	Frequency
1	9
2	9
3	13
4	21
5	32
6	36
7	23
8	41
9–15	16

Calculate an estimate of the mean and the standard deviation of the data. Draw a relative frequency histogram of the data and use it to estimate the proportion of heights more than two standard deviations away from the mean. Compare this with what you would expect from a normal distribution.

2 The salaries of a group of 200 graduates were recorded when the graduates first found employment after leaving university. The cumulative frequency distribution below shows the results.

Salary (£)	Cumulative frequency
≤ 12 500	7
≤ 13 000	35
≤ 13 500	102
≤ 14 000	164
≤ 14 500	197
≤ 15 000	200

Plot the data on normal probability paper and show that it is reasonable to assume that the data are normally distributed. Use your graph to estimate the mean and standard deviation of the data.

3 The following data refer to the masses of a group of 200 adult males.

Mass (m) in kg	Frequency
$50 \leq m < 55$	4
$55 \leq m < 60$	28
$60 \leq m < 65$	47
$65 \leq m < 70$	41
$70 \leq m < 75$	46
$75 \leq m < 80$	26
$80 \leq m < 85$	8

a) Estimate the mean and standard deviation of these data and plot a relative frequency density histogram.

b) Plot the data on normal probability paper and use this diagram to get a second estimate of the mean and standard deviation of the data.

4 For normally distributed data, about 16 per cent of the variate is more than one standard deviation below the mean, and about 16 per cent is more than one standard deviation above the mean.

Check this statement with the discussion above, which states that about 68 per cent of the normal model's variate is within one standard deviation of the mean.

Using the graph on page 659, use the 50th percentile on the cumulative proportion scale to estimate the mean length of pebbles. Then use the 84th percentiles to estimate the standard deviation of the lengths, which is given by their difference divided by 2.

Compare these estimates with the actual sample mean length of 8.02 mm and sample standard deviation of 1.82 mm.

CALCULATING NORMAL PROBABILITIES

Tables of the distribution function of N(0, 1)

The standardised value of a random variable is important when using the normal probability model. The process of standardisation allows direct comparison of an observation from one distribution with one from another distribution. It also allows probabilities to be estimated for any normal model from the standardised normal variate.

Suppose that X is a random variable which is normally distributed with mean μ and variance σ^2. The notation for this is generally:

$$X \sim N(\mu, \sigma^2)$$

The process of standardising an observation, x, of X produces the value, z, where:

$$z = \frac{x - \mu}{\sigma}$$

The random variable, Z, defined in this way is the standardised normal variate with mean equal to zero and variance equal to unity i.e.

$$Z \sim N(0, 1)$$

The density function for Z is usually given the symbol $\phi(z)$ {ϕ is the lower case Greek f and is pronounced phi}. The form for $\phi(z)$ is:

$$\phi(z) = \frac{1}{\sqrt{2\pi}} e^{-\frac{1}{2}z^2} \quad \text{where} \quad -\infty < z < \infty$$

Knowledge of the probability for a range of values of Z allows us to write down the probability for the corresponding range of another normal variate. For instance:

$$P(-1 < Z < 2) \approx 0.8186$$

implies that, in the normal model:

$$P(6.20 < \text{pebble length} < 11.66) \approx 0.8186$$

This is because the standardised values are:

$$2 = \frac{\text{pebble length} - 8.02}{1.82}$$

and:

$$-1 = \frac{\text{pebble length} - 8.02}{1.82}$$

Rearranging these produces the given values. Have a go at showing that:

$$P(3.66 < \text{honeysuckle length} < 6.18) \approx 0.8186$$

for the model of the distribution of lengths of honeysuckle leaves.

The real value of this correspondence between all normal variates and the Z variate lies in the tabulation of probabilities for Z. The table on page 706 shows the commulative probability function (known as the **distribution function**), $\Phi(z)$. Φ is the upper case Greek letter phi.

$$\Phi(z) = P(Z < z)$$

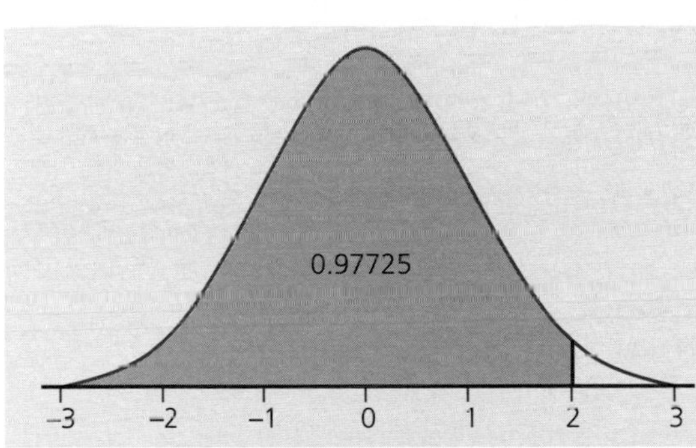

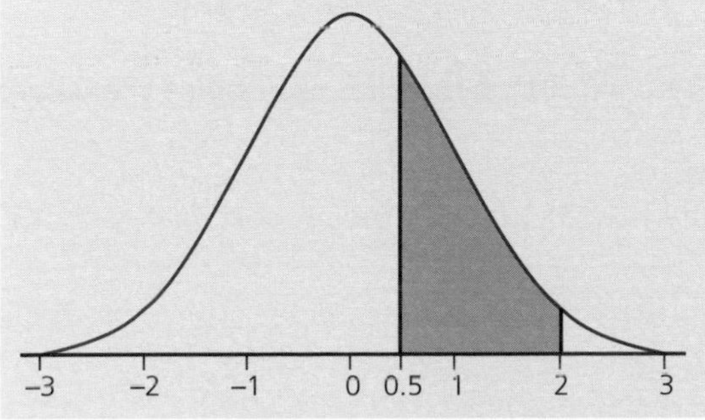

The tables give values for $Z \geq 0$. How does the symmetry of the density function make it possible to find $\Phi(z)$ for $Z < 0$?

Have a look in the tables to find $\Phi(2)$. You should find that:

$$\Phi(2) = P(Z < 2) = 0.977\,25$$

This is the area under the curve for the density function of the standard normal probability model shown here.

To find the probability:

$$P(0.5 < Z < 2)$$

we need to find the difference:

$$P(Z < 2) - P(Z < 0.5)$$

i.e.

$$\Phi(2) - \Phi(0.5)$$

Reading directly from the tables, this is:

$$0.977\,25 - 0.691\,46 \approx 0.2858$$

However, to find:

$$P(-1 < Z < 2) = \Phi(2) - \Phi(-1)$$

we need to make use of the symmetry of the density function to evaluate $\Phi(-1)$. This is not available directly from the tables but can be found from $\Phi(+1)$.

This diagram helps to illustrate their general relationship.

$$\Phi(-a) = 1 - \Phi(a)$$

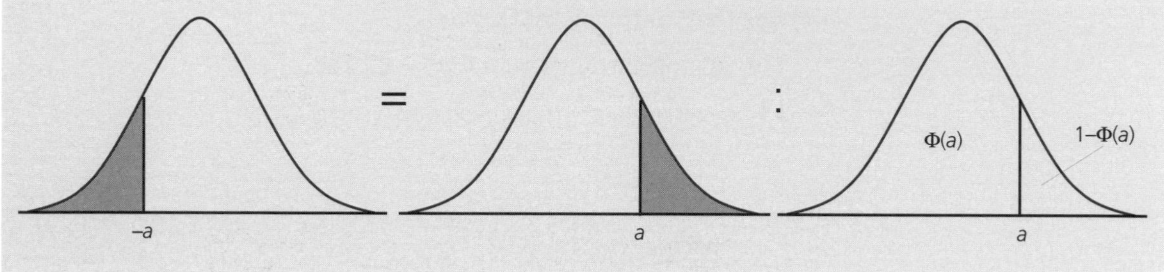

This results in:

$$\begin{aligned} P(-1 < Z < 2) &= \Phi(2) - \Phi(-1) \\ &= 0.977\,25 - (1 - \Phi(1)) \\ &= 0.977\,25 - (1 - 0.841\,34) \\ &\approx 0.8186 \end{aligned}$$

Example 34.1

Use the distribution function tables to find the following.

a) $\Phi(0.88)$ ***b)*** $\Phi(1.367)$ ***c)*** $\Phi(-0.81)$ ***d)*** $\Phi(-2.305)$

Solution

a) *This is a straightforward case of the row for* $Z = 0.8$ *and then the column for 0.08 which produces* $\Phi(0.88) = 0.810\,57$.

b) *To find* $\Phi(1.367)$, *we use the tables to find* $\Phi(1.36) = 0.913\,08$. *Then, we go to the column for 7 in the proportional parts, which shows 112. These digits must be added to the end digits of* $\Phi(1.36)$. *This is equivalent to saying:*

$$\begin{aligned} \Phi(1.367) &= 0.913\,08 + 0.001\,12 \\ &= 0.914\,20 \end{aligned}$$

Since proportional parts have been used, the final answer should be given as:

$$\Phi(1.367) \approx 0.9142$$

c) $\Phi(-0.81)$ *is the same as* $1 - \Phi(0.81)$, *hence the tables give the value:*

$$1 - 0.79103 = 0.20897$$

d) $\Phi(-2.305) = 1 - \Phi(2.305)$

$$= 1 - (0.989\,28 + 0.000\,13) \text{ using the proportional parts '13'}$$
$$= 0.010\,59$$
$$\approx 0.0106$$

Example 34.2

Calculate the following probabilities, given that Z is a standardised normal variate.

a) $P(Z > 0.85)$ ***b)*** $P(0.083 < Z < 0.945)$ ***c)*** $P(-1.62 < Z < 2.35)$
d) $P(Z > -1.65)$ ***e)*** $P(|Z| < 1.375)$

Solution

a) *The concept of complementary events implies:*

$P(Z > 0.85) = 1 - P(Z \leq 0.85)$

Since Z is a continuous variate, there is no distinction between $P(Z \leq 0.85)$ *and* $P(Z < 0.85)$*. This suggests that:*

$$\begin{aligned} P(Z > 0.85) &= 1 - P(Z < 0.85) \\ &= 1 - \Phi(0.85) \\ &= 0.197\,66 \end{aligned}$$

b) $$\begin{aligned} P(0.083 < Z < 0.945) &= \Phi(0.945) - \Phi(0.083) \\ &= (0.826\,39 + 0.001\,27) - (0.531\,88 + 0.001\,19) \\ &\approx 0.2946 \end{aligned}$$

c) $$\begin{aligned} P(-1.62 < Z < 2.35) &= \Phi(2.35) - \Phi(-1.62) \\ &= 0.990\,61 - (1 - \Phi(1.62)) \\ &= 0.990\,61 - (1 - 0.947\,38) \\ &= 0.937\,99 \approx 0.9380 \end{aligned}$$

d)

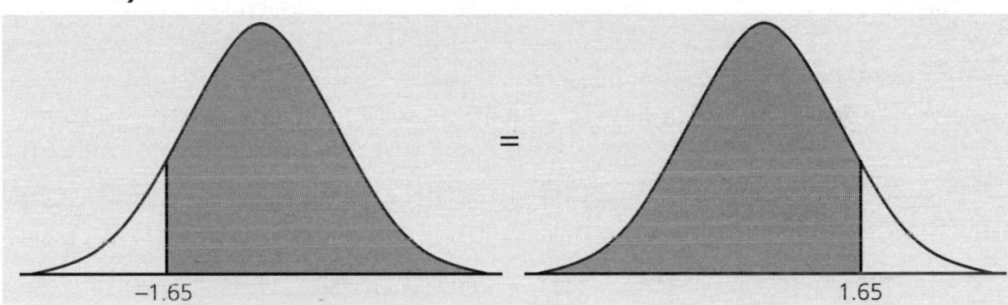

$P(Z > -1.65)$ *has the same value as* $P(Z < +1.65)$ *since the curve is symmetric. This leads to the straightforward result:*

$$\begin{aligned} P(Z > -1.65) &= \Phi(1.65) \\ &= 0.950\,53 \end{aligned}$$

e) *This requires interpretation of* $|Z| < 1.375$*. This modulus in an equality is equivalent to the double inequality:*

$-1.375 < Z < 1.375$

Hence:

$$\begin{aligned} P(-1.375 < Z < 1.375) &= \Phi(1.375) - \Phi(-1.375) \\ &= \Phi(1.375) - (1 - \Phi(1.375)) \\ &= 2\Phi(1.375) - 1 \\ &= 2(0.914\,66 + 0.000\,80) - 1 \\ &\approx 0.8309 \end{aligned}$$

Example 34.3

a) *Given that X is a random variable with distribution modelled by the normal,* $N(5, 1.44)$*, estimate the probability that an observation of X is less than 6.8.*

b) *If* $X \sim N(8, 0.04)$*, calculate* $P(X > 8.4)$*.*

Solution

a) *The notation,* $N(5, 1.44)$*, says that the mean of X is 5 and that the variance is 1.44. Hence the standard deviation is 1.2. Standardised values of X are distributed as* $N(0, 1)$*. The standardised value of 6.8 is* $\frac{6.8-5}{1.2} = 1.5$*, hence the probability:*

$$\begin{aligned} P(X < 6.8) &= P(Z < 1.5) \\ &= \Phi(1.5) = 0.933\,19 \end{aligned}$$

b) *Since* $X \sim N(8, 0.04)$*, standardising* $\frac{X-8}{\sqrt{0.04}} \sim N(0, 1)$ *produces a standard normal variate.*

$$\begin{aligned} P(X > 8.4) &= P\left(Z > \frac{8.4-8}{0.2}\right) \\ &= P(Z > 2) \\ &= 1 - \Phi(2) \\ &= 0.022\ 75 \end{aligned}$$

Tables of percentage points of N(0, 1)

The students enjoying their field work week measured lengths of the coastal flower known as Sea Pinks. Tragically, they lost the data collected apart from two pieces of information. Eighty-five per cent of the lengths were less than 20 cm. Thirty-nine per cent were more than 18 cm. What other information can be gleaned from these two bits?

It seems reasonable to model the distribution of lengths as a normal variate:

$$X \sim N(\mu, \sigma^2)$$

with mean equal to μ and standard deviation equal to σ. Under these circumstances, the standardised variate $\frac{X-\mu}{\sigma}$ is N(0, 1).

Hence, the two pieces of information available are equivalent to:

$$P(X < 20) = P\left(Z < \frac{20-\mu}{\sigma}\right) = 0.85$$

$$P(X > 18) = P\left(Z > \frac{18-\mu}{\sigma}\right) = 0.39$$

The first of these can be written in terms of the distribution function as:

$$\Phi\left(\frac{20-\mu}{\sigma}\right) = 0.85$$

hence

$\frac{20-\mu}{\sigma}$ must be equal to 1.036 since $\Phi(1.036) = 0.85$.

The second relationship, concerning $P\left(Z > \frac{18-\mu}{\sigma}\right)$ can, with care, be written in terms of the distribution function:

$$1 - \Phi\left(\frac{18-\mu}{\sigma}\right) = 0.39$$

hence:

$$\Phi\left(\frac{18-\mu}{\sigma}\right) = 0.61$$

The 'percentage points' tables indicate:

$$\Phi(0.279) = 0.61$$

So this indicates that $\frac{18-\mu}{\sigma}$ is equal to 0.279.

So far the information has yielded two equations involving the unknown mean and standard deviation:

$$\frac{20-\mu}{\sigma} = 1.036 \quad \text{and} \quad \frac{18-\mu}{\sigma} = 0.279$$

These can be rewritten as linear equations:

$$20 - \mu = 1.036\sigma \quad \text{and} \quad 18 - \mu = 0.279\sigma$$

Subtracting the second equation from the first eliminates μ and produces:

$$(20 - \mu) - (18 - \mu) = 1.036\sigma - 0.279\sigma$$

$$\Rightarrow 2 = 0.757\sigma$$

From this the standard deviation can be estimated as:

$$2 \div 0.757 \approx 2.64$$

Similarly, we can find that $\mu \approx 17.3$.

Example 34.4

Information of a normal variate, X, indicates that:
$P(X < 6.3) = 0.995$
and
$P(X < 4.9) = 0.75$
Use this information to obtain estimates of the mean and standard deviation of X.

Solution
Assume that μ and σ are the required mean and standard deviation. Standardising the values 6.3 and 4.9 it is possible to write the information in terms of $\Phi(Z)$:

$$\Phi\left(\frac{6.3 - \mu}{\sigma}\right) = 0.995 \quad \textit{and}$$
$$\Phi\left(\frac{4.9 - \mu}{\sigma}\right) = 0.75$$

The 'percentage points' table indicates:
$\Phi(2.576) = 0.995$ *and* $\Phi(0.674) = 0.75$
Hence, two equations result:

$$\frac{6.3 - \mu}{\sigma} = 2.576 \quad \textit{and} \quad \frac{4.9 - \mu}{\sigma} = 0.674$$

These can be solved to produce:
$\sigma \approx 0.736$ *and* $\mu \approx 4.40$

EXERCISES

34.2 CLASSWORK

KEY SKILLS
N 3.2b
N 3.2c
N 3.2d

1 Use a calculator to determine the following.

a) $P(4 < x < 5)$ when $X \sim N(3, 4)$
b) $P(25.6 < x < 32.8)$ when $X \sim N(28, 25)$
c) $P(18.7 \leq x \leq 19.6)$ when $X \sim N(20, 0.8^2)$
d) $P(1 < x \leq 2.2)$ when $X \sim N(0, 1)$

2 Use tables of the standard normal variate to estimate the following.

a) $P(|Z| > 1.23)$ **b)** $P(0.153 < Z < 1.47)$ **c)** $P(-0.34 < Z < 1.04)$
d) $P(Z < 1.645)$ **e)** $P(|Z - 1| < 1.5)$ **f)** $P(Z > 1.854)$

3 Use tables to estimate the value of a standard normal variate when:

a) $\Phi(Z) = 0.945$ **b)** $\Phi(-Z) = 0.372$
c) $\Phi(Z - 1) = 0.75$ **d)** $\Phi(1 - Z) = 0.05$

4 Assume that $X \sim N(1.52, 0.442)$.

a) Calculate:
   i) $P(x > 0.8)$ ii) $P(0.75 < x < 2.25)$.

b) Determine the value of a if $P(x < a) = 0.99$.

c) Calculate the quartiles of X, and hence the interquartile range.

5 Calculate the mean and standard deviation of each of the following normally distributed variates given that:

a) $P(X < 2.60) = 0.739$ and $P(X > 1.30) = 0.897$

b) $P(Y < 9.49) = 0.005$ and $P(Y > 9.52) = 0.0435$

c) $P(W > 80.5) = 88\%$ and $P(W < 92.5) = 34\%$

EXERCISES

34.2 HOMEWORK

1 Jars of coffee are stated to contain 200 g. In fact, there is a legal requirement that at least 95 per cent of jars must contain not less than the printed weight.

a) If the weight of coffee is normally distributed, with $\sigma = 0.4$ g, find the minimum setting for the mean weight which will conform with this requirement.

b) When the mean is at this setting, calculate the interquartile range of the weights.

2 Examination marks are normally distributed with a mean of 45 per cent and a standard deviation of 18 per cent. The pass mark is 40 per cent.

a) If 'A' grades are awarded for marks of 70 per cent and over what proportion of candidates obtain an A grade?

b) What is the probability that a randomly-chosen candidate with an A grade achieved over 75 per cent in the examination?

c) What is the probability that a randomly-chosen candidate who failed the examination achieved less than 30 per cent?

d) What proportion of candidates who pass the examination obtain an A grade?

3 Given that $X \sim N(6, 25)$:

a) use tables to calculate $P(X > 11)$

b) calculate $P(5 \le X \le 7)$

c) find a value t such that $P(X < t) = 0.85$

d) find a value s such that $P(X \le s) = 0.77$.

CONSOLIDATION EXERCISES FOR CHAPTER 34

1 Assume that the life of a watch battery may be modelled using a normal distribution with mean 2 years and standard deviation 0.25 year.

a) The manufacturer quotes life expectancy of 18 months. What proportion of batteries may be expected to expire before the quoted time?

b) Consumer protection legislation is introduced in which manufacturers are required to quote a life expectancy which should be exceeded by 99.5 per cent of the batteries. What should this be?

2 Ball bearings emerge from a production line. The diameter of these is modelled as a random variable following a normal distribution. Given that 99 per cent of the production have diameters in excess of 4.90 mm and that 2.5 per cent are more than 5.1 mm in diameter, determine the mean and standard deviation of the model.

3

Class	$x \le 5$	$5 < x \le 7$	$7 < x \le 9$	$9 < x \le 10$
Frequency, f	5	17	38	26
Class	$10 < x \le 11$	$11 < x \le 12$	$12 < x \le 14$	$14 < x \le 16$
f	29	29	49	32
Class	$16 < x \le 18$	$x > 18$		
f	16	9		

a) Plot the data on normal probability paper and interpret your result.

b) Assume that the distribution of the data may be modelled using the random variable $X \sim N(12, 12)$. Determine the frequencies expected by this model in the same classes as in the table.

4 The UK operates a 'first past the post' electoral system. A cluster sample of 135 constituencies is selected. A measure of the closeness of the election in each constituencies is given in the table.

a) Calculate an estimate of the mean assuming that the lower bound of the '$x < 0.1$' class is zero.

Measure, x	$x < 0.1$	$x < 0.2$	$x < 0.3$	$x < 0.4$
Cumulative number of constituencies	23	31	50	73
x	$x < 0.5$	$x < 0.6$	$x < 0.7$	$x < 0.8$
Cumulative number of constituencies	94	117	128	132
x	$x < 0.9$	$x < 1.0$		
Cumulative number of constituencies	135	135		

b) Use your mean to obtain an estimate of the standard deviation of the measure.

c) Plot the data on normal probability paper and use the plot to estimate mean and standard deviation. Compare the results with your calculations.

d) To what extent does your plot support the hypothesis that this measure is normally distributed?

e) Use the chi-squared test to judge the hypothesis that N(0.35, 0.04) is an appropriate model.

5 Eggs are graded according to length L mm. A size 3 egg is one for which $60 < L < 65$. An egg producer finds that 37 per cent of her eggs are larger than size 3 while 21 per cent are smaller. Assume that L is normally distributed.

a) Show the information given on a sketch of the distribution of L.

b) Write down two equations involving the mean and standard deviation and solve them.

Further investigation shows that **i)** $L > 70$ for about seven per cent of eggs, and **ii)** $L < 55$ for less than one per cent of eggs.

c) Determine whether **i)** is consistent with the distribution found in **b)**.

d) Determine whether **ii)** is consistent with the distribution found in **b)**.

(MEI Question 4, Paper S2, January 1994)

6 A certain type of light bulb has a lifetime which is normally distributed with mean 1100 hours and standard deviation 80 hours.

a) Find the probability that a randomly chosen bulb will last at least 1000 hours.

b) Find the lifetime which is exceeded by 95 per cent of bulbs.

A newly-installed light fitting takes six of these bulbs. The lifetimes of the bulbs are independent of one another.

c) Show that the probability that the light fitting can run for 1000 hours without any of the bulbs failing is a little over 0.5.

d) The probability that the light fitting can run for t hours without any of the bulbs failing is 0.95. Find t.

(MEI Question 4, Paper S2, Summer 1993)

7 A factory makes steel rods and steel tubes. The internal diameter X of a steel tube is normally distributed with mean 3.50 cm and standard deviation 0.03 cm.

a) Find the probability that a randomly selected tube has an internal diameter less than 3.48 cm.

The diameter Y of a steel rod is normally distributed with mean 3.45 cm and standard deviation 0.03 cm.

b) Find the probability that a randomly selected rod has a diameter greater than 3.40 cm and less than 3.51 cm.

(EDEXCEL Paper T1, Question 6, January 2000)

Summary

The *normal probability distribution* is a distribution used to model many symmetrically distributed continuous variates where a bell-shaped density function is appropriate.

- $X \sim \mathrm{N}(\mu, \sigma^2) \Rightarrow \mathrm{f}(x) = \dfrac{1}{\sigma\sqrt{2\pi}} \mathrm{e}^{-\frac{1}{2}\left(\frac{x-\mu}{\sigma}\right)^2}$
- $Z \sim \mathrm{N}(0, 1) \Rightarrow \phi(z) = \dfrac{1}{\sqrt{2\pi}} \mathrm{e}^{-\frac{1}{2}z^2}$
- X may be standardised as a Z-variate using the linear transformation:

$$Z = \frac{X - \mu}{\sigma}$$

- The distribution function for Z is known as $\Phi(z)$.
- A linear graph on **normal probability paper** of the cumulative proportion of a random v appropriateness of a normal model.

Generating Evidence for Key Skills

To generate evidence for Application of Number students must plan and carry through at least one substantial and complex activity that includes tasks for N3.1, 2 and 3. Similarly for Information Technology students must plan and carry through at least one substantial activity that includes tasks for IT3.1, 2 and 3.

For Communication Key Skills, students can provide evidence for each of the tasks separately for C3.1a, 1b, 2 and 3.

There are many naturally occurring opportunities to develop skills for Application of Number, IT and Communications throughout the course e.g.:

1 Developing Skills for Application of Number

- N 3.1 Plan and interpret information from two different types of sources e.g. colleting data for statistical analysis or mechanics experiments.
- N 3.2 Carry out multistage calculations e.g. Calculating statistical parameters, using mechanics formulae, checking results. – Statistics chapters
- N 3.3 Interpret results of calculations e.g. results of statistical analysis, mechanics experiment – present findings using graphs and diagrams.

2 Developing Skills for Information Technology

- IT 3.1 Plan and use different sources to search e.g. collecting data from web sites CD ROMs for statistical activities
- IT 3.2 Explore develop and exchange e.g. using spreadsheets and graphs plotting software to investigate curve sketching, functions, transformations, and iterative procedures.
- IT 3.3 Present information from different sources.. e.g. using charts and graph facilities to present statistical information or properties of functions; using word-processing and charts to present findings from a modelling activity or exploration

3 Developing Skills for Communication

- C 3.1a Contribute to a group discussion e.g. any group activity where provides opportunities for discussion- introducing a new topic, strengths and weaknesses of using a particular approach to a modelling problem.
- C 3.1b Making a presentation e.g. Findings from an experiment, results of research for a statistics assignment

- C 3.2 Read and synthesise information e.g. Read a theory passage from a chapter in this textbook. Read a similar passage from another source. Prepare a summary of key points which includes ideas from both sources
- C 3.3 Write two different types of document e.g. Write up the results of an assignment in statistics or an experiment in mechanics

Generating evidence

Developing substantial tasks

With careful reference to the specifications and guidelines the following activities could be adapted to enable students to generate evidence for Application of Number and Information Technology.

In many cases the activities could be structured to provide evidence for Communication Skills (presenting findings to the class) and Working with Others (exchanging data in groups). The mathematical modelling activities could provide evidence for Problem Solving.

- **page 19**

Set an investigation into either "tides" or "lighting-up times" in the local area.

Students collect their own data from sources e.g. Internet.

Present the data in graphical form and use a trial and error method to fit a graph of the form $x = a \cos bt + c$

- **page 70–71**

Set an investigation into the most effective tool for presenting data in a scatter diagram and finding the line of best fit e.g. graphics calculators, Excel spreadsheets, graph plotting software, by hand

Students give a class presentation to the class, justifying their choice. *Evidence for communication skills*

- **page 94**

A discussion on the advantage and disadvantages of the various methods of solving quadratic equations. *Evidence for communication skills*

- **page 219**

A presentation to an audience of non-mathematics about how mortgage repayments are calculated or how the proceeds of a regular investment is estimated. *Evidence for communication skills*

- **page 501**

Carry out one of the modelling tasks.

Present the model to the class, stating the assumptions you have made, with reasons. Including diagrams. Invite questions from the class about the appropriate of your modelling assumption and discuss alternatives. *Developing problem solving skills and evidence for communication skills*

- **chapter 24**

Explore different software packages and calculators to investigate the path of a rocket e.g. spreadsheet methods or a graph-plotting programme (e.g. omigraph) to achieve similar results. *Developing working with others – if different groups investigate different methods*

- **page 515**

Class discussion. *Evidence for communication skills*

- **page 517**

Include a careful record of results and plot the points on a graph. *Find the line of best fit.*

- **page 529**

Set Exercise 28.1 classwork question 1 as an investigation. *Students collect their data for a purpose*

- **page 560**

Develop Exercise 29.2 classwork question 2 as an investigation.

Students collect data from their own school/college

Choose appropriate measures of dispersion and location

Draw conclusions

- **chapter 33**

Set an investigation based on theory for chapter 33.

Students collect their own data from sources such as the web

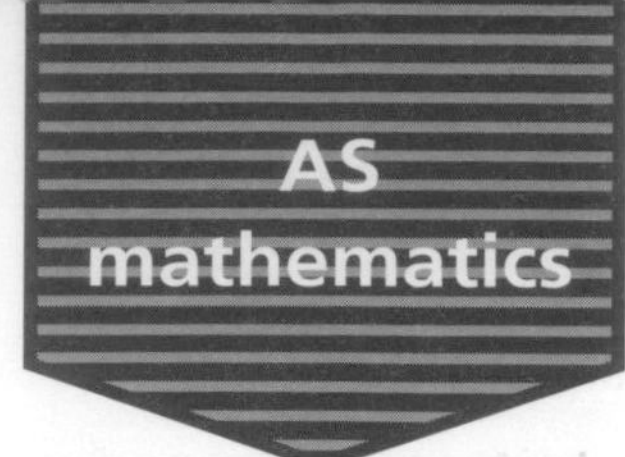

Answers

CHAPTER 1
Problem solving in mathematics

Exercises 1.1 *(p.5)*

1 c) i) 8.8 cm **ii)** 7 cm **iii)** 530 g
d) $l = 7 + 0.01m$
2 c) £178.50, 143
e) i) $d = 500 - 2p$
ii) $s = 1.5p - 125$
3 b) $y = -0.4x + 260$ **c) i)** 2000
ii) 2025

Exercises 1.2 *(p.9)*

1 c) i) £18.13 **ii)** side 3.3 ft
d) $c = 0.5l^2 + 6l$ **e) ii)** £23, side 2.7 ft **iii)** $c = 0.5l^2 + 6l + 5$
2 c) i) 240 ft **ii)** 28.7 mph
d) $d = v + 0.05v^2$
f) i) 420 ft **ii)** 21.9 mph

Exercises 1.3 *(p.14)*

1 c) $w = \dfrac{330}{f}$ **e)** 0.825 m
f) 220 cycles per second
2 a) $F = \dfrac{409600000}{d^2}$ **c)** 1.5 N
d) 755 km
3 a) 10 cm square base, 5 cm height
b) $A = 2x^2 + \dfrac{2000}{x}$, cube side 7.94 cm

Exercise 1.4 *(p.17)*

1 c) i) 14.2 **ii)** 4.96 years
d) $q = 10 \times 1.15^t$
2 c) i) 7.43 **ii)** 3.32 weeks
d) $r = 20 \times 0.5^t$
3 c) i) 70°C **ii)** 15.5 min
d) $T = 100 \times 0.8^{0.2t}$

Exercises 1.5 *(p.22)*

1 b) i) 11 hours **ii)** 9 November to 2 February
c) $h = 12 + 6\sin(30m°)$
2 c) i) 11.7 m **ii)** from 14 to 22 s
d) $h = 9 - 8\cos(10t°)$

CHAPTER 2
Basic algebra

Exercises 2.1 class *(p.27)*

1 19 **2** 9.5 **3** 15 **4** 39 **5** 8
6 −3 **7** 19 **8** 10 **9** −4 **10** 1
11 2 **12** 3.5 **13** $-\frac{5}{8}$ **14** 2.5

Exercises 2.1 home *(p.27)*

1 83 **2** 0.3 **3** 2.8 **4** 28 **5** 6
6 8.75 **7** −3.5 **8** $\frac{1}{3}$ **9** − 0.2
10 3 **11** 1.75 **12** $1\frac{5}{7}$ **13** $3\frac{2}{3}$
14 3.5

Exercises 2.2 class *(p.30)*

1 a) $3x + 12$ **b)** $12 - 3x$
c) $-4x - 20$ **d)** $14p - 21q$
e) $2x^2 - 6x$ **f)** $2x^2 + 6x$
g) $6pr - 3pq$ **h)** $-3pq - 6pr$
i) $5a^2 - 5ab + 5ac$
j) $5a^2 + 5ab - 5ac$
k) $6r^2 - 10rs + 2rt$
m) $-6r^2 + 10rs - 2rt$
2 a) $5x + 11$ **b)** $x - 5$ **c)** $x - 8$
d) $16 - 17x$ **e)** $4x^2 + 7x$
f) $-9x$ **g)** $6x + 9$ **h)** $ab - ac$
i) $-3p - 5q$ **j)** $5x - 4y$
3 a) $5(2a - b)$ **b)** $7(x + 3)$
c) $3(4y + 1)$ **d)** $3x(4y - 1)$
e) $x(7x - 5)$ **f)** $7t(t - 5)$
g) $ab(a - b)$ **h)** $5d(3c + 4e)$
i) $5(r - 4s + 3t)$
j) $3x(2x + 10y - 5)$

Exercises 2.2 home *(p.30)*

1 a) $18x + 12$ **b)** $-72x - 64$
c) $10 - 14x$ **d)** $3 - 4x$
e) $64a - 16b$ **f)** $24a - 36b$
g) $28m^2 + 24m$ **h)** $-x^2 - 9x$
i) $4x - 20x^2$ **j)** $-10t^2 - 25t$
k) $x^2 + xy - xz$
l) $-xy + y^2 + yz$
m) $-24a^2 + 24ab - 3ac$
n) $8a^2 - 12ab - 4a$
2 a) $15x + 105$ **b)** $8 - x$
c) $3x - 69$ **d)** $30x + 8$
e) $12t + 6$ **f)** $-31x - 28$
g) $67x^2 - 38x$
h) $25x^2 - 2x + 28$ **i)** x
j) $2xy + 4xz$ **k)** $20x - 63$
l) $5a - 47b$
3 a) $4(7x + 6)$ **b)** $7(6 - 5a)$
c) $3(1 - x)$ **d)** $2m(2m + 5)$
e) $y(8y - 3)$ **f)** $2a(a + 9)$
g) $xy(8x - 7y)$ **h)** $3a(2ad + b)$
i) $x(1 - x + 7y)$
j) $6t(4t - 7u^2 - 5)$

Exercises 2.3 class *(p.31)*

1 3.5 **2** 5.4 **3** −2 **4** 5 **5** −5.8
6 2 **7** −2 **8** 0.25 **9** 0.8 **10** 4
11 −11 **12** 1.25

Exercises 2.3 home *(p.31)*

1 3.75 **2** −10 **3** 1 **4** −16 **5** 3
6 −4 **7** −0.5 **8** $11\frac{2}{3}$ **9** $-2\frac{1}{9}$
10 −15.5 **11** $\frac{34}{53}$ **12** $\frac{17}{26}$

Exercises 2.4 class *(p.33)*

1 10 **2** 6 **3** 0.3 **4** 6 **5** 15
6 13 **7** −1 **8** −10 **9** −3 **10** 5
11 8 **12** 1 **13** 13 **14** 7 **15** 2

Exercises 2.4 home *(p.34)*

1 24 **2** 0.6 **3** $1\frac{1}{9}$ **4** −18 **5** 4.8
6 $-11\frac{9}{17}$ **7** $\frac{1}{74}$ **8** −7 **9** $\frac{2}{3}$ **10** −1
11 −53 **12** $1\frac{9}{67}$ **13** 3.1 **14** $-\frac{1}{6}$
15 $\frac{9}{37}$ **16** −3.6 **17** $3\frac{2}{7}$ **18** 0.25
19 $-1\frac{9}{14}$ **20** $-2\frac{5}{73}$

Exercises 2.5 class *(p.35)*

1 $3(x + 1)^2(x - 1)$
2 $2(a - 1)(a + 1)$
3 $(x + a)(x - a)^2$
4 $g(y - 2)(y - 1)$ **5** x
6 $\dfrac{a^2 + 2}{a}$ **7** $\dfrac{17}{12x}$
8 $\dfrac{2}{(x + 1)(1 - x)}$ **9** $\dfrac{8 - a^2}{(2 - a)(4 - a)}$
10 $\dfrac{x^2 + x + 1}{x(x + 1)}$ **11** $\dfrac{3 - y}{2(y - 1)(y + 1)}$
12 $\dfrac{-1}{(x - b)(a - b)}$

Exercises 2.5 home *(p.36)*

1 $x(x - 1)(x + 1)^2$
2 $2(x - 1)(x + 2)$
3 $6(x + 1)^3$
4 $y(y - a)(y + a)(y - 1)(y + 2)$
5 x
6 $\dfrac{a + 2}{a}$ **7** $\dfrac{17}{6x}$
8 $\dfrac{4}{(x + 2)(2 - x)}$ **9** $\dfrac{-y^2 - 3}{(3 + y)(1 - y)}$
10 $\dfrac{2a^2 - a + 1}{a(a - 1)}$ **11** $\dfrac{3 - x}{x(x - 1)(x + 1)}$
12 $\dfrac{a^3 - a^2 + 3a + 1}{2a(a - 1)(a + 1)}$

Exercises 2.6 class *(p.39)*

1 $u = v - at$ **2** $a = \dfrac{2A}{h} - b$
3 $d = \dfrac{u - a}{n - 1}$ **4** $n = \dfrac{u - a + d}{d}$
5 $y = 5x - 12$ **6** $x = \dfrac{y + 12}{5}$

7 $y = \frac{20-4x}{5}$ **8** $x = \frac{20-5y}{4}$

9 $s = \frac{3r+5}{8}$ **10** $p = \frac{2q+rw}{5}$

11 $d = \frac{a(b-c)}{e}$

12 $b = \frac{de}{a} + c$ **13** $e = \frac{g(f-7)}{3}$

14 $g = \frac{3e}{f-7}$ **15** $a = b$

16 $x = \frac{s-q}{p-r}$ **17** $m = \frac{-5n}{7}$

18 $m = \frac{5n}{3n-5}$ **19** $x = \frac{ab+2}{a+2}$

20 $x = \frac{bd}{a+b-d}$

21 $x = \frac{y+1}{y-1}$ **22** $x = \frac{2y+5}{2y+1}$

Exercises 2.6 home *(p.39)*

1 $x = \frac{a-c}{b}$ **2** $s = \frac{v^2-u^2}{2a}$

3 $t = \frac{2s}{u+v}$ **4** $v = \frac{2s}{t} - u$

5 $m = \frac{y-y_1}{x-x_1}$ **6** $r = \frac{c}{2\pi}$

7 $w = \frac{gp}{f}$ **8** $h = \frac{A}{2\pi r} - r$

9 $y = \frac{7x-3}{9}$ **10** $x = ag - 3y$

11 $n = \frac{3x-7y}{2m}$ **12** $\frac{3a-5m}{2}$

13 $a = \frac{18x-2}{3}$ **14** $y = mx - am + b$

15 $x = \frac{a-b}{6}$ **16** $x = \frac{3ay+14y}{2-3a}$

17 $y = \frac{nx-mx}{m+n}$ **18** $y = \frac{2x-3}{x+1}$

19 $f = \frac{8x}{m+5}$ **20** $x = \frac{m}{y-c}$

Exercises 2.7 class *(p.43)*

1 $x > 2$ **2** $x \geq 4$ **3** $x < 7$
4 $x \leq -5$ **5** $x > 1$
6 $x \geq 2.125$ **7** $x > 2.2$
8 $x \leq -0.5$ **9** $2 \leq x \leq 5$
10 $-11 < x < -3$ **11** $x < 4, x > 10$
12 $x > 2$ **13** $-5 \leq x \leq 2$
14 $x \leq -1.2, x \geq 2$

Exercises 2.7 home (p.43)

1 $x < 0.8$ **2** $x \leq 5$ **3** $x < 0.875$
4 $x > -8$ **5** $x \geq \frac{7}{9}$ **6** $x \leq \frac{31}{47}$
7 $x > -2$ **8** $x > -\frac{5}{32}$
9 $-2 < x < 11$
10 $1\frac{2}{3} \leq x \leq 4$
11 $x < 1, x > 5$
12 $x > 2$ **13** $5 \leq x \leq 11$
14 $x \leq -3.4, x \geq 6.6$

Exercises 2.8 class *(p.47)*

1 **a)** 9 **b)** $\frac{1}{4}$ **c)** 1 **d)** $35x^8$
e) $8a^5b^5$ **f)** $32a^5b^5$
g) $-64x^9y^6$ **h)** $3r^2s^2$
i) $\left(\frac{3ab^2}{4c^2}\right)^3$ **j)** $\frac{3p^3}{7q}$

2 **a)** $\frac{1}{8}$ **b)** 7 **c)** 343 **d)** $\frac{16}{81}$ **e)** $\frac{81}{16}$
f) $\frac{1}{5}$ **g)** $\frac{5}{2}$ **h)** $\frac{7}{2}$ **i)** $\frac{3}{2}$ **j)** $1\frac{1}{3}$

3 **a)** $n = -3$ **b)** $n = 2$ **c)** $n = 4$
d) $n = \frac{8}{27}$ **e)** $n = 343$
f) $n = 4$ **g)** $n = -4$
h) $n = \frac{1}{2}$ **i)** $n = \frac{1}{3}$ **j)** $n = -\frac{2}{3}$
k) $n = -\frac{1}{2}$

Exercises 2.8 home *(p.47)*

1 **a)** 32 **b)** 25 **c)** 1 **d)** $15y^{11}$
e) $40a^8b^8c^6$ **f)** $11^9a^{18}b^9$
g) $-243m^{10}n^{15}p^{20}$
h) $\frac{a^2}{2b^2}$ **i)** $\frac{4x}{y^2}$ **j)** $\frac{25r^2t^2}{49s^4}$

2 **a)** $\frac{1}{32}$ **b)** 8 **c)** 512 **d)** $\frac{1}{8}$ **e)** $\frac{27}{64}$
f) $\frac{64}{27}$ **g)** $\frac{2}{5}$ **h)** $\frac{7}{4}$ **i)** $\frac{9}{2}$ **j)** $\frac{4}{3}$

3 **a)** $n = 3$ **b)** $n = 2$
c) $n = \frac{1}{10}$ **d)** $n = \frac{64}{125}$ **e)** $n = 216$
f) $n = 0$ **g)** $n = 3$
h) $n = \frac{1}{2}$ **i)** $n = -2$

Exercises 2.9 class *(p.50)*

1 $3\sqrt{2}$ **2** $4\sqrt{2}$ **3** $2\sqrt{7}$ **4** $5\sqrt{3}$
5 $3\sqrt{2}\sqrt{5}$ **6** $\sqrt{3}\sqrt{5}\sqrt{23}$ **7** $13\sqrt{3}$
8 $100\sqrt{2}\sqrt{3}$ **9** $\frac{1}{2}\sqrt{3}$ **10** $\frac{5}{3}\sqrt{2}$
11 $8\sqrt{3}$ **12** $2\sqrt{2}$ **13** $\sqrt{5}$ **14** $18\sqrt{2}$
15 $5\sqrt{2}-2$ **16** $\sqrt{2}$ **17** $7\sqrt{2}$
18 $\sqrt{3}-3$ **19** 20 **20** -2 **21** $\frac{5\sqrt{2}}{2}$
22 $\frac{\sqrt{3}}{3}$ **23** $\sqrt{7}$ **24** $\frac{\sqrt{5}\sqrt{6}}{2}$
25 $\frac{1}{6}\left(3\sqrt{2}-2\sqrt{3}\right)$ **26** $\frac{15\sqrt{7}+14}{21}$
27 $\frac{1}{2}\left(\sqrt{3}-1\right)$ **28** $7\sqrt{5}-14$
29 $\frac{1}{7}\left(3+\sqrt{2}-3\sqrt{3}-\sqrt{2}\sqrt{3}\right)$
30 $4-\sqrt{5}\sqrt{3}$

Exercises 2.9 home *(p.51)*

1 $2\sqrt{11}$ **2** $5\sqrt{5}$ **3** $1000\sqrt{7}$
4 $8\sqrt{5}$ **5** $3\sqrt{29}$ **6** $4\sqrt{19}$
7 $4\sqrt{31}$ **8** $29\sqrt{5}$ **9** $\frac{4}{5}\sqrt{2}$
10 $\frac{3}{4}\sqrt{3}$ **11** $7\sqrt{7}$ **12** $6\sqrt{2}$
13 $16\sqrt{3}$ **14** $7\sqrt{3}$ **15** $7\sqrt{3}+6$
16 0 **17** $14+2\sqrt{5}$ **18** 4
19 $-12\sqrt{13}$ **20** $x-y$ **21** $\frac{7\sqrt{2}}{2}$
22 $-\frac{4\sqrt{5}}{5}$ **23** $2\sqrt{7}$
24 $\sqrt{13}$ **25** $\frac{\sqrt{3}\sqrt{7}}{3}$
26 $\frac{1}{15}\left(3\sqrt{5}+5\sqrt{3}\right)$
27 $2+\sqrt{3}$ **28** $\frac{1}{2}\left(5-\sqrt{3}\right)$
29 $\frac{1}{3}\left(4-\sqrt{7}\right)$
30 $2+\sqrt{5}\sqrt{2}-\sqrt{5}-2\sqrt{2}$

Consolidation Exercises for Chapter 2 *(p.51)*

1 **a)** -1 **b)** $\frac{4}{9}$ **c)** 0.25
2 **a)** $30x - 35$ **b)** $-15p - 24p^2$
3 **a)** $29x^2 + 7x$ **b)** $-5x$
4 **a)** $3ab(3a + 2b)$
b) $5x(4y + 1 - 4x)$
5 **a)** 5 **b)** -0.6 **c)** -2
6 **a)** 0.7 **b)** $2\frac{5}{9}$ **c)** 2.4 **d)** 0.25
7 **a)** x **b)** $\frac{2x-4}{x(x-1)}$
c) $\frac{a^3+a^2+2a}{(a-1)(a+1)}$
d) $\frac{-x^3-4x^2-2x-1}{x(x-1)(x+1)^2}$
8 **a)** $k = \frac{m+n-fm}{2}$
b) $c = ax - am - bm$
c) $g = \frac{7b}{4a-1}$ **d)** $y = \frac{3x+1}{x+2}$
e) $x = \frac{40m-9}{24m+1}$
9 **a)** $x < 1$ **b)** $-2\frac{2}{3} \leq x < -1$
c) $x < -1$
10 **a)** $\frac{1}{49}$ **b)** $10a^5$ **c)** $6a^6b^7$
d) $4p^2q^7$ **e)** $3r^4s^3t^2$
f) $\frac{81}{16}x^4y^4z^8$
11 **a)** $25a^2$ **b)** a^{-3} **c)** $a^{\frac{5}{2}}$
d) $16a^{-4}$ **e)** $4a^{\frac{1}{2}}$ **f)** $a^{-\frac{3}{2}}$
g) $3a^{\frac{1}{2}}$ **h)** $27a^{12}$
12 **a)** $x = \pm 0.8$ **b)** $x = 7$ **c)** $a = -3$
d) $x = 2$ **e)** $\frac{1}{256}$ **f)** $x = 0$
g) $x = -6$ **h)** $x = 3$ **i)** $\frac{1}{2}$
13 **a)** $14\sqrt{3}$ **b)** $6\sqrt{2}$ **c)** $-93\sqrt{5}$
d) $-8 + 3\sqrt{2}$ **e)** $-\frac{13}{22}+\frac{7}{22}\sqrt{3}$
f) $\frac{4}{3}+\frac{\sqrt{7}}{3}$ **g)** $\frac{15}{37}-\frac{\sqrt{3}}{37}$

h) $\frac{1}{2}+\frac{1}{2}\sqrt{5}$

14 a) $5\sqrt{5}$ **b)** $\frac{4\sqrt{2}}{5}$ **c)** $15+5\sqrt{7}$

d) $\frac{11}{4}-\frac{3}{4}\sqrt{13}$

15 i) $\frac{1}{49}$, 0.25 **ii)** $\frac{\sqrt{x}}{2}$

16 $90 < x < 110$
$453 < n < 472$

CHAPTER 3
Linear functions

Exercises 3.1 class *(p.57)*

1 36 km (165, 38)
2 a) 6.7, (5, 2.5) **b)** 9.43, (–1,2.5)
c) 8.54, (–2.5, 1)
3 a) XY = 5, YZ = 5, XZ = √50
b) isosceles, right-angled
c) M(2.5, 1.5) **d)** 12.5
4 a) M(7, 0), N(4, 4)
b) PR = 10, MN = 5
5 a) E(–1, 3), F($-\frac{1}{2}$, $\frac{3}{2}$), G($\frac{7}{5}$, $\frac{5}{2}$), H(3, 4),
b) EF = GH, so EFGH is a parallelogram

Exercises 3.1 home *(p.57)*

1 (199, 46), 52.9 km
2 a) 6 **b)** 10.3 **c)** 7.28 **d)** 11.7
e) 14.2 **f)** 11.2
3 a) (6, –1) **b)** (2, 4.5) **c)** (3.5, –2)
d) 1, –0.5) **e)** (2.5, –7)
f) (–1.5, –1.5)
4 a) 9.90, 13, 13
c) (3.5, 3), (–2.5, 5.5)
5 a) 13.2, 13.2, 13.2, 13.2
b) (3.5, 0.5), (3.5, 0.5)
c) PR = 21.2, QS = 15.6

Exercises 3.2 class *(p.61)*

2 AF = $\frac{12}{7}$, HD = $-\frac{2}{5}$,
AD = $-\frac{7}{3}$, CH = $\frac{1}{12}$
3 Gradient DE = gradient EF = 0.5, common point E
4 Gradient AC = gradient DH = –0.4
5 BD is parallel to FH
6 Gradient BC = $-\frac{7}{2}$, gradient DG = $\frac{2}{7}$, product = –1
7 EG and GF, AC and CD
8 I (1, 0)
9 EG and GF perpendicular ⇒ right-angled triangle

Exercises 3.2 home *(p.61)*

2 2, –0.1, 0.15
5 e.g. (–5, –3)

6 1, PN
7 (13, –5), (7, –10) or
(3, 7), (–3, 2)
8 (–10, 2)
9 (5, 2), (2, –4) (–7, –4), (–10, 2), (–7, 8), (2, 8)

Exercises 3.3 class *(p.66)*

1 a) 2, –5 **b)** –3, 10 **c)** –1, 7
d) –0.8, 6 **e)** $\frac{1}{3}$, 1.5 **f)** $-\frac{4}{3}$, 4
2 i) (–4, 0), (0, 8) **ii)** (3, 0), (0, 12)
iii) (6, 0), (0, 4)
iv) (5, 0), (0, 10)
v) (6, 0), (0, –4.5)
vi) (3, 0), (0, 2.5)
3 a) $y = 3x - 5$ **b)** $y = 7 - 2x$
c) $y = 8$ **d)** $5y + 2x + 12 = 0$
e) $y = 2x + 3$
4 a) $y = 4x - 21$ **b)** $y = 3 - 3x$
c) $3y + 2x - 3 = 0$
5 a) $5y - x + 2 = 0$
b) $3y - x - 1 = 0$
c) $5y + 13x - 14 = 0$
6 a) (4, 3) **b)** –1 **c)** $y = x - 1$
7 a) $y = x - 4$ **b)** $y = 7 - x$
d) AB = $3\sqrt{2}$ = 4.24,
CD = $\frac{7\sqrt{2}}{2}$ = 4.9
Area = 10.5 units^2
8 a) $3y - 4x + 3 = 0$

Exercises 3.3 home *(p.67)*

1 a) 1, 2 **b)** –3, 2
c) –2, 0 **d)** –0.5, –3.5
e) –0.1, 4.8 **f)** 0, 7
2 a) ($-\frac{6}{7}$, 0), (0, 6), 7
b) (1.5, 0), (0, 6), –4
c) ($\frac{2}{3}$, 0), (0, $\frac{2}{9}$), $-\frac{1}{3}$
d) ($1\frac{2}{7}$, 0), (0, 1.8), –1.4
e) ($-\frac{2}{3}$, 0), (0, $\frac{4}{9}$), $\frac{2}{3}$
f) (0, –7.1), 0
3 a) $y = 7x + 4$ **b)** $27x + 3y = 2$
c) $12y = 16x + 3$
4 a) $y = 3x - 23$ **b)** $5x + y = 3$
c) $3y = 2x - 23$
5 a) $6y = 5x + 2$
b) $13x + 5y + 66 = 0$
c) $6x + 14y + 11 = 0$
6 a) $3x - y + 6 = 0$
b) $2x + 3y + 6 = 0$
c) $4x + y + 27 = 0$
d) $5x + 2y - 2 = 0$
7 a) (2, 2.5) **b)** 0.3
c) $6y + 20x = 55$
8 $4y = 2x + 7$

Exercises 3.4 class *(p.70)*

1 b) $F = 1.8C + 32$ **c)** 32 **d)** –40
2 b) 6 years, 796 g
c) $m = 135a - 14$
d) 391 g **e)** 7.5 years
3 b) $R = 0.15T + 15$
d) i) 34.5 ohms, **ii)** $T < -33$°C,
iii) –100°C, no

Exercises 3.4 home *(p.71)*

1 b) $y = 0.06x + 0.03$
c) 0.09 mm
2 b) Yes, $y = 0.03x + 1.5$
c) 5.43 million **d)** –1.5 million!
3 b) $y = 310 - 2.2x$
c) i) 3: 55.2, **ii)** 3: 20

Consolidation Exercises for Chapter 3 *(p.72)*

1 a) √32, √72, √104, 90° **b)** 1, –1
c) MA = MB = √26
2 $5x - 6y = 2$
3 b) $v = 5.6t - 0.8$
c) 5.6 mph per second
4 c) $b = 0.06a + 25$
d) $b = 0.06a + 40$
e) 7100 g (2 s.f.)
5 a) $2x + y = 20$ **b)** $3y = x + 4$
6 $8.4 < x < 9$

CHAPTER 4
Quadratic functions

Exercises 4.1 class *(p.78)*

1 i) b) (0, 5) **c)** (1, 0), (5, 0)
d) $x = 3$ **e)** (3, –4)
ii) b) (0, 3) **c)** (–3, 0), (1, 0)
d) $x = -1$ **e)** (–1, 4)
iii) b) (0, –5) **c)** (–2.5, 0), (0.5, 0)
d) $x = -1$ **e)** (–1, –9)
iv) b) (0, 25) **c)** (–2.5, 0), (5, 0)
d) $x = 1.25$ **e)** (1.25, 28.125)
v) b) (0, –16) **c)** (–4, 0), (4, 0)
d) $x = 0$ **e)** (0, –16)
vi) b) (0, 25) **c)** (–2.5, 0), (2.5, 0) **d)** $x = 0$ **e)** (0, 25)
vii) b) (0, 0) **c)** (0, 0), (4, 0)
d) $x = 2$ **e)** (2, –12)
viii) b) (0, –9) **c)** (–3, 0) **d)** $x = -3$
e) (–3, 0)
2 (–1.75, 15.125)
3 a) 192 m **b)** 192 m **c)** $x = 96$
4 a) 23.6 min **b)** 41.6 min
c) 10.5 min, 9.7

Exercises 4.1 home *(p.79)*

1 a) (0, 4) **b)** (0, 7)
c) (0, 0) **d)** (0, 0)
e) (0, –7) **f)** (0, –3.5)
2 $x = 0.5$

3 (6.25, −15.125)
4 a) 0.818 sec
b) 0.235 sec, 1.67 m

Exercises 4.2 class *(p.84)*

1 a) $x^2 + 13x + 40$
b) $x^2 + 3x - 40$
c) $x^2 - 13x + 40$
d) $2x^2 + 17x - 9$
e) $4y^2 - 11y + 6$
f) $15x^2 + 23x + 4$
g) $4t^2 + 4t - 15$
h) $3a^2 - 8ab - 3b^2$
i) $16x^2 + 8x + 1$ **j)** $4x^2 - 12x + 9$
k) $16z^2 - 1$ **l)** $c^2 - 49$
m) $15x^2 + 40x - 15$
n) $12x^2 - 60xy + 75y^2$
2 a) $2x^2 - 6x - 29$ **b)** $26x$
c) $x^2 + 17x - 21$
d) $13x^2 - 23x - 39$
e) $-a^2 - 18ab - 6b^2$
f) $22x^2 - 5xy - 8y^2$
g) $-20x^2 - 140x + 202$
3 a) $(x + 5)(x + 4)$
b) $(x - 5)(x + 4)$
c) $(x + 5)(x - 4)$
d) $(x - 7)(x - 5)$
e) $(y - 9)(y + 7)$
f) $(x + 3)^2$ **g)** $(x - 7)^2$
h) $(2x + 1)(x + 1)$
i) $(3x + 5)(x + 4)$
j) $(2x - y)(x + 3y)$ **k)** $(4a - 5b)^2$
l) $5(4x + 3)(x + 4)$
m) $3(2x + 5)^2$
n) $x(2x - 7)(x + 3)$
4 a) $(x - 7)(x + 7)$
b) $(10 - t)(10 + t)$
c) $(p - q)(p + q)$
d) $(8s - 5)(8s + 5)$
e) $(11t - 1)(11t + 1)$
f) $(6a - b)(6a + b)$
g) $(3e - 7f)(3e + 7f)$
h) $10(x - 2)(x + 2)$
i) $5(3 - 2x)(3 + 2x)$
j) $x(3 - 7x)(3 + 7x)$
k) $5(8x - 5)(8x + 5)$
l) $ab(a - b)(a + b)$

Exercises 4.2 home *(p.85)*

1 a) $x^2 + 5x + 4$ **b)** $x^2 + 3x - 4$
c) $x^2 - 5x + 4$
d) $6x^2 + x - 7$
e) $2t^2 - 23t + 56$
f) $27x^2 + 57x + 28$
g) $32x^2 - 92x + 63$
h) $2x^2 - 3xy - 2y^2$
i) $25x^2 + 30x + 9$
j) $36x^2 - 60x + 25$
k) $x^2 - 64$ **l)** $49u^2 - 4$
m) $216x^2 - 48x - 64$
n) $81x^3y + 108x^2y^2 + 36xy^3$
2 a) $2x^2 + 6x - 44$
b) $2x^2 + 54$ **c)** $4x^2 + 8x + 4$
d) $14x^2 + 30x + 27$
e) $39a^2 + 37ab - 84b^2$
f) $-4xy - 8y^2$
g) $78x^2 + 293x - 273$
3 a) $(x + 2)(x + 5)$
b) $(x - 5)(x + 2)$ **c)** $(x - 5)(x - 2)$
d) $(8 - x)(x - 4)$ **e)** $(t - 8)(t + 2)$
f) $(x - 5)^2$ **g)** $(x + 11)^2$
h) $(x - 5)(3x - 1)$ **i)** $(x - 3)(6x + 1)$
j) $(a + 2b)(7a - b)$ **k)** $(9x + 2y)^2$
l) $2(2x + 5)(3x - 4)$
m) $8(5x - 7)^2$
n) $x(25x^2 - 195x - 84)$
4 a) $(x - 4)(x + 4)$
b) $(7 - u)(7 + u)$
c) $(a - 2b)(a + 2b)$
d) $-4(2x - 3)(2x + 3)$
e) $(3x - 1)(3x + 1)$
f) $4(a - 3b)(a + 3b)$
g) $(8x - 9y)(8x + 9y)$
h) $5(3x - 2)(3x + 2)$
i) $3(9p - 4q)(9p + 4q)$
j) $5a(2a - b)(2a + b)$
k) $-t(4t - 9)(4t + 9)$
l) $4xy(3x - 5y)(3x + 5y)$

Exercises 4.3 class *(p.89)*

1 0, 7 **2** 4, 8
3 3 **4** −2, 4
5 4 **6** −5, 5
7 0, 17 **8** 0, 2
9 −4, 0 **10** −7, 7
11 −5, 5 **12** −7, 7
13 −1.5, 1.5 **14** none
15 none **16** −2, −3
17 −6, −9 **18** 1, 3
19 −5, 8 **20** −4, 1
21 −3, 4 **22** 1
23 0.5, 5 **24** −2, $2\frac{1}{3}$
25 $-2\frac{1}{2}, -\frac{2}{3}$ **26** −7, 0.4
27 $-1\frac{1}{3}, 2\frac{1}{2}$ **28** $-\frac{2}{3}$
29 −4 **30** −3, 2
31 −1.5, 4 **32** −3, −2, 2, 3
33 −3, −2 **34** 1.2 sec, 2 sec
35 b) 70 m by 45 m
36 b) 5, 12, 13

Exercises 4.3 home *(p.90)*

1 0, −2 **2** −3, 3
3 −3, 0.5 **4** −2, 4
5 $\frac{2}{3}, 1\frac{1}{2}$ **6** none
7 −4, 0 **8** 0, 3
9 0, $1\frac{2}{3}$ **10** $-\sqrt{17}, \sqrt{17}$
11 $-\sqrt{26}, \sqrt{26}$ **12** $-\sqrt{10}, \sqrt{10}$
13 −4, 4 **14** none
15 −5, 0 **16** −3, −1
17 −17, −3 **18** 4, 8
19 2, 5 **20** 3
21 −2, 3 **22** 1
23 $-\frac{1}{7}, 1$ **24** −7, 2
25 $1\frac{1}{2}, \frac{1}{3}$ **26** −2.5, 1.5
27 $-\frac{1}{3}$ **28** $1\frac{1}{3}, 1\frac{1}{2}$
29 2, 6 **30** −3, 6
31 −1, 1
32 b) 6, 8, 10 **c)** $3d, 4d, 5d$
33 a) 27, 29 **b)** 35, 44
34 11

Exercises 4.4 class *(p.95)*

1 2, 6 **2** −18, 1
3 −14, 6 **4** −3, $-\frac{1}{3}$
5 −2, $\frac{5}{9}$
6 −1, $1\frac{1}{11}$ **7** −2.12, 0.786
8 −0.773, −0.369
9 −4, 1 **10** $\frac{2}{3}$, 3
11 0.382, 2.62 **12** $-\frac{2}{3}$, 5
13 −0.907, 2.57
14 −1.5, 0.8 **15** none
16 −136, 25 **17** none
18 −1.45, 3.45 **19 d)** 1.62

Exercises 4.4 home *(p.95)*

1 −10, −2 **2** −4, 5
3 −9, 20 **4** −1.13, 2.27
5 −0.08, −4.67 **6** 0.551, 5.45
7 −8.53, −0.469 **8** −0.135, 2.47
9 −7, −1 **10** −1.69, 1.19
11 −0.549, 1.22 **12** 0.4, 2
13 none **14** 0, $1\frac{2}{7}$
15 $\frac{3}{4}, 1\frac{1}{3}$ **16** $-10\frac{2}{7}$, 14
17 −1.18, 0.847 **18** −1.73, 1.73
19 −18.5, 30.5 **20** −11.6, 0.603

Consolidation Exercises for Chapter 4 *(p.97)*

1 a) $x^2 + 5x - 36$ **b)** $6x^2 - 5x - 6$
c) $25 - 20x + 4x^2$
d) $7x^2 - 7x - 69$ **e)** $43x + 96$
2 a) $(x - 7)(x - 13)$
b) $(x + 11)(2x - 1)$
c) $2(2x + 5)(3x + 2)$
d) $4(5x^2 - 30x + 9)$
e) $5(7x - 1)(7x + 1)$
3 a) $(x - 10)^2 - 9$
b) $2(x + 5)^2 - 15$
c) $8.25 - (x - 0.5)^2$
d) $4(x - 2)^2 - 9$
4 a) $4(x + 0.75)^2 + 4.75$
b) (−0.75, 4.75), $x = -0.75$

5 a) (2, 1), $x = 2$
b) (–1, –3), $x = -1$
c) (1, 5), $x = 1$

6 $a\left(x+\frac{b}{2a}\right)^2+\frac{4ac-b^2}{4a}$

a) $b^2 > 4ac$
b) $b^2 = 4ac$ c) $b^2 < 4ac$

7 a) $y = 2x^2 - 10$
b) $y = (x + 2)^2 + 5$
c) $y = x(x - 4)$
d) $y = 20 - (x - 2)^2$

8 $x = -0.5$ or 1.5 $y = -3.5$ or -1.5

9 $x = \frac{1}{3}$ or $x = 1$

10 $\{x: -5 < x < 1.75\}$
$x = 0$ or $x = -1$

11 a) $-2 \pm \sqrt{3}$ b) $\frac{1}{4}(5 \pm \sqrt{17})$
c) $\frac{1}{6}(-1 \pm \sqrt{61})$ d) $\frac{1}{8}(1 \pm \sqrt{113})$

12 $x = 4$ or $x = -5$

13 $1 \pm \sqrt{13}$

14 $-6 > k > 6$
i) $a = 2\sqrt{3},\ b = -3$,
least value = –3
ii) $x = 3\sqrt{3}$ or $\sqrt{3}$

CHAPTER 5 Simultaneous equations and quadratic inequalities

Exercises 5.1 class *(p.104)*

1 $x = 6, y = 6$. 2 $x = 2\frac{4}{7}, y = \frac{2}{7}$.
3 $p = 7, r = 2$.
4 $x = -1.3, y = 3.4$.
5 (10, 1), (6, 6), (1, 3).
6 All meet at (7,4)
7 a) Lines coincident, infinite number of solutions
b) Lines parallel, no solutions
8 Median equations: $x + 4y = 6$, $x = 2$, $4y = 3x - 2$ (2, 1)
9 a) PQ = PR = $\sqrt{50}$ b) $y = 8 - x$
c) $y = x$ d) (4, 4) e) 15
10 b) $t = 20, s = 50$

Exercises 5.1 home *(p.105)*

1 $x = -\frac{5}{7}, y = 3\frac{1}{7}$
2 $x = \frac{20}{21}, y = -\frac{16}{21}$
3 $x = 4, y = 2$
4 $x = \frac{23}{39}, y = -\frac{11}{39}$
5 (0.5, –0.5)
6 $8x + 12y + 9 = 0$ and $4x + 6y = 3$ are parallel (1.5, –1.75), (0, 0.5)
7 (6, –8)
8 a) ii) b) i) c) iii) d) (–12, –12)
9 $(-1\frac{15}{23}, -\frac{17}{23})$
10 40 first class, 10 second class

Exercises 5.2 class *(p.107)*

1 (–2, 0), (4, 6)
2 (–2.5, 18.5), (0.5, 3.5)
3 none
4 (–2, 2), $(8, -\frac{2}{9})$
5 $(1\frac{2}{3}, 2\frac{2}{3})$, (3, 2)
6 (–9.52, 5.88), (7.65, 1.59)

Exercises 5.2 home *(p.107)*

1 (–1, 4), (4, 19)
2 (–5.15, 10.1), (1.49, 5.68)
3 (2, 2.25), (3, 1.5)
4 (1, 5), (2.5, 8)
5 (10, 9)
6 (13, 10)

Exercise 5.3 class *(p.110)*

1 $-\frac{1}{3} < x < \frac{1}{3}$ 2 $x \le -\frac{1}{3}, x \ge \frac{1}{3}$
3 no x values
4 $0 < x < \frac{3}{2}$ 5 $-2 < x < 4$
6 all x values
7 all x values except –2
8 all x values except 2
9 $x < -4.83, x > 0.828$
10 $x < -0.828, x > 4.83$

Exercises 5.3 home *(p.110)*

1 $-2.646 < x < 2.647$
2 no x values
3 $x < -3.606, x > 3.606$
4 $-5 \le x \le 2$
5 $-4 \le x \le -1$
6 $x < 0, x > 2$
7 $-0.449 \le x \le 4.449$
8 $-1.618 \le x \le 0.618$
9 $x < -0.291, x > 2.291$
10 $-0.646 < x < 4.646$

Consolidation Exercises for Chapter 5 *(p.110)*

1 a) $x = 5, y = 1$ b) $x = -2, y = 3$
c) $a = -1, b = 2$ d) $a = 2, b = 3$
2 a) $x + 2y = 8$ b) $x + 2y = 3$, (1, 1)
c) AP = BQ = PQ = $\sqrt{5}$
3 a) (–1, 5), (3, 7), (0, 7)
b) 36.9°, 26.6°, 116.6°
4 a) $b + s = 20, 30b + 20s = 480$
b) $b = 8, s = 12$
5 a) $(5x + 3)(x - 2)$
b) $\{x: x < -0.6$ or $x > 2\}$
6 a) $-3 < x < 4$ b) $1 < x < 2$
c) $-1 < x < 1.5$ d) $x < -2, x > 3$
7 $y^2 + 2y + 1 = 0$, (2, –1)
8 a) $(3x - 7)(2x - 1)$
b) $x < \frac{1}{2}, x > 2\frac{1}{3}$
c) (0, 7), $(2\frac{2}{3}, 4\frac{1}{3})$
9 $-1\frac{15}{17}$, 2
10 (–1, 1), (3, 5)
11 $(-\frac{2}{3}, 9)$, (3, –2)
12 $3 < x < 4$
13 i) $x = 3$ ii) $y = 3x - 7$ is a tangent to $y = x^s - 3x + 2$

CHAPTER 6 Cubic and polynomial functions

Exercises 6.1 class *(p.116)*

1 b) (–1.53, 13.1), (1.53, –1.13)
c) –3, 1, 2
2 b) none c) –0.246
3 b) (0, 0), (2.67, –9.48) c) 0, 4
4 b) (2.22, 9.11), (0.451, 6.37)
c) 3.70
5 b) no max, (1.14, –7.07)
c) –1.10, 2.05
6 b) (–1.5, 4.69), no min
c) –2.26, 1

Exercises 6.1 home *(p.116)*

1 b) (–1.73, 10.4), (1.73, –10.4)
c) –3, 0, 3
2 b) none c) 1
3 b) (0, 0), (1.67, –4.63) c) 0, 2.5
4 b) (–0.667, 4.52), (–4, –14)
c) –5.47, –1.74, 0.210
5 b) (0, 0), (–2.83, –64), (2.83, –64) c) –4, 0, 4
6 b) (–0.573, 3.11) no min
c) –1.08, 0.160

Exercises 6.2 class *(p.119)*

1 a) $2x^2 + 4x - 3$, $6x - 13$
b) $4x^2 - 5x + 24$, $4x^3 - 2x^2 - 3x - 6$
c) $3x^4 + x^3 + 5x^2 - 9x - 8$, $3x^4 - x^3 + 5x^2 + 9x - 8$
d) $x^5 + 4x^3 + x^2 - x + 5$, $-x^5 + 6x^3 - x^2 - x + 11$
2 a) $3x^3 + 5x^2 + 17x + 10$
b) $10x^3 - 17x^2 + 8x - 1$
c) $x^4 + 5x^3 + 19x^2 + 34x + 40$
d) $2t^4 - 6t^3 - 21t^2 + 11t - 30$
e) $t^5 - 2t^4 - 18t^3 + 27t^2 - 22t + 20$
f) $2x^5 + 7x^4 + 6x^3 + 59x^2 + 10x - 21$
3 a) $13x^3 - 13x^2 + 79x - 43$
b) $7t^3 - 5t^2 - t + 23$
c) $-4x^3 + 90x^2 - 12x - 92$
4 a) $x^3 + 6x^2 + 2x - 10$ i) 3 ii) 1
b) $-2x^2 + 6x + 29$ i) 2 ii) 0
c) $-2x^3 - 3x^2 + 20x + 30$
i) 3 ii) –2
d) $-2x^6 - 13x^5 + 5x^4 + 136x^3 + 159x^2 - 60x - 90$ i) 6 ii) 136
e) $x^4 + 13x^3 + 35x^2 - 6x - 109$
i) 4 ii) 13
f) $16x^4 + 96x^3 + 216x^2 + 216x + 81$ i) 4 ii) 96

Exercises 6.2 home (p.120)

1 a) $4x^2 + 3x - 4$, $3x + 4$
b) $3x^3 + x^2 - 6x$, $x^3 - x^2 - 6x + 8$
c) $x^4 - 2x^3 - 2x^2 + 10$, $x^4 - 4x^3 + 2x^2 + 2$
d) $x^5 - 2x^2 + 8$, $-x^5 + 4x^2 + 8x$

2 a) $x^4 - x^2 - 2$, 4
b) $2x^3 - 10x^2 + 9x + 9$, 3
c) $2x^4 - 9x^3 + 12x^2 - 11x + 6$, 4
d) $-18x^5 + 9x^4 - 30x^3 + 24x^2 - 14x + 4$, 5
e) $x^8 - 3x^7 + 4x^6 + 2x^4 - 7x^3 + 11x^2 - 4x$, 8
f) $4x^6 - 4x^5 - 33x^4 + 33x^3 + 62x^2 - 36x - 40$, 6

3 a) $3x^3 - 2x^2 + 9x - 5$ **b)** $4x$
c) $x^4 - x^3 + 9x^2 - 3x + 31$

4 a) $x^3 + 4x^2 + 9$ **i)** 3 **ii)** 4
b) $-x^2 + 3x - 11$ **i)** 2 **ii)** -1
c) $3x^3 + 9x^2 - 6x + 4$ **i)** 3 **ii)** 9
d) $3x^3 - 2x^2 + 27x - 18$ **i)** 3 **ii)** -2
e) $2x^5 + 6x^4 + 18x^3 + 54x^2$ **i)** 5 **ii)** 54
f) $6x^5 - 18x^4 - 243x^2 - 729$ **i)** 5 **ii)** -243

Exercises 6.3 class (p.123)

1 $(x - 4)(x - 1)(x + 3)$
2 $(x - 5)(x + 2)(2x - 1)$
3 $(x - 2)(x - 1)(x + 3)$
4 $(x - 2)^2(x + 1)$
5 $(x - 2)(x + 3)(3x - 1)$
6 $(x - 3)(x - 1)(x + 2)(x + 4)$
7 $(x - 3)(x + 1)(2x - 1)(2x + 7)$
8 $(x + 4)(5x - 2)(x^2 - x - 5)$

Exercises 6.3 home (p.123)

1 $(x - 3)(x - 2)(x - 1)$
2 $(2x - 1)(x^2 + 1)$
3 $(x + 3)(2x - 1)(2x + 1)$
4 $(x - 1)(x^2 + x + 5)$
5 $(x + 1)^2(x^2 - x + 1)$
6 $(x - 3)(3x + 1)(x^2 + 4)$

Exercises 6.4 class (p.127)

1 a) $-3.5, -1, 0.5, 3$ **c)** $x < -3.5$ or $-1 < x < 0.5$ or $x > 3$, $-3.5 \le x \le -1$ or $0.5 \le x \le 3$
2 a) $-2.5, 2$ **c)** $x < -2.5$ or $x > 2$, $-2.5 \le x \le 2$
3 a) $-4, 1, 2$ **c)** $-4 < x < 1$ or $x > 2$, $x \le -4$ or $1 \le x \le 2$
4 a) 0.6, 5 **c)** $0.6 < x < 5$ or $x > 5$, $x \le 0.6$ or $x = 5$
5 a) $-6.19, -1, -0.807, 4$ **c)** $x < -6.19$ or $-1 < x < -0.807$, $x > 4$, $-6.19 \le x \le -1$ or $-0.807 \le x \le 4$
6 a) $-3, -1, 1$ **c)** $-1 < x < 1$ or $x > 1$, $x \le 1$ or $x = 1$
7 $f(x) = x^3 + x^2 - 6x$
8 $f(x) = x^3 + 2x^2 - 4x - 8$
9 $f(x) = 18 + 18x - 2x^2 - 2x^3$
10 $f(x) = x^3 + 0.5x^2 - 12.5x + 6$

Exercises 6.4 home (p.128)

1 a) $-3, -1.5, 2$ **c)** $x < -3$ or $-1.5 < x < 2$, $-3 \le x \le -1.5$ or $x \ge 2$
2 a) $-4, 0.382, 2.62$ **c)** $x < -4$ or $0.382 < x < 2.62$, $-4 \le x \le 0.382$ or $x \ge 2.62$
3 a) $-1, -0.457$ or 1.457 **c)** $x < -1$ or $-0.457 < x < 1.457$, $-1 \le x \le 0.457$ or $x \ge 1.457$
4 a) $-1, 1.5$
c) $-1 < x < 1.5$, $x \le -1$, $x \ge 1.5$
5 a) $-4, -3, -2, -1$ **c)** $-4 < x < -3$ or $-2 < x < -1$, $x \le -4$ or $-3 \le x \le -2$, or $x > -1$
6 a) $-1.85, -1, 1, 1.35$
c) $-1.85 < x < -1$ or $1 < x < 1.35$, $x \le -1.85$ or $-1 \le x \le 1$ or $x \ge 1.35$
7 a) $-3, -1.73, 1, 1.73$ **c)** $x < -3$ or $-1.73 < x < 1$ or $x > 1.73$, $-3 \le x \le -1.73$ or $1 \le x \le 1.73$
8 a) $-2.5, -1, 0, 2$
c) $x < -2.5$ or $0 < x < 2$, $-2.5 \le x \le 0$ or $x \ge 2$
9 a) 1, 3 **c)** $x > 3$, $x \le 3$
10 $f(x) = -x^3 + 6x^2 - 8x$
11 $f(x) = \frac{1}{4}x^3 - \frac{3}{4}x^2 - \frac{5}{2}x + 6$
12 $f(x) = -2x^3 - x^2 + 8x - 5$
13 $f(x) = 15x^3 - 21x^2 - 18x$

Consolidation exercises for Chapter 6 (p.129)

1 b) $f(x) = (x - 3)(x + 4)(x^2 + 2x + 2)$, $x^2 + 2x + 2 = 0$ has no real roots
2 $f(x) = 5x^3 - 10x^2 - 5x + 10$
3 a) $k = -34$, **b)** $-2.5, 0.5, 1.5$
4 b) ii) $p = 1, q = 3, a = 0.5$
iv) $h = 0.1$
5 b) $(x - 3)(x^2 - 2)$ **c)** $-\sqrt{2}$, $\sqrt{2}$, 3
d) $-\sqrt{2} - 1$, $\sqrt{2} - 1$, 2
6 $a = 1, b = -4, (x + 1)$
7 $x < 2$ or $3 < x < 4$
8 b) $b = 1, c = 3, a = -2$
c) $y = -2x^3 + 10x^2 14x + 6$
9 b) $\frac{-3+\sqrt{5}}{2}$, $\frac{-3-\sqrt{5}}{2}$
10 b) $2x^2 - x - 5$
c) $\frac{1+\sqrt{41}}{4}$, $\frac{1-\sqrt{41}}{4}$,
11 $(x + 1)(x - 4)(3x + 2)$

CHAPTER 7
Differentiation 1

Exercises 7.1 class (p.134)

1 $2x$ **2** $10x$ **3** $6x^2$
4 $4x^3$ **5** $12x^3$ **6** $2x + 1$
7 $2x + 5$ **8** $3x^2 - 3$

Exercises 7.1 home (p.135)

1 1 **2** -5
3 $8t$ **4** $5t^4$
5 $2t - 2$ **6** $2t - 3$
7 $3t^2 - 12t + 12$ **8** $2t - 8$

Exercises 7.2 class (p.138)

1 $20x$ **2** -5
3 $3x^2 - 4x$
4 $21x^6 - 20x^4 + 6x^2$
5 $9x^2 - 12$ **6** $2x - 8$
7 $4x + 1$ **8** $3x^2 - 16x + 15$
9 $20x$ **10** -5
11 $3x^2 - 4x$
12 $21x^6 - 20x^4 + 6x^2$
13 $4x$, 20 **14** $2 - 3x^2$, 1.25
15 $6x - 21$, 0
16 $15x^2 - 20x$, 35
17 $6x^2 - 10x + 1$, 1
18 $3x^2 - 6x + 10$, 19
19 $2 - 8t$, -6
20 $45t^2 - 4t - 8$, 41
21 (1, 7)
22 (3, 2), (−3, 8)
23 (0, 0), (1.5, −1.69)
24 $(-\frac{1}{3}, -\frac{4}{27})$, (1, 0)
25 (1, −7), (−1, −23)
26 -1 **27** -7, 7
28 $A(-\frac{2}{3}, 9.59)$, $B(1.5, -4.25)$

Exercises 7.2 home (p.138)

1 $15x^2$ **2** $4x^3 + 3$
3 $-10 + 20x - 30x^2$
4 5 **5** 0
6 $3u^2 - 2u + 5$
7 $98x^6 - 50x^4$ **8** $30t - 70$
9 $15x^2$ **10** $4x^3 + 3$
11 $-10 + 20x - 30x^2$ **12** 5
13 0, 0 **14** -5, -5
15 $4x$, 4 **16** $8x$, 0
17 $6t^2 + 2t - 5$, 15
18 $4t^3 - 6t^2 + t - 1$, -1
19 $4t - 10$, 6
20 $36t^2 - 96t + 15$, -33
21 (−0.707, −0.25), (0, 0), (0.707, −0.25)
22 $(-1\frac{2}{9}, \frac{1}{9})$ **23** H(2, −6), (−1, 0)
24 (1.423, 0.385), (2.577, −0.385)
25 a) i) 11, **ii)** 5, **iii)** -7, 7
b) $(-\frac{5}{6}, -4\frac{1}{12})$

26 a) i) –4, **ii)** 21, –12, 28
b) (–3.694, 12.60), (0.361, –20.75)
27 (–0.5, –8.125), (1, –7) **28** b

Exercises 7.3 class *(p.141)*
1 a) 0, 89, 208, 405, 728
b) 90, 96, 150, 252, 402
2 a) 12 m **b)** $20t - 6t^2$
d) –4 m s^{-2} **e)** $3\frac{1}{3}$ sec
3 a) 4000 **b)** 5

Exercises 7.3 home *(p.141)*
1 a) 0 m s^{-1}, **b)** 10 m s^{-1}
c) –10 m s^{-2}
2 a) $24 - 6t$ **c)** 48 cm
d) s = 21, 36, 45, 21;
v = 18, 12, 6, 18;
down, down, up, up
3 b) i) 55, **ii)** –40 **c)** $8\frac{2}{3}$

Exercises 7.4 class *(p.144)*
1 a) 9, –7 **b)** (0.25, 1.125)
2 a) 21, –6, 6 **b)** (1.414, –1.657), (–1.414, 9.657)
3 (2.5, 20.25) max
4 (2.5, 0) min
5 (0, 9) max $(2\frac{2}{3}, -\frac{13}{27})$ min
6 (1, 4) max, (3, 0) min
7 (0, 0) inflexion, (3, 27) max
8 (–2, 19) max, (0, 3) min, (2, 19) max
9 (0, –10) min, (2, 6) inflexion

Exercises 7.4 home *(p.145)*
1 a) –24 (decreasing), 12 (increasing), –24 (decreasing)
b) (–1, –7), (2, 20)
2 a) –12, 0, 12
b) (0, 0), (0.5, 0.0625), (1, 0)
3 (–2.5, –0.25) min
4 (–5, 0) max
5 $(\frac{1}{3}, -\frac{37}{54})$ max, (2, –3) min
6 (–1.22, –3.25) min, (0, –1) max, (1.22, –3.25) min
7 (–2, 0) inflexion
8 (–1, –4) min, (1, 12) max, (3, –4) min
9 none

Exercises 7.5 class *(p.147)*
1 a) $y = 30 - x$ **b)** $A = 30x - x^2$
c) 15, 225 m^2, square
2 Site A: **a)** $2x + y = 60$
b) $A = 60x - 2x^2$
c) 450 m^2, $x = 15$, $y = 30$
Site B: **a)** $2x + y = 68$
b) $A = 68x - 2x^2 - 40$
c) 538 m^2, $x = 17$, $y = 34$
3 b) $x = 9$, $y = 8$ A = 432 m^2
4 a) 12 miles from A **b)** B
5 b) $V = \pi h(400 - \frac{1}{4}h^2)$
c) $h = 23.1$, $r = 16.3$, 19 350 cm^2
6 $x = 0$, $r = \frac{200}{\pi} \approx 63.7$

Exercises 7.5 home *(p.148)*
1 75 m by 100 m
2 51 mph
3 A_1: 25 m square, A_2: 25 m by 12.5 m
4 c) $\frac{18}{\pi+4} \approx 2.52$ m^2

Consolidation Exercises for Chapter 7 *(p151)*
1 a) $3x^2 - 1$ **b)** 6 **c)** 2
d) $y = 2x + 8$ **e)** (1, 6)
2 a) $3x^2 + 6x + 4$
3 a) 0, 0 **b)** (1, 1)
c) i) (–1.414, –0.943), (1.414, 0.943)
ii) (–3.08, –0.520), (–1.59, –1.00), (1.59, 1.00), (3.08, 0.520)
d) i) –2.45, 0, 2.45 **ii)** 0
4 $c = 5000 + 250n$, $a = 13500$, $b = -20$ £462.50, 4250, £898 125
5 b) A: (–1, 0) B: $\left(\frac{5}{3}, \frac{256}{27}\right)$
6 a) B: (0, –14)
c) (1, –11), $\left(\frac{7}{3}, \frac{329}{27}\right)$
7 b) $x = 0$, $x = \pm 2\sqrt{2}$
c) OP = 0

CHAPTER 8
Integration 1

Exercises 8.1 class *(p.159)*
1 a) 23.75 **b)** 15 **c)** 14.5 **d)** $42\frac{2}{3}$
2 a) 31.5 **b)** 42.5 **c)** 0.16
3 a) (2, 0), 2 **b)** (–1, 0), 15
c) (–4, 0), $\frac{1}{2}$
4 a) 40 m s^{-1} **b)** 20 s **d)** 400 m
e) $A(t) = 40t - t^2$, 75 m
5 b) $A(t) = 0.4t^2 + t$
c) amount of bacteria
d) 7.6 million

Exercises 8.1 home *(p.160)*
1 a) 41.25 **b)** $53\frac{1}{3}$ **c)** 8.5
d) 36.25
2 a) 8 **b)** 7.5 **c)** $5\frac{5}{6}$
3 a) 0.5 **b)** 6.5 **c)** 8.5
4 a) 24 m s^{-1} **b)** 4 s
d) $24t - 3t^2$, 2 m **e)** $\frac{1}{12}$s
5 b) $\frac{t^2}{3500} + \frac{t}{175}$
c) Amount of cola that has leaked out
d) 1 litre **e)** 33 s

Exercises 8.2 class *(p.165)*
1 a) $12\frac{1}{3}$ **b)** $29\frac{1}{3}$ **c)** $42\frac{2}{3}$ **d)** $20\frac{1}{4}$
2 a) 3.75 **b)** $\frac{1}{6}$ **c)** 12.8 **d)** 72
3 $6\frac{1}{3}$ **4** $57\frac{1}{6}$ **5** $21\frac{1}{3}$
6 13.5 **7** $10\frac{2}{3}$ **8** $10\frac{2}{3}$ **9** $58\frac{2}{3}$

Exercises 8.2 home *(p.166)*
1 a) $85\frac{1}{3}$ **b)** 20 **c)** 41.25 **d)** 22.5
2 a) 18.6 **b)** 1.5 **c)** $10\frac{2}{3}$ **d)** 256
3 $21\frac{1}{3}$ **4** $\frac{2}{3}$ **5** 0.5
6 0.5625 **7** 36 **8** $2\frac{2}{3}$ **9** $\frac{1}{3}$

Exercises 8.3 class *(p.169)*
1 a) $7x + c$ **b)** $x^4 + c$ **c)** $2x^3 + c$
d) $\frac{1}{3}x^3 - 2x^2 + 5x + c$
e) $\frac{1}{8}x^8 + c$
f) $\frac{1}{3}x^3 + \frac{1}{2}x^2 - 12x + c$
g) $x^4 - \frac{4}{3}x^3 + c$
h) $\frac{1}{4}x^4 + 2x^3 + 6x^2 + 8x + c$
2 a) $2x^2 - 7x + c$
b) $\frac{1}{4}x^4 - \frac{1}{3}x^3 + c$
c) $\frac{2}{5}x^5 + 4x^2 + c$
d) $\frac{7}{3}x^3 - 14x^2 + 28x + c$
3 a) $y = x^2 + 3$
b) $y = 2x^2 + 5x + 2$
c) $y = 10x - x^3 - 8$
d) $y = \frac{1}{4}x^4 + \frac{1}{3}x^3 + \frac{5}{12}$
e) $y = \frac{2}{3}x^3 - x^2 - 5$
h) $y = \frac{3}{4}x^4 + \frac{5}{3}x^3 - \frac{3}{2}x^2 - 5x - 3$

Exercises 8.3 home *(p.169)*
1 a) $-3x + c$ **b)** $x^5 + c$
c) $0.04x^5 + c$ **d)** $0.5x^7 + c$
e) $\frac{1}{3}x^3 + \frac{1}{2}x^2 + c$
f) $\frac{1}{3}x^3 - \frac{3}{2}x^2 + 2x + c$
g) $1.2x^5 + 5.25x^4 + c$
h) $6.75x^4 + 9x^3 + 4.5x^2 + x + c$
2 a) $1.5x^2 - 4x + c$
b) $\frac{1}{6}t^6 - \frac{1}{4}t^4 + c$
c) $\frac{1}{6}x^3 - \frac{5}{2}x^2 + \frac{25}{2}x + c$
d) $0.25x^4 + x^3 + x^2 + c$
3 a) $y = 0.5x + 0.5$
b) $y = 4x^2 - 32$
c) $y = 11x - x^2 - 18$
d) $y = 11x - \frac{2}{3}x^3$
e) $y = \frac{1}{4}x^4 + \frac{4}{3}x^3 - \frac{225}{4}$
f) $y = \frac{27}{4}x^4 - 18x^3 + 18x^2 - 8x$

Consolidation Exercises for Chapter 8 *(p.170)*

1 $20\frac{5}{6}$
2 a) P(2, 20), Q(4, 16)
b) Area L = 28; area R = 36
3 a) $19\frac{8}{15}$ **b)** $1049\frac{1}{3}$
4 a) A(4, 0) B(–4, 8)
c) $13\frac{1}{3}, -2\frac{2}{3}$
d) $32 - (13\frac{1}{3} - 2\frac{2}{3}) = 21\frac{1}{3}$
5 a) A(–1, 4), B(2, 4)
b) 12 – 5.25 = 6.75
c) AB = OC = 3
6 a) $p = -7, q = -2$
b) C: (6, 17) **c)** $\frac{4}{3}$
7 a) P: (–1, 5) Q: (2,2)
8 i) $\frac{32}{3}$ **ii) b)** 3.175

CHAPTER 9
Trigonometry 1

Exercises 9.1 class *(p.177)*

1 a) i) –315°, –45°, 315°,
ii) –225°, –135°, 135°, 225°
b) i) –315°, –225°, 135°,
ii) –135°, –45°, 225°, 315°
c) i) –315°, –135°, 225°,
ii) –225°, –45°, 135°, 315°
2 a) –330°, –150°, 210°
b) –300°, –120°, 240°
c) –210°, –30°, 150°, 330°
d) –240°, –60°, 120°, 300°
3 a) 14.5°, 165.5°
b) 240°, 300°
c) 75.5°, 284.5°
d) 150°, 210°
e) 68.2°, 248.2°
f) 120°, 300°
4 a) –81.4°, 81.4° **b)** none
c) –120°, 120°
d) –160.7°, –19.3°
e) –95.7°, 84.3°
f) 60°, 120° **g)** –36.9°, 143.1°
h) –150°, 30°

Exercises 9.1 home *(p.178)*

2 a) $\frac{\sqrt{3}}{2}, -\frac{1}{2}, -\sqrt{3}$
b) $\frac{1}{2}, -\frac{\sqrt{3}}{2}, -\frac{1}{\sqrt{3}}$
c) $-\frac{1}{2}, -\frac{\sqrt{3}}{2}, \frac{1}{\sqrt{3}}$
d) $-\frac{\sqrt{3}}{2}, \frac{1}{2}, -\sqrt{3}$
3 a) 36.9°, 143.1°
b) 228.6°, 311.4°
c) 53.1°, 306.9°
d) 138.6°, 221.4°
e) 31.0°, 211.0°
f) 143.1°, 323.1°
4 a) –126.9°, –53.1°
b) –110.5°, 110.5°
c) none **d)** –21.8°, 158.2°
e) none **f)** –19.9°, 19.9°
g) –89.4°, 90.6° **h)** 30°, 150°

Exercises 9.2 class *(p.180)*

1 a) 36.9°, 323.1°
b) 22.6°, 157.4°
c) 60.3°, 240.3°
d) 107.5°, 252.5°
e) 202.0°, 338.0°
f) 112.6°, 292.6°
2 a) 26.6°, 63.4°, 206.6°, 243.4°
b) 18.9°, 108.9°, 198.9°, 288.9°
c) 268.9° **d)** 236.1°
e) 24.6°, 95.4°, 144.6°, 215.4°, 264.6°, 335.4° **f)** 318.8°
3 a) 38.3°, 141.7°, 218.3°, 321.7°
b) 52.9°, 127.1°, 232.9°, 307.1°
c) 41.4°, 138.6°, 221.4°, 318.6°
d) 60°, 120°, 240°, 300°
4 a) –149.0°, –31.0°, 31.0°, 149.0°
b) –130°, 110° **c)** none
d) –150°, –120°, –60°, –30°, 30° 60°, 120°, 150°
e) –60°, 60°
f) –131.8°, –120.2°, –59.8°, –48.2°, 12.2°, 23.8°, 84.2°, 95.8°, 156.2°, 167.8°
g) –93.7°, 86.3° **h)** none

Exercises 9.2 home *(p.181)*

1 a) 44.4°, 135.6°
b) 66.4°, 293.6° **c)** 69.4°, 249.4°
d) 204.6°, 335.4°
e) 104.5°, 255.5°
f) 113.2°, 293.2°
2 a) 22.8°, 157.2°, 202.8°, 337.2°
b) 16.3°, 76.3°, 136.3°, 196.3°, 256.3°, 316.3°
c) 249.7° **d)** none
e) 18.4°, 71.6°, 198.4°, 251.6°
f) 230.8°
3 a) 48.2°, 131.8°, 228.2°, 311.8°
b) 39.2°, 140.8°, 219.2°, 320.8°
c) 42.4°, 137.6°, 222.4°, 317.6°
d) 49.8°, 130.2°, 229.8°, 310.2°
4 a) none **b)** –178.5°, –29.5°
c) 41.8°, 138.2° **d)** none
e) –148.3°, –121.7°, –58.3°, –31.7°, 31.7°, 58.3°, 121.7°, 148.3° **f)** none **g)** –60°, 60°
h) –144.4°, –54.4°, 35.6°, 125.6°

Exercises 9.3 class *(p.185)*

1 b) 03:00 and 15:00, 09:00 and 21:00 **c) i)** 4.2 m, **ii)** 04:20 and 16:20 **iii)** 3 h 20 min
d) i) 4.17 m **ii)** 04:23 and 16:23
iii) 3 h 26 min
2 a) $a = 4, b = 30, c = 18$
b) i) 20° C
ii) 4, 5, 6, 7, 8
3 a) $a = -0.5, c = 1.5$
c) i) after 0.5, 2.5, 3.5, 5.5 s,
ii) 0.6 to 0.9 s, 2.1 to 2.4 s, 3.6 to 3.9 s, 5.1 to 5.4 s

Exercises 9.3 home *(p.186)*

1 a) $a = -0.25, b = 192$
c) $0.35 < t < 0.59$, $1.38 < t < 1.53$, $2.23 < t < 2.47$, $3.16 < t < 3.41$, $4.10 < t < 4.34$
d) i) 1.875 m, **ii)** 1.522 m
2 a) $h = \sin 12t$
b) $h = 5 + \sin 12t$
c) i) 5.87 m, **ii)** 4.13 m,
iii) 4.79 m
3 a) $y = 4\cos(22.5t)$
b) $y = 0.5\sin(5400t)$

Exercises 9.4 class *(p.189)*

1 a) –120° **b)** 22.5° **c)** –330°
d) 75° **e)** 315°
2

Degrees°	Radians
0	0
30	$\frac{\pi}{6}$
60	$\frac{\pi}{3}$
90	$\frac{\pi}{2}$
120	$\frac{2\pi}{3}$
150	$\frac{5\pi}{6}$
180	π
210	$\frac{7\pi}{6}$
240	$\frac{4\pi}{3}$
270	$\frac{3\pi}{2}$
300	$\frac{5\pi}{3}$
330	$\frac{11\pi}{6}$
360	2π

3 a) 1.75 **b)** –0.506
c) 5.36 **d)** –3.49
e) 17.5
4 a) 114.6° **b)** 28.6°
c) 361.0° **d)** 99.2°
5 a) $\frac{\pi}{2}, \frac{3\pi}{2}$ **b)** $0, \pi, 2\pi$
c) $\frac{\pi}{6}, \frac{11\pi}{6}$
d) $\frac{\pi}{4}, \frac{3\pi}{4}, \frac{5}{4}\pi, \frac{7\pi}{4}$
6 b) i) $0, \pi, 2\pi$ **ii)** $\frac{\pi}{2}, \frac{3\pi}{2}$
iii) $\frac{\pi}{6}, \frac{5\pi}{6}, \frac{7\pi}{6}, \frac{11\pi}{6}$
iv) $\frac{\pi}{4}, \frac{3\pi}{4}, \frac{5\pi}{4}, \frac{7\pi}{4}$

Exercises 9.4 home *(p.190)*

1 **a)** 45° **b)** –30° **c)** 300°
d) –105° **e)** 225°

2 **a)** 0.349 **b)** 1.26 **c)** 6.98
d) –2.44 **e)** 13.3

3 **a)** 85.9° **b)** 22.9 **c)** 171.9
d) 286.5 **e)** 412.5

4 **b) i)** $\frac{\pi}{2}$, $\frac{3\pi}{2}$
ii) $\frac{\pi}{3}$, $\frac{2\pi}{3}$
iii) $\frac{\pi}{4}$, $\frac{3\pi}{4}$, $\frac{5\pi}{4}$, $\frac{7\pi}{4}$

5 **c) i)** $-\frac{\pi}{2}$, $\frac{\pi}{2}$ **ii)** $-\pi$, 0, π
iii) $-\frac{2\pi}{3}$, $-\frac{\pi}{3}$, $\frac{\pi}{3}$, $\frac{2\pi}{3}$
iv) $\frac{-3\pi}{4}$, $\frac{-\pi}{4}$, $\frac{\pi}{4}$, $\frac{3\pi}{4}$

6 **c) i)** -2π, $-\pi$, 0, π, 2π
ii) $\pm\frac{7\pi}{4}$, $\pm\frac{5\pi}{4}$, $\pm\frac{3\pi}{4}$, $\pm\frac{\pi}{4}$
iii) $\pm\frac{5\pi}{3}$, $\pm\frac{4\pi}{3}$, $\pm\frac{2\pi}{3}$, $\pm\frac{\pi}{3}$
iv) $\pm\frac{11\pi}{6}$, $\pm\frac{7\pi}{6}$, $\pm\frac{5\pi}{6}$, $\pm\frac{\pi}{6}$
v) $\pm\frac{3\pi}{2}$, $\pm\frac{\pi}{2}$

Exercises 9.5 class *(p.192)*

1 **a)** PQ = 5.50 cm
POQ = 9.62 cm²
[shaded] = 3.50 cm²
b) PQ = 26.18 cm
POQ = 130.90 cm²
[shaded] = 105.90 cm²

2 $\theta = \frac{4}{3}$ radian = 76.4°
Area AOB = 150 cm²

3 θ = 28.65°, area = 36 cm², volume = 72 cm³

4 r = 6.25 cm
θ = 2.56 radians = 146.7°

5 perimeter = 61.96 cm, area = 100π – 41.56 = 272.59 cm²

6 **a)** 0.199 m²
Water is travelling at 0.228 m s⁻¹.

7 **a)** area of ΔPQR = 43.30 cm²
b) area S = 43.30 + 3(9.06) = 70.50 cm²

8 perimeter of cross-section=19.13 m

9 $\frac{1}{2}r^2(\theta - \sin\theta)$, θ = 1.28

10 $r = \frac{1}{4}l$, area = $\frac{1}{8}l^2$, θ = 2

Exercises 9.5 home *(p.193)*

1 **a) i)** 4.4 cm **ii)** 9.24 cm²
iii) 1.60 cm²
b) i) 10.47 cm **ii)** 26.18 cm²
iii) 15.36 cm²

2 $\theta = 4.62^c$, area = 24.375 cm

3 r = 5.76 cm, $\theta = 4.34^c$

4 **a)** 1.107 m²
b) speed of the water = 0.54 m s⁻¹

5 material needed = 10 708 m²

7 $\frac{1}{2}r^2(\alpha = \sin\alpha)$, $\alpha \approx \sin\alpha$

9 **a)** ∠CAB = 0.5857 radians
b) i) perimeter of R = 4.5142 cm
ii) area ACX = 2.635 65 cm²
iii) area of R = 0.296 cm²

Exercises 9.6 class *(p.196)*

1 **a)** θ = 126.87°, 306.87°
b) θ = 90°, 270°
c) θ = 63.4°, 116.6°, 243.4°, 296.6°
d) θ = 30°, 150°

2 **a)** θ = 210°, 330°
b) θ = 60°, 120°, 240°, 300°
c) θ = 0°, 360°
θ = 131.8°, 228.2°
d) θ = 36.87°, 323.13°
θ = 180°

3 **a)** 30°, 150°, 221.8°, 318.2°
b) 51.8°, 308.2°
c) 14.5° or 165.5°, 199.5° or 340.5°
d) 36.87°, 323.13°

4 **a)** –1.89 radians, 1.25 radians
–1.107 radians, 2.03 radians
b) –2.03 radians, 1.107 radians
–2.68 radians, 0.47 radians
c) 0.27, 2.87
d) –2.78, 0.37, –1.94, 1.21
e) –0.48, –2.67

5 **a)** f(1) = 0,
f(s) = (s – 1) (2s – 1)(2s +1)
b) 1.57,0.52, 2.62, –0.52, –2.62

Exercises 9.6 home *(p.197)*

1 **a)** 63.4°, 243.4°
b) 45°, 135°, 225°, 315°
c) 70.5°, 109.5, 250.5, 289.5°
d) 45°, 225°

2 **a)** 30°, 150°, 19.5°, 160.5°
b) ±160.5°, ±19.5°
c) –116.6, 63.4. –135, 45
d) θ = –90°, 53.1°, 126.9°
θ = –90°

3 **a)** $\frac{\pi}{6}$, $\frac{5\pi}{6}$, $\frac{7\pi}{6}$, $\frac{11\pi}{6}$
b) 0.075^c, 3.07^c
c) 1.21^c, 4.35^c, 0.35^c, 3.51^c

4 3.48 radians, 5.94 radians, 0.52 radians, 2.62 radians

5 **a)** (s + 1)(s + 2)(2s – 1)(2s + 1)
b) $\frac{3\pi}{2}$, $\frac{\pi}{6}$, $\frac{5\pi}{6}$, $\frac{7\pi}{6}$, $\frac{11\pi}{6}$

Consolidation Exercises for Chapter 9 *(p.197)*

1 6, 2 (90, 6), (210, 6), (330, 6) (30, 2), (150, 2), (270, 2)

2 **c)** 60°, 180°, 300°,
2, –1.125

3 3, –1, 60°, 120°, 240°, 300°

4 30°, 150°, 210°, 330°

5 **a)** 15 hr **b)** 30 June,
1 January or 27 December
c) $n = 12 - 6\cos(\frac{360}{365}x + 10)$

7 **b)** 1.614 **c)** 36° **d)** 90°

8 **a)** 9.775 **b)** 7.80625

9 **a)** –4 **b)** –2 **c)** $\frac{5\pi}{4}$, $\frac{7\pi}{4}$

10 $15\sin^2\theta + \sin\theta - 2 = 0$
19.5°, 160.5°, 203.6°, 336.4°

CHAPTER 10
Sequences and series 1

Exercises 10.1 class *(p.203)*

1 **a)** $u_1 = 1$, $u_{k+1} = u_k + 4$,
$u_k = 4k - 3$ **b)** $u_1 = 1$,
$u_{k+1} = -2u_k$, $u_k = (-2)^{k-1}$
c) $u_1 = 16000$, $u_{k+1} = u_k\frac{1}{4}$,
$u_k = 16000\ (0.25)^{k-1}$
d) $u_1 = 1$, $u_{k+1} = u_k +$
$(3k^2 + 3k + 1)$, $u_k = k^3$

2 **a)** 55 **b)** 55 **c)** 55 **d)** 60

3 **a)** $\sum_{k=1}^{25} k^2$ **b)** $\sum_{k=1}^{15} k(k+1)$ **c)** $\sum_{k=1}^{100} \frac{1}{k}$

4 **a) i)** 4, $4\frac{2}{3}$, $4\frac{8}{9}$, $4\frac{26}{27}$,
ii) $u_k = 5 - \left(\frac{1}{3}\right)^{k-2}$, **iii)** 5
b) i) 2, $\frac{2}{3}$, $\frac{6}{5}$, $\frac{10}{11}$,
ii) $u_k = 1 + \frac{3(-1)^{k-1}}{2^{k+1} + (-1)^k}$, **iii)** 1

Exercises 10.1 home *(p.203)*

1 **a)** $u_1 = 65$, $u_{k+1} = u_k - 9$,
$u_k = 74 - 9k$
b) $u_1 = 1$, $u_{k+1} = 0.9u_k$,
$u_k = (0.9)^{k-1}$
c) $u_1 = 1$, $u_{k+1} = u_k + (k + 1)$,
$u_k = \frac{1}{2}k(k + 1)$
d) $u_1 = 1$, $u_{k+1} = u_k / (u_k+1)$,
$u_k = \frac{1}{k}$

2 **a)** $\frac{341}{280}$ **b)** 63 **c)** 85 **d)** 85

3 **a)** $\sum_{k=1}^{10} 2k^3$ **b)** $\sum_{k=2}^{12} k(k+3)$
c) $\sum_{k=1}^{21} (-1)^{k+1}\frac{1}{k}$

4 **a) i)** $-\frac{1}{4}$, $-\frac{13}{16}$, $-\frac{61}{64}$, $-\frac{253}{256}$
ii) $u_k = -1 + \frac{3}{4^{k-1}}$ **iii)** –1
b) i) 3, $\frac{3}{2}$, $\frac{12}{5}$, $\frac{30}{17}$, $\frac{3}{2}$,
ii) $2 + \frac{5(-2)^{k-3}}{(-3)^{k-1} + 2^{k-3}}$, **iii)** 2

Exercises 10.2 class *(p.207)*

1 **a)** 11 **b)** 34, 26
c) 13, 6, –1, –8, –15
d) $3\frac{1}{4}, 4\frac{3}{4}, 5\frac{1}{2}, 6\frac{1}{4}$

2 **a)** 10 **b)** 8 **c)** 19 **d)** 11

3 **a)** $u_k = 3k - 1$,
$S_n = \frac{1}{2}n(3n + 1)$,
$u_{10} = 29$, $S_{10} = 155$
b) $u_k = 3\frac{3}{4} - \frac{3}{4}k$,
$S_n = \frac{1}{2}n(6\frac{3}{4} - \frac{3}{4}n)$, $u_{10} = -3\frac{3}{4}$,
$S_{10} = -3\frac{3}{4}$
c) $u_k = 3k - 16.5$,
$S_n = \frac{1}{2}n(3n - 30)$,
$u_{10} = 13.5$, $S_{10} = 0$
d) $u_k = (k - 1)x$,
$S_n = \frac{1}{2}n((n - 1)x)$,
$u_{10} = 9x$, $S_{10} = 45x$
e) $u_k = p + 2(k - 1)q$,
$S_n = n(p + (n - 1)q)$,
$u_{10} = p + 18q$,
$S_{10} = 10(p + 9q)$
f) $u_k = p + (2 - k)q$,
$S_n = \frac{1}{2}n(2p + (3 - n)q)$,
$u_{10} = p - 8q$,
$S_{10} = 5(2p - 7q)$

4 $u_k = 1.5k + 2$, $u_8 = 14$

5 $S_n = n(4 + n)$, $S_8 = 96$

6 **a)** 279.5 **b)** 92 **c)** 93.5 **d)** 188.5

7 124.8

8 10

9 **a)** 74 m **b)** 12 s

Exercises 10.2 home *(p.208)*

1 **a)** 20 **b)** 17.5, 15, 12.5, 10, 7.5
c) 1, $\frac{5}{3}$ **d)** $2\frac{1}{6}$, $1\frac{1}{6}$

2 **a)** 11 **b)** 12 **c)** 13 **d)** 14

3 **a)** $u_k = 2k$, $S_n = n(n + 1)$,
$n_8 = 16$, $S_8 = 72$
b) $u_k = 21 - 4k$,
$S_n = n(19 - 2n)$,
$u_8 = -11$, $S_8 = 24$
c) $u_k = 10 - 5k$,
$S_n = \frac{1}{2}5n(3 - n)$, $u_8 = -30$,
$S_8 = -100$
d) $u_k = 30 - (k - 1)x$,
$S_n = \frac{1}{2}n(60 - (n - 1)x)$,
$u_8 = 30 - 7x$, $S_8 = 240 - 28x$
e) $u_k = p - 4(k - 1)q$,
$S_n = n(p - 2(n - 1)q)$,
$u_8 = p - 28q$, $S_8 = 8(p - 14q)$
f) $u_k = p + q + (k - 1)(p + 2q)$,
$S_n = \frac{1}{2}n(2(p + q) + (n - 1)(p + 2q))$,
$u_8 = 8p + 15q$, $S_8 = 36p + 64q$

4 $u_k = 2k + 1$, $u_{11} = 23$

5 $S_n = \frac{1}{2}n(5n - 13)$, $S_{10} = 185$

6 **a)** 688 **b)** –18 **c)** 1500 **d)** 1550

7 2

8 6

9 460 men, £705 600

Exercises 10.3 class *(p.213)*

1 **a)** 5, 625 **b)** –9, 3 **c)** 10, 2.5
d) 1, $\frac{9}{64}$, $\frac{27}{512}$ **e)** x^4, x^6, x^{10}
f) $p^{11}q^6, p^9q^5, p^7q^4, p^5q^3$

2 **a)** 10 **b)** 6 **c)** 10
d) 10 (32, ..., $\frac{1}{8}$, $\frac{1}{16}$)

3 **a)** $u_k = 2^{k-1}$,
$S_n = 2^{n-1}$ $u_8 = 128$, $S_8 = 255$
b) $u_k = 500(\frac{1}{2})^{k-1}$,
$S_n = 1000(1 - (\frac{1}{2})^n)$, $u_8 = 3\frac{29}{32}$,
$S_8 = 996\frac{3}{32}$
c) $u_k = 16(-\frac{1}{2})^{k-1}$,
$S_n = \frac{32}{3}\left(1 - \left(-\frac{1}{2}\right)^n\right)$,
$u_8 = -\frac{1}{8}$, $S_8 = 10\frac{5}{8}$
d) $u_k = (\frac{1}{x})^{k-1}$,
$S_n = \dfrac{1-\left(\frac{1}{x}\right)^n}{1-\frac{1}{x}}$,
$u_8 = \frac{1}{x^7}$, $S_8 = \dfrac{1-\left(\frac{1}{x}\right)^8}{1-\frac{1}{x}}$

4 $u_k = 2700(\frac{4}{3})^{k-1}$, $u_5 = 8533\frac{1}{3}$

5 $r = \pm 0.6$,
$S_n = 25\,000(1 - (0.6)^n) \Rightarrow$
$S_5 = 23\,056$,
$S_n = 6250(1 - (0.6)^n)$,
$S_5 = 6736$

6 **a)** $r = 1.5 \Rightarrow a = 32$,
$r = -1.5 \Rightarrow a = -32$
b) 32, 48, 72, 108, 162, 243, 364.5, 546.75 –32, 48, –72, 108, –162, 243, –364.5, 546.75
c) $S_n = 64(1.5^n - 1) \Rightarrow$
$S_8 = 1576.25$,
$S_n = 12.8(1 - (-1.5)^n) \Rightarrow$
$S_8 = -315.25$

7 7

8 10

9 **a)** $u_k = 20 \times 1.1^{k-1}$
b) 18th week **c)** 912 km (3 s.f.)

Exercises 10.3 home *(p.214)*

1 **a)** $u_k = 2 \times 3^{k-1}$, $S_n = 3^{n-1}$,
$u_{10} = 39\,366$, $S_{10} = 59\,048$
b) $u_k = 27(\frac{1}{3})^{k-1}$,
$S_n = \frac{81}{2}\left(1 - \left(\frac{1}{3}\right)^n\right)$,
$u_{10} = 0.0014$, $S_{10} = 40.5$
c) $u_k = 12(-\frac{1}{2})^{k-1}$,
$S_n = 8(1 - (-\frac{1}{2})n)$,
$u_{10} = -0.0234$, $S_{10} = 7.99$
d) $u_k = (\frac{\pi}{2})^k$,
$S_n = \dfrac{\left(\frac{\pi}{2}\right)^n - 1}{\frac{\pi}{2} - 1}$,
$u_{10} = 91.45$, $S_{10} = 248.9$

2 $u_k = 21 \times 2^{k-1}$, $u_9 = 5376$

3 $u_k = 18(\frac{1}{3})^{k-1}$,
$u_9 = \frac{2}{2187} \approx 0.000\,91$

4 **a)** $r = \pm\frac{2}{3}$=, $a = 2$
b) 2, $\frac{4}{3}, \frac{8}{9}, \frac{16}{27}, \frac{32}{81}, \frac{64}{243}$
or 2, $-\frac{4}{3}, \frac{8}{9}, -\frac{16}{27}, \frac{32}{81}, \frac{64}{243}$
c) $S_n = 6(1 - (\frac{2}{3})^n) \Rightarrow$
$S_{10} = 5.896$
or $S_n = \frac{6}{5}(1 - (-\frac{2}{3})^n) \Rightarrow$
$S_{10} = 1.179$

5 **a) i)** 0.2 mm **ii)** 0.4 mm
iii) 0.8 mm **b)** 0.1×2^n
c) i) 12.8 mm **ii)** 10.24 cm
iii) 3.28 m **d)** 20 folds

6 **a)** 210 by 297, 62 370 mm²
b) 148.5 by 210, 297 by 420, 420 by 594, 594 by 840, 840 by 1188
c) 31 185, 124 740, 249 480, 498 960, 997 920 mm² **d)** $\frac{1}{2}$
e) $\frac{1}{\sqrt{2}}$ **f)** 1 m², 210.224 by 297.302
g) A10: area 974.5 mm² (26.25 by 37.125),
A(–2): area 4 m² (1680 by 2376)

7 18 weeks

8 **a)** 3 bounces **b)** 6 bounces

9 **a)** pays £10 000,
b) pays £10 485.75

Exercises 10.4 class *(p.218)*

1 **a)** diverges **b)** 10 **c)** 64
d) diverges

2 **a)** $\frac{2}{3}$ **b)** $\frac{3}{11}$ **c)** $\frac{1}{27}$ **d)** $\frac{1}{7}$ **e)** $\frac{5}{13}$ **f)** $\frac{1}{101}$

3 **a)** 160 **b)** $53\frac{1}{3}$

4 **a)** –54 or 27 **b)** $333\frac{1}{3}$ or $142\frac{6}{7}$

5 36, 9, 2.25, 0.5625, 0.140 625

6 $r = 0.6$, $a = 60$

7 **a)** 1.08 m **c)** 20 m

Exercises 10.4 home *(p.219)*

1 **a)** diverges **b)** $\frac{1}{3}$ **c)** 0.54
d) diverges

2 **a)** $\frac{7}{9}$ **b)** $\frac{16}{9}$ **c)** $\frac{4}{33}$ **d)** $\frac{41}{333}$

3 **a)** 1822.5 **b)** –911.25

4 $r = 0.75$; 20, 15, 11.25, 8.4375
5 $a = 2$; 2.00, 1.83, 1.68, 1.54, 1.41, 1.29 (2 d.p.)
6 **a)** 125 **b)** 18th term **c)** 19
7 **a)** 0.9 **b)** Yes, for $-1 < r < 0$

Consolidation Exercises for Chapter 10 *(p.221)*

1 $a = -4, d = 7$
2 $a = 0, d = 4$
3 **a)** $n = 33, d = 3.5$ **b)** 1450
4 **a) i)** £70 620, **ii)** £1062
5 **a) i)** £3370, **ii)** £5679
b) £52 423
6 **a) i)** $14n + 11$ **ii)** $n(7n + 18)$
b) 880 cans
7 **a)** 1.08 **b)** £29 985 **d)** £1500
8 **a) i)** 15 cm **ii)** 41.5 m
b) i) ar^9 **ii)** $a = 0.0301$, $r = 1.25$
9 **a)** $a + 4d = 205$, $a + 18d = 373$
b) $d = 12, a = 157$ **c)** 28
10 **b)** 1500 m
11 **a)** $q = -\frac{1}{2}$ **b)** $q = 5$ ratio $= \frac{3}{4}$
$q = -\frac{1}{2}$ ratio $= -2$
c) 14 **d)** 867.62
12 **b)** 200 **c)** $\frac{1000}{3}$ **d)** 8.95×10^{-4}
13 **a)** 1 hour 21 minutes
c) 3 hours 51 minutes
14 **i) a)** 2, 4, 8, 16 **b)** GP $u_n = 2^n$
iii) $N + 2(2^N - 1)$

CHAPTER 11 Differentiation and integration 2

Exercises 11.1 class *(p.228)*

1 $x = 1$ $y = 2$ is a local minimum
asymptotes $y = x$, $y = 0$, $x = -1$, $y = -2$ is a local maximum
2 x-intercept (2, 0), minimum point (–1.59, –2.52)
3 2.4 units
4 **a)** $2rh + 0.5\pi r^2 = 500$
b) $r = 11.83$

Exercises 11.1 home *(p.228)*

1 asymptotes $y = x$, $x = 0$, no stationary points
2 x-axis intercepts (2, 0), (–2, 0), asymptote $x = 0$
3 **a)** $p = \frac{540}{n} + 0.01$
c) 1103
4 $f = \frac{1}{T}$, $T = 0.0039$ s

Exercises 11.2 class *(p.233)*

1 **a)** $-\frac{7}{x^2}$ **b)** $\frac{24}{x^3}$ **c)** $5 + \frac{48}{x^4}$
d) $-\frac{6}{x^2} - 15$ **e)** $\frac{15}{2\sqrt{x}}$ **f)** $\frac{2}{x^{\frac{3}{2}}}$
g) $\frac{3}{2}\sqrt{x} - \frac{4}{\sqrt{x}}$
h) $8x + \frac{5}{2}x^{\frac{3}{2}} = 8x + \frac{5}{2}x\sqrt{x}$
2 **a)** (1, 2) is a local minimum, (–1, –2) is a local maximum
b) $(-3\frac{1}{3}, 3\frac{4}{3})$ is a local maximum
c) $(3, \frac{2}{9})$ is a local maximum, $(-3, -\frac{2}{9})$ is a local minimum
d) (4, 4) is a local maximum
e) (5.76, –19.9065) is a local maximum
f) $(36, -\frac{25}{6})$ is a local minimum
4 **a)** $h = \frac{500}{x^2}$ **b) i)** $A = x^2 + \frac{2000}{x}$
ii) $A = 2x^2 + \frac{2000}{x}$
c) i) $x = 10$, $h = 5$, $A = 300$ cm²
ii) $x = \sqrt[3]{500}$, $h = \sqrt[3]{500}$, $A = \frac{3000}{\sqrt[3]{500}}$ cm²
5 **a)** $h = \frac{2}{\pi r^2}$ **b)** $A = \pi r^2 + \frac{4}{r}$
c) $r = \sqrt[3]{\frac{2}{\pi}}$; $h = r$ in this case
6 **a)** $2x + \frac{338}{x}$ **b)** $x = 13$ m so minimum length = 52 m

Exercises 11.2 home *(p.234)*

1 **a)** 4 **b)** 0.2 **c)** 24 **d)** $6\frac{1}{16}$
e) $\frac{31}{9}$ **f)** 13 **g)** $\frac{9}{4}$
2 **a)** $\left(-\frac{2}{2^{\frac{3}{2}}}, -\frac{3}{2^{\frac{1}{3}}}\right)$ is a local maximum
b) $\left(2, \frac{1}{4}\right)$ is a local maximum
c) $\left(\sqrt{15}, \frac{2\sqrt{15}}{45}\right)$ is a local maximum, $\left(-\sqrt{15}, \frac{2\sqrt{15}}{45}\right)$ is a local minimum
d) $\left(\frac{25}{9}, \frac{125}{27}\right)$ is a local maximum
e) (3.2, 4.5795) is a local maximum
f) (100, –0.15) is a local minimum
4 **a)** $A = 24x^2 + \frac{16464}{x}$
b) $x = 7$ cm
c) $A = 3528$ cm² is a minimum value
5 **a)** $V = \pi r^2 h = 512\pi$, $S = 2\pi r^2 + 2\pi r$
b) $S = 2\pi r^2 + \frac{1024\pi}{r}$
c) $r = \sqrt[3]{256}$ gives a minimum value of $\frac{1536}{\sqrt[3]{256}}$
d) $\frac{d^2S}{dr^2} > 0$
e) $S = 192\sqrt[3]{2\pi}$; $h = 8\sqrt[3]{4\pi^2}$
6 $180\sqrt[3]{2} = 227$ cm (to nearest cm)
7 **i)** $x = c$ **ii)** $v = \sqrt{2k}$

Exercises 11.3 class *(p.237)*

1 **a)** $f''(x) = 6x$, $f''(2) = 12$
b) $f''(x) = 2a$, $f''(-1) = 2a$
c) $f''(x) = 2 - \frac{6}{x^4}$, $f''(-1) = -4$
d) $f''(x) = \frac{(4 + 3x)}{4x^{\frac{3}{2}}}$, $f''(4) = -\frac{1}{2}$
2 **a)** (1, –2) is a local minimum: $f''(1) = 18 > 0$
(–2, 25) is a local maximum: $f''(-2) = 18 < 0$
b) (2, 3) is a local minimum: $f''(2) = \frac{3}{2} > 0$
c) $(\frac{1}{4}, -\frac{1}{4})$ is a local minimum: $f''(\frac{1}{4}) = 2 > 0$
d) (0, 7) is a local minimum: $f''(0) = 4 > 0$
(1, 8) is a local maximum: $f''(1) = -8 < 0$
(–1, 8) is a local maximum: $f''(-1) = -8 < 0$
3 **a)** (1, 13) **b)** (0, 0), $\left(\frac{2}{3}, -\frac{16}{27}\right)$
c) (1, –10) (–1, 10)
d) (2.25, –8.4375)
4 **a) i)** – 20m s^{-2} **ii)** 1.5 s
b) i) 5 m s^{-2} **ii)** 0.5 s

Exercises 11.3 home *(p.237)*

1 **a)** $f''(x) = x + 1$, $f''(2) = 3$
b) $f''(x) = 5 - 3x$, $f''(2) = -1$
c) $f''(x) = 12x + \frac{6}{x^3}$, $f''(-1) = -18$
d) $f''(x) = \frac{3}{2}(8 - 5\sqrt{x})$, $f''(5) = \frac{3}{2}(8 - 5\sqrt{5}) \approx -4.7705$
2 **a)** (0, 10) is a local minimum, $f''(x) = 6 > 0$
(2, 14) is a local maximum, $f''(x) = -6 < 0$
b) $\left(-\frac{1}{2}\sqrt[3]{10}, \frac{3}{2}\sqrt[3]{100}\right)$ is a local minimum, $f''\left(-\frac{1}{2}\sqrt[3]{10}\right) = 12 > 0$
c) (5.76, 39.8131) is a local maximum, $f''(5.76) = -6 < 0$
d) (2, 10) is a local minimum, $f''(2) = 6 > 0$
(4, 4) is a local maximum, $f''(4) = -6 < 0$
3 **a)** $\left(\frac{2}{3}, -\frac{70}{27}\right)$
b) (0, 0), $\left(\frac{3}{4}, -\frac{81}{128}\right)$

c) no points of inflexion
d) $\left(\frac{5}{2}, 0\right)$

4 a) i) $a = -3.6$ m s^{-2}
ii) $t = 1$ s or $t = 5$ s
b) i) $a = -\frac{15}{16}$ m s^{-2} ii) $t = 3$ s
c) i) $\frac{3\sqrt{5}}{8} = 0.84$ m s^{-2} ii) $t = \frac{9}{16}$s

Exercises 11.4 class *(p.239)*

	tangent	normal
1	$y = 4x - 9$	$y = -\frac{1}{4}x - \frac{1}{2}$
2	$y = -6x$	$y = \frac{1}{6}x + \frac{37}{6}$
3	$y = -3x - 12$	$y = \frac{1}{3}x - \frac{16}{3}$
4	$y = \frac{5}{3}x + 15$	$y = -\frac{3}{5}x + \frac{177}{5}$
5	$y = -4t$	$s = \frac{1}{4}t + \frac{17}{4}$
6	$y = -6x + 10$	$y = \frac{1}{6}x + \frac{23}{6}$
7	$y = 8x + 24$	$y = -8x + 40$ (1, 32)
8	$y = 4x - 11$	$y = 4x + 21$
9	$p = -0.6$	$q = -12.24$

Exercises 11.4 home *(p.239)*

	tangent	normal
1	$y = -8x - 20$	$y = \frac{1}{8}x + 4.5$
2	$s = -12t + 30$	$s = \frac{1}{12}t + \frac{35}{6}$
3	$y = 3x - 4$	$y = -\frac{1}{3}x - \frac{2}{3}$
4	$y = 12x - 8$	$y = -\frac{1}{12}x + \frac{49}{12}$
5	$y = 6x + 12$	$y = -\frac{1}{6}x + 36\frac{2}{3}$
6	$y = \frac{7}{2}x - \frac{9}{2}$	$y = -\frac{2}{7}x - \frac{5}{7}$
7	$24y = 2x + 1$	$24y = -2x + 5$ $(1, \frac{1}{8})$
8	$y = -\frac{1}{3} + 36\frac{1}{3}$	$y = -\frac{1}{3}x + 3$
9	$y = -4x$, $y = 17x - 24$, $y = 12x + 36$	

Exercises 11.5 class *(p.242)*

1 a) $-\frac{7}{x} + c$ b) $\frac{6}{x^2} + c$
c) $-\frac{3}{2x}(4 + 5x^3) + c$
d) $10x\sqrt{x} + c$ e) $-8\sqrt{x} + c$
f) $\frac{2\sqrt{x}}{15}(3x^2 - 40x) + c$
g) $\frac{2x^3}{21}(14 + 3\sqrt{x}) + c$
h) $-\frac{9}{x}(1 + 2\sqrt{x}) + c$

2 a) 3 b) 76 c) $\frac{31}{4} = 7.75$
d) 16
e) 7.0083 (to 4 d.p.) $\left(= \frac{17}{5}\sqrt{6} - \frac{14}{15}\sqrt{2}\right)$
f) 3.5156 (to 4 d.p.)

3 a) 10 b) 7.5 c) $\frac{63}{6} = 12.6$
d) $\frac{625}{6} = 104.167$
e) $\frac{48\sqrt{6}}{5} = 23.5151$ f) $\frac{1}{12}$ g) $\frac{9}{32}$

4 a) 2 b) $\frac{155}{3} = 51.67$
c) $\frac{64}{3} = 21.33$ d) $\frac{20}{3} = 6.67$

5 a) $f(x) = 5x - 4\sqrt{x} - 3$, $f(4) = 9$
b) $f(x) = 4x + \frac{3}{x}$, $f(4) = \frac{67}{4} = 16.75$
c) $f(x) = 6x\sqrt{x} + 2$, $f(4) = 50$
d) $f(x) = \frac{1}{x^3} - \frac{1}{x^2} + 2$, $f(4) = \frac{125}{64} = 1.9531$

Exercises 11.5 home *(p.243)*

1 a) $-\frac{1}{4x^2} + c$ b) $\frac{5}{8x^8} + c$
c) $x^3 + \frac{1}{x^3} + c$
d) $\frac{77}{3}x^3 + \frac{33}{2x^4} + c$
e) $2\sqrt{x} + \frac{2}{3}x\sqrt{x} + c$
f) $\frac{2}{3}x\sqrt{x} - 2\sqrt{x} + c$
g) $\sqrt{x}(x - 1) + c$
h) $\frac{2}{5}x^{\frac{5}{2}} - \frac{7}{2}x^2 + c$
i) $-\frac{2}{3x^{\frac{3}{2}}} + c$ j) $\frac{2}{5}x^{\frac{5}{2}} - 8\sqrt{x} + c$

2 a) $\frac{20}{9}$ b) 54.4 $\left(\frac{272}{5}\right)$
c) 15.11 d) $\frac{20}{9}$ e) $\frac{8}{21}$ f) $\frac{1}{6}$

3 a) $\frac{3}{2}$ b) 0.2508 (4 d.p.) c) 1
d) $4 - \frac{8}{3}\sqrt{2} = 0.2288$ (to 4 d.p.)
e) 8.5
f) $\frac{3}{5}(6 + \sqrt{2}) = 4.4485$ (to 4 d.p.)
g) $\frac{1}{110} = 0.0091$ (to 4 d.p.) h) $\frac{41}{3}$

4 a) $\frac{1}{3}$
b) $\frac{15}{5} - 8\ln 2 = 1.9548$ (to 4 d.p.)
c) $\frac{70}{3} - 8\sqrt{6} = 3.7341$ (to 4 d.p.)
d) $\frac{17}{3}$

5 a) $f(x) = 6\sqrt{x} - x - 3$, $f(2) = 6\sqrt{2} - 5$
b) $f(x) = 3x + \frac{7}{2x^2} - \frac{11}{2}$, $f(2) = \frac{11}{8} = 1.375$
c) $f(x) = \frac{2\sqrt{x}}{3}(3 - x) + \frac{19}{3}$, $f(2) = \frac{1}{3}(19 + 2\sqrt{2}) = 7.2761$
d) $f(x) = \frac{1}{x^4} - \frac{1}{x^3} + 2$, $f(2) = \frac{31}{16}$

Consolidation Exercises for Chapter 11 *(p.245)*

1 b) $V = 4x\left(25 - \frac{x^2}{3}\right)$
c) $\frac{100}{3}$ cm^3 (when $x = 5$ cm)
d) $V''(5) = -40 < 0$

2 b) i) local minimum at (2, 2)
ii) $x = -1.31$

3 (–2, –4) local maximum, (2, 4) local minimum; $\{x: |x| > 2\}$

4 a) $k = 8$ b) –4

5 a) 6 b) i) $y = 6x - 7$
ii) $(2 + \sqrt{6}, 5 + 6\sqrt{6})$

6 a) $\frac{3}{2}x^{-\frac{1}{2}} + 2x^{-\frac{3}{2}}$
b) $2x^{\frac{3}{2}} - 8x^{\frac{1}{2}} + c$ c) $6 - 2\sqrt{3}$

7 a) $-\frac{2}{3}x^{\frac{3}{2}} + 5x - 8x^{\frac{1}{2}} + c$ b) $\frac{7}{3}$

8 c) 1200

9 (0, 0) local minimum; (4,32) local maximum $\{x: x < 0\}$ and $\{x: 4 < x\}$ $y = 12x - 8$

CHAPTER 12 Functions

Exercises 12.1 class *(p.251)*

1 a) range $\{y$: 16, 10, 7, –2$\}$, one-to-one
b) range $\{y$: 13, –3$\}$, many-to-one
c) range $\{y$: –2, –5, 5, 2$\}$, one-to-one
d) range $\{y$: 2, 6$\}$, many-to-one
e) range $\{y$: 0$\}$, many-to-one

2 a) range $\{y: 2 \le y \le 9\}$, one-to-one
b) range $\{y: 0 \le y \le 50\}$, many-to one
c) range $\{y: -2.5 \le y \le 18\}$, many to one
d) range $\{y: 0 \le y \le 9\}$, many-to-one
e) range $\{y: -2 \le y \le 20\}$, many-to-one
f) range $\{y: 0 \le y < \infty\}$, one-to-one
g) range $\{y: 0 \le y < \infty\}$, many-to-one
h) range $\{y: - < y \le 0\}$, one-to-one

Exercises 12.1 home *(p.251)*

1 a) range $\{y$: –4, 0, 4, 6, 8$\}$, one-to-one
b) range $\{y$: 19, 1, –5,$\}$, many-to-one
c) range $\{y$: 4, 2, $1\frac{1}{3}$, 1$\}$, one-to-one
d) range $\{y$: 6, 0$\}$, many-to-one
e) range $\{y$: 3, 0, –3$\}$, one-to-one

2 a) range $\{y: -1 \le y \le 7\}$, one-to-one
b) range $\{y: -\frac{1}{2} \le y \le 6\frac{1}{2}\}$, one-to-one
c) range $\{y: 0 \le y \le 12\frac{1}{2}\}$, many-to-one
d) range $\{y: -0.125 \le y \le 45\}$, many-to-one
e) range $\{y: 0 \le y \le 12\}$, many-to-one
f) range $\{y: y \ge 0\}$, many-to-one

g) range $\{y: -4 \le y \le -0.4\}$, many-to-one
h) range $\{y: -39 \le y \le 39\}$, many-to-one

Exercises 12.2 class *(p.253)*

1 a) i) $2(5 - x)$ **ii)** $5 - x^2$
iii) $25 - 20x + 4x^2$
b) i) 14 **ii)** 1 **iii)** 81
c) $x = 1, 4$
3 x
4 $\frac{x}{1 + 2x}$
5 a) $f(g(x))$ **b)** $h(f(x))$ **c)** $g(h(x))$
d) $g(f(x))$ **e)** $f(h(x)$ **f)** $h(h(x))$
6 b) $f(x) = x$, $g(x) = 25 - x^2$, $h(x) = \sqrt{x}$

Exercises 12.2 home *(p.254)*

1 a) $3x^3 - 4$ and $(3x - 4)^3$
b) i) 20 **ii)** 8 **c)** $x = 3$
2 i) x **ii)** x
3 $3(x^2 + 1)^2 + 2(x^2 + 1) - 4$
4 $\sqrt{4-x^2}$, $2 - x$
5 $\frac{x^2}{4(2x^2-1)}$, $-(4x^2 + 24x + 31)$
6 domain $\{x: x \ge 0\}$
$f(x) = x^{\frac{2}{3}}$, $g(x) = 1 - x$, $h(x) = \sqrt{x}$

Exercises 12.3 class *(p.258)*

1 $x + 4$ **2** $\frac{x}{3}$ **3** $\frac{x+4}{3}$ **4** $\frac{7-x}{2}$
5 $\frac{12}{x} - 1$ **6** $x^3 + 3$
7 $\sqrt{\frac{x-5}{2}}$ **8** $\sqrt{x} - 2, x \ge 4$
9 a) i) $k = 0$ **ii)** $\{f : 2 \le f \le \infty\}$
iii) $f^{-1}(x) = \sqrt{x-2}$
b) i) $k = 3$ **ii)** $\{f : 0 \le f \le \infty\}$
iii) $f^{-1}(x) = \sqrt{x} + 3$
c) i) $k = -1$ **ii)** $\{f : f \le 5\}$
iii) $f^{-1}(x) = -1 + \sqrt{5-x}$
d) i) $k = 2$ **ii)** $\{f : f \ge -1\}$
iii) $f^{-1}(x) = 2 + \sqrt{1+x}$
10 a) i) $k = 5$ **ii)** $f^{-1}(x) = 5 - \frac{20}{x}$
iii) $\{f^{-1}: x \ne 0\}$,
range $\{f : -\infty < f < \infty\}$
b) i) $k = 2$
ii) $f^{-1}(x) = \frac{5+2x}{x-1}$
iii) $\{f^{-1}: x \ne 1\}$,
range $\{f: -\infty < f < \infty\}$
c) i) $k = -2\frac{1}{2}$ **ii)** $f^{-1}(x) = \frac{5x+2}{3-2x}$
iii) $\{f^{-1}: x \ne 1\frac{1}{2}\}$,
range $\{f: -\infty < f < \infty\}$
11 b) $x \ne \frac{a}{b}$ **c)** $f^{-1}(x) = \frac{4-x}{4x+1}$

Exercises 12.3 home *(p.259)*

1 $f^{-1}(x) = x + 3$ **2** $f^{-1}(x) = \frac{1}{6}x$
3 $f^{-1}(x) = \frac{1}{2}(x - 3)$
4 $f^{-1}(x) = \sqrt[4]{x}$ **5** $f^{-1}(x) = \sqrt[3]{3x}$
6 $f^{-1}(x) = 4x^2 - 6$
7 $f^{-1}(x) = \frac{4}{x} - 2$
8 $f^{-1}(x) = \sqrt{\frac{x+1}{3}}$
9 a) i) $k = 0$ **ii)** $\{y: y \le 3\}$
iii) $f^{-1}(x) = \sqrt{3-x}$
b) i) $k = -2$
ii) $\{y: y \ge -5\}$
iii) $f^{-1}(x) = \sqrt{x+5} - 2$
c) i) $k = 2.5$
ii) $\{y: y \ge -0.25\}$
iii) $f^{-1}(x) = \frac{5}{2} + \frac{1}{2}\sqrt{1+x}$
d) i) $k = -4$ **ii)** $\{y: y \le 7\}$
iii) $f^{-1}(x) = -4 + \sqrt{7-x}$
10 a) i) $k = -5$
ii) $f^{-1}(x) = \frac{2}{x} - 5$ **iii)** $\{x : x \ne 0\}$
b) i) $k = 5$
ii) $f^{-1}(x) = \frac{5x}{2+x} \{x: x \ne -2\}$
c) i) $k = 4$
ii) $f^{-1}(x) = \frac{3+4x}{x-2}$
iii) $\{x : x \ne 2\}$
11 a) $\frac{9}{5}, 32$
b) ii) $f^{-1}(x) = \frac{5}{9}(x - 32)$
d) $x = -40$

Exercises 12.4 class *(p.261)*

1 a) translation 3 units // y-axis
b) translation –7 units // y-axis
c) translation 2 units // x-axis
d) translation –5 units // x-axis
e) stretch, factor 4 // y-axis
f) stretch, factor $\frac{1}{3}$ // y-axis
g) reflection in x-axis
h) translation –3 units // x–axis
2 a) $y = x^2 - 5$ **b)** $y = x^2 + 3.5$
c) $y = (x - 4)^2$ **d)** $y = (x + 7)^2$
e) $y = 3x^2$ **f)** $y = \frac{1}{3}x^2$
3 a) stretch, factor 2 // y-axis, translation 6 units // y-axis
b) translation 3 units // y-axis, stretch, factor 2 // y-axis
c) translation –5 units // y-axis, stretch, factor $\frac{1}{3}$ // y-axis
d) stretch, factor $\frac{1}{3}$ // y-axis, translation –1 units // y-axis
e) translation –4 units // y-axis, reflection in x-axis
f) reflection in x-axis, translation 4 units // y-axis
g) translation –4 units // x-axis, stretch, factor 3 // y-axis
h) translation 1 unit // x-axis, stretch, factor 5 // y-axis
i) translation 2 units // x-axis, translation 3 units // y-axis
j) translation –5 units // x-axis, translation –7 units // y-axis
k) translation –3 units // x-axis, stretch, factor 2 // y-axis, translation 5 units // y-axis
l) translation –4 units // x-axis, reflection in x-axis
m) translation –4 units // x-axis, reflection in x-axis, translation 7 units // y-axis
n) translation –6 units // x-axis, stretch, factor 0.4 // y-axis, translation –4.4 units // y-axis
o) translation 3 units // x-axis, stretch, factor 2 // y-axis, reflection in x-axis, translation 10 units // y-axis
p) translation –2 units // x-axis, stretch, factor 5 // y-axis, translation 3 units // y-axis, reflection in x-axis
4 a) $y = 2x^2 - 5$ **b)** $y = -3x^2$
c) $y = 0.5(x - 3)^2$ **d)** $y = -(x + 5)^2$
e) $y = (x - 2)^2 + 5$ **f)** $y = 9 - x^2$
g) $y = 3(x + 4)^2 - 7$
h) $y = 4 - (x - 6)^2$

Exercises 12.4 home *(p.262)*

2 a) $y = 6x^2$ **b)** $y = (x - 3)^2$
c) $y = x^2 + 3$ **d)** $y = (x + 0.5)^2$
e) $0.2x^2$ **f)** $x^2 - 8$
3 a) $y = (x - 5)^2 + 5$ **b)** $y = 7x^2 - 1$
c) $y = -4x^2$ **d)** $y = 0.5(x^2 + 3)$
e) $y = -x^2 - 6$ **f)** $y = -0.7(x - 5)^2$
g) $y = 7(x + 2)^2 + 3$
h) $y = 2(x - 9)^2 - 3$

Exercises 12.5 class *(p.266)*

1 a) $y = (x + 2)^2 + 7$
b) $y = (x - 3)^2 - 4$
c) $y = (x - 2.5)^2 - 9.25$
d) $y = (x + 1.5)^2 - 10.25$
e) $y = (x + 0.5)^2 + 0.75$
f) $y = (x - 3.5)^2 - 12.25$
2 a) $y = 2(x - 2)^2 - 3$
b) $y = 3(x + 1)^2 - 10$
c) $y = 5(x - 0.5)^2 + 6.75$
d) $s = 3(t - \frac{1}{6})^2 + 4\frac{11}{12}$
e) $d = 5(t + 0.2)^2 - 12.2$
f) $y = 12.25 - (x + 1.5)^2$
g) $y = 15\frac{1}{3} - 3(x + 1\frac{2}{3})^2$
h) $y = 35.02 - 12(z - \frac{23}{24})^2$
3 a) $x = 1$, $(1, -4)$
b) $x = -2.5$, $(-2.5, 1.75)$
c) $x = 1.25$, $(1.25, 5.4375)$
d) $x = 1$, $(1, 7)$
e) $x = 0.3$, $(0.3, -0.45)$
f) $x = 5$, $(5, 25)$
g) $x = -0.5$, $(-0.5, 12.25)$
h) $t = 0$, $(0, 4)$
4 a) ii) $x = 500$, **iii)** $(500, -222)$
b) 2.5 m

5 b) ii) 720 m^2, **iii)** 8 m, 7.5 m

Exercises 12.5 home *(p.267)*

1 a) $y = (x - 5)^2 + 3$
b) $y = (x - 1.5)^2 + 0.75$
c) $y = (x + 6)^2 - 9$
d) $y = (x - 2.5)^2 - 5.75$
e) $y = (x + 3.5)^2 - 12.25$
f) $y = x^2 + 7$
2 a) $y = 2(x + 3)^2 - 11$
b) $y = 3(x - 6)^2 + 1$
c) $s = 3(t - 2.5)^2 - 23.75$
d) $y = 8(x - 0.125)^2 + 8.875$
e) $y = 4 - (x - 7)^2$
f) $y = 0.5 - 2(x - 0.5)^2$
g) $y = 3(x - \frac{1}{3})^2 + \frac{2}{3}$
h) $y = -1.2 - 5(x - 0.6)^2$
3 a) (0, 7), (2, 3) **b)** (0, 8), (0, 8)
c) (0, –4), (–1, –5)
d) (0, 7), (–2.5, 0.75)
e) (0, 57), (4, –7)
f) (0, 1), (–0.5, 1.25)
g) (0, –5), ($-\frac{2}{3}$, $-7\frac{2}{3}$)
h) (0, –23), (0.9, –18.95)
4 b) 225 feet **c)** 62 feet
d) 125 feet
5 b) 1.2 m by 2.4 m, 1.6 m by 1.6 m

Exercises 12.6 class *(p.270)*

1 i) b) (0, 3), **c)** $2 \le y \le 4$
ii) b) (0, 0), (180, 0), (360, 0), **c)** $-1 \le y \le 1$
iii) b) (0, 2), (90, 0), (270, 0), **c)** $-2 \le y \le 2$
iv) b) (0, 1), **c)** $1 \le y \le 3$
v) b) (0, –3), (90, 0), (270, 0), **c)** $-3 \le y \le 3$
vi) b) (0, 1), (30, 0), (90, 0), (150, 0), (210, 0), (270, 0), (330, 0), **c)** $-1 \le y \le 1$
vii) b) (0, 0), (90, 0), (180, 0), (270, 0), (360, 0), **c)** $\infty \le y \le \infty$
viii) b) (0, 1), (90, 0), (270, 0), **c)** $-1 \le y \le 1$
ix) b) (0, 0.5), (150, 0), (330, 0), **c)** $-1 < y < 1$
2 b) i) stretch, factor 0.5 // x-axis
ii) translation –1 unit // y-axis
iii) stretch, factor $\frac{1}{3}$ // x-axis
iv) translation –60 // x-axis
v) stretch, factor $\frac{1}{3}$ // x-axis, stretch, factor $\frac{1}{2}$// y-axis
vi) stretch, factor $\frac{1}{2}$ // y-axis, translation 3 units // y-axis
vii) stretch, factor 2 // x-axis
viii) stretch, factor 2 // x-axis, stretch, factor 5 // y-axis
ix) translation –60 // x-axis, stretch, factor 3 // y-axis
x) translation –60 // x-axis, translation –5 unit // y-axis
3 i) b) $y = 4\cos x$,
c) (0, 4), (180, –4), (360, 4)
ii) b) $y = \cos x - 3$,
c) (0, –2), (180, –4), (360, –2)
iii) b) $y = \cos(0.4x)$, **c)** (0, 1)
iv) b) $y = \cos 3x - 5$,
c) (0, –4), (60, –6), (120, –4), (180, –6), (240, –4), (300, –6), (360, –4)
v) b) $y = 4\cos(x + 90)$,
c) (90, –4), (270, 4)
vi) b) $y = -\cos(x - 120°)$,
c) (120, –1), (300, 1)
vii) b) $y = 3\cos(x + 45) + 3$,
c) (135, 0), (315, 6)
viii) b) $y = 1.5\cos(0.5x) - 3.5$,
c) (0, –2), (360, –5)

Exercises 12.6 home *(p.271)*

1 i) b) (0, 3), **c)** $3 \le y \le 5$
ii) b) (0, 2), **c)** $1 \le y \le 3$
iii) (0, 3), (90, 0), (270, 0)
c) $-3 \le y \le 3$
iv) b) (0, 0), (180, 0), (360, 0)
c) $-2.5 \le y \le 2.5$
v) b) (0, 0), (60, 0), (120, 0), (180, 0), (240, 0), (300, 0), (360, 0)
c) $-\infty \le y \le \infty$
vi) b) (0, 0.5), (150, 0), (330, 0),
c) $-1 \le y \le 1$
vii) b) (0, –1), (30, 0), (150, 0), (270, 0), **c)** $-2 \le y \le 0$
viii) b) (0, 2.863), **c)** $1 \le y \le 3$
2 b) i) stretch, factor $\frac{1}{3}$ // y-axis
ii) translation 4 units // y-axis
iii) stretch, factor $\frac{1}{6}$ // x axis
iv) translation 90 units // x-axis, reflection in y–axis
v) stretch, factor $\frac{1}{6}$ // x-axis, reflection in x-axis
vi) stretch factor $\frac{1}{2}$ // x-axis, stretch factor $\frac{1}{3}$ // y-axis
vii) stretch, factor 3 // x-axis, translation 2 units // y-axis
viii) stretch, factor 3 // x-axis, stretch, factor 6 // y-axis
3 b) i) $y = 0.5\sin x$ **ii)** $y = \sin 4x$
iii) $y = \sin(x - 60°)$
iv) $y = 2\sin x + 1$ **v)** $y = -\sin 2x$
vi) $y = \sin(x + 30°) - 2$
vii) $-2.5\sin(x - 90°)$
viii) $y = -0.25\sin(0.5x)$

Exercises 12.7 class *(p.276)*

1 a) i) a translation through –3 units // x-axis
b) i) a stretch, factor 2 // y-axis
c) i) stretch, factor 2 // x-axis
d) i) stretch, factor $\frac{1}{2}$ // y-axis *followed by* translation through –4 units // y-axis
e) i) translation through 2 units // x-axis *followed by* reflection in the x axis
f) i) stretch, factor 2, // x-axis *followed by* stretch, factor 2 // y-axis.
g) i) translation through –5 units // x-axis *followed by* reflection on the y-axis
h) i) stretch, factor $\frac{1}{2}$ // x-axis *followed by* translation through 1 unit // x-axis *followed by* stretch, factor 3 // y-axis
2 a) i) $\frac{1}{3}g(x)$ **b) i)** $g(x + 3)$
c) i) $-g\left(\frac{1}{2}x\right)$ **d i)** $g(-x) + 4$
e) i) $g([-x] - 4)$
f) i) $-g\left(\frac{1}{2}(x+3)\right)$
3 c) {f: $x > 1$}, {g : $g(x) \ge 0$} {h: $x > -2$}, {h : $h(x) \ge 0$}
4 a) $h(x) = \sqrt{25 - x^2}$
b) stretch, factor $\frac{25^2}{4}$ // y-axis stretch, factor $\frac{5}{2}$ // x-axis
5 a) odd **b)** even **c)** even
d) odd **e)** odd **f)** even
g) neither **h)** even

Exercises 12.7 home *(p.277)*

1 a) i) translation through –1 units // x-axis
b) i) stretch, factor 3 // y-axis
c) i) stretch, factor $\frac{1}{2}$ // x-axis
d) i) stretch, factor $\frac{1}{2}$ // y-axis *followed by* translation through 2 units // y-axis
e) i) translation through 3 units // x-axis
f) i) translation through 3 units // x-axis *followed by* stretch, factor 2 // y-axis
g) i) translation through 4 units // x-axis *followed by* reflection in the y-axis
h) i) stretch, factor $\frac{1}{2}$ // x-axis *followed by* translation through 1 unit // x-axis *followed by* stretch, factor 3 // y-axis *followed by* translation through 4 units // y-axis.
2 a) i) $g(x - 3)$ **b) i)** $2g(x)$
c) i) $g(3x) + 4$ **d) i)** $g(-x) - 2$

e) i) $g(3[x-3])+4$

3 a) i) $\sin(-x)$ **b) i)** $-\sin x$
c) i) $f(-x)=-f(x)$ **d) i)** $\cos x$
ii) $-\cos x$, $\cos x$ is an even function; $\tan x=-\tan x$, $\tan x$ is an odd function

4 a) translation through 2 units // x-axis
b) $\sqrt{9-(x-2)^2}$

5 a) even **b)** neither **c)** even
d) odd **e)** neither **f)** even
g) neither **h)** odd **i)** even
j) neither

Consolidation Exercises for Chapter 12 *(p.278)*

1 a) $\{y : y \geq 1\}$ **b)** 1, 0
c) $-2\frac{1}{3}$, 3 **d)** $-1\frac{1}{2}$

2 $(-1, 2)$

3 a) $\{x : x \leq 3\}$ **b)** $0 < k < 4$
c) f one-to-one, g many-to-one
d) $\{x: 0 \leq x \leq 4\}$, $\{y: 0 \leq y \leq 2)$

5 a) $4x^2+4x+4$
b) $\{y : y \geq 3\}$
c) $x = 3$

6 a) i) $gf(2) = 3$
ii) $h(x) = x^2 - 1$
b) There are no limitations to x, f or g, $x \in \Re$, f : $f(x) \in \Re$, g : $g(x) \in \Re$
c) $g^{-1}(x) = x + 2$, $x \in \Re$
d) $x \geq 0$, $y \geq 1$

7 b) $y = 2.5\cos(0.5x) - 3$
c) $(0, -0.5)$, $(360, -5.5)$

8 translation through -2 units // x-axis; stretch, factor 4, // y-axis stretch, factor 4, // y-axis *followed by* translation through 2 units // x-axis

9 a) $y = \frac{10}{(x-3)^2}$, asymptotes $y = 0$, $x = 3$
b) $y = \frac{10}{x^2} - 3$, asymptotes $y = -3$, $x = 0$
c) $y = \frac{30}{x^2}$, asymptotes $y = 0$, $x = 0$
d) $y = \frac{10}{-x^2} + 3$, asymptote $y = 3$, $x = 0$

10 a) translation through 3 units // x-axis
b) reflection in x-axis then translation through 10 units // y-axis
c) reflection in x-axis *followed by* a stretch, factor 3, // y-axis
d) translation through $\frac{3}{2}$ // x-axis *followed by* stretch, factor $\sqrt{2}$ // y-axis

11 a) $\{y: y \geq \frac{9}{4}\}$ **b)** $\frac{4}{x^2} - \frac{6}{x}$
c) $\left(\frac{4}{3}, -\frac{9}{4}\right)$

12 b) $\frac{1}{2}$, $\frac{3}{2}$

14 a) $f^{-1}: x \to \frac{1+x}{4}$
b) $gf = \frac{3}{8x-3}$; $x \in \Re$, $x \neq \frac{3}{8}$
c) 0.826, -0.076

15 i) $y \geq 1$ **ii)** $f^{-1}: x \to (x-1)^2$
iii) $1 + x$ **iv)** $y = 1 + |x|$

CHAPTER 13 Algebra 2

Exercises 13.1 class *(p.283)*

1 A=1, B=2 **2** A=2, B=3
3 A=3, B=3 **4** A=3, B=2
5 A=1, B=2 **6** A=2, B=3, C=1
7 A=–1.5, B=1, C=0.5
8 A=1, B=2, C=1
9 A=2, B=3, C=–1
10 A=–1, B=2, C=–3
11 A=0.5, B=3, C=–0.5
12 A=–4, B=0.5, C=3 (maximum value = 3)
13 A=4, B=–1, C=7 (minimum value = 7)
14 a) $6x^3 + 7x^2 - 6x + 1$
b) $x^3 + 2x^2 - 17x + 6$
c) $2x^4 - x^3 + 2x^2 + 3x - 2$
d) $6x^4 - x^3 + 6x^2 - 3x + 2$

Exercises 13.1 home *(p.283)*

1 A=1, B=–2 **2** A=0.5, B=1.5
3 A=1, B=2 **4** A=2, B=3, C = 1
5 A=–2, B=3 **6** A=–1, B=2, C=–4
7 A=0.5, B=1.5, C=1
8 A=–0.5, B=1, C=0.5
9 A=2, B=–3, C=2
10 A=3, B=1, C=–2
11 A=–2, B=3, C=1
12 A=–2, B=–1.5, C=–0.5 (maximum value = –0.5)
13 A=9, B=–1/3, C=7 (minimum value = 7)
14 a) $3x^3 - x^2 - 6x + 4$
b) $2x^3 - 3x^2 - 13x - 6$
c) $2x^4 - x^3 - 9x^2 + 13x - 5$
d) $3x^4 + 7x^3 + 2x^2 + 5x - 3$

Exercises 13.2 class *(p.287)*

1 $2x - 1 - \frac{4}{(x-1)}$
2 $2x^2 - x + 7 - \frac{2}{(x-5)}$
3 $x^3 - 2x + 2 + \frac{(2x-3)}{(x^2+x+1)}$
4 $4x + 8 + \frac{12x-7}{x^2-2x+1}$
5 $x^2 + 2x + 2$
6 $x^2 + 2x - 3 + \frac{(-x^2+x+1)}{(x^3+x^2-x+1)}$

Exercises 13.2 home *(p.287)*

1 $x^2 - 7x + 12$
2 $6x^2 + 3x + 11 - \frac{12}{(2-3x)}$
3 $x^3 + x + 1 + \frac{x+3}{x^2-x+2}$
4 $x^2 - x + 3 - \frac{(2x+2)}{(x^2+x+1)}$
5 $3x^2 + 2x^2 - 5x + 0.5 + \frac{6x-2.5}{2x^2+1}$
6 $x^2 + ax + a + \frac{(1-a)}{(x+1)^2}$

Exercises 13.3 class *(p.289)*

1 $\frac{5(x+1)}{6x(x-1)}$ **2** $\frac{2x^2(x+3)}{5(x-2)}$
3 $\frac{(3+x)}{(3-x)}$ **4** $\frac{1}{x}$
5 $\frac{(x+2)(2x-1)}{(x-2)(x+4)}$ **6** $\frac{(5-13x)}{(3x-1)(2-5x)}$
7 $\frac{(3x+5)}{(x+3)(x-1)(x+1)}$
8 $\frac{x^2-2x-5}{(x-3)(x+1)(x+3)}$
9 $\frac{10x^2+77x-46}{(x-3)(x+7)(2x-1)}$
10 $\frac{-x^2-10x+5}{(x+3)(x-1)}$

Exercises 13.3 home *(p.289)*

1 $\frac{(x-3)(x-1)}{4x}$ **2** $\frac{-3x(1-x)}{2(x+7)(2x-3)}$
3 $\frac{(1-3x)}{(1-x^2)^2}$ **4** $\frac{2}{(1-x)}$
5 $\frac{(x+3)(2x+3)}{5x^2(x-3)}$ **6** $\frac{1-3x}{(2x+1)(x+3)}$
7 $\frac{5x^2-2x+5}{(x+1)(x-2)(x^2+3)}$ **8** $\frac{-3x^2-8x-11}{(x+1)(x+3)(2x-1)}$
9 $\frac{3x^2+15x+36}{(x+1)(x+5)(x+3)}$ **10** $\frac{2x^2-20x-12}{(2x-1)(x+7)}$

Consolidation Exercises for Chapter 13 *(p.290)*

1 $a = 2$, $b = 1$, $c = -7$, $d = 6$
2 $A = 2$, $B = -1$, $C = 3$ (minimum value = 3)
3 $A = 5$, $B = -2$, $C = -1$
5 $-3x + 2$
6 $\frac{3x^2-54x-9}{2(x-2)(x+3)}$
7 $\frac{2x^3+15x^2+x+6}{(x-1)(x+3)(x^2+x+1)}$
8 $(x-1)(2x+3)(x^2+x+1)$
9 $x^2 + 2x - a + 3$

CHAPTER 14 Sequences and series 2: binomial expansions

Exercises 14.1 class *(p.294)*

1 a) $a^6 + 6a^5b + 15a^4b^2 + 20a^3b^3 + 15a^2b^4 + 6ab^5 + b^6$
b) $p^5 - 5p^4q + 10p^3q^2 - 10p^2q^3 + 5pq^4 - q^5$

c) $6561r^8 + 87\,480r^7 + 510\,300r^6 + 1\,701\,000r^5 + 3\,543\,750r^4 + 4\,725\,000r^3 + 3\,937\,500r^2 + 1\,875\,000r + 390\,625$

2a) 495

b) $a^{12} + 12a^{11}b + 66a^{10}b^2 + 220a^9b^3$

3 a) $x^4 + 12x^3y + 54x^2y^2 + 108xy^3 + 81y^4$

b) $32f^5 + 240f^4g + 720f^3g^2 + 1080f^2g^3 + 810fg^4 + 243g^5$

c) $6561x^8 - 34\,992x^7y + 81\,648x^6y^2 - 108\,864x^5y^3 + 90\,720x^4y^4 - 48\,384x^3y^5 + 16\,128x^2y^6 - 3072xy^7 + 256y^8$

4 a) $84a^6$

b) 180

c) $-448p^3$

d) $316\,800\,000f^5$

e) $-77\,520$

f) $\binom{20}{r}.(-1)^{20-r}\,.\,x^r$

5 a) 78 **b)** 84 **c)** 2 427 570

Exercises 14.1 home *(p.295)*

1 a) $m^5 + 5m^4n + 10m^3n^2 + 10m^2n^3 + 5mn^4 + n^5$

b) $2187 - 5103a + 5103a^2 - 2835a^3 + 945a^4 - 189a^5 + 21a^6 - a^7$

c) $16x^4 + 96x^3 + 216x^2 + 216x + 81$

2 a) $252x^5y^5$

b) $x^{10} - 10x^9y + 45x^8y^2 - 120x^7y^3$

3 a) $a^5 + 10a^4b + 40a^3b^2 + 80a^2b^3 + 80ab^4 + 32b^5$

b) $16\,384a^7 - 57\,344a^6b + 86\,016a^5b^2 - 71\,680a^4b^3 + 35\,840a^3b^4 - 10\,752a^2b^5 + 1792ab^6 - 128b^7$

c) $0.015\,625m^6 - 0.375m^5n + 3.75m^4n^2 - 20m^3n^3 + 60m^2n^4 - 96mn^5 + 64mn^6$

4 a) $4b$ **b)** 225 173 520

c) $1056p^{10}$ **d)** $11\,160\,261b^2$

e) -192 **f)** $\binom{8}{n}2^{8-n}$

5 a) 2000 **b)** -17496

c) 66 542

Exercises 14.2 class *(p.297)*

1 a) $1 + 10x + 45x^2 + 120x^3 + 210x^4$

b) $1 - 7x + 21x^2 - 35x^3 + 35x^4$

c) $1 + 12x + 54x^2 + 108x^3 + 81x^4$

d) $1 + 6x + 16.5x^2 + 27.5x^3 + 30.9375x^4$

e) $1 - 2x + 1.667x^2 - 0.741x^3 + 0.185x^4$

f) $1 + 8ax + 28a^2x^2 + 56a^3x^3 + 70a^4x^4$

2 a) $1 - 3x - 3x^2 + 25x^3$

b) $1 + 19x + 160x^2 + 780x^3$

c) $3 - 44x + 255x^2 - 720x^3$

d) $5 + 7x + 4x^2 + 1.12x^3$

3 $n = 5, a = 2$

4 a) $a = 4, b = -1$

b) $a = -\frac{44}{9}, b = \frac{1}{9}$

5 0.817 to 3 s.f.

6 277 to 3 s.f.

7 a) 1.0121 to 5 s.f.

b) 60 240 to 5 s.f.

c) 16 270 to 5 s.f.

8 0.989

Exercises 14.2 home *(p.298)*

1 a) $1 + 15x + 105x^2 + 455x^3 + 1365x^4$

b) $1 - 9x + 36x^2 - 84x^3 + 126x^4$

c) $1 + 35x + 525x^2 + 4375x^3 + 21\,875x^4$

d) $1 + 4x + \frac{22}{3}x^2 + \frac{220}{27}x^3 + \frac{55}{9}x^4$

e) $1 - \frac{10}{3}x + \frac{40}{9}x^2 - \frac{80}{27}x^3 + \frac{80}{81}x^4$

f) $1 - 10ax + 45a^2x^3 - 120a^3x^3 + 210a^4x^4$

2 a) $1 + 9x + 35x^2 + 77x^3$

b) $1 - 17x + 120x^2 - 460x^3$

c) $3 - 215x + 6732x^2 - 120\,204x^3$

d) $8 + 23x + 30x^2 + 23.375x^3$

3 $a = -6, n = 9$

4 $b = 2$ or $\frac{4}{7}$, $a = -3$ or $5\frac{4}{7}$

5 $n = 10$

6 0.709 to 3 s.f.

7 525.98 to 5 s.f.

8 $\delta = 0.0061$

Exercises 14.3 class *(p.303)*

1 a) $1 - x + x^2 - x^3 + x^4$, $|x| < 1$

b) $1 + \frac{3}{2}x - \frac{9}{8}x^2 + \frac{27}{16}x^3 - \frac{405}{128}x^4$, $|x| < \frac{1}{3}$

c) $1 + \frac{2}{3}x + \frac{1}{3}x^2 + \frac{4}{27}x^3 + \frac{5}{81}x^4$ $|x| < 3$

d) $2\left(1 + \frac{x}{24} - \frac{x^2}{576} + \frac{5x^3}{41472} - \frac{5x^4}{497\,664}\right)$ $|x| < 8$

2 a) 1.02

b) 9.80 to 3 s.f.

c) 2.03

3 $1 - 2x + 2x^2 - 2x^3$

4 0.816

5 $a = \frac{1}{2}, P = -1, Q = \frac{3}{4}$

6 $n = -\frac{1}{5}, r = \frac{15}{2}, |x| < \frac{2}{15}$

Exercises 14.3 home *(p.303)*

1 a) $1 - 6x + 24x^2 - 80x^3$ $|x| < \frac{1}{2}$

b) $1 + 0.2x + 0.004x^2 + 0.008x^3$, $|x| < 5$

c) $3(1 + 0.0123x - 0.000\,151x^2 + 3.14 \times 10^{-6}x^3)$, $|x| < 27$

d) $1 + 3.5x - 6.125x^2 + 21.4375x^3$, $|x| < \frac{1}{7}$

2 a) 0.975 **b)** 11.8 **c)** 2.00

3 $1 + 1.5x + 0.875x^2 + 0.6875x^3 + 0.5859x^4$

4 $a = 4, b = -\frac{9}{64}$

5 $1 + 0.5x + 0.375x^2 - 0.1875x^3 + 0.023\,437x^4$, $-0.8 \le x \le 1.1$

6 $1 - \frac{2.667}{x} - \frac{7.111}{x^2} - \frac{31.61}{x^2}, \left|\frac{8}{x}\right| < 1$

Consolidation Exercises for Chapter 14 *(p.305)*

1 240

2 a) $P = (\frac{1}{2}, -1)$

b) $8x^3 - 36x^2 + 54x - 27$

c) $I = \int_{\frac{3}{2}}^{\frac{5}{2}} \left(x^2 - \frac{9}{2}x^3 + \frac{27}{4}x - \frac{27}{8}\right)\mathrm{d}x$

d) 0.25 **e)** 3

3 a) $x = -\frac{1}{2} + \frac{1}{2}\sqrt{1-4p}$ or $x = -\frac{1}{2} - \frac{1}{2}\sqrt{1-4p}$

b) $A = -2$ $B = -2$ $C = -4$, valid for $p : -0.25 \le p \le 0.25$

c) $x = -(2p^3 + p^2 + p)$ (1)

$x = 2p^3 + p^2 + p - 1$ (2)

d) $x = -0.112, x = -0.888$

4 b) $\frac{4096}{729} + \frac{2048}{81}x + \frac{1280}{27}x^2 + \frac{1280}{27}x^3$

5 a) $1 + 24x + 264x^2 + 1760x^3$

b) $x = 0.01$; 1.26816

c) 1.2682417945625

d) 0.00045%

6 a) $n = 8$ **b)** $\frac{35}{8}$

7 $1 + 5x + 10x^2 + 10x^3 + 5x^4 + x^5$ 45

8 $1 + x + \frac{3}{2}x^2$ $|x| < \frac{1}{2}$

CHAPTER 15
Trigonometry 2

Exercises 15.1 class *(p.310)*

1 a) $\frac{\sqrt{6}}{4} + \frac{\sqrt{2}}{4}$ **b)** $\frac{3-\sqrt{3}}{3+\sqrt{3}}$

c) $\frac{\sqrt{6}}{4} + \frac{\sqrt{2}}{4}$ **d)** $\frac{\sqrt{3}+3}{3-\sqrt{3}}$

e) $\frac{\sqrt{2}}{4} - \frac{\sqrt{6}}{4}$ **f)** $\frac{\sqrt{6}}{4} - \frac{\sqrt{2}}{4}$

2 a) $\frac{1}{2}$ **b)** $\frac{1}{2}$ **c)** $\sqrt{3}$

3 a) $\frac{171}{221}$ **b)** $\frac{220}{221}$ **c)** $-\frac{171}{140}$

4 a) $\frac{44}{125}$ **b)** $\frac{3}{5}$ **c)** $\frac{44}{117}$

5 0 **7a)** $\frac{5}{2}$ **b)** 2 **c)** 175.24°

8 36.9°

9 $\frac{\tan 60° + \tan 30°}{1 - \tan 60° \tan 30°}$, tan 90° = ∞

10 18.43°   11 45°, 225°

14 a) $\tan x = \frac{(1+k)}{(1-k)} \tan\alpha$

b) 60°, 240°

15 15°, 195°   16 –76.64°, 103.36°

17 156.2°, 336.2° P: (156.2°, 0.81), Q: (336.2°, –0.81)

Exercies 15.1 home (*p.311*)

4 a) sin 104° b) sin 4° c) cos 40°

d) –cos 60° e) $\sin \frac{\pi}{2}$ f) sin $3x$

g) cos $2x$ h) sin x

5 a) $\frac{\sqrt{2}}{4}(\sqrt{3}+1)$ b) $\frac{\sqrt{2}}{4}(\sqrt{3}-1)$

c) $2+\sqrt{3}$

7 a) $\frac{4}{5}, \frac{4}{3}, \frac{5}{13}, \frac{5}{12}$

b) $\frac{63}{65}, \frac{33}{65}, \frac{16}{65}, \frac{56}{65}, \frac{63}{16}, \frac{33}{56}$

8 $\cos(A+B) = \frac{33}{65}$,

$\tan(A-B) = \frac{16}{63}$

9 $\frac{1}{4}, \frac{1}{4}, \frac{1}{4}, -\frac{1}{4}$

10 $\frac{1}{4}(\sqrt{6}-\sqrt{2}), \frac{1}{4}(\sqrt{6}+\sqrt{2})$, $\frac{1}{4}(\sqrt{2}-\sqrt{6}), \frac{1}{4}(\sqrt{6}+\sqrt{2})$

11 a) $\beta = \alpha + \theta$

c) $\theta = \arctan\frac{1}{7}$ = 0.1419rad or 8.13°

15 $a = -5$, $b = 8$

Exercises 15.2 class (*p.315*)

1 a) $\frac{3}{5}$ b) $\frac{4}{5}$ c) $\frac{24}{25}$ d) $\frac{7}{25}$ e) $\frac{24}{7}$

2 a) 0.96 b) –0.28 c) –0.5376

3 a) $-\frac{527}{625}$ b) $-\frac{336}{625}$ c) $\frac{336}{527}$

7 a) $\frac{2\sqrt{5}}{25}$ b) $-\frac{91}{125}$

8 a) $\frac{\pi}{2}, \frac{5\pi}{6}, \frac{3\pi}{2}, \frac{11\pi}{6}$

b) 0.4636, $\frac{\pi}{2}$, 3.6052, $\frac{3\pi}{2}$

9 a) 60°, 180°, 300° b) 90°

c) 56.44°, 123.56°, 270°

Exercises 15.2 home (*p.315*)

1 A translation of 1 unit parallel to the y axis, $2\cos^2 x = \cos 2x + 1$.

2 a) $\frac{\sqrt{3}}{2}$ b) $\frac{\sqrt{2}}{2}$ c) $\frac{\sqrt{3}}{2}$ d) 0 e) $\sqrt{3}$

3 a) i) $\frac{\sqrt{7}}{4}$ ii) $\frac{3\sqrt{7}}{8}$ iii) $\frac{1}{8}$ iv) $3\sqrt{7}$

b) $\frac{3\sqrt{7}}{32}, -\frac{31}{32}, -\frac{3\sqrt{7}}{31}$

4 a) i) $\frac{2\sqrt{5}}{5}$ ii) $-\frac{4}{5}$ iii) $\frac{3}{5}$ iv) $-\frac{4}{3}$

b) $-\frac{24}{25}, -\frac{7}{25}, \frac{24}{7}$

5 $4\cos^3 x - 3\cos x$

6 b) $\frac{336}{625}$

7 a) 60°, 300°

b) 30°, 150°, 194.5°, 345.5°

8 $\tan\frac{\theta}{2}$

Exercises 15.3 class (*p.320*)

1 a) translation of +36.87° x–axis, $3\cos x + 4\sin x = 5\sin(x + 36.87°)$

b) translation of –53.13° x–axis, $3\cos x + 4\sin x = 5\cos(x - 53.13°)$

2 a) $13\sin(x + 157.38°)$, $13\cos(x - 292.62°)$

b) $25\cos(x + 73.74°)$, $25\sin(x - 196.26°)$

3 a) $\sqrt{2}\cos(x - 45°)$ or $\sqrt{2}\cos(x - 0.7854)$

b) $5\cos(x - 36.87°)$ or $5\cos(x - 0.6435)$

4 a) $5\cos(x + 233.13°)$ or $5\cos(x + 4.0689)$

b) $13\cos(x + 22.62°)$ or $13\cos(x + 0.3948)$

5 a) $\sqrt{5}\sin(x - 26.57°)$ or $\sqrt{5}\sin(x - 0.4637)$

b) $\sqrt{12}\sin(x - 60°)$ or $\sqrt{12}\sin(x - \frac{\pi}{3})$

6 a) $\sqrt{41}\sin(x + 51.34°)$ or $\sqrt{41}\sin(x + 0.8961)$

b) $\sqrt{3}\sin(x + 54.74°)$ or $\sqrt{3}\sin(x + 0.9554)$

7 $17\sin(x - 61.93°)$

a) greatest value = 17, least value = –17

b) greatest value = ∞, least value = –∞

8 a) maximum value = 2, minimum value = –2, turning points (150°, –2), (330°, 20)

b) maximum value = 20, minimum value = –14, turning points (118.07°, –14), (298.07°, 20)

c) maximum value = ∞, minimum value = –14, turning points (45°, $\frac{1}{\sqrt{2}}$), (225°, $-\frac{1}{\sqrt{2}}$)

d) maximum value = 169, minimum value = 0, turning points (67.38°, 169), (157.38°, 0), (247.38°, 169), (337.38°, 0)

Exercises 15.3 home (*p.321*)

1 a) translation of +67.38°// x-axis, $13\sin(x + 67.38°)$

b) translation of –22.67°// x-axis, $13\cos(x - 22.67°)$

2 a) $5\cos(x + 53.13°)$, $5\sin(x + 143.13°)$

b) $17\cos(x + 61.93°)$, $17\sin(x - 208.07°)$

3 a) $\sqrt{3}\cos(x - 35.26°)$ or $\sqrt{3}\cos(x - 0.6154)$

b) $\sqrt{10}\cos(x - 18.43°)$ or $\sqrt{10}\cos(x - 0.3217)$

4 a) $2\cos(x + 60°)$ or $2\cos(x + \frac{\pi}{3})$

b) $5\cos(x + 36.87°)$ or $5\cos(x + 0.6435)$

5 a) $5\sin(x - 53.13°)$ or $5\sin(x - 0.9273)$

b) $\sqrt{2}\sin(x - 45°)$ or $\sqrt{2}\sin(x - \frac{\pi}{4})$

6 a) $\sqrt{53}\sin(x + 74.05°)$ or $\sqrt{53}\sin(x + 1.2924°)$

b) $\sqrt{130}\sin(x + 15.26°)$ or $\sqrt{130}\sin(x + 0.2663)$

7 $25\cos(x - 73.74°)$

a) greatest value = 25, least value = –25

b) greatest value = ∞, least value = –∞

8 a) maximum value = $\sqrt{13}$ at x = 146.31, minimum value = $-\sqrt{13}$ at x = 326.31°

b) maximum value = 2 + $\sqrt{58}$ at x = 293.2°, minimum value = 2 – $\sqrt{58}$ at x = 113.2°

c) maximum value = ∞, minimum value = –∞, turning points (144.74°, $-\frac{1}{\sqrt{3}}$), (324.74°, $\frac{1}{\sqrt{3}}$),

d) maximum value 13 at x = 56.31° and 236.31°, minimum value 0 at x = 146.31° and 326.31°

Exercises 15.4 class (*p.323*)

1 a) 2.000 b) 1.015

c) –0.364 d) 0

e) 2 f) 2

g) $\frac{4}{3}$ h) $\frac{4}{3}$

2 a) 2 b) –1 c) –1

d) ∞ e) –1 f) –9.233

3 a) 60°, 300°

b) 191.54°, 348.46°

c) 9.74°, 80.26°

d) 25.66°, 154.34°

e) θ = 316.4

f) no solution

g) 30°, 60°, 120°, 150°, 210°, 240°, 300°, 330°

h) 53.13°, 306.87°

4 **a)** π **b)** 0.25, 2.89 **c)** 0.38, 3.52 **d)** 0.52, 1.05 **e)** 0.42, 2.72 **f)** 0.89, 1.94 **g)** no solution **h)** 0.79, 2.36, 3.93, 5.50

Exercises **15.4 home** *(p.323)*

1 **a)** 1.06 **b)** –1.31 **c)** 0 **d)** ∞ **e)** $\frac{4}{3}$ **f)** $\frac{4}{3}$ **g)** 1.19 **h)** 1.19

2 **a)** $\frac{1}{\sqrt{3}}$ **b)** $\sqrt{2}$ **c)** $\frac{2}{\sqrt{3}}$ **d)** ∞ **e)** ∞ **f)** 4.21

3 **b) i)** $\theta = 0, \pi, 2\pi$ **ii)** $\frac{\pi}{2}, \frac{3\pi}{2}$ **iii)** $0, \pi, 2\pi$

4 **a)** 0.52, 3.67 **b)** 3.67, 5.76 **c)** no solution **d)** 1.47, 3.05 **e)** 0.28, 1.81, 2.37 **f)** no solution **g)** 0.98, 2.55 **h)** no solution

Exercises **15.5 class** *(p.325)*

1 **a)** sec θ **b)** sin θ **c)** cosec θ **d)** $\tan^4 \theta$ **e)** sin θ **f)** 1

Exercises **15.5 home** *(p.325)*

1 **a)** cos θ **b)** $\sin^3 \theta$ **c)** tan θ **d)** $\frac{1}{2}\cos\theta$

Consolidation Exercises for Chapter 15 *(p.327)*

1 **b)** 61.32°, 241.32°

2 0.6155, 3.75707

3 150°, 330°

4 $(3n + 1)\frac{\pi}{3}$

5 $t = -2 \pm \sqrt{7}$ or $t = 0.6458$ and –4.6458, $x = 180n + 32.85°$ and $x = 180n - 77.85°$

6 0°, 60°, 180°, 300°, 360°

7 **a)** 30°, 150°, 270° **b)** 51.33°, 128.67° **c)** 0°, 180°, 210°, 330°, 360°

8 0.3747, 2.7669

9 **a)** 90°, 210°, 270°, 330° **b)** 0°, 180°, 360° **c)** 0°, 180°, 270°, 360° **d)** 0°, 30°, 150°, 180°, 360° **e)** 90°, 216.87°, 323.13° **f)** 60°, 120°, 240°, 300°

10 $\cos 4x \equiv \cos^2 2x - \sin^2 2x \equiv 2\cos^2 2x - 1 \equiv 1 - 2\sin^2 2x$
a) 0°, 30°, 150°, 180°, 210°, 330°, 360° **b)** 105°, 165°, 285°, 345°

11 $0, \frac{\pi}{4}, \pi, \frac{3\pi}{4}, \frac{5\pi}{4}, \frac{7\pi}{4}, 2\pi$

12 **a)** 0°, 180°, 360° **b)** 39.2°, 140.8° **c)** 35.3°, 144.7°, 215.3°, 324.7°

13 $R = 17$, $\alpha = 61.93°$, –208.07°, 151.93°

14 **a)** 103.3°, 330.5° **b)** 50.5°, 256.3° **c)** 0°, 90°, 360° **d)** 106.27°, 180°

15 **a)** $82.62° + 360n$, $322.62° + 360n$ **b)** $360n$, $109.5° + 360n$ **c)** $45° + 360n$ **d)** $360n$; $360n - 143.2°$

16 **a)** $2n\pi + 0.476$, $2n\pi + 1.378$ **b)** $2n\pi + 0.1$, $2n\pi + 5.8$ **c)** $2n\pi - 0.13$, $2n\pi - 2.23$ **d)** $2n\pi$, $2n\pi - \frac{2\pi}{3}$

17 $360n \pm 60° + 73.74°$, 13.74°, 133.74° **a)** 27.48°, 267.48° **b)** 6.87°, 66.87°, 186.87°, 246.87°

18 $\sqrt{5}\sin(x + 26.57°)$, 0°, 126.87°, 360° **a)** 0°, 253.74° **b)** 0°, 42.29°, 120°, 162.29°, 240°, 282.29°, 360°

19 $\frac{\pi}{12}, \frac{5\pi}{12}, \frac{13\pi}{12}, \frac{17\pi}{12}$

20 **a)** $5\sin(x + 36.97°)$ **b)** 5 **c)** 143.13°, 323.13°

21 15°, 75°, 195°, 255°

22 0°, 30°, 150°, 180°, 210°, 330°, 360°

23 **a)** $p = 4r\cos\theta + 2r\sin\theta$ **b)** maximum value of $a = r^2$ when $\theta = \frac{\pi}{4}$ **c)** p is maximum when $\tan^{-1}\frac{1}{2} = 26.57°$ $a = 0.8r^2$

24 **a)** $a = 2$, $b = \sqrt{3}$ **b)** $\sqrt{7}\sin(x + 40.89°)$ **c) i)** $x = 49.10°$ **ii)** $x = 0°$

25 **a)** $\cos x \cos\alpha - \sin x \sin\alpha$ **b)** $\sqrt{29}\cos(x + 68.2°)$ **c)** maximum value is $\sqrt{29}$ at $x = 291.8°$ minimum value is $-\sqrt{29}$ at $x = 111.8°$ **d)** 235.65°, 347.95°

26 **a)** $R = 17$ **b)** $A = 61.9°$ **c)** maximum value = 17 **d)** 298.1°

27 **b)** 5.76 **c)** 0.40, 4.84 **d)** 3.4

28 **a)** $R = \sqrt{10}$, $\alpha = 18.43°$ **b)** 90°, 306.86° **c)** $\sin x = 1$ or $\sin x = -\frac{4}{5}$

29 $\cos 15 = \frac{\sqrt{2}}{4}(1 + \sqrt{3})$

30 1.355, 4.496

31 $\frac{\pi}{6}, \frac{\pi}{2}, \frac{5\pi}{6}$

32 36°, 156°, 84°

CHAPTER 16
Exponentials and logarithms

Exercises **16.1 class** *(p.335)*

1 **a)**

x	3	2	1	0	1	2	3
y	0.037	0.111	0.333	1	3	9	27

c) $x \approx 2.7$

d)

x	–3	–2	–1	0	1	2	3
gradient	0.04	0.12	0.37	1.1	3.3	9.9	29.7

2 **a)** $x \approx 2.73$

3 $x \approx -1.58$

4 **b)** reflection in y-axis. **c)** reflection in y-axis followed by a translation $\frac{1}{2}$ unit // x-axis *or* reflection in y-axis followed by stretch, factor 2, // y-axis

6 **c)** $\alpha = 0.741$, $\beta = 5.47$

7 **c) i)** 4 million **ii)** 81.27 yrs

8 **b) i)** Drug B **ii)** Drug A **c)** $t = 2.63$ h and $C = 1.238$ mg/ml

Exercises **16.1 home** *(p.336)*

1 **a)**

x	–3	–2	–1	0	1	2	3
y	0.008	0.04	0.2	1	5	25	125

c) $x \approx 1.7$ **d)** 24.8

2 **a)** $x = 1.68$

3 **a)** $x = -1.89$

4 **b)** reflection in y-axis **c)** translation through –1 // x-axis *or* a stretch, factor 5, // y-axis **d)** translation through 1 unit // x-axis *or* stretch, factor $\frac{1}{5}$, // y-axis

6 **b)** $\alpha = 1.20$

7 **c)** 63 627 visitors **d)** during the 16th year

8 $\frac{R}{R_0} = \frac{1}{10}(3.2^n + 4)$, $n = -2$

Exercises **16.2 class** *(p.340)*

1 **a)** $y = \log_{10}x$ is a reflection in $y = x$ of 10^x.

3 **a)** $8 = 2^3$ **b)** $100\,000 = 10^5$ **c)** $3 = a^b$ **d)** $x = a^5$ **e)** $1 = a^0$ **f)** $q = p^y$

4 **a)** $\log_3 9 = 2$ **b)** $\log_{11} 1 = 0$ **c)** $\log_8 2 = \frac{1}{3}$ **d)** $\log_n m = 2$ **e)** $\log_x 2 = y$ **f)** $\log_{10} q = p$

5 **a)** 2.18 **b)** 0.70 **c)** 0.93 **d)** 1.20 **e)** 6.99 **f)** 1.28

6 **a)** 125.90 **b)** 15 848.93 **c)** 8.37 **d)** 632.46

e) 2.49 f) –0.34
g) $x = 1.35$ h) $x = 4.11$
i) $x = 1.83$, $x = 0.69$

7 a) $\log_a \frac{63}{125}$ b) $\log_2 8pq^2$
c) $\log\left(\frac{r^2s^3}{100t^4}\right)$ d) $\log(x^{\frac{1}{2}}y^{\frac{1}{3}})$
e) $\log_a(x-2)^2$ f) $\log_2(x+1)^2$

8 a) $\log_2 u + \log_2 v$
b) $2\log_3 u + 3\log_3 v$
c) $a\log u + b\log v - \log w$
d) $\frac{1}{2}\log_a u + 2\log_a v + \frac{1}{3}\log_a w$
e) $\frac{3}{2}\log u + \frac{5}{2}\log u$
f) $3\log_{10} v + 2$ g) $-2\log w$
h) $\log(u-1) + \log(v+1) - \log(w-2)$

Exercises 16.2 home *(p.341)*

3 a) $128 = 2^7$ b) $1\,000\,000 = 10^6$
c) $7 = a^b$ d) $x = a^{31}$
e) $1 = a^0$ f) $s = r^p$

4 a) $\log_7 49 = 2$ b) $\log_{130} 1 = 0$
c) $\log_{16} 4 = \frac{1}{2}$ d) $\log_{10} 0.01 = -2$
e) $\log_p r = 3$ f) $\log_{10} q = -p$

5 a) $x = 2.23$ b) $x = 0.52$
c) $x = 0.65$ d) $x = 0.28$
e) $x = 8.45$ f) $x = 8.45$

6 a) $x = 12.59$ b) $x = 316.23$
c) $x = 6.32$ d) x 0.099
e) $x = 50$ f) $x = 0$
g) $x = 36.31$ h) $x = 1.73$

7 a) $\log_a\left(\frac{4}{3}\right)$ b) $\log_3\left(\frac{rs^2}{9}\right)$
c) $\log\left(\frac{10xy^2}{t^5}\right)$ d) $\log\left(\frac{r^2}{s}\right)^{\frac{1}{8}}$
e) $\log_a(x+3)^2$
f) $\log_5(x^2+x+1)$

8 a) $\log_3 r + \log_3 s$
b) $4\log_4 s + \log_4 t$
c) $m\log r + n\log s + p\log t$
d) $\frac{1}{2}\log_a r - 3\log_a s$
e) $\frac{4}{3}\log s + \frac{5}{3}\log t$ f) $2\log_{10} r - 2$
g) $-(\log_a r + \log_a s + \log_a t)$
h) $\log(2r+1) + \log(3s-2) - \log(t+3)$

Exercises 16.3 class *(p.343)*

1 9.34×10^5 times greater
2 $E = 5.77 \times 10^{17}$ J
3 $L = 63.01$ dB
4 a) $\frac{S_1}{S_6} = 100$ b) 4.79×10^5
c) 1.74×10^{-12}

Exercises 16.3 home *(p.344)*

1 31 times stronger
2 $\frac{E_1}{E_2} = 11.086$
4 a) 7.96, the solution is alkaline.
b) 1×10^{-5} moles per litre

Exercises 16.4 class *(p.346)*

1 a) 2.1206 b) –1.8261
c) 0.7157 d) –0.9308
e) 11.4922 f) 0.1610
g) 1.0767 h) 1.3856
2 a) 2.7268 b) –1.5850
3 a) $x = 0.1260$ b) $x = 17.6549$
c) $x = 0.3562$, $x = 0$
d) $x = -1.5806$
4 $n = 66$

Exercises 16.4 home *(p.346)*

1 a) 3.2406 b) –0.6990
c) –0.2075 d) 0.3398
e) 4.0137 f) 1.8957
g) –4.1918 h) 3.1739
2 a) 1.6826 b) –1.8928
3 a) $x = 2$, $x = 1.5850$
b) $t = -1.3502$
c) $p = 0.732$ d) $x = -0.0534$
4 The least value of n is 9.

Exercises 16.5 class *(p.349)*

1 $y = 4x^{\frac{1}{2}}$
2 $y = 5 \times \left(\frac{3}{2}\right)^x$
3 $w = 3x^{-2.5}$
4 $u = 2.5t^{1.6}$
5 a) $\lambda = 1.4$, $C = 15\,971.81$
b) $P = 15971.81\ V^{-1.4}$, $P = 25.31$
6 $P = 17.1 \times 10^{(0.0133t)}$
7 $T = 0.01 \times 1.03^x$ in the year 2081

Exercises 16.5 home *(p.350)*

1 $\log(x) - \log(y)$ $y = 3.4x^{2.7}$
2 $t - \log(x)$ $x = 0.3 \times 4.1^t$
3 $t - \log(p)$ $p = 1.5 \times 2.72^t$
4 $\log(t) - \log(p)$ $p = 1.5 \times t^{2.16}$
5 $M = 0.04 \times 108^l$
6 $\mu = 48.38T^{-2.06}$
7 $H = 16.16M^{0.93}$, $H = 614.45$

Consolidation Exercises for Chapter 16 *(p.352)*

1 a)

x	–3	–2	–1	0	1	2	3
y	0.1875	0.375	0.75	1.5	3	6	12

c) $x = 2.3$ d) 0.13, 0.26, 0.52, 1.04, 2.08, 4.16, 8.32
2 a) $x = 2.32$
3 b) i) $d = 57$ cm ii) $t = 22$ weeks
c) $t = 21.6$ weeks
4 *either* a translation through –1 unit // x-axis *or* a stretch, factor 2 // y-axis.
5 b) local maximum is (2.89, 1.13)
6 $a = 0.90$, $k = 0.039$
$\frac{dy}{dx} = -0.3$ at $x = 20$
7 $t = 2.630$
8 $y = 3.(0.02)^x$, satisfies neither of the laws, $s = 4.2.t^{1.7}$
9 Since log – log graph is linear, $N = AT^B$
$\Rightarrow N = 200T^{1.5}$, $A = 200$, $B = 1.5$
10 $yx^{0.50} = 56 \Rightarrow n = 0.50$, $k = 56$
11

$\log x$	0.477	0.778	1.000	1.176	1.301
$\log y$	1.017	1.468	1.801	2.065	2.253

b) Since log-log is a linear relationship, $y = Ax^n$.
c) $A = 2$, $n = 1.5$
12 b) $y = ab^x \Rightarrow \log y = \log(ab^x)$
$= \log a + x\log b$, $Y = mX + C$
where $Y = \log y$, $m = \log b$, $X = x$, $C = \log a$
c)

x	0.000	1.000	2.000	3.000	4.000
$\log y$	1.079	1.231	1.398	1.568	1.724

$y = 11.87 \times (1.45)^x$
13 a) $b = 1.32$, $a = 2.27$, $x = 2.817$
b) $b = 10^m$, $a = 10^c$

CHAPTER 17 The Exponential and the natural logarithmic functions

Exercises 17.1 class *(p.359)*

1 a) £2251.02 b) £2253.65
c) £3187.70
2 a) 6.09% b) 8.24%
c) 10.51%
3 a) £5986.09 b) £2983.65
c) £1822.12
4 a) 8.66 yrs b) 13.73 yrs.
5 a) 20.009 b) 1.396
c) 0.135 d) 1.948
6 A: APR = 8.35%, B: APR = 8.11% therefore choose bank A
7 a) i) APR = 12.89%
ii) APR = 12.96%
b) A: £916.77,
B: £919.66, £2.89

Exercises 17.1 home *(p.360)*

1 a) £3963.46 b) £3965.43
c) £6517.76
2 a) 5.10% APR b) 11.57% APR
c) 9.42% APR
3 a) £1832.10 b) £1436.89
c) £7968.28
4 a) 5 yrs 7 months
b) 8 yrs 9 months
c) 11 yrs 1 month
5 £20 702.63 in 2000,
£143.88 in 1900
6 A: 5.875% APR
B: 5.654% APR
7 a) 7.389 non-oscillating
b) 0.368 oscillating
c) 1.649 non-oscillating
d) 0.607 oscillating

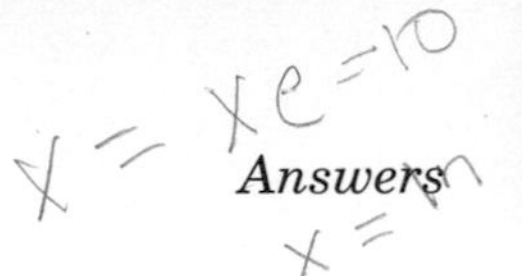

Exercises 17.2 class *(p.362)*

2 a) i) at $y = 2$, $x = 1.897$
ii) at $x = 1$, $\frac{dy}{dx} = 0.815$
b) i) at $y = 4$, $x = 3.386$
ii) at $x = 1$, $\frac{dy}{dx} = 0.368$
c) i) at $y = 3.5$, $x = -0.560$
ii) at $x = 1$, $\frac{dy}{dx} = -0.736$
d) i) at $y = 5.3$, $x = -1.609$
ii) at $x = 1$, $\frac{dy}{dx} = 4.077$
e) i) at $y = -2$, $x = 4.605$
ii) at $x = 1$, $\frac{dy}{dx} = -0.824$
f) i) at $y = 0.9$, $x = \pm 0.325$
ii) at $x = 1$, $\frac{dy}{dx} = -0.736$

3 a) stretch, factor 2 // y-axis followed by reflection in x-axis
b) reflection in y-axis followed by translation through –10 units // y-axis
c) stretch, factor 2 // x-axis
d) stretch, factor $\frac{1}{2}$ // x-axis followed by translation through –5 units // y-axis

4 a) 13.86 yrs **b)** $\frac{dP}{dt} = 4121.80$

5 b) i) $t = 8$, $v = £2018.97$
ii) $t = 4.581$ yrs
c) $R = 20\%$

Exercises 17.2 home *(p.363)*

2 a) i) at $y = 0.75$, $x = 0.981$
ii) at $x = 1$, $\frac{dy}{dx} = -5.437$
b) i) at $y = 3$, $x = 0$
ii) at $x = -1$, $\frac{dy}{dx} = 0.812$
c) i) at $y = -18$, $x = 0.999$
ii) at $x = -1$, $\frac{dy}{dx} = -0.149$
d) i) at $y = 20$, $x = -1.004$
ii) at $x = -1$, $\frac{dy}{dx} = 20.086$
e) i) at $y = 4$, $x = \pm 0.8326$
ii) at $x = -1$, $\frac{dy}{dx} = 10.873$

3 a) stretch, factor $\frac{1}{5}$ // y-axis
b) translation through –1 unit // x-axis
c) stretch, factor $\frac{1}{2}$, // x-axis followed by translation through 3 units // x-axis
d) stretch, factor $\frac{1}{2}$ // x-axis followed by reflection in y-axis followed by stretch, factor 2.5 // y-axis
e) reflection in the y-axis followed by translation through –1 unit // y-axis followed by reflection in x-axis followed by stretch, factor 4 // y-axis.

4 a) i) N will increase
ii) N will decrease **iii)** $N = N_o$
b) i) $N = 5.18 \times 10^{25}$
ii) $N = 2.69 \times 10^{47}$
iii) $N > 10^{100}$

5 b) i) $Q = 3.679$ mg
ii) $t = 11$ h 30 mins
iii) $\frac{dQ}{dt} = -0.7358$ mg s^{-1}

Exercises 17.3 class *(p.365)*

1 a) ln 21 **b)** ln 15 **c)** ln ba^n
2 a) 10 **b)** $\frac{1}{7}$ **c)** 5 **d)** x **e)** $\frac{4}{5}$ tan x
4 b) translation of –ln 5 units // y-axis *or* stretch, factor 5 // x-axis
5 b) i) 2ln x **ii)** $\frac{1}{2}$ln x
c) $y^{-1} = e^{x/2}$, $y^{-1} = e^{2x}$
6 b) reflection in the x-axis
d) $y^{-1} = e^{-x}$

Exercises 17.3 home *(p.365)*

1 a) ln 24 **b)** ln 40 **c)** ln 25
2 a) 1 **b)** 2 **c)** 25 **d)** x^4
3 a) e^{12} **b)** $e^5 + e^7$ **c)** e^{-2}
5 b) translation of ln 5 units // y-axis *or* stretch, factor $\frac{1}{5}$ // x-axis
6 b) i) stretch, factor 3 // y-axis
ii) stretch, factor $\frac{1}{3}$ // y-axis
c) $y^{-1} = e^{x/3}$, $x \in \Re$
$y^{-1} = e^{3x}$, $x \in \Re$

Exercises 17.4 class *(p.368)*

1 a) $x = \ln 10 = 2.30$
b) $t = \frac{1}{5} \ln 15 = 0.54$
c) $x = \frac{1}{2} \ln \frac{5}{8} = -0.24$
d) $x = -\ln \frac{15}{4} = -1.32$
e) $t = -\frac{1}{3} \ln \frac{10}{7} = -0.12$
2 a) $x = e^3 = 20.09$
b) $x = e^{-\frac{5}{2}} = 0.08$
c) $x = \sqrt[7]{e^{2.1}} = e^{0.3} = 1.35$
d) $x = 8992.27$ **e)** $x = 3$
3 a) $x = 1.39, 1.10$
b) $t = 0.3466$ **c)** no (real) solution
4 In the year 2005
5 a) 78%, 28.9%
b) 5590 yrs (to nearest year)
6 2512.94
7 a) 90°C **b)** 5.61×10^{-3}
c) 2 min 31 s
8 a) when $k = 0.693$, $A = 20$
b) 17.5 **c)** $t = 4.32$
9 b) $t = 6$ hrs

Exercises 17.4 home *(p.369)*

1 a) $x = \ln 5 = 1.61$
b) $x = \frac{1}{4}\ln \frac{7}{3} = 0.21$
c) $x = -\ln \frac{3}{2} = -0.41$ **d)** $x = 0$
e) $x = \ln 1.5 + 2 = 2.41$
2 a) $x = e^7 = 1096.63$
b) $x = e^{\frac{3}{4}} = 2.12$
c) $x = 2$ **d)** $x = 0.28$ **e)** $x = 3$
3 a) $x = 1.61$ $x = 0.69$ **b)** $x = 0.23$
c) no real solutions
d) no solutions
e) $x = \pm 1.32$
4 a) $M_0 = 80$ g **b)** $k = 0.069$
c) i) $M = 20$ g **ii)** $M = 2.5$ g
d) $t = 33$ days
5 a) $k = 0.021$, $t = 32.89$ days
b) 13.51 yrs **c)** 1.51×10^{-3} s
6 a) 10 h 20 min **b)** $N = 2500$
c) 7 812 500 bacteria
7 after 10 h $N = 450\,000$
8 3.58×10^{-3}
a) $N = 61.5$ million
b) $N = 61.7$ million
c) $N = 73.6$ million
9 a) i) 933.90 mbar
ii) 887.43 mbar
iii) 862.56 mbar
b) $x = 205\,853$ feet

Consolidation Exercises for Chapter 17 *(p.372)*

1 a) APR = 10.47%
b) APR = 8.24%
c) APR = 12.75%
2 a) B **b)** F **c)** A **d)** E **e)** C **f)** D
3 a) 783.71 years old **b)** no
4 a) $L = 70$, $D = 6$, $a = \ln \frac{2}{3}$
b) 3 days **d)** 70 mg
5 e) 20 000
6 a) 409 g **b)** 34.7 years
7 a) $a = 5$, $k = 0.462$ (3 s.f.)
b) $y = 5e^{0.462(x-3)}$
8 a) $e^x - 5$ **b)** 1.61 **c)** $p = 25$
9 a) $f^{-1}: x \to \frac{1}{5}(2 + e^x)$
b) $x \in \Re$ **c)** 1.878
10 330
11 b) $V = 100x - \frac{4}{3}x^3$ **c)** $333\frac{1}{3}$
d) $\frac{d^2V}{dx^2} < 0$
12 i) 200°C **ii)** 12.8 minutes
iii) 5°C min^{-1}

CHAPTER 18 Differentiation and integration 3

Exercises 18.1 class *(p.380)*

1 a) 1.75 **b)** 0.067 **c)** –1.35
d) –18.0 **e)** 22.1
f) 0.233 **g)** 0.221 **h)** 4.82
i) $\frac{5}{8}$ **j)** $-\frac{1}{5}$ **k)** 7.5 **l)** 2.718
2 a) $f'(x) = 2e^{2x} - 0.5$, $x = 0.506$
b) $f'(x) = -0.2e^{-0.8x}$, $x = -4.89$
c) $f'(x) = \ln(4)\, 4^{-x}$, $x = 0.5$
d) $f'(x) = -\frac{2}{x}$, $x = \frac{8}{3}$

3a) $(\ln 2, 2 - 2\ln 2)$ is a local minimum

b) $\left(\frac{5}{6}\ln\frac{25}{6}, \frac{35}{6} + \frac{25}{6}\ln\frac{26}{6}\right)$ $= (1.189, 11.79)$ is a local maximum

c) $(1.5, 3 - 3\ln 1.5) = (1.5, 1.784)$ is a local minimum

d) $(2, 24\ln 2 - 8) = (2, 8.636)$ is a local maximum

e) $\left(\frac{4}{7}, \frac{8}{7} - 7\ln\frac{4}{7}\right) = (0.5714, 6.203)$ is a local minimum

4 a) $-3000e^{-0.6}$ $(= -1646.43)$ £ per year

b) $\frac{10}{3}\ln 5 = 5.36$ years

5 a) $f(t) = 2500 \times 2^{\frac{1}{3}t}$

b) $f'(t) = \frac{2500\ln 2}{3} 2^{\frac{1}{3}t}$

c) $t = 3 + \frac{3\ln 3}{\ln 2} = 7.75$ hours

6 a) $f''(x) = e^x$, 1

b) $f''(x) = -\frac{2}{x^2}$, -2

c) $f''(x) = (\ln 2)^2.2^x$, 3.84

d) $f''(x) = -4e^{2x}$, -29.56

7 a) $y = 2 - 2x$, $y = 2 + \frac{1}{2}x$

b) $y = 9x - 1$, $y = -\frac{1}{9}x - 1$

c) $y = 5 - x$, $y = x + 3$

d) $y = 8x - 5$, $y = -\frac{25}{8} - \frac{1}{8}x$

Exercises 18.1 home *(p.381)*

1 a) $0.25e$ **b)** $21e^{14}$

c) e^6 **d)** -3.5

e) $6(e^6 + e^{-6})$ **f)** $-6e^{-4} + 84$

g) $7^5\ln 7$ **h)** $-4000\ln 5$

i) $\frac{1}{15}\ln 10$ **j)** $\frac{7}{5}$

k) $\frac{1}{2}$ **l)** $-\frac{1}{9}$ **m)** $3\frac{2}{3}$

2 a) $f'(x) = \frac{1}{2}(e^x - e^{-x})$, $x = 0$

b) $f'(x) = 1 - \frac{1}{x}$, $x = 3$

c) $f'(x) = \frac{1}{2\sqrt{x}} - \frac{1}{2x}$, $x = 1$

d) $f'(x) = \frac{1}{2}(e^x + e^{-x})$,
$x = \ln(\sqrt{5} + 2)$ or $x = \ln(\sqrt{5} - 2)$

3 a) $(2\ln 2, 2 - 2\ln 2)$ is a local minimum

b) $\left(\frac{1}{2\sqrt{3}}, \frac{1}{4}(1 + \ln 12)\right) =$ $(0.2887, 0.8712)$ is a local minimum

c) $(\ln 2, 8 - 12\ln 2)$ is a local minimum

d) $(-1, -\frac{1}{4})$ is a local minimum

e) $(1, -2)$ is a local maximum

4 b) $c'(t) = k(be^{-bt} - ae^{-at})$ rate of decay of drug in bloodstream

c) $\frac{1}{(a-b)}\ln\left(\frac{a}{b}\right)$

d) maximum value of $c(t)$ ($b > a$ for positive $c(t)$)

5 a) $t = \frac{1}{2}$ hour **b)** $P = 2000e^{2t\ln 2}$

c) $P'(1) = 16\,000\ln 2$, $P'(2) = 64\,000\ln 2$

6 a) $f''(x) = e^{x/2}$, $e^{-1/2}$

b) $f''(x) = \frac{2}{x^2}$, $\frac{2}{9}$

c) $f''(x) = 5(\ln 3)^2\, 3^{-x}$, 3.484

c) $f''(x) = (\ln 3)^2 3^x - (\ln 2)^2 2^x$, 0.162

7 a) $y = \frac{ex}{4}$, $y = -\frac{4}{e} + \frac{e^2 + 16}{e}$

b) $y = 14t - 7$, $y = -\frac{t}{14} + \frac{1}{28}$

c) $y = -11x + 1$, $y = -\frac{x}{11} + 1$

d) $y = 7x - 6$, $y = -\frac{x}{7} + \frac{8}{7}$

Exercises 18.2 class *(p.384)*

1 a) $4e^x + c$ **b)** $-e^{-x} + c$

c) $3e^{2x} + c$ **d)** $-\frac{2}{3}e^{-3x} + c$

e) $\frac{2^x}{\ln 2} + c$ **f)** $-\frac{(0.5)^{2x}}{2\ln 2} + c$

g) $-\frac{3^{-x}}{\ln 3} + c$ **h)** $-\frac{5^{-2x}}{2\ln 5} + c$

2 a) $4\ln x + c$ **b)** $-3\ln x + c$

c) $\frac{1}{2}x^2 - 9\ln x + c$

d) $2\ln x + \frac{5}{x} + c$

3 a) 3.19 **b)** 4 **c)** 2.43

d) 21.5 **e)** 22.6 **f)** 11.4

g) -1.58 **h)** 10.8

4 a) $34 - \frac{15}{\ln 2} = 12.3596$

b) $e^3 - e^{-1}$ **c)** $30 + 10e^{-4}$

d) $16\ln 2$ **e)** $(e^1 - e^{-1})$

f) $e^1(2\ln 2 + 1) - 1$

5 a) $\frac{1}{2}e^{2x+3} + c$ **b)** $\frac{1}{4}e^{4x-7} + c$

c) $\frac{1}{a}e^{ax+b} + c$ **d) i)** $\frac{1}{5}(e^{1.5} - e^{-1})$

ii) $e - e^{-1}$ **iii)** $2(e - e^{-1})$

6 $e^2 - e - \ln 1.5$

Exercises 18.2 home *(p.385)*

1 a) $\frac{7}{3}e^{3x} + c$ **b)** $-\frac{1}{2}e^{-2x} + c$

c) $-4e^{-3x} + c$

d) $-3e^{-3x} - 3e^{-5x} + c$ **e)** $\frac{5^x}{\ln 5} + c$

f) $\frac{(0.25)^{-x}}{\ln 4} + c$ or $\frac{2^{2x}}{\ln 4} + c$

g) $\frac{7^{3x}}{3\ln 7} + c$ **h)** $-\frac{8^{-4x}}{4\ln 8}$

2 a) $11\ln x + c$ **b)** $-17\ln x + c$

c) $13\ln x - \frac{1}{2}x^2 + c$

d) $7\ln x - \frac{15}{x} + \frac{1}{2x^2} + c$

3 a) $\frac{13}{10}(e^{1.5} - 1)$ **b)** $\frac{1}{4}$ **c)** $\frac{4\sqrt{5}}{5\ln 5}$

d) $\frac{1}{3}\ln 4$ **e)** $\frac{8}{\ln 2} - \frac{37}{3}$

f) $-\frac{e^{-15}}{3} - \frac{207}{4}$ **g)** $10 - 25\ln\left(\frac{3}{2}\right)$

h) $\frac{124}{25\ln 5}$

4 a) $\frac{8}{\ln 3} - \frac{3}{\ln 2}$ **b)** $\frac{15}{2\ln 2} - \frac{32}{4}$

c) $\ln 3 + e^{-1} - e^{-3}$

d) $\frac{3}{2}e^{-1} - e^{-2}$ **e)** $e + e^{-1}$

f) $\frac{98\sqrt{7}}{5} - \frac{9}{5}\sqrt{\frac{3}{2}} + \frac{1}{\ln 1.5}\left(\frac{3}{2}\sqrt{\frac{3}{2}} - 1 - 1.5^7\right)$

(= 14.1085 to 4 d.p.)

5 a) $\frac{1}{3}e^{3x+5} + c$ **b)** $\frac{1}{4}e^{4x-11} + c$

c) $\frac{1}{a}e^{ax+b} + c$ **d) i)** $\frac{1}{2}(e^{-1} - e^{-3})$

ii) $e - e^{-1}$ **iii)** $2(e^{-1} - e^{-2})$

6 a) $\frac{14}{3} - 2\ln 2$

Exercises 18.3 class *(p.388)*

1 a) 36π **b)** 32π **c)** $\frac{32\pi}{5}$ **d)** $\frac{24\pi}{\ln 2}$

e) $50\pi(4e^{-2} - e^{-4} + 1)$

2 a) $\frac{16^3\pi}{3}$ **b)** $\frac{49\sqrt{3}\pi}{5}$ **c)** 4π

3 a) i) (0, 0), (3, 0) **iii)** $\frac{1296\pi}{5}$

b) i) (0, 0), (6, 0) **iii)** $\frac{27\pi}{4}$

4 a) $\frac{19 \times 2^7\pi}{15}$ **b)** $\frac{3\pi}{10}$

5 a) 3 **b)** $\frac{21\pi}{2}$

6 a) $y = \frac{a}{h}x$ **d)** $\frac{\pi a^2(h^3 - b^3)}{3h^2}$

Exercises 18.3 home *(p.389)*

1 a) $\frac{6272\pi}{3}$ **b)** $\frac{9\pi}{2}$ **c)** $\frac{384\pi}{7}$

d) $\frac{40\pi}{\ln 3}$ **e)** $\frac{\pi}{2}(8\ln 2 - 5)$

2 a) $\frac{9\pi}{4}$ **b)** $\frac{3^5 2\pi}{5}$ **c)** 8π

3 a) $\frac{5^4\pi}{6}$ **b)** $\frac{64\pi}{21}$

4 a) $\frac{128\pi}{15}$ **b)** $\frac{2\pi}{35}$

5 a) $3\ln 2 + 6$ **b)** $\left(12\ln 2 + \frac{27}{2}\right)\pi$

6 d) $\frac{\pi}{3}(a - b)^2(2a + b)$

Consolidation Exercises for Chapter 18 *(p.390)*

1 $a = 0.90$, $k = 0.039$, $\frac{dy}{dx} = -0.3$

2 a) 1.65, 65%

b) $k = 0.5008$ (to 4 d.p.) (or $k = \ln 1.65$ exactly)

d) 0.5

3 a) 117π **b)** 24π **c)** $\frac{\pi}{2}(e^5 - 1)$

d) $192\pi\ln 2$ **e)** $\frac{\pi}{2}(e^2 - 1)$ **f)** $\frac{7\pi}{8}$

4 a) $\frac{13}{6}$ **b)** $\frac{59\pi}{15}$

5 a) 162π **b)** $\frac{567}{8}\pi$ **c)** $c = 1$

d) $c^3 - 75c - 88 = 0$, $c = -1.196$

6 a) $k = 8$ **b)** -4 **c)** 1.72

7 a) $0.5e^{0.5x} - \frac{1}{x^2}$

c) $2e^{0.5x} + \ln(x) + c$ **d)** 10.03

8 $f(x) = \frac{1}{4}e^{2x} - 3x^2 - \frac{5}{4}$

9 $\frac{3}{2}e^4 - \frac{7}{2}$

10 $a = 50.4$, $k = 0.12$, $11.02\ mm^2\ h^{-1}$

CHAPTER 19
Numerical methods

Exercises 19.1 class (p.397)

1 **b)** [1, 2] **c)** 1.33
2 **b)** [–5, –4], [–2, –1], [1, 2]
c) –4.57, –1.64, 1.20
3 **b)** [–5, –4], [1, 2] **c)** –4.99, 1.94
4 **b)** [0, 1], [1, 2] **c)** 0.793, 1.64
5 **b)** –1.73, –1.62
6 **b)** $2 - 2x - 4x^3$ **c)** (0.590, 8.71)
7 **b)** $\pm\sqrt{2}$
8 **b) i)** 1.4 (4 steps) **ii)** 1.43 (8 steps)
iii) 1.429 (11 steps)
c) 10 steps

Exercises 19.1 home (p.397)

1 **b)** [1, 2] **c)** 1.28
2 **b)** [–1, 1], [4, 5] **c)** 0, 4.58
3 **b)** [–1, 0], [1, 2]
c) –0.775, 1.93
4 **b)** [–1, 0] **c)** –0.927
5 **b)** 1.38. 1.62
6 **b)** $2x + e^x$ **c)** (–0.352, 0.827)
7 **a)** 0.329, 1.911, –1.786
b) (0.329, 0.658), (1.911, 3.822), (–1.786, –3.572)
8 **b)** 0.318
c) infinite number of roots, all in the interval [–0.5, 0.5]

Exercise 19.2 class (p.402)

1 **b)** 0.761
2 **b)** 0.297
3 **b)** 0.610
4 –1.88, 0.347, 1.53

Exercises 19.2 home (p.403)

1 **b)** $-3 - 6x^2 < 0$ for all x **c)** 1.28
2 **b)** 1.39 **c)** –1.07, 4.68
3 **a)** (0.728, 5.63) **b)** minimum
4 **b)** ±4.47

Exercises 19.3 class (p.407)

1 **b)** –1.59
2 **b)** –1.39, 0.145, 1.24
3 **b)** 0.178, 1.70
4 **b)** –2.21, 1.24
5 **b)** 3.35
6 **c)** –3.98, 1.75
7 $x_{n+1} = \frac{x_n(3a - x_n^3)}{2a}$, 3.16
8 (–2.41, –16.1), (–0.265, 0.412), (1.17, –5.28)
9 **b) i)** 0.806 in 25 steps
ii) 0.806 in 4 steps

Exercises 19.3 home (p.408)

1 **b)** 2.29
2 **b)** –3.88, –1.22, 2.11
3 **b)** –1.67, 0.195
4 **b)** –1.45, –0.747, 0.681
5 **b)** –1.19, 4
6 **b)** –1.31 **c) i)** division by zero
ii) initial sequence erratic
7 $x_{n+1} = \frac{x_n(4a - x_n^3)}{3a}$, 2.15
8 (–0.459, 0.729), (0.910, 1.73), (3.73, –10.2)
9 **b) i)** –0.726 in 22 steps
ii) –0.726 in 4 steps

Exercises 19.4 class (p.413)

1 **a)** 9.125 **b)** 0.693 **c)** 2.19
d) 1.48
2 **b)** $y = 4 - x^2$ **c)** 3.00
d) 3.10, 3.14, 3.14
3 23.99

Exercises 19.4 home (p.414)

1 **a)** 65.8 **b)** 0.784 **c)** 4.02
d) 31.0
2 40.6 m
3 **a)** $6 + \frac{\pi}{2}$ **b)** 7.57 **d)** 7.37 (3 sf)
e) about 50

Consolidation Exercises for Chapter 19 (p.416)

1 1.935
2 **a)** 1.733 **b)** 1.620, 1.666
3 1.969
4 2.002, 2 iterations
5 13.80
6 No, 55 weeks
7 **a)** –4, 1, 0.268, 3.732 **c)** 0.16
8 **b)** 1.442
9 **b)** 1.327 **c)** $p = -1.25$
d) –2.642
10 **a)** $q = -0.25$ **b)** 0.1888
11 1.374 radians

CHAPTER 20
Mechanics and the real world

Exercises 20.1 class (p.424)

1 **a)** No **b)** Yes or No (students may feel length of car is significant) **c)** Yes **d)** No
3 **a)** No **b)** No **c)** Yes

Exercises 20.1 home (p.424)

1 **a)** Yes **b)** Yes unless close to poles or bar **c)** No **d)** Yes
2 **a)** e.g. car wheel, football, rolling marble
b) e.g. golf ball, snooker or pool ball, boomerang
3 At the 'centre' of the child, probably a little above the swing seat.
4 **a)** No **b)** Yes **c)** No

CHAPTER 21
Force

Exercises 21.1 class (p.428)

1 **a)** Yes **b)** No **c)** No **d)** No
e) Yes if the skateboard travels in a straight line. **f)** Yes **g)** No
3 **a)** The speed is likely to increase, until it reaches a maximum.
b) If friction is constant then the net force is constant however if friction depends on speed then the net force is likely to reduce in magnitude.

Exercises 21.1 home (p.428)

1 **a)** Yes **b)** No **c)** Yes **d)** No
e) No **f)** Yes **g)** Yes
2 **a)** The lorry moves at constant speed in a straight line.
b) When they have come to rest at the end of the jump.
c) If the ice is so smooth that there is no friction.
d) If the buoyancy force is equal to the force of gravity.
3 **a)** Increases to a maximum.
b) Decreases to zero.
4 **a)** Decreases to zero.
b) Decreases to zero.

Exercises 21.2 class (p.430)

1 **a)** 245 N **b)** 0.0294 N
c) 17 640 N
2 900 kg
4 No, unless air resistance is significant.
5 104 N
6 2.8×10^{-7} N
7 15.1 m s^{-2}
8 290.2 N
9 3.46×10^8 m

Exercises 21.2 home (p.431)

1 **a)** 666.4 N **b)** 0.49 N
c) 1.96×10^6 N
2 286 grams
4 Fall together in both cases, but slower on the moon.
5 384.8 N
6 15 m s^{-2}
7 1.76×10^{28} kg
8 37.43 N
9 6.05 m s^{-2}

Exercises 21.3 class (p.435)

1 **a)** 735 N **b)** 5.88 N **c)** 6.53 N
d) 49 N

3 Reaction forces have magnitude 19.6 N, 68.6 N and 98 N.
4 6
5 **a)** 78.4 N to left
b) 29.4 N to right
6 **a)** 280 N **b)** 200 N
7 294 N
8 **a)** 10 143 N **b)** 7326 N
9 **b)** Between box and sledge 98 N. Between sledge and ground 205.8 N. **c)** No
10 **a)** 4900 N **b)** 3332 N
c) 9 **d)** 1200 N

Exercises 21.3 home *(p.436)*

1 **a)** 490 N **b)** 4.9 N **c)** 19 600 N
2 **a)** 49 N Equal force on each wheel. **b)** 12250 N Equal force on each wheel.
4 Forces due to gravity: 245 N on sledge and 1470 N on box. Reaction forces: 1470 N between box and sledge, and 1715 N between sledge and ground.
5 2352 N on bottom of box, 2058 N on top of box.
6 **a)** 8 N to left **b)** 2 N to right
c) 0 N **d)** 1 N to left
7 **a)** 695.8 N **b)** 146.1 N.
8 $0.581 \le \mu \le 0.867$.
9 **a)** 3920 N **b)** P
10 **a)** 2450 N
b) greater than 3920 N
c) Rear wheels 500 N, front wheels 4400 N.

Exercises 21.4 class *(p.439)*

1 14.7 N
2 **a)** 0.49 N **b)** Decreases going up, increases going down.
3 **a)** 49 N, 39.2 N **c)** 9.8 N
4 **a)** 4.9 N **b)** 3.43 N **c)** 3.43 N
5 **b)** 19.6 N, 49 N **c)** 3.2 N, 8 N
6 **a)** $T \le 5684$N **b)** $T = 5684$ N
c) $T > 5684$ N
7 2450 N
8 **a)** 29.4 N, 49 N
b) 29.4 N, 0.6
c) 29.4 N, 19.6 N, 0.125

Exercises 21.4 home *(p.440)*

1 **a)** 88.2 N **b)** 10.20 kg
2 **a)** 10 N **b)** 1.02 kg
3 **a)** 98 N **b)** 66.64 N
4 **b)** 98 N, 127.4 N
c) 98 N, 127.4 N
5 **a)** 58.8 N, 1.2
b) 29.4 N, 39.2 N, 0.1
6 490 N, 735 N, Top two cables have equal tensions.
7 **a)** 58.8 N, 39.2 N, 9.8 N
b) 1.176 m, 0.784 m, 0.196 m

Consolidation Exercises for Chapter 21 *(p.442)*

2 **a)** Buoyancy force = mg
c) Equal in magnitude as it goes through its equilibrium level.
3 **b)** Friction causes the marble to roll.
5 No

CHAPTER 22 Vectors and forces

Exercises 22.1 class *(p.447)*

1 **a)** $28.19\mathbf{i} + 10.26\mathbf{j}$
b) $-45.89\mathbf{i} - 65.53\mathbf{j}$
c) $-21.13\mathbf{i} + 45.32\mathbf{j}$
d) $4.91\mathbf{i} - 3.44\mathbf{j}$
2 **a)** $\begin{pmatrix} 4 \\ 6.93 \end{pmatrix}$ **b)** $\begin{pmatrix} 9.40 \\ -3.42 \end{pmatrix}$
c) $\begin{pmatrix} -8.68 \\ 49.24 \end{pmatrix}$ **d)** $\begin{pmatrix} -20 \\ -34.64 \end{pmatrix}$
3 **a)** $5\mathbf{i} + 3\mathbf{j}$, 5.83 N, 31.0° to $\mathbf{i}$
b) $-1.5\mathbf{i} - 0.866\mathbf{j}$, 1.732 N, −150° to $\mathbf{i}$ **c)** $4.52\mathbf{i} + 7.74\mathbf{j}$, 8.96 N, 59.7° to $\mathbf{i}$
4 **a)** 15.62 N, 50.2° **b)** 35.78 N, 63.4° **c)** 13.60 N, 36.0°
d) 102.4 N, −77.6° **e)** 20 N, −143.1° **f)** 5 N, 126.9°
5 **a)** 3.61 N, 33.7° to $\mathbf{i}$
b) 9.22 N, 130.6° to $\mathbf{i}$
c) 4.47 N, −153.4° to $\mathbf{i}$
d) 2.24 N, 153.4° to $\mathbf{i}$
6 **a)** $5.14\mathbf{i} + 6.13\mathbf{j}$ **b)** $5.20\mathbf{i} + 3\mathbf{j}$
c) $80\mathbf{i}$ **d)** $59.1\mathbf{i} + 10.4\mathbf{j}$

Exercises 22.1 home *(p.448)*

1 **a)** $6\mathbf{j}$ **b)** $49.24\mathbf{i} + 8.68\mathbf{j}$
c) $-13.79\mathbf{i} + 2.43\mathbf{j}$
d) $18.79\mathbf{i} - 6.84\mathbf{j}$
e) $-3\mathbf{i} - 5.20\mathbf{j}$
f) $3.54\mathbf{i} + 3.54\mathbf{j}$
2 **a)** $\mathbf{i} - \mathbf{j}$ **b)** $2.36\mathbf{i} + 1.05\mathbf{j}$
c) $5.63\mathbf{i}$
3 **a)** $\begin{pmatrix} 2.05 \\ 5.64 \end{pmatrix}$ **b)** $\begin{pmatrix} 28.19 \\ -10.26 \end{pmatrix}$
c) $\begin{pmatrix} -86.60 \\ 50 \end{pmatrix}$ **d)** $\begin{pmatrix} -20.52 \\ -56.38 \end{pmatrix}$
4 **a)** 10.4 N, 73.3° to $\mathbf{i}$
b) 125 N, −61.4° to $\mathbf{i}$
c) 89.2 N, −160.3° to $\mathbf{i}$
d) 44.7 N, 153.4° to $\mathbf{i}$
e) 10 N, −53.1° to $\mathbf{i}$
f) 62.2 N, 11.1° to $\mathbf{i}$
5 **a)** 8.06 N, 29.7° to $\mathbf{i}$
b) 6.32 N, −18.4° to $\mathbf{i}$
c) 10.2 N, −11.3° to $\mathbf{i}$
d) 10 N, 126.9° to $\mathbf{i}$
6 **a)** $-64.20\mathbf{i} - 13.97\mathbf{j}$, 65.7 N, 167.7°
b) $10\mathbf{i} + 40.36\mathbf{j}$, 41.6N, 76.1°

Exercises 22.2 class *(p.453)*

1 **a)** 490 N **b)** Cable 1: $-T\cos 30°\mathbf{i} + T\cos 60°\mathbf{j}$
Cable 2: $-490\mathbf{j}$ Rod: $R\mathbf{i}$
c) $T = 980$ N, $R = 849$ N
d) 498 N, 980 N, 762 N
2 **b)** $-T_1\cos 50°\mathbf{i} + T_1\cos 40°\mathbf{j}$
$T_2\cos 40°\mathbf{i} + T_2\cos 50°\mathbf{j}$ $-mg\mathbf{j}$
c) 37.8 N **d)** 5.99 kg
3 **b)** $R\mathbf{j}$, $F\mathbf{i}$, $-392\cos 80°\mathbf{i}$ $-392\cos 10°\mathbf{j}$ **c)** $R = 386$ N, $F = 68.1$ N **d)** $F < 196$ N
4 **b)** Equal in magnitude but opposite in direction.
c) 45 m s^{-1} **d)** 20.9 m s^{-1}
5 **a)** $376.2\mathbf{i} + 36.26\mathbf{j}$
b) $-376.2\mathbf{i} - 36.26\mathbf{j}$
c) 378 N, −174.5° to $\mathbf{i}$
d) 25.8° **e)** No because the cables will sag.
6 **a)** 31.5 N **b)** 16.5 N
7 **a)** 346 N
b) 452 N and 399 N
8 **b)** $(1637 - F)\mathbf{i} + (11\,646 - R)\mathbf{j}$
c) 1637 N

Exercises 22.2 home *(p.454)*

1 **a)** $-1121\mathbf{i} + 684\mathbf{j}$
b) $1121\mathbf{i} - 684\mathbf{j}$
c) 1313 N, 31.4°
2 **a)** $(T_2 - T_1 \cos 50°)\mathbf{i} + (T_1 \cos 40° - 400)\mathbf{j}$
b) 522 N **c)** 336 N
3 **b)** $-649\mathbf{i} - 9287\mathbf{j}$
c) $F = 649$ N, $R = 9287$ N
4 **a)** 21.5 N **b)** Rope probably not horizontal, there will be some friction. **c)** 21.8 N
5 **a)** 159 N **b)** 0.231
c) No account has been taken of other forces such as air resistance on the skier. Estimate the magnitude of the air resistance.
6 $Q = 299$ N, $P = 51.8$ N
7 2521 N
8 **a)** 11.8 N, 14.7 N **b)** 1.68 kg

Consolidation Exercises for Chapter 22 *(p.456)*

1 3.82 N, 9.7°
2 a) 77.8 N, 60 N
3 a) 19.9 N
b) 3.46 N
4 b) i) 125 N **ii)** 43.3 N
c) 0.35
5 24.0 N, 27.1 N,
6 a) 17.3 N **b)** 21.3 N

CHAPTER 23 Kinematics in one dimension

Exercises 23.1 class *(p.461)*

1 a) 700 m **b)** $140T$, zero gradient so zero acceleration
2 a) $\frac{1}{15}$ m s^{-2}, $v = \frac{1}{15}t$
b) i) $3\frac{1}{3}$ m **ii)** $53\frac{1}{3}$ m **iii)** $\frac{T^2}{30}$
3 a) 9.8 m s^{-2} **b)** $s = 4.9t^2$ **c)** 1.92 s
4 b) $v = 10 + 1.2T$
c) i) 65 m **ii)** $10T + 0.6T^2$

Exercises 23.1 home *(p.461)*

1 a) 200 m **b)** $20t$ m
2 a) $\frac{1}{3}$, $\frac{1}{3}$ m s^{-2}
b) $v = \frac{1}{3}t$ **c) i)** 4.17 m
ii) 37.5 m **iii)** $\frac{1}{6}t^2$
d) For example speed increases more rapidly at first, a greater distance would be travelled.
3 a) 0.8 m s^{-2} **b)** $0.4t^2$
c) 1.73 s, 1.39 m s^{-1}
4 b) 15 s **c)** 225 m **d)** –2 m s^{-2}

Exercises 23.2 class *(p.464)*

1 a) 1.43 s **b)** 14 m s^{-1}
2 a) 0.114 m s^{-2} **b)** 5 m s^{-2}
c) 1.219 m s^{-2}.
That the accelerations are constant.
3 a) 4.77 m **b)** 9.66 m s^{-1}
4 a) –3.6 m s^{-2} **b)** 1.67 s
5 a) –1.12 m s^{-2}
b) Yes, after 178.6 m. **c)** 10.7 s
d) 1.61 m s^{-2} **e)** 4.35 s
f) 15.1 s **g)** 13.3 m s^{-1}
h) Constant acceleration.
6 3840 m
7 65 m
8 a) 4.43 m s^{-1} **b)** 3.70 m s^{-1}
c) 49 cm

Exercises 23.2 home *(p.465)*

1 a) 0.2 m s^{-2} **b)** 2 m s^{-2}
c) –1.2 m s^{-2}
2 a) $t = 0.204$ s
b) 1.204 m **c)** 4.86 m s^{-1}
3 18 m s^{-2}
4 a) –1.995 m s^{-2}, 6.72 s
b) 501 m, 22.4 s
5 a) 600 m **b)** 60 s
6 a) aT **b)** $20aT - aT^2$
c) $\frac{1}{15}$ m s^{-2}, $\frac{1}{3}$ m s^{-1}
7 a) 2 m s^{-2}, 10 s **b)** 20 m s^{-1}
c) 200 m
8 a) 5.56 m s^{-1}, 0.0031 m s^{-2}
b) The cyclist will probably reach a constant speed and remain at that speed for most of the ride.

Consolidation Exercises for Chapter 23 *(p.466)*

1 b) 5 s **c)** 3 m s^{-1}
2 a) 10 m s^{-1}, 2.5 m s^{-2}
b) 1.78 s, 5.06 m s^{-2}
c) B is always in front, but A catches up at the end.
3 b) $45T$-562.5
c) 37.5 s
4 b) 5400 m **c)** 112 s
5 ii) 380 m 332 N
6 a) 0.625 m s^{-2}, 0,
–0.417 m s^{-2}
b) 32.5 m
c) Cyclist, 5 s
d) Not if you always use the same point.

CHAPTER 24 Motion and vectors

Exercises 24.1 class *(p.473)*

1 a) $t = 0$ $\mathbf{r} = 0 + 0\mathbf{j}$
$t = 1$ $\mathbf{r} = 4\mathbf{i} + 0.1\mathbf{j}$
$t = 2$ $\mathbf{r} = 8\mathbf{i} + 0.4\mathbf{j}$
$t = 4$ $\mathbf{r} = 16\mathbf{i} + 1.6\mathbf{j}$
$t = 6$ $\mathbf{r} = 24\mathbf{i} + 3.6\mathbf{j}$
2 a) $\mathbf{r}_A = 10\mathbf{j}$ $\mathbf{r}_B = 8\mathbf{i} - 2\mathbf{j}$
b) $4\mathbf{i} + 4\mathbf{j}$, 045°, 5.66 km
c) Note $\mathbf{r} = 3\mathbf{i} + 5.5\mathbf{j} \Rightarrow t = 1.5$.
3 a) $t = 0$ $\mathbf{r}_A = 8\mathbf{i} + 4\mathbf{j}$
$\mathbf{r}_B = 0\mathbf{i} + 0\mathbf{j}$
$t = 2$ $\mathbf{r}_A = 12\mathbf{i} - 2\mathbf{j}$
$\mathbf{r}_B = 8\mathbf{i} + 4\mathbf{j}$
$t = 3$ $\mathbf{r}_A = 14\mathbf{i} - 5\mathbf{j}$
$\mathbf{r}_B = 12\mathbf{i} + 6\mathbf{j}$
c) 2 s, 7.21 m
4 a) $t = 0$ $\mathbf{r} = 0\mathbf{i} + 2\mathbf{j}$
$t = 0.5$ $\mathbf{r} = 7.5\mathbf{i} + 5.75\mathbf{j}$
$t = 1.0$ $\mathbf{r} = 15\mathbf{i} + 7\mathbf{j}$
$t = 1.5$ $\mathbf{r} = 22.5\mathbf{i} + 5.75\mathbf{j}$
$t = 2.0$ $\mathbf{r} = 30\mathbf{i} + 2\mathbf{j}$
c) $0 \le t \le 2.18$ **d)** 32.75
e) Where do you place a particle on a javelin, at the middle or one end?
5 a) $t = 0$ $\mathbf{r} = 0\mathbf{i} + 0\mathbf{j}$
$t = 1$ $\mathbf{r} = 0.5\mathbf{i} + 0.48\mathbf{j}$
$t = 2$ $\mathbf{r} = 1\mathbf{i} + 1.12\mathbf{j}$
$t = 3$ $\mathbf{r} = 1.5\mathbf{i} + 1.92\mathbf{j}$
c) In the **j** direction.
6 a) $t = 0$ $\mathbf{r} = 0\mathbf{i} + 0\mathbf{j}$
$t = 1$ $\mathbf{r} = 20\mathbf{i} + 37\mathbf{j}$
$t = 3$ $\mathbf{r} = 60\mathbf{i} + 63\mathbf{j}$
$t = 3.5$ $\mathbf{r} = 70\mathbf{i} + 63.875\mathbf{j}$
$t = 4$ $\mathbf{r} = 80\mathbf{i} + 64\mathbf{j}$
c) Horizontally
7 a) $2\mathbf{i} + 1\mathbf{j}$
b) $a = 0.2$, $c = 0.3$
c) $b = 0.9$, $d = 0.35$

Exercises 24.1 home *(p.474)*

1 a) $t = 0$ $\mathbf{r} = 0\mathbf{i} + 0\mathbf{j}$
$t = 1$ $\mathbf{r} = 4.5\mathbf{i} + 3\mathbf{j}$
$t = 2$ $\mathbf{r} = 10\mathbf{i} + 6\mathbf{j}$
$t = 3$ $\mathbf{r} = 16.5\mathbf{i} + 9\mathbf{j}$
2 a) $t = 0$ $\mathbf{r} = 0\mathbf{i} + 2\mathbf{j}$
$t = 1$ $\mathbf{r} = 3\mathbf{i} + 9\mathbf{j}$
$t = 2$ $\mathbf{r} = 6\mathbf{i} + 6\mathbf{j}$
c) 9.2 m **d)** 2.56 s **e)** 7.67 m
3 a) $t = 0$ $\mathbf{r} = 0\mathbf{i} + 0\mathbf{j}$
$t = 1$ $\mathbf{r} = 3\mathbf{i} + 0.1\mathbf{j}$
$t = 2$ $\mathbf{r} = 6\mathbf{i} + 0.4\mathbf{j}$
$t = 3$ $\mathbf{r} = 9\mathbf{i} + 0.9\mathbf{j}$
$t = 4$ $\mathbf{r} = 12\mathbf{i} + 1.6\mathbf{j}$
c) Arrow in **j** direction.
4 c) $0 \le t \le 12$
5 a) B, with the higher path
b) B, 0.94 s
6 a) $t = 2.5$ s
b) Yes
7 a) $(\frac{16}{3}, \frac{40}{9})$, (6, 5)
b) 3.91 m

Exercises 24.2 class *(p.477)*

1 a) $3.83\mathbf{i} + 3.21\mathbf{j}$
b) $-72.08\mathbf{i} + 45.04\mathbf{j}$
c) $-0.42\mathbf{i} - 2.97\mathbf{j}$
3 a) Car cruising on a straight road.
b) Rocket as it beings to accelerate from a launch pad.
c) Car going round a roundabout.
4 a) A: $5\mathbf{j}$, 5 **B:** $-1\mathbf{i} - 4\mathbf{j}$, 4.12,
C: $4.2\mathbf{i} - 5\mathbf{j}$, 6.53
c) C is fastest and B is slowest.

5 A: 102 m s^{-1}, 078.7°
B: 161.6 m s^{-1}, 158.2°
C: 164.9 m s^{-1}, 194.0°
6 40.05 m s^{-1}, 2.9°
7 a) $-2\mathbf{i}$, $1.4\mathbf{i} + 1.4\mathbf{j}$ **b)** 3.53 s
c) $0.360\mathbf{i} - 0.869\mathbf{j}$ **d)** $0\mathbf{i} + 0\mathbf{j}$
8 e) 0, 0, 13.43 m s^{-1}

Exercises 24.2 home *(p.478)*

1 a) $0.96\mathbf{i} + 0.28\mathbf{j}$
b) $-5.64\mathbf{i} - 2.05\mathbf{j}$
c) $24.57\mathbf{i} - 17.21\mathbf{j}$
3 a) $3500\mathbf{i} + 6062\mathbf{j}$
b) $7.29\mathbf{i} + 12.63\mathbf{j}$, 14.58 m s^{-1}
c) Greater than or equal to 14.58 m s^{-1}
4 a) A: 9.43 m s^{-1}, 058.0°,
B: 5 m s^{-1}, 143.1°,
C: 6.32 m s^{-1}, 198.4°
b) $1080\mathbf{i} - 600\mathbf{j}$
c) The ship would probably follow a curved path.
5 a) $33.0\mathbf{i} - 3.2\mathbf{j}$
b) $-17.6\mathbf{i} - 55.6\mathbf{j}$
c) 58.4 m s^{-1}, 197.5°
6 a) 2.01 m s^{-1} **b)** 5.7°
c) $2.01\mathbf{i} + 0.07\mathbf{j}$
7 a) $40\mathbf{i}$ **b)** $35\mathbf{i}$ **c)** $49.85\mathbf{i} + 1.74\mathbf{j}$
8 a) 12.8 m s^{-1} at 38.7° to the horizontal **b)** 0.8 s, 8 m
c) For example
$\mathbf{v} = (10 - 2.5t)\mathbf{i} + (8 - 10t)\mathbf{j}$
d) No account of factors other than gravity which would change the vertical motion.

Exercises 24.3 class *(p.482)*

1 a) $1.4\mathbf{i} + 1.4\mathbf{j}$ **b)** $2.4\mathbf{i} + 4.4\mathbf{j}$
c) $19.1\mathbf{i} + 29.1\mathbf{j}$
2 a) $\mathbf{v} = 180\mathbf{i} - 10t\mathbf{j}$.
$\mathbf{r} = 180t\mathbf{i} + (1.5 - 5t^2)\mathbf{j}$
b) 0.55 s, 98.6 m **c)** 180 m s^{-1}
3 a) $200\mathbf{i}$, $80\mathbf{i}$
b) $2600\mathbf{i} + 1200\mathbf{j}$, $160\mathbf{i} + 120\mathbf{j}$
4 a) $\mathbf{r} = t^2\mathbf{i} - 0.75t^2\mathbf{j}$
b) 11.25 m
c) 7.5 m s^{-1}
5 a) $3.83\mathbf{i} + 3.21\mathbf{j}$, $-3.76\mathbf{i} + 1.37\mathbf{j}$
b) $-75.9\mathbf{i} - 18.5\mathbf{j}$.
6 a) $\mathbf{v} = 2\mathbf{i} + 0.5t\mathbf{j}$
$\mathbf{r} = 2t\mathbf{i} + 0.25t^2\mathbf{j}$
c) 10.2 m s^{-1}, 40 m
d) Unlikely to be constant due to buoyancy and resistance.
7 a) $23\mathbf{i} + 19\mathbf{j}$
c) $\mathbf{v} = 23\mathbf{i} + (19 - 10t)\mathbf{j}$.
$\mathbf{r} = 23t\mathbf{i} + (19t - 5t^2)\mathbf{j}$
d) 3.86 s, 89 m
e) An over estimate

8 a) $4\mathbf{i} + 2\mathbf{j}$, constant acceleration
b) 156.5 m s^{-1}

Exercises 24.3 home *(p.483)*

1 a) $1.2\mathbf{i}$
b) $\mathbf{v} = 1.2\mathbf{i} + 0.1t\mathbf{j}$
c) $\mathbf{v} = 1.2\mathbf{i} + 0.15\mathbf{j}$, $\mathbf{r} = 1.8\mathbf{i} + 0.1125\mathbf{j}$ **d)** No
2 a) $7.66\mathbf{i} + 6.43\mathbf{j}$
b) $\mathbf{r} = 7.66t\mathbf{i} + (6.43t - 5t^2 + 2)\mathbf{j}$
c) $t = 1.54$ s, $0 \le t \le 1.54$
d) 11.8 m
3 a) $5.13\mathbf{i} + 14.10\mathbf{j}$, $11.82\mathbf{i} - 2.08\mathbf{j}$ **b)** $13.4\mathbf{i} - 32.4\mathbf{j}$
c) Constant acceleration. A model where acceleration peaks.
4 b) $50\mathbf{i} - 200\mathbf{j}$ **c)** 206 m s^{-1}
d) $0 \le t \le 6.24$ s
5 a) $\pm 25\mathbf{j}$ **b)** $3.4\mathbf{i} \pm 15\mathbf{j}$ **c)** 77.2°
6 a) $0.5t^2\mathbf{i} - 0.025t^2\mathbf{j}$
b) $0.50\,06t^2$
c) 6.32 s, $6.32\mathbf{i} - 0.316\mathbf{j}$, 6.33 m s^{-1}
7 a) $\mathbf{a} = 0.1\mathbf{i} + 0.4\mathbf{j}$, $\mathbf{v} = 0.1t\mathbf{i} + 0.4t\mathbf{j}$
b) $15\mathbf{i} + 80\mathbf{j}$
8 37.8 m, 38.4 m
9 13.45 m s^{-1}, 54.83 on 24.2°

Consolidation Exercises for Chapter 24 *(p.484)*

1 a) i) 500 s **ii)** $10000\mathbf{i}$
iii) 100 m s^{-1}
2 a) $\mathbf{r} = 20t\mathbf{i}$
$\mathbf{s} = (300+10t)\mathbf{i} + 10t\mathbf{j}$
b) AB = $(300-10t)\mathbf{i} + 10t\mathbf{j}$
c) 15 s
d) 30 s

CHAPTER 25
Newton's first and second laws

Exercises 25.1 class *(p.488)*

1 784 N
2 780 N, travelling in a straight line.
3 a) 45 kg s^{-1} **b)** 1350 N
c) $R = 40v + 200$, 1400 N
4 Moves along a tangent at a constant speed.
5 462 N
6 a) 62.4 N **b)** 62.4 N
7 a) 3.4 m s^{-1} **b)** 3.9 m s^{-1}
8 216 N

Exercises 25.1 home *(p.489)*

1 676.2 N
2 2080 N
3 a) $R = 10 + 9v$ **b)** 55 N
4 At a tangent to the curve.
5 74°
6 13317 N
7 a) 640 N
b) 903 N
8 a) $R = 98v$
b) 8 m s^{-1}

Exercises 25.2 class *(p.491)*

1 a) 15 000 N **b)** 1.96 N
2 a) 6.67 m s^{-2} **b)** 26667 m s^{-2}
3 a) 5715 N **b)** 5704 N
c) 5616 N
4 a) -7.5 m s^{-2} **b)** 60 m **c)** 4 s
5 a) -7.84 m s^{-2} **b)** 19.4 m s^{-1}
c) Air resistance – will increase the initial speed.
6 a) $0.098\mathbf{i} + 1.5\mathbf{j}$ **b)** 0.601 N
7 a) $3.08\mathbf{i} - 20.00\mathbf{j}$
b) $0.62\mathbf{i} - 4.00\mathbf{j}$
c) 4.05 m s^{-2} at 81.3° below $\mathbf{i}$.
8 a) 400 N **b)** 83.6°, 268 N
c) 2 needed.
9 a) 769 N **b)** 4.27 m s^{-1}
c) 3.42 m s^{-1}

Exercises 25.2 home *(p.492)*

1 a) 0.0294 N **b)** 15 000 N
2 a) 3.75 m s^{-2} **b)** 10 000 m s^{-2}
3 a) 6867 N **b)** 6720 N **c)** 6860 N
4 a) -2.70 m s^{-2} **b)** 18.5 m
c) 3.7 s
5 a) $10.7\mathbf{i} + 2.6\mathbf{j}$ **b)** $5.34\mathbf{i} + 1.3\mathbf{j}$
c) 5.5 m s^{-2} at 13.8° above $\mathbf{i}$
6 a) $-190\mathbf{i} + (R - 710)\mathbf{j}$
c) $-2.54\mathbf{i}$ **d)** 74.7 N
7 a) 101 N **b)** 1.36 m s^{-2}
c) 11.68 m s^{-1}
8 1142 N
9 b) $0.125\mathbf{j}$ **c)** $\mathbf{v} = 0.5\mathbf{i} + 0.125t\mathbf{j}$, $\mathbf{r} = 0.5t\mathbf{i} + 0.0625t^2\mathbf{j}$
e) $0.5\mathbf{i} + 1.25\mathbf{j}$, $15\mathbf{i} + 31.25\mathbf{j}$

Exercises 25.3 class *(p.496)*

1 a) $1750 - T$, $T - 250$
b) $1750 - T = 1000a$, $T - 250 = 700a$ **c)** 868 N, 0.882 m s^{-2}
d) 11.3 s
2 a) i) $\frac{1}{4}g$ **ii)** $\frac{1}{9}g$ **iii)** 0
b) $\dfrac{(M-m)g}{M+m}$
3 a) 2.8 m s^{-2} **b)** 0.7 m s^{-2}
4 a) $\frac{2}{9}$m s^{-2} **b)** 4444.4 N
c) 8888.9 N
5 a) 0.754 m s^{-2}
b) 0.101 m s^{-2}, 27.2 N

6 a) 4.29 m s^{-2}
b) 2.06 m s^{-2} 38.7 N

Exercises 25.3 home *(p.497)*

1 a) Block: $T - 10$ Mass: $19.6 - T$
b) $a = \frac{T-10}{5}$ and $a = \frac{19.6-T}{2}$
c) $T = 16.86$ N, $a = 1.37$ m s^{-2}
2 a) 33.7 N, 1.37 m s^{-2}
b) 3.27 N, 3.27 m s^{-2}
c) 17.2 N, 1.2 m s^{-2}
3 a) $49 - T$, $T - 19.6$
b) $\frac{49-T}{5}, \frac{T-19.6}{2}$
c) 28 N, 4.2 m s^{-2}
d) There is no resistance and tension constant in string.
4 a) 900 N **b)** 2200 N
5 a) 0.517 m s^{-2} **b)** 33.3 N.
6 a) 3.41 m s^{-2}, 40.6 N

Consolidation Exercises for Chapter 25 *(p.498)*

1 a) 194.5 N **b)** 3.24 m s^{-2}
2 a) 10.1 N **b)** 153.4°
3 a) 109 N **c)** 1.08 m s^{-2}
d) i) increases **ii)** no change
4 17.64 N, 0.98 m s^{-2}
5 a) $\frac{3mg}{2}$ **b** 0.5

6 a) i) $\frac{pmg}{2}$
b) i) $p + q = 12$
ii) $p = 9$, $q = 3$
7 i) a) 1.4 m s^{-2}, 3.36 N
b) 0.845 s
ii) a) smaller **b)** larger
c) smaller
8 b) i) $\frac{3g}{25}$ **ii)** $\frac{36mg}{25}$

CHAPTER 26
Momentum and collisions

Exercises 26.1 class *(p.504)*

1 a) 4 kg m s^{-1}
b) 4 000 000 kg m s^{-1}
c) 9.5 kg m s^{-1}
2 Momentum of 16 g greater in magnitude, both have the same direction.
3 Constant magnitude, but variable direction.
4 10.5 m s^{-1}
5 2.19 kg m s^{-1}

Exercises 26.1 home *(p.504)*

1 a) 476 kg m s^{-1}
b) 200 000 kg m s^{-1}
c) 0.012 kg m s^{-1}
2 No. It may have constant magnitude, but will vary in direction.
3 Momentum has constant magnitude.
4 9526 kg m s^{-1}
5 2.70 kg m s^{-1}

Exercises 26.2 class *(p.506)*

1 a) 0.4125 Ns **b)** 0.275 Ns
2 a) 750 Ns **b)** 625 N
3 a) 7500 Ns **b)** 3750 N
4 b) 544 Ns **c)** 454 N
5 a) –180 Ns **b)** –0.4 m s^{-1}
6 a) 3.48 Ns **b)** 34.8 N
7 a) 22.5 m s^{-1} **b)** 30 m s^{-1}
8 $m\sqrt{(2g)}\,(\sqrt{h} + \sqrt{H})$

Exercises 26.2 home *(p.507)*

1 a) 0.24 Ns **b)** 0.48 m s^{-1}
2 a) –0.24, 0.12, defining up as positive **b)** 0.36 Ns **c)** 0.72 N
3 a) 3 Ns **b)** 5 N **c)** Increase to a maximum and decrease.
4 a) 375 Ns **b)** Extend t and reduce F. **c)** 208 N **d)** 1250 N
5 6842 N, 10833 N
6 a) 180000 Ns
b) 22500 N
7 a) $\frac{7mU}{4}$ **b)** $\frac{7mU}{4T}$
8 $m\left(\sqrt{u^2+2gh}+\frac{1}{2}\sqrt{3gh}\right)$

Exercises 26.3 class *(p.512)*

1 a) 0.7 kg m s^{-1}
b) 0.7 kg m s^{-1}
c) 3.5 m s^{-1}
2 a) 18 kg m s^{-1} **b)** 5.25 m s^{-1}
3 2.6 m s^{-1}
4 8.87 m s^{-1}
5 6 m s^{-1}
6 3 m s^{-1}
7 6 m s^{-1}
8 $1\frac{2}{3}$ m s^{-1}

Exercises 26.3 home *(p.513)*

1 a) 0.03 kg m s^{-1}
b) 0.03 kg m s^{-1}
c) 0.248 m s^{-1}
2 a) –5 kg m s^{-1} **b)** –5 kg m s^{-1}
c) $v = 1$ m s^{-1}
3 0.9 m s^{-1}
4 2 kg
5 18 grams
6 30 cm s^{-1}
7 49 m s^{-1}
8 Direction remains unchanged but speed reduced to 0.9 m s^{-1}

Consolidation Exercises for Chapter 26 *(p.515)*

1 i) 0.15 **ii)** 0.4, 0.0667 or 0.133
2 0.8
3 a) $\frac{5u}{4}$ **b)** $\frac{21mu}{4}$ **c)** $\frac{25u^2}{24g}$
4 a) 4.8 m s^{-1} **b)** 43200 Ns
c) 3600 N
5 a) 4 s **b)** no **c)** 7.2 m s^{-1}

CHAPTER 27
Moments, couples and equilibrium

Exercises 27.1 class *(p.519)*

1 a) 259 Nm **b)** –300 Nm
c) –64 Nm **d)** –150 Nm
2 a) –35 Nm, 40 Nm
b) 5 Nm, rotates anticlockwise
3 a) –60 Nm **b)** –164 Nm
c) –100 Nm **d)** 340 Nm
4 –280 Nm
5 a) 3 m **b)** 6 m
c) 0.5 m **d)** 2 m
6 –30 Nm

Exercises 27.1 home *(p.520)*

1 a) 90 Nm **b)** 5.76 Nm
c) –63 Nm **d)** 0
2 a) 1.2 m
b) –19.6 Nm, Bob goes down.
3 a) 5 Nm **b)** –4 Nm
c) 3.2 Nm **d)** –46 Nm
4 1.2 Nm
5 0.8 m
6 a) 2 m **b)** 1.33 m **c)** 0.889 m

Exercises 27.2 class *(p.522)*

1 c) $130\frac{2}{3}$ N
2 b) is true.
3 a) A, 700 N; B, 1000 N
b) A, 1190; B, 1490 N
4 a) Nothing
b) 23 Nm, –23 Nm, 0 Nm
5 a) 245 N **b)** stays the same
6 1.71 m from A, 0.14 m from B

Exercises 27.2 home *(p.308)*

1 M = 98 N, N = 882 N
2 a) 3 **b)** Greater
3 a) 180 N and 320 N
b) 425 N and 565 N
4 52.5 kg
5 a) 588 N **b)** 1568 N
c) 588 N
6 a) 784 N, 1470 N
b) 0.2 m

Consolidation Exercises for Chapter 27 *(p.524)*

1 5.6 m
2 5/6 m
3 **b)** 80 kg
4 **b)** 2352 N **c)** 2058 N

CHAPTER 28
Data

Exercises 28.1 class *(p.529)*

3

1	2	3	4	5	6
15	20	22	23	11	4

Exercises 28.1 home *(p.529)*

1 a), d), e) are continuous; b), c) are discrete
2 **a)** qualitative, discrete
b) quantitative, continuous
c) quantitative, discrete
d) quantitative, discrete
e) quantitative, discrete
f) qualitative, discrete
g) quantitative, continuous

Exercises 28.2 class *(p.538)*

1 **a)**

Class	f
$300 \le x < 400$	1
$400 \le x < 500$	3
$500 \le x < 600$	10
$600 \le x < 700$	4
$700 \le x < 800$	2

b)

Class	f
$0.6 \le x < 0.7$	4
$0.7 \le x < 0.8$	8
$0.8 \le x < 0.9$	7
$0.9 \le x < 1.0$	1

2 **a)** *Unit = 1*
1F 5
1S 7 7 6 6 7 6
1E 9 8 8 9
2O 0 1
2T 2
b) *Unit = 100*
1E 8 8 9
2O 1 0
2T 3
2F 5
c) *Unit = 0.001*
0– 3
0+ 8 9 8 8
1– 0 1 1
3 23, 20, 24, …, 50
4 *Unit = 1*
O 0 1 0 0 0 0 1 0 1 1 1 1
T 2 3 2 2
F 5 4
S
E 9 8
1O 1 0 0 0
1T 2 2 2 2 2
5 **a)** 25, 30, 35, 45, 55
b) 3, 5, 5, 10, 10; frequency density $\propto$ 20, 4, 2.4, 0.5, 0.1
6 **b) i)** 14%, **ii)** 63%

Exercise 28.2 home *(p.540)*

1 **a)** 10, 10, 20, …, 490
b) 0.00, 0.01, 0.02, …, 0.14
2 *Unit = 1*
3 7
4 8 3
5 9 0 2 6
6 4 8 5 0 5 3
7 5 9 6 2 9
8 3 8
3 *Unit = 10*
7+ 8 8 9 9 9
8– 0 0 0 0 1 1 1 1 2 2 3 3 3 4 4 4
4 *Unit = 0.1*
1O 1
1T
1F 4 4 4 4
1S 6 6 7 6 7 7 6 7 7
1E 8 8 9 9 8 8 9
2O 0 1 0 1
2T 2 3 3
2F 4 5
6 **b)** 53%

Consolidation Exercises for Chapter 28 *(p.541)*

1 **a)** continuous **b)** discrete
c) continuous **d)** discrete
e) discrete continuous
f) discrete
2 **a)** qualitative, discrete
b) quantitative, continuous
c) qualitative, discrete
d) quantitative, discrete
e) qualitative, discrete
f) quantitative, discrete
5 **a)** Use a five-part stem with unit = 10
6 **a) i)** 24.5 **ii)** 19.5
7 **a) i)** 15.5 **ii)** 12.5
b) 9.5, 3, 3, 3, 3
c) frequency density $\propto$ 3.16, 6, 5, 2.33, 1.67
8 *Unit = 1*
0+ 5 8
1– 4 2 4
1+ 7 6 7 9
2– 2 0
2+ 6
3– 1
9 **a) i)** discrete
ii) class boundaries are disjointed
b) i) identify upper bound

CHAPTER 29
Summary statistics 1

Exercises 29.1 class *(p.554)*

1 mode = 3; median = 4
2 **a)** 44 **b)** 44
3 **b)** 734 (depends on classes)
c) actual 680
4 0.3, 13.5
5 **b)** 583.7, 585.8 **c)** 587.3

Exercises 29.1 home *(p.555)*

1 **c)** 7
2 520–529 **a)** 524 **b)** 524
3 **a)** *Unit = 0.1*
depth
1 14 7
6 15 2 3 6 6 6
12 16 7 7 7 8 8 9
(5) 17 3 3 4 8 9
13 18 2 2 4 4 7 7 8
6 19 3 6
4 20 2 4 5
1 21 2
b) 17.6
4 Unit = 0.1 depth
a) 3 45 2 3 5
8 46 1 2 3 6 7
14 47 1 1 2 5 7 8
21 48 0 1 3 5 6 6 9
(7) 49 2 2 3 5 6 7 8
27 50 0 0 1 2 3 5 5 6 7 8 9
16 51 0 1 2 3 4 5 6 7 7
7 52 0 2 3 7
3 53 2 5 6
b) 49.8 **c)** 49.9
5 **c)** 24 **d)** 2.6

Exercises 29.2 class *(p.560)*

1 **a)** 40.7 **b)** 0.667, 40.7
2 **a)** 2.25 **b)** 2.25 **c)** 2
3 **a)** 0.755, 368.9 **b)** 368.9
4 **a)** 25.07

Exercises 29.2 home *(p.561)*

1 **a)** 52.9 **b)** 55.7
2 **a)** 1.98 **b)** 1.98 **c)** 2
3 **a)** 0.877, 163.8 **b)** 163.8
4 65.85

Exercises 29.3 class *(p.567)*

1 **a)** 54
b) 7, 16, 21, 18, 8, 9; 58.0
2 **a)** increase in weight
b) i) 3.29, **ii)** 2.91
d) positively skewed

3 £6.25
5 **a)** £185.40, £208.20
b) +12.3%

Exercises 29.3 home *(p.568)*

1 **a)** 0.517 sec **b)** 0.508 sec
c) positively skewed
2 **b)** **i)** 11.9 cm, **ii)** 9.25 cm
c) positively skewed
3 13.4 g
4 **a)** 20 **b)** 12 **c)** 26
5 **b)** 41.75

Consolidation Exercises for Chapter 29 *(p.569)*

1 **a)** 35–39 **b)** 38.02
2 **a)** 13.0 cm **b)** 9.9 cm
3 **a)** 73 **b)** 75.1
c) positively skewed
4 **a)** 7, 7 **b)** 7, 7
e) symmetric, positively skewed, positively skewed, negatively skewed
5 £7.77
6 105
7 24.9
8 **b)** 50.5 **c)** 50.2
9 **a)** 4 **b)** 3.9 **c)** 4
10 **a)** 1.35 kg **c)** 14 to 15
d) 1.86, 0.523
e) 1.74, 1.51, 2.15 **f)** positive

CHAPTER 30
Summary statistics 2

Exercises 30.1 class *(p.578)*

1 **a)** 5, 4 **b)** 0.6, 0.3
c) 46, 17.5 **d)** 0.8, 0.325
2 **a)** 9 **b)** 0.4
c) 320 **d)** 4.6
3 **a)** 3.21
b) 0.04, 1.37, 13.7, 15.8
c) positive skew
4 **a)** 4.35, 3.01, 7.93
b) –2.09, 12.85 **c)** 15.8
5 **a)** 5, 23.75, 35.83, 51.67, 65;
10,30,41,48,70;
10, 20, 30.83, 38.33, 70;
10, 33.33, 44, 53.33, 90

Exercises 30.1 home *(p.579)*

1 **a)** 10, 7 **b)** 39, 23
c) 1.3, 0.7 **d)** 23, 8
2 **a)** 6 **b)** 60.5
c) 101.8 **d)** 510
3 22.7, 26.4, 39.4
4 **a)** 30.1; 33.5, 28.0
b) 22.5, 39.17, 44.5
d) 20.0; 44.5 far out
5 **a)** 11.6, 7.6, 13.9
12.8, 11.0, 15.4
b) 0, 7.6, 11.6, 13.9, 40;
0. 11.0, 12.8, 15.4, 40

Exercises 30.2 class *(p.585)*

1 4.0 **a)** 3.47 **b)** 3.47
2 **a)** 2.143 **a)** 2.143
3 24.7, 108.91, 10.44
4 16.58

Exercises 30.2 home *(p.586)*

1 17.3 **a)** 0.81 **b)** 0.81
c) likely to be innaccurate by 0.5 yr, but could be 0.9 yr
2 **a)** 1.08 **b)** 1.08
3 **a)** 0.644, 2.074, 1.44
b) 3.144, 2.074, 1.44
4 £2.60, £1.77

Consolidation exercises for Chapter 30 *(p.590)*

1 **b)** 53.35, 41.26, 64.02; negative
2 negative skew **c)** 252, 6.52
d) **i)** increase **ii)** decrease
3 **a)** £208.42, £18.30
b) £4644.40
c) £246.39, £38.40
4 **a)** 6,5
b) more than 2 standard deviations from mean
c) **I)** retain, possibly elder sibling
ii) error – discard
d) 5, 5 **e)** reduce both
f) positive, remains positive
5 **a)** **i)** 16.23 **ii)** 12.3, 20.6; 8.3
6 **a)** frequency density ∝ 21, 64, 66, 48, 36, 21, 16, 12, 5.5, 2.4
b) 3.13, 2.51
7 **b)** similar averages and maximum mark; A has a greater range and marks are relatively symmetric, B's marks are positively skewed
8 **a)** negatively skewed
d) 68.6, 9.52 **e)** 49.5, 14.85
9 **a)** 30.1, 25.4, 37.2 **b)** positive

CHAPTER 31
Probability

Exercises 31.1 class *(p.603)*

1 **a)** $\frac{1}{4}$, $\frac{1}{52}$, $\frac{1}{26}$
b) **i)** C, K **ii)** C, RK **iii)** K, RK
2 **a)** $\frac{33}{95}$ **b)** $\frac{48}{95}$
3 **a)** $\frac{5}{8}$ **b)** $\frac{3}{5}$

Exercises 31.1 home *(p.604)*

1 $\frac{8}{64}$, $\frac{30}{64}$
2 **b)** $\frac{11}{28}$
3 **a)** **i)** $\frac{6}{13}$ **ii)** $\frac{6}{13}$ **iii)** $\frac{1}{6}$ **iv)** $\frac{1}{6}$
b) **i)** $\frac{10}{13}$ **ii)** $\frac{4}{13}$ **iii)** $\frac{1}{4}$ **iv)** $\frac{1}{10}$
4 **a)** $\frac{9}{16}$ **b)** $\frac{5}{9}$

Exercises 31.2 class *(p.608)*

1 **a)** 12 **b)** $\frac{1}{3}$
2 15 890 700
3 **a)** 12 376 **b)** 1200

Exercises 31.2 home *(p 609)*

1 240
2 **a)** 8! **b)** 2 × 6!
3 **a)** 406 192 **b)** **i)** 250 800
ii) 38 760 **iii)** 319 770

Consolidation Exercises for Chapter 31 *(p.611)*

1 **a)** $\frac{1}{2}$ **b)** $\frac{1}{4}$ **c)** $\frac{5}{12}$
2 **a)** $\frac{1}{2}$ **b)** $\frac{3}{8}$ **c)** $\frac{1}{4}$
3 **a)** $\frac{1}{16}$ **b)** $\frac{1}{4}$ **c)** $\frac{1}{4}$
4 $\frac{7}{15}$
5 **b)** **i)** $\frac{1}{3}$ **ii)** $\frac{1}{6}$ **iii)** $\frac{1}{4}$ **iv)** $\frac{1}{6}$
6 **a)** $\frac{1}{4}$ **b)** $\frac{1}{2}$ **c)** $\frac{16}{169}$
d) $\frac{88}{169}$ **e)** $\frac{1}{26}$
7 **a)** $\frac{t(t-1)}{(l+s)(l+s-1)}$
b) $\frac{s(s-1)}{(l+s)(l+s-1)}$
c) $\frac{2st}{(t+s)(t+s-1)}$
8 24
9 **a)** 6! **b)** 3 × 5!
c) 3 × 5! **d)** 192
10 **a)** 5005 **b)** **i)** 540 **ii)** 4921
11 **a)** 56 **b)** 0.218 75
12 **a)** 13 860 **b)** 210 **c)** 4620
13 **a)** 2 598 960 **b)** 1287
c) 0.0020
14 **a)** **i)** $\frac{3}{4}$ **ii)** $\frac{9}{16}$ **iii)** $(\frac{3}{4})^5$ **iv)** $(\frac{3}{4})^N$
b) 33
15 0.6
16 **b)** **i)** $\frac{1}{5}$ **ii)** $\frac{2}{5}$ **iii)** 0 **c)** $\frac{1}{2}$
17 **a)** $\frac{2}{3}$ **c)** $\frac{1}{4}$ **d)** $\frac{23}{60}$ **e)** $\frac{15}{23}$
18 **a)** 0.62 **b)** $\frac{1}{31}$
19 **a)** $\frac{17}{35}$ **b)** $\frac{12}{25}$ **c)** $\frac{97}{175}$
20 **b)** $2.7l$ **c)** $\frac{1}{45}$
21 **a)** 65 780 **b)** 0.000 015 2
c) 0.966 464 0
22 **a)** 13 983 816
b) 0.000 000 071 5

c) i) 0.435 965 ii) 0.413 019
iii) 0.132 378 iv) 0.018 622

23 12

24 a) 0.125 b) 0.273

25 0.125

26 a) 0.25 b) 0.48 c) 0.26

27 a) (A) 0.006 67 (B) $\frac{1}{2}$ (C) $\frac{2}{3}$
b) $\frac{2}{9}$ c) $\frac{1}{2}$

28 a) independent b) neither
c) mutually exclusive

29 a) 0.545 b) 0.455 c) 0.3

31 a) 11/24 b) 11/60
c) 19/20 d) 143/800

32 a) 11/15 b) 3/8

33 a) 4989600 b) 4/165

CHAPTER 32
Expectation

Exercises 32.1 class *(p.621)*

1 ii) a) $\frac{1}{32}$ b) –21.6p c) no

2 a) 0.002 b) 0.23; 3.9p

3 a) 282 500 b) no

4 a) no b) £126.67

5 a) 0.015 625, 0.5625, 0.421 875
b) 0.1875 clockwise

Exercises 32.1 home *(p.622)*

1 5.6p

2 b) no c) loss of 16.7p

3 a) i) £102.50 ii) £107.50
b) i) £205, £82, £82, £41
ii) £178.22, £71.29, £71.29 £35.64

4 a) i) $(\frac{1}{6})^5$ ii) $1-(\frac{5}{6})^5-(\frac{1}{6})^5$
b) 10p c) 60p

Exercises 32.2 class *(p.626)*

1 3.5, $\frac{35}{12}$

2 2, 1

3 $\frac{1}{36}, \frac{3}{36}, \frac{5}{36}, \frac{7}{36}, \frac{9}{36}, \frac{11}{36}$; 4.47, 1.97

4 a) i) $\frac{1}{6}$ ii) $\frac{1}{2}$ iii) $\frac{1}{3}$
b) 1.17, 0.472

5 $\frac{1}{36}, \frac{2}{36}, \frac{3}{36}, \frac{4}{36}, \frac{5}{36}, \frac{6}{36}, \frac{5}{36}, \frac{4}{36}, \frac{3}{36}, \frac{2}{36}, \frac{1}{36}$, 0, $\frac{35}{6}$

Exercises 32.2 home *(p.627)*

1 a) 6.54 b) 9.94

2 2.25, 1.59

3 a) 2.5, 1.25 b) $\frac{5}{3}, \frac{20}{9}$

4 5.25, 10.35

5 8.5, $\frac{95}{12}$

Exercises 32.3 class *(p.628)*

1 a) 3 b) 6 c) 9 d) 12
e) 10 f) 20 g) 9 h) 12

2 275.50, 330.60

3 a) 7 b) 12.69 c) 1.41
Var(Y) = 3^2 × Var(X)

4 9.5; £1500, 0.6

5 a) £11.875, 8.297
b) £28.325, 46.51

Exercises 32.3 home *(p.630)*

1 a) 2.1 b) –3.2 c) 4.2
d) –3.2 e) 4.9 f) 7

2 £250, 36 000

3 a) 3.8 b) 3.36 c) 0.84
Var(Y) = 2^2 × Var(X)

4 a) $C = 10 + 24X$
b) £78.40, 361.44

5 187.5; 0.4

Exercises 32.4 class *(p.633)*

1 a) 0.05

3 b) 0, 1
c) 1

4 a) U(-2, 2)
b) 0
c) 2
d) i) 2 ii) 8 iii) 8

Exercises 32.4 home *(p.634)*

1 a) U(1, 12)
c) mean 11.5

2 a) –3.5
b) 1.708

3 a) R: U(0, 4); S: U(5, 9)
b) 2; 7
c) 2

4 a) 3.5, 1.25 b) -4.5, 1.25
c) –4.5, 1.25 d) 3, 5
e) –2, 5 f) 12, 5
g) 10.5, 1.25) h) 22.5, 31.25

Consolidation Exercises for Chapter 32 *(p.634)*

1 0.2p

2 loss of 2.4p

3 $\frac{1}{2}, \frac{2}{7}, \frac{1}{7}, \frac{2}{35}, \frac{1}{70}$; 1.8

4 1

5 1.39p

7 a) 0.35 b) 3.2

8 a) $\frac{1}{56}$ b) $\frac{10}{56}$ c) 1.125

9 1.373, 0.488

10 £6375

11 14.62, 17.04; yes, probability > 0.5

12 a) 0.2, 0.2 b) uniform c) 2

13 b)

0	1	2	4
$\frac{1}{4}$	$\frac{1}{3}$	$\frac{5}{18}$	$\frac{1}{36}$

c) 1

14 a) 0.4 b) 0.3 c) 2.6 d) 1.44
e) 15.6

CHAPTER 33
Algebra 2

Exercises 33.1 class *(p.643)*

1 a) – 0.173 b) – 0.2226
c) – 17.3
d) – 0.2226; r is unchanged by the linear transformations

2 b) yes c) i) 14.5 ii) 1278.2
iii) 18 697.5 d) 0.863

3 a) (1, 63.5)
b) i) –0.909 ii) –0.747

4 0.9298, strong positive linear correlation

Exercises 33.1 home *(p.644)*

1 b) 3.364 c) 0.553

2 a) E b) i) 0.698 ii) 0.913

3 a) positive b) negative
c) none d) positive

4 no change

Exercises 33.2 class *(p.650)*

1 d) 0.962, positive linear correlation
e) $p = 23.5a - 49.7$ f) 2665

2 a) $y = 5.06 + 1.40x$ b) 19.1
c) x is factor and is integer

3 a) –0.7851, yes b) 32.4
c) $x = 69.6 - 0.885y$

4 A a) –0.8578
b) $y = 0.304 - 0.0172x$
d) i) 0.218 ii) 0.046 iii) –0.126
e) 5, within range, reasonably linear, reliable
15, within range, non-linear, unreliable
25, out of range, unreliable
B a) 0.9944, closer to unity
c) 0.031

5 a) 0.8895
b) 0.9694
c) $A = 1.03a^2 - 14.7$

Exercises 33.2 home *(p.652)*

1 a) –0. 9979 c) $x = 33.5 - 2.66y$
d) x controlled

2 a) $y = 0.6x + 0.414$
b) 0.8823 c) 2.869

3 a) 0.9876, yes b) time is factor
c) $y = 0.0259t - 0.703$
d) i) 20.0 g
ii) 51.1; second one is unreliable

4 a) $y = 0.991 - 0.107x$
b) $y^{-1} = 2.062 - 1.077x^{-1}$

Consolidation Exercises for Chapter 33 *(p.653)*

1 b) 0.9692 **c)** yes
2 a) $y = 139 + 1.05x$ **b)** 186
c) increase in length for each unit increase in mass
3 a) 0.9281
b) suggests a linear model may be appropriate
4 a) 0.7496, evidence supports linear correlation
b) appears non-linear
c) 0.8381, squared is better
5 b) $y = 0.231 - 0.011\,x^{-1}$
c) 0.0014 **d)** outlier
e) model fits data without (0.2, 0.269) better
6 b) $y = 8{,}64 + 9.89x$
c) b represents cost of each additional day, a represents a fixed cost **d)** £117
e) no, out of range of data
7 b) $y = 0.952x - 35.5$
c) i) 141, in range, little variability, should be accurate
ii) 198, in range but much variability, unlikely to be accurate
iii) 250, out of range, unreliable
d) bias readings to upper end, say 215 up to 250
8 a) 0.3377 **b)** not significant
c) reduces it, exclude the point
9 a) ii) $y = 0.613 + 0.0259x$
iii) 2.7; out of range, data not linearly related
c) use new line for reliable estimate; carry out trials around 80 g
10 b) $h = 22.6 + 0.821a$

CHAPTER 34

The normal probability model

Exercises 34.1 class *(p662)*

1 b) i) 65.4 **ii)** 13.4
c) i) 65.4 **ii)** 52.0, 78.8
iii) 38.6, 92.2
d) i) 4% **ii)** 68.1% **iii)** 27.9%
e) 5%, 68%, 27%
2 e) 19% **f)** 55 mph
4 b) 137.4, 763.9
c) i) 5.9% **ii)** 69.4% **iii)** 24.7%

Exercises 34.1 home *(p.663)*

1 6.0, 2.6; 7.3% compared with 5%
2 £13 500, £540
3 a) 67.7, 7.22

Exercises 34.2 class *(p.669)*

1 a) 0.158 **b)** 0.516
c) 0.256 **d)** 0.145
2 a) 0.219 **b)** 0.368
c) 0.484 **d)** 0.950
e) 0.685 **f)** 0.032
3 a) 1.598 **b)** 0.327
c) 1.674 **d)** 2.645
4 a) i) 0.861 **ii)** 0.741
b) 3.07 **c)** 1.07, 1.97; 0.90
5 a) 2.16, 0.682
b) 9.508, 0.00700
c) 98.98, 15.73

Exercises 34.2 home *(p.670)*

1 a) 200.658 **b)** 0.539
2 a) 8.2% **b)** 0.580
c) 0.518 **d)** 13.5%
3 a) 0.159 **b)** 0.159
c) 11.18 **d)** 9.70

Consolidation Exercises for Chapter 34 *(p.670)*

1 a) 2.3% **b)** 1 year 4 months
2 5.01, 0.0467
3 a) reasonably linear, normal model may fit
b) 5.4, 13.2, 29.7, 22.2, 26.1, 28.4, 54.5, 39.4, 20.6, 10.4
c) 13.47 < 16.919 difference not significant at 5% level
4 a) 0.37 **b)** 0.211
e) 14.3, 16.3, 23.6, 26.7, 23.6, 16.3, 8.9, 3.8, 1.2, 0.3; model does not fit data
5 b) 63.54, 4.394 **c)** 3%, yes
d) 2.6%, no
6 a) 0.8944 **b)** 968 hours
c) 0.5117 **d)** 909 hours
7 a) 0.2525 **b)** 0.9295

Tables of statistics

Standard normal probability distribution function **Proportional parts**

z	0.00	0.01	0.02	0.03	0.04	0.05	0.06	0.07	0.08	0.09	1	2	3	4	5	6	7	8	9
0.0	0.50000	0.50399	0.50798	0.51197	0.51595	0.51994	0.52392	0.52790	0.53188	0.53586	40	80	119	159	199	239	279	319	358
0.1	0.53983	0.54380	0.54776	0.55172	0.55567	0.55962	0.56356	0.56749	0.57142	0.57535	39	79	118	158	197	237	276	315	355
0.2	0.57926	0.58317	0.58706	0.59095	0.59483	0.59871	0.60257	0.60642	0.61026	0.61409	39	77	116	155	193	232	271	309	348
0.3	0.61791	0.62172	0.62552	0.62930	0.63307	0.63683	0.64058	0.64431	0.64803	0.65173	38	75	113	150	188	225	263	300	338
0.4	0.65542	0.65910	0.66276	0.66640	0.67003	0.67364	0.67724	0.68082	0.68439	0.68793	36	72	108	144	180	216	252	288	324
0.5	0.69146	0.69497	0.69847	0.70194	0.70540	0.70884	0.71226	0.71566	0.71904	0.72240	34	69	103	137	171	206	240	274	309
0.6	0.72575	0.72907	0.73237	0.73565	0.73891	0.74215	0.74537	0.74857	0.75175	0.75490	32	65	97	129	161	194	226	258	291
0.7	0.75804	0.76115	0.76424	0.76730	0.77035	0.77337	0.77637	0.77935	0.78230	0.78524	30	60	90	120	151	181	211	241	271
0.8	0.78814	0.79103	0.79389	0.79673	0.79955	0.80234	0.80511	0.80785	0.81057	0.81327	28	56	83	111	139	167	195	222	250
0.9	0.81594	0.81859	0.82121	0.82381	0.82639	0.82894	0.83147	0.83398	0.83646	0.83891	25	51	76	102	127	152	178	203	229
1.0	0.84134	0.84375	0.84614	0.84849	0.85083	0.85314	0.85543	0.85769	0.85993	0.86214	23	46	69	92	115	138	161	184	207
1.1	0.86433	0.86650	0.86864	0.87076	0.87286	0.87493	0.87698	0.87900	0.88100	0.88298	21	41	62	82	103	124	144	165	185
1.2	0.88493	0.88686	0.88877	0.89065	0.89251	0.89435	0.89617	0.89796	0.89973	0.90147	18	37	55	73	91	110	128	146	164
1.3	0.90320	0.90490	0.90658	0.90824	0.90988	0.91149	0.91308	0.91466	0.91621	0.91774	16	32	48	64	80	96	112	128	144
1.4	0.91924	0.92073	0.92220	0.92364	0.92507	0.92647	0.92785	0.92922	0.93056	0.93189	14	28	42	56	70	84	98	112	126
1.5	0.93319	0.93448	0.93574	0.93699	0.93822	0.93943	0.94062	0.94179	0.94295	0.94408	12	24	36	48	60	72	84	96	108
1.6	0.94520	0.94630	0.94738	0.94845	0.94950	0.95053	0.95154	0.95254	0.95352	0.95449	10	20	31	41	51	61	72	82	92
1.7	0.95543	0.95637	0.95728	0.95818	0.95907	0.95994	0.96080	0.96164	0.96246	0.96327	9	17	26	35	43	52	60	69	78
1.8	0.96407	0.96485	0.96562	0.96638	0.96712	0.96784	0.96856	0.96926	0.96995	0.97062	7	14	22	29	36	43	50	58	65
1.9	0.97128	0.97193	0.97257	0.97320	0.97381	0.97441	0.97500	0.97558	0.97615	0.97670	6	12	18	24	30	36	42	48	54
2.0	0.97725	0.97778	0.97831	0.97882	0.97932	0.97982	0.98030	0.98077	0.98124	0.98169	5	10	15	20	24	29	34	39	44
2.1	0.98214	0.98257	0.98300	0.98341	0.98382	0.98422	0.98461	0.98500	0.98537	0.98574	4	8	12	16	20	24	28	32	36
2.2	0.98610	0.98645	0.98679	0.98713	0.98745	0.98778	0.98809	0.98840	0.98870	0.98899	3	6	10	13	16	19	22	25	29
2.3	0.98928	0.98956	0.98983	0.99010	0.99036	0.99061	0.99086	0.99111	0.99134	0.99158	3	5	8	10	13	15	18	20	23
2.4	0.99180	0.99202	0.99224	0.99245	0.99266	0.99286	0.99305	0.99324	0.99343	0.99361	2	4	6	8	10	12	14	16	18
2.5	0.99379	0.99396	0.99413	0.99430	0.99446	0.99461	0.99477	0.99492	0.99506	0.99520	2	3	5	6	8	9	11	12	14
2.6	0.99534	0.99547	0.99560	0.99573	0.99585	0.99598	0.99609	0.99621	0.99632	0.99643	1	2	4	5	6	7	8	10	11
2.7	0.99653	0.99664	0.99674	0.99683	0.99693	0.99702	0.99711	0.99720	0.99728	0.99736	1	2	3	4	5	5	6	7	8
2.8	0.99744	0.99752	0.99760	0.99767	0.99774	0.99781	0.99788	0.99795	0.99801	0.99807	1	1	2	3	3	4	5	6	6
2.9	0.99813	0.99819	0.99825	0.99831	0.99836	0.99841	0.99846	0.99851	0.99856	0.99861	1	1	2	2	3	3	4	4	5
3.0	0.99865	0.99869	0.99874	0.99878	0.99882	0.99886	0.99889	0.99893	0.99896	0.99900	0	1	1	2	2	2	3	3	3
3.1	0.99903	0.99906	0.99910	0.99913	0.99916	0.99918	0.99921	0.99924	0.99926	0.99929	0	1	1	1	1	2	2	2	3
3.2	0.99931	0.99934	0.99936	0.99938	0.99940	0.99942	0.99944	0.99946	0.99948	0.99950	0	0	1	1	1	1	1	2	2
3.3	0.99952	0.99953	0.99955	0.99957	0.99958	0.99960	0.99961	0.99962	0.99964	0.99965	0	0	0	1	1	1	1	1	1
3.4	0.99966	0.99968	0.99969	0.99970	0.99971	0.99972	0.99973	0.99974	0.99975	0.99976	0	0	0	0	1	1	1	1	1
3.5	0.99977	0.99978	0.99978	0.99979	0.99980	0.99981	0.99981	0.99982	0.99983	0.99983	0	0	0	0	0	0	0	0	0

Φ	0.00	0.01	0.02	0.03	0.04	0.05	0.06	0.07	0.08	0.09
0.5	0.000	0.025	0.050	0.075	0.100	0.126	0.151	0.176	0.202	0.228
0.6	0.253	0.279	0.305	0.332	0.358	0.385	0.412	0.440	0.468	0.496
0.7	0.524	0.553	0.583	0.613	0.643	0.674	0.706	0.739	0.772	0.806
0.8	0.842	0.878	0.915	0.954	0.994	1.036	1.080	1.126	1.175	1.227
0.9	1.282	1.341	1.405	1.476	1.555	1.645	1.751	1.881	2.054	2.326

Φ	0	0.001	0.002	0.003	0.004	0.005	0.006	0.007	0.008	0.009
0.95	1.645	1.655	1.665	1.675	1.685	1.695	1.706	1.717	1.728	1.739
0.96	1.751	1.762	1.774	1.787	1.799	1.812	1.825	1.838	1.852	1.866
0.97	1.881	1.896	1.911	1.927	1.943	1.960	1.977	1.995	2.014	2.034
0.98	2.054	2.075	2.097	2.120	2.144	2.170	2.197	2.226	2.257	2.290
0.99	2.326	2.366	2.409	2.457	2.512	2.576	2.652	2.748	2.878	3.090

Φ	0.5%	1.0%	2.0%	2.5%	5.0%	10.0%						
1 − Φ							10.0%	5.0%	2.5%	2.0%	1.0%	0.5%
z	−2.576	−2.326	−2.054	−1.960	−1.645	−1.282	1.282	1.645	1.960	2.054	2.326	2.576

Random number table

23505	32408	00972	75953	27778	02240	98776	76255	35351	35730	08152	72896
84744	91235	85344	22723	97935	84372	13292	28162	29463	44734	78899	85427
67135	02152	34778	47377	18502	50742	24514	06370	95004	36152	79402	45594
33591	15583	96977	60192	44159	59332	74309	01316	50806	75379	24918	87070
57787	57248	89698	41776	52546	33597	87944	63145	81875	39865	38955	22913
14766	54285	52523	20721	06003	72173	69945	97350	93210	03392	01552	63127
45926	78875	83938	97158	27463	85241	47795	07886	43518	64679	75598	16054
78938	89726	40968	70279	84951	22225	30919	51919	43655	72606	28982	12951
59369	01028	62588	03664	52707	06334	87055	11072	63671	21627	93451	62562
30962	04554	03732	30794	79584	97655	59797	67924	00586	78601	56219	03616
27874	57190	80930	57080	51382	37294	34005	28287	31632	05457	21800	64011
47651	74469	43485	56113	93057	93002	63100	51545	03706	27973	88920	89087
31431	83282	43730	43006	61880	86284	50366	26745	53003	64851	39700	40594
75415	03441	26142	78621	52412	60563	74920	29887	05783	86082	96278	15336
24897	35940	68834	59572	72705	29934	05583	93433	99119	21725	67146	16111
32969	70116	59106	34163	24965	50167	81174	37670	20332	69765	83978	71301
87833	57604	12336	50895	20521	68370	22046	23914	42885	76263	56131	38447
91167	03154	31650	54722	23301	36239	31521	97178	64194	18987	31871	70386
58277	79938	16566	24973	35469	45707	85744	86713	76028	00206	30121	44449
56471	15945	06962	32146	47734	70351	29692	24522	67548	32305	29239	56412
58151	67936	18313	92678	58406	21529	64561	55445	69088	16396	09472	20839
99436	19991	11724	74357	49339	12500	21952	87811	45155	39804	23392	22234
25808	78720	23661	13185	62144	14508	34347	06116	84674	63687	57372	43121
22522	09270	10011	79451	55023	03390	05459	19040	92354	12203	54542	83984
83960	82719	47408	41168	60103	39533	59263	15805	57077	56831	36050	85170
65484	72838	34333	78561	54851	09256	51502	86839	65282	42651	07545	10767
03625	20785	62258	63419	39187	97844	91034	99656	50821	97208	15212	20855
78131	16692	70347	00396	85685	97622	00500	60893	09574	44518	13208	20855
15673	22384	39905	13615	78544	00238	77761	60618	77041	24887	66032	36594
57485	97418	61853	31389	69163	63071	69175	60365	25143	86177	00083	03325
93761	46283	22309	57562	32438	93946	03023	92889	48511	87037	08272	12047
74412	45238	37078	37604	57874	81430	48212	60258	02791	33847	46434	99449
31770	53625	22111	64275	07936	57060	56774	15297	77697	20999	47345	28709
38744	77136	07184	57549	54621	97858	55852	48261	95110	75124	73032	29955
28359	44192	51026	64701	48047	28759	88462	29886	33070	79827	65324	50024

Index